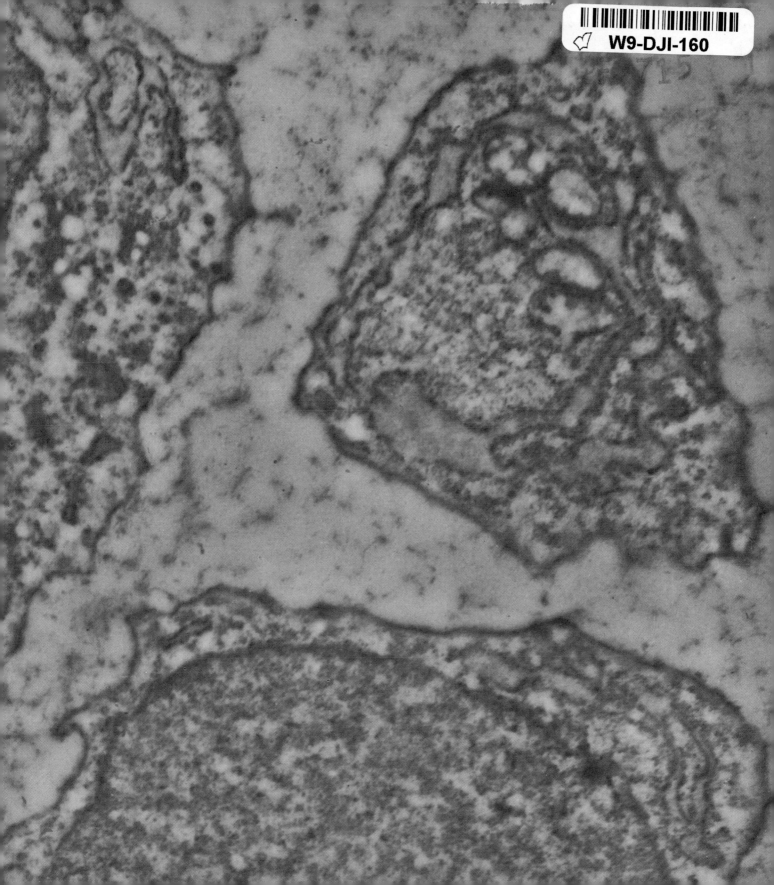

THE SCIENCE OF
BIOLOGY

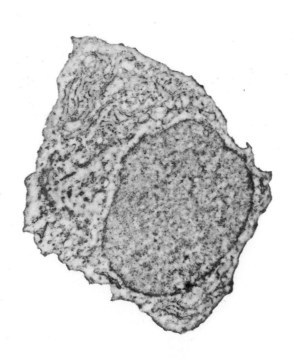

THE SCIENCE OF
BIOLOGY

PAUL B. WEISZ, *Professor of Biology, Brown University*

McGRAW-HILL *Book Company, Inc. New York Toronto London* 1959

This book is set in Caledonia, a type face designed for

Linotype by the American graphic designer W. A. Dwiggins.

The boldface headings are Spartan Heavy. Drawings

are by Joseph and Eva Cellini. Charts are by Wallace Boyd.

To Lillian

PREFACE

THIS IS A completely new book, new in conception and organization, new in depth and coverage, new in verbal and pictorial presentation. It evolved from the author's earlier *Biology*, which was an initial effort to introduce into a college text a measure of the maturity and dynamism of contemporary biology. Classroom use showed where this earlier effort was successful, and where it could be improved. Students, teachers, and the author's own experience contributed to the appraisal, and the accumulated information was used as a guide in the preparation of the present volume. As the preparation progressed, it became clear that this book would not be simply a cursory revision but an altogether new text, warranting publication as an original edition.

Designed to serve both the terminal student of biology and the prospective major, this book above all attempts to provide *understanding* of biological processes and principles. Its aim is analysis and synthesis, not mere cataloguing of data. The approach is determined by the results of modern research and is steeped in the same framework of thought that today orients professional biologists. But this book does not simply pay lip service to the recent advances. It shuns the superficial and glib and pursues each topic to considerable depth. Yet it remains within the grasp of the beginner.

The arrangement of the subject matter may be adapted easily to widely different types of courses. The first two parts of the book examine primarily the *organizational* aspects of living matter. After an introductory chapter on the nature of science, Part One considers the living world as a whole. It ranges in time from the origin of life to the present, and in space, from atoms and molecules to species, communities, and the global environment. Against this background of the broad scope of the biological domain, Part Two concentrates on the living substance as such. The discussion here deals in detail with the molecular properties and the composition of protoplasm, and with its structural and functional aggregation into cells and organisms. One of the important subsidiary objectives of these early sections is to give the reader a basic feeling for protoplasmic chemicals and their activities, essential for any appreciation of modern biology.

The first parts form the foundation for the remainder of the book, which emphasizes primarily the *operational* aspects of living matter. Part Three is an account of metabolism. The treatment here is thoroughly up to date, avoiding the many oversimplifications that have somehow become almost hereditary in discussions of this particular topic at this level. Parts Four, Five, and Six deal with self-perpetuation. Under the headings of steady-state control, reproduction, and adaptation, these concluding portions examine the living functions based on metabolism. Here again the presentation is oriented toward analysis rather than mere description, and it culminates the various concepts of molecular, cellular, and organismic biology developed in the earlier parts.

Thus the organization of the subject matter is functionally and pedagogically coherent, one portion building easily and naturally on the preceding portion. But the parts are not interwoven so tightly that they cannot be disengaged. The instructor may readily fit the book to the structure of his own course; he may conveniently discuss, for example, plant and animal types, ecological biology, or any other topic at points which differ from those suggested by the chapter sequence.

The tactical handling of any segment of the subject matter is extensive in scope and intensive in depth. Many topics are introduced for the first time, their inclusion virtually being demanded by the present state of biological knowledge. Thus a book of this kind can no longer afford to be silent about, for example, the structure and function of DNA, the principles of morphogenesis and differentiation, the genetic basis of post-Darwinian evolutionary theory, or the molecular details of photosynthesis and respiration. But it is clear that merely making passing reference to these or any other topics, simply for the sake of "covering" them, would be worse than useless. Instead, a patient chapter-length treatment, with thorough step-by-step exposition, is offered when an important phase of modern biology is introduced.

Both student and instructor are kept in mind in the auxiliary teaching aids which accompany the book. Close to 800 new, functional illustrations are integrated with the text. A glossary is appended at the end, and a series of provocative review questions is given after each chapter. Included there, too, are references to pertinent collateral readings, with particular emphasis on short, popular, readable articles. Finally, a revised and enlarged Laboratory Manual is offered, tailored primarily to fit the text but equally adaptable to widely different laboratory programs.

Thus the book should fulfill the objective for which it was written, namely, to communicate the excitement and challenge of modern biology, and at the same time to satisfy the text requirement of any beginning college course in biology. The book is balanced in coverage, and presents a unified, integrated view of the living world, without concern over botanical, zoological, or other static compartmentalizations. Featuring not only breadth but also urgently needed depth, it discourages mere assimilation of memorized "facts," but encourages acquisition of mature understanding. Coincidentally, it satisfies the criteria for a sound textbook as set forth by the Committee on Educational Policies of the Biology Council.[1] If it contributes to bringing more life to the teaching and learning of the science of life, then its long preparation will have been well worth the effort.

I am grateful to Dr. Walter J. Kenworthy, Brown University, for his continued interest in the growth of this book, his critical reading of portions of the manuscript, and his keen judgment, which has done much to improve many a chapter. I wish to thank the editors of the *Providence Journal and Evening Bulletin*, who have permitted the inclusion in Chap. 1 of substantial portions of an article on science published previously in their paper. And sincere thanks are due, individually and collectively, to many friends and colleagues, both at Brown and elsewhere, and to several laboratories and business organizations, who have kindly supplied photographs for use in this book.

PAUL B. WEISZ

[1]Biology Council, Committee on Educational Policies, "Improving College Biology Teaching," National Academy of Sciences, National Research Council Publication 505, 1957, pp. 66–70.

CONTENTS

THE SCIENCE OF
BIOLOGY

1

THE NATURE OF SCIENCE

OUR CURRENT CIVILIZATION is so thoroughly permeated with science that, for many, the label "scientific" has become the highest badge of merit, the hallmark of progress, the dominant theme of the age of atoms and space. No human endeavor, so it is often claimed, can really be worthwhile or of basic significance unless it has a scientific foundation. Moreover, advertisements loudly proclaim the "scientific" nature of consumer goods, and their "scientifically proved" high quality is attested to by "scientific" experts. Human relations too are supposed to be "scientific" nowadays. Conversation and debate have become "scientific" discussions, and in a field such as sports, if one is a good athlete, he is a "scientific" athlete.

There are even those who claim to take their religion "scientifically" and those who stoutly maintain that literature, painting, and other artistic pursuits are reducible to "science," really. And then there are those who believe that science will eventually solve "everything" and that, if only the world were run more "scientifically," it would be a much better place.

Yet in contrast to this widespread confidence in things and activities which claim to be, and in a few cases actually are, scientific, large segments of society doubt and mistrust scientists as persons. To many, the scientist is somehow queer and "different." He is held to be naïve and more or less uninformed outside his specialty. He is pictured as a cold, godless calculating machine, living in a strange, illusory world of his own.

Many circumstances in our civilization conspire to foster such false, stereotyped notions about science and scientists. However, no one who wishes to consider himself properly educated can afford to know about the meaning of science only what popular misconceptions, and "common knowledge," may have taught him. Especially is this true for one who is about to pursue studies in a modern science such as biology.

What then *is* the actual meaning of science? How did truly scientific undertakings develop, and how does science "work"? What can it do and, more especially, what can it not do? How does science differ from other forms of activity, and what place does it have in the scheme of modern culture?

The Origin of Science

Science began in the distant past, long before human history was being recorded. Its mother was tribal *magic*.

The same mother also gave birth to religion and, probably even earlier, to art. Thus science, religion, and art have always been blood brothers. Their methods differ, but their aim is the same: to understand and interpret the universe and its workings and, from this, to promote the material and spiritual welfare of man, where possible.

This was also the function of tribal magic. For long ages, magic was the rallying point of society, the central institution in which were concentrated the accumulated wisdom and experience of the day. The execution of magical procedures was in the hands of specially trained individuals, the medicine men and their equivalents. These were the forerunners of the scientists and the clergymen of today. How did science and religion grow out of magic? We may illustrate by means of an example.

Several thousand years ago, it was generally believed that magical rites were necessary to make wheat grow from planted seeds. In this particular instance, the rites took one of two forms. Either man intensified his sexual activity, in a solemn spring festival celebrated communally in the fields, or he abstained completely from sexual activity during the planting period.

The first procedure was an instance of *imitative* magic. The reasoning was that, since sowing seeds is like producing pregnancy in a woman, man could demonstrate to the soil what was wanted and so induce it to imitate man and be fertile. The second procedure, an instance of *contagious* magic, grew out of the assumption that only a limited amount of reproductive potency was available to living things. Consequently, if man did not use up his potency,

that much more would become available for the soil. Depending on the tribe, the time, and the locality, either imitative or contagious magic might have been used to attain the same end, namely, to make the earth fruitful.

The fundamental weakness of magic was, of course, that it was unreliable. Sometimes it worked, and sometimes it did not work. Bad soil, bad grain, bad weather, and insect pests often must have defeated the best magic. In time, man must have realized that magical rites actually played no role in wheat growth, whereas soil conditions, grain quality, and good weather played very important roles. This was a momentous discovery—and a scientific one.

Magic became science when man accidentally found, or began to look for, situations which could be predictably controlled without magical rituals. In many situations where magic seemed to work successfully most of the time, man discovered an underlying scientific principle.

Yet there remained very many situations where magic did not work and where scientific principles could not be found. For example, in spite of good soil and good weather, wheat might not have grown because of virus or fungus infections. Such contingencies remained completely beyond understanding up to very modern times, and early man could only conclude that unseeable, uncontrollable "somethings" occasionally defeated his efforts. These somethings became spirits and gods. And unless prayers and sacrificial offerings maintained the good will of the gods, their wrath would undo human enterprise. Thus magical rituals evolved into primitively religious ones.

At this stage, medicine men ceased to be magicians and instead assumed the dual role of priest and scientist. Every personal or communal undertaking required both scientific and religious action: science, to put to use what was known; religion, to protect against possible failure by inducing the unknown to work on man's side.

In time, the "two-way" medicine man disappeared and made way for the specialized scientist and priest. In both religion and science, shades of the old magic lingered on for long periods. The religions still retain a high magical content today, and the sciences only recently dissociated from magic-derived pseudosciences such as alchemy, astrology, and the occult arts.

Throughout the early development of science and religion, emphasis was largely on practical matters. Science was primitively technological, and religion too was largely "applied," designed to deal with the concrete practical issues of the day. Man was preoccupied mainly with procuring food, shelter, and clothing, and science and religion served these necessities. Later, as a result of technological successes, more time became available for contemplation and cultural development, and this is when researchers and theorists appeared alongside the technologists, and theologians alongside the clergymen.

The Forms of Science

Today there are three types of scientists carrying on two kinds of science.

One kind of scientist may be symbolized as a man who sits by the river on nice afternoons and who whittles away at a stick and wonders about things. Strange as it may seem to some, the most powerful science stems from such whittlers. Whereas most people who just sit manage merely to be lazy, a few quietly boil with rare powers and make the wheels of the world go round. Thinker-scientists of this sort usually are not too well known by the general public, unless their thoughts prove to be of outstanding importance. Newton, Einstein, Darwin, and Freud are among the best known.

A second kind of scientist is the serious young man in the white coat, reading the dials of monster machines while lights flash and buzzers purr softly. This picture symbolizes the technician, the lab man, the trained expert who tests, experiments, and works out the implications of what the whittler has been thinking.

The third kind of scientist is a relatively new

phenomenon. He goes to an office, dictates to secretaries, and spends a good part of his time in conferences or in handling contracts, budgets, and personnel. This symbolizes the businessman-scientist, who gets and allocates the funds which buy time and privacy for the whittler and machines for the lab man.

Note, however, that every scientist worthy of the name actually is a complex mixture of philosopher, technician, and businessman all rolled into one, and none is a "pure" type. But the relative emphasis varies greatly in different scientists.

Whatever type mixture he may be, a scientist works either in basic research, often called **pure science,** or in technology, often called **applied science.**

Basic research is done primarily to further man's understanding of nature. Possible practical applications of the findings are here completely disregarded. Scientists in this field are more frequently of the philosopher–lab-man type than in technology. They may be found principally in university laboratories and research institutes and, in lesser numbers, in industry and government. They have little to show for their efforts beyond the written accounts of their work; hence it is comparatively hard for them to convince nonscientists that they are doing anything essential. However, government and every enlightened industry today either support independent research or conduct such research. And the public is beginning to realize that pure science is the soil from which applied science must develop.

Technology is concerned primarily with applying the results of pure science to practical uses. No lesser inventiveness and genius are required in this field than in basic research, though here the genius is more of a commercial and less of a philosophical nature. Physicians, engineers, crime detectives, drug manufacturers, agricultural scientists, all are technologists. They have services and tangible products to sell; hence the public recognizes their worth rather readily.

Here again, note that no scientist is pure researcher or pure technologist. Mixtures are in evidence once more, with emphasis one way or the other. Moreover, technology is as much the fertilizer of basic research as the other way round. As new theories suggest new ways of applying them, so new ideas for doing things suggest further advances in research. Thus, in most research today, pure and applied science work hand in hand. Many conclusions of pure science cannot be tested before the technologist thinks up the means of testing. Conversely, before the technologist can produce desirable new products, years of basic research may first be required. In so far as every basic researcher must use equipment, however modest, he is also a technologist; and in so far as every technologist must understand how and why his products work, he is also a basic researcher.

It follows that any science shrivels whenever either of its two branches ceases to be effective. If for every dollar spent on science an immediate, tangible return is expected, and if the budding scientist is prevented from being a whittler by the necessity of producing something salable, then basic research will be in danger of drying up. And when that happens, technology too will become obsolete before long.

The Procedure of Science

Everything that is science ultimately has its basis in the **scientific method.** Both the powers and the limitations of science are defined by this method. And wherever the scientific method cannot be applied, there cannot be science.

Taken singly, most of the steps of the scientific method involve commonplace procedures carried out daily by every person. Taken together, they amount to the most powerful tool man has devised to know and to control nature.

OBSERVATION

All science begins with *observation,* the first step of the scientific method.

At once this delimits the scientific domain; something that cannot be observed cannot be investigated by science. However, observation need not be direct. Atomic nuclei, for example, or magnetism cannot be perceived directly through our sense organs. But their effects can be observed with instruments. Similarly, mind cannot be observed directly, but its effects can be, as expressed, for example, in behavior.

For reasons which will become clear presently, it is necessary, furthermore, that an observation be *repeatable,* actually or potentially. Anyone who doubts that objects fall back to the ground after being thrown into the air can convince himself of it by repeating the observation. One-time events on earth are outside science.

Correct observation is a most difficult art, acquired only after long experience and many errors. Everybody observes, with eyes, ears, touch, and all other senses, but few observe correctly. Lawyers experienced with witnesses, artists who teach students to draw objects in plain view, and scientists who try to see nature all can testify to this.

This difficulty of observation lies largely in unsuspected bias. People forever see what they *want* to see, or what they think they *ought* to see. It is extremely hard to rid oneself of such unconscious prejudice, and to see just what is actually there, no more and no less. Past experience, "common knowledge," and often teachers can be subtle obstacles to correct observation, and even experienced scientists may not always avoid them. That is why a scientific observation is not taken at face value until several scientists have repeated the observation independently and have reported the same thing. That is also a major reason why one-time, unrepeatable events normally cannot be science.

A scientific piece of work is only as good as the original observation. Observational errors persist into everything that follows, and the effort may be defeated before it has properly begun.

PROBLEM

After an observation has been made, the second step of the scientific method is to define a *problem*.

In other words, one asks a question about the observation. How does so and so come about? What is it that makes such and such happen in this or that fashion? Question asking additionally distinguishes the scientist from the layman; everybody makes observations, but not everybody shows further curiosity.

More significantly, not everyone sees that there may actually be a problem connected with an observation. During thousands of years, even curious people simply took it for granted that a detached, unsupported object falls to the ground. It took genius to ask, "How come?" and few problems, indeed, have ever turned out to be more profound.

Thus scientists take nothing for granted, and they ask questions, even at the risk of irritating others. Question askers are notorious for getting themselves into trouble, and so it has always been with scientists. But they have to continue to ask questions if they are to remain scientists. And society has to expect annoying questions if it wishes to have science.

Anyone can ask questions. However, good questioning, like good observing, is a high art. To be valuable scientifically, a question must be *relevant*, and it must be *testable*. The difficulty is that it is often very hard or impossible to tell in advance whether a question is relevant or irrelevant, testable or untestable. If a man collapses on the street and passers-by want to help him, it may or may not be irrelevant to ask when he had his last meal. Without experience one cannot decide on the relevance of this question, and a wrong procedure might be followed.

As to the testability of questions, it is clear that proper testing techniques must be available, actually or potentially. This cannot always be guaranteed. For example, Einstein's fame rests, in part, on showing that it is impossible to test whether or not the earth moves through an "ether," an assumption held for many decades. All questions about an ether therefore become nonscientific, and we must reformulate associated problems until they become testable. Einstein did this, and he came up with relativity.

In general, science does best with "How?" or "What?" questions. "Why?" questions are more troublesome. Some of them can be rephrased to ask "How?" or "What?" But others such as "Why does the universe exist?" fall into the untestable category. These are outside the domain of science.

HYPOTHESIS

Having asked a proper question, the scientist proceeds to the third step of the scientific method. This involves the seemingly quite unscientific procedure of guessing. One guesses what the answer to the question might conceivably be. Scientists call this postulating a *hypothesis*.

Hypothesizing distinguishes the scientist still further from the layman. For while many people observe and ask questions, most stop there. Some do wonder about likely answers, and scientists are among these.

Of course, a given question may have thousands of *possible* answers but only one *right* answer. Chances are therefore excellent that a random guess will be wrong. The scientist will not know whether his guess was or was not correct until he has completed the fourth step of the scientific method, *experimentation*. It is the function of every experiment to test the validity of a scientific guess.

If experimentation shows that the first guess was wrong, the scientist then must formulate a new hypothesis and once more test for validity by performing new experiments. Clearly, the guessing and guess testing might go on for years, and a right answer might never be found. This happens.

But here again, artistry, genius, and experience usually provide shortcuts. There are good guesses and bad ones, and the skilled scientist is generally able to decide at the outset that, of a multitude of possible answers, so and so many are unlikely answers. His knowledge of the field, his past experience, and the experience of others working on related problems normally allow him to reduce the many possibilities to a few likelihoods.

This is also the place where hunches, intuitions, and lucky accidents aid science enormously. In one famous case, so the story has it, the German chemist Kekule went to bed one night after a fairly alcoholic party and dreamed of six monkeys chasing one another in a circle, the tail of one held in the teeth of the other. Practically our whole chemical industry is based on that dream, for it told the sleeping scientist what the long-sought structure of benzene was—as we now know, 6 carbon atoms "chasing" one another in a circle. And benzene is the fundamental parent substance for thousands of chemical products.

The ideal situation for which the scientist generally strives is to reduce his problem to just two distinct alternative possibilities, one of which, when tested by experiment, may then be answered with a clear "yes," the other with a clear "no." It is exceedingly difficult to streamline problems in this way, and with many it cannot be done. Very often the answer obtained is "maybe." However, if a clear "yes" or "no" does emerge, scientists speak of an elegant piece of work, and such performances often are milestones in science.

EXPERIMENT

Experimentation is the fourth step in the scientific method. At this point, science and nonscience finally and completely part company.

Most people observe, ask questions, and also guess at answers. But the layman stops here: "My answer is so logical, so reasonable, and it sounds so 'right' that it must be correct." The listener considers the argument, finds that it is indeed logical and reasonable, and is convinced. He then goes out and in his turn converts others. Before long, the whole world rejoices that it has the answer.

Now the small, kill-joy voice of the scientist is heard in the background: "Where is the evidence?" Under such conditions in history, it has often been easier and more convenient to eradicate the scientist than to eradicate an emotionally fixed public opinion. But doing away with the scientist does not alter the fact that answers without evidence are at best unsupported opinions, at worst wishful thinking and fanatical illusions. Experimentation can provide the necessary evidence, and whosoever then experiments after guessing at answers becomes truly "scientific" in his approach, be he a professional scientist or not.

On the other hand, experiments do not guarantee a scientific conclusion. For there is ample room within experimentation and in succeeding steps to become unscientific again.

Experimentation is by far the hardest part of scientific procedure. There are no rules to follow; each experiment is a case unto itself. Knowledge and experience usually help technically, but to design the experiment, to decide on the means by which a hypothesis might best be tested, that separates the genius from the dilettante. The following example will illustrate the point:

Suppose that you observe that a chemical substance X, which has accidentally spilled into a culture dish full of certain disease-causing bacteria, kills all the bacteria in that dish. Problem: Can drug X be used to protect human beings against these disease-causing bacteria? Hypothesis: yes. Experiment: You go to a hospital and find a patient with that particular bacterial disease and inject some of the drug into the patient.

Possible result no. 1: Two days later the patient is well. Conclusion: hypothesis confirmed. You proceed to market the drug at high prices. Shortly afterwards, users of the drug die by the dozens, and you are tried and convicted for homicide.

Possible result no. 2: Two days later the patient is dead. Conclusion: The drug is worthless, and you abandon your project. A year later a colleague of yours is awarded the Nobel prize for having discovered a drug X which cures a certain bacterial disease in man—the same drug and the same disease in which you had been interested.

In this example, the so-called experiment was not an experiment at all.

First, no allowance was made for the possibility that people of different age, sex, eating habits, prior medical history, hereditary background, etc., might react differently to the same drug. Obviously, one would have to test the drug on many categories of carefully preselected patients, and there would have to be many patients in each such category. Besides, one would make the tests first on mice, or guinea pigs, or monkeys.

Second, the quantity of drug to be used was not determined. Clearly, a full range of dosages would have to be tested, for each different category of patient. We tacitly assume, moreover, that the drug is a pure substance; that is, it does not contain traces of other chemicals which might obscure, or interfere with, the results. If impurities are suspected, whole sets of separate experiments would have to be made.

Third, and most importantly, no account was taken of the possibility that your patient might have become well, or have died, in any case, even without your injecting the drug. What is needed here is **experimental control;** for every group of patients injected *with* drug solution, a precisely equal group must be injected with plain solution, *without* the drug. Then, by comparing results in the control and the experimental groups, one can determine whether or not the recovery or death of patients is really attributable to the drug.

Note that every experiment requires at least two parallel tests or sets of tests, identical in all respects except one. Of these parallel tests, one is the control series, and it provides a standard of reference for assessing the results of the experimental series. In drug experiments on people, not fewer than about 100,000 to 200,000 test cases, half of them controls, half of them experimentals, would be considered adequate. It should be easy to see why a single test on a single test case may give completely erroneous conclusions. Many repetitions of the same test, under as nearly identical conditions as possible, and at least one control test for each of the experimental tests—these are always prerequisite for any good experiment.

While an actual drug-testing program would be laborious, expensive, and time-consuming, the design of the experiment is nevertheless extremely simple. There are few steps to be gone through, and it is fairly clear what these steps must be. But there are many experiments where the tests themselves may not take more than an hour or two, while several years may have to be spent to think up appropriate, foolproof plans for these tests.

And despite a most ingenious design and a most careful execution, the result may still not be a clear yes or no. In a drug-testing experiment, for example, it is virtually certain that not 100 per cent of the experimental, drug-injected group will recover, nor 100 per cent of the untreated control group will remain sick.

The actual results might be something like 70 per cent recovery in the experimentals, and something like 20 per cent recovery in the controls. The experimentals here show that 30 per cent of the patients with that particular disease do not recover despite treatment, and the controls show that 20 per cent of the patients get well even without treatment. Moreover, if 70 out of every 100 experimental patients recover, then 20 out of these 70 were not actually helped by the drug, since, from the control data, they would have recovered even without treatment. Hence the drug is effective in only 70 per cent minus 20 per cent, or 50 per cent of the cases.

Medically, this may be a major accomplishment, for having the drug is obviously better than not having it. But scientifically, one is confronted with an equivocal "maybe" result. It will probably lead on to new research, based on the new observation that some people respond to the drug and some do not, and to the new problem of why and what can be done about it.

The result of any experiment represents **evidence.** That is, the original guess in answer to a problem is confirmed as correct or is invalidated. If invalidated, a new hypothesis, with new experiments, must be thought up. This is repeated until a hypothesis may be hit upon which can be supported with confirmatory experimental evidence.

As with legal evidence, scientific evidence can be strong and convincing, or merely suggestive, or poor. In any case, nothing has been proved. Depending on the strength of the evidence, one merely has a basis for regarding the original hypothesis with a certain degree of confidence.

Our new drug, for example, may be just what we claim it to be when we use it in this country. In another part of the world it might not work at all, or it might work better. All we can confidently say is that our evidence is based on so and so many experiments with American patients, American bacteria, American drugs, and that under specified hospital conditions, and with proper allowance for unspotted errors, the drug has an effectiveness of 50 per cent. Experimental results are never better or broader than the experiments themselves.

This is where many who have been properly scientific up to this point become unscientific. Their claims exceed the evidence; they mistake their partial answer for the whole answer; they contend to have proof for a fact, while all they actually have is some evidence for a hypothesis. There is always room for more and better evidence, or for new contradictory evidence, or indeed for better hypotheses.

THEORY

Experimental evidence is the basis for the fifth and final step in the scientific method, the formulation of a *theory*.

When a hypothesis has been supported by really convincing evidence, best obtained in many different laboratories and by many independent researchers, and when the total accumulated evidence is unquestionably reliable within carefully specified limits, then a theory may be proposed.

In our drug example, after substantial corroborating evidence has also been obtained from many other test localities, an acceptable theory would be the statement that "in such and such a bacterial disease, drug *X* is effective in 50 per cent of the cases."

This statement is considerably broader than the experiments on which it is based. Theories always are. The statement implies, for example, that drug *X*, regardless of who manufactures it, will be 50 per cent effective anywhere in the world, under any conditions, and can be used also for animals other than man.

Direct evidence for these extended implications does not exist. But inasmuch as drug *X* is already known to work within certain limits, the theory expresses the belief, the *probability*, that it may also work within certain wider limits.

To that extent every good theory has *predictive* value. It prophesies certain results. In contrast to nonscientific prophecies, scientific ones always have a substantial body of evidence to back them up. Moreover, the scientific prophecy does not say that something will certainly happen, but only that something is *likely* to happen, with a stated degree of probability.

A few theories have proved to be so universally valid and to have such a high degree of probability that they are spoken of as **natural laws.** For example, no exception has ever been found to the observation that, if an apple is disconnected from a tree and is not otherwise supported, it will fall to the ground. A law of gravitation is based on such observations.

Yet even laws do not pronounce certainties. For all practical purposes, it may well be irrational to assume that some day an apple will rise from a tree, yet there simply is no evidence that can absolutely guarantee the future. Evidence can be used only to estimate probabilities.

Most theories actually have rather brief life spans. For example, if, in chickens, our drug *X* should be found to perform not with 50 per cent but with 80 per cent efficiency, then our original theory becomes untenable and obsolete. And the exception to the theory becomes a new observation, beginning a new cycle of scientific procedure.

Thus new research might show that chickens contain a natural booster substance in blood which materially bolsters the action of the drug. This might lead to isolation, identification, and mass production of the booster substance, hence to world-wide improvement in curing the bacterial disease. And we would also have a new theory of drug action, based on the new evidence.

Thus science is never finished. One theory predicts, holds up well for a time, exceptions are found, and a new, more inclusive theory takes over—for a while. We may note in passing that old theories do not become incorrect but merely obsolete. Development of a new airplane does not mean that earlier planes can no longer fly. New theories, like new airplanes, merely range farther and serve more efficiently than earlier ones, but the latter still serve for their original purposes. Science is steady progression, not sudden revolution.

Clearly, knowledge of the scientific method does not by itself make a good scientist, any more than knowledge of English grammar alone makes a Shakespeare. At the same time, the demands of the scientific method should make it evident that scientists cannot be the cold, inhuman precision machines they are so often, and so erroneously, pictured to be. Scientists are essentially artists, and they require a sensitivity of eye and of mind as great as that of any master painter, and an imagination and keen inventiveness as powerful as that of any master poet.

The Limitations of Science

Observing, problem posing, hypothesizing, experimenting, and theorizing—this sequence of procedural steps is both the beginning and the end of science. To determine what science means in wider contexts, we must examine what scientific method implies and, more especially, what it does not imply.

THE SCIENTIFIC DOMAIN

First, scientific method defines the domain of science: *Anything to which the scientific method can be applied, now or in the future, is or will be science; anything to which the method cannot be applied is not science.*

This helps to clarify many a controversial issue. For example, does science have something to say about the concept of God? To determine this, we must find out if we can apply the scientific method.

Inasmuch as the whole universe and everything in it may be argued to be God's work, one may also argue that He is observable. It is possible, furthermore, to pose any number of problems, such as "Does he exist, is the universe indeed His doing, and is He present everywhere and in everything?" One can also hypothesize; some might say "yes," some might say "no."

Can we design an experiment about God? To be reliable, we would need experimental control, that is, two otherwise identical situations, one with God and one without. Now, what we wish to test is the hypothesis that God exists and is universal, i.e., that He is everywhere. Being a hypothesis thus far, this could be right or wrong.

If right, He would exist and exist everywhere; hence He would be present in *every* test we could possibly make. Thus we would never be able to devise a situation in which God is not present. But we need such a situation in order to have a controlled experiment.

But if the hypothesis is wrong, He would not exist, hence would be absent from *every* test we could possibly make. Therefore, we would never be able to devise a situation in which God *is* present. Yet we would need such a situation for a controlled experiment.

Right or wrong, our hypothesis is untestable either way, since we cannot run a controlled experiment. Hence we cannot apply the scientific method. The point is that the concept of God is outside the domain of science, and science cannot legitimately say anything about Him. He cannot be tested by science, because its method is inapplicable.

It should be carefully noted that this is a far cry from saying "Science disproves God," or "scientists must be godless; their method demands it." Nothing of the sort. Science specifically leaves anyone perfectly free to believe in any god whatsoever or in none. Many first-rate scientists are priests; many others are agnostics.

Science commits you to nothing more, and to nothing less, than adherence to scientific method.

Such adherence, it may be noted, is a matter of faith, just as belief in God or confidence in the telephone directory is a matter of faith. Whatever other faiths they may or may not hold, all scientists certainly have strong faith in the scientific method. So do those laymen who feel that having electric lights and not having bubonic plague are good things.

THE SCIENTIFIC AIM

A second consequence of the scientific method is that it defines the aim and purpose of science: *The objective of science is to make and to use theories.*

Many would say that the objective of science is to discover truth, to find out facts. We must be very careful here about the meaning of words. "Truth" is popularly used in two senses. It may indicate a temporary correctness, as in saying "It is true that my hair is brown." Or it may indicate an absolute, eternal correctness, as in saying "In plane geometry, the sum of the angles in a triangle is 180°."

From the earlier discussion on the nature of scientific method, it should be clear that science cannot deal with truth of the absolute variety. Something absolute is finished, known completely, once and for all. But science is never finished. Its method is unable to determine the absolute. Besides, once something is already known absolutely, there is no further requirement for science, since nothing further needs to be found out. Science can only adduce evidence for temporary truths, and another term for "temporary truth" is "theory." Because the word "truth," if not laboriously qualified, is ambiguous, scientists try not to use it at all.

The words "fact" and "proof" have a similar drawback. Both may indicate either something absolute or something temporary. If absolute, they are not science; if temporary, we have the less ambiguous word "evidence." Thus, science is content to find evidence for theories, and it leaves truths, proofs, and facts to others.

Speaking of words, "theorizing" is often popularly taken to mean "just talk and speculation." Consider, however, how successfully theorizing builds bridges!

SCIENCE AND VALUES

A third important implication of the scientific method is that *it does not make value judgments or moral decisions.*

It is the user of scientific results who may place valuations on them. But the results by themselves do not carry built-in values. And nowhere in the scientific method is there a value-revealing step.

The consequences of this are vast. For example, the science which produced the atomic bomb and penicillin cannot, of itself, tell whether these products are good things or bad things. Every man must determine this for himself as best he can. The scientist who discusses the moral aspects of nuclear weapons can make weightier statements than a layman only in so far as he may know more about what damage such weapons may or may not do. This will certainly influence his opinions. But whatever opinion he gives, it will be a purely personal evaluation made as a citizen, and any other scientist—or layman—who is equally well informed about the capacities of the weapons may conceivably disagree completely. Human values are involved here; science is not.

In all other types of evaluations as well, science is silent and noncommittal. Beauty, love, evil, happiness, virtue, justice, liberty, property, financial worth, all these are human values which science cannot peg. To be sure, love, for example, might well be a subject of scientific research, and it might show much about what love is and how it works. But such research could never discover that love is wonderful, an evaluation clear to anyone who has done a certain amount of nonscientific research.

It also follows that it would be folly to strive for a strictly "scientific" way of life or to expect strictly "scientific" government. Certainly the role of science might profitably be enlarged in areas of personal and public life where science can make a legitimate contribution. But a completely scientific civilization, adhering strictly to the rules of the scientific method, could never tell, for example, whether it is right or wrong to commit murder, or whether it is good or bad to love one's neighbor. Science cannot and does not give such answers. To be sure, this does not imply that science does away with morals. It merely implies that science cannot determine whether or not one ought to have moral standards, or what particular set of moral standards one ought to live by.

SCIENCE AND PURPOSES

A fourth implication of the scientific method is that *it cannot reveal purposes.*

No step in the method can yield such revelations. Just as the things science discovers do not have built-in values, so they also do not have built-in purposes. To be sure, scientific results may be employed toward various purposes, but this is a different matter.

Does the universe exist for a purpose? Does man live for a purpose? You cannot hope for an answer from science, for science is not designed to tackle such questions. Moreover, if you already hold certain beliefs in these areas, you cannot expect science either to prove or to disprove them for you.

Many arguments have been attempted to show purpose from science. For example, it has been maintained by some that the whole purpose of the evolution of living things was to produce man. Here the evidence supporting the theory of evolution is invoked to prove that man was the predetermined goal from the very beginning.

This implies several things besides the conceit that man is the finest product of creation. It implies, for example, that nothing could ever come after man, for he is supposed to be the last word in living magnificence. As a matter of record, man is sorely plagued by an army of parasites which cannot live anywhere except inside people. And it is clear that you cannot have a man-requiring parasite before you have a man.

Many human parasites did evolve after man. Thus, the purpose argument at best would show that the whole purpose of evolution was to produce those living organisms which cause influenza, diphtheria, gonnorrhea, and syphilis. This even the most ardent purpose arguer would probably not care to maintain.

Those who claim to see the goal of evolution in man do not know their biology in other ways. For the available evidence simply does not support the notion of goal-directed evolutionary trends. If any pattern is discernible, it is the pattern of chance, of opportunistic seeping into all possible livelihood niches offered by the environment, of extinction here and flourishing there, quite depending on what random heredity and changing environmental conditions allow.

Moreover, orchids, houseflies, and hundreds of other living types are just as recent products of evolution as man. One could therefore claim just as well, and just as untenably, that the purpose of evolution was to produce orchids or houseflies, man merely being a convenient backdrop.

The essential point is that any purpose-implying argument, in this or in any other issue, stands on quicksand the moment science is invoked as a witness. For to say such and such is the goal, the ultimate purpose, is to state a human value. And we already know where science stands in this respect.

If one is so inclined, he is of course perfectly free to believe that man is the pinnacle of it all. Then the rest of the universe with its billions of suns, including the living worlds which probably circle some of them, presumably are merely immense and fancy scenery for the microscopic stage on which man struts about. One may believe this, to be sure, but one cannot maintain that such beliefs are justified by evidence from science.

This, then, is the voice of science: a voice without truths, without values, without purposes.

And it is precisely because science is unfettered by such concepts that it advances. After centuries of earnest deliberation, mankind still does not agree on what truth is, values still change with the times and with places, and purposes remain as unfathomed as ever. On such shifting sands it has proved difficult to build a knowledge of nature. What little of nature we really know, and are likely to know in the foreseeable future, stands on the bedrock of science and its powerful tool, the scientific method.

The Language of Science

SCIENCE AS A WHOLE

Fundamentally, science is a *language,* a system of communication. Religion, art, politics, English, and French are among other such languages. Like them, science enables man to travel into new countries of the mind and to understand, and be understood, in such countries. Like other languages, science too has its grammar—the scientific method, its authors and its literature—the scientists and their written work, and its various dialects or forms of expression—physics, chemistry, biology, etc.

Indeed, science is one of the few truly universal languages, understood all over the globe. Art, religion, and politics are also universal. But each of these languages has several forms, so that Baptists and Hindus, for example, have little in common either religiously, artistically, or politically. Science, however, has the same single form everywhere, and Baptists and Hindus do speak the same scientific language.

It should be clear that no one language is "truer" or "righter" than any other. There are only *different* languages, each serving its function in its own domain. Many an idea is an idiom of a specific language and is best expressed in that language. For example, the German *Kindergarten* has been imported as is into English, and the American "baseball" has gone into the world without change. Likewise, one cannot discuss morality in the language of science, or thermodynamics in the language of religion, or artistic beauty in the language of politics; to the extent that each system of communication has specific idioms, there is no overlap or interchangeability among the systems.

On the other hand, many ideas can be expressed equally well in several languages. The English "water," the Latin "aqua," and the scientific "H_2O" are entirely equivalent, and no one of these is truer or righter than the others. They are merely different. Similarly, in one language man was created by God; in another man is a result of chance reactions among chemicals and of evolution. Again, neither the scientific nor the religious interpretation is the truer. If the theologian argues that everything was made by God, including scientists who think that man is the result of chance chemical reactions, then the scientist will argue back that chance chemical reactions created men with brains, including those theological brains which can conceive of a God who made everything. The impasse is permanent, and within their own systems of communication the scientist and the theologian are equally right. Many, of course, assume without warrant that it is the compelling duty of science to prove or disprove religious matters, and of religion, to prove or to disprove scientific matters.

The point is that there is no single "correct" formulation of any idea which spans various languages. There are only *different* formulations, and in given circumstances, one or the other may be more useful, more satisfying, or more effective. Clearly, he who is adept in more than one language will be able to travel that much more widely and will be able to feel at ease in the company of more than one set of ideas.

We are, it appears, forever committed to multiple standards, according to the different systems of communication we use. But we have been in such a state all along, in many different ways. Thus, the color red means one thing politically, something else in a fall landscape, and is judged by a third standard in the fashion world. Or consider the different worth of the same dime to a child, to you, and to the United States Treasury. To be multilingual in his interpretation of the world has been the unique heritage of man from the beginning. Different proportions of the various languages may be mixed into the outlook of different individuals, but science, religion, art, politics, spoken language, all these and many more besides are always needed to make a full life.

BIOLOGY

Within the language of science, biology is an important dialect, permitting travel in the domain of *living things*. Man probably was a biologist before he was anything else. His own body in health and disease; the phenomena of birth, growth, and death; and the plants and other animals which gave him food, shelter, and clothing undoubtedly were matters of serious concern to even the first of his kind. The motives were sheer necessity and the requirements of survival. These same motives still prompt the same biological studies today; agriculture, medicine, and fields allied to them are the most important branches of modern applied biology. In addition, biology today is strongly experimental, and pure research is done extensively all over the world. Some of this research promotes biological technology; all of it increases our understanding of how living things are constructed and how they operate.

Over the decades, the frontiers of biological investigations have been pushed into smaller and smaller realms. Some 100 to 150 years ago, when modern biology began, the chief interest was the whole plant or the whole animal, how it lived, where it could be found, and how it was related to other whole living things. Such studies have been carried on ever since, but, in addition, techniques gradually became available for the investigation of progressively smaller parts of the whole, their structures, their functions, and their relationships to one another. Thus it happened that, during the past few decades, the frontiers of biology were pushed down to the chemical level. And while research with larger biological units continues as before, the newest biology attempts to interpret living opera-tions in terms of the chemicals which compose living creatures.

Biology here merges with chemistry. Today there are already many signs that the next frontier will be the atoms which in their turn compose the chemicals, and biology tomorrow will undoubtedly merge with atomic physics. Such a trend is quite natural. For ultimately, living things are atomic things. Penultimately, they are chemical things, and only on a large scale are they plants and animals. In the last analysis, therefore, biology must attempt to show how atoms, and chemicals made out of atoms, are put together to form, on the one hand, something like a rock or a piece of metal and, on the other, something like a flower or a human baby.

This book is an outline of how successful the attempt has been thus far.

REVIEW QUESTIONS

1. What are the aims and the limitations of science? Review fully. In what sense is science a language, and how does it differ from other similar languages?

2. What characterizes the different present-day forms of science and the different specializations of scientists?

3. Review the steps of the scientific method, and discuss the nature of each of these steps. Define "controlled experiment."

4. How would you show by controlled experiment:
   a. Whether or not temperature affects the rate of growth of living things?
   b. Whether or not houseflies can perceive differently colored objects?
   c. Whether or not plants use up some of the soil they grow in?

5. Suppose that it were found in question 4*a* that, at an environmental temperature of 28°C, the growth of fertilized frog eggs into tadpoles occurs roughly twice as fast as at 18°C. What kinds of theories could such evidence suggest?

6. What are the historical and the modern relations of science and religion? Which of the ideas you have previously held about science should you now, after studying this chapter, regard as popular misconceptions?

7. Can you think of observations or problems which so far have not been investigated scientifically? Try to determine in each case whether or not such investigation is inherently possible.

8. Why is mathematics not considered to be a science?

9. Consider the legal phrases "Do you swear to tell the truth and nothing but the truth?" and "Is it not a fact that on the night of . . . ?" If phrases of this sort were to be used in a strictly scientific context, how should they properly be formulated?

10. Biology is called one of the *natural sciences,* all of which deal with the composition, properties, and behavior of matter in the universe. Which other sciences are customarily regarded as belonging to this category, and what distinguishes these from one another and from biology? What are *social sciences?* Do these too operate by the scientific method?

SUGGESTED COLLATERAL READINGS

Those who wish to read more on the general nature of science may find any of the following books particularly instructive:

Conant, J. B.: "Science and Common Sense," Yale University Press, 1951.

————: "On Understanding Science," Yale University Press, 1947.

————: "Modern Science and Modern Man," Columbia University Press, 1952.

Russell, B.: "The Scientific Outlook," Norton, 1931.

Baker, J. R.: "The Scientific Life," Macmillan, 1943.

Sullivan, J.: "The Limitations of Science," Mentor 35, or Viking, 1933.

Arber, A.: "The Mind and the Eye," Cambridge, 1954.

Beveridge, W. I. B.: "The Art of Scientific Investigation," Norton, 1957.

Excellent accounts of various historical aspects of science may be found in the following:

Dampier, W. C.: "A History of Science," 3d ed., Macmillan, 1942.

Singer, C.: "A History of Biology," rev. ed., Schuman, 1950.

A GOOD PLAN of procedure in a study of living things is to begin with a characterization of the broad domain with which biology deals, namely, the whole living world in time and in space.

Just what is life? How was it created originally in the far distant past? And how did such first life become the living world of today? Questions like these are clearly fundamental, and a discussion of the **origin of life** undoubtedly should be part of any broad characterization of the living world.

Within this world, the outstanding object and basic unit is the individual living creature, the **organism.** What is an organism? What is it made of, and what are its properties? And what exactly distinguishes it from an inanimate object? A general characterization of the living world certainly must deal fully with these issues.

Numbers of organisms are grouped together into local **communities.** A human observer especially is likely to be aware of the communal, strikingly social organization of his own kind. And if he looks farther afield, the regional groupings of plant and other animal populations are bound to attract his attention too. An examination of the living community evidently should be included in a broad characterization of life.

Finally, even the most casual observer of the living world cannot fail to notice its most general characteristic, namely, that it exists within a larger **environment** and that this environment influences it greatly. Clearly, a discussion of the environment and of its role in life should be part of any broad characterization.

The following four chapters are devoted to these topics. We begin at the beginning, with the origin of life.

PART

THE LIVING WORLD

2

IN THE BEGINNING: MOLECULE AND CELL

A STUDY of the original creation of living matter gives us important glimpses into the very nature of life. For before there were living creatures, there were only chemicals; and before there were chemicals, there were only atoms. Therefore, by tracing the origin of life, we may learn how the atoms and the chemicals came to be arranged into "living" wholes. The insight so gained may then serve later as the fundamental backdrop against which all other life processes may be viewed and studied.

To be sure, our understanding of the origin of life is at present far from complete. Much of what is known about it is simply a backward projection of living types and living activities encountered today.

For example, biologists deduce from viruses, bacteria, and other primitive existing forms what the earliest living forms might have been like. Other clues come from astronomy, physics, and geology, sciences which contribute information about the probable physical character of the ancient earth. Important data are also provided by ingenious chemical experiments, designed to duplicate in the laboratory some of the steps which many centuries ago may have led to the beginning of life.

All this, supplemented to no small degree by speculation, today enables us to give a preliminary but plausible account of living origins. This account contains just enough detail to suggest how life *could* have arisen from nonlife. And it contains more than enough detail to show what we mean by the term "living."

Since, in large measure, the story of life and its origin is written in the language of chemistry, we first must understand something of that language. We therefore begin this story with an outline of its grammar.

The Chemical Background

ATOMS AND MOLECULES

The universe is made up of 92 different basic kinds of materials, called chemical **elements. Atoms** are the unimaginably small units of these elements. The atoms of different elements differ in mass, or "weight." Hydrogen atoms are the lightest; uranium atoms are the heaviest. Man has learned to create artificially a number of elements still heavier than uranium.

Each element is given a chemical symbol, often the first or the first two letters of its English or Latin name. Thus the symbol for hydrogen is H, that for carbon is C, that for silicon is Si. Consult Table 1 for others. To represent 1 atom of an element, one simply writes the appropriate symbol. For example, if not otherwise specified, the letter H stands for 1 atom of hydrogen.

Under given conditions of temperature, pressure, and concentration, most atoms are able to attach to, and to remain linked to, certain other atoms. Such combinations of 2 or more atoms are called **molecules.** A molecule is the smallest unit of a **compound.** Molecule is to compound as atom is to element.

TABLE 1. Some common chemical elements

Element	Symbol	Number of possible bonds
Hydrogen	H	1
Sodium	Na	1
Potassium	K	1
Chlorine	Cl	1
Iodine	I	1
Calcium	Ca	2
Magnesium	Mg	2
Sulfur	S	2
Oxygen	O	2
Copper	Cu	1, 2
Iron	Fe	2, 3
Carbon	C	2, 4
Silicon	Si	4
Aluminum	Al	3
Nitrogen	N	3, 5
Phosphorus	P	3, 5

To make atoms link together into a molecule, work must be done. That is, an external force, or better, an external source of **energy**, must provide the "cement" which will hold the atoms together. Put another way, to form a bond between 2 atoms, *bond energy* must be supplied from the outside. In different cases, different forms of energy may be used. For example, heat, light, electricity, X rays, and mechanical pressure are different forms of energy, and each of them may do the work necessary to combine given atoms into a given molecule (Fig. 2.1). The bond energy which then holds these atoms together is said to be *chemical* energy.

By virtue of the bond energies between its atoms, every molecule holds energy "in storage." If by appropriate means a bond between 2 atoms is broken, the atoms separate and the bond energy is released. The amount of this energy equals the amount which had to be supplied originally to link the atoms together.

Each kind of atom has a fixed, limited bonding capacity. That is, it can form only so many bonds with other atoms (see Table 1). For reasons which need not be examined here, a few types of atoms cannot form any bonds. The atoms of the elements helium, neon, and argon are among these. Such elements are chemically completely inert, and their atoms cannot participate in the formation of molecules.

Atoms of hydrogen, and of a number of other elements, may form single bonds. For example, one H atom may combine with exactly one other H atom. Each here uses up its entire bonding capacity: H + H → H—H. The single bond is indicated by the short line between the H's. One hydrogen atom could also combine with 1 atom of chlorine, which also can form only a single bond: H + Cl → H—Cl.

Two, three, four, and even five bonds may be formed by the atoms of other elements. For example, oxygen, nitrogen, and carbon may form 2, 3, and 4 bonds, respectively. We may symbolize these bonding capacities by writing

The 2 bonds of an oxygen atom could hold, for example, 1 hydrogen atom each. The resulting molecule, *water,* may be written H—O—H. Or both bonds of 1 oxygen atom could hold a second oxygen atom: O=O. Or the 4 bonds of 2 oxygen atoms could satisfy the bonding capacity of 1 carbon atom: O=C=O.

An atom may combine with several different kinds of atoms. For example, in the molecule

$$Cl-\overset{\displaystyle H}{\underset{\displaystyle H}{C}}-O-H$$

the 4 bonds of the carbon atom hold 4 atoms of three different elements: Cl, H, and O. Not all atomic combinations possible on paper can actually occur in nature. The principles pertinent here are known, but they need not be discussed in the present context.

In symbolizing a molecule, it is not necessary to show the distribution of the bonds as above. The molecule may be depicted in such a way that only the types and numbers of the component atoms are indicated, without reference to the bonds. In this procedure, the number of like atoms is written as a subscript to the chemical symbol. For example, the hydrogen molecule H—H may be written also as H_2. Water (H—O—H) may be written also as H_2O. The molecule O=C=O above, depicting the structure of carbon dioxide, may be written also as CO_2. If more than one molecule of a particular type is to be represented, the appropriate number is put before the molecular formula. For example, $5H_2O$ means five water molecules.

It should be clear that molecules differ in size and mass according to the number and the types of atoms in them. Thus, H_2O is larger and heavier than H_2. Some molecules are extremely large, containing hundreds or thousands of atoms each. As we shall see, very large molecules are particularly characteristic of living systems.

The chemical properties of a molecule are determined by the *numbers,* the *types,* and the *spatial arrangement* of the component atoms. Two

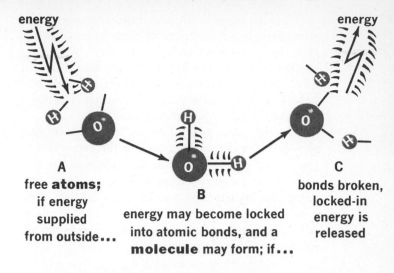

FIG. 2.1. External energy is needed to make atoms combine into a molecule. When the atomic combination is disrupted, the energy originally put in is released.

molecules may contain the same atoms, but if these are arranged differently, the molecules will have different properties. For example,

$$Cl-\overset{\displaystyle H}{\underset{\displaystyle H}{C}}-O-H \quad and \quad H-\overset{\displaystyle Cl}{\underset{\displaystyle H}{C}}-O-H$$

contain identical atoms, and both molecules may be symbolized as CH_3OCl. But since their atoms are bonded in different patterns, they are, in fact, different kinds of molecules.

MOLECULES AND REACTIONS

With certain exceptions unimportant in the present context, free atoms today do not exist naturally on the surface of the earth. As we shall see shortly, atoms probably were free at one time, just after the origin of the earth. Later, however, atoms which could combine with others did so. Ever since, the earth has been very largely a collection of molecules.

But molecules are not absolutely permanent structures. If two or more of them come into contact, they may **react** with one another and thereby change into different kinds of molecules. Virtually all chemical events on earth, including those which have led to, and now occur within, living systems, are *contact reactions among molecules.*

In the most general terms, a molecular reaction changes the number and/or the types and/or the spatial arrangements of the atoms in the participating molecules. More specifically, four main categories of reactions may be distinguished. First, 1 or more atoms of 1 molecule may trade places with 1 or more atoms of another. This is an **exchange** reaction. For example,

$$H-Cl + Na-O-H \rightarrow H-O-H + Na-Cl$$

hydrochloric   sodium   water   sodium
acid   hydroxide   chloride

Second, 2 or more molecules may add together and form a single, larger molecule. This is a **synthesis** reaction. For example,

$$CO_2 + H_2O \rightarrow H_2CO_3$$
carbon   water   carbonic
dioxide   acid

Third, 1 molecule may break up into 2 or more smaller molecules. This is a **decomposition** reaction, and it is the reverse of synthesis. For example,

$$H_2CO_3 \rightarrow CO_2 + H_2O$$

Lastly, the numbers and types of atoms in a molecule may remain the same, but the pattern of the atoms changes. This is a **rearrangement** reaction. For example,

$$Cl-\overset{\overset{\displaystyle H}{|}}{\underset{\underset{\displaystyle H}{|}}{C}}-O-H \rightarrow H-\overset{\overset{\displaystyle Cl}{|}}{\underset{\underset{\displaystyle H}{|}}{C}}-O-H$$

Note that, in every equation illustrating a reaction, the *total* numbers and types of atoms to the left of the arrow equal exactly the totals to the right of the arrow; in the reaction as a whole,

atoms are neither gained nor lost. It is important to make sure that equations *balance* in this fashion, whenever a reaction is depicted symbolically.

A molecular reaction possible on paper can occur actually only under appropriate conditions. What these conditions must be varies for different reactions. Temperature, pressure, and the concentration of participating molecules are some of the governing factors.

Since a reaction among molecules makes, breaks, or rearranges the bonds between some of the atoms and since bonds represent chemical energy, *energy changes* are likely to accompany the reaction. In synthesis, for example, at least 1 atom of 1 molecule becomes linked to at least 1 atom of another molecule; the new link combines the reacting molecules into a single larger one. But as noted earlier, to forge a link bond energy must be supplied from the outside. Hence, a certain amount of energy must be put into a synthesis reaction if such a reaction is to occur. Symbolically,

$$A + B + \text{energy} \rightarrow A-B$$

This describes an **endergonic,** or energy-*requiring,* reaction (Fig. 2.2). The energy becomes incorporated into the new molecule *A—B.*

Conversely, in a decomposition, at least one existing bond is broken, and the energy of that bond is released:

$$A-B \rightarrow A + B + \text{energy}$$

This symbolizes the **exergonic,** or energy-*yielding,* reaction. Under suitable conditions, energy obtained from a decomposition may be used to make possible a synthesis. This happens frequently in living systems, as we shall see. Energy changes usually also accompany molecular exchanges and rearrangements. Thus

$$A-B + C-D \rightarrow A-C + B-D \pm \text{energy}$$

and

$$A \rightarrow B \pm \text{energy}$$

With this as a general background, we are now ready to examine the origin of life.

Initial Events

THE EARLY EARTH

Living creatures on earth are a direct product of the earth. There is now little doubt that living things owe their origin entirely to certain physical and chemical properties of the ancient earth. Nothing supernatural was involved—only time and natural physical and chemical laws operating within the peculiarly suitable earthly environment. Given such an environment, life probably *had* to happen. And it undoubtedly happened, and may even now be happening, elsewhere too, in other solar systems, if environmental conditions there are approximately similar to those of the early earth.

These early conditions trace back to the origin of the solar system as a whole. The best available evidence indicates that the sun and earth are both about 4½ to 5 billion years old. Several hypotheses have been proposed to explain the process of formation. According to one, now widely accepted, the whole solar system formed from a hot, rapidly rotating ball of gas. This gas was made up of free atoms. Hydrogen atoms probably were the most abundant, and other, heavier kinds were present in lesser quantities. The sun was formed when most of this atomic gas, hence most of the hydrogen, gravitated toward the center of the ball. Even today, the sun is composed largely of hydrogen atoms. A swirling belt of gas remained outside the new sun. Eddies formed in this belt, and in time it broke up into a few smaller gas clouds. These spinning spheres of fiery matter constituted the early planets.

The Earth thus probably started out as a glowing mass of free hydrogen and other types of atoms. These eventually became sorted out according to weight. Heavy ones, such as iron and nickel, sank toward the center of the earth, where they are still present today. Lighter atoms, such as silicon and aluminum, formed a middle shell. The very lightest, such as hydrogen, nitrogen, oxygen, and

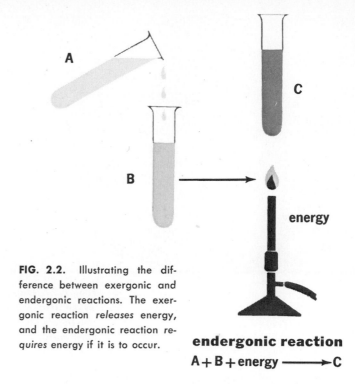

FIG. 2.2. Illustrating the difference between exergonic and endergonic reactions. The exergonic reaction *releases* energy, and the endergonic reaction *requires* energy if it is to occur.

energy

endergonic reaction
A + B + energy ⟶ C

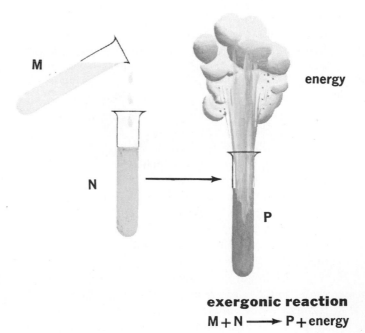

energy

exergonic reaction
M + N ⟶ P + energy

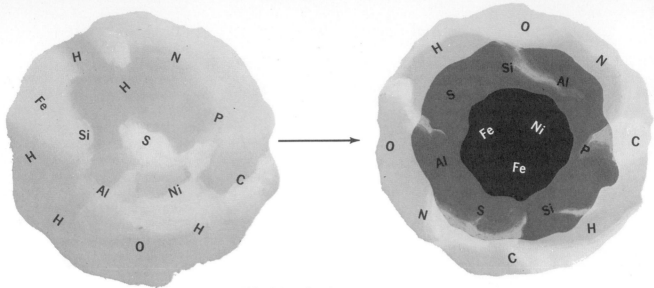

FIG. 2.3. The elements composing the early earth became sorted out according to weight. Heavy elements like iron (Fe) sank to the center, lighter ones like silicon (Si) formed a middle shell, and very light elements like hydrogen (H) collected into an outer mantle.

carbon, collected in the outermost layers (Fig. 2.3).

At first, temperatures were probably too high for the formation of molecules. Excessive heat disrupts the bonds between atoms as fast as such bonds might form. But under the influence of the cold of cosmic space, the earth began to cool down gradually. And in time, low enough temperatures prevailed to permit a relatively stable bonding together of atoms. Molecules then appeared in profusion, and free atoms disappeared.

With this, we reach the beginning of the chemical history of the earth, which henceforth will accompany the physical history. Conditions were apparently appropriate for a remarkable series of reactions, synthesis reactions in particular. After free atoms had combined into small simple molecules, some of these subsequently combined into larger molecules. Some of these in turn later combined into still larger molecules. After several more of such rounds of chance synthesis, spread out through many millions of years, certain extremely large molecules had formed which possessed unique, "living" properties.

As far as they are known or suspected, what are the details of these life-producing reactions?

THE FIRST ROUND

The Early Atmosphere

Among the lightest and most abundant materials in the surface gas of the early earth were, as noted above, atoms of hydrogen, oxygen, carbon, and nitrogen. Therefore, when temperatures became low enough to allow the formation of molecules, the atoms of these four elements must have played a conspicuous role. Of the four, the most reactive is hydrogen. That is, hydrogen combines more readily with O, N, and C than these three combine with one another. Three types of molecules therefore must have appeared in the earth's outer layers:

H atoms combined with O atoms, producing molecules of

$$H—O—H \quad \text{or } H_2O \quad \text{or water}$$

H atoms combined with N atoms, producing molecules of

$$H-\overset{\displaystyle H}{\underset{\displaystyle H}{N}} \quad \text{or } NH_3 \quad \text{or ammonia}$$

H atoms combined with C atoms, producing molecules of

$$H-\overset{\displaystyle H}{\underset{\displaystyle H}{C}}-H \quad \text{or } CH_4 \quad \text{or methane}$$

Temperatures were such that these three compounds persisted as gases, and the earth henceforth had an outer *atmosphere* containing large quantities of these three.

We have indirect evidence that these events actually occurred, not only on earth but on some of the other planets as well. For example, today on the cold, distant planet Jupiter water, ammonia, and methane appear to be present in the form of permanently frozen solids. Apparently, the initial chemical events there were as on earth, but at that great distance from the sun, the surface of the planet probably froze before much further chemical change could occur. The modern earth, to be sure, does not have an ammonia-methane atmosphere. We shall soon see how the present "air" may have developed.

Energy for the formation of water, ammonia, and methane may have come from the sun, in the form of X rays, ultraviolet rays, heat, and light. Moreover, the heat of the earth probably was itself still sufficiently intense to forge atoms into molecules, yet no longer intense enough to disrupt the molecules formed.

In time, as the gas ball which was the earth continued to cool, temperatures became low enough to allow some of the gases to liquefy, and some of the liquids in turn to solidify. Heavy substances near the center of the earth probably tended to liquefy and solidify first. But the pressure produced by the weight of the overlying materials generated so much heat that any tendency to solidify was counteracted. To this day the earth contains a hot, liquid or semiliquid center. On the other hand, the middle shell of lighter substances did congeal, and a solid, gradually thickening crust developed. As it thickened and cooled, it wrinkled and folded and gave rise to the first mountain ranges. Overlying this crust was the outer atmospheric mantle, which at prevailing temperatures still remained gaseous.

The Early Ocean

Then the rains started. All the water on earth up to this stage was in the atmosphere, forming clouds probably hundreds of miles thick. The solidifying crust underneath at first was sufficiently hot that any liquid water would boil away instantly. But eventually the crust became cool enough to hold water in liquid form, and then rain began falling in unceasing, centuries-long downpours. Basins and shallows filled up, and torrential rivers tore down from the mountains. The oceans formed in this way.

Dissolved in these seas were some of the atmospheric ammonia and methane, compounds which persist as gases at temperatures at which water is liquid. Also accumulating in the ocean were salts and minerals. At first there were none, but as the rivers eroded the mountainsides and dissolved them away, and as violent tides battered the shores and reduced them to powder, salts and minerals came to be added to the ocean in increasing quantities. Moreover, massive submarine bursts of molten lava probably erupted frequently through the earth's crust, and they too added their substance to the mineral content of the world's waters (Fig. 2.4). Thus the oceans acquired their saltiness relatively early, and to a small extent they became saltier still during subsequent ages.

The formation first of water, methane, and ammonia and second of large bodies of *liquid* water containing methane, ammonia, and many minerals in solution was the key event which made the later origin of life possible. Water was, and is now, the most essential single component of living

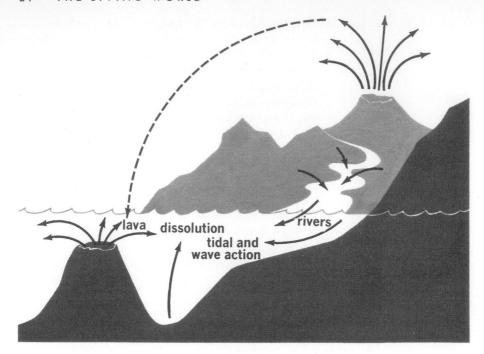

FIG. 2.4. The original sources of oceanic salt. Some derived from volcanoes, both submarine and terrestrial; some was dissolved out of the sea bottom; a third source was tidal action, which crumbled and dissolved the shore lines; and a good deal of salt also came from the land surface, leached out by rain and rivers.

matter. On an average, two-thirds, and often as much as 90 per cent or more, of anything living is water; and the presence of water in bulk over three-fourths of the earth's surface is today of profound importance in the economy of living things. The fundamental role of water traces primarily to two of its properties.

First, water is virtually the best of all possible solvents. It dissolves more of more substances than practically any other liquid, and this means that it is an ideal medium for chemical reactions. Chemical processes also occur in gases and solids, but many more can occur in liquids, and much more readily. Since living processes are based on chemical processes, the abundant supply of liquid water on the early earth was a promising circumstance.

Second, water was originally the only good source of hydrogen and oxygen. Both elements have exceedingly useful properties, and the construction of a living system on a chemical basis virtually demands their availability. But, as noted, free hydrogen atoms and free oxygen atoms became unavailable soon after the origin of the earth. Water molecules then came to serve as the prin-

cipal suppliers. Water remains today virtually the only usable source of hydrogen and one of the important sources of oxygen.

Thus oceanic water set the stage for a second round of reactions toward the formation of living matter. The actors on this stage were the various materials dissolved in water, plus water itself. And the title role was played by the carbon of methane.

THE SECOND ROUND

Properties of Carbon

Carbon, with a bonding capacity of 4, is a most versatile element. In the case of methane, all 4 bonds of carbon hold H atoms:

$$
\begin{array}{c}
\text{H} \\
| \\
\text{H---C---H} \\
| \\
\text{H}
\end{array}
$$

But any one or more of these may be exchanged rather readily with other kinds of atoms. For example, if methane is allowed to react with chlorine or chlorine-containing molecules, 1, 2, 3, or all 4 of the H atoms of methane may be replaced by Cl atoms. The resulting compounds will be CH_3Cl, CH_2Cl_2, $CHCl_3$, and CCl_4, of which the third is the most familiar: $CHCl_3$ is *chloroform*, an anesthetic. The H atoms of methane may also be replaced by many elements other than chlorine and by several different ones at the same time.

Therefore, in the oceans of the early earth, methane must have reacted with the numerous other simple compounds present there, and a large variety of carbon-containing molecules must have come into existence. Among the important compounds which reacted with methane were methane itself, as well as carbon-containing molecules formed from methane. This points up the most interesting property of carbon: many carbon atoms may link directly to one another, in an almost infinite variety of patterns. Thus if we start with methane, one of its H atoms may be replaced by a carbon atom derived, for example, from another methane molecule:

The free bonds of the added carbon may be filled by more H atoms or by other atoms, including more carbon atoms:

Molecules containing long *chains* of carbon can be formed in this way:

Moreover, the carbon at one end of such a chain may combine with the carbon at the other end, and carbon *rings* will be produced. Benzene is a good example of this:

Many additional combining possibilities exist. For example, carbon chains can be branched, rings and chains can become joined to one another, and any of these "patterns in carbon" can extend into three as well as two dimensions. Such carbon structures form molecular "skeletons," as it were, and the free bonds of the skeletons can be fleshed out with other atoms—hydrogen and oxygen, for example.

Clearly, carbon-to-carbon combinations introduce the possibility of tremendous *complexity*, as well as *variety*, into molecular structure. In fact, carbon-containing substances display more complexity and more variety than all other chemicals put together. Note also that two molecules with even slightly differently arranged carbon skeletons are different kinds of molecules and possess different chemical properties.

Compounds of Carbon

The formation of molecules containing several linked carbons from methane and substances which reacted with methane was a critical phase of the early history of living matter. Today, carbon-to-carbon combinations occur almost exclusively within living matter, or in materials derived from living and once living matter. For this reason, such chemicals are called **organic** compounds. This contrasts with water, mineral substances, metallic materials, and other **inorganic** compounds, which do not contain linked carbons. Inorganic substances make up the nonliving world, but they are also found in substantial quantities in the living.

Among the many kinds of organic compounds undoubtedly formed in the early seas, five particular groups came to have special significance in later events. The first of these groups consisted of molecules with a few carbons each, arranged in chains. The only other atoms of these molecules were H's and O's, present in a 2:1 ratio. Probably formed originally from methane and water, such molecules represent the group of chemicals known as **carbohydrates.**

The most familiar carbohydrates are the **sugars.** The sugar **glucose** is an important example. A glucose molecule possesses 6 carbons in a chain, and to it are joined 12 atoms of hydrogen and 6 of oxygen. Hence the atomic formula of glucose is $C_6H_{12}O_6$. The detailed arrangement of the atoms here (and of compounds discussed below) is indicated in Fig. 2.5. Not all sugars possess 6 carbons. For example, we shall soon encounter some with only 5 carbons, and others with more than 6 carbons.

The second group of subsequently significant organic compounds included **glycerin.** A molecule of this substance possesses a 3-carbon skeleton, with 8 atoms of hydrogen and 3 of oxygen attached. The atomic formula therefore is $C_3H_8O_3$.

A third group too consisted entirely of carbon, hydrogen, and oxygen. Here again the carbons were arranged in chains, from 2 to 20 or more atoms long. These substances were the **fatty acids.** In all fatty acids, only hydrogen is attached to the carbons, except at one end of the chain. Here 2 oxygen atoms are present in addition to hydrogen (consult Fig. 2.5).

A fourth group of early compounds comprised the **amino acids.** Their carbon skeleton was, and is today, either a chain or a ring, and the identifying feature of these acids is the presence of *nitrogen,* in addition to carbon, hydrogen, and oxygen. The nitrogen occurs here in the form called an *amino group.*

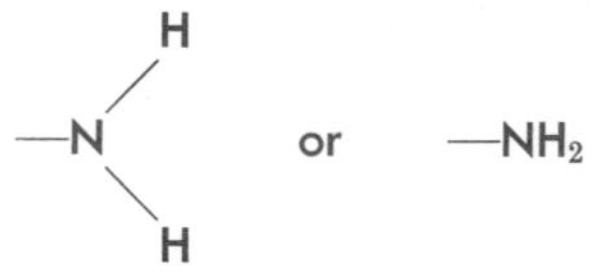

$$-N\begin{array}{c}H\\[4pt]\\[4pt]H\end{array} \qquad \text{or} \qquad -NH_2$$

This group undoubtedly was derived from ammonia by the removal of 1 H atom from NH_3. In each amino acid, at least one amino group is joined to the carbon skeleton.

Finally, the fifth group of important organic materials included the **purines** and **pyrimidines.** The molecular skeleton here is always a ring structure. The rings consist primarily of carbon atoms, but several nitrogen atoms are included as well. As Fig. 2.5 shows, a pyrimidine molecule is built of one such ring, and purines have a double-ring skeleton.

For a summary of these chemical events of the second round of early reactions, consult Fig. 2.6.

What was the energy source for these synthe-

FIG. 2.5.   The chemical structure of various types of molecules probably formed during a second round of reactions.

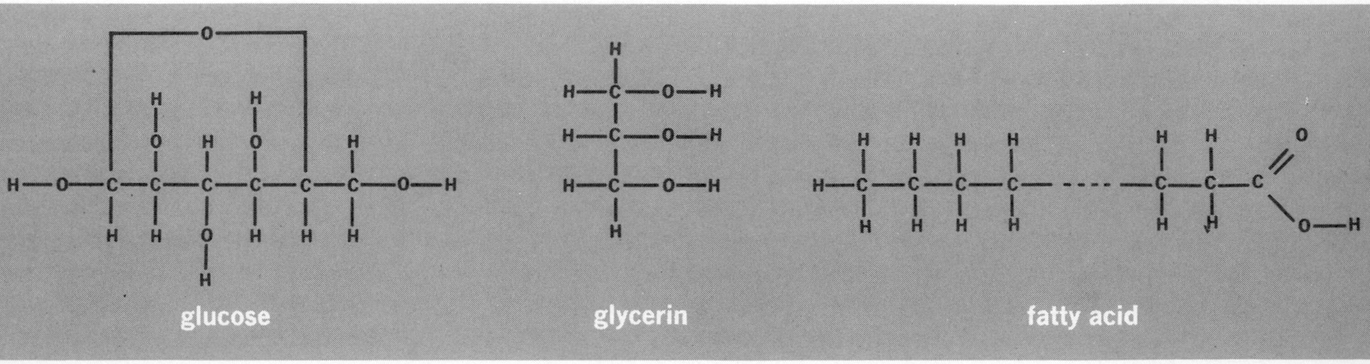

glucose   glycerin   fatty acid

ses, and what is the evidence that such reactions actually occurred?

Of the two sources of energy already mentioned earlier, one may still have played a significant role. The surface temperature of the earth by then was below the boiling point of water, and earth heat could no longer have been very effective. However, the ultraviolet rays and much other high-energy radiation from the sun still penetrated down to earth in unabated intensity. Some of this radiation could well have provided the necessary energy for reactions among methane, ammonia, and water.

Moreover, another new energy source was by then available also: powerful electric discharges in lightning, which must have occurred almost continuously in the early cloud-laden, storm-lashed atmosphere. Like solar radiation, lightning too is capable of producing chemical reactions. Either lightning or solar energy could have acted directly on the gas molecules of the atmosphere, as still happens today to some extent. The resulting aerial chemicals could then have been washed down into the seas by rain.

Alternatively, reactions could have taken place directly in the waters of the ocean, where methane and all other necessary ingredients were dissolved. Or atmosphere and ocean both could have been reaction sites at the start. Later reactions undoubtedly occurred primarily in the ocean.

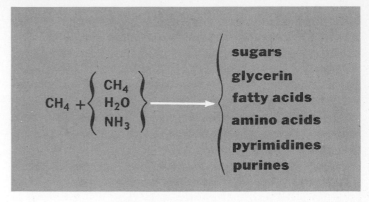

FIG. 2.6.   Summary of the second round of reactions. Interaction of methane with itself, water, and ammonia probably resulted in the compounds shown on the right.

That such events could indeed have taken place was demonstrated dramatically in recent laboratory experiments (see Suggested Readings, page 45). Methane gas, ammonia gas, and water were put together in a flask, and electricity was discharged into this mixture for several days, to simulate the lightning discharges of the early earth. When the contents of the flask were then examined, many sugars, amino acids, fatty acids, and other simple organic compounds were found to be present!

Thus there is good reason to think that, under

amino acid   pyrimidine   purine

the impact of early energy sources, simple gases and inorganic materials reacted with one another and gave rise to a variety of organic materials which accumulated in the ancient seas. These organic materials were not very complex as yet, but they contained the all-important carbon-to-carbon combinations. This was the key which was to open the door to life, for it made possible the synthesis of even larger molecules, with larger carbon skeletons and many novel chemical properties.

THE THIRD ROUND

Once started, the joining of carbon molecule to carbon molecule continued. Among the organic substances already present, some must have reacted with one another and with inorganic materials, and highly complex new types of molecules must have formed.

Specifically, sugars combined with one another. The result was a series of larger new molecules containing very long carbon chains. Some of the **polysaccharides** formed in this way are quite familiar. For example, *starch, cellulose,* and *glycogen* are polysaccharides, each consisting of a dozen or more sugar molecules joined together. The early synthesis of polysaccharides was to prove important for the development of living systems, for, as we shall see, polysaccharides are good building materials and excellent sources of chemical energy. They still function in these capacities today.

In another series of reactions, glycerin combined with various fatty acids. **Fats** were formed in this manner. They too proved to be very good sources of energy, and as building materials they came to be even more widely useful than polysaccharides.

By far the most important new construction materials formed were the **proteins**. These consist of amino acids, joined together in exceedingly complex ways. A tremendous number of amino acid molecules—in the order of 100,000 or more

—can combine to form a protein, and the geometrical pattern of such unions can vary almost infinitely. As a result, proteins are not only among the largest molecules in existence but also among the most varied structurally. Primarily because of their complexity and variety, they became the most widely adaptable building materials in the formation of living matter.

The development of proteins was important also for another crucial reason: some proteins could enormously *speed up reactions* among other molecules. Chemists know several methods by which a molecular reaction may be accelerated. Application of heat, for example, is a procedure employed frequently. Many reactions can be speeded up without heating, by adding what are called *catalysts.* We shall see later how such materials produce this effect. Here we note only that many proteins may act as catalysts and that protein catalysts are called **enzymes.** With the appearance of proteins, therefore, the chemical tempo in the early oceans could quicken substantially. And from the beginning right to the present, "living" was to become a function of *enzyme-accelerated reactions.*

Another group of supermolecules, at least as varied and complex as proteins, developed from the purines and the pyrimidines. Some of these each combined with two other kinds of substances: a 5-carbon sugar and phosphate, which was, and is now, one of the inorganic mineral components present in the ocean. Two types of combinations thus formed, *purine-sugar-phosphate* and *pyrimidine-sugar-phosphate.* Either of these is known as a **nucleotide.** Hundreds and thousands of different nucleotide molecules then combined with one another, producing exceedingly complex supermolecules called **nucleic acids.**

We may summarize these various reactions of the third round as in Fig. 2.7.

It was the development of nucleic acids that made the ultimate formation of living matter a virtual certainty. The crucial event occurred during a fourth round of reactions.

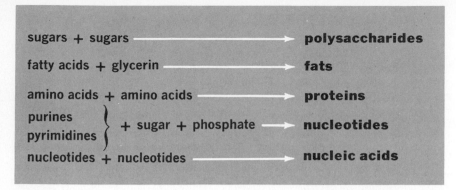

FIG. 2.7. Summary of the third round of reactions. Interactions shown to the left of the arrows probably resulted in the compounds shown on the right.

Later Events

THE FOURTH ROUND

The process of progressive chemical synthesis continued; some of the polysaccharides, fats, proteins, and nucleic acids combined with one another in various ways. Among the resulting giant molecules were the **nucleoproteins,** combinations of nucleic acids and proteins. These are the largest and most complex molecules known. Their total complexity combines the very considerable complexities of the individual nucleic acids and proteins.

Reproduction

There are good reasons to believe that, sooner or later during their history, nucleoproteins featured several radically new properties. The most significant of these was that certain nucleoprotein molecules could make exact replicas of themselves; that is, they could *reproduce!*

At first glance it may seem utterly fantastic that a mere molecule should be able, by its own efforts, to make a copy of itself. But the process becomes quite plausible if we consider its details, which research is just now beginning to unravel.

In making an exact copy of any object, it is necessary, first, to duplicate the individual component parts of that object, and then to arrange the duplicate parts in such a way that the whole assembly will match the original. Therefore, if a copy of a nucleoprotein molecule is to be made, duplicate sugars, amino acids, phosphates, purines, and pyrimidines are required. In the early ocean, these component parts of a nucleoprotein already existed in abundance. Some of them had combined to form the original nucleoproteins, and the rest could serve later as ready-made duplicate building materials. Hence nucleoprotein reproduction became mainly a matter of *arranging* already existing raw materials into larger wholes which would match precisely the original nucleoproteins.

Nucleoprotein molecules are long, extended, fibrous structures. As we shall see in a later chapter, the individual sections of such a molecule have chemical affinity for like sections. That is, any segment along a nucleoprotein molecule is able to attach to itself matching building materials from the environment. Consequently, if all required duplicate building materials are present in the vicinity of a nucleoprotein molecule, these materials may in time become attached along the nucleoprotein in matching order. To complete the copying process, it is then necessary only to link

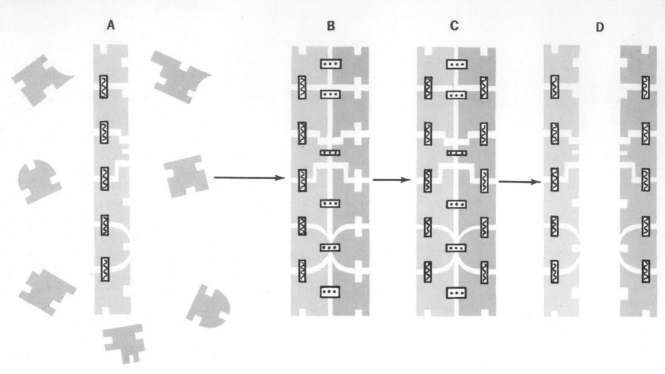

FIG. 2.8. Diagrammatic symbolization of nucleoprotein reproduction. **A,** a preexisting nucleoprotein molecule (light shading), surrounded by raw materials needed for the construction of a nucleoprotein duplicate (dark shading). **B,** a raw material of a given type has affinity for a corresponding component of a nucleoprotein, and the raw materials so attach in matching sequence to the preexisting nucleoprotein. **C,** the correctly positioned raw materials link up with each other. **D,** the new nucleoprotein molecule so created separates from the original "model." Model and replica are identical in composition.

together the "correctly" positioned duplicate parts (Fig. 2.8).

In rough outline, this is how nucleoprotein reproduction is believed to have occurred in the early seas and to occur now (see Chap. 18 for a detailed discussion). Essentially, the process represents a shortcut of the original nucleoprotein creation. Thus, the very first nucleoproteins had formed through random, many million-years-long sequences of reactions: by the chance combination of sugars, phosphates, purines, and pyrimidines into nucleotides; by the chance combination of nucleotides into nucleic acids; by the chance com-

bination of amino acids into proteins; and by the final chance combination of proteins and nucleic acids. But with the appearance of the first nucleoproteins, *models* became available which could substantially accelerate the formation of more nucleoproteins. Each slowly created first nucleoprotein could serve as a "recipe," or a blueprint, by means of which appropriate sugars, amino acids, purines, etc., could be combined directly, in a single step, and without complete dependence on chance, into exactly matching nucleoproteins.

Ever since, reproduction fundamentally has

meant only this: relatively rapid construction of a duplicate of a pre-existing model, out of simpler raw materials put together in a pattern matching the model. In living reproduction, the model itself carries out the matching and the putting together, and the finished duplicate may then in turn serve as a new model. In this way, descendants of the earliest nucleoproteins have followed one another in an unbroken succession down to the present.

Nucleoproteins were the first, and, as far as we know, they now are the only kinds of molecules to be endowed with this capacity of *self-duplication*. This remarkable property is strictly a consequence of their particular structural make-up and atomic complexity. Put the right types and numbers of atoms together in the right way, and the whole will have the property of reproduction. In principle this is not any more mysterious, though more surprising, than that some other chemical combination of atoms should have the property of being strongly acid, for example, and thus capable of eating a hole through steel. Reproduction, we are led to conclude, is no more and no less than one of the properties potentially inherent in matter made out of atoms. By extension, all life is no more and no less than this, as we shall see.

Nutrition

A prerequisite for reproduction was, and is now, availability of varied building materials. Therefore, the multitude of inorganic and organic compounds in the early seas came to be significant as **nutrients.** The first nucleoproteins, we note, introduced not only the phenomenon of reproduction but also that of *nutrition;* organic nutrients or *foods,* such as sugars, amino acids, purines, etc., together with inorganic nutrients such as phosphates and water, made reproduction possible.

As nucleoprotein reproduction transformed more and more nutrients into more and more nucleoproteins, which reproduced in their turn, ever-increasing amounts of the free nutrient molecules of the seas were being used up. Indeed, the rate of conversion of nutrients into nucleoproteins probably was more rapid from the start than the rate of creation of fresh food molecules out of methane, ammonia, and water.

Another complication probably intensified the increasingly heavy drain on the free foods of the ocean. We are not sure exactly how or when it may have happened, but physical conditions on earth eventually changed in such a way that new supplies of sugars, amino acids, and other foods could no longer be formed. Perhaps the frequency of lightning discharges decreased to such an extent that methane, ammonia, and water could no longer combine in appreciable quantities. Or, perhaps because of other changes in the atmosphere, the necessary high-energy solar radiation could no longer penetrate to the earth's surface in as great an intensity as before. Quite a number of physical changes of this sort may be envisaged which would have been sufficient to stop any further synthesis of free foods. And the existing supply of such foods was being used up increasingly by the multiplying nucleoproteins.

Clearly, with the appearance of reproducing nucleoproteins, it became only a question of time when the ocean would be completely empty of free molecular foods, as empty of them as it is today. This must have meant the emergence of **competition** as a new condition of existence; through their property of being able to withdraw food molecules from the sea, nucleoproteins in effect began to compete for available supplies. Under such circumstances, another new property of nucleoproteins, fully as significant as that of reproduction, came to play an increasingly important role.

Evolution

As a class, nucleoproteins are exceedingly stable molecules. That is, unlike the structures of most other kinds of molecules, nucleoprotein structure is not easily disrupted by the many physical and chemical hazards encountered on earth. Occasionally, however, minor structural changes may be produced by various chemical and physical agencies. When this happens the altered nucleoprotein structure is itself very stable, and during reproduction the changed condition is transmitted faithfully into the replica (Fig. 2.9). Such stable, *inheritable* changes in nucleoproteins are known as **mutations.** They alter the properties of nucleoproteins in major or minor ways.

Thus, if mutations occurred in successive offspring generations, as undoubtedly happened, a single parent nucleoprotein could have given rise to a number of differently structured descendant lines. Each such mutated line would feature new and different characteristics. Some of these might, by chance, have proved to be very advantageous. For example, a mutation might have enabled a nucleoprotein to utilize as building materials previously unusable types of organic molecules. Or mutations might have allowed several nucleoprotein molecules to attach to one another and to form a united molecular aggregate. By virtue of consisting of more than one active molecule, such an ag-

FIG. 2.9. Nucleoprotein stability and mutation. The properties of a parental nucleoprotein molecule are passed on unchanged to descendant molecules; if a mutation alters the properties of one of the descendants, then the altered condition is stable and is itself passed on unchanged.

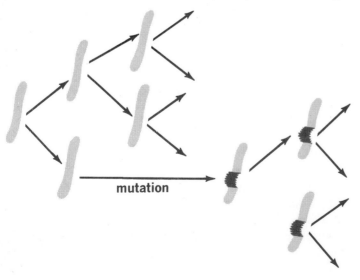

mutation

gregate might have been more effective in collecting foods than the same molecules individually. Primitive forms of **cooperation** may have arisen in this manner.

Through chance mutations of this sort, given strains of nucleoproteins probably developed significant advantages over other strains in the competition for foods. The former would subsequently be able to reproduce faster and to leave more offspring, whereas the latter might not even find enough foods among the slowly dwindling supplies to reproduce at all.

The final outcome would be nucleoprotein **evolution:**

1. Origin of new types by chance mutation
2. More effective competition, hence preferential reproduction, of some of the new types over the older strains
3. Inheritance of the most successful new properties by an increasing fraction of the total nucleoprotein population
4. Eventual extinction of the least successful types

Through such evolution, a succession of diverse nucleoproteins undoubtedly came into existence. And the elements of competition, cooperation, mutation, reproduction, inheritance, and preferential survival have governed evolution ever since (see Chap. 29). We may sum up this fourth round of processes as in Fig. 2.10.

With the development of nucleoproteins, a borderline stage between life and nonlife had evidently been reached. Nucleoprotein molecules displayed some of the properties we now recognize as being characteristic of living matter, but truly living creatures were yet to arise. This happened in a fifth round of processes.

THE FIFTH ROUND

Protoviruses

Progressive depletion of free nutritive materials, and nucleoprotein evolution, shaped the ensuing course of history.

As food supplies dwindled gradually, competi-

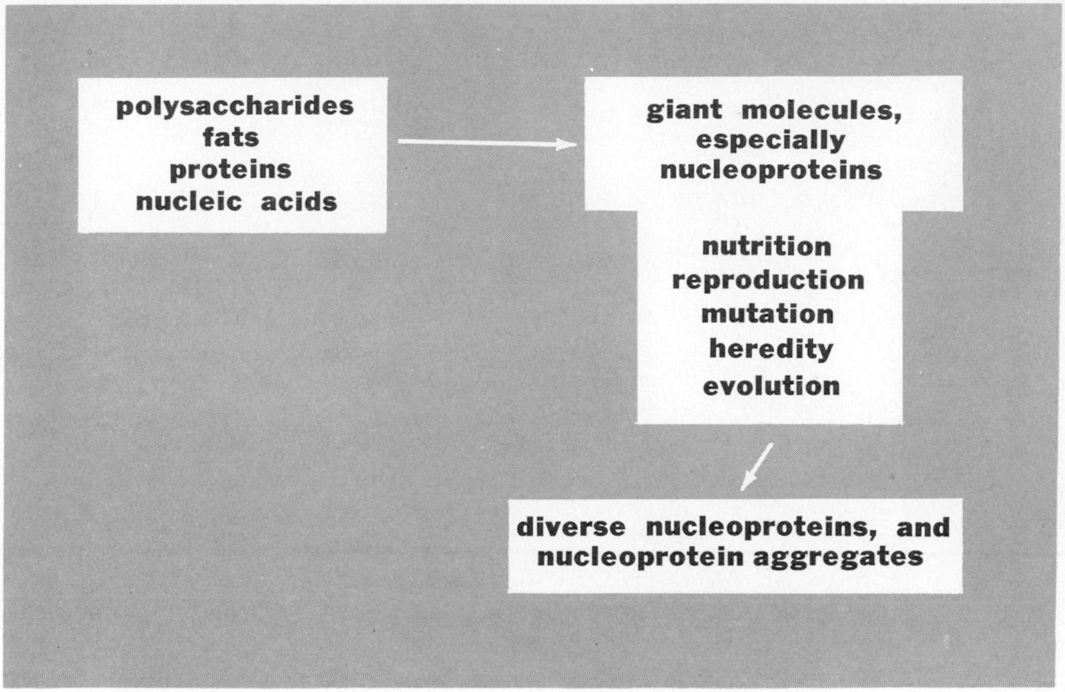

**polysaccharides
fats
proteins
nucleic acids**

→

**giant molecules,
especially
nucleoproteins**

**nutrition
reproduction
mutation
heredity
evolution**

↓

**diverse nucleoproteins, and
nucleoprotein aggregates**

FIG. 2.10. Summary of the fourth round of reactions. The properties and processes which presumably characterized the earliest nucleoproteins are listed under nucleoproteins.

tion among nucleoproteins for available raw materials must have become increasingly intense. Among mutations which may have enhanced the competitive abilities of nucleoproteins probably were those which increased the stickiness of these molecules. Complex organic substances, proteins, for example, tend to be sticky in any case, as everyone knows who has ever handled egg white, or meat, or glue. Nucleoproteins are extraordinarily sticky, and mutational changes among the first of their kind may have reinforced this property to different degrees. Thus, as indicated above, some of the early nucleoproteins may have been able to clump together into aggregates.

Such aggregates in turn may have been able to accumulate more or less extensive *shells* of nutrients around themselves (Fig. 2.11). Carried about, such shells would represent readily available reserve foods, not easily accessible to other, competing nucleoproteins. We note that, under the environmental conditions then prevailing, any chance mutation which happened to enhance the aggregative tendencies of nucleoproteins would

have been favored preferentially. And such mutations would have promoted the evolution of more or less extensive clumps of varied molecules.

In some such manner presumably, a *viruslike*, or **protovirus**, stage of development was attained.

FIG. 2.11. Diagram to show how early nucleoproteins may have acquired more or less extensive shells of other organic and inorganic materials and may thus have given rise both to protoviruses and to the first cells.

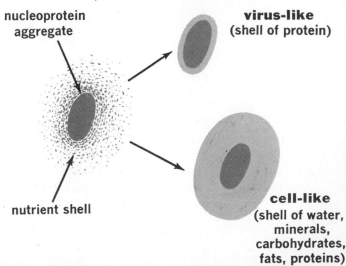

nucleoprotein
aggregate

virus-like
(shell of protein)

nutrient shell

cell-like
(shell of water,
minerals,
carbohydrates,
fats, proteins)

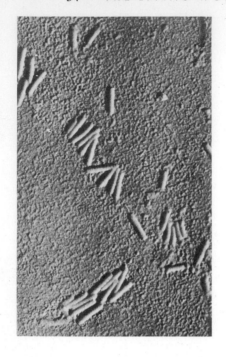

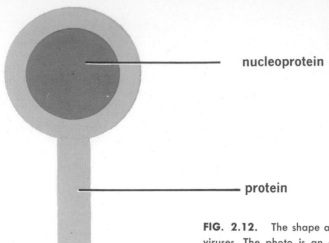

nucleoprotein

protein

FIG. 2.12. The shape and structure of modern viruses. The photo is an electron micrograph of rod-shaped viruses. Virus types of many other shapes are known. The diagram shows the typical composition of viruses, with nucleoprotein in the center and a protein shell on the outside. (Photo courtesy of R. W. G. Wyckoff, "Electron Microscopy," Interscience Publishers, Inc., 1949.)

A virus today is a clumped collection of nucleoprotein molecules, surrounded by a thin shell of protein molecules (Fig. 2.12). Viruses reproduce under appropriate conditions, and they mutate and evolve. Indeed, modern viruses resemble the postulated early protoviruses so closely that they may be their direct descendants. However, modern viruses are all parasites. That is, they display "living" properties only within plant or animal hosts. Outside such hosts, they are simply inert, nonreproducing chemicals.

Largely because of this parasitic nature of modern viruses, some biologists doubt that viruses are derived directly from early protoviruses. They suggest, instead, that modern viruses are degenerate descendants of some later, advanced living creatures. This is a possible but not a necessary conclusion. Plant and animal hosts today supply modern viruses with foods for reproduction just as the early ocean must have supplied the protoviruses. If these protoviruses had been removed from the nutrient-containing ocean, they too would

have been merely inert, nonreproducing chemicals. Clearly, the early ocean must have been "host" to the protoviruses in precisely the same way as plants and animals are host to modern viruses now. And later, after the free foods of the early ocean had become exhausted, the protoviruses may have found substitute sources of foods within the plants and animals then in existence. Parasitic protoviruses may have arisen in this manner, and these could have been the ancestors of the modern viruses (see also below).

Cells

The early protovirus stage still did not represent a truly "living" stage, just as present-day viruses too form a border group between life and nonlife. But the same process of aggregation which may have led to protoviruses probably also led to the first fully living forms. As indicated, an early viruslike unit may have been made up of a nucleoprotein aggregate and a thin surrounding protein coat. Living structures may have arisen by the accumulation of much more than merely protein around a nucleoprotein core. Some of the early nucleoprotein aggregates probably managed to invest themselves with very extensive layers of varied nutrients, organic as well as inorganic, including considerable amounts of water (Fig. 2.11).

The first **cells** may have come into being in this fashion: microscopic drops made of diverse compounds present in the ocean, each surrounded by a fine membrane, and possessing one, or probably more than one, nucleoprotein aggregate in the interior. Such cells undoubtedly were endowed with all the properties already developed in the protoviruses; that is, they could draw raw materials from the sea, and by virtue of their nucleoproteins, they could reproduce, mutate, and evolve. But, in addition, the multitude of varied chemicals around the nucleoproteins must have equipped cells with many new properties. All these, old and new, concentrated together in the confines of a tiny droplet of watery matter, amounted to what we now recognize as "living." Thus, with the evolution of the first cells, probably some 2 billion years ago, the border domain between the nonliving and the living had been traversed. Henceforth, the earth possessed entities which were clearly alive: single-celled **organisms.**

Cell Functions

What were the new properties of these cellular organisms? One of them probably came to be crucial for all the others: cells were able to carry on **respiration.** That is, they could use some of the foods accumulated within them as sources of energy. As we have seen in an earlier part of this chapter, bond energy holds together the atoms of every molecule, and every molecule is therefore a store of a certain amount of energy. By decomposing a molecule into smaller atomic groups or individual atoms, some or all of the stored chemical energy may be liberated. Organic molecules are particularly rich potential sources of bond energy,

and such foods now were components of cells. In effect, therefore, decomposition reactions involving food molecules within cells could become respiration, and, through it, cells could produce their own energy.

One of the byproducts of respiration was, and still is, carbon dioxide (CO_2). In time, more and more respiring cells produced more and more of this gas, which passed from the cells into the ocean. Some of it dissolved there, and the remainder escaped into the atmosphere. Thus a gas not previously present in appreciable quantities began to accumulate, and we note that the physical character of the earth already was beginning to be changed by living processes. Atmospheric carbon dioxide is known to be a screen against high-energy solar radiation. The progressive accumulation of the gas in the early atmosphere therefore must have meant that certain forms of solar energy were gradually becoming unavailable on the earth's surface. As we shall see, environmental CO_2 was to affect the further development of living matter in other ways as well.

The ability of early cells to produce energy within their substance made other, energy-requiring processes possible. With internal energy, all the synthesis and exchange and rearrangement reactions which previously had occurred in the open ocean could now occur inside cells. They could also occur faster and more surely, for all the reaction ingredients were aggregated closely together, and proteins were directly on hand to serve as reaction-accelerating enzymes. Furthermore, since internal energy could be produced steadily, reactions within cells could become independent of chance lightning or high-energy solar radiation.

As a result, cells could **synthesize** not only duplicate nucleoproteins, but all their other complex organic constituents as well, out of raw materials still obtained from the sea. These manufactured substances accumulated within cells and led to increases in cell size, or **growth.** And with duplicates of all cellular components available inside cells, reproduction was not necessarily confined to

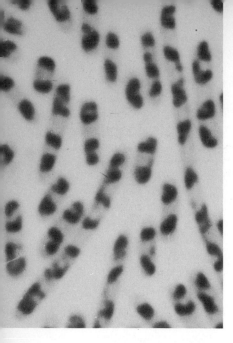

FIG. 2.13. The dispersed nucleoprotein of bacteria. The name of the bacteria shown here is *Escherichia coli.* Some of the cells occur as single individuals; others are joined into chains. Staining makes the nucleoproteins appear as dark bodies. Note the dispersion of these bodies throughout the cytoplasm of a bacterial cell. (Courtesy of the Society of American Bacteriologists, from A. G. Smith, *J. Bacteriol.*, vol. 59, 1950.)

with new properties consequently could form, and during the life of a cell, these could change cellular structure and/or behavior. In this way, cells could undergo internal **development.**

Finally, the various cellular activities came to be harmonized and mutually adjusted in rate and amount to the requirements of the moment. As we shall see later, the nucleoproteins within cells came to play particularly important roles in such control of cellular activities. Through nucleoproteins, cells could maintain a self-adjusting **steady state,** despite fluctuations of environmental conditions. Today, certain cellular nucleoproteins still serve as the ultimate directors and adjusters of cell function, in addition to their ancient role in reproduction and evolution. These modern cellular nucleoproteins are called **genes,** and we shall see in a later chapter how they carry out their multiple jobs. Here we merely note that the original free nucleoproteins of the ancient seas probably have left descendants not only in the form of modern viruses but also in the form of the genes found in all cells of all living creatures.

In sum, early cells were undoubtedly capable of respiration and synthesis; they could grow, di-

nucleoprotein duplication, but **division** of an entire cell into two new ones could occur.

Moreover, with a profusion of different molecules available within cells, entirely new chemical reactions became possible, such as had not occurred previously in the ocean. New endproducts

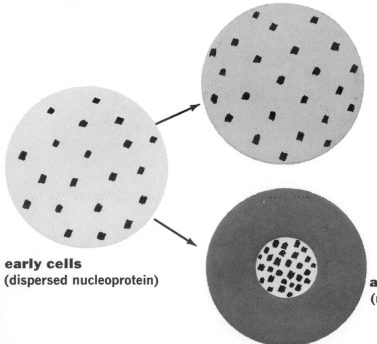

early cells
(dispersed nucleoprotein)

bacterial cells, blue-green algae
(nucleoprotein still dispersed)

all other modern cells
(nucleoprotein collected within nucleus)

FIG. 2.14. In some of the descendants of the first cells, nucleoprotein aggregates must have remained dispersed throughout the cell substance, as in the ancestors. Such cells are represented today by the bacteria and the blue-green algae. In other descendants, the nucleoprotein aggregates must have collected together into a single cell nucleus. All modern cell types other than bacteria and blue-greens feature such a nucleated condition.

vide, and develop, and they could maintain steady states. In addition, they were able to nourish themselves, to reproduce their nucleoproteins, to mutate, and to evolve. Together, these various capacities established their "living" character.

More than one gene-containing nucleoprotein clump was probably present in the earliest cells. In the descendants of some of these, the several clumps apparently remained dispersed more or less at random through the cellular structure. Such an arrangement is still encountered today in the most primitive types of cells known, notably the **bacteria** (Fig. 2.13). As in the case of viruses, the exact ancestry of modern bacteria is somewhat in doubt. But, in structure as well as function, bacteria now living are very close to our conception of what some of the first cells might have been like, and the latter may conceivably have been the ancestors of modern bacteria.

In another early group with several nucleoprotein clumps per cell, the clumps apparently did not stay dispersed. Instead, they became collected together into a single structure, the cell **nucleus.** Early cells possessing a distinct gene-containing nucleus undoubtedly were the ancestors of the vast majority of modern cells (Fig. 2.14).

The fifth round of "genesis" may therefore be summed up as in Fig. 2.15. In a subsequent round, the first plants and animals were to make their appearance.

FIG. 2.15. Summary of the fifth round of reactions. Note the additional new processes and properties which undoubtedly characterized the first cells.

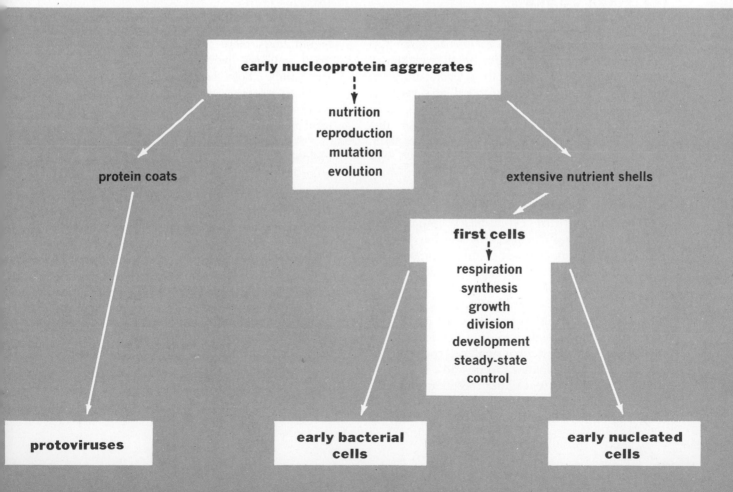

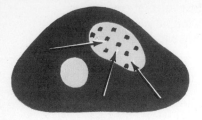
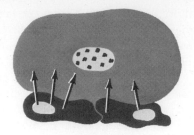
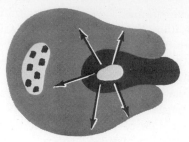

parasitism   **saprophytism**   **animalism**

FIG. 2.16. The three noncreative methods of obtaining food. In parasitism, one organism obtains food from another living one (a small parasitic cell is shown inside a larger host cell). In saprophytism, food is obtained from dead organisms or from organic derivatives of other organisms. And in animalism, one organism eats another, in whole or in part, and obtains food in this manner. These three methods are noncreative because they merely redistribute already existing foods and do not create new supplies.

THE SIXTH ROUND

As the free foods of the ocean were being used up more, the distinct prospect loomed large that the new life would soon suffer death from starvation. But through their capacity of evolution, living organisms were, and still are today, able to *adapt* to changing environments and to develop new, more suitable ways of life. The early organisms did, in fact, not succumb. On the contrary, they flourished and gave rise to the far-flung, richly diversified living world of today.

Parasites, Saprophytes, and Animals

One of the first evolutionary responses to dwindling food supplies probably was the development of **parasitism.** If foods could not be obtained from the open ocean, they still could be obtained within the bodies of living cells (Fig. 2.16). For example, a protovirus would solve its supply problem neatly if it could penetrate right into a cell, bacterial or nucleated, and use the foods accumulated in such a host. Or a small cell could survive similarly if it could manage to invade a larger cell. Methods of infecting cellular hosts undoubtedly evolved early, and today all viruses, as well as many of the bacteria and nucleated organisms, are

infective and parasitic. To be sure, parasitic invasion puts considerable stress on a host organism. Evolution would henceforth operate to make potential hosts more resistant to infection—and to make potential parasites more infective. As we know today, hosts have never quite succeeded in avoiding infection altogether, and parasites have never quite succeeded in circumventing the powerful defenses evolved by the hosts.

For many of the early organisms, parasitism undoubtedly was an effective new way of life. Another new way which required relatively little evolutionary adjustment was **saprophytism.** Here an organism drew food molecules not from the decreasing supply in the ocean but from the bodies of dead or decaying cells (Fig. 2.16). Many early bacterial groups probably adopted this comparatively easy method of getting food and became the ancestors of the many modern saprophytic bacteria. Note that organic decay is a *result* of the nutrient-gathering activities of saprophytic bacteria. Before the development of saprophytism, decay was unknown on earth. Today, saprophytic bacteria are so abundant that virtually any substance derived from once living matter begins to decay almost immediately after exposure to air or water.

A third new way of surviving despite dwindling food supplies was to develop means of *eating* other living cells whole (Fig. 2.16). This required the evolution of cellular *mouths* or equivalent engulfing structures and of devices to extract usable food molecules from the swallowed organisms. Many of the early nucleated cells took this evolutionary path, and they were the first **animals.**

But all three of these new food-gathering procedures were essentially self-limiting. Parasitism, saprophytism, and animalism merely increased the rate of utilization of existing foods, and they did not add new foods to the global supply. Clearly, if a totally new food source had not become available, life would have had to cease sooner or later.

Chemosynthesizers

What was needed fundamentally was a new way of making organic substances, preferably right within cells. The original way, in which sun and lightning made methane, ammonia, and water combine, was no longer adequate, if it occurred at all at that late period. But the raw materials for a new process were still available in abundance. Water was in inexhaustible supply, and, in addition to methane, there now existed an even better source of carbon, obtainable directly within cells: carbon dioxide, byproduct of respiration. Given CO_2 and water, organic molecules could be manufactured in cells, provided that a new source of energy could be found. Organic molecules themselves were good potential energy sources, but these were the very substances which were fast disappearing and thus needed to be built in new ways. And the inadequacy of the earlier solar- and electric-energy sources was the reason why a new source became necessary at all.

Certain of the primitive bacterial organisms did find new external sources of energy: in sulfur, in iron, in nitrogen, and in a number of other metallic and nonmetallic materials obtainable from the environment. Several groups of the early bacteria must have evolved in such a way that they could absorb various inorganic molecules into their substance and there make them undergo chemical reactions. In some of these reactions chemical

bonds were broken and energy was released. Such energy could then be used within the cells to combine CO_2 and water into food molecules (Fig. 2.17). The whole process is called **chemosynthesis.** Certain bacteria living today still manufacture foods in this manner (see Chap. 8). Note that the energy-procuring phase of chemosynthesis differs from respiration in that the sources of energy in chemosynthesis are *inorganic* rather than scarce organic molecules.

Judging from the results some 2 billion years later, early chemosynthesis apparently was only a limited solution of the energy- and food-supply problem. Possibly it depended too much on particular inorganic materials, available only in par-

FIG. 2.17. The general pattern of chemosynthesis. With energy obtained from inorganic nutrients, the organism creates new organic nutrients out of carbon dioxide and water.

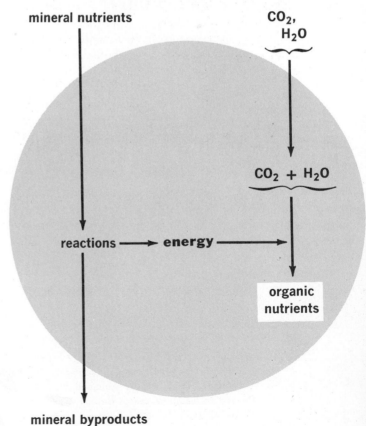

mineral nutrients

CO_2, H_2O

$CO_2 + H_2O$

reactions → energy →

organic nutrients

mineral byproducts

ticular localities. A more generally useful solution required a steady, more nearly universal energy source. Such a source was the sun.

Photosynthesizers

High-energy solar radiation could no longer be had on the earth's surface in sufficient amount. But radiation of lower energy content, especially *light,* beamed down to earth as predictably and dependably as could be desired. If sunlight could be used, the energy problem, hence the food problem, would be solved. Indeed, sunlight became the ultimate energy supplier for the vast majority of organisms, and it has played this role ever since.

Utilization of light energy within cells requires a cellular light-trapping device. Certain kinds of molecules are known to be photosensitive; that is, they are able to absorb light and trap more or less of its energy. By chance reactions, such molecules may have formed very early in the open ocean, along with all the others we have discussed. Recent laboratory experiments have actually shown that, if, at proper temperatures, carbon dioxide gas and ammonia gas are allowed to react with certain silicon-containing compounds, then fairly complex organic molecules are formed which are excellent light trappers. Reactions like these were entirely feasible in the early ocean. And it is likely that some of the resulting photosensitive molecules were among the many materials which collected to-

gether and formed cells. Certain cells would have possessed primitive light-trapping equipment, and such molecules could have been improved upon gradually through evolution.

Alternatively, light-trapping molecules might have been manufactured directly within cells already in existence, as one of the new materials produced by cellular synthesis. Or again, photo-sensitive compounds may have formed in the ocean and may by chance have been incorporated into some of the parasitic organisms. These in turn may have imported the compounds into host cells.

However it may have happened in detail, some of the early cellular organisms eventually came to possess molecules which were more or less efficient in trapping the energy of sunlight. Released subsequently within such cells, this energy could be used to combine CO_2 and water into organic molecules (Fig. 2.18). The most efficient of the early light-trapping substances has been per-

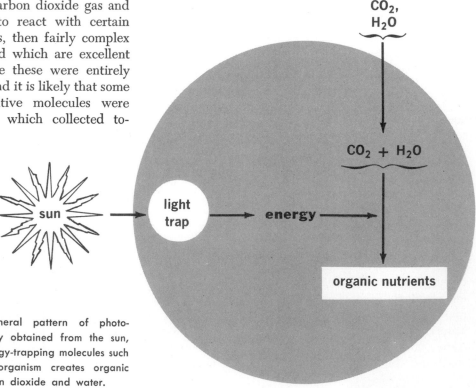

FIG. 2.18. The general pattern of photosynthesis. With energy obtained from the sun, and by means of energy-trapping molecules such as chlorophyll, the organism creates organic nutrients out of carbon dioxide and water.

petuated to the very present. It is green, and we call it **chlorophyll.** The new process, in which sunlight and chlorophyll promote the combination of CO_2 and water into foods, is called **photosynthesis.**

With this new source of organic molecules assured, it did not matter that free primeval foods in the ocean finally disappeared. Photosynthesizing cells could make foods for themselves, animals could eat such cells and then each other, parasites could invade photosynthesizers or animals, and saprophytes in turn could find foods in the dead bodies of any of these. Consequently, excepting only the chemosynthesizers, which made their own foods, all other organisms were saved from premature extinction by photosynthesis. Today photosynthesis still supports all living creatures except the chemosynthesizers.

At least two groups of organisms developed photosynthetic capacity. One included certain early bacteria, and their descendants are still living. They are called *purple sulfur bacteria,* found in many sulfur ponds and sulfur springs. These bac-

teria contain a red pigment which masks the color of chlorophyll. The other, subsequently more important photosynthesizing group included some of the early nucleated cells. These were the ancestors of modern green **plants.**

We note that, sooner or later after the appearance of the first cells, four kinds of organisms and five kinds of food-getting methods were in existence. The organisms were the protoviruses, the early bacteria, the first green plants, and the first animals. The last three of these were single-celled, and the last two developed from nucleated cells. The food-getting methods were parasitism, saprophytism, eating, chemosynthesis, and photosynthesis. Only the last two added to the net global supply of foods. Exactly when which kind of organism developed which kind of food-getting process is more or less uncertain, but the evolutionary pattern as such is relatively clear. We may summarize it as in Fig. 2.19.

In a final round, the physical earth was to acquire more or less recognizably modern features.

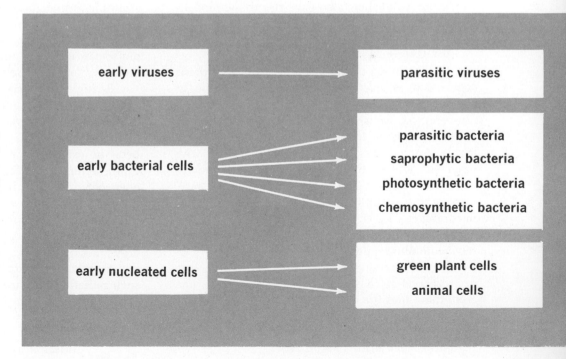

FIG. 2.19. Summary of the sixth round of reactions. This shows how the earliest living things became diversified according to the methods of food getting they evolved.

$$CH_4 + 2O_2 \longrightarrow CO_2 + 2H_2O$$

$$4NH_3 + 3O_2 \longrightarrow 2N_2 + 6H_2O$$

$$O_2 + 2O_2 \longrightarrow 2O_3, \text{ozone}$$

$$\text{metals, minerals} + O_2 \longrightarrow \text{ores, rocks}$$

$$\text{organisms} + O_2 \longrightarrow \text{aerobic respiration}$$

FIG. 2.20. Summary of the seventh round of reactions, the "oxygen revolution." Oxygen resulting from photosynthesis reacted with other materials as shown and brought about the changes indicated.

THE SEVENTH ROUND

The direct descendants of the first green plants and the first animals are undoubtedly living today: **algae** originated from the early plants; **protozoa** from the early animals. These modern groups still are primarily single-celled. But as we shall see in the next chapter, the ancestral cellular stocks which produced them also gave rise to the modern multicellular plants and animals.

The Oxygen Revolution

In the course of this evolution, photosynthesis occurred to an ever-increasing extent and brought about far-reaching changes in the physical environment. As we shall see later, a byproduct of photosynthesis is free molecular oxygen (O_2), a highly reactive gas which combines readily with other substances. Before the advent of photosynthesis, free oxygen had not existed since the early days of the earth, when oxygen atoms were still uncombined. Later, such small quantities of free oxygen as might occasionally have formed would have combined quickly with materials in the vicinity. Now, increasingly large amounts of free oxygen escaped from plant cells into the ocean and from there into the atmosphere. The gas must have reacted promptly with everything it could, and this probably initiated a slow, profound "oxygen revolution" on earth (Fig. 2.20).

Oxygen probably reacted with methane and transformed it into carbon dioxide:

$$CH_4 + 2O_2 \rightarrow CO_2 + 2H_2O$$

Oxygen also must have reacted with ammonia and converted it into molecular nitrogen (N_2):

$$4NH_3 + 3O_2 \rightarrow 2N_2 + 6H_2O$$

These events ultimately transformed the ancient atmosphere into the modern one, which no longer contains methane and ammonia. Instead, it consists mainly of water vapor, carbon dioxide, and molecular nitrogen, plus large quantities of free molecular oxygen itself.

At higher altitudes, under the impact of high-energy radiation from space, oxygen molecules combined with one another. The result was a layer of *ozone* (O_3). This layer, several miles up, has been in existence ever since. Ozone formed an even better screen than carbon dioxide against deep penetration of high-energy radiation. Consequently, organisms which evolved after the establishment of the ozone layer lived in an environment more or less completely free of high-energy radiation. This is why modern advanced plants and animals are comparatively unadapted to such radiation and are killed by even small doses

FIG. 2.21. Overall summary of the seven rounds of genesis described in this chapter.

Round 1: formation of H_2O, CH_4, NH_3

Round 2:

H_2O

CH_4

NH_3

$\longrightarrow$

monosaccharides
glycerin
fatty acids
amino acids
pyrimidines
purines

Round 3:

monosaccharides + monosaccharides $\longrightarrow$ polysaccharides

fatty acids + glycerin $\longrightarrow$ fats, lipids

amino acids + amino acids $\longrightarrow$ proteins $\longrightarrow$ enzymes

pyrimidines
purines $\Big\}$ + ribose + phosphate $\longrightarrow$ nucleotides

nucleotides + nucleotides $\longrightarrow$ nucleic acids

Round 4:

nucleic acids + proteins $\longrightarrow$ nucleoproteins
reproduction
mutation
nutrition
aggregation

Round 5:

nucleoproteins + organic shells $\longrightarrow$ protoviruses, early cells

synthesis
growth
development
division
internal control
fermentation $\longrightarrow$ CO_2 byproduct

Round 6:

protoviruses, early cells $\longrightarrow$ chlorophyll

parasites

animals
saprophytes
chemosynthesizers

photosynthesizers: $\Big\{$ CO_2 + H_2O

plants

sugar, O_2 byproduct

Round 7: oxygen revolution:

O_2 + methane $\longrightarrow$ CO_2

O_2 + ammonia $\longrightarrow$ N_2

O_2 + oxygen $\longrightarrow$ O_3, ozone

O_2 + metals $\longrightarrow$ ores, rocks

O_2 + organisms $\longrightarrow$ aerobic respiration

of it. By contrast, early viruses, bacteria, and primitive nucleated cells had evolved before the large-scale formation of ozone and had become more or less well adapted to space radiation. Their modern relatives have inherited this radiation resistance and now can withstand exposures to X rays and similar energies that would kill an army of men.

Free oxygen also reacted with the solid crust of the earth and converted most pure metals and mineral substances into *oxides*—the familiar ores and rocks of which much of the land surface is now made. A few relatively unreactive metals like gold resisted the action of oxygen, but others could not. And if today we wish to obtain pure iron or aluminum, for example, we must smelt or otherwise process appropriate ores, to separate out the firmly bound oxygen.

Free oxygen, finally, made possible a new, much more efficient form of respiration. The earliest cells decomposed food molecules without oxygen, a method of energy production named *fermentation,* or **anaerobic** (without air) respiration. However, if oxygen is available, it may participate in respiration. The amount of energy then obtained, per unit amount of food consumed, is much greater than in fermentation. When free environmental oxygen began to accumulate in quantity, newly evolving organisms developed means to utilize this gas. Thus an **aerobic** (with air) form of respiration came into existence, and it soon became the standard way of extracting energy from foods.

Nevertheless, fermentation persists today in all living organisms. Many primitive forms, for example, certain bacteria, still can respire only by fermentation, and we surmise that their original ancestors had already existed before the oxygen revolution. Organisms which evolved during and after this revolution inherited the capacity to ferment foods. But aerobic respiration became the main process, and fermentation was relegated to play an auxiliary role. As a result, most modern plants and animals normally respire aerobically, but if oxygen is temporarily unavailable, fermentation may still occur. We shall discuss this in detail in Chap. 15.

We note that the effects and activities of the early organisms greatly altered the physical character of the earth and also the biological character of the organisms themselves. So it has been ever since, even if never again so dramatically and incisively: the physical earth creates and influences the development of the biological, and the biological earth then reciprocates by influencing the development of the physical.

RESUME   We have traced the major stages of the earth's early history, as these are understood today (see Fig. 2.21). In these seven non-Biblical rounds of "genesis," no one point really qualifies as a "beginning" of life. The cell is the major product of the seven rounds, and we regard this product as being alive. But the earlier nucleoprotein already possessed some of the characteristic properties. Nucleoproteins in turn did not originate them but acquired them piecemeal from various simpler molecules. The potential of life clearly traces back to the individual atoms, and the creation of life out of atoms was but a step-by-step exploitation of their properties. Each of the steps spanned literally eons of chemical evolution, and any one step overlapped and intergraded with the next unimaginably slowly.

Thus, unlike Athena, who sprang fully formed and armed from Zeus's head, life did not burst forth from the ocean finished and ready. Instead, life *developed,* and here is perhaps the most dramatic illustration that small beginnings may have surprisingly large ends. Development has been the hallmark of life ever since, and life today is still unceasingly forming and molding. Indeed it will never be finally "finished" until its last spark is extinguished.

1. Consider the following equation:

$$Ca(OH)_2 + 2HCl \rightarrow CaCl_2 + 2H_2O$$

    a. Identify the different atoms by name, and determine the bonding capacity of each.

    b. Rewrite the equation so as to show the atomic bonds within each molecule.

    c. Is the equation balanced?

    d. Is this an exchange, synthesis, decomposition, or rearrangement reaction?

2. Review the role of (*a*) temperature, (*b*) water, (*c*) organic compounds, and (*d*) enzymes in the origin of life.

3. What is chemical energy, and what makes organic compounds particularly good sources of such energy?

4. Review the chemical composition and general structure of carbohydrates, fats, proteins, and nucleic acids. What are sugars, amino acids, fatty acids, and purines?

5. What are the principal properties of nucleoproteins, and what roles have these properties probably played in the origin of life? What are genes?

6. How are protoviruses, bacterialike cells, and nucleated cells believed to have evolved?

7. With what properties were the first cells probably endowed, and what is the nature of these properties?

8. What are nutrients? What factors may have contributed to their disappearance from the early ocean, and in what different ways have early organisms then obtained foods? Review the general nature of each of these ways.

9. What was the physical character of the earth at the time it formed, before life originated, and after life originated? Review the principal events of the oxygen revolution.

10. Review the whole step-by-step sequence of events by which cellular life is now believed to have originated.

Those who wish to brush up in greater detail on basic chemistry are urged to consult any of a number of introductory chemistry texts to be found in public and college libraries or to ask their instructors for specific recommendations. A list of some of such texts is given at the end of Chap. 6, page 148.

The following are excellent key accounts of the probable origin of the Earth and of life. The last article cited describes the experiments referred to above, in which inorganic gases are transformed into organic substances found in living matter.

Gamov, G.: The Origin and Evolution of the Universe, *Amer. Scientist,* vol. 39, 1951.

Urey, H.: The Origin of the Earth, *Sci. American,* vol. 187, 1952.

Oparin, A.: "The Origin of Life," 3d ed., Dover, 1957.

Wald, G.: The Origin of Life, *Sci. American,* vol. 191, 1954.

Schroedinger, E.: "What Is Life?" Macmillan, 1945.

Miller, S. L.: Genesis by Lightning, *Sci. American,* vol. 189, 1953.

3

CELL
AND ORGANISM

THE RESULT OF GENESIS was the living **organism.** The first cells were organisms, and in the course of time they evolved into different organisms, some still unicellular like their ancestors, others multicellular. The living world today is a varied collection of unicellular and multicellular organisms.

In the first part of this chapter, we inquire into the basic common nature of all living organisms. What does being "alive" actually mean? How does a living organism differ from a dead one and from a nonliving structure like a machine? In the second and third parts, we examine some of the fundamental differences among organisms. What can the unicellular type do that the multicellular cannot, and vice versa? In what general ways do individual cells perform the functions of life, and in what patterns are such cells aggregated into multicellular organisms? Finally, how did multicellular types actually arise from early unicellular ancestors, and what, broadly, are the present results of this evolution?

The Nature of Organism

FUNCTIONAL CHARACTERISTICS

Every organism is a variation on the functional and structural themes elaborated a few billion years ago. Thus, from a functional standpoint, all organisms perform the various activities which early cells had already performed. These activities may be grouped into two broad categories of functions, namely, **metabolism** and **self-perpetuation.**

Metabolism comprises the functions of **nutrition, respiration,** and **synthesis** and all processes associated with these three. Nutrition provides the raw materials for life. Respiration extracts energy from some of the raw materials. With a portion of this energy, synthesis transforms the other raw materials into structural components of living matter.

46

The remainder of the energy and all the structural components then make self-perpetuation possible (Fig. 3.1).

In principle, metabolism occurs also in inanimate machines. A machine may be designed to take on "nourishment" in the form of fuel and raw materials. The fuel may provide operating energy, and, with it, the raw materials may then be processed into nuts, bolts, shafts, and other structural components out of which such a machine is built. If, for one reason or another, any one of these processes should stop, the machine would cease to operate, even though it is still whole and intact. Similarly, if a metabolic function of an organism is stopped, the organism becomes nonoperational and dies.

Metabolism therefore may be said to run the machinery of life. But metabolism, having equivalents in inanimate nature, is not the distinguishing feature of living nature. That distinguishing feature is, rather, self-perpetuation. Self-perpetuation ensures that the machinery *continues* to run indefinitely, *without* outside help, and *despite* internal or external changes which would otherwise stop its operation.

Based on the energy and the structural components supplied by metabolism, self-perpetuation itself includes three principal activities: **steady-state control, reproduction,** and **adaptation** (Fig. 3.2). All three allow the organism to cope with the disruptive and destructive effects of the *environment,* in far greater measure than the operations of any machine can do. And it is primarily this which puts the organism into the category of the living, and the machine into that of the inanimate.

Fundamentally, *steady-state* controls permit the organism to receive **information** from within itself and from the external environment and to act on this information in a *self-preserving* manner. The information is received in the form of **stimuli,** and the self-preserving actions are **responses.** Thus, with the aid of energy and building materials, steady-state controls cause the organism to procure fresh nutritive raw materials when past supplies are used up; adjust respiration and synthesis in rate and amount according to the requirements of the moment; channel the energy of respiration into protective physical responses like movement, and into protective chemical responses like poison manufacture; and channel the products of synthesis into repairing damaged parts of the organism, into completely replacing irreparable parts, and into constructing additional parts, hence into growth (Fig. 3.3).

Many machines of advanced, modern design have ingenious steady-state controls built into them too. For example, such controls may make a machine automatically self-"feeding" and self-adjusting. But no machine is as yet self-protecting, self-repairing, or self-healing to any major extent, and no machine

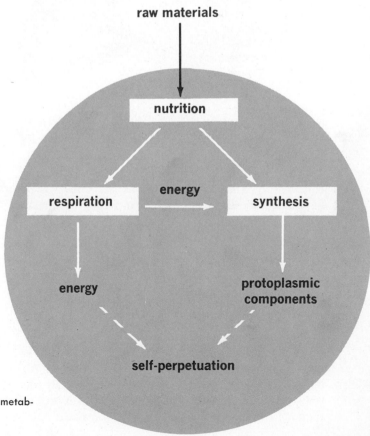

FIG. 3.1. The interrelations of the main processes of metabolism and the main results of metabolism.

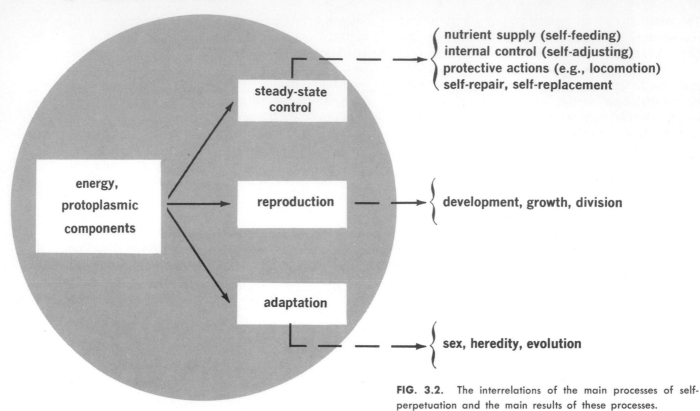

nutrient supply (self-feeding)
internal control (self-adjusting)
protective actions (e.g., locomotion)
self-repair, self-replacement

steady-state control

energy, protoplasmic components

reproduction

development, growth, division

adaptation

sex, heredity, evolution

FIG. 3.2. The interrelations of the main processes of self-perpetuation and the main results of these processes.

certainly is self-growing. On the other hand, it is known today how, theoretically, such a fully self-controlled, self-preserving machine could be built. If it is ever built, it will have steady-state controls conceivably quite as effective as the ones which have been standard equipment in living organisms for a billion years.

Steady-state controls permit an organism to live as long as it inherently can. Life span is invariably limited because, like any other parts of an organism, those which maintain steady states are themselves subject to wear and tear, to breakdown, and to accidental destruction. When some of its controls become inoperative for any such reason, the organism suffers disease. Other, still intact controls may then initiate self-repair. In time, however, so many controls break down simultaneously that too few remain intact to effect repairs. The organism then is in an irreversibly *unsteady state,* and it must

die. In this regard, the organism again resembles a machine. For even the most carefully serviced apparatus eventually becomes scrap, and the destructive impact of the environment ultimately can never be denied.

But unlike a machine, the organism here outwits the environment; before it dies, the organism may have *reproduced.* With the help of energy and raw materials, the living organism has grown in size, and growth in size subsequently permits subdivision and growth in numbers. Reproduction in a sense anticipates and compensates for unavoidable individual death. And through reproduction over successive generations, the tradition of life may be inherited and carried on indefinitely (Fig. 3.4).

Reproduction implies a still poorly understood capacity of *rejuvenation.* The material out of which the offspring is made is part of the parent, hence is really just as old as the rest of the parent. Yet the one lives and the other dies. Evidently, there is a profound distinction between "old" and "aged." Reproduction also implies the capacity of **development,** for the offspring is almost always not only smaller than the parent but also less nearly complete in form and function.

In its capacity of reproduction, the organism far outclasses any inanimate system. No machine self-reproduces, self-rejuvenates, or self-develops. However, it may be noted once again that the theoretical knowledge of how to build such a machine now exists. A device of this kind would metabolize, maintain steady states, and eventually "die" but, before that, would reproduce. It would be *almost* living. If it had the additional capacity of adaptation it would be fully living—and here too the theoretical know-how is already available!

Adaptation is the final requirement for circumventing destructive effects of the environment. For steady-state controls and reproduction as such cannot counteract major, long-term environmental change. Over thousands and millions of years, climates may become altered profoundly; ice ages may come and go; mountains, oceans, vast tracts of land may appear and disappear. Moreover, living organisms themselves may in time alter the nature of a locality in major ways. Consequently, two related organisms many reproductive generations

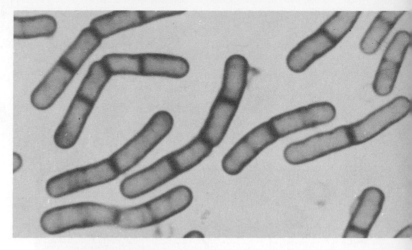

FIG. 3.4. Reproduction: growth in size, followed by subdivision and growth in numbers. The bacteria shown here are named *Bacillus megatherium,* and they are stained to show the cell walls. These organisms have grown in length for a period of time, and as the transverse partitions show, are now in various stages of reproduction by subdivision. Repeated at intervals, reproduction may maintain the bacterial protoplasm indefinitely. (Courtesy of Dr. C. F. Robinow and the Society of American Bacteriologists.)

FIG. 3.3. Steady-state controls in living organisms bring about repair of damaged or lost parts, as in this fiddler crab, which is in the process of regenerating the large claw it has lost. (Carolina Biological Supply Co.)

apart could find themselves in greatly different environments. And whereas the steady-state controls of the ancestor may have coped effectively with the early environment, these same controls, if inherited unchanged by the descendant, could be overpowered rapidly by the new environment. Hence, in the course of reproductive succession, organisms must change *with* the environment if they are to persist. They actually do change through adaptation. **Evolution** is the means of adaptation, and evolution in turn is made possible through mutation and also through sex and heredity, as we shall see (Fig. 3.5).

To define, then, the fundamental meaning of "living," we may say that **any structure which metabolizes and self-perpetuates is alive.** And we find further that *the metabolic functions of nutrition, respiration, and synthesis make possible the self-perpetuative functions of steady-state control, reproduction, and adaptation.*

FIG. 3.5. Illustrating the process of adaptation, or change *with* the environment. The upper figure (left) is a drawing of a placoderm, a type of fish long extinct but very common some 300 million years ago. Fishes of this group were the ancestors of modern fish, of which one, a muskellunge, is shown in the lower figure. Evidently, in this evolutionary history, as in most others, descendants changed as their physical and biological environment changed and remained adapted to this changing environment. (Placoderm, Chicago Natural History Museum; muskellunge, courtesy of E. P. Haddon, U.S. Fish and Wildlife Service.)

A first implication of this is that any structure which does not satisfy the above *in every particular* is either nonliving or is dead if it was once alive. Every nonliving or dead object on earth sooner or later decomposes and crumbles to dust under the impact of the environment. But every living object metabolizes and self-perpetuates and so may avoid such a fate. We come to realize that living matter, though soft and weak to the touch, is actually far more durable than the strongest steel, far more permanent than the hardest granite. Oceans, mountains, even whole continents have come and gone several times during the last 2 billion years, but living matter has persisted indestructibly during that time and, indeed, has become progressively more abundant.

A second implication of the definition above is that the property of life basically does not depend on a particular substance. *Any* substance, of whatever composition, will be "living" provided that it metabolizes and self-perpetuates. It happens that only one such substance is now known. It is shaped into organisms, and it is a complex mixture of many inorganic and organic compounds, as outlined in the preceding chapter. We call this type of material "living matter," or **protoplasm.** But if some

day we should be able to build a fully metabolizing and self-perpetuating system out of nuts, bolts, and wires, then it too will have to be regarded as being truly alive. Similarly, if some day we should encounter, on another planet out in space, a metabolizing and self-perpetuating entity made up of hitherto completely unknown materials, it also will have to be considered living.

A third implication is that a comprehensive study of organisms must deal with four major topics:

1. The changing *environment,* which created the organism, which supplies the nutritive raw materials for metabolism, and which orients the self-perpetuation of the organism

2. *Protoplasm,* the material which possesses the properties of life, and out of which organisms are made

3. *Metabolism,* which maintains living processes

4. *Self-perpetuation,* which endows organisms with potential immortality

A glance at the table of contents will show that this book is structured along these very lines.

The above characterizes organisms from the functional standpoint. What is their structural character?

STRUCTURAL CHARACTERISTICS

During the process of genesis in the early seas, the keynote and central running theme were progressive *aggregation.* As we have seen, atoms aggregated into simple molecules, simple molecules aggregated into complex ones, complex molecules aggregated into molecular clumps, and clumps and other molecules eventually aggregated into cells. These combinatorial events were a progressive expression of the inherent bonding potential of atoms. We recall the energy requirement in making such potentials actual.

The successive stages of aggregation may be regarded as successively higher **levels of organization of matter.** As noted, each level features new properties over and above those found at lower levels. For example, a molecule exhibits new prop-erties over and above those of the individual atoms. Similarly, a cell exhibits important properties in addition to those of the molecular aggregates which compose it. Such additional properties in a sense represent the dividend on the energy required to raise one level to the next higher.

The aggregative tendencies which led to higher organizational levels did not cease to operate with the formation of cells. Multicellular organisms arose in due course, and, within them, a number of supra-

FIG. 3.6.   The hierarchy of levels in the organization of matter.

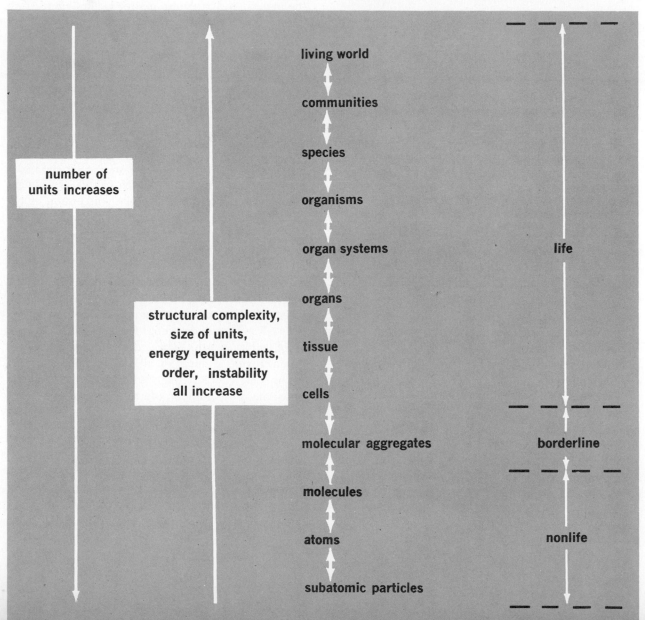

number of
units increases

structural complexity,
size of units,
energy requirements,
order, instability
all increase

living world

communities

species

organisms

organ systems

organs

tissue

cells

molecular aggregates

molecules

atoms

subatomic particles

life

borderline

nonlife

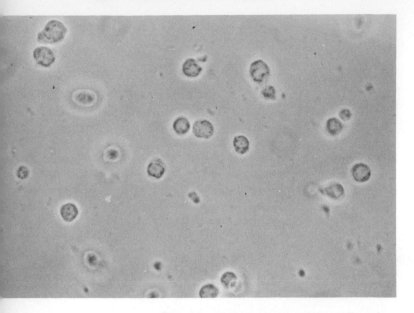

FIG. 3.7. Disaggregated tissue cells of a mouse embryo, cultured in nutrient solution. Originally these cells were part of a compact tissue. Disaggregation destroyed the tissue level of organization but did not destroy the cellular level; the individual cells shown here remain alive. (Courtesy of Dr. Clifford Grobstein, Stanford University.)

cellular levels came to be established. Above the level of the **cell** today is the **tissue,** defined as an aggregation of like cells performing similar functions. Above the tissue level is the **organ,** a cooperative aggregation of several different tissues. And above the organ level is the **organ system,** a cooperative aggregation of several different organs. Several organ systems make up modern multicellular organisms.

Aggregation has carried also beyond the organism. A few individual organisms of one kind together may make up a **family.** Large numbers of families of one kind may make up a **society.** All organisms, families, and societies of the same kind together form a **species.** Different species aggregate into a local **community.** And the sum of all local communities represents the whole living world (Fig. 3.6).

As we shall see, each of these living levels fea-

tures properties beyond those of lower ones. Also, each of these levels is structurally more complex than lower ones, for it combines the complexities of all lower levels and has an additional complexity of its own. Moreover, each level includes fewer members than the preceding. Thus there is only one living world, but there are uncountable numbers of atoms. We note, in sum, that from atom to living world, matter is organized into a *hierarchy* of structural levels.

From this, we arrive at *structural* characterizations of life, nonlife, and death. Up to the level of the molecular aggregate, matter is nonliving. At all higher levels matter is living, provided that, at *each* such level, metabolic and self-perpetuative functions are carried out. To be living, a society, for example, must metabolize and self-perpetuate on its own level, as well as on every subordinate level, down to the molecular aggregate.

As life is organized by levels, so is death. Structural death occurs when one level is disrupted or decomposed into the next lower. For example, if a tissue is disaggregated into separate cells, the tissue ceases to exist. Structural death of this sort always entails functional death also, i.e., disruption of the metabolic and self-perpetuative processes of the affected level. But note that disruption of one level need not necessarily mean disruption of lower levels. If a tissue is decomposed into cells, the cells may carry on as individuals; if a family is disrupted, the member organisms may survive on their own (Fig. 3.7). On the other hand, death of one level does always entail death of higher levels. If many or all of its tissues are destroyed, the whole organ will be destroyed; if many or all of its families are dismembered, a society may cease to exist. In general, the situation is comparable to a pyramid of cards; removal of a top card need not affect the rest of the pyramid, but removal of a bottom card usually topples the whole structure. We recognize that neither life nor death is a singular state but is organized and structured into levels.

The aggregation of living matter into a hierarchy of levels has a number of operational consequences. Thus, as already noted, energy must be expended to create a higher organizational level.

Energy must also be supplied thereafter to maintain the organization. For example, if the energy supply to the cell, the organ, or the organism is stopped, death and decomposition soon follow, and reversion to lower levels occurs. Similarly, maintenance of a family or a society requires work, over and above that needed to maintain the organization of subordinate units.

This requirement is an expression of the **second law of thermodynamics,** one of the most fundamental laws of nature: *if left to itself, any system tends toward a state of greatest disorder.* "Randomness," "stability," and "probability" are equivalent to this meaning of disorder. When we say that a system has a higher level of organization, we also say that the system exhibits a high degree of order, that it is nonrandom. The second law tells us that such a system is unstable and improbable and that if we leave it to itself it will eventually become disordered and therefore more stable. Living systems are the most ordered, unstable, and improbable systems known. If they are to avoid the fate predicted by the second law, a price must be paid. That price is energy—energy to push the order up, against the constant tug to tear the order down.

With each new level attained, the energy expenditure nets new properties. One of these is united, integrated function: nonaggregated structure means independent function, and, by extension, **competition;** aggregated structure means joint function and, by extension, **cooperation.** Atoms, for example, may remain structurally independent, and they may then be in functional competition for other suitable atoms with which they might aggregate. Once they do aggregate into a molecule, they have lost structural independence and cannot but function unitedly, as a single cooperative unit. Similarly, cells may remain independent structurally, and they may compete for space and raw materials. But if they aggregate into a tissue, they surrender their independence and become a cooperative, integrated unit.

This generalization applies at every other organizational level as well (Fig. 3.8). The results on the human level are very familiar. Men may be independent and competing, or they may give up a

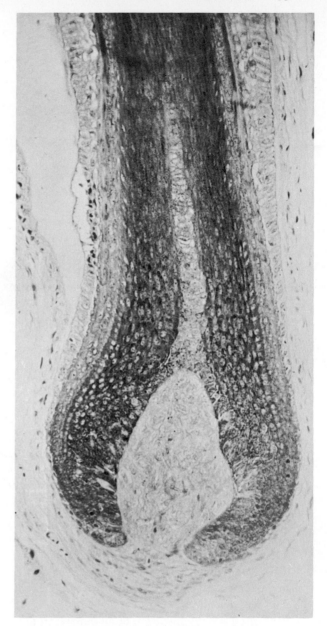

FIG. 3.8. Photomicrograph through mammalian skin, showing the base (follicle) of a hair. Many different types of tissues may be seen, which cooperate to produce and maintain this organ. In so doing, these tissues surrender much of their freedom and independence of action. (Courtesy of Dr. William Montagna, Brown University.)

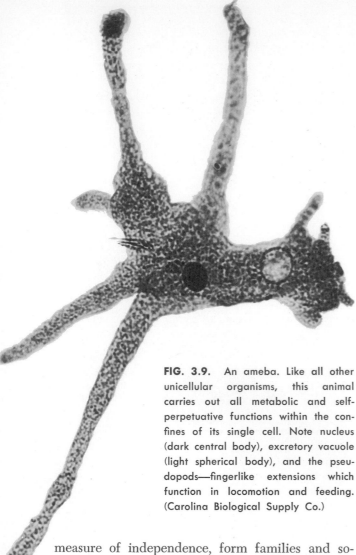

FIG. 3.9. An ameba. Like all other unicellular organisms, this animal carries out all metabolic and self-perpetuative functions within the confines of its single cell. Note nucleus (dark central body), excretory vacuole (light spherical body), and the pseudopods—fingerlike extensions which function in locomotion and feeding. (Carolina Biological Supply Co.)

measure of independence, form families and societies, and start cooperating. Note here that sociological laws governing human society are based on, and are reflections of, the more fundamental laws governing the organization of all matter, from atoms to the whole living world.

Note also that competition and cooperation are not in any basic sense willful, deliberate, planned, or thought out; atoms or cells neither think nor have political or economic motives. Structural units of any sort simply *function,* as their internal make-up dictates. And the automatic result of such

functioning among independent units may be competition; among aggregated units, cooperation. To be sure, human beings may *decide* to compete or to cooperate, but this merely channels, reinforces, makes conscious, and is superimposed on what they would necessarily do in any event. *Reasoned* cooperation is the most recent result of the ancient aggregative tendency of matter, and the evolution of reason may be regarded as nature's way of ensuring the possibility of a very close cooperation among organisms.

Competition with other units of the same or lower levels and cooperation within units of higher levels are direct consequences of the hierarchical organization of matter, and both are as inseparably characteristic of life as respiration or reproduction. Another important consequence, and a result of cooperation, is operational efficiency; the cooperating aggregate is more efficient in performing the functions of life than its subordinated components separately and competitively. For example, a given number of nonaggregated cells must expend more energy and materials to survive than if that same number of cells were integrated into a tissue. Similarly for all other organizational levels.

The underlying reason for this difference is that, in the aggregate, duplication of effort may be avoided. For example, in a set of nonaggregated cells, every cell is exposed to the environment on all sides and must therefore expend energy and materials on all sides to cope with the impact of the environment. However, if the same cells are aggregated into a disk or a ball, only the outermost cells are in direct contact with the environment, and inner cells then need not channel their resources into protective activities.

In one such form or another, savings in energy and materials, and corresponding gains in efficiency, almost always result from aggregation. If energy is the price paid to create and maintain higher organizational levels, then the return is greater efficiency and less waste, hence comparatively cheaper operation. This basically is what has favored more and more aggregation in matter generally, and in living matter particularly, despite the second law. As a result of this, also, evolution has produced multicellular organisms rather than only bigger and better unicellular organisms.

Our characterization thus far has shown organisms to be ordered, organized aggregates above a certain level of structural complexity, carrying out the functions of metabolism and self-perpetuation. We have also found that it is comparatively expensive to maintain living levels of organization but that this expense yields cooperative, dependent functioning of subordinate units, with important gains in efficiency.

One further feature must be discussed to complete the characterization. This feature, also made possible by the hierarchical organization, is **specialization.**

Specialization

THE PRINCIPLE

The unicellular organism carries out all metabolic and self-perpetuative functions within the confines of its minute bit of protoplasm. In many instances, the performance of even one function requires most or all of the operational resources of the cell. For example, in a bacterium, an ameba, or a single-celled alga, the *entire* cell surface is designed to serve as gateway for entering raw materials and exiting wastes. The *entire* substance of the cell functions to distribute materials within it. And *all* parts of the cell may be required directly in locomotion or in feeding, for example (Fig. 3.9).

Very often, therefore, two such functions cannot be performed at the same time. In an ameba, because locomotion and feeding *each* necessitate action by the *whole* cell surface, performance of one of these functions more or less precludes simultaneous performance of the other. We shall find, moreover, that reproduction too involves the operational equipment of the *whole* cell, and in an ameba this necessitates temporary suspension of both feeding and locomotion.

Mutual exclusion of some functions by others is a common occurrence in all unicellular forms. That such an arrangement is nevertheless successful is proved by the existence of a multitude of single-celled organisms today. However, that such an arrangement is not particularly efficient is shown by the abundance of existing multicellular forms, which have an improved functional design; in a cooperating aggregate, all cells need not carry out all functions. Instead, some cells may channel all their resources into performing one function, other cells into performing another function, and the total work may be divided up in this manner among the many available cells. Thus each cell becomes a *specialist* in one or a few jobs, and it performs these for the benefit of the whole aggregate (Fig. 3.10).

Such **division of labor** is the most important expression of cooperation within an aggregate, and such *specialization* is the most important factor leading to gains in efficiency. We may draw a rough analogy by considering a shoemaker on the one hand and a shoe factory on the other. Assume

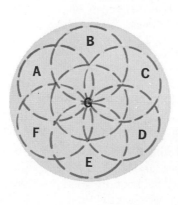
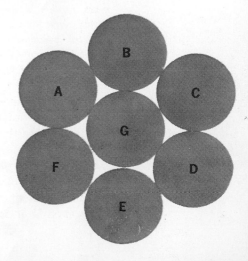

FIG. 3.10. The principle of specialization. The single-celled organism (left) must carry out all required functions (symbolized by letters) within the limits of one cell. In the multicellular organism (right), on the other hand, each cell may specialize to carry out a single function only, with resulting gains in efficiency.

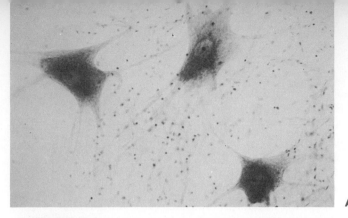
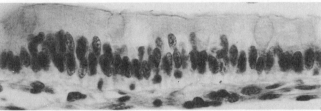
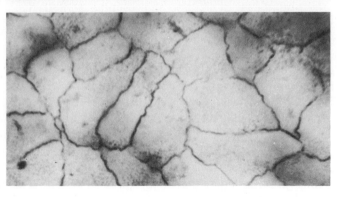

FIG. 3.11. **A**, highly specialized cells (nerve cells); **B**, less highly specialized cells (gut cells); **C**, relatively unspecialized cells (peritoneal membrane). Nerve cells never divide, gut cells divide more or less frequently, and membrane cells divide very frequently. (Nerve and gut cells, General Biological Supply House, Inc.; membrane cells, courtesy of Dr. B. J. Serber, College of Medicine, New York University.)

that both turn out a product of comparable quality. The shoemaker must devote his whole attention first to one operation, then to the next. And as he now uses one machine and then another, most of his machinery stands idle for most of the time. It takes fairly long to make a pair of shoes, and time means energy. All the equipment must be kept in good working order, even if it is not constantly used.

And the cost of maintenance, the rent, the light bill, the food bill, etc., will be relatively large in proportion to the value of the goods produced. In contrast, shoe production in a factory is faster and cheaper. The work is divided among a team of cooperating specialists, each servicing only one machine or, perhaps, a few which can easily be handled simultaneously. Installations are used more fully and more continuously. Therefore, in proportion to the value and the volume of goods produced, overhead and cost of upkeep are relatively smaller than in the one-man shoe shop.

This principle of industrial economics holds also for the living organism. In the multicellular system, some cells may become specialized to acquire food, for themselves as for all other cells. These other cells then need not perform that function but may concentrate their energy and materials into carrying out other, specialized jobs. Some of the cells, for example, may develop particular sensitivity to stimuli and, as specialized sensory cells, may then serve in a manner beneficial to the whole aggregate. Analogously for other vital activities. This not only avoids duplication of effort, but each effort is carried out without dilution by parallel efforts.

In the multicellular system, therefore, the *individual* cell does not perform all the functions necessary for survival. But the system as a whole does. We already know that the price of efficiency is more maintenance energy and loss of independence. We now note that another price is loss of functional **versatility**, through individual specialization. But since specialization is accompanied by cooperative division of labor within an aggregate, efficiency *and* overall versatility may both be attained.

As we shall see, these principles of specialization apply at all organizational levels.

THE PATTERN

All cells of a multicellular organism possess apparatus for certain irreducible "housekeeping" functions. *Every* cell must absorb, synthesize, respire, and excrete, and must be responsive at least to its immediate environment. These functions cannot be specialized. Performed continuously and simultaneously in every cell, they are the bedrock of survival. In addition to performing these housekeeping activities, a cell of a multicellular organism usually exercises one or more functions for which it is specialized.

Each function requires a structure designed to perform that function. Specialization in function therefore hinges on specialization in structure. Certain functions require more intricate structural equipment than others. Hence, on the basis of operational complexity, we may distinguish different *degrees* of cellular specialization. By that criterion a nerve cell, for example, is more highly specialized than a cell forming part·of a membrane. We may also estimate the degree of specialization from the *number* of cells which ordinarily carry out a given activity. For example, many a highly specialized brain cell exercises unique steady-state functions which very few other brain cells can duplicate. But the activities of a less specialized membrane-forming cell are also performed by a huge number of other similar cells.

A multicellular organism is actually composed of three general categories of cells: *very highly specialized, less highly specialized,* and *relatively unspecialized* cells (Fig. 3.11). Among these, the degrees of specialization are a rough inverse measure of functional versatility; the more highly a cell is specialized, the fewer functions it performs. Thus, the very highly specialized cells of an organism generally perform just one main function, apart from housekeeping activities. For example, the operational resources of nerve cells, or of blood cells, are focused so completely on executing one particular main function that they are too "preoccupied" to carry out other functions, such as reproduction.

On the other hand, the operational capacities of a cell are not likely to be exhausted by one activity if that activity is not too complex. Also, where many cells may perform the same function, overall efficiency may not be seriously reduced if a few of them do something else temporarily; actually this may often be an advantage. In line with this, we find a large group of less highly specialized cells which carry out one fairly complex main function, but they also reproduce and may perform other activities toward their own survival (e.g., gut cells).

Cells in the third group are even less specialized, and they may perform a multiplicity of functions. At least two classes of such cells may be distinguished. One includes *reproductive* and *embryonic* cells. They are still undeveloped, and they may give rise to all the various specialized and unspecialized cell types which make up a multicellular organism (Fig. 3.12). Most plants and many animals exploit this developmental and functional versatility of embryonic cells. As such organisms mature into adulthood, they retain within them reservoirs of embryonic cells, left over from earlier developmental stages. These cells perpetuate by division, and they represent a self-renewing reserve of relatively unspecialized cells, capable of developing into many of the specialized cell types normally present in the adult organism. Specialized cells lost through injury, for example, may in many cases be replaced by the delayed development of the embryonic reserve cells.

A second class of cells capable of performing a variety of nonhousekeeping functions includes al-

FIG. 3.12. The rat cells shown here are growing in a nutrient-rich medium. They are called fibroblasts, connective tissue cells of a certain kind, which in the body may perform a considerable variety of functions, depending on environmental conditions.

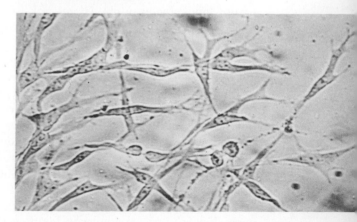

most all adult plant cells and certain animal "connective tissue" cells (Fig. 3.12; also Chap. 7). These cells are not permanently specialized. In response to particular environmental conditions, they may now carry out one function, then another. For example, virtually any plant cell may, under appropriate environmental stimulation, perform the function of any other plant cell. Thus it is well known that a piece of stem, for example, when planted underground, may become root, or that a piece of root, when freed of soil, may sprout leaves. Animal connective tissue cells generally remain connective tissue cells. But within these limits, a wide variety of successive functions may be performed by one cell, in response to different environmental stimuli. In man, for example, such a cell may now manufacture elastic fibers; may then migrate in the body fluids and engulf foreign bodies; may subsequently become a fat-storing cell, or a pigment cell; may later contribute to scar-tissue formation; and may eventually resume any of these functions once more. In these transformations, the superficial appearance of a plant or animal cell changes, but basic structural characteristics probably do not.

Note that, although the cells of an organism differ in degree of specialization, extreme degrees do not exist; no cell is ever *completely* specialized, and none is *completely* unspecialized. Even the most specialized cell performs housekeeping activities in addition to its specialized function; hence it is still fairly versatile. And even the most unspecialized cell is still sufficiently specialized to require a very *particular* environment and very *particular* foods, for example. In general, cells can be only *relatively* more or less specialized or unspecialized.

We may wonder why the multicellular organism contains relatively less specialized cells at all. From what has been said earlier about comparative efficiencies, would it not be best if *every* function of the organism were the responsibility of uniquely specialized cells which, like nerve cells, performed one major job (beyond housekeeping activities) and no other? Probably not. Such a design would not take into account the condition that certain functions need not be performed continuously. For example, it would be highly wasteful to maintain a permanent set of specialized scar-tissue cells—the organism might never sustain an injury. Analogously, it is a decided advantage that, in plants and in many animals, reproductive organs are fully developed only during seasons when reproduction actually occurs. We may note that the actual design of the multicellular system permits the greatest possible economy of energy and materials. Thus, continuous functions are indeed the responsibility of sets of permanently specialized cells. But functions required intermittently, or only under unusual circumstances, are carried out by versatile, **pluripotent** cells: as we have seen, either embryonic reserve cells specially developed for given jobs or cellular "jacks of many trades," like animal connective tissue cells.

We may therefore characterize the multicellular organism as a cooperating aggregate of interdependent, variously specialized cells. And we note that the greater the cellular specialization, the more limited is the functional versatility, and the greater consequently is the mutual interdependence and cooperation among cells.

To the basic advantage of specialization, namely, increased efficiency and economy in the performance of fewer functions, may be added some others. One type of additional advantage may be illustrated as follows: The function of breathing—absorbing oxygen into the organism and releasing carbon dioxide—requires the presence of relatively thin boundaries, or the gases cannot penetrate. The single-celled organism possesses such boundaries in its surface membranes. But their very thinness precludes any great degree of protection against evaporation, pressure, or physical injury, for example. Analogous boundaries in multicelled organisms are represented by sheets of thin, flat cells specialized for gas exchange. But such sheets, being specialized, now need not cover the whole body exterior; a small area exposed to the atmosphere may serve the whole organism adequately. Consequently, the rest of the external body surface can be built more sturdily—an obvious advantage. As in man, moreover, the breathing tissue (lungs) may be tucked well into the interior of the body for further protection and need be connected with the outer atmosphere only by tubes (Fig. 3.13).

Still another type of advantage arises from specialization. Differently specialized cells may cooperate toward a *composite* function. Each cell here contributes its bit to the composite, and the overall functional result may be wholly novel, totally beyond the capacities of any single cell. For example, although every bacterium is sensitive to light, no bacterium can "see." Quite apart from unique specializations required, seeing is a function necessitating the cooperation of *many* different cells—and the bacterium is merely *one* cell.

This points up an important general characteristic of specialization. The evolutionary transformation of unicellular into multicellular organisms has involved *more* than a mere parceling out, among many cells, of the structures and functions already in existence in the ancestral cell. A one-man shoe shop does not become a factory merely by installing existing machinery in a larger plant. Bigger and better machines are likely to be required to make a factory pay. In much the same way has the parceling out of ancestral cellular functions been accompanied by significant improvements in the performance of each. Thus, the protoplasm of a bacterium is merely sensitive to light, but a specialized light-receptor cell of the eye distinguishes wavelengths and intensities of light, responds to different light stimuli in different specialized ways, and does all this faster and with more precision. In many other cases too, entirely new specialized cell functions have evolved, which the unspecialized ancestral cell neither possessed nor required. It is this refining and sharpening, this enhancing of the operational capacity of a cell in the course of evolution, which, probably more than any other factor, has made specialization and multicellularity pay off.

How have unicellular organisms actually evolved into multicellular ones?

The Origin of Multicellularity

The creation of the first cells, achieved possibly as early as 1½ to 2 billion years ago, completed the earliest and longest major phase of living evolution. We have described its main features

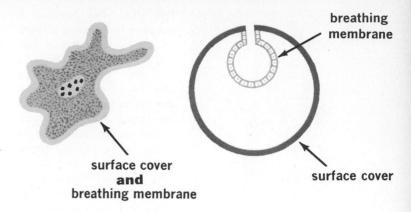

FIG. 3.13.   In a single-celled organism (left), the whole body surface functions in breathing, which means that the surface must remain thin, hence relatively poorly protected. In a multicellular organism (right), on the other hand, a specialized breathing membrane such as a lung may be tucked into the body, and most of the body exterior may then be more sturdily built.

in the preceding chapter. The following second phase involved the diversification of some of the ancestral cells into an enormous variety of unicellular descendant organisms and the evolution of other ancestral cells into the first multicellular organisms. During a third phase, the early multicellular types themselves diversified greatly and gave rise to the basic multicellular forms represented abundantly today. The origin and elaboration of multicellularity evidently must be sought in the last two phases. The many other aspects of these periods of evolution will be discussed in Chap. 29.

UNICELLS

A considerable amount of evolutionary "experimenting" had to occur before the multicellular pattern, with tissues, organs, and organ systems, became firmly entrenched. Certain forms existing today, transitional between single cells and complex multicellular types, bear witness of this.

Given the primitive single-celled free-living or-

FIG. 3.14. Two protozoa, illustrating the principle of multiple internal specialization. Left, model of *Paramecium*. Note the elaborate surface, including cilia, the gullet pocket leading into the animal from the anterior (upper) end, the food-containing vacuoles, and one of the nuclei, at mid-body. Bottom, photomicrograph of *Stentor*. Note prominent chain of nuclei, the dark anterior whorl of the gullet, and the posterior holdfast. (*Paramecium*, American Museum of Natural History; *Stentor*, courtesy of Dr. Roman Vishniac, Albert Einstein College of Medicine.)

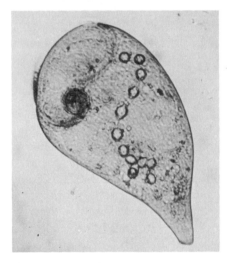

able, each can be assigned to a different machine, and all the equipment in the room then may be used simultaneously and continuously. The speed and the volume of production thereby increase, and the relative costs of maintenance and of finished goods decrease. Operational improvement here results from *multiple internal specialization:* each worker specializes in running some of the equipment. This kind of improvement is exhibited in the evolutionary history of unicellular organisms.

Some bacteria, algae, and protozoa today are still *primitively* single-celled, without much internal specialization, presumably like their original ancestors. Modern bacteria, for example, as already noted in Chap. 2, and also the *blue-green algae*, do not even possess a distinct nucleus. Genetic nucleoproteins are present, but they are not collected together within a nuclear membrane. All other algae and all protozoa do possess typical nuclei, and we may regard the development of these bodies as one of the first steps in the process of internal specialization.

In some of the nucleated forms, internal cellular specialization subsequently went a good deal further. For example, algae developed *chloroplasts*, structures specialized to carry out the function of photosynthesis. Chloroplasts presumably had not been, and are not now, present in the primitive photosynthetic bacteria, in which the equipment for photosynthesis is dispersed loosely throughout the cell.

Among unicellular animals, internal specialization became particularly pronounced in the *ciliate protozoa*. In these, the body surface is covered by fine, bristlelike projections called *cilia*. The organisms *Paramecium* and *Stentor* (Fig. 3.14) are good examples. Here one portion of the cell is permanently specialized as a primitive mouth. The ciliated body surface is permanently specialized as a locomotor apparatus and as a device which creates food-bearing currents in the water. A permanently specialized excretory structure is present within the cell. And, as in *Stentor*, one end of the cell may be permanently specialized as an anchoring holdfast. A more detailed examination reveals many other internal specializations. In such a cell, clearly,

ganism as the starting point, we may almost predict the direction of further evolution from our shoeshop analogy. Assuming that the operational efficiency of the one-man, one-room shop can be improved, how could maximum improvement be achieved by a minimum of reorganization? Two different patterns of reorganization might be attempted.

One of these is fairly obvious: The shoemaker hires a few helpers. With several workers avail-

many more functions can be carried out simultaneously and continuously than, for example, in an ameba or a bacterium. In ciliate protozoa, consequently, the relative cost of each function, in terms of energy and materials, is probably less than in more primitive single-celled organisms.

However, this pattern of operational improvements has not progressed very much farther after it first developed, and it has *not* led to the modern multicellular organism. The reason undoubtedly lies in the limitations inherent in multiple internal specialization.

We may illustrate by referring again to our analogy. No matter how we reorganize the one-room shop, it remains, after all, still only a one-room shop. We cannot enlarge any one machine unduly, nor add too many new ones, if there is to be space for others. And as we increase the number of helpers, they will soon get in one another's way. Consequently, beyond a certain degree of operational improvement, any further attempts at internal specialization would make matters worse rather than better. We may enlarge the whole room, to be sure. Indeed, ciliate protozoa like *Stentor*, visible with the unaided eye, are among the largest cells in existence. But beyond a certain cell size, oxygen can no longer penetrate rapidly into the interior, which in a large cell is relatively distant from the surface, and problems of mechanical support and cohesion arise which a single cell cannot solve.

Thus, the pattern of multiple internal specialization evolved as far as it could, and then the operational efficiency attained could at best be perpetuated without further gains. This pattern, characteristic today mainly of numerous algae and protozoa, now forms a separate, still exceedingly successful, but essentially unprogressive evolutionary branch of life.

Incidentally, this should show, contrary to what many mistakenly believe to be the case, that "the ameba" is *not* the ancestor of man. Amoebae and all other living unicellular types are merely modern *contemporaries* of man, and both have had separate, independent histories for a billion years (Fig. 3.15). An original common ancestor of both certainly existed, but this ancestor could not have been the ameba itself; like modern multicellular forms, modern unicellular ones are themselves comparative latecomers in evolution. Both groups trace back, somewhat like brothers, to a common, very early, primitive, unicellular ancestral type.

MULTICELLS

To find the origin of multicellularity we must go back in time to the primitive, internally not very specialized ancestral single cell—in our analogy, to the one-room, one-man shop without helpers. Given that starting point, there is another way of achieving operational improvement, though it is not so direct and immediate as the one just discussed. Suppose that we initially changed nothing in the one-room shop itself but built a series of such shops, one next to the other. So far there is little change in overall efficiency. However, the opportunity now exists for the several shops to cooperate, so that each carries out a different phase of the production process.

We begin to recognize the specialized pattern: operations in the various shops can be simultaneous

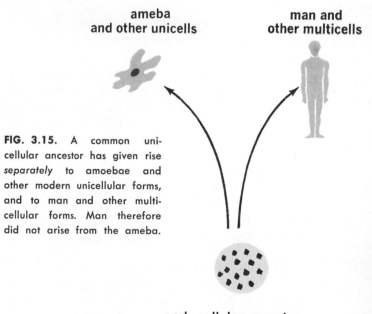

FIG. 3.15. A common unicellular ancestor has given rise *separately* to amoebae and other modern unicellular forms, and to man and other multicellular forms. Man therefore did not arise from the ameba.

ameba
and other unicells

man and
other multicells

early cellular ancestor

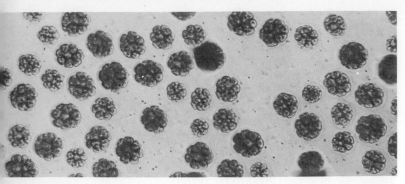

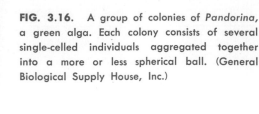

FIG. 3.16. A group of colonies of *Pandorina*, a green alga. Each colony consists of several single-celled individuals aggregated together into a more or less spherical ball. (General Biological Supply House, Inc.)

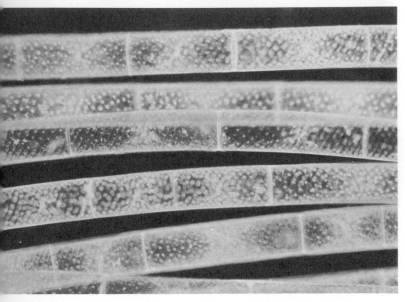

FIG. 3.17. Portions of *Spirogyra* filaments. Note the cross walls which mark the limits of individual cells. These cells are quite alike, and each may persist on its own. (General Biological Supply House, Inc.)

and continuous and correspondingly cheap. The one man in each shop may discard the many machines he ceased using when he specialized, and so may create ample room to install a bigger, better, and more efficient machine for his one specialized function. No function will then get in the way of any other, and new functions can be added simply by adding to the number of one-man shops. Clearly, multiple specialization *among many* cells offers a far greater potential for operational improvement than multiple specialization *within one* cell.

Primitive Aggregates

An early phase in the evolution of multicellularity, in line with the analogy above, has been the formation of **colonies** of like, relatively unspe-

cialized, independent cells. If, by successive cell divisions, one cell gives rise to many, and if the cells so produced stick together, then a colony would be formed. Colonial life has its own advantages. For where conditions have proved favorable for one cell, they are likely to be favorable also for many like cells. Indeed, when colonies first arose during cellular evolution, some of the organisms retained this level of development and through their descendants perpetuated it into the present (Fig. 3.16).

Other ancestral colonial organisms, however, evolved farther, from colonies of independent cells to colonies of cooperating, specialized cells. In this transition, teamwork probably developed by degrees, as currently living forms tend to indicate.

For example, in the green alga *Spirogyra* (see Fig. 3.17), the bottom cell of the filament is specialized as a holdfast anchoring the entire colony. But all other cells are still alike and essentially independent.

Among seaweeds, e.g., *Fucus,* a common brown alga attached to rocks on the seashore, some of the cells may be specialized as a holdfast; others may form air bladders which float the whole cellular aggregate; still others may specialize into reproductive structures.

Slime molds consist of separate, independent ameboid cells. At certain times, large numbers of these cells migrate together and form a continuous colony (Fig. 3.18). The whole aggregate then develops into a reproductive structure—an example of rather close cooperation among primitive cells.

In *sponges,* cellular cooperation and specialization are still more advanced. Some cells in these animals are specialized to produce feeding currents in the water; others are skeletal cells, i.e., they

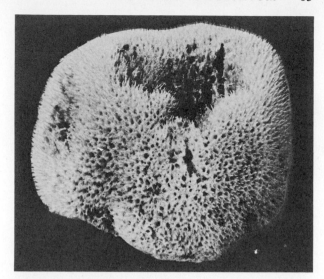

FIG. 3.19.   The horny skeleton of a toilet sponge. This quite complex structure was formed by cooperating skeletal cells, each contributing a tiny bit to the horny mesh of fibers. (U.S. Fish and Wildlife Service.)

secrete solid internal supporting elements; still others specialize as contractile cells; and the whole aggregate forms an architecturally rather complex organism (see Fig. 3.19).

In all such cases, however, the cells still retain a considerable amount of independence. A sponge, for example, can be pressed through cheesecloth, so that the cells become separated from one another. If the loose cells are then heaped fairly closely together, they will slowly migrate until they make mutual contact and will build themselves into a new sponge! Cooperation is clearly in evidence, but even drastic interference with it does not yet endanger survival.

Tissues and Organs

From colonies of variously specialized, cooperating cells, the transition to true tissues can be envisaged readily. The first tissues undoubtedly were single- or double-layered aggregations of cells which were molded either into flat sheets or into hollow sacs; every cell required direct contact with the nutrient- and oxygen-supplying sea, and a one- or two-layered sheet or sac permits such contact

FIG. 3.18.   The ameboid cells of a slime mold, migrating together and eventually forming a compact aggregate. A reproductive structure will then develop from the aggregate. (Second part of figure courtesy of J. T. Bonner, *J. Exp. Zool.,* vol. 106, p. 7.)

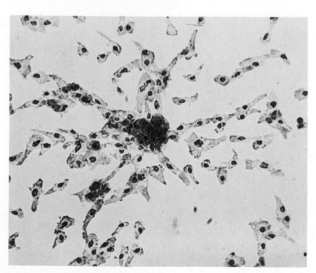

two-layered sheet

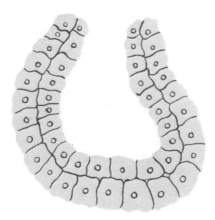

two-layered sac

FIG. 3.20. *Each cell of an organism is in direct contact with the environment if the organism is constructed as either a one- or a two-layered sheet, or a one- or a two-layered sac.*

(Fig. 3.20). Modern descendants of such early tissue-possessing organisms include certain of the algae among plants and certain of the coelenterates among animals (Fig. 3.21; see also Chap. 29).

Development of third and additional tissue

layers hinged on solutions of a number of new problems created by extensive multicellularity. For example, in a compact, bulky aggregate, cells in the interior would no longer be in direct contact with the sea. This would necessitate devices for ferrying foods and oxygen from the surface to the interior, waste and CO_2 from the interior to the surface, and all types of materials from point to point within the aggregate. Moreover, mere bulk would present a new problem, for a large collection of cells would be affected greatly by gravity. Internal mechanical supports would therefore be required. And if, in addition to being rigidly supported, the aggregate were to be flexible and capable of motion, then the antigravity supports would have to be made in sections, and these would have to be held together in some way. Finally, in a large aggregate of cells, as in an orchestra, a conductor would be required. For if the whole were to function harmoniously, individual cells would have to play the right tune, at the right time, in the right intensity.

In time, the descendants of the early one- and two-layered organisms actually did evolve specializations which solved these functional problems one by one. Among animals, for example, sea water accumulated *between* two primary tissue layers could serve very well as distributing and transporting *body fluid*. Establishment of additional tissues between the original layers then became possible, for the new layers could be serviced by the body fluid. With more tissues so available within the organism, some could become specialized *skeletal* structures. This in turn made possible further increases in the size and complexity of organisms.

We may note, in general, that as chance evolutionary innovations created new problems, further chance innovations solved these problems and created new ones in their turn. In the course of this stepwise evolutionary progression, specialized tissues also began to function cooperatively and became organs, and close cooperation among organs produced the organ system. Eventually, a tremendous variety of very complex forms arose which had solved the problems of multicellular life through up to 10 specialized organ systems:

The **integumentary** system, including skin and skin appendages, serving as outer cover and protective device for the whole organism

The **circulatory, breathing,** and **excretory** systems, which ferry foods, gases, and wastes between skin and the interior, and within the interior

The **alimentary** system, which processes available foods into usable ones

The **skeletal** and **muscular** systems, which provide support, protection, and the means of motion

The **reproductive** system, which propagates the multicellular individual

The **nervous** and hormone-producing **endocrine** systems, which coordinate the activities of all organs and systems into a harmonious pattern

In different organisms, some or others of these systems did not arise. For example, plants are without alimentary, breathing, excretory, muscular, and nervous systems: plants photosynthesize foods, hence need not move to find it; and as we shall see, hormonal coordination suffices in plants, and gas transport and excretion can be accomplished on the tissue and organ level.

However few or many organ systems a modern multicellular organism possesses, we note that they evolved by degrees from ancestral structures consisting of one, two, and later three and more tissue layers. To this day, the development of the eggs and embryos of all advanced multicellular animals first passes through one-, two-, and three-layered stages (see Chap. 26), and only then does the complex structural elaboration of the organism take place.

Organisms

In this brief outline of the historical elaboration of multicellularity, it may have been noted that evolution has produced a living diversity patterned like a branching bush. We shall have a great deal more to say about this in later chapters. But we may emphasize here that, in each ancestral form, some members merely retained the gains of earlier evolution and passed them on more or less unchanged right to the present. Other members, however, made new gains through further evolution. Whenever such chance innovations proved to be disadvantageous, the organisms became extinct. But when the innovations were successful, the or-

FIG. 3.21. *Volvox,* a colonial organism consisting of many individual flagellate cells. The cells are arranged as a single-layered sphere, with each cell in direct contact with the water environment. In the interior of the sphere are several offspring colonies, which develop there and eventually burst through the parent. (General Biological Supply House, Inc.)

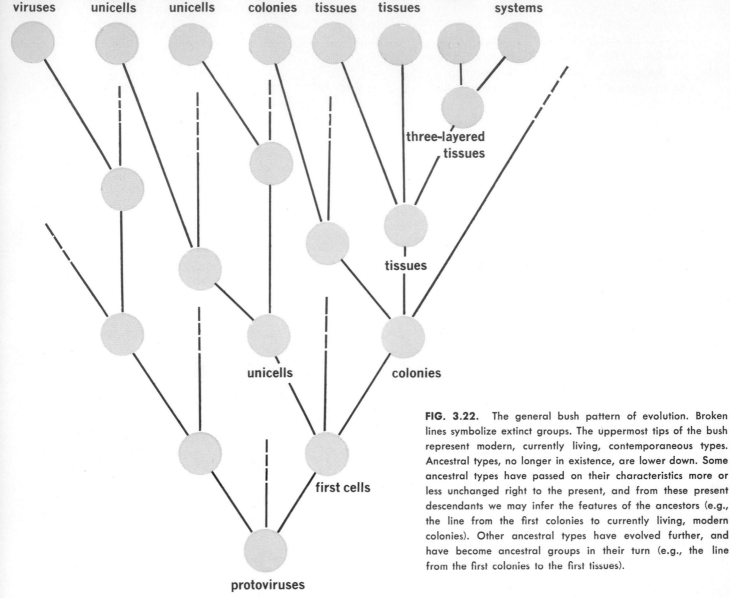

modern
viruses

primitive
unicells

advanced
unicells

modern
colonies

sheet
tissues

sac
tissues

organs

organ
systems

three-layered
tissues

tissues

unicells

colonies

first cells

protoviruses

FIG. 3.22. The general bush pattern of evolution. Broken lines symbolize extinct groups. The uppermost tips of the bush represent modern, currently living, contemporaneous types. Ancestral types, no longer in existence, are lower down. Some ancestral types have passed on their characteristics more or less unchanged right to the present, and from these present descendants we may infer the features of the ancestors (e.g., the line from the first colonies to currently living, modern colonies). Other ancestral types have evolved further, and have become ancestral groups in their turn (e.g., the line from the first colonies to the first tissues).

ganisms thrived and became a new ancestral group in their turn (Fig. 3.22).

Today, therefore, the earth is populated with modern representatives of most of the successive evolutionary stages of the past. **Viruses**, probable remnants of the ancient prelife, still abound. **Bacteria** include the descendants of probably the most primitive of the true organisms. Plants include the

nonphotosynthesizing **fungi** and the large group of photosynthesizing **algae**. Some of these are still primitively unicellular; some are unicellular but greatly specialized internally; some are colonial; and some have reached the tissue and even the organ level of construction. Various algal types now are terrestrial, but most are still aquatic. Plants on the organ and organ-system level include **mosses**, ferns, and related terrestrial forms, and, above all, the **seed plants.** This most abundant of all present plant groups more or less completely dominates the modern landscape with its herbs, shrubs, and trees.

Animals have become even more diversified. Among the highly successful groups are the **proto-zoa,** which include unicellular forms internally specialized to varying degrees, and some colonial types. **Sponges** may be regarded as primitive tissues. The tissue level proper has been attained by the **coelenterates,** familiar representatives of which include the jellyfishes and sea anemones.

Most other animals feature organs and organ systems. Because man is one of their number, **vertebrate** animals, characterized by possession of a vertebral column, are more generally familiar than **invertebrate** animals. But, even discounting protozoa, sponges, and coelenterates, invertebrates are far more numerous, and they include the most abundant kinds of all living organisms. A good measure of abundance is the number of known species. Among plants, some 250,000 to 300,000 different living species have been identified so far. Many more probably exist, still undiscovered. Among animals, 1½ million or so species are already known. Of these, only some 50,000 are vertebrates, and all the rest are invertebrates. Known insect species alone add up to close to a million, and these are more numerous today than all other plant and animal species combined. A detailed survey of modern plant and animal types will be found in Chaps. 30 and 31.

RESUME We have found that the characteristics of organisms, and of their organ systems, organs, and tissues, are determined by, and are reflections of, the characteristics of their constituent cells. But note that the whole is more than the sum of its parts.

To cite an analogy from the nonliving world, a collection of carbon atoms, for example, may be either soot, graphite, or diamond, according to *how* the atoms are grouped together. Each different grouping here endows the whole with unique properties, over and above those of the sum of the individual carbon atoms. Similarly, an integrated cellular aggregate possesses properties not exhibited by a mere random heap of cells. The difference is a result of **organization,** of pattern of arrangement. Just as a cell is the sum of its molecules *plus* internal organization, so also is a multicellular whole the sum of its cells *plus* organization. Only through its specialized organization does the multicellular aggregate become "organism."

By virtue of the specializations of its cells, tissues, organs, and systems, the entire multicellular organism is itself specialized. It is a dependent, necessarily cooperating member of a larger living fabric: the social group, the whole species, the community of several species, the physical environment which encompasses all. Even man is so specialized. He requires a terrestrial environment of particular properties, a social community of variously specialized human beings, a community of wheat, cattle, and other food organisms. Thus, the specializations of his body allow him to pursue no other but a characteristically human mode of life.

We conclude, therefore, that the large result of cellular specialization is *adaptation* of the whole organism: ability to live in a particular biological and physical environment, and ability to pursue a particular way of life within that environment.

This leads us to our next topic, namely, an examination of the place of the individual organism within larger aggregations of organisms.

1. What is metabolism? Self-perpetuation? What are the principal component functions of each of these, and what specific roles do these functions play toward the maintenance of life?

2. What are the fundamental differences between inanimate and living systems? Discuss carefully and fully.

3. Define organism, living, cellular specialization, death.

4. Review the hierarchy of levels in the organization of matter, and discuss how living matter is characterized in terms of levels.

5. Review the relationship of levels of organization to energy, to aggregation, to complexity, to competition and cooperation, and to operational efficiency.

6. In terms of cellular specializations, how does a cell of a single-celled organism differ from a cell of a multicellular organism?

7. What functional features characterize a very highly, a less highly, and a relatively incompletely specialized cell? Give a concrete example of each.

8. What are the functional advantages of high and of low degrees of specialization? Cite examples of specialization on the organism, society, species, and community levels of organization.

9. Review the probable evolutionary history of multicellularity. How is a colony of cells different from a tissue? What are the broad main types of organisms in existence today, and what distinguishes these from one another?

10. What are the organ systems of man, and which familiar organs belong to each of these systems? What are the organ systems of a plant?

Most of the subject matter introduced here is elaborated substantially in subsequent chapters, and appropriate readings are recommended in those later contexts. Suggested here are several articles, the last two reprinted in a book which contains much useful information and good reading on many other biological subjects.

Scatchard, G.: The Social Behavior of Molecules, *Amer. Scientist,* vol. 38, 1950.

Burkholder, P.: Cooperation and Conflict among Primitive Organisms, *Amer. Scientist,* vol. 40, 1952.

Bonner, J. T.: The Social Amebae, *Sci. American,* vol. 180, 1949.

————: Volvox, a Colony of Cells, *Sci. American,* vol. 182, 1949.

Kemeny, J. G.: Man Viewed as a Machine, *Sci. American,* vol. 192, 1955.

Parker, G. H.: Criteria of Life, *Amer. Scientist,* vol. 41, 1953.

Holmes, S. J.: How Life Becomes Complex, in I. W. Knobloch, "Readings in Biological Science," Appleton-Century-Crofts, 1948.

Young, R. T.: The Living Machine, in I. W. Knobloch, "Readings in Biological Science," Appleton-Century-Crofts, 1948.

BEING A SPECIALIZED ENTITY, every organism depends on other organisms for some essential product or process; no organism can survive in strict isolation. Cooperative aggregations of organisms are as ancient as organisms themselves, and as the ones evolved, so did the others. Moreover, the same principles and consequences of aggregation described previously for infraorganismic levels of organization hold also for supraorganismic ones.

In this chapter, we shall deal with two major supraorganismic levels of the living world, the **species** and the **community**. As one of the specialized aggregations subordinated to the species level, we shall also examine the **society**, and as one of the expressions of community living, we shall discuss parasitism and other **symbiotic associations**.

The Species

THE NATURE OF A SPECIES

The Species Concept

Individual organisms of the same kind are aggregated into a series of organizational units. The smallest such unit is the **family**, a rather temporary type of association not necessarily characteristic of every kind of organism. Also more or less temporary, and typical of only certain organisms, are the larger associations of families of the same kind into **tribes** and of tribes of the same kind into **societies**. But, whether or not like organisms form families, tribes, and societies, they always form local **populations**.

A population is a relatively permanent grouping of organisms of the same kind, encountered among all types of organisms. The dandelions in a field, the pines in a forest, the earthworms in a plot of soil, the minnows in a pond, and the people in a village, all are examples of local populations. Individual organisms multiply and die, emigrate or

4

SPECIES AND COMMUNITY

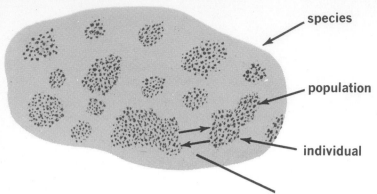

species

population

individual

occasional
interbreeding
between populations

FIG. 4.1. The interrelation between individuals, populations, and species. Interbreeding occurs frequently among the individuals of a population and occasionally among the population of a species. Individuals of two different species do not interbreed in nature.

immigrate, but collectively the population persists. It may split into subpopulations, or it may fuse with adjacent sister populations, yet the basic character of the group as a whole does not thereby change. Structurally, the geographic extent of a population may vary vastly, from the space in a laboratory test tube to a space of continental or oceanic proportions. Likewise, population density may vary greatly. Functionally, the fundamental unifying link of a population is that its members interbreed more or less preferentially with one another. However, occasional interbreeding with members of sister populations does occur. A population thus is a reproductively cohesive unit, integrated more loosely with other such units (Fig. 4.1).

The sum of all the populations of the same kind, and thus the sum of all the organisms of the same kind, forms a **species.** For example, all the dandelions on earth, all the bullfrogs on earth, all the human beings on earth, each group represents a species. Even more so than the population, the species is a universal, very permanent, self-perpetuating organization.

If "species" is defined as above as the sum of all organisms of the same kind, what does the phrase "of the same kind" actually mean? Is a 4-ft Pygmy

of the Ituri Forest in Africa the "same kind" of organism as a 7-ft member of the neighboring Watusi tribe, and is either the "same kind" of organism as a New York businessman? Is the fishlike bullfrog tadpole the "same kind" of organism as a bullfrog adult? Clearly not, and we may note that the definition of species as "the totality of organisms of the same kind" is wanting because the word "kind" is exceedingly vague.

As a second approximation, therefore, we might say that a species is the sum of all organisms specialized structurally and functionally the same way. This would help to put Pygmies, Watusis, and New Yorkers into the same species, where they should be, but we could not properly put men and women, for example, or bullfrog tadpoles and adults, into the same species. The basic difficulty here is that every single organism actually differs in many structural and functional respects from every other organism, and no two are ever exactly alike. Even identical twins differ structurally and

FIG. 4.2. Individual variation. These two umbrella birds belong to the same species, namely *Cephalopterus ornatus*. But they are members of different populations, and the structural differences between the birds are quite pronounced. Technically, these birds are said to belong to different subspecies of the same species (cf. Chap. 28). (New York Zoological Society.)

functionally to some extent, however small. We say that organisms exhibit **individual variation** (Fig. 4.2).

Yet that men and women, and tadpoles and frogs, naturally "belong together" is clearly evident, and biologists usually have little trouble in recognizing a species and distinguishing between species. Underlying this basic distinctiveness of a species is a relatively close historical link between its member organisms. *Relatedness* is as good a criterion of group character, and often a better one, than structure and function. We may say, therefore, as a third approximation, that a species is a collection of structurally and functionally similar organisms which, genetically, embryologically, and evolutionally, are more closely related to one another than to any other organisms.

But note that this definition too still has elements of vagueness, for the phrase "more closely related than" may be interpreted with considerable latitude. All organisms on earth are related to one another; all are different from one another; and in this continuous spectrum of historical relation and difference, it is often difficult or impossible to decide exactly where one species ends and the next related one begins. Relatedness puts bullfrog tadpoles and adults into the same species, but this would also put grass frogs into the same species as bullfrogs. Yet it should not.

Evidently, what is needed is a criterion other than relatedness, one which introduces discontinuity into the continuous spectrum of historical relation and individual variation. Such a criterion is the breeding pattern among organisms. As a fourth and most nearly adequate definition, we may regard a species as *a group of closely related, structurally and functionally similar organisms, which in nature interbreed with one another, but which do not interbreed with organisms of other groups* (Fig. 4.3).

All bullfrog populations on earth are in actual or potential reproductive contact. Similarly, any grass frogs from any part of the world may interbreed. Bullfrogs and grass frogs may, and do, coexist in the same localities; yet despite this constant proximity they do not interbreed. Hence they represent different species.

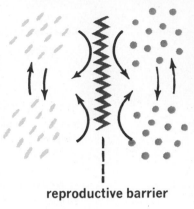

species A   species B

FIG. 4.3. In nature, a reproductive barrier of some sort always prevents interbreeding between populations of different species. Interbreeding is limited to populations *within* a species.

reproductive barrier

Isolation and Speciation

That two different types of organisms *do not* interbreed in nature does not necessarily mean that they *cannot* interbreed. In many cases, members of different species may be brought together in the laboratory, and there they interbreed perfectly well. For example, swordtails and platys, two species of tropical fish (Fig. 4.4), may have offspring in the

FIG. 4.4. Platyfish female at top, swordfish male at bottom. These animals belong to different species, and in nature they do not interbreed. But they can and do interbreed in the laboratory. (Courtesy of Dr. Myron Gordon and the Genetics Laboratory, New York Zoological Society.)

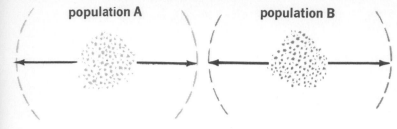

population A   population B

FIG. 4.5.   If two populations of the same species are too far apart, the migratory range of one may not intersect that of the other. Individuals of population A then cannot meet individuals of population B, and interbreeding does not occur. If the reproductive separation persists for a long time, two new species may arise in this manner from the original one. Distance is often a major factor in speciation.

laboratory quite readily. But in nature they almost never do; swordtails live in the headwaters of rivers, platys in the lower stream beds, and normally the two simply do not meet.

In general, absence of reproductive contact indicates the presence of some kind of *barrier* to interbreeding. In many cases, as between bullfrogs and grass frogs, the barrier is biological, and interbreeding then is impossible regardless of the degree of proximity. Thus, bullfrogs and grass frogs have incompatible structures and functions, cross-mating cannot occur, and sperms from one cannot successfully fertilize the eggs of the other. In numerous cases, the eggs and sperms of different groups are compatible, yet effective natural biological barriers still exist. For example, the breeding season in one group may occur a few weeks earlier or later than in another; or the members of one group may be active only at night, those of another only in the daytime. Despite proximity, interbreeding will be impossible under such circumstances.

In many instances, as in the case of the swordtails and platys, the reproductive barriers are not biological but environmental. Impassable mountains, unfordable rivers, pronounced climatic differences, or merely great distances between one territory and another may make contact between groups impossible, and reproductive isolation will be the consequence. Interbreeding can still occur

if the isolating condition is removed, but in nature this does not normally happen.

On the contrary, the development of new environmental isolating conditions is the usual cause of **speciation,** the origin of new species by the splitting of one into two. For example, if an original parental species ranges over a given large territory, physical barriers may arise in the course of time which may prevent interbreeding between populations at opposite ends of the territory. With reproductive communication so lacking, the bond of close hereditary relatedness can no longer be maintained, and in the isolated populations, evolution may henceforth follow entirely different courses. In effect, the parental species will be split into two new ones (Fig. 4.5). At first, the descendant species will still be rather similar structurally and functionally. In time, however, evolutionary changes are likely to introduce progressively pronounced differences, including biological barriers to interbreeding. These would add to, and reinforce, the environmental ones already in existence. Speciation by this means is the principal way in which new species evolve. Such a process takes, on an average, about 1 million years. In Chap. 28 we shall hear more about speciation, and we shall find also that the concept of "species" has important genetic aspects.

Note that, apart from the discontinuity of reproductive communication between species, the range of individual variations within one species may be directly continuous with the range within a closely related species. It may happen, therefore, that two organisms from two different species might differ less in structure and function than two organisms from the same species.

The extent and form of the individual variations within a species constitute an integral part of species character. What is the nature of these variations?

VARIATIONS

Types of Variations

All variations within a species are superimposed on a basic set of structural and functional characteristics common to all member organisms. For example, no matter in what way or to what degree human beings might differ, they never differ so much that their human status cannot be recognized.

Two classes of variations may be distinguished, **inheritable** and **noninheritable** ones. The first are produced by gene mutations and are controlled by genes. They may therefore be transmitted to offspring. Noninheritable variations are the result of developmental processes within organisms and are not controlled genetically. They therefore disappear from a species with the death of the individuals which feature such variations. Evidently, only inheritable variations can be significant in species evolution.

If a man is an athlete, his muscular system is likely to be developed much more than in the average person. This is an individual variation, and a noninheritable one; the state of muscular development does not depend on heredity, primarily, but only on whether or not a person goes in for athletics. On the other hand, the blood type, the skin color, and the hair color of an individual are examples of hereditary variations (Fig. 4.6). They are part of the genetic inheritance from parents and earlier forebears and will, in turn, influence the traits of future offspring generations. Many variations exist which are inherited but which may be modified subsequently in noninheritable fashion. For exam-

ple, body weight is a general, inherited species characteristic, but what the actual weight of an individual will be depends partly on his habits. Similarly, a generalized level of intelligence "runs in the family" and is inherited, but actual mental capacities depend on the thought training of each individual.

In many, and probably in the majority, of instances, the variations within a species are correlated with variations in the environment. Among birds and mammals, for example, man not excepted, clear-cut structural differences accompany differences in climatic temperatures. In warm climates, for example, individuals of a species tend to have smaller body size, longer ears, tails, and other protrusions, and darker body colors than fellow members of the species living in cold climates. Such structural variations are said to be **adaptive;** that is, they are advantageous to the individuals in the different environments. Smaller bodies and longer ears, for example, make for a large body surface relative to the body volume. Evaporation rates therefore are comparatively high, and the cooling effect of such enhanced evaporation is of considerable benefit in a warm climate. Conversely for the cool climate. In many instances it may be very difficult to recognize the adaptive value of a variation. And some variations conceivably may be **nonadap-**

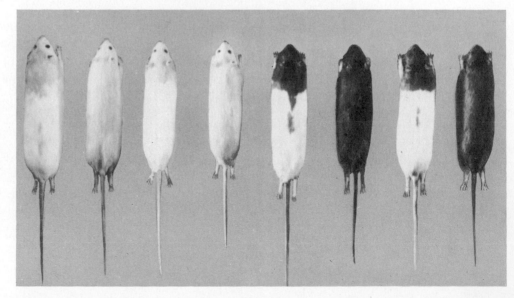

FIG. 4.6. Inheritable variations. These are litter-mate rats, produced by the same two parents. Considerable variation in coat color is evident. Such differences arise because even brothers and sisters of the same family may be different genetically. Hereditary (i.e., gene-controlled) variations tend to be more pronounced, the less related the given members of a species. (American Museum of Natural History.)

tive, without inherent advantage to the possessors. Human eye-color differences may possibly, but not certainly, be in this category.

Polymorphism

Because of the individual variations of its members, a species is said to exhibit **polymorphism,** i.e., to be composed of individuals of many shapes. The sex differences between the males and females of most organisms are instances of **dimorphism,** a form of polymorphism (Fig. 4.7). But polymorphism may be far more pronounced than in the examples cited up to now. Two individuals may be so different structurally and functionally that their common traits become evident only through the most careful study. Many coelenterate species are highly poly-

morphic. For example, *Physalia,* the Portuguese man-of-war, is a colonial coelenterate common on the surface of warm seas (Fig. 4.8). A colony is made up of several dozens or hundreds of individuals, and several classes of polymorphs are present: *feeding* individuals, with tentacles and mouths adapted for the ingestion and digestion of small fish; *protective* individuals, whose long trailing tentacles are equipped with batteries of sting cells which paralyze prey and ward off predators; individuals modified into the air-filled *float,* which buoys the whole colony; *reproductive* individuals, which manufacture sex cells and propagate the species. A more familiar example of pronounced polymorphism is the variety of individuals found in insect societies: queens, drones, soldiers, workers, and others, all

FIG. 4.7. Courtship of fur seals. Female on left, male on right. Sexual dimorphism is illustrated strikingly here, the male being far larger and darker in color than the female. Special forms of polymorphism of this sort occur very widely in the animal kingdom. (Courtesy of V. B. Scheffer, U.S. Fish and Wildlife Service.)

structurally and functionally very dissimilar (see below).

All instances of polymorphism are expressions of organismic *specialization*. And where organisms exhibit great polymorphic diversity, a high degree of cooperative interdependence is also manifest. In *Physalia*, for example, only the feeding individuals can feed, and the whole colony depends on that. Only the protective individuals can protect, and all other polymorphs depend on that also. And only the whole, tightly integrated colony is a self-sufficient unit. Indeed, such units display all the elements of a primitive **society**. In one form or another, a high degree of polymorphism is always characteristic of societies, as the following section will show.

The Society

A society is subordinated to both the species and the population; it is a grouping of organisms *within* a population. All organisms live in groups, and in most cases the population is the smallest group within the species. Some kinds of organisms band together into smaller, more closely knit groups as well, and the society is one of these. Where social groups occur, ties of heredity, function, and tradition are strong, and these usually limit the reproductive contact with other societies of the population. Tribal and family units may or may not occur within a society.

Societies are characteristic only of animals. Also, all societies have evolved independently of one another, and the most advanced societies occur in the most advanced animals: insects and vertebrates. Structural and/or functional polymorphism is pronounced in both groups, as is cooperative interdependence of the member organisms.

INSECT SOCIETIES

Highly developed societies occur among termites, ants, bees, and wasps. In these, each member organism is structurally adapted from birth to carry out specific functions in the society. Insect societies,

FIG. 4.8. Model of *Physalia*, the Portuguese man-of-war. Each tentacle suspended from the gas-filled float represents a portion of a single coelenterate individual. The several different types of tentacles here indicate the high degree of polymorphism encountered in this colony. (American Museum of Natural History.)

organized somewhat differently in each of the four groups just named, operate in fixed, stereotyped, largely unlearned behavior patterns. In its rigid, inflexible ways, the insect society resembles a human dictatorship, except that among insects there is no dictator, no rule by force; each member is guided by inherited, instinctive reactions, unable to carry out any functions other than those for which built-in instincts exist. Insects *can* learn, though only to a limited extent. For example, a bee

FIG. 4.9. Honeybees. Worker on left, queen in middle, drone on right. (U.S. Department of Agriculture.)

may be taught to respond differently to different colors and scents, and it may learn a new route to its hive if the hive has been moved.

Social insects have this in common: they build intricate *nests,* and their societies are stratified into *structurally* distinct castes. In each of the four groups, different species form societies of different degrees of complexity. We may profitably examine the organization of a few of the more complex associations.

Honeybees

A colony of honeybees (Fig. 4.9) is made up of three social ranks: a *queen,* tens or hundreds of male *drones,* and from 20,000 to 80,000 *workers.* The queen and the stingless drones are fertile, and their main functions are reproductive. The smaller-bodied workers are all sterile females. They build the hive, ward off enemies, collect food, feed the queen and the drones, and nurse the young.

When a hive becomes overcrowded, the queen together with some drones and several thousand workers secedes from the colony. The emigrants swarm out and settle temporarily in a tree or other suitable place until a new hive is found (Fig. 4.10). In the old hive, meanwhile, the workers which remain behind raise a small batch of the old queen's eggs in large, specially built honeycomb cells. These

FIG. 4.10. A swarm of bees, emigrated from a parental hive and searching for a new hive. (U.S. Department of Agriculture.)

eggs develop into new queens. The first one to emerge from its cell immediately searches out the other queen cells and stings their occupants to death. If two new queens happen to emerge at the same time, they at once engage in mortal combat until one remains victorious. The young queen, her succession now undisputed, soon mates with one of the drones. In a nuptial flight high into the air, she receives millions of sperms which are stored in an abdominal receptacle. The sperms from this single mating last through the entire egg-laying career of the queen.

Among the eggs laid individually into honeycomb cells (Fig. 4.11), some escape fertilization, even in a young queen. None is fertilized in an older queen once her sperm store is exhausted. Unfertilized eggs develop into drones. Fatherless development of this sort, or **natural parthenogenesis,** is widespread among social insects and a number of other animal types, e.g., rotifers, water fleas, brine shrimp (see Chap. 31). Fertilized eggs develop into larvae, and these either into queens or into workers, depending on the type of food the larvae receive from their worker nurses. Larvae to be raised into workers are fed a "regular" diet of plant pollen and honey. Queens form when the larvae receive an especially rich royal jelly, containing pollen, honey, and comparatively huge amounts of certain vitamins (e.g., pantothenic

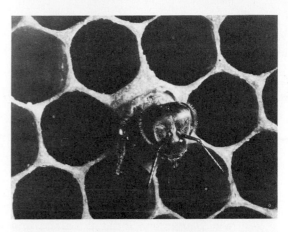

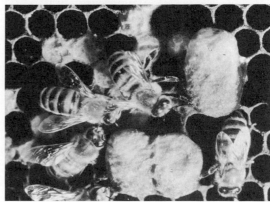

FIG. 4.11. Left, queen bee laying eggs, surrounded by attendants. Top, above, nurse bee feeds and cleans the larvae in the brood cells. Middle, a worker bee just hatching out from its brood cell. Bottom, two enlarged brood cells, capped over with wax, in which queen bees are being raised. (All photos copyright © Walt Disney Productions.)

FIG. 4.12. A queen ant. (Ward's Natural Science Establishment, Inc.)

acid). But new queens are not raised while the original queen remains in the hive, healthy and fertile. If the queen produces eggs faster than honeycomb cells can be built, she receives less food from her attendants. Egg production then slows down. Conversely, if she is behind in her egg laying, she is fed more intensively.

In the six weeks or so of its life, a worker bee does not perform the same duties continuously. The age of a bee determines what work it can do; housekeeping tasks are performed by young bees; food-collecting trips are made by older ones. On a food-collecting trip, the bee gathers pollen, rich in protein, and nectar, a thin sugar solution. Pollen is carried home in *pollen baskets* on the hind legs; nectar is swallowed into the *honey crop*, a specialized part of the alimentary tract, where saliva partially digests the sugar of nectar. On arriving at the hive, the bee first passes a security check on the way in, then unloads its pollen into one cell, and regurgitates its nectar into another. Other bees which happen by pack the pollen tight and start converting nectar into honey. They rapidly beat their wings close to a nectar-filled cell, a process which is continued until most of the water has evaporated. Every now and then a bee samples the product (probably more a matter of hunger than of professional pride in the work). And when the honey is just right (or when all the bees standing by have had their fill?) the cell is sealed up with

wax. This is the principal food store for the winter. Pollen is unobtainable at that time and, being perishable, cannot be stored as readily.

Bees, and other social insects as well, possess remarkable powers of orientation and communication. On food-collecting trips, bees have been shown to navigate by the sun; they are able to relate the position of their hive with the direction of polarized light coming from the sun; hence they may steer a beeline course home from any compass point. On arrival in its hive, a scouting bee which has found a food-yielding field of flowers communicates with its fellow workers by means of an *abdominal dance,* a side-to-side wiggle of the hind portion of the bee's body. The violence of the dance gives information about the richness of the food source. Flight distance is indicated by the duration of the dance, and flight direction, by the specific body orientation the dancing bee assumes on the honeycomb surface.

Specific external stimuli elicit specific group responses among bees. For example, in winter bees cling together in compact masses. Animals in the center always work their way out; those near the surface work their way in. A clump of bees thereby withstands freezing, even when exposed to very low temperatures. Smoke calms bees, as is well known. The animals react to smoke by rushing to their food stores and gorging themselves with honey. They are too busy at that time to sting an intruder. This is probably an inherited adaptive response to fire. Smoke might indicate a burning tree, and it is of obvious advantage if the bees are well fed when they are forced to abandon their nest. Similarly adaptive is the expulsion of all drones from the colony at the approach of winter; not contributing to the well-being of the colony, males merely use up food which is at a premium in the cold season. Reactions such as these might appear to be thought out. Yet bees probably do not "reason" at all.

Other Insect Societies
Structurally polymorphic castes, functionally polymorphic division of labor, and group behavior are in evidence also among other social insects (Figs. 4.12 and 4.13). Many species of ants and

termites include, in addition to sterile wingless workers, sterile wingless *soldiers,* strong-jawed, heavily armored individuals which accompany work crews outside and keep order within the nest. Soldiers in many cases cannot feed themselves and are cared for by workers. Besides a winged fertile queen and one or several winged fertile males (*kings*), ant and termite societies may maintain structurally distinct lesser "royalty," probably developed by overfeeding larvae: not enough to produce queens, but enough to produce workers.

Agricultural societies occur among both termites and ants. Certain termite species make little garden plots of wood, excrement, and dead termites. There they plant and rear fungi for food. *Leaf-cutting ants,* similarly, prepare pieces of leaves upon which fungi are grown. The fungi are systematically pruned and cared for by gardening details.

Dairy ants exist which keep aphids, tiny green insects (plant lice), as food suppliers. The aphids secrete honeydew, a sugar- and protein-containing mixture, on which the ants depend. A common

FIG. 4.13. Portion of termite nest. In central chamber note queen, her abdomen swollen with eggs, being cared for by workers. Winged king in lower right corner, larval queen in upper left corner. (Courtesy of C. E. Simmons, Buffalo Museum of Science.)

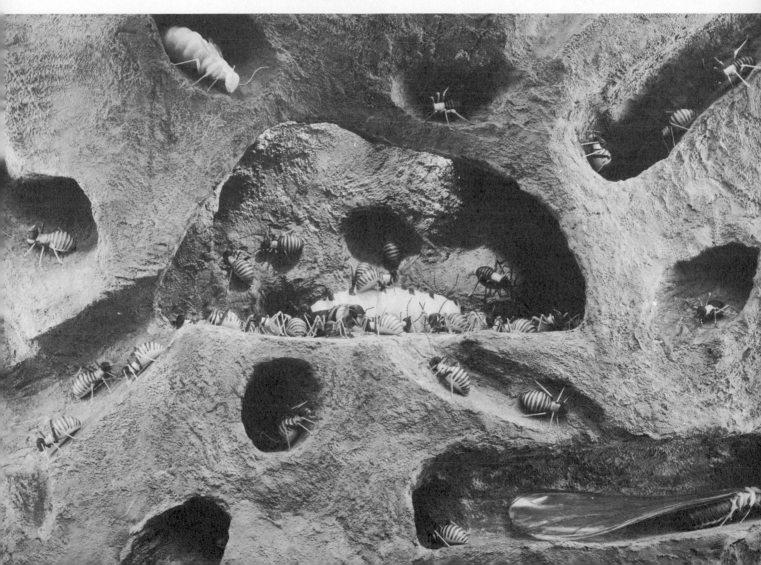

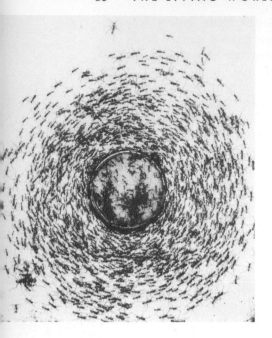

FIG. 4.14. Army ants. Opposite, queen; far left, marching column, circling endlessly. (American Museum of Natural History.)

species of garden ant, for example, places "domesticated" plant lice on the roots of corn. The aphids feed there, and the ants thereafter milk these "ant cows" by gently stroking them. At the approach of winter, the aphids are carried into the ant nest and are put back on corn roots the following spring.

Certain desert ants, called *honeypot ants*, collect nectar from flowers and feed it to some of their fellow workers which are kept within the nest. These "living bottles" become greatly distended and serve as bacteria-free storage bins; during the dry season they dispense drops of honey to their thirsty mates.

Slave-making ants exist which can neither build nests, feed themselves, nor care for their larvae. They form workerless soldier societies capable only of making raids on other ant species. These victims are robbed of their pupae. The captive pupae mature, and the emerging slaves then care for their masters, performing all the functions they would have carried out in their own nest.

Tropical *army ants* (also called *driver* or *legionary* ants; see Fig. 4.14) march across country in raiding expeditions. They travel in columns, and

larger-bodied "officer" ants march alongside. Everything living in the path of such columns is devoured, even large animals, including man, if these should be unable to move away. The instinctive, unreasoned nature of insect behavior is shown particularly well in these ants. If a column of army ants is made to travel in a circle, so that the first animals of the column come to march right behind the last, then these ants will continue to circle, endlessly. And unless they are diverted by an outside agency, they may march themselves to death. Each ant evidently is so completely "disciplined" from birth that it is capable only of following the ant before it, and incapable of thinking itself out of even a slightly changed situation.

Among insect societies generally, the structural and behavioral fixity of each individual constitutes a potential long-range disadvantage. Death of a queen bee and the destruction of honeycomb cells which contain larvae still young enough to be reared into queens usually spell the end of a bee colony; new workers are not produced, and old ones die out. Local eradication of the fungus on which agricultural termites depend and the destruction of their gardens spell the end of the termite colony, its members not being equipped to grow any other food. The victims of slave-making ants could better preserve their colony if all the workers could be mobilized into defending soldiers at the moment of attack.

Among insects, destructive social crises of this sort are offset by the establishment of numerous colonies and by enormous reproduction rates; the safety of the species lies in the number of its individuals. We recognize, however, that immediate advantages would accrue if, in addition to safety through numbers, the society were organized more flexibly, if each member could perform the functions of every other member, and if the colony as a whole could learn to adopt new ways of life in the face of changed environmental conditions. Flexible social organization is actually in evidence to greater or lesser degree among vertebrate groups.

VERTEBRATE SOCIETIES

The Pattern

In contrast to insects, and apart from individual differences associated with the sexual dimorphism of males and females, the members of vertebrate societies are more or less alike at birth in structural and functional potential. Later polymorphism is predominantly functional and behavioral and is based on variations in physical strength, in developed skills, in mental acuity, and in some cases on social tradition. As in insects, on the other hand, the main determinant of behavior is inherited instinct, tempered here with a more or less thin veneer of *learning* and *reasoning*. Learning goes hand in hand with *training*, and both are made possible largely by **family** groupings. The subdivision of the advanced vertebrate society into family units is one of its main distinctions.

Schools of fish, flocks of birds, packs of European wolves, herds of deer are among the most primitive of the associations within the vertebrate group. Functional polymorphism is not particularly pronounced. In travel, the individual which happens to be in the lead position, usually a male, guides the group temporarily. Other males, often stationed along the outskirts of the group, may take the lead in frequent rotation. The advantages of such associations are largely protective; many eyes see more than two; a closely huddled herd stays warm; a group is more effective in attack and in defense. Family life within such groups may or may not be evident. There is hardly any in schools of fish. But a duck or a doe trains its young. Families maintain spatial unity within the society. For example, in a herd of seals resting on an island, males take up stations at more or less regular intervals, and each male gathers his family around him. The individual patriarch jealously guards his territory, driving off bachelor males and keeping a sharp eye on his females (see Chap. 5, Fig. 5.17). Social life among beavers is more cooperative and rather more advanced. *Several* families may pool their efforts in woodcutting and dam building. All share the benefits of this teamwork, which clearly serves more than mere protection.

Migrations

Social herding very often is associated with extensive animal **migrations.** These may be undertaken in search of richer or safer pastures, in response to seasonal changes in climate, or to reach geographically fixed breeding grounds. Eels, seals, salmon, and many types of birds are among familiar migrants. When not migrating, solitary individuals or families of these animals may be dispersed widely over a considerable territory. At specific times, as if on cue, individuals draw together from far and near to a common jumping-off point, and then they travel together to their destination, as a band.

These phenomena are among the most intriguing in all biology. How do these organisms know where to gather before the journey? How do they time their arrival there, often exactly to the day? And what leads them unerringly to their destination, thousands of miles away in many cases? The navigation problem is sufficiently puzzling among forms which make the same trip every year, like seals and birds. If nothing else, a remarkable memory for landmarks, prevailing winds, or ocean currents may be indicated. The problem becomes even more puzzling, however, when none of the migrating animals has ever been at its destination. This is the case among eels.

The spawning grounds of both European and American eels are situated in the deep waters of the Sargasso Sea, southeast of Bermuda and northeast of Puerto Rico. The eggs hatch there, and the near-microscopic larvae, or *elvers,* then travel toward the coasts; larvae of American eels turn west, those of the European eel turn east. The spawning beds of the American type lie farther west. Differences in the direction of ocean currents probably contribute to the initial separation of the two species.

Elvers of the American species travel for about a year before they reach continental waters—and maturation of the larvae requires just 1 year. The voyage of European elvers lasts 3 years—and their maturation requires precisely 3 years!

In coastal estuaries the elvers metamorphose. The glassy transparency of the larval body changes to an opaque brown-gray, and the fishlike larval shape changes to the characteristic elongated form of the adult. Adult males remain in estuaries. Females ascend rivers and settle in headwaters and in lakes. Some 7 to 15 years now pass. Then the females migrate back to the estuaries, rejoin the males, and all head out into the Atlantic. Reproductive organs mature during the migration, and upon arrival in the Sargasso, the females spawn and the males fertilize the eggs. The adults then die.

How do the adults find their breeding grounds? It is hardly conceivable that they memorize the route in reverse when they make the trip as immature larvae, a decade earlier. And how do the larvae find coastal waters from which to ascend rivers?

In eels particularly, and in migrating animals generally, all the evidence has manifestly not been assembled as yet. But much is known, and almost that much remains unexplained. However, whatever the mechanics of migrations might be, the adaptive value of banding together during travel is clear.

Families

Not all vertebrate societies migrate, and not in all cases are families grouped into herds. Solitary families are common, among both monogamous and polygamous species. Fish such as sticklebacks, birds such as parrots, and mammals such as bears and wolverines are monogamous and may mate for life. Such family groups are organized like human families.

Solitary polygamous families may approach the numerical proportions of flocks or herds, as in chickens. Such a group is usually made up of a single dominant male, a series of females, their young, and sometimes a few unrelated young bachelor males. The rule of the dominant male is frequently challenged by the bachelors. If one of these succeeds in defeating his opponent in battle, the loyalty of the females is transferred to the winner. In this way the group is assured of continuously fit, healthy leadership, and the number of males is also held to proportions commensurate with the number of available females.

An interesting social organization exists among the females of a polygamous family. In a flock of chickens, for example, hens are ranked according to a definite **peck order.** A given hen may peck with impunity all hens below her in social rank but may be pecked in turn by all hens above her in the scale. If a new hen is introduced into the flock, she undertakes, or is made to undertake, a pecking contest with each fellow hen. Winning here and losing there, she soon finds her level in the society. A high ranking carries with it certain advantages, such as precedence to the food trough and a position of prestige on the perch. Very-high-ranking birds often are so aggressive that they persistently reject the attentions of the rooster. More submissive hens then produce most of the offspring. Social rankings of a similar nature are found also among female elephants as well as in most other polygamous families.

Human society has had its prehistoric beginnings in the solitary nomadic family. Later arose associations of families into clans and tribes, groupings roughly equivalent to herds among other mammals. Still retaining its familial foundation, the society of the village, the city, and the nation gradually emerged. Today, the trend is toward large-scale associations of nations, a process of social consolidation which may eventually encompass the entire species.

The success of vertebrate societies as a whole lies primarily in the functional versatility of the individual. In the insect society, as we have noted, reproduction of the majority is suppressed, and reproduction of the minority serves not only toward the new formation of individuals, but also toward the new formation of the whole society. Thus, among insects, the fate of social institutions hinges on the fate of a single female, and her genes alone provide continuity from one social generation to the next. By contrast, virtually all members of a vertebrate society are reproducers (Fig. 4.15). Social continuity consequently is founded more broadly, and reproduction of any one individual is less critical for the propagation of social institutions.

The phenomenon of "society" as a whole appears to be bound up with advanced evolutionary status; both insects and vertebrates today stand at the apex of their respective evolutionary lines (see Chap. 29). And although different in origin and detailed organization, remarkably similar patterns of social behavior are in evidence; ants and man are unique among animals in making deliberate war, in practicing slavery, in pursuing agriculture, and in domesticating other organisms.

Society in all its forms is subordinated to the larger local population and to the still larger species. Populations of social and nonsocial organisms in turn are subordinated to the local community, an aggregation type that occupies our attention next.

The Community

A community is a local association of populations of several *different* species. A pond with its various plant and various animal populations is a community; so is a forest, a meadow, a section of

FIG. 4.15. Social continuity in insect and vertebrate societies. Among insects, continuity hinges on a single female. But among vertebrates, *all* individuals are reproducers.

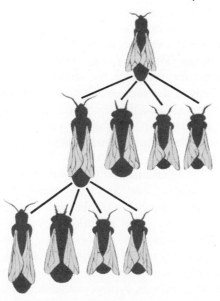

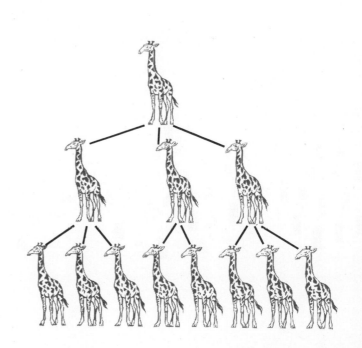

ocean shore, or a village with its people, trees, grasses, bacteria, cats, dogs, and other plants and animals (Fig. 4.16). The sum total of all communities makes up the whole living world.

The boundaries between communities are not primarily biological, as between species, but are primarily geographical and environmental. And the *kind* of community likely to be found in a given territory depends largely on the physical and chemical nature of that territory. For this reason, we shall discuss the different specific types of communities in the next chapter, in a context which stresses the environmental aspects of the living world. Here we shall deal with the general characteristics of all types of communities, and with the forces which govern their structure. As noted earlier, an account of symbiotic associations will be a part of this discussion.

FIG. 4.16. When the territorial ranges of several species overlap, populations of these different species may come to coexist within a given limited area. The organisms in such an area represent a community.

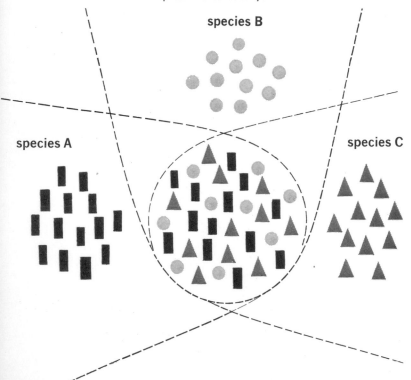

CYCLES AND BALANCES

Like other living entities, a community grows, develops, passes through a relatively stable mature phase, reproduces, and ultimately dies. The time scale is in hundreds and thousands of years.

Such communal life cycles result from an interplay between organisms and their environment. Being specialized, different organisms are adapted to, and must therefore live in, different environments. The physical character of a given region consequently determines what types of organisms can settle there originally. Temperature, winds, amount of rainfall, the chemical composition of the surroundings, latitude and altitude, soil conditions, and other similar factors decisively influence what kinds of plants will be able to survive in a given locale. Vegetation, in turn, as well as the physical character of the locale, has a selective effect on the types of animals that may successfully settle in the region.

By its very presence, however, a given set of organisms gradually alters local conditions. Raw materials are withdrawn from the environment in large quantities, and metabolic wastes are returned. To the extent that these wastes differ from the original raw materials, the environment becomes altered. Moreover, the components of dead organisms also return to the environment, but not necessarily in the same place, nor necessarily in the same form, in which they were obtained. In time, organisms thus bring about profound redistributions and alterations of vast quantities of the earth's substance.

This means that later generations of the original organisms may find the changed local environment no longer suitable, and the members of the community must resettle elsewhere or die out. A new community of different plants and animals may come to occupy the territory, and as this community now alters the area according to its own specializations, type replacement, or **communal succession,** may eventually follow once more. We note how closely the nonliving and the biological components of the environment are interlinked: change in one produces change in the other.

Communal succession of this sort may ulti-

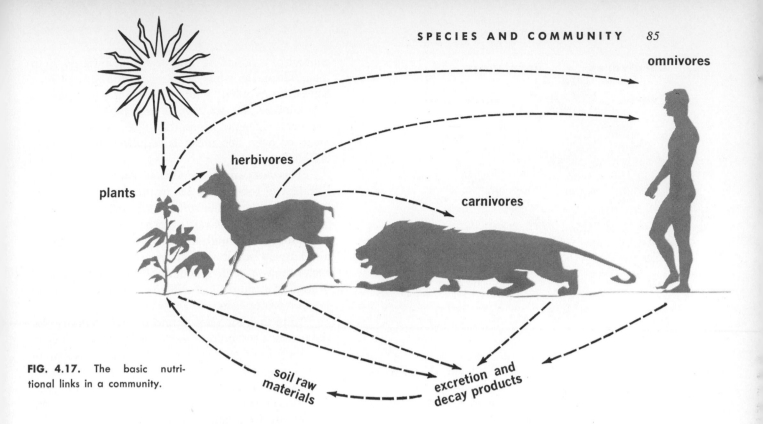

FIG. 4.17. The basic nutritional links in a community.

mately lead to the establishment of a **climax community**: a set of organisms which alters the local environment in such a way that the original conditions are repeatedly re-created more or less exactly. The North American prairie and forest belts are good examples of climax communities; so are the communities in deserts, large lakes, and in the ocean. Such associations are relatively stable, and they are perpetuated within a territory as long as local conditions are not altered drastically by climatic or geological upheavals. If that happens, communal death usually follows. Development of new communities by immigration, or major evolutionary adjustment of the remnants of the old community, may then occur.

In a community, as on all other levels of living organization, *turnover* occurs continuously; individuals of the various populations emigrate or die out and are replaced by others. The important point is that, in a climax community, this flux is automatically self-adjusting, so that the community remains internally *balanced* and exhibits a numerical steady state. That is, in all populations present, the num-

bers of individuals remain relatively constant. In a large, permanent pond, for example, the number of frogs, minnows, and any other organisms, plant or animal, will be more or less the same from decade to decade. Annual fluctuations are common, but over longer periods of time, constancies of numbers are characteristic in most natural communities.

What creates and controls these striking numerical balances? Three main factors do so: **food, reproduction,** and **protection,** the three principal links which make the members of a community interdependent.

NUTRITIONAL LINKS

In every stable community, green plants produce their own food and grow; herbivorous animals eat the plants; carnivorous animals eat each other or herbivores; the elimination products and the dead bodies of all plants and all animals replenish the ocean or the soil; and this, plus solar energy and raw materials from the environment, then makes new plant growth possible (Fig. 4.17).

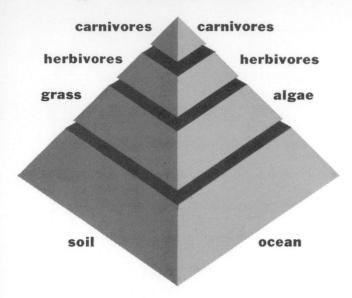

FIG. 4.18. The general pattern of food pyramids. Soil and ocean support plant life, herbivorous animals subsist on the plants, and carnivorous animals subsist on the herbivores.

In such cycles, a pound of food eaten by an animal does not make a pound of new animal protoplasm. Much of the food is water; some components are indigestible altogether; some escape digestion in their passage through the gut. Nor is the energy

content of a pound of food usable quantitatively in metabolism, since loss of energy in the form of heat cannot be avoided. Therefore, when one organism eats another, this transfer of protoplasm is not 100 per cent efficient. *More* than 300 lb of antelope meat, or even lion meat, is required to produce a 300-lb lion.

This inescapable condition leads to the establishment of **food pyramids** in the community (Fig. 4.18). So many tons of soil can support only so many *fewer* tons of grass. Grass in turn supports herbivores which together weigh less than the grass. And only a relatively small weight of carnivores can find sustenance in such a community. Several acres of ground thus might just suffice to support 150 lb of human protoplasm.

Note that such a pyramid of total weights also delineates a pyramid of individual numbers and individual sizes; prey is generally smaller than predator; hence the balanced community may contain millions of individual grasses, but only one man.

Pyramids of this sort are one of the most potent factors in balancing communal populations. For significant variations of numbers at any level of a pyramid entail automatic adjustments at every other level. For example, overpopulation of carnivores soon results in the depletion of herbivores, since a greater number of herbivores is eaten. This depletion leads to starvation of carnivores and decimation of their numbers. Underpopulation of carnivores then results in overpopulation of herbivores, since fewer herbivores are eaten. But the fewer carnivores can be well fed; hence they may reproduce relatively rapidly, and this increases their

FIG. 4.19. Population balance between carnivores and herbivores. A large carnivore population reduces the herbivore population by predation (top). This eventually decreases the food supply of carnivores and leads to starvation and decrease of the carnivore population (bottom right). This in turn then permits the herbivore population to flourish again (bottom left), which also permits an increase in the numbers of carnivores. The cycle repeats in this manner.

FIG. 4.20. Several different food chains, each culminating in a different organism, may be supported by a single plot of ground.

number again (Fig. 4.19). The cycle then repeats. As a result, although the numbers undergo short-term fluctuations, they remain relatively constant over the long term.

The territory of a given community usually supports more than one food pyramid. Each of these is characterized by a different **food chain,** culminating in a different predator. For example, a lion would find it extremely expensive in terms of locomotor energy to live on insects, worms, or even lizards and mice. Bigger prey, like antelope or zebra, is obviously more appropriate. On the other hand, insects and worms are suitable food for small birds; and small birds, lizards, and mice provide adequate diet for larger predator birds. In this example, two food pyramids are based on the same plot of land. The pattern is generally much more complex. Different types of plants in one territory may sustain many different herbivores. These may form the basis of different, intricately interlocking animal food chains. As in the case of elephants, a herbivore may itself represent the peak of a food pyramid (Fig. 4.20).

It may be noted also that, in a balanced community, total live protoplasm and the physical en-

vironment yield just enough dead organic matter and other raw materials to replenish the soil or the ocean, thus permitting the quantitative perpetuation of the various food pyramids above ground or in water. In such delicate nutritional interdependencies, minor fluctuations are rebalanced fairly rapidly. But serious interference, by disease, by man, or by physical factors, is likely to topple the whole pyramid.

In this respect, man's impact has often been particularly disastrous. To cite just one instance, through ignorance, under the guise of "sport," through bounty payments, in the name of trade, and equipped with gun and torturous steel trap, man has virtually written the end of the age of mammals in the "civilized" world. Practically every such drastic imbalancing of terrestrial food pyramids entails a rapid spreading of insect and other

FIG. 4.21. The photo shows the remains of a cornfield after attack by grasshoppers. (U.S. Department of Agriculture.)

pests, which destroy economically important crops and so cost billions every year (Fig. 4.21).

Control measures instituted by conservation biologists and Federal agencies do much to protect natural resources, and the taxpayer's purse, from losses due to severe upsets in the communal balance of populations. For example, in the fight against disease-causing or otherwise crop-destroying pests, one biological method of control is based on a study of food pyramids. If a pest organism invades new territory, the natural enemies which have held it in check in its original habitat are searched for. One of these enemies is then introduced into the new region, after investigation has shown that it is likely to fit into the new food pyramid and is not likely to become a pest itself. In this way the English sparrow, for example, has been introduced in New England against the gypsy moth caterpillar. The ladybird beetle has been brought from Australia to California, where a destructive scale insect threatened the citrus industry. A parasitic fly from British New Guinea has successfully held down the sugar-cane weevil in Hawaii.

Yet as in so many problems of health, personal or national, while remedial measures are good, preventive measures are better, safer, and cheaper. And preventive measures include, above all, a minimizing of thoughtless human interference with delicate natural balances.

REPRODUCTIVE LINKS

A familiar and most important instance of reproductive interdependence within a community is that of the pollinating activity of insects. In some well-known cases of remarkable specialization, a given insect visits only one or a few specific flower types for pollen and nectar, and the flower in turn is structurally adapted to facilitate entry of the insect (e.g., snapdragons). Such intimate reciprocity testifies to a closely correlated evolutionary development of animal and plant. It is fairly obvious how such interdependence contributes to population balance: reduction of the insect population entails reproductive restriction of the plant, and vice versa. Similarly significant in balancing the reproductive growth of plant populations is the seed-dispersing activity of birds and mammals.

Other examples of reproductive dependence are many. Birds such as cuckoos lay eggs in nests of other birds. Insects such as gall wasps embed their eggs deep in the tissues of particular plants, where the hatching larvae find food and protection. Other insects deposit eggs on or under the skin of various animals. Certain wasps, for example, kill tarantulas and lay their eggs in them (see Fig. 4.29).

Reproductive growth and geographic expansion of a community are intimately correlated with nutritional balances. In new territory, a pioneer association of populations will first form a small food pyramid, occupying perhaps only part of the available territory. The pyramid may still be too "low" to support any big herbivores or carnivores. Abundance of food and absence of competition promote high reproduction rates and a rapid increase of numbers, at all levels of the pyramid. The base of the pyramid therefore widens, and a larger area of the territory will be occupied. Sizable herbivores and even a few larger carnivores may gradually be assimilated into the community. As a result, the rate of predation will increase, which in turn will slowly decrease the net reproductive population gain. A turning point will be reached eventually. Prior to it the community grows at an *increasing* rate; after it the community still grows, but at a *decreasing* rate. Net expansion finally comes to a standstill, and from then on the pyramid retains relatively stable proportions (Fig. 4.22).

In such a growth pattern, it is assumed that territorial and numerical expansion can follow its inherent trend without external restriction. Yet geographic and biological barriers often delimit an area. A small forest may be surrounded by water, or by land on which trees cannot grow; a meadow may be ringed in by forest, or a valley by high mountains. In such cases, growth of the community is stopped before its inherent potential is fully expressed. The food pyramid on such a limited territory may never become high enough to support large herbivorous or carnivorous members; one searches in vain for stag in a tiny forest, for large

fish in a small pond, but the one is likely to abound in worms, mice, and small birds, the other in algae, protozoa, and frogs.

In a community incapable of further expansion, steady reproduction may produce a centrifugal **population pressure.** This may be relieved by emigration of the overflow population. If emigration is not possible, or if it is not sufficiently effective, numbers will be decimated by starvation, or even sooner by epidemic diseases. The latter spread rapidly through an overpopulated, undernourished, spatially delimited community. Even if disease affects only one of the component species, the whole communal web is likely to be disrupted.

PROTECTIVE LINKS

Examples of protective interdependence of organisms within a community are numerous. The many ways in which forests and grasslands house and hide large and small animals are commonplace. Protective devices here usually involve *camouflage,* of body colors or of body shapes. Probably the most remarkable instance of color camouflage is the phe-

FIG. 4.22. Population growth and geographic expansion. As the number of individuals increases, more territory will be occupied and the food pyramid will become wider and higher (left part of diagram). Growth rates are indicated in curve at right; increasing rates are in evidence prior to a turning point (arrow), decreasing rates thereafter.

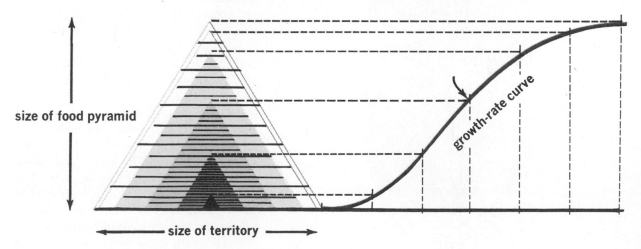

FIG. 4.23. The shape of many insects mimics that of plant parts on which these animals habitually live. Far left, a dead-leaf butterfly, which, when its wings are folded, remarkably resembles a leaf. Opposite, a praying mantis, colored green, resembling a thin stem. Lower left, a leaf insect, whose resemblance to a leaf is exceptionally striking. (Butterfly, General Biological Supply House, Inc.; others, U.S. Department of Agriculture.)

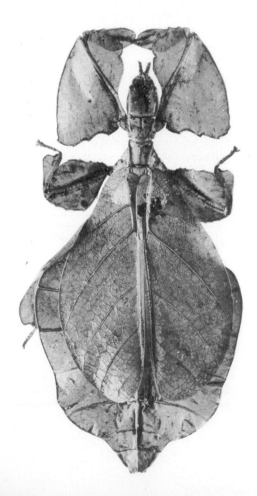

nomenon of **mimicry**, widespread particularly among butterflies and moths. In certain of these animals, pigmentation patterns exist which are virtually indistinguishable from those of other, unrelated species. Usually those species are mimicked which are strong or fast and have few natural enemies. The advantage is that an animal resembling, even superficially, another more powerful one will be protected too, by scaring off potential predators.

Insects also display a variety of structural camouflages. For example, the individuals of certain species possess the detailed shape of leaves, of branches, or of thorns (Fig. 4.23). This serves not only defensively but also as a disguise against potential victims.

Other protective devices vary widely in type. Various birds and some mammals mimic the song and voice of other species, either defensively or as an aggressive lure. The hermit crab protects its soft abdomen in an empty snail shell of appropriate size. Schools of small pilot fish scout ahead of large sharks, leading their protectors to likely prey. Significant protection is also afforded by man, through domestication, game laws, parks, and sanctuaries.

In these and other similar instances, overpopulation reduces the relative amount of protection available against enemies or adverse climates. Through this, protective opportunities become powerful controlling factors of communal population balances.

These various considerations show clearly that the member populations of a community are specialized nutritionally, reproductively, and protectively. Thus, carnivorous populations cannot sustain themselves on plant food and not even on every kind of animal food. Herbivorous populations require plants and are incapable of hunting for animals. The populations of green plants depend on soil or ocean, and the populations of saprophytic bacteria cannot do without dead protoplasm. These are profound specializations in structure and function, and they imply loss of individual self-sufficiency, as well as a need for cooperative interdependence. Communal associations of populations evidently are a *necessity*. They are but extensions, on a higher biological level, of the necessarily cooperative aggregations of cells into tissues, organs, and organisms.

Indeed, the development of "community" is as integral a part of organic evolution as the development of individual organisms. Events were *not* such that a particular organism first evolved structurally and functionally in a certain way and then happened to find the right community into which it could fit. Rather, the community existed from the very beginning, and all its member populations evolved *together;* the community itself evolved. The histories of the bumblebee and the snapdragon are linked as intimately as the histories of every man's hand and foot.

A community within a given territory includes not only organisms which live in loose cooperative association. It also includes organisms which live together in more or less permanent physical contact. Two individuals of different species may be joined so intimately that one lives right *within* the other. All such instances of physically intimate living together, of members of *different* species, are instances of **symbiosis,** a special form of communal life.

Symbiosis

THE PATTERN

A free association in which an animal habitually shelters under a plant might, in a relatively simple evolutionary step, become an association in which the animal and the plant have entered a more permanent protective union. A plant which depends on some animal for seed dispersal might advantageously live in, or on, the animal altogether, not only at the time of seed production, but throughout life. A soil bacterium, or a scavenging protozoon, living on the undigested elimination products of larger forms, might find a surer food supply if it could adapt to an existence right in the gut cavity of its supplier.

Among ancestral populations of free-living forms, ample opportunity existed for the development of such symbiotic relationships. These opportunities were exploited to the full, and many associations arose in which two organisms of different plant or animal species came to live together in intimate, lasting physical contact. Today there is no major group of plants or animals which does not include symbiotic species; and there is no individual plant or animal, man not excepted, which does not play **host** to at least one **symbiont.**

The phenomenon of symbiosis is expressed in two basic patterns. In **facultative** associations, two different organisms "have the faculty" of entering a more or less intimate symbiotic relationship. But they need not necessarily do so, being able to survive as free-living forms. In **obligatory** associations, on the other hand, one organism *must* unite symbiotically with another, usually a specific one, if it is to survive. The ancestors of obligatory symbionts have invariably been free-living organisms which, in the course of history, have lost the power of living on their own. Before becoming obligatory symbionts, they formed facultative associations with organisms on which they came to depend more and more.

Symbionts affect each other in different ways. Thus, **mutualism** describes a relationship in which

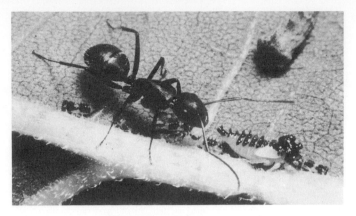

FIG. 4.24. Mutualistic symbiosis. The photo shows a carpenter ant protecting a larva of a tree hopper insect. The larva benefits from the protection and in return secretes sugary honeydew, which is licked off by the ant and serves as its food. (Courtesy of E. W. Teale.)

both associated partners derive some benefit, often a vital one, from living together. **Commensalism** benefits one of the partners, and the other is neither helped nor harmed by the association. **Parasitism** is of advantage to the parasite but is detrimental to the host to greater or lesser extent. These categories intergrade imperceptibly, and in many boundary cases clear-cut distinctions cannot be made.

MUTUALISM

An example of a loose mutualistic association is the tickbird-rhinoceros relationship. The tickbird feeds on skin parasites of the rhinoceros, and in return the latter is relieved of irritation and obtains warning of danger when the sharp-eyed bird flies off temporarily to the security of the nearest tree. Another example is the relationship between dairy ants and aphids, already cited earlier in the section on insect societies. The ant obtains food from the aphid, and the aphid in turn secures protection, food, and care from the ant. These two examples also illustrate the difference between facultative and obligatory mutualism: Both tickbird and rhinoceros can get along without each other if necessary. But the ant cannot do without

its aphids, and the aphid cannot do without its ants (Fig. 4.24).

A somewhat greater degree of physical intimacy is exhibited in the mutualistic symbiosis of sea anemones and hermit crabs. Sea anemones attach themselves to empty snail shells, and hermit crabs use these shells as protective housings. The sea anemone, an exceedingly slow mover by itself, is thus carried about on the shell of the hermit crab —an obvious advantage to the anemone in its search for food and in geographic dispersal. The hermit crab in turn benefits from the disguise. Moreover, since the anemone is not a dainty eater, scraps of food become available to the crab when the anemone catches prey. This is a facultative association: sea anemones and hermit crabs may, and largely do, live on their own.

An example of rather more intimate mutualism is provided by **lichens**, grayish and yellowish incrustations commonly found on rock surfaces. These crusts actually are primitive plants— more specifically, plant-plant associations of photosynthesizing single-celled algae and saprophytic, threadlike fungi. The meshes of the fungal threads support the algae, and they also hold rain water like a sponge. The algae produce food, for themselves and for the fungus. The fungus in turn contributes water, nitrogenous wastes, and respiratory carbon dioxide, substances which allow for continued photosynthesis and food production. Lichens may consequently survive in relatively dry terrestrial environments. The fungus can live alone in a water-sugar medium, and the alga may persist by itself in mineral-containing water. Separately, they are merely two types of organisms not particularly different from many others like them. But together, they become a combination of considerable evolutionary importance. Lichens were among the first organisms capable of eking out a terrestrial existence. Contributing to the crumbling of rock and the formation of soil, they paved the way for a larger-scale colonization of the land (see Chaps. 5 and 30).

The most intimate form of mutualism involves algae, protozoa, and bacteria which live in the gut cavity or within the cells of host organisms. Many free-living protozoa (e.g., a species of *Paramecium*) and coelenterates (e.g., several species of *Hydra*) harbor green, single-celled algae within their translucent bodies. The algae supply food and oxygen, as in lichens, and in turn receive protection, water, and other materials essential for continued photosynthesis.

In the gut of termites live flagellate protozoa which secrete an enzyme capable of digesting the cellulose of wood. Termites chew and swallow wood, the intestinal flagellates then digest it, and both organisms share the resulting carbohydrates. Thus, to the detriment of man, termites may exploit unlimited food opportunities open to very few other animals. And the protozoa receive protection and are assured of a steady food supply.

Virtually every animal which possesses an alimentary canal houses billions of intestinal bacteria, particularly in the lower gut. These bacteria draw freely on materials not digested or not digestible by the host, and as a result of their activities, they initiate fecal decay (see Chap. 12). The host generally benefits from the auxiliary digestion carried out by the bacteria and in many instances is also dependent on certain of the bacterial byproducts. For example, man and other mammals obtain many vitamins in the form of "waste" materials released by the bacterial symbionts of the gut.

Mutualistic associations may sometimes develop into parasitic ones. In the course of successive generations, a relationship originally beneficial to both partners may change into an association in which one partner gradually comes to live at the expense of the other. For example, a given beneficial intestinal symbiont might easily "develop a taste" for gut-wall tissue or might become capable of penetrating through the gut wall into the blood stream. In effect, the host would then support a parasite.

COMMENSALISM

Just as the chance association of two free-living organisms may develop into mutualism, so an analogous chance association may develop into com-

mensalism. Since the commensal neither harms nor helps its host, the host neither resists nor fosters the relationship in any way.

For example, a species of small tropical fish finds shelter in the cloaca of sea cucumbers. The fish darts out for food and returns, to the utter indifference of the host. The so-called suckerfish (Fig. 4.25) possesses a dorsal fin which is modified into a holdfast device. By means of it, the fish attaches to the underside of sharks and thereby secures scraps of food, wide geographic dispersal, and protection. The shark neither benefits nor suffers in any respect. Barnacles may attach to the skin of whales, an association which secures geographic distribution and wider feeding opportunities for the sessile crustaceans. In this instance, a trend toward parasitism is in evidence; in some cases the barnacles send rootlike processes into the whale, outgrowths which eat away bits of host tissue.

These and most other existing commensalistic unions tend to be facultative. For a symbiont is not likely to be allowed to impose on a host, in intimate, obligatory fashion, unless the host derives at least some benefits from such an imposition and therefore fosters the association, or unless the sym-

FIG. 4.25. Commensalistic symbiosis. Shark with three suckerfish attached to underside. (New York Zoological Society.)

FIG. 4.26. Mistletoe, parasitic on branch of pine tree. (U.S. Forest Service.)

biont has overcome the host's defenses and is frankly parasitic. Consequently, although obligatory commensalistic associations may have evolved quite often, most of them have probably been unstable; they would soon have changed either into mutualism or into parasitism.

We note that both commensalism and mutualism may develop into parasitism. Also, commensalism may first become mutualism, then parasitism. Finally, of two associated organisms, one may be parasitic from the outset. Evidently, all symbiotic roads may eventually lead to parasitism, and none, or virtually none, leads away from it. Parasitic symbiosis is by far the most stable, by far the most widespread.

PARASITISM

Parasitic Ways of Life

It has probably become apparent in the above that symbiosis revolves largely, though not exclusively, around the problem of food. We might suspect, therefore, that symbiosis in general, and

parasitism in particular, would be most prevalent among organisms in which competition for food is most intense. This is actually the case. Although there exist occasional parasitic green plants (e.g., mistletoes, Fig. 4.26), photosynthesizing organisms by and large are not under competitive pressure for basic nutrients; air, water, and sunlight are present everywhere, in inexhaustible quantities. Parasitism flourishes primarily among organisms which must obtain food from other protoplasm: in viruses, in bacteria, in fungi, and in animals.

All viruses today are parasitic. Of the bacteria, those which are not photosynthetic or saprophytic are parasitic. Among fungi, some are saprophytic, the rest are parasitic. And in animals, many major groups are wholly parasitic; virtually all others include important parasitic subgroups (see Chaps. 30 and 31).

The list suggests, and indeed we have seen in Chap. 2, that parasitism is almost as old as life itself. So advantageous and economical is the parasitic mode of living that many parasites may be infested with smaller parasites of their own, and these in turn may support still smaller ones. For example, a mammal may harbor parasitic worms; these may be invaded by parasitic bacteria; and the bacteria may be infected by *bacteriophages,* i.e., viruses which parasitize bacteria (Fig. 4.27). **Hyperparasitism** of this sort is very common. It represents a natural exploitation of the very condition of parasitism. Inasmuch as the parasite is generally smaller than the host, and inasmuch as one host may support many parasites, parasitic and hyperparasitic relationships form inverted food pyramids, contained within the pyramids of the larger community.

The first problem a potential parasite faces is the defense mobilized by a potential host. Attachment to the outer body surface can be prevented only with difficulty, particularly if the host does not possess limbs. Numerous **ectoparasites** exploit this possibility. Equipped with suckers, clamps, or adhesive surfaces, they hold onto skin or hair, and with the aid of cutting, biting, or sucking mouth parts, or with rootlike outgrowths, they feed on the body fluids of the host. Examples: many fungi among plants; leeches, lice, ticks, mites, lampreys, among animals.

Endoparasites, within the body of the host, must breach more formidable defenses. Cellular enzymes in plant and animal, digestive juices and strong acids in the alimentary tract, antibodies in the blood, white blood cells, and other cells which engulf foreign bodies in ameboid fashion, these are among the defensive agents which guard against the invader. Overcoming them means *specialization:* development of enzyme- and antibody-resistant outer coverings, as in bacteria and fungi; tough cuticles, as in most parasitic worms; development of cyst walls and calcareous capsules; development of hooks or clamps with which to hold onto the gut wall; development of enzymes which, when secreted, erode a path through host tissues.

Specialization also involves the selection of *specific* hosts. Highly advanced parasites cannot pick a host at random, even if many similar ones offer the same type of food. During the evolution of a parasite, structural and functional specializations have developed in adaptation to particular hosts only. Thus, most parasites enter a host's body by fixed routes, then settle in fixed regions, as if, in the course of time, they had learned to channel their attack through points of weakness characteristic of particular hosts.

Breaching the host's defenses is a perennial problem to the parasite. No sooner has it developed an avenue to a comfortable existence than the infected individual is discriminated against in his environment; healthy individuals of the host species which have evolved a resistance to the parasite have a better chance of surviving. Large-scale infection of a population with blood parasites, for example, will lead to the preferential survival of those hosts which, through random mutations, develop specific antibodies or other means of combating the infectious agents. Hence if a parasite is to prevail against defenses continually improved by evolution, it too must readjust and evolve. Through its own random mutations, it must develop new means of attack.

We recognize that parasite and host evolve *together,* first the parasite, then the host being one

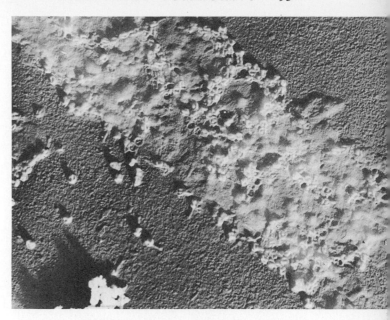

FIG. 4.27. Electron micrograph of the remnants of a bacterium after attack by bacteriophages. The virus parasites are the small rodlets with knobbed ends. Bacteriophage viruses are illustrated also in Fig. 24.2. (Courtesy of R. W. G. Wyckoff, "Electron Microscopy," Interscience Publishers, 1949.)

jump ahead. The very fact that free-living organisms exist today at all signifies that they are resistant to a good many potential parasites by which they are constantly besieged. The very fact that parasites continue to exist signifies that free-living organisms are not completely resistant—and they probably can never be, in view of the evolutionary inventiveness of the parasites.

It may be noted in this connection that it is to the obvious advantage of the parasite to keep the host alive. We find, indeed, that the virulence of a parasite often decreases with time. When a parasite-host relationship is first established, the invader is likely to be **pathogenic,** that is, disease-producing. Two parallel evolutionary trends tend to reduce this pathogenicity. One is natural discrimination against infected hosts, as indicated above; the least resistant will be eliminated through plagues and epidemics. At the same time, less virulent

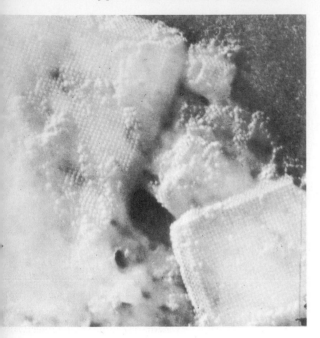

FIG. 4.28. Crystals of virus protein. In this state viruses are nonliving. They exhibit living properties only when present within host cells. (Courtesy of R. W. G. Wyckoff, "Electron Microscopy," Interscience Publishers, 1949.)

strains of the parasite will be favored, for when the host is killed, the killer is generally killed as well. Therefore, the more virulent the parasite, the more difficult is its perpetuation. Many parasites are only mildly pathogenic, or not at all, often indicating long association with a particular host.

FIG. 4.29. A caterpillar of a sphinx moth, parasitized by the pupae of another insect species. (Courtesy of E. W. Teale.)

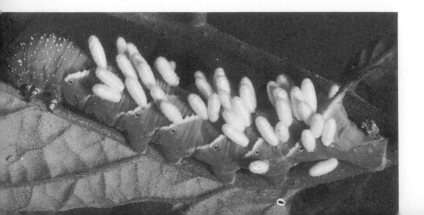

Parasitic Degeneracy

Once established in the body of a host, the parasite may pursue a life of comparative ease. Embedded in food, it needs no locomotor equipment, few sense organs, no fast nervous reflexes. Indeed, structural and functional **degeneracy** is a nearly universal characteristic of parasites. Here we encounter the ultimate expression of the principle that loss of self-sufficiency tends to be proportional to the degree of interdependence of organisms.

Structural degeneracy is pronounced in *tapeworms,* for example. These parasites (see Fig. 4.30) possess only a highly rudimentary nervous system, a rudimentary muscular system, and not even a vestige of a digestive system; almost like blotting paper, the worms soak up the food juices of the host gut through their body walls. Even more degenerate is the adult of *Sacculina,* a crustacean which parasitizes its not too remote relatives, crabs. The parasitic adult is little more than a formless, semifluid mass of cells which spreads through a crab like a malignant tumor, literally reducing the host to an empty shell. The invader later produces sperms and eggs, and fertilized eggs then develop into recognizably typical, free-swimming crustacean larvae. These attach to crabs, enter them, and metamorphose into the degenerate adults.

Degeneracy also extends to metabolic activities. In particular, the synthetic capacities of a parasite are almost invariably restricted. For example, in the presence of nitrogen sources and simple carbohydrates like glucose, a free-living soil bacterium or fungus may synthesize amino acids, proteins, vitamins, numerous antibiotics useful to man, in short, all the complex compounds which make up bacterial or fungal protoplasm. By contrast, a parasitic bacterium or fungus promptly dies when given nitrogenous and simple organic substances alone; it has become dependent on its host for most of the components of its protoplasm.

In this respect, the modern virus is the most degenerate. It cannot metabolize or self-perpetuate at all except within living host cells. Removed from cells, it becomes a lifeless crystal of complex chemicals; and it may resume metabolic and self-perpetuative activities only when it is reintroduced into living protoplasm (Fig. 4.28). Other parasites may be free-living at least at some stage of their life cycle—as eggs, as larvae, or as adults. Viruses are never free-living. Their parasitism is total, complete, obligatory. But as we have seen in Chap. 2, their ancestors may have been free-living.

Parasitic degeneracy is probably an adaptive advantage; the degenerate condition may be more economical than the fully developed condition of the free-living ancestor. A tapeworm, for example, being structurally degenerate, may concentrate all its resources into parasitizing the host, and it need not divert energy and materials into maintaining elaborate nervous, muscular, or digestive systems, which are unnecessary in this particular way of life.

Parasite Reproduction

In one respect parasites are far from degenerate: reproduction. In this function they are as prolific as the most prolific free-living forms. The practical necessity of an enormous reproductive potential is correlated with a major problem confronting the parasite, particularly the endoparasite, namely, how to get from one host to another. The problem is severely compounded by the requirement that not any new host will do. Another individual of the same host species must be found.

Parasites succeed in two ways, both of which involve reproduction: **active transfer** and **passive transfer.** In the former, one stage of the life cycle of the parasite is free-living *and* motile; that is, this stage transfers from one host to another through its own powers of locomotion. For example, the adult phase may be parasitic, and the free-living embryo or larva may be capable of locomotion, as in *Sacculina.* Or the larval phase may be the parasite, the adult then being free-living and capable of locomotion. This is the case in a number of parasitic insects which deposit their eggs within or on individuals of other species (Fig. 4.29).

Passive transfer is encountered among parasites in which *no* phase of the life cycle is capable of locomotion. Propagation here is accomplished by wind, by water, or by **intermediate hosts.** The latter offer a means of transfer which is not quite

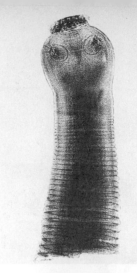

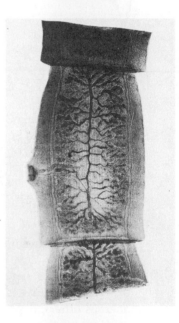

FIG. 4.30. Tapeworm. Top, head; middle, segmental sections near middle of body; bottom, segmental sections near hind end of body. Tree-shaped structures in middle and bottom photos are reproductive organs. Note eggs, filling segments in right photo, and genital pores, opening on the sides of the segments. (General Biological Supply House, Inc.)

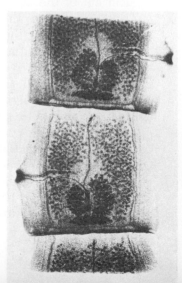

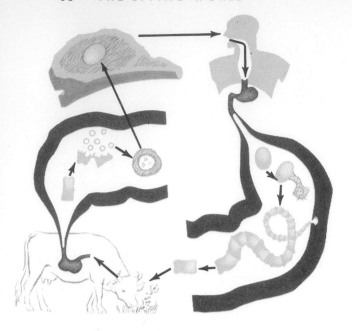

FIG. 4.31. The life cycle of a tapeworm. Ripe sections of the worm pass with the feces from the human gut. Eggs are released from these sections in the gut of cattle. Tapeworm embryos then encapsulate in beef muscle, and the embryos become adults in the intestine of man.

as chancy as random distribution by wind or water. The principle involved is well illustrated in the propagation of tapeworms.

These parasites of man (Fig. 4.30), like numerous others, exploit one of the easiest routes into and out of the host, namely, the alimentary tract. Entering through the host's mouth by way of eaten food, and leaving through the anus by way of feces, some, like tapeworms, spend their adult life directly in the gut cavity of the host. Others utilize the gut as a springboard from which to invade interior tissues. The problem is to transfer offspring from one human host to another by passive means. Tapeworms accomplish a first phase of this readily; mature eggs are released to the outside with the host's feces.

Since man does not eat feces, the eggs evidently cannot reach new human hosts directly. However, tapeworms ingeniously take advantage

of the food pyramids of which man is a member: man eats beef, and cattle eat grass. A ready-made pathway from grass to man thus exists, and the transfer chain becomes complete if, as happens on occasion, human feces are deposited on grass. Tapeworm eggs clinging to such vegetation may then be eaten by cattle.

In the intestine of a cow, a tapeworm egg develops into an embryo, and such an embryo bores a path through the gut wall into the cow's bloodstream. From there the embryo is carried into beef muscle, where it encapsulates and matures. If man then eats raw or partially cooked beef, the capsule surrounding the young tapeworm is digested away in the human gut, and the free worm now hooks on to the intestinal wall of its new host (Fig. 4.31).

This history illustrates a very widely occurring phenomenon. A considerable number of parasites utilize well-established food pyramids in transferring to new hosts. Often there is more than one intermediate host, as in the life cycle of the *Chinese liver fluke* (Fig. 4.32). The adults of this parasite infest the liver of man. Fertilized eggs are released via the bile duct into the gut of the host, and they pass to the outside with the feces. If the feces get into ponds or rivers, as happens frequently, some of the eggs may be eaten by snails.

In the tissues of a snail, each egg develops into a larva, called a **miracidium.** By asexual means, this larva then develops *many* smaller larvae, called **sporocysts.** *Each* of these subsequently gives rise to many **redia** larvae, which feed on snail tissue and grow. Then *each* of the rediae produces yet another set of many larvae, called **cercariae.**

These fourth-generation larvae escape from the snail and swim about freely. If within a short time they happen to find a fish, they bore into it and encapsulate in muscular tissue. And if man subsequently eats raw or incompletely cooked fish, the young adult flukes find their way from the human gut into the liver.

Note that this cycle involves two intermediate hosts, the snail and the fish. Transfer is partly passive (man to snail, fish to man), partly active (snail to fish). Note particularly the asexual, multiple-stage, larva-within-a-larva type of development. Characteristic of flukes generally, it constitutes a highly efficient method of enormously increasing the number of reproductive units. A single fluke egg is estimated to yield a final total of some 10,000 cercariae—and a single adult fluke may produce many ten thousands of eggs! Hence the chances become fairly good that at least some of the millions or billions of larvae will reach final hosts.

Through active locomotion, through physical agents such as air and water, and through routes involving food pyramids and intermediate hosts, parasites have solved their transfer problems most successfully. So successfully, indeed, that there are many more parasites in existence than free-living forms.

That parasites have shaped the course of human history at least as much as man himself is today recognized widely. That the parasitic way of life—not that of man, not that of the insect, not that of the plant—is really the dominant way on earth is even more significant. Man often holds parasitism in utter contempt. In his ethical code it becomes a way of despicable insidiousness. But, purely as a question of ethics, we may ask which is the more contemptible: predator man, who ruthlessly hunts down his victim as a matter of "necessity"; the "gentle" herbivore, who tramples a hundred plants for every ten he devours; or the well-adapted parasite who, if he could, would be the first to prolong the life of his host?

Ethics aside, parasitism specifically, and symbiosis generally, illustrate most strikingly how very intimately the members of a living community are interdependent.

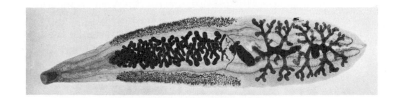

FIG. 4.32. Photo: Chinese liver fluke, adult. Note sucker at anterior (narrow) end of body and dark-stained reproductive organs. Diagram: life cycle of a liver fluke. **A,** Adult in liver of man; **B,** egg, passing out with feces and eaten by snail; **C,** in the snail, the egg develops into a miracidium larva; **D,** from it develop many sporocysts; **E,** from each sporocyst larva in turn form many redia larvae; **F,** each redia gives rise to many cercaria larvae; **G,** cercariae escape from the snail and encapsulate in fish muscle. The encapsulated larvae then grow into adults in the gut and liver of man. (Photo, Ward's Natural Science Establishment, Inc.)

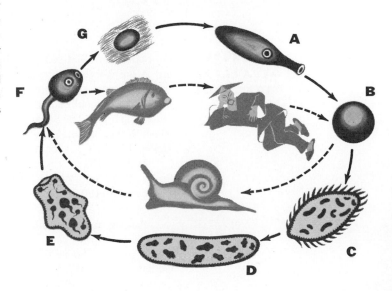

1. What, specifically, is a population, a society, a species, a community, a symbiotic association? Make sure that you understand the interrelation of these units.

2. How do new species arise, and in what general ways are two sister species different?

3. What are individual variations? Distinguish between inheritable and noninheritable variations, and give examples of each. Why are noninheritable variations without direct importance in species evolution? What are adaptive variations?

4. Define polymorphism, and give several examples. What varieties of polymorphism are encountered within societies?

5. Review the organization of some insect and vertebrate societies, and contrast these organizations. What is the social significance of family groupings, and where do the latter occur? What is the significance of animal migrations? Of peck orders?

6. Define communal succession, climax community, food pyramid, food chain, mimicry. Review the nutritional, reproductive, and protective links which hold the members of a community together. How are long-range numerical population balances maintained? In what ways are populations, species, and communities specialized?

7. What are the various forms of symbiosis, and how are they defined? Give concrete examples of each.

8. Which broad groups of organisms include, or consist entirely of, parasites? What is hyperparasitism, ectoparasitism, endoparasitism?

9. What general structural and functional characteristics distinguish parasites from free-living organisms? How do parasites transfer from host to host?

10. Describe the life cycles of tapeworms and liver flukes, and review the general significance of intermediate hosts.

SUGGESTED
COLLATERAL
READINGS

On populations and communities, the first book cited is a small classic and "must" reading. More detailed information may be obtained from the second and third books, and the fourth is a standard text which may be valuable for additional references:

Elton, C.: "Animal Ecology," Macmillan, 1937.

Ousting, H. T.: "The Study of Plant Communities," Freeman, 1948.

Allee, W. C.: "Animal Aggregations," University of Chicago Press, 1931.

Hesse, R.,. W. C. Allee, and K. P. Schmidt: "Ecological Animal Geography," 2d ed., Wiley, 1951.

Smith, R. F., and W. W. Allen: Insect Control and the Balance of Nature, *Sci. American,* vol. 190, 1954.

Among many popular books and articles on social animals, the following are excellent:

Tinbergen, N.: "Social Behavior in Animals," Wiley, 1953.

Collias, N.: Social Life and the Individual among Vertebrate Animals, *Ann. N.Y. Acad. Sci.,* vol. 51, 1950.

Guhl, A. M.: The Social Order of Chickens, *Sci. American,* vol. 194, 1956.

Haskins, C. P.: "Of Societies and Men," Norton, 1951.

Imms, A. D.: "Social Behavior in Insects," Methuen, 1947.

Von Frisch, K.: "Bees, Their Vision, Chemical Senses, and Language," Cornell University Press, 1950.

Krough, A.: The Language of the Bees, *Sci. American,* vol. 179, 1948.

Various aspects of symbiosis are popularly described in the following:

Cleveland, L. R.: An Ideal Partnership, *Sci. Monthly,* vol. 67, 1948.

De Kruif, P.: "Microbe Hunters," Harcourt, Brace, 1928.

Zinsser, H.: "Rats, Lice, and History," Little, Brown, 1935.

Bigger, J. W.: "Man against Microbe," Macmillan, 1939.

Lwoff, A.: The Life Cycle of a Virus, *Sci. American,* vol. 190, 1954.

Burnet, F. M.: Viruses, *Sci. American,* vol. 184, 1951.

Luria, S. E.: The T2 Mystery, *Sci. American,* vol. 192, 1955.

Schwartz, B.: Animal Parasites Transmissible to Man, in I. W. Knobloch, "Readings in Biological Science," Appleton-Century-Crofts, 1948.

IN THIS CHAPTER, we add the finishing touches to our characterization of the living world; our scale of view now becomes global, and we examine the living world as a whole.

Different environments harbor different kinds of communities, and an inquiry into the nature of these various communal homes, or **habitats,** forms our first topic. The second topic deals with the physical, chemical, and geological forces which affect the habitats and the organisms in them and which actually govern environmental conditions on the entire earth. In other words, we shall examine the large-scale nature of the **global environment.**

The Communal Habitats

With the possible exception of the most arid deserts, the high frozen mountain peaks, and the perpetually icebound polar regions, probably no place on earth is devoid of life. The large subdivisions of this planetary home are the **aquatic** and the **terrestrial** habitats. Both range from equator to pole and from a few thousand feet below to a few thousand feet above sea level. **Ocean** and **fresh water** are the principal components of the aquatic habitat, and **air** and **soil** of the terrestrial.

THE OCEANIC HABITAT

The Ocean Basin

Even the land dweller will appreciate readily that the sea is not a single, unified environment. Indeed, an examination of its structure and of its content of living matter shows clearly that this birthplace of life features nearly as many distinct subenvironments as the land.

All ocean basins have roughly the form of an inverted hat (Fig. 5.1). A gently sloping **continental shelf** stretches away from the coastline for an average distance of about 100 miles (discounting

5

COMMUNITY AND ENVIRONMENT

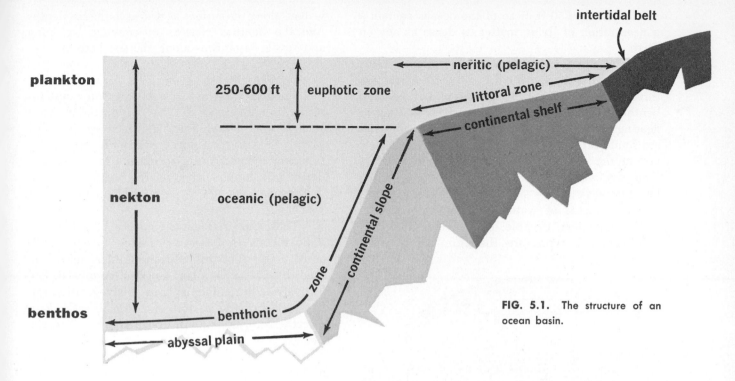

FIG. 5.1. The structure of an ocean basin.

often extreme deviations from this average). The angle of descent then changes more or less abruptly, and the shelf grades over into a steep **continental slope.** Characteristically, this slope is scored deeply by gorges and canyons, carved out by slow rivers of mud and sand discharging from estuaries. Several thousand feet down, the continental slope levels off into the ocean floor, a more or less horizontal expanse known as the **abyssal plain.** Mountains rise from it in places, with peaks sometimes so high that they rear up above sea level as islands. Elsewhere, the plain may be scarred by deep rifts, e.g., the Mindanao trench off the Philippines which, plunging 35,000 ft down, is the lowest part of the earth's crust.

Three major environments may be distinguished in such a basin. The sea floor from the shore out to the edge of the continental shelf forms the **littoral** zone. Its most important subenvironment is the narrow **intertidal** belt, between the high- and low-tide lines. Beyond the littoral, the sea floor along the continental slope and the abyssal

plain constitutes the **benthonic** environment. The third principal environment is the **pelagic**—the water itself which fills the ocean basin. This environment includes a **neritic** subdivision over the littoral zone and an **oceanic** subdivision over the benthonic zone.

A most important vertical subdivision of the pelagic environment is brought about by the sun. Acting directly or via the overlying medium of air, the sun produces "weather" in the surface layers of the sea—waves, currents, storms, evaporation, seasons, daily climatic rhythms, and other changes. Deep water is not so affected. Moreover, sunlight penetrates into water only to an average depth of about 250 ft, and to at most 600 ft in certain seas. Within this sunlit layer, called the **euphotic** zone, light dims progressively to zero with increasing distance from the surface. The most significant consequence of this is that photosynthesizing vegetation can exist only in the uppermost layers of the sea. Animal life directly dependent on plant foods therefore must remain near the surface too. As a result, the top 250 ft or so of the oceans contain a concentration of living matter as dense as any on earth.

On the basis of its relationship to these various environments, marine life has been classified into three general categories: **plankton, nekton,** and **benthos.** Plankton includes all passively drifting or floating forms. Most of them are microscopic and are found largely in the surface waters of the sea, i.e., in the euphotic zone. Even though some of them possess locomotor systems, they are nevertheless too weak or too small to counteract currents and movements of water. Nekton comprises the active swimmers, capable of changing stations at will. Nektonic types are therefore found in all

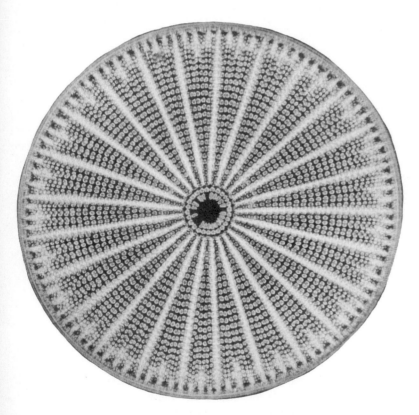

FIG. 5.2. The finely sculptured silicon shell of a diatom. Other examples of these single-celled components of phytoplankton are illustrated in Chap. 30, Fig. 30.9. (General Biological Supply House, Inc.)

waters, along the surface as well as in the sea depths. And the benthos consists of crawling, creeping, and sessile organisms along the sea bottom.

The Open Euphotic Zone

Since they do not possess locomotor systems, plants in open water can stay within the range of sunlight only if they float. And since protoplasm is slightly heavier than water, passive floating is possible only if an organism possesses a special floating device or a large surface relative to its volume, or if it is small enough to be buoyed up by the salt water.

Thus, the predominant marine flora is planktonic. It consists of teeming trillions of algae, which, as a group, probably photosynthesize more food than the rest of the plant kingdom combined. Collectively called **phytoplankton,** this vegetation represents the richest pasture on earth; directly or indirectly, it forms the nutritional basis of all marine life.

Most of the algal types included in this "grass of the sea" are microscopic (see also Chap. 30). Unquestionably the most abundant are the **diatoms.** Each of these single-celled plants is enclosed within a delicate, intricately sculptured, silicon-containing shell (Fig. 5.2). Reddish **dinoflagellates** also abound in surface waters, sometimes in populations so dense that they tint acre upon acre of ocean with a coppery hue (e.g., "red" tides). Like other flagellates, dinoflagellates are equipped with flagella and may move like animals (see Chap. 30). Other marine algae include many types of variously pigmented forms, and some of these, as well as countless numbers of marine bacteria, are bioluminescent. They emit flashes of cold light, which dot the night seascape with a billion pin points of greenish fire.

Surrounded on all sides by raw materials and bathed in sunlight, the passively drifting phytoplankton community inhabits a highly favorable, chemically rather stable environment. Death rate through animal feeding is great—a whale may strain a ton of diatoms from the ocean daily—but rapid reproduction sufficiently offsets it. Physical and climatic changes do not affect an algal cell too

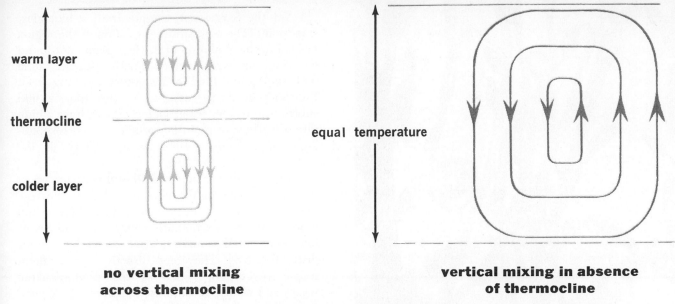

warm layer

thermocline

colder layer

equal temperature

**no vertical mixing
across thermocline**

**vertical mixing in absence
of thermocline**

FIG. 5.3. Temperature layering of surface water, as in summer, leads to the formation of a *thermocline* and poor vertical circulation of water (left). In early spring, late fall, and winter, surface waters acquire the same temperature as deeper layers; hence the thermocline disappears, and vertical mixing becomes possible.

greatly. In winter, the temperature of surface waters may fall below the freezing point, but the salts of the ocean prevent actual freezing. Cold merely reduces the rate of metabolic processes, and algal life continues, at a slower pace.

Indeed, low temperatures promote algal growth. For when surface temperatures are high, as in tropical waters throughout the year, and in northern and southern waters in summer, pronounced **temperature layering** of water prevents much vertical mixing. A warm water layer is less dense and thus lighter than a colder layer below it; hence it "swims" on top of the colder layer without mixing. Under such conditions, organisms in the warm layer deplete the surface waters of mineral raw materials, and at death these materials sink down without being brought back to the surface by vertical mixing (Fig. 5.3). As a result, the amount of surface life is limited, and warm seas are actually relatively barren.

By contrast, when surface and deeper waters have roughly the same low temperature, vertical mixing becomes possible, and minerals are re-

circulated more readily. Surface life may therefore be more abundant. The perennially cold arctic, antarctic, and subpolar waters actually support huge permanent populations of algae. And as is well known, the best commercial fishing grounds are in the high north and south, not in the tropics, and the best fishing seasons are spring and fall, not summer.

In certain circumscribed regions, phytoplankton also includes larger, multicellular algae—flat, sheetlike seaweeds, often equipped with specialized air bladders which aid in keeping the organisms afloat. Such seaweeds may sometimes aggregate in considerable numbers over wide areas, particularly if a region is ringed in by ocean currents and therefore remains relatively isolated and stagnant. The Sargasso Sea in mid-Atlantic is a good example. This sea has figured prominently in marine lore. For example, stories are told of ships trapped in "floating jungles," rapidly overgrown by plants, and sunk without a trace. Such accounts are wholly legendary, since the flora is nowhere dense enough to prevent a ship's passage.

FIG. 5.4. Sargassum weed, a brown alga. The bulbous structures are air bladders. A species related to the one shown in the photo forms the principal seaweed of the Sargasso Sea. (General Biological Supply House, Inc.)

FIG. 5.5. Plankton. From left to right: phytoplankton is illustrated in the first two photos; various algal types are shown. In the next two illustrations of zooplankton, the first catch is dominated by comb jellies (ctenophores), and the catch at far right, by fish eggs and small, shrimp-like copepods. (U.S. Fish and Wildlife Service.)

Yet the Sargasso *is* unique from a biological standpoint. The comparative isolation of the region has led to the evolution of distinct plants not found elsewhere on earth, and an equally distinct fauna finds shelter and food in this vegetation (Fig. 5.4). Buoyancy in the Sargasso, as in other tropical and subtropical waters, is particularly great, since a high rate of surface evaporation produces a correspondingly high, buoyancy-promoting salinity of the water.

Living side by side with the phytoplankton in the open waters of the euphotic zone is the **zooplankton**: protozoa, eggs, larvae, tiny shrimp, and other crustacea (particularly *copepods*), and countless other small animals carried along by surface drift (Fig. 5.5). They feed directly on the microscopic vegetation; hence as the phytoplankton waxes and wanes, so does the zooplankton. A good part of the nekton, largely fishes and marine mammals, comes into these waters, to feed either on zooplankton or on phytoplankton directly.

The Coastal Region

Nearer to shore, in the waters above the littoral, the problem of remaining afloat is not so critical for a plant as in open water, for here even a bottom dweller is likely to be within the range of sunlight. The problem, rather, is to remain attached to solid ground, for close to shore the force of waves and of ground swells is considerable. In the intertidal belt, moreover, an even more profound problem is the ebbing of water twice daily and the consequent rhythmic alternation between aquatic and

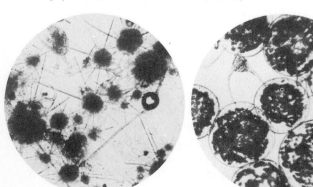

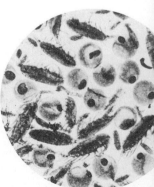

essentially terrestrial conditions. Also, in waters in and for miles beyond estuaries, fresh water discharging from rivers mixes with ocean water, a circumstance introducing additional environmental inconstancies. Being the meeting ground of water, land, and air, the intertidal belt is actually among the most violently changing environments on earth.

Vegetation here, and in the littoral and the overlying neritic region as a whole, is again largely algal. In addition to the planktonic types, attached plants abound. Most of these are equipped with specialized holdfasts which anchor the organisms to underlying ground. Green, brown, and red algae are particularly common. For example, the soft, slippery mats of vegetation encrusting rocks along the shore are familiar to many, as is *Fucus,* a common leathery brown alga found in dense populations on coastal rock (Fig. 5.6). We shall hear more about specific kinds of algal vegetation, along the coasts and elsewhere, in Chap. 30.

The fauna of the littoral, neritic, and intertidal environments includes representatives of practically all animal groups. In addition to the abundant zooplankton, sessile and creeping types occur which are variously adapted to rocky, muddy, or sandy bottoms. The animals make use of all conceivable dwelling sites—tide pools left on rock by ebbing water, crevices and hollows in and under rock, burrows in sand or mud, the sheltered water among vegetation and among sessile animal growths, empty shells and other skeletons of dead animals, flotsam and jetsam along the shore and in deeper water, etc. Among the very abundant nektonic animals in these regions, largely fish, many normally do not stray very far from a particular home, even though an efficient locomotor system would permit them to do so. They foray into surrounding waters for food and mates, but they always tend to return to the same base of operations. However, another group of nektonic animals consists of perpetual wanderers without permanent homes.

The Deep-sea Environment

The contrast between the surface environments within reach of the sun and those underneath is dramatic. As the ones are forever fluctuating, so

are the others perennially steady and relatively unchanging. The deep ocean is still little explored and, for many, this "last frontier" has acquired a romance and mystery all its own. Several unique physical conditions characterize this world of the sea depths.

First, the region is one of eternal night. In the total absence of sunlight, the waters are pervaded with a perpetual blackness of a kind found nowhere else on earth.

Second, seasons and changing weather are practically absent. Localized climatic changes do

FIG. 5.6. A portion of *Fucus,* a common brown alga found attached to rocks on the seashore. Note the air bladders along the leaflike body. The bulbous structures at the ends of the body contain sex organs. (General Biological Supply House, Inc.)

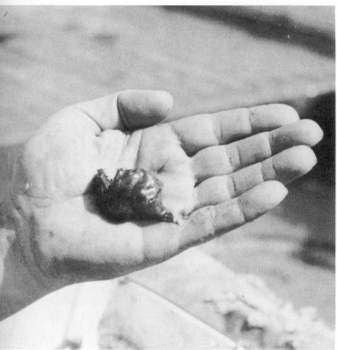

FIG. 5.7. Deep-sea fishes. Top, two kinds of oceanic angler fishes. The animal at left is a female. The structure above the eye is a parasitic male, which is carried about permanently attached. This neatly solves the problem of finding mating partners in the dark. The "beard" of the animal at right is probably luminescent. Many of these large-mouthed, dagger-toothed fishes are surprisingly small, as the angler fish photo at bottom indicates. (Bottom, courtesy of D. M. Owen, Woods Hole Oceanographic Institute; others, American Museum of Natural History.)

occur, as a result of occasional submarine volcanic activity or, more regularly, through deep-sea currents. These produce large-scale shifts of water masses and, incidentally, bring oxygen to even the deepest parts of the ocean. Being beyond the influence of the sun, the deep waters are cold, unchangingly so. Temperatures range from about 10°C at the top of the dark zone to about 1°C along the abyssal plain.

Third, water pressure increases steadily from the surface down, 1 atmosphere (atm) for every 33 ft of descent. Thus, in the deepest trenches of the ocean, the pressure is about a thousand times as great as at sea level.

And fourth, a continuous slow rain of the dead remnants of surface organisms drifts down toward the sea bottom. Much of this material, particularly the organic fraction, dissolves completely during the descent. But much microscopic mineral matter reaches the abyssal plain, where it forms ever-thickening layers of ooze. Accumulating over the millennia, the older layers eventually compress into rock. Vertical-bore samples of such rock have revealed a great deal of the past history of the oceans and their once-living surface inhabitants.

Contrary to early beliefs that life should be impossible in such an environment, a surprisingly rich diversity of organisms has been found to exist practically everywhere in the free water, and along the floor, of the deep sea. The community is uniquely and exclusively *animal*—photosynthesizing plants are confined to the sunlit surface. Virtually all animal groups are represented, many by —to us—strange and bizarre types uniquely adapted to the locale (Fig. 5.7).

If a deep-sea animal is to avoid death from explosion or implosion, its internal pressure must equal the external pressure of the water. A few of the nektonic animals, toothed whales, for example, are adapted to resist the harmful effects of rapid changes of external pressure, and these animals are capable of traversing the whole ocean from bottom to surface. They may therefore feed directly on the rich food supplies in surface waters. But the bulk of the deep-sea nekton is adapted to particular water pressures only, and given animals are rigidly confined to limited pressure zones at given depths. Such animals therefore must obtain food either from the dead matter drifting down from the surface—a meager source, particularly in deeper water—or from within the nekton itself.

This last condition makes the deep sea the most fiercely competitive environment on earth. The very structure of the animals underscores their violently carnivorous, "eat-or-be-eaten" mode of existence. For example, most of the fishes have enormous mouths equipped with long, razor-sharp teeth, and many can swallow fish larger than themselves.

Since the environment is pitch-black, one of the critical problems for these animals is to *find* food to begin with. A highly developed pressure sense provides one solution. Turbulence in the water created by nearby animals can be recognized and, depending on the nature of the turbulence, may be acted upon either by flight or by approach.

Another important adaptation to the dark is bioluminescence. Many of the deep-sea animals possess light-producing organs on the body surface, of different shapes, sizes, and distributions in different species. The light patterns emitted may include a variety of colors and probably serve partly in species recognition; identification of a suitable mate, for example, must be a serious problem in an environment where everything appears equally black. Another function of the light undoubtedly is to warn or to lure. Some of the bioluminescent lures have evolved to a high degree of perfection. Certain fish, for example, carry a "lantern" on a stalk protruding from the snout (Fig. 5.8). An inquisitive animal attracted to the light of the lantern will discover too late that it has headed straight into powerful jaws.

THE FRESH-WATER HABITAT

Physically and biologically, the link between ocean and land is the fresh water. Rivers and lakes were the original invasion routes over which some of the descendants of ancestral marine organisms reached land and, in the process, evolved into terrestrial forms. Certain of the migrant types never

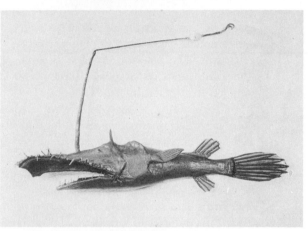

FIG. 5.8.   Two kinds of deep-sea angler fishes with stalked, luminescent "lanterns" over the mouth. Note the vertical position of the mouth in the upper animal. This facilitates catching prey lured to the light of the lantern. (American Museum of Natural History.)

completed the transition but settled along the way.

Among these, some adapted to the brackish water in estuaries and river mouths, or to a life spent partly in the ocean, partly in fresh water. Very many types could leave the ocean entirely and adapt to an exclusively fresh-water existence. The descendants of this large group include bacteria and algae and also representatives of most major animal types. Some of the ancestral fresh-water organisms later managed to gain a foothold on land, but they still had to spend part of their lives in or near fresh water. Frogs and other amphibia, and many insects, are among their modern descendants. Thus, organisms which inhabit the fresh water for part or all of their lives today constitute a rich and major subdivision of the biological world.

Three main conditions distinguish the fresh-water environment from that of the ocean. First, the salt content is substantially lower. In an organism which has evolved, and still lives, in the sea, the internal salt concentration of protoplasm matches that of the marine environment. If such an organism moves to fresh water, the external salt concentrations will be much lower than the internal. For reasons to be explained in the next chapter, the result of this is that water will be pulled from the environment, through the body surface, into the organism. The amount of water in protoplasm will therefore tend to increase, and protoplasm will tend to become diluted.

Fresh-water organisms evidently require, and they actually possess, efficient bailing devices to eliminate the water they continuously ship. Excretory systems, and also digestive systems and gills, serve in this water-balancing function (Fig. 5.9). In animals inhabiting estuaries, where external salt concentrations fluctuate almost continuously, and in organisms whose life cycle includes both marine and fresh-water phases, water- and salt-balancing mechanisms are particularly well developed.

A second general condition characterizing much of the fresh-water environment is the presence of strong, swift currents. Except in large lakes, passively floating life so typical of the ocean surface is therefore not likely to be encountered. On the contrary, the premium will be either on maintaining firm anchorage along the shores and bottoms of rivers or on ability to resist and to overcome the force of currents by muscle power.

Indeed, fresh-water plants are strongly rooted, and fresh-water animals generally are powerful swimmers. The eggs of such animals are enveloped by sticky jelly coats which adhere firmly to plants or other objects in the water (Fig. 5.10). And even the young are strongly muscled from the moment they hatch.

We may note in this connection that most modern fish, and vertebrates in general, probably are an evolutionary product of the fresh water, not of the ocean. The ancestors of vertebrates were marine; they laid small, relatively yolk-free eggs which developed rapidly; and the adults were small and not very muscular. Some of the descendants of these forms then evolved adaptations which permitted them to become successful in fresh water. Principally, eggs enlarged and became very yolky. Well supplied with food in this manner, the eggs could develop slowly and for a relatively long period, which allowed ample time for the elaboration of internal structures, muscular systems included. At hatching, therefore, the young were already well muscled and could maintain station against river currents.

The first fish probably arose in this way, as forms well adapted to the fresh-water environment. Some of these early fish stayed in fresh water, and their descendants may still be encountered there today. Others, however, invaded the ocean, returning along the reverse route their ancestors had taken. Thus marine fish came into being, and today these are among the dominant life forms of the ocean. A third group of the early fresh-water fish took the path to land, and from these eventually evolved the modern land vertebrates—

FIG. 5.9. In a fresh-water organism, the protoplasm contains far more salt and other dissolved substances than the external environment. Water therefore tends to be drawn into such organisms, and they must continuously bail out the excess.

fresh-water exterior

salt-water interior

water continuously pulled in   excess water must be bailed out amphibia, reptiles, birds, and mammals, including man. Large, yolky eggs are still characteristic of vertebrates today, a silent reminder of their probable fresh-water origin (see also Chaps. 29 and 31).

A third major distinction between fresh water and ocean is that the former, with the exception of only the very large lakes, is affected much more by climate and weather than any part of the latter. Bodies of fresh water often freeze over in winter and may dry up completely in summer. Water temperatures change not only seasonally but also daily, frequently to a considerable extent. Gales or flood conditions may bring bottom mud and silt to the surface and upset the fresh-water habitat in major ways. A large number of factors may alter flow conditions and produce, for example, stagnant water, or significantly altered chemical content, or situations facilitating infectious epidemics. We note that the fresh water shares the environmental inconstancies of the land in very large measure. Notwithstanding the aquatic nature of the fresh-water habitat, its living component reflects the ebb and flow of land life as much as that of ocean life.

With a few notable exceptions, major plant and animal groups found in the ocean also have representatives in fresh water. Bacteria and algae occur richly in fresh water as well as in the ocean, and these organisms have become highly successful on land too. Aquatic algae have probably given rise to all other plants, and these—fungi, mosses, ferns, and the seed plants—are fundamentally terrestrial; the advantage of direct exposure to sun and air has made the land a very favorable environment for plants.

Among animals, however, not one major group has left the water entirely, and of those which have reached fresh water, only a few advanced subgroups have been able to colonize the land successfully: some snails, some worms, some vertebrates, and most arthropods (insects, spiders, and related forms). The reason for this continued preference of an aquatic environment is readily appreciated. On the one hand, access to direct sunlight is of no particular advantage to an animal. On the other, locomotion is accomplished with least effort in water, support against gravity is greatest

FIG. 5.10. Frog eggs. Note the jelly coat surrounding each egg. This jelly holds the egg masses together and attaches them to vegetation and other objects in the water. (General Biological Supply House, Inc.)

in water, and plant and animal food is plentiful in water.

Thus, several major groups in the plant kingdom, but none in the animal kingdom, today are entirely terrestrial; and actually only one major animal group is predominantly terrestrial: the arthropods, to which the insects belong.

THE TERRESTRIAL HABITAT

That land environments differ vastly in character is eminently clear to a land dweller as efficient and far-ranging as man. It should also be clear that, regardless of which particular subdivision of the terrestrial environment one considers, the sustaining foundations of all land life are **air** and, directly or indirectly, also **soil;** air and soil are to the terrestrial habitat what the surface waters of the ocean are to the marine.

Like air, soil is itself a terrestrial home, pro-

FIG. 5.11. The desert habitat. In this particular view, Joshua cacti are the predominant plants. (Courtesy of E. P. Haddon, U.S. Fish and Wildlife Service.)

viding a habitat for a vast array of subsurface organisms. And by creating the conditions necessary for the survival of all other terrestrial plants and animals, man included, soil becomes a major agency which transforms terrestrial environments into life-sustaining "habitats." Two other agencies play a vital role here: annual **temperature** and **rainfall.** As these vary with geographic latitude and altitude, they divide the soil-covered land surface into a number of distinct habitat zones: *desert, grassland, rain forest, deciduous forest, taiga,* and *tundra.*

The Tropics and Subtropics

In the tropics are found regional representatives of the first three of the six habitats just named. They are characterized here by comparatively high annual temperatures and by daily temperature variations which are greater than the seasonal variations. Differences in the amount of precipitation largely account for the different nature of these habitats.

A **desert** (Fig. 5.11) usually has less than 10 in. of rain per year, concentrated largely in a few

FIG. 5.12. Grassland habitat. The photo shows a landscape in Arizona. (U.S. Department of Agriculture.)

heavy cloudbursts. Desert life is well adapted to this. Plants, for example, grow, bloom, are fertilized, and produce seeds, all within a matter of days after a rain. Since the growing season is thus greatly restricted, such plants stay relatively small. Leaf surfaces are often reduced to spines and thorns, minimizing water loss by evaporation (see also Chap. 8). Desert animals too are generally small, and they include many burrowing forms which may escape the direct rays of the sun under the ground surface. In most deserts, the "warm-blooded" mammals and birds are comparatively rare or are absent altogether; maintenance of constant body temperature is difficult or impossible under conditions of great heat and practically no water. By contrast, animals which match their internal temperature to the external, the so-called "cold-blooded" forms, can get by much more easily.

Grassland, as everyone well knows, is not an exclusively tropical habitat but extends into much of the temperate zone as well (Fig. 5.12). The more or less synonymous terms "prairie," "pampas," "steppe," "puszta," and many other regional designations underscore the wide distribution of this habitat. The common feature of all grasslands is intermittent, erratic rainfall, amounting to about 10 to 40 in. annually. Grasses of various kinds, from short buffalo grass to tall elephant grass and thickets of bamboo, are particularly adapted to irregularly alternating periods of precipitation and dryness. Grassland probably supports more species of animals than any other terrestrial habitat. Different kinds of mammals are particularly conspicuous.

In those tropical and subtropical regions in which torrential rains fall practically every day, and where a well-defined rainy season characterizes the winter, plant growth continues the year round. Lush **rain forests** have developed here (Fig. 5.13), typified particularly by the communal coexistence of up to several hundred different species of trees. Rain forests are the "jungles" of the adventure tale. They cover much of central Africa, south and southeast Asia, Central America, and the Amazon basin of South America. Trees in such

FIG. 5.13. Above: the habitat of the rain forest. Many dozens of different plant types, coexisting in dense formations, are generally characteristic of it. Right: a subtropical palm forest. The trees of such forests may retain their foliage the year round. (Rain forest, National Park Service; palm forest, U.S. Forest Service.)

the wind. As a result, the forest floor is exceedingly humid and quite dark, and it is populated by plants requiring only a minimum of light. Animal communities too are stratified vertically, according to the several very different habitats offered between canopy and ground. The tropical rain forest is singularly quiet during the day, but it erupts into a cacophony of sound at night, when the largely nocturnal fauna becomes active.

The Temperate and Polar Regions

In the temperate zone, apart from extensive grasslands and occasional deserts, the most characteristic habitat is the **deciduous forest** (Fig. 5.14). The fundamental climatic conditions here are cold winters, warm summers, and well-spaced rains bringing some 30 to 40 in. of precipitation per year. The habitat is characterized also by seasonal temperature variations which are greater than the daily variations. Winter makes the growing season discontinuous, and the flora is adapted to this; trees are largely deciduous, that is, they shed their leaves and hibernate; and small annual plants produce seeds which withstand the cold weather. A deciduous forest differs from a rain forest in that trees are spaced farther apart and in that far fewer species are represented. Compared with the hun-

FIG. 5.14. The habitat of the deciduous forest. In this type of forest, characteristic of the temperate zone, the trees lose their leaves during the winter. (National Park Service.)

forests are normally so crowded together that they form a continuous overhead canopy of branches and foliage, which cuts off practically all the sunlight, much of the rain water, and a good deal of

FIG. 5.15. The habitat of the taiga. Note the predominance of a single species of tree over large areas, characteristic of the taiga generally. (National Park Service.)

dreds of tree types in the one, there may be only some 10 or 20 in the other. Maple, beech, oak, elm, ash, and sycamore are among the common trees of a deciduous forest. The many familiar animal types in this habitat include deer, boars, raccoons, foxes, squirrels, and, characteristically, woodpeckers.

North of the deciduous forests and the grasslands, across Canada, northern Europe, and Siberia, stretches the **taiga** (Fig. 5.15). This is a habitat of long, severe winters and of growing seasons limited largely to the few months of summer. Hardy conifers, spruce in particular, are most representative of the flora, and moose, wolves, and bears of the fauna. The taiga is preeminently a zone of forests. These differ from other types of forests in that they usually consist of a single species of tree. Thus, over a large area, spruce, for example, may be the only kind of tree present. Another conifer species might be found in an adjacent, equally large area. Occasional stands of hardy deciduous trees are often intermingled with conifers. An accident of geography makes the taiga a habitat characteristic of the northern hemisphere only; little land exists in corresponding latitudes of the southern hemisphere.

The same circumstance makes the **tundra,** most polar of terrestrial habitats, a predominantly northern phenomenon (Fig. 5.16). Much of the tundra lies within the Arctic Circle; hence its climate is cold, and there may be continuous night during the winter season and continuous daylight, of comparatively low intensity, during the summer. Some distance below the surface, the ground is permanently frozen, and above ground, frost can form even during the summer—plants often freeze solid and remain dormant until they thaw out again. The growing season is very brief, as in the desert, but in the tundra the limiting factor is temperature, not water supply. Plants are low, ground-hugging forms, and trees are absent. Lichens, mosses, coniferous and other shrubby growths, and herbs with brilliantly colored flowers, all blooming simultaneously during the growing season, are characteristic of the habitat. Conspicuous among the animals are hordes of insects, particularly flies, and a considerable variety

of mammals: caribou, arctic hares, lemmings, foxes, musk oxen, and polar bears. Birds are largely migratory, leaving for more southern latitudes with the coming of winter.

Life does not end at the northern margin of the tundra but extends farther into the ice and bleak rock of the soilless polar region. Polar life is almost exclusively animal. And it is not fundamen-

FIG. 5.16. The habitat of the tundra. Note complete absence of trees in both views. (Courtesy of U. C. Nelson and H. C. Oberholser, U.S. Fish and Wildlife Service.)

FIG. 5.17. The polar and subpolar habitat, based on the sea. The photo shows a group of fur seals on an island in the far north. Note the polygamous, familial organization: a single male, several females, and their young. (Courtesy of V. B. Scheffer, U.S. Fish and Wildlife Service.)

tally terrestrial but is based on the sea (e.g., walrus, seals, penguins; Fig. 5.17).

Mountain Environments

The horizontal sequence of habitats between equator and pole is repeated more or less exactly in a vertical direction, along the slopes of mountains (Fig. 5.18). Here too temperature and precipitation are the decisive variables. On a high mountain in the tropics, for example, the succession of habitats from mountain base to snow line is tropical rain forest, deciduous forest, coniferous forest, and lastly, low shrubby growths and lichens. The farther north a mountain is situated, the more northern a habitat covers its base, and the fewer habitats cover its slopes. In the taiga, for example, the foot of a mountain is coniferous forest, and the only other habitat higher along the slopes is the zone of low shrubby plants. Thus, habitat zones which are spread over thousands of miles latitudinally are telescoped altitudinally into a few thousand feet.

The foregoing should make it clear that the nature of any kind of habitat, hence the nature of its living communities, is determined by a few persistently recurring variables. Among them are solar light, solar heat, geographic latitude, vertical depth and altitude, rainfall, wind and water currents, and the chemical composition of the locale. Variables like these are of global importance, and together they add up to the large-scale "environment."

With this we reach the highest organizational level on earth: the earth itself as a unit and its integrated living and nonliving components, both changing with time.

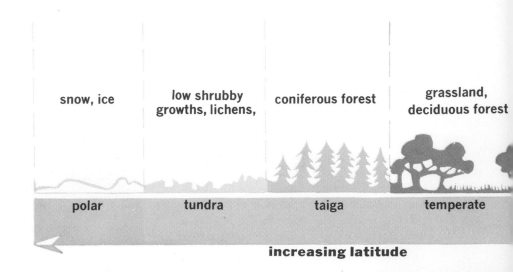

snow, ice   low shrubby growths, lichens,   coniferous forest   grassland, deciduous forest

polar   tundra   taiga   temperate

increasing latitude

The Global Environment

It is hard to fix a boundary between living matter and environment. Neither certainly "stops" at one's skin. Environment extends out beyond the Earth into the universe, and so, for all we know, may living matter. *Both* also reach inward to organs, tissues, cells, down to the smallest components of the atom; any *part* of living matter is as much "environment" to any other part as the physical medium in which living matter exists.

The most important single observation we can make about the earthly environment as a whole is that it is forever changing, on every scale from the submicroscopic to the global. As a direct consequence, living matter too must constantly change: it must adjust internally if it is to maintain steady states; it must reproduce if it is to offset environmental destruction; and it must evolve if it is to stay adapted to its surroundings. As we have seen, the very origin of living matter was itself a result of environmental change, and protoplasm subse-

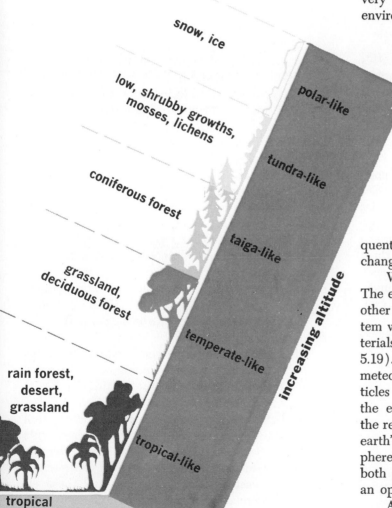

FIG. 5.18. The sequence of habitat zones between equator and pole is repeated altitudinally, between the foot and the tip of a mountain.

quently became a powerful cause of continued change.

What, fundamentally, moves the environment? The earth as a whole, hence protoplasm and every other subordinate part, is an **open system**: a system which, unlike a **closed system**, exchanges materials and/or energy with its surroundings (Fig. 5.19). To be sure, if we discount the occasional meteorite and the negligible mass of atomic particles coming from space, nothing material enters the earth from the outside. And if we discount the relatively few molecules which may escape the earth's gravitational field from the top of the atmosphere, nothing material leaves. However, *energy* both enters and leaves, and this makes the earth an open system.

A broad spectrum of solar energy, from heat rays to X rays, beams in every microsecond, and an enormous amount of energy radiates away, prin-

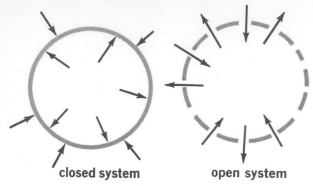

closed system   open system

FIG. 5.19. In a closed system, nothing enters or leaves. In an open system, materials, energy, or both, may either enter or leave.

cipally in the form of heat. As a result, the earth's material substance can never attain static equilibrium. For so long as the sun shines and the earth spins, energy flux will create balance-upsetting disturbances. Every imbalance creates new imbalances of its own, and as a general consequence, the earth's environment is forever changing.

Changes occur predominantly in rhythmic, patterned **cycles.** Daily and seasonal climatic cycles are familiar examples. Other environmental cycles may be less readily discernible, particularly if their scale is too vast or too minute, or if they occur too fast or too slowly for direct observation. The three major aspects of the environment are the physical, the chemical, and the biological. Correspondingly, we may distinguish three main classes of environ-

FIG. 5.20. The global water cycle. Evaporated water eventually returns to earth through precipitation.

mental cycles: **geophysical, geochemical,** and **biological.** The last, which include population cycles within communities and cycles of communal succession, in effect have already been dealt with earlier. Here therefore we shall discuss only the first two types, in particular, their interrelation with the biological component of the environment.

GEOPHYSICAL CYCLES

These include, principally, **climatic** and **geological** changes, produced partly by solar and other astrophysical causes, partly by events on and within the earth itself.

Climatic Change

A discussion of climate ultimately becomes a discussion of *water* and of the temperature changes to which water is subjected. For the earth is a world of water. The most ubiquitous mineral on the planet, water covers 73 per cent of the earth's surface entirely, and it is present in the atmosphere, in rocks, indeed in virtually all objects and all regions. The climate role of water may be appreciated by imagining an earth without water. Every day would be a baking, burning, radiation-riddled holocaust, and every night, a rigor gripped in cosmic cold. We may note that water in atmosphere and ocean provides immense protective and moderating cushions, the one screening out large amounts of high-energy radiation from space, the other retaining much of the energy which does penetrate.

The world's waters play a principal part in the following climatic cycles:

1. **Evaporation** of warmed water produces humidity and clouds. Subsequent rain and snow form rivers, which replenish the ocean (Fig. 5.20).

2. Ocean water warmed in the tropics becomes light and rises to the surface, whereas cool polar water sinks. These up-down displacements bring about massive horizontal shifts of water between equator and pole. The rotation of the earth introduces east-west displacements, and these effects, reinforced substantially by similarly patterned, wind-producing air movements, result in **oceanic currents.** These influence climatic conditions not only within the seas, but also in the air and on land (Fig. 5.21).

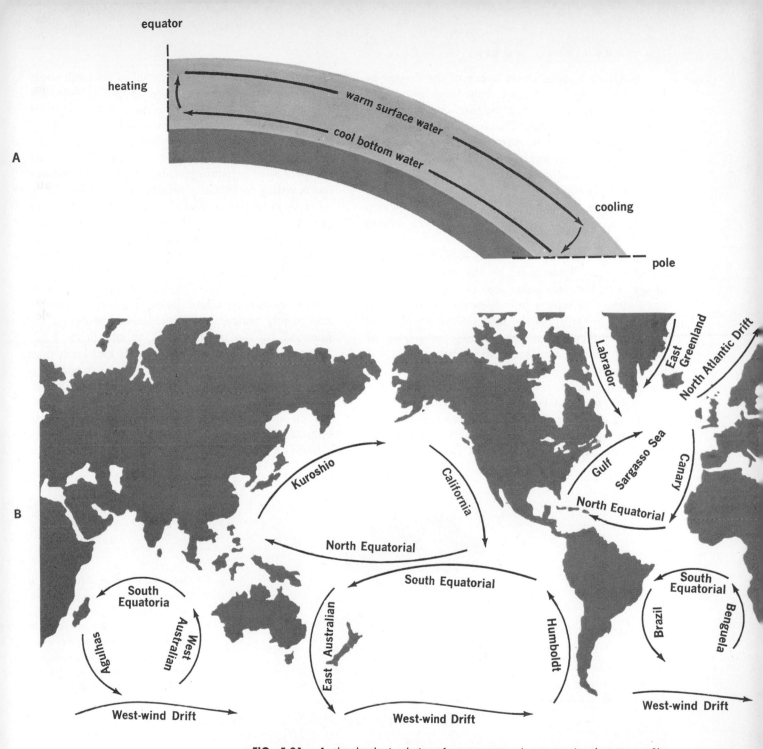

FIG. 5.21. **A**, the depth circulation of ocean water. A cross-sectional ocean profile between equator and pole is shown. Water warmed in equatorial regions rises, and water cooled in polar regions sinks. This produces a north-south and up-down circulation as indicated. However, this basic equator-to-pole movement is modified by the rotation of the earth, by winds, and by the position of the continents. In surface view, the actual circulation so produced is illustrated in **B**. The names and flow directions of the chief currents are shown.

3. Of all liquids, water is one of the slowest to heat or cool, and it stores a very large amount of thermal energy. The oceans thus become huge reservoirs of solar heat. The result is that sea air chilled by night, or in winter, becomes less cold owing to **heat radiation** from water warmed by day, or in summer, and that sea air warmed by day, or in summer, becomes less hot owing to heat absorption by water cooled by night, or in winter. Warm or cool onshore winds then moderate the inland climate in daily and seasonal patterns.

4. Over long periods of time, global climatic conditions are determined by the relative amount of water locked into **polar ice.** Temperature variations averaging only a few degrees over the years, produced by still poorly understood geophysical changes, suffice for major advance or retreat of polar ice. During the last million years, "ice ages" have developed and waned rhythmically, and warm *interglacial* periods, characterized by ice-free poles, have intervened between successive advances of ice. Four glaciation cycles have occurred, each lasting in the order of 60,000 to 200,000 years. At the present time, the earth is slowly emerging from the last ice age, which reached its peak some 50,000 to 20,000 years ago (see Chap. 29). As polar ice is melting, water levels are now rising and coast lines are gradually being submerged. If trends during the past 50 years are reliable indications, the earth appears to be warming up generally. Deserts are presently expanding; snow lines on mountains are receding to higher altitudes; in given localities, more days of the year are snow-free; and the flora and fauna native to given latitudes are slowly spreading poleward. It is difficult to be sure whether these changes are merely part of a short warm cycle or are really indicative of a long-range trend.

Directly or indirectly, these and other climatic cycles materially affect living matter; organisms are largely water, and protoplasmic water is influenced by the weather just as any other kind. Even man, who like other mammals and birds possesses an internal temperature- and evaporation-regulating mechanism, feels the effect of climate in all parts of the body, as everyone well knows.

In some instances, living matter in turn affects climate. For example, the trees of tropical jungles release so much water vapor that the air over vast

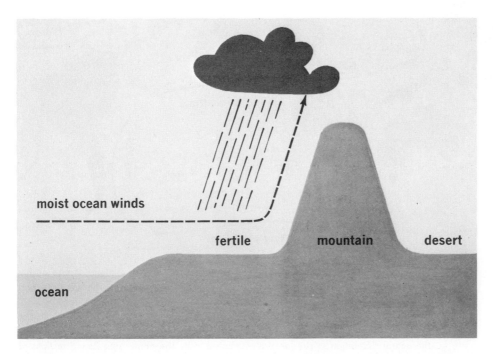

FIG. 5.22. The effect of a mountain on climate. A mountain deflects moisture-rich ocean winds upward and causes rain to remain confined to the slope facing the ocean. That slope will therefore be fertile, but the far slope will become a desert.

areas remains permanently saturated with moisture. Significant on an even larger scale is the release of carbon dioxide by plants and animals, and by the industrial installations of modern man. As this gas accumulates, it adds to the heat-retaining potential of the atmosphere. Over the millennia, therefore, CO_2 may contribute to the development of warmer climates all over the globe.

Geological Change

Geological cycles generally span thousands and millions of years, and their effects on living organisms are often so profound that the only adequate response is rapid evolution.

One of the most important cycles here involves **diastrophism,** followed by **gradation.** Diastrophism is the vertical uprising of large tracts of the earth crust. Major parts of continents, or indeed whole continents, may undergo such diastrophic movements. They occur when a land mass is pushed up from below or is subjected to great lateral pressure, generated in adjacent portions of the earth crust. Uplifting or upbuckling then follows. Changes of this sort take place exceedingly slowly. They are counteracted, equally slowly, by gradation, i.e., the leveling of land by erosion.

The most striking instance of diastrophism-gradation cycles is mountain building and mountain leveling. Presently the youngest, hence the highest, mountain ranges are the Himalayas, the Rockies, the Andes, and the Alps. All of them were thrown up some 70 million years ago, and we may note that the earth's crust in these regions is not completely settled even now.

Quite apart from the tremendous upheaval caused by mountain formation itself, such an event has long-lasting climatic consequences. A high, massive mountain barrier is likely to interfere drastically with continental air circulation. For example, moisture-laden ocean winds may no longer be able to pass across the barrier. Continual rain will therefore fall on the near side, and the region may become lush and fertile. By contrast, the far side will be arid, and desert conditions are likely to develop (Fig. 5.22). Two good examples: fertile California on the ocean side of the Rockies, and the deserts of Arizona and New Mexico on the other; fertile India on the

FIG. 5.23. The cutting, erosional effect of a river. This canyon was channeled out by the stream flowing through it. (U.S. Department of Agriculture.)

ocean side of the Himalayas, and the belt of deserts north of them. Plants and animals living on either side of a newly formed mountain range must adapt to the new environmental conditions by evolution. As we shall see, periods of extensive mountain building have always been followed by major evolutionary turnover among organisms (see Chap. 29).

In time, even the highest mountains wear away by gradation, principally through the erosive action of water. Thus, water and gravity produce shearing, canyon-cutting rivers (Fig. 5.23). Water and low temperatures produce grinding, rock-pulverizing glaciers, and as freezing water expands in rocky crevices, it carves boulders and stones off the face of a mountain. Water and high temperatures produce corrosive humidity, and water dissolves rock by chemical action. Water, wind, and sun in

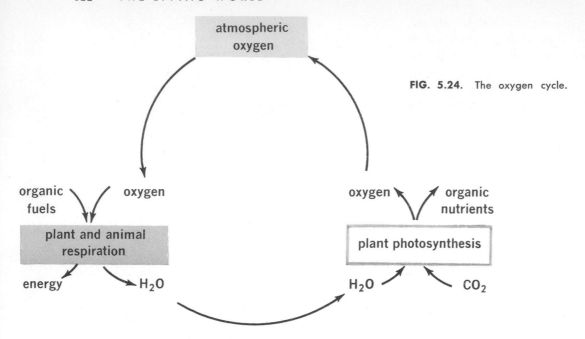

FIG. 5.24. The oxygen cycle.

time thus reduce mountain to hill, and hill eventually to plain.

Interplay between land and sea produces other geological cycles. Land is eroded away as wind-whipped waves batter the shore, topple cliffs, crumble stone, and wash out beaches. But new land appears where rivers deposit silt and where tongues of land or growing sand bars cut off shallow, slowly evaporating arms of the sea.

Another land-sea cycle is brought about by the alternate growth and recession of polar ice. With the fluctuation of ice, the sea level falls or rises; hence coastal lands around the globe enlarge or disappear. Also, narrow bridges of land may emerge or submerge, and the outline of continents may change. Note here that diastrophic movements too may bring about a change in the contours of the continents.

In still another cycle, submarine volcanic action may thrust up new oceanic islands, and existing islands may become submerged. Living matter itself on occasion contributes to the growth of new land. For example, coral islands and atolls are the products of countless sessile coelenterates, which extract calcium salts from the sea and build their skeletons from them. When the animals die, their offspring build onto the skeletons of their forebears. On an even larger scale, myriads of tiny marine surface organisms die every second, and, as noted above, their microscopic skeletal shells rain down to the sea floor. There they accumulate layer by layer for millions of years, building up here and there into thick rocky crusts. These may eventually be exposed as new land.

The many components of unending geophysical change thus include temperature, pressure, gravitation, radiation, evaporation, ice, humidity, wind, waves, dissolution, corrosion, erosion, and the heaving of the earth crust. Living matter must cope with them or die. Moreover, living matter must also cope with geochemical change.

GEOCHEMICAL CYCLES

Partly owing to geophysical change, partly owing to the metabolic activity of living organisms, all chemical constituents of the earth's surface circulate in vast cycles. Protoplasm is an important component in these. The entire substance of living matter is composed of materials drawn ultimately from the physical surroundings, and after a temporary stay in protoplasm, all these materials return to the earth, often to contribute again to new living matter. On a finite planet, such *conservation* of materials is a fundamental requirement for long-continued perpetuation of life.

Water

The basic cycle is the sea-air-land-sea circulation which, as described above, is maintained by evaporation and precipitation (see Fig. 5.20). Living organisms are interposed at all points; sea, air, and land all contribute water to protoplasm. Such water is turned over fairly quickly—much of it is soon returned to sea, air, or land by excretion and evaporation. A relatively constant amount is retained within protoplasm until death, when that quantity too passes back into the environment.

Atmospheric Gases

The present atmosphere consists mainly of oxygen, O_2 (about 20 per cent); carbon dioxide, CO_2 (about 0.03 per cent); nitrogen, N_2 (about 79 per cent); water (in varying amounts, depending on climatic conditions); and minute traces of inert gases (helium, neon, krypton, argon, xenon). Excepting the inert gases, all these components of air are vital protoplasmic raw materials, and they are drawn either directly from the air or from natural waters in which they are dissolved.

Atmospheric oxygen enters plants and animals as a respiratory gas, and it eventually passes back to the environment as a byproduct of photosynthesis. In an intervening step of this cycle, oxygen appears as water; as we shall see later, the function of oxygen in respiration is to collect hydrogen. The water so formed by the combination of oxygen and hydrogen either remains in protoplasm temporarily or is excreted immediately. Environmental or protoplasmic water then serves as a raw material in photosynthesis, during which the oxygen in water is liberated

and is returned to the environment (Fig. 5.24; also Chaps. 11 and 15).

Atmospheric carbon dioxide is the carbon source of protoplasm. This gas enters the living world through photosynthesis, in which it is a fundamental raw material. Photosynthesis converts CO_2 into organic substances, and these then serve as nutrients for plants and, indirectly, for animals. Some of the nutrients are used subsequently in respiration, which returns one fraction of CO_2 to the environment. The remaining nutrients, containing the rest of the CO_2 building blocks, are incorporated into the protoplasmic structure of plants and animals. After death, protoplasm decays by bacterial action, and the CO_2 is released in the process (Fig. 5.25). Note that the CO_2 content of air also increases through combustion of industrial fuels, through forest and other fires, and to some extent also through occasional additions from the interior of the earth (e.g., volcanic eruptions).

Atmospheric N_2 is the principal nitrogen source for living organisms. However, molecular nitrogen (N_2) is rather inert chemically, and the majority of organisms actually cannot use it directly. For example, man obtains an abundance of aerial nitrogen

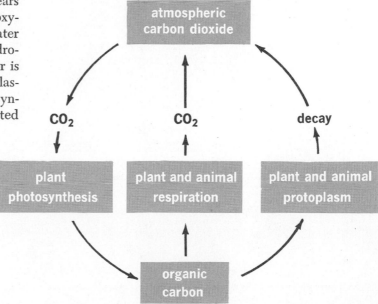

FIG. 5.25. The carbon cycle.

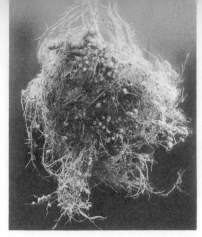

FIG. 5.26. Nodules of nitrogen-fixing bacteria on roots. (U.S. Department of Agriculture.)

with every breath, yet all of it is again exhaled, unchanged and unused. The situation is essentially similar in all other animals. In general, animals can use nitrogen only if it is obtained in the form of certain nitrogen-hydrogen combinations, for example, amino groups ($-NH_2$). Such combinations are found in other animals or in plants. Ultimately, therefore, the principal nitrogen sources of animals must be plant foods. Plants in turn may obtain nitrogen-hydrogen combinations by manufacturing them out of **nitrates,** i.e., mineral substances which contain $-NO_3$ groups. These occur in solution in

the water of soil and ocean, and plants absorb them from there.

The only organisms able to make use of atmospheric N_2 directly are **nitrogen-fixing** microorganisms, certain bacteria and blue-green algae which live in soil and water. These incorporate aerial nitrogen into the structure of their protoplasm and produce nitrogen-hydrogen combinations which may become available to green plants. Legumes in particular may obtain most or all of their nitrogenous supplies directly from nitrogen-fixing bacteria; some of the latter live in nodules on the roots of leguminous plants (Fig. 5.26). Other N fixers are free in soil, and their fixed nitrogen eventually becomes available in the form of environmental nitrate, usable by green plants generally.

Nitrogen incorporated in plant and animal protoplasm returns to soil and water through decay. Excretion products, and ultimately the dead bodies of plants and animals, are decomposed by **decay-causing** organisms, largely bacteria and fungi. The final nitrogenous endproduct of decay is *ammonia* (NH_3). This compound is utilized by two other groups of bacteria. One group, the **nitrifying** bacteria, converts ammonia into nitrates, and this adds

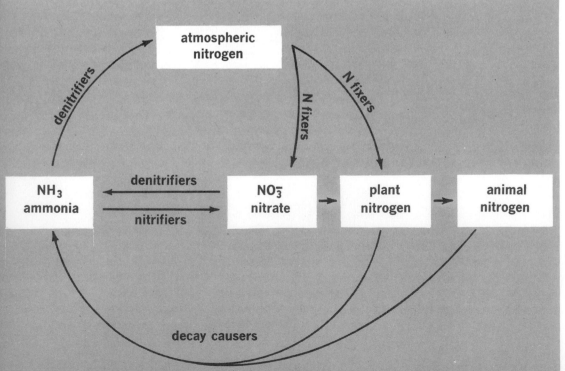

FIG. 5.27. The nitrogen cycle.

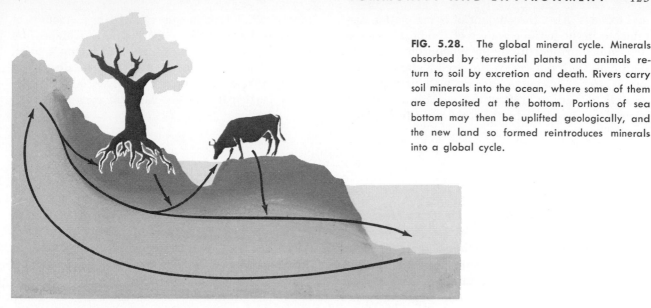

FIG. 5.28. The global mineral cycle. Minerals absorbed by terrestrial plants and animals return to soil by excretion and death. Rivers carry soil minerals into the ocean, where some of them are deposited at the bottom. Portions of sea bottom may then be uplifted geologically, and the new land so formed reintroduces minerals into a global cycle.

to the available nitrate supply in the environment. The second group, the **denitrifying** bacteria, tends to reduce the nitrate supply, for they convert —NO_3 back into NH_3. Moreover, denitrifiers transform some of the NH_3 into molecular nitrogen (N_2), which returns to the atmosphere. We shall hear more about the chemical activities of these various groups of bacteria in Chap. 8. Here we note that they represent vital links in the global nitrogen cycle. The main features of this cycle are outlined in Fig. 5.27.

Mineral Solids

Turnover of the solid components of the earth's surface is correlated with the geological cycles discussed above. Rock and sand are slowly eroded by water, and most of the constituents of stone thereby become dissolved minerals and salts. The usable supply of nitrates, for example, may be enriched in this manner. These inorganic substances are carried by rain into rivers and soil. There they may be used as nutrients by plants and animals. After the organisms die, the inorganic components return to river and soil, thus completing a continental mineral cycle.

Soil minerals leach into rivers, and rivers drain into the ocean. Hence as the land is slowly being denuded of mineral compounds, the seas fill with them. Another cycle exists in the ocean: marine flora and fauna incorporate required minerals into their protoplasm, and upon death these materials are reclaimed by the sea.

Completion of the global mineral cycle involves the settling of bones, shells, and other mineral precipitates on the ocean floor and subsequent upthrusting of the sea bottom, or the dropping of sea level, exposing new land (Fig. 5.28).

Each of the geochemical cycles here considered turns over billions of tons of materials. Clearly, the maximum quantity of living matter that can be supported on earth depends on the *least* plentiful raw material circulating in the environment. Despite the dense cover of protoplasm now carpeting the earth, available quantities of most raw materials are still well in excess of currently required amounts. However, because of the uninterrupted, global growth of living matter for 2 billion years, a few key materials are already in relatively short supply.

In particular, mineral phosphates and nitrates have become significant limiting factors. For example, soils may often be burdened with so much vegetation that they may become exhausted, unless artificially enriched with fertilizers—largely phosphates and nitrates. Also, the amount of living matter sustainable in the surface waters of the ocean is now determined principally by the amounts of available phosphates and nitrates. Water itself is often in short supply, as the example of deserts well illustrates. In general, the upper limit to the possible amount of protoplasm is not set by the *total* quantity of given raw materials existing on earth. Huge amounts of minerals, for example, exist within mountains, but these supplies are unavailable to living matter. Clearly, the significant factor is the locally *usable* supply, that is, that quantity of material which actively participates in geochemical cycles.

RESUME

We have completed our characterization of the living world. From atom through molecule, nucleoprotein, cell, organism, species, community, to the whole environment, the ever recurring theme has been progressive aggregation; the ever recurring result, progressive interdependence, cooperation, specialization, and greater economy and efficiency in maintaining and perpetuating life.

The aggregative process has not yet entirely saturated the living hierarchy. Thus, the social level exists, but it is rare, and in our own case it is certainly not startlingly perfected as yet. The species level exists, but the member populations of the whole species are not so cooperative as the member organisms of a population. Room for organizational improvement is actually ample at all levels. Moreover, origination of altogether new levels, interpolated between existing ones, is also well within the bounds of possibility. The modern drawing together of mankind into ever larger aggregates of nations may be just such an interpolation. If so, the net result of such aggregative processes should be predictable: more efficient, cooperative survival, at the expense of more or less of the independence of the subordinated units.

REVIEW QUESTIONS

1. What is the structure of an ocean basin? What are the major subenvironments in such a basin, and what role does the sun play in creating some of these subenvironments? What physical conditions characterize the various subenvironments?

2. Define phytoplankton, zooplankton, nekton, and benthos. Give specific examples of each. Where in the ocean are each of these types of organisms found? Why is life in tropical waters generally less abundant than in temperate and subpolar waters?

3. What physical and biological conditions characterize the sea depths?

4. Review the essential physical differences between oceanic and fresh-water environments. What major types of organisms occur in fresh water, and in what general ways are they adapted to this environment? What major types of organisms are terrestrial?

5. What are the main terrestrial habitats, and what physical and biological conditions characterize each of these? In what way are latitudinal terrestrial habitats related to altitudinal habitats?

6. Why is the global environment always changing and never stable? What are open and closed physical systems? What are the main categories of ways in which the global environment is changing?

7. How do the world's waters influence climates? How does the formation of mountains influence climates? Cite examples.

8. Review some of the major geological cycles which produce environmental change. What role does water play in geological cycles?

9. Review the global water, oxygen, carbon dioxide, and nitrogen cycles. How many different bacterial groups play a part in the nitrogen cycle, and what is the specific role of each group? How does man obtain his nitrogen supply?

10. Review the general pattern of mineral cycles. Can you list various biological roles of phosphate and calcium? On the basis of this, make diagrams showing the pattern of global phosphate and calcium cycles.

SUGGESTED COLLATERAL READINGS

The text by Hesse, Allee, and Schmidt cited at the end of Chap. 4 will be valuable as a reference for most topics dealing with habitats and environments. Specific habitats are well described in the following first-rate accounts:

Coker, R. C.: "This Great and Wide Sea," 2d ed., University of North Carolina Press, 1949.
Carson, R.: "The Sea around Us," Oxford, 1951.
Ommanney, F. D.: "The Oceans," Oxford, 1949.
Ryther, F. H.: The Sargasso Sea, *Sci. American,* vol. 194, 1956.
Walford, L. A.: The Deep-sea Layers of Life, *Sci. American,* vol. 185, 1951.
Vevers, H. G.: Animals of the Bottom, *Sci. American,* vol. 187, 1952.
Beebe, W.: "Half a Mile Down," Harcourt, Brace, 1934.
Berrill, N. J.: "The Living Tide," Dodd, Mead, 1951.
Buxton, P. A.: "Animal Life in Deserts," Longmans, 1923.
Went, F. W.: The Ecology of Desert Plants, *Sci. American,* vol. 192, 1955.
Beebe, W.: "Edge of the Jungle," Little, Brown, 1950.
Nicholas, G.: Life in Caves, *Sci. American,* vol. 192, 1955.
Deevey, E. S.: Life in the Depths of a Pond, *Sci. American,* vol. 185, 1951.
Daubenmire, R. F.: "Plants and Environment," Wiley, 1947.
Tiffany, L. H.: "Algae, the Grass of Many Waters," Charles C Thomas, 1939.

The global environment and its physical, chemical, geological, and biological aspects are variously discussed in the following:

Henderson, L. J.: "Fitness of the Environment," Macmillan, 1913.
Kimble, G. H. T.: The Changing Climate, *Sci. American,* vol. 182, 1950.
Cole, Lamont Cook: The Ecosphere, *Sci. American,* vol. 198, 1958.
Kamen, M. D.: Discoveries in Nitrogen Fixation, *Sci. American,* vol. 188, 1953.
Osborn, F.: "Our Plundered Planet," Little, Brown, 1948.
Vogt, W.: "Road to Survival," Sloane, 1948.
Von Engeln, O. D., and K. S. Caster: "Geology," McGraw-Hill, 1952.

THE PRECEDING SEQUENCE of chapters was a characterization of the living world as a whole. The present sequence begins a more detailed characterization of living structures and functions.

We have found that living matter, **protoplasm,** is structured by levels and that we regard it as living because it carries out the functions of metabolism and self-perpetuation. Our immediate objective is to take a closer look at protoplasm and to examine its properties and its internal organization in greater detail.

Specifically, we inquire first into the chemical and physical **behavior** of protoplasm, on which all biological behavior is based. We then reconsider the **molecules** out of which protoplasm is made, and we examine the ways in which these molecules are aggregated into **cells.** Cells in their turn make up the organisms of the living world. Accordingly, we shall study the internal organization, and the resulting ways of life, of whole **plants** and **animals.**

The following four chapters deal with these topics. They also serve to set the stage for a later detailed analysis of protoplasmic functions.

PART

2

THE LIVING SUBSTANCE

6

PROTOPLASM: BASIC PROPERTIES

REGARDLESS OF WHERE, when, or how we examine the structure of any bit of protoplasm, we ultimately find it to consist entirely of chemicals—atoms and molecules. And regardless of what particular function of protoplasm we examine, that function is ultimately always based on the chemical and physical properties of the protoplasmic atoms and molecules.

The nature of these protoplasmic chemicals has already been discussed briefly in Chap. 2: water and other *inorganic* substances; and carbohydrates, fats, proteins, nucleoproteins, and other *organic* substances. We shall later deal with the composition of these again, in greater detail. Here we regard them as given and concentrate primarily on their **chemical** and **physical properties.**

Considered singly, most of these properties are encountered also in inanimate systems, and very few are uniquely protoplasmic. However, protoplasm is quite unique as a result of a particular *combination* of properties, and it is the combination which endows it with the potential of life. In the following, we shall be concerned with various individual properties contributing importantly to this living potential.

Chemical Properties

The most important of these is that protoplasmic molecules undergo large numbers of **chemical reactions** with one another. The presence of large amounts of water materially facilitates this property; water dissolves most of the other protoplasmic constituents, and chemical reactions take place especially well in **aqueous solution.**

Protoplasm is not a static, passive material. Hundreds of reactions occur simultaneously every second, and, through them, protoplasm is in continuous chemical turmoil. To the human observer, a tree may appear to be a rather placid, inactive structure. But if the tree's molecules could be seen, they would all

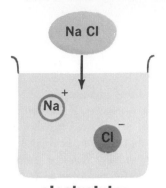

electrolyte:
molecule ionizes in water

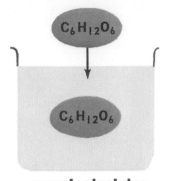

nonelectrolyte:
molecule stays intact in water

FIG. 6.1. Electrolytes and non-electrolytes. Electrolytes (e.g., NaCl) dissociate in water into ions (Na^+, Cl^-), whereas non-electrolytes (e.g., $C_6H_{12}O_6$, sugar) remain intact.

be noted to be in constant, violent motion, colliding with one another and, as a result, reacting and changing. Consequently, the tree as a whole changes continuously, and so indeed does every kind of protoplasm.

The main kinds of chemical reactions taking place in protoplasm have already been outlined in Chap. 2: exchange, synthesis, decomposition, and rearrangement reactions. But to describe a reaction completely and so to appreciate its significance in protoplasmic events, it is not sufficient merely to determine which of the above four categories it belongs to. Certain other characteristics must be specified in addition. First, does the reaction involve *ionized* or *nonionized* reactants? Second, what *energy changes* accompany the reaction? Third, how is the reaction *catalyzed?* And fourth, how does the reaction obey the law of *mass action?*

These questions point to basic chemical properties of all protoplasmic reactions. What are the underlying principles?

IONIZATION

When they are dissolved in water, as in protoplasm, some kinds of molecules do, and some do not, remain intact. Those which do not remain intact break up, or **dissociate,** into two or more electrically charged atoms or groups of atoms, called **ions.** For example, table salt, sodium chloride (NaCl), is an ionizing substance. In protoplasm, or in water gen-

erally, it dissociates into a positively charged sodium ion (Na^+) and a negatively charged chloride ion (Cl^-):

$$NaCl \rightarrow Na^+ + Cl^-$$

sodium   sodium   chloride
chloride   ion   ion

The solution now contains an equal number of such positive and negative ions, and it therefore remains electrically neutral as a whole. Electric neutrality is always preserved in solutions of ionized substances. But the presence of ions, rather than of whole molecules, makes possible the conduction of electric currents through the solution. Substances which ionize are also called **electrolytes;** those which do not ionize, **nonelectrolytes.** Protoplasm contains both kinds (Fig. 6.1).

Depending on their chemical nature, different types of ions may carry different amounts of electric charge. One, two, or three charges, positive or negative, per ion are common. For example,

$$KCN \xrightarrow{H_2O} K^+ + CN^-$$

potassium   potassium   cyanide
cyanide   ion   ion

$$H_2SO_4 \xrightarrow{H_2O} H^+ + H^+ + SO_4^=$$

sulfuric   hydrogen   sulfate
acid   ions   ion

$$Fe(OH)_3 \xrightarrow{H_2O} Fe^{+++} + OH^- + OH^- + OH^-$$

ferric   ferric   hydroxyl
hydroxide   ion   ions

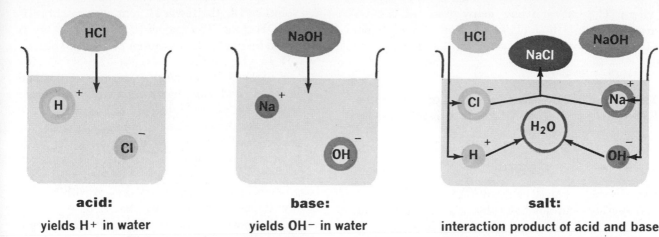

acid:
yields H+ in water

base:
yields OH⁻ in water

salt:
interaction product of acid and base

FIG. 6.2. When placed into water, an acid releases hydrogen ions (H⁺), and a base releases hydroxyl ions (OH⁻). A salt is an interaction product of an acid and a base.

In the second equation above, note that sulfuric acid dissociates in such a way that *hydrogen ions* (H⁺) are produced. Any compound which dissociates so as to yield hydrogen ions is called an **acid.**

Analogously, any compound which dissociates so as to yield *hydroxyl ions* (OH⁻), as in the third equation above, is a **base** or an **alkali.**

A compound resulting from the chemical interaction of an acid and a base is a **salt** (Fig. 6.2). Sodium chloride (NaCl) is a salt because it is formed by the interaction of hydrochloric acid (HCl) and sodium hydroxide (NaOH):

HCl + NaOH → NaCl + H₂O
acid   base   salt

If a substance is an electrolyte, it is either an acid or a base or a salt. Chemists distinguish between "strong" acids and "weak" acids, strong bases and weak bases, and strong salts and weak salts. The basis for such distinctions is the *extent* to which an electrolyte is ionized. In a strong acid, for example, all, or practically all, of the acid molecules are ionized. In a weak acid, on the other hand, only a few of the acid molecules are ionized; the others remain intact as molecules (Fig. 6.3). The situation is analogous for bases and salts.

It is often important to determine the "strength" of a solution of electrolytes, i.e., its degree of acidity or alkalinity. This can be done with appropriate electrical apparatus, by measuring the relative number of H⁺ and OH⁻ ions present in the solution. The result is expressed as a number, called the **pH** of the solution. Mathematically, pH has been defined arbitrarily by the equation

$$pH = \log \frac{1}{[H^+]}$$

FIG. 6.3. In a strong acid, many molecules are dissociated into ions (many single white and black particles); in a weak acid, very few of the molecules are dissociated (many joined pairs of white and black particles).

strong acid:
many ions,
few molecules

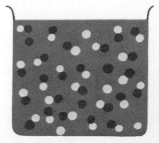

weak acid:
few ions,
many molecules

where [H⁺] indicates how many grams of H⁺ ions are present in 1 liter (l) of solution. For example, pure water ionizes to a very slight degree:

$$H_2O \rightarrow H^+ + OH^-$$

Measurement shows that, in a liter of pure water, 0.0000001 gram (g) of H⁺ ions is present. The pH of pure water therefore is

$$pH_{water} = \log \frac{1}{0.0000001} = 7$$

Since water contains as many H⁺ ions as OH⁻ ions, it is neither acid nor basic, but *chemically neutral.* We may note that any solution will be chemically neutral, and will have a pH of 7, if its net H⁺ ion concentration is as in pure water.

Suppose that a given mixture of dissolved electrolytes contains so much acid that, in a liter of the mixture, there is 0.1 g of H⁺ ions present, i.e., 1 million times as many as in pure water. Then the pH of that mixture would be

$$pH = \log \frac{1}{0.1} = 1$$

We may note in general that, the *lower* than 7 the pH of a solution, the *more acid* it is; i.e., the more H⁺ ions are present relative to OH⁻ ions. Analogously, the higher than 7 the pH, the *more alkaline*

is a solution; i.e., the fewer H⁺ ions are present relative to OH⁻ ions. The maximum possible acidity is indicated by pH 0; the maximum possible alkalinity, by pH 14 (Fig. 6.4).

Protoplasm, containing a mixture of ionized acids, bases, and salts, has a pH usually very near neutrality. For example, the pH of human blood is 7.3. However, some types of protoplasm may be characteristically more acid (e.g., lemons) or basic (e.g., many pond organisms). A living system does not tolerate significant variations of its normal acid-base balance, and its pH must remain within fairly narrow limits. If these limits should be exceeded, major chemical and physical disturbances would result which would be lethal. For example, protoplasmic proteins would be destroyed (see below).

We shall find later that many normal processes within protoplasm yield small amounts of excess acids or bases. But such small additions produce only negligible alterations of the pH. This is largely because protoplasm is **buffered;** that is, it is protected to some extent against pH change.

For example, suppose that we consider a solution of sodium bicarbonate (NaHCO₃), a salt which is normally present in protoplasm. This salt is more or less completely ionized into sodium ions (Na⁺) and bicarbonate ions (HCO₃⁻). If, now, a little hydrochloric acid (HCl) is added, we should

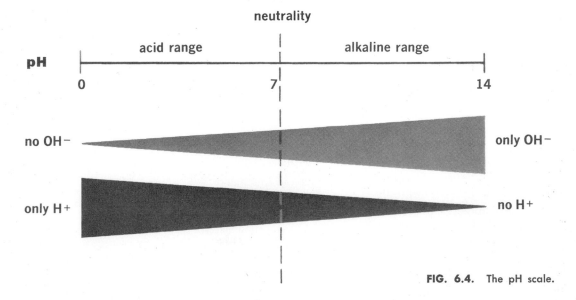

FIG. 6.4. The pH scale.

expect the solution to become more acid. Actually, however, the pH change will be rather slight. This is because the hydrogen ions of hydrochloric acid (H^+) have a chance to react with the bicarbonate ions (HCO_3^-). The result is the formation of carbonic acid (H_2CO_3):

$$NaHCO_3 \rightarrow Na^+ + HCO_3^-$$
$$HCl \rightarrow H^+ + Cl^-$$
$$\overline{H^+ + HCO_3^- \rightarrow H_2CO_3}$$

Carbonic acid is a *weak* acid; that is, only comparatively few of its molecules can become ionized. But the solution above at first contains very many H^+ and HCO_3^- ions, far more than a carbonic acid solution can actually hold. Therefore, H^+ and HCO_3^- will combine into whole carbonic acid *molecules*, as above, until the amounts of these ions are reduced appropriately. In effect, the free H^+ ions of the added HCl are being "taken out of circulation," and the HCl consequently will not be able to change the pH appreciably.

We say that the presence of HCO_3^- ions *buffers* the solution, i.e., protects it from major pH change if a little acid is added. Analogous buffering effects against added bases are produced by a number of positively charged ions. Inasmuch as protoplasm contains complex mixtures of various electrolytes, it is buffered by virtue of its composition. The bicarbonate ion and also carbonate ions ($CO_3^=$) and phosphate ions ($PO_4^\equiv$) are among the most important buffers in protoplasm. To be sure, if protoplasm, or any buffered solution, is flooded with large quantities of additional acids or bases, then buffer protection will become insufficient and pH will change.

For simplicity, chemical reactions involving electrolytes are often *written* as if the reactants were whole molecules rather than ions. For example, instead of writing

$$H^+ + Cl^- + Na^+ + OH^- \rightarrow Na^+ + Cl^- + H_2O$$

we may write, less precisely,

$$HCl + NaOH \rightarrow NaCl + H_2O$$

But note that reactions among electrolytes are always reactions among ions, not molecules, regardless of the manner of symbolization.

ENERGETICS

As noted in Chap. 2, one requirement for any chemical reaction is *contact* among the participating molecules. Such contact is brought about principally by **heat;** the heat energy of the environment causes molecules to vibrate uninterruptedly, in random motions. The higher the temperature, the more violent are the molecular motions. Indeed, the amount of molecular vibration is a measure of heat. At $-273°C$, the theoretical absolute zero of temperature, heat is, by definition, entirely absent, and all molecules are stationary. However, every known natural or experimentally produced environment always contains at least some heat, and molecular vibrations are proportional to the temperature.

Thus all molecules, be they in a gas, a liquid, or in a solid, are subjected by environmental heat to a certain amount of motion, or **thermal agitation.** And as molecules so jostle one another about, they collide. Such collisions represent the contacts which make chemical reactions possible. The higher the temperature, the more collisions there are, and the faster therefore the chemical reactions (Fig. 6.5).

It can be shown that every temperature increase of 10°C approximately doubles to triples the speed of reactions. A **temperature coefficient,** conventionally designated by the letter Q, expresses how many times a reaction is speeded up by any stated increase of temperature. It can be shown that $Q_{10} = 2$ to 3, for chemical reactions generally. This statement reads: a 10° rise of temperature speeds reactions two to three times. The implications for protoplasmic reactions are important. For example, the chemical reactions in the protoplasm of a housefly or a green plant will occur twice or three times as fast on a day which is 10°C warmer than another.

Different kinds of chemical reactions require different degrees of thermal agitation. In some cases, the molecular agitation brought about by ordinary room temperature may suffice to allow a reaction to proceed. For example, water and metallic sodium react "spontaneously," i.e., at room temperature. But mix water and fat at room temperature and nothing happens. Here, and in most other protoplas-

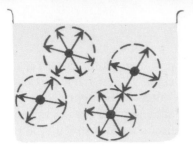

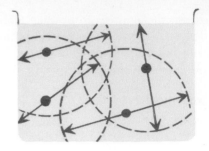

FIG. 6.5. When molecules are agitated only a little (left), they collide infrequently and reactions are therefore slow. But when molecules are agitated greatly (right), they collide often and reactions are rapid.

low temperature:
weak thermal agitation,
few collisions, hence
slow reaction

high temperature:
intense thermal agitation,
many collisions, hence
fast reaction

mic reactions, much more violent molecular vibration, and more frequent collision, is required before reactions become appreciable.

In many cases, therefore, heating is necessary to make a reaction occur. The energy so supplied is called **activation energy.** It represents the heat required to increase the thermal agitation just enough to start a reaction. Different quantities of activation energy are necessary for different kinds of reactions.

Once a reaction is under way, minimum thermal agitation, hence a minimum environmental temperature, must be maintained if the reaction is to continue. For many reactions, this means that external heating must continue. But some reactions generate heat on their own, and such heat may suffice to sustain them. We have already spoken of *exergonic,* energy-yielding, reactions in Chap. 2:

$$A + B \rightarrow C + D + \text{energy } (E)$$

If, here, the released energy escapes, as is usually the case, it may raise the temperature of the immediate environment enough to maintain the reaction. Continuous external heating is then not necessary (Fig. 6.6). Such self-maintaining reactions operate like many familiar mechanical devices. A motor, for example, must first be started up and warmed up to a required temperature; i.e., activation energy must be supplied from the outside. But once the motor is running, its fuel-burning reactions usually generate enough energy to sustain their own operating temperature.

Exergonic reactions, indeed, may generate so much heat that they not only sustain themselves but also provide sufficient extra energy to activate and maintain *endergonic,* or energy-requiring, reactions. Thus, in the endergonic reaction

$$A + B + E \rightarrow C + D$$

activation energy must be supplied just as before to start the reaction. This is not shown in the equation. Thereafter, the supply of external energy must be continued, first, to maintain the operating temperature of the reaction and, second, to provide the E without which the reaction could not proceed. All such energy requirements could be satisfied by the energy yield of exergonic reactions. This is actually the general case in protoplasm. Exergonic reactions here release sufficient energy to sustain themselves as well as all endergonic reactions (Fig. 6.7).

Clearly, the energetics of reactions are important attributes of chemical processes: the environment and in some cases the reacting molecules provide energy; and this energy supply in turn determines whether or not a reaction is possible at all, and how fast such a reaction can occur.

CATALYSIS

Inasmuch as most protoplasmic reactions require high activation energies, it should follow that most living processes should require environments far hotter than room temperature. This is evidently not the case. Indeed, if protoplasm were heated substantially above room temperature it would quickly be killed. It remains true, nevertheless, that, at the comparatively low temperatures at which protoplasm normally exists, thermal agitation as such is insufficient to activate many reactions. How then are living processes possible? How are sufficient molecular collisions brought about without additional heat? The answer lies in *catalysis*—acceleration of reactions by means of **catalysts** rather than heat.

Protoplasmic catalysts are invariably proteins, and they are called **enzymes**. Virtually every one of the thousands of protoplasmic reactions is speeded up enormously by a particular enzyme protein. Without these, the reactions could not occur fast enough at ordinary temperatures to sustain life. Thus, enzymes are a supplement to thermal agitation, a device through which reactions requiring high temperatures in test tubes can occur at low temperatures in protoplasm.

How does an enzyme work? Best available evidence indicates that it combines temporarily with the reacting molecules. Mutual contact of these molecules is then no longer a matter of chance collision but a matter of certainty. Hence faster reaction.

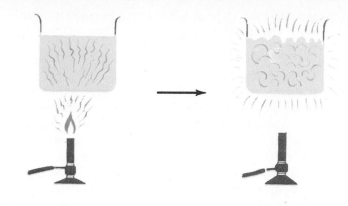

activation energy supplied from outside to start reaction   **once reaction started, enough energy released to be self-sustaining**

FIG. 6.6. External energy activates a reaction (left), and if the reaction is exergonic, it may generate so much heat that it becomes self-sustaining (right). External energy then need no longer be applied.

The protein nature of enzymes is essential to this reaction-accelerating effect. As already pointed out in Chap. 2, protein molecules are huge, and they each consist of very many joined, variously arranged amino acids. Hence, according to its particular internal structure, a protein has one of an almost infinite number of gross physical shapes. It also has a unique surface geometry, distinct from that of other types of proteins. The nature of the sur-

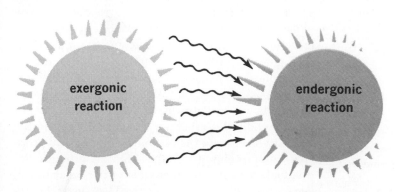

exergonic reaction   **endergonic reaction**

self-sustaining   **sustained by exergonic system**

FIG. 6.7. Exergonic reactions sometimes may generate so much energy that they sustain not only themselves but also endergonic reactions.

face appears to be the key to enzyme action. Consider the reaction

glucose + fructose → sucrose

Glucose has a given unique surface geometry, and so does fructose. Enzymatic acceleration of this reaction may now occur if the surfaces of both glucose and fructose happen to fit closely into the surface of a particular protein molecule. In other words, if the reacting molecules can become attached to a suitably shaped surface of an enzyme, then these molecules will be so close to each other that they may react chemically (Fig. 6.8). The enzyme itself remains relatively passive here. It only provides a uniquely structured "platform" on which particular molecules may become trapped. Such trapping brings reacting molecules into contact far faster than chance collisions at that temperature. Hence accelerated reactions. Held by the enzyme, glucose and fructose react and become sucrose, and sucrose then disengages from the enzyme surface.

In enzyme-accelerated reactions, it is customary to speak of reacting molecules such as glucose and fructose as the **substrates.** When substrate molecules are attached to an enzyme, the whole is referred to as an **enzyme-substrate complex.** Formation of such complexes may be thought of as a "lock-and-key" process. Only particularly shaped keys fit into particularly shaped locks. Just so, only certain types of molecules will establish a close fit with a given type of enzyme protein. For example, the enzyme in Fig. 6.9 may be effective in reactions involving substrates **a** or **b,** but not in those involving **c.**

Differences in the surface configuration of different types of proteins undoubtedly account for the phenomenon of **enzyme specificity;** a given type of

enzyme normally accelerates only one particular type of reaction. For example, the enzyme in the glucose-fructose reaction above, called *invertase,* is specific and catalyzes *only* that particular reaction. In protoplasm, there are actually almost as many different kinds of enzymes as there are different kinds of reactions. This specificity of enzymes is an important corollary of the more general phenomenon of *protein specificity,* about which more will be said in the next chapter. Because of protein specificity, some proteins are enzymes and some are not; if a protein happens to have a surface into which some other molecules could fit, then that protein could function as an enzyme in reactions involving those molecules.

Several other characteristics of enzymatic reactions may now be noted. If we assume the general reaction $A + B → C + D$ to be accelerated by an enzyme, we may write

$$A + B + enz. → A \cdot B \cdot enz.$$
$$C \cdot D \cdot enz. → C + D + enz.$$

Note here that the enzyme molecule reappears unchanged at the end of the reaction, free to combine with a new set of starting substrates. We conclude again that enzymes, and catalysts in general, are *passive* participants of reactions and are not themselves affected by the reactions. Because of this, very small amounts of enzymes, used over and over, can catalyze large quantities of substrates.

Note further that a given enzyme can speed up a reaction in *either* direction; the reaction sucrose → glucose + fructose is accelerated by the *same* enzyme, namely, invertase, that speeds up the reaction glucose + fructose → sucrose. This is understandable if we keep in mind that enzymes are primarily passive-reaction platforms. Thus, enzymes only influence reaction **speeds;** other factors govern the direction of a reaction, as we shall see shortly.

Enzymes share the chemical and physical properties of proteins generally. Like all proteins, individual enzyme molecules wear out or break down, even under normal conditions. They must be replaced by resynthesis from raw materials—reactions

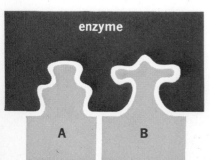

FIG. 6.8. The surfaces of molecules **A** and **B** fit into the surface of the enzyme. Reaction between **A** and **B** is thus speeded up, for contact between **A** and **B** does not depend on chance collision.

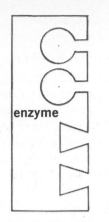
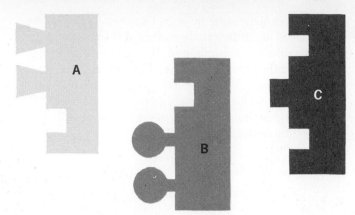

FIG. 6.9. Reactants **A** and **B** fit partially into the surface of the enzyme but reactant **C** does not. Hence the enzyme may speed up reactions involving **A** and **B** but not those involving **C**.

which themselves require enzymes. Like all proteins also, enzymes are extremely sensitive to changes of temperature, pH, pressure, metallic poisons, and other agents. Coagulated enzyme proteins usually are not effective catalytically, undoubtedly because coagulation destroys the unique surface geometry of the molecule (see Chap. 7).

Many substances which are not normally present in protoplasm may, if introduced into living matter, combine with given protoplasmic enzymes, and so act as poisons; by attaching to enzymes, such poisons prevent the normal protoplasmic substrates from combining with the enzymes. Since protoplasmic enzymes are present only in rather small

amounts, small quantities of such poisons, or **enzyme inhibitors,** may block certain normal reactions completely. This may be fatal. On the other hand, enzyme inhibition also accounts for the beneficial effect of many drugs (Fig. 6.10).

Enzymes may be classified according to the kind of substrate they affect. For example, any enzyme accelerating reactions of carbohydrates is called a **carbohydrase.** Invertase, above, is a carbohydrase. Analogously, **proteinase** and **lipase,** for enzymes catalyzing reactions of proteins and of fatty substances (= lipids), respectively. A suffix *-ase* always signifies that the substance in question is an enzyme. Note, however, that names of enzymes need

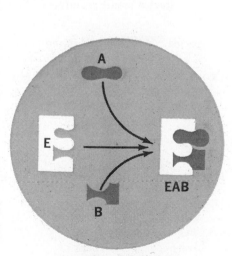

reaction of A and B
possible with aid of enzyme E

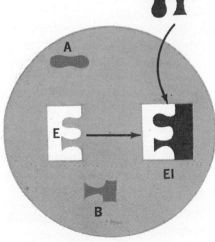

reaction of A and B
blocked by enzyme inhibitor I

FIG. 6.10. The principle of enzyme inhibition. The enzyme **E** normally speeds up reactions involving reactants **A** and **B**. But if an inhibitor molecule **I** is supplied from the outside, which fits into the surface of **E**, then **I** may combine with **E** preferentially, thus preventing the normal reaction of **E, A,** and **B**. Poisons may be what they are because of such inhibiting effects. On the other hand, if **E** with **A** and **B** gives an abnormal disease-producing reaction, then a beneficial drug may be introduced which acts as **I** and so prevents the disease.

not necessarily end in *-ase*. Enzymes may also be classified according to the nature of the reaction they catalyze. For example, one distinguishes "splitting" and "synthesizing" enzymes, "transferring" enzymes (*transferases*), and "rearranging" enzymes (*mutases*). In writing an enzymatic reaction symbolically, the name of the enzyme is conventionally put over the reaction arrow. Thus,

$$\text{glucose} + \text{fructose} \xrightarrow{\text{invertase}} \text{sucrose}$$

We have found that, like thermal agitation, enzymes increase the rate of contact among molecules, and so they increase the rate of reactions. But thermal agitation and enzymes are not the only two conditions to do so. A third is the **concentration** of the molecules present.

MASS ACTION

It should be readily apparent that the more molecules there are in a given reaction system, the more frequently will thermal agitation produce molecular collisions, and the more quickly may substrates become attached to enzymes. It follows that *the speed of a reaction is proportional to the concentrations of the participating molecules.* This is known as the **law of mass action** (Fig. 6.11).

This law actually predicts more than the speed of reactions. By implication, it also predicts the **direction** and the **amount** of reactions. In principle, all *chemical reactions are reversible;* that is, if they can occur in one direction, they can also occur in the opposite direction. Suppose that we consider the reversible protoplasmic reaction

$$1 \text{ glycerin} + 3 \text{ fatty acids} \rightleftharpoons 1 \text{ fat} + 3 \text{ water}$$

If glycerin, fatty acids, fat, and water molecules come into mutual contact, as happens often in protoplasm, in which direction will the reaction proceed? Will fat form, or will fat disappear? The law of mass action gives the answer: if glycerin and fatty acids are present in higher concentrations than fat and water, then the reaction will go to the *right;* but if fat and water are present in higher concentrations, then the reaction will proceed to the *left.* Put differently, if more collisions occur between glycerin and fatty acids, more fat and water will form; and if more collisions occur between fat and water, more glycerin and fatty acids will form.

Mass action clearly determines the direction of a reaction. How long will such a reaction continue in a given direction, i.e., what is the amount of reaction? Suppose that we started out with high concentrations of glycerin and fatty acids and a zero concentration of fat and water:

$$\text{glycerin} + \text{fatty acids} \rightarrow$$

The reaction proceeds to the right at a certain speed. But as glycerin and fatty acids are transformed, their concentrations decrease. And as the first few molecules of fat and water appear, they can react together and start a small reaction to the *left:*

$$\text{glycerin} + \text{fatty acids} \overset{\longrightarrow}{\underset{\leftarrow}{}} \text{fat} + \text{water}$$

The *net* accumulation of fat therefore will now occur at a slower pace than at the beginning. With time,

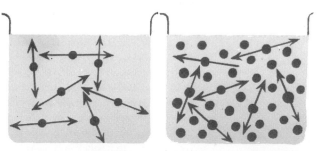

low concentration: few collisions, hence **slow reaction**

high concentration: many collisions, hence **fast reaction**

FIG. 6.11. The principle of mass action. At left, few molecules are present, and the concentration is low. Collisions are therefore infrequent; hence reaction speed is also low. At right, at the same temperature as at left, many molecules are present, and the concentration is high. Collisions at right are therefore frequent; hence reaction speed is high.

the net reaction to the right will become slower and slower; as more and more fat and water form, reacting increasingly to the left, less and less glycerin and fatty acids remain, reacting decreasingly to the right. An **equilibrium** will be reached when the left-hand reaction occurs as fast as the right-hand one. No further *net* increase of fat and water will take place thereafter, and the net reaction stops:

glycerin + fatty acids $\rightleftharpoons$ fat + water

In short, a reaction continues in a given direction until an equilibrium point is reached. At that point certain quantities of reactants are present, and so long as the equilibrium is maintained, the reaction in one direction occurs as fast as in the other. Hence the net quantities of all substances present do not change.

This holds if the reaction system is left to itself and nothing is added or removed. Suppose, however, that we *removed* fat (or water) as fast as it formed. Then, because fat (or water) is not allowed to accumulate, a reaction to the left cannot take place. Hence the reaction to the right will continue, an equilibrium point will not be reached, and all the glycerin and fatty acids present initially will eventually be converted into fat and water. The reaction to the right will proceed to completion, and the yield of fat and water will then be maximal.

In protoplasm, reactions often proceed to completion, i.e., to maximum yield, if one of the substances formed is an escaping gas ($\uparrow$) or a relatively insoluble precipitate ($\downarrow$). For this is equivalent to removing one of the end products as fast as it is formed. For example,

carbonic acid $\rightarrow$
water + carbon dioxide gas $\uparrow$
calcium ion + phosphate ion $\rightarrow$
calcium phosphate (bone) $\downarrow$

Another way of preventing establishment of an equilibrium in the glycerin-fat reaction above would be to keep *adding* glycerin and fatty acids to the reaction system. The concentrations of glycerin and fatty acids then would always remain high, and according to the law of mass action, the reaction would always be "driven" to the right. More and more fat and water would form as more and more

glycerin and fatty acids were added. Situations of this sort also occur in protoplasm. For example, the continuing supply of food materials through eating prevents protoplasmic reactions from reaching long-term equilibria.

Note that the rules of mass action also apply to the energy changes of exergonic and endergonic reactions. Consider the reversible reaction

$A \rightleftharpoons B + E$ (energy)

Proceeding to the right, the reaction is exergonic. E here is as much an endproduct as B, and if E escapes as fast as it is produced, the reaction to the right will not reach equilibrium but will proceed to completion. Equilibrium could be reached only if the reaction were completely energy-insulated, that is, if none of the energy produced could escape the system. Such insulation cannot be achieved in practice, and reactions of this type always do tend to go to completion. The reverse reaction is endergonic. Here E must be added continuously if all of B is to be converted into A. If the supply of E is stopped prematurely, the reaction to the left will cease, and the reverse reaction to the right will supervene and proceed to completion.

CONCLUSION

We may now summarize all the foregoing and specify the universal chemical properties of protoplasm as follows: The water component dissolves most of the other components and maintains many of them in an ionized state. Protoplasm thus becomes a complex mixture of acids, bases, salts, and nonelectrolytes. Some of the protein components in this mixture function as enzymes. These, plus the temperature of the environment and the concentrations of the protoplasmic constituents, permit numerous reactions at various speeds, in various directions, and in various amounts. As a result of such reactions, energy exchanges occur, concentrations change, and chemical composition as such becomes changed.

New sets of reactions now become possible among the altered constituents, and such reactions alter chemical conditions in turn. If, as is normally the case, changes in the external environment occur at the same time, the diverse chemical events in protoplasm will be affected accordingly. Living matter consequently is forever in chemical flux. Perhaps the most remarkable outcome of these uninterrupted processes is that protoplasm remains "living" throughout.

Accompanying and greatly influencing these many chemical events are physical ones. What is the nature of these?

Physical Properties

Clearly, protoplasm is neither a true solid nor a true liquid but a system composed of both solid and liquid components. Any such system can be classified as belonging to one of three categories, depending on the size of the solid particles (Fig. 6.12). If all particles are very small, for example, small ions or molecules, then the system is a true **solution.** Since crystals can readily form from it, such a system is also called a *crystalloid.* If all particles are very large, e.g., the size of soil grains, they soon settle out by gravity at the bottom of a container. Such a system is a coarse **suspension.** But if all particles are of intermediate size, they neither form a solution, i.e., do not easily crystallize, nor settle out. Such a system is a **colloid.**

The particles in a colloid range in diameter from $\frac{1}{1,000,000}$ to $\frac{1}{10,000}$ millimeter (mm). The larger figure corresponds very nearly to the limit of vision under a good microscope. In biological practice, the unit $\frac{1}{1,000}$ mm = 1 micron (1 μ) is frequently used. Hence the colloidal range is from $\frac{1}{1,000}$ to $\frac{1}{10}$ μ.

Protoplasm is largely a colloidal system. It consists of a **liquid phase**—water containing dissolved ions and small molecules—and a **dispersed phase**—very large molecules, including proteins and others, and aggregates of molecules.

Among other colloidal systems are milk, mayonnaise (colloidal fat droplets and protein in water); fog (colloidal water droplets in air); cigarette smoke (colloidal ash in air); cheese (colloidal air in fat-protein); ruby glass (colloidal gold in a solid). Eight general types of colloidal systems are possible: a gas within either a solid or a liquid; a liquid within either a liquid, a solid, or a gas; and a solid within either a liquid, a solid, or a gas. Liquids within liquids are called **emulsions.**

PROTOPLASMIC COLLOIDS

What are some of the properties of colloids? What, first, prevents colloidal particles in protoplasm from settling out?

As noted above, the molecules of a liquid are under continuous thermal agitation, the more intensely the higher the temperature. When the liquid freezes, molecular motion is reduced sharply. Above the boiling point, molecules move so rapidly that many escape; i.e., the liquid vaporizes at great rate. If dispersed particles are present in a liquid, they are buffeted and bombarded constantly by the molecules of the liquid. Very large particles are unaffected by these tiny forces, and they fall straight to the bottom of a container. But smaller bodies of colloidal size may be pushed back and forth, up and down. Gravitational pull may thereby be counteracted partly or wholly, and the particles thus may

solution

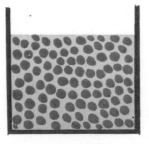

colloid

coarse suspension

FIG. 6.12. The *size* of the particles in water determines whether they will form a solution, a colloid, or a coarse suspension.

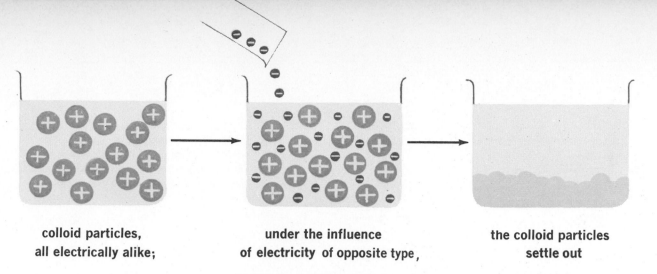

colloid particles,
all electrically alike;

under the influence
of electricity of opposite type,

the colloid particles
settle out

FIG. 6.13. Colloid particles carry similar electric charges—in this illustration, positive ones (left). These charges make the particles repel one another, and so keep them suspended. If electricity of the opposite type is added (middle), the colloid charges are neutralized, and the particles settle out (right).

be kept suspended. This random movement of small particles is called **Brownian motion** and is easily demonstrable under the microscope.

Brownian movement aids in keeping colloidal particles from settling out, but they cannot remain suspended by this force alone. Colloids stay dispersed mainly because of their **electrical charges.** All solid particles of a given colloidal system are either electropositive or electronegative. Since like charges repel, the particles are kept apart. If the charge is neutralized by electricity of opposite type, the colloid particles do settle out (Fig. 6.13).

Protoplasmic colloids undergo reversible **sol-gel transformations,** also called **phase reversals.** If large numbers of colloidal particles are added to the system or, alternatively, if water is gradually withdrawn, the particles are brought closer together, and they come into contact with one another eventually. Rod-shaped particles then pile up like a log jam; round or irregular particles interlock in intricate ways. In effect, the original dispersed phase now is a continuous spongelike network which holds water within its meshes, in discontinuous droplets. This is the **gel** state of a colloid. The quasi-solid, pliable aspect of protoplasm, as in skin or muscle, or of protein colloids generally, as in Jello and gelatin, is due to the gel condition. We may understand, therefore, how even systems like jellyfish, which contain as

much as 90 per cent or more water, can maintain definite form and shape.

Conversely, addition of water to a colloidal system, or removal of dispersed particles, results in greater fluidity, the **sol** state of a colloid (Fig. 6.14). In protoplasm, sol and gel states alternate normally and repeatedly in accordance with local variations of particle concentrations. Boundary protoplasm is more or less permanently in a gel state.

Increased temperature may convert a gel into a sol; at higher temperature, colloidal particles in a gel become more agitated, and the gelled meshwork is disrupted (e.g., liquefaction of Jello by heating). Many other physical and chemical influences, such as low or high pH or pressure, affect sol-gel conditions. For example, cream, a sol, when churned (i.e., when put under pressure), yields butter, a gel. Butter in turn can be creamed, that is, returned to the sol state.

All colloids **age.** The particles in a young, freshly formed colloidal system are enveloped by layers of *bound water;* water molecules are held against the particle surfaces by electrochemical attraction. It is largely because of these forces that water within a gel does not "run out" through the gel meshes. With time, however, the binding capacity of the particles decreases, and some of the water does run out. The colloid "sets"; that is, it contracts and gelates pro-

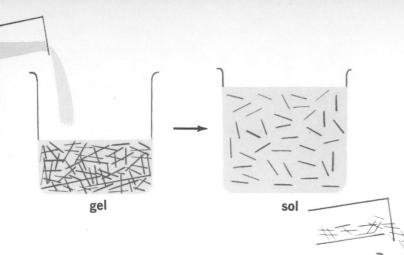

FIG. 6.14. Phase reversals. A gel may be transformed into a sol either by adding more liquid (top) or by withdrawing solid particles. And a sol may be transformed into a gel either by adding more solid particles (bottom) or by withdrawing liquid.

gressively (e.g., exudation of water from long-standing milk curd, custard, mustard, etc.). Such aging of colloids may be a factor contributing to the aging of living systems.

Migratory movements occur in colloids, and also in true solutions, as a direct result of the thermal agitation of the particles. If ions, molecules, or colloidal particles are unevenly distributed, more collisions take place in more concentrated regions. For example, if a particle in the circle in Fig. 6.15 is displaced by thermal agitation, or by Brownian bombardment, *toward* a region of higher concentration, it will soon be stopped in its track by collision with other particles. But if it is displaced *away* from a high concentration, its movement will not be interrupted as soon, since neighboring particles are farther apart. On an average, therefore, a greater number of particles are displaced into more dilute regions than into more concentrated ones. In time, particles throughout the system will become distributed evenly. This equalization resulting from migration of particles is called **diffusion.**

MEMBRANES AND PERMEABILITY

The boundary between a colloidal system and a different medium (air, water, solid surfaces, or another colloid of different type) is called an **interface.** The molecules there are usually subjected to complex physical forces which act on, and from, both sides of the interface. The result is that the molecules at the interface pack together tightly and become *oriented* in parallel, in layers, or both; an *interfacial membrane* forms (e.g., the "skins" on puddings, custards, boiled milk; Fig. 6.16). On surface protoplasm, as on the surfaces of cells, for example, such molecular skins are called *plasma membranes.* If the plasma membrane on the surface of a cell is punctured, a new membrane develops over the opening within seconds, before appreciable amounts of the interior can flow out.

Protoplasmic membranes are the gateways through which the molecular traffic into and out of protoplasm must pass. How do materials get through such membranes?

Plasma membranes have different **permeability** to different substances. Most membranes are completely permeable to water; that is, water molecules can pass through freely in either direction. As for other materials, organic or inorganic, there is no rule by which their passage potential can be determined beforehand. In general, three classes of materials can be distinguished: those that can pass through a membrane in either direction; those that can pass in one direction but not in the other; and those that cannot penetrate at all. These categories vary considerably for different membranes.

FIG. 6.15. Diffusion. In the initial state, particles are distributed unevenly. A given particle (for example, the circled one) will therefore have more freedom of movement in the direction of lower concentrations. This eventually leads to an even distribution of particles, as in the end state shown at right.

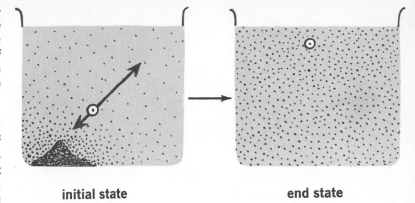

initial state   end state

In the past, traffic through living membranes has been compared with traffic through nonliving ones, like cellophane. Such nonliving membranes let water or small ions through, but not proteins, for example. Particle penetration here can be explained rather readily in terms of diffusion. Ions, for example, would strike the barrier; most of them would bounce off, but some would pass through *pores* in the membrane. If the ion concentration is greater on one side of the membrane than on the other, more ions on an average would migrate into the dilute side, thus equalizing concentrations.

However, a hypothesis postulating diffusion through pores is generally inadequate for living membranes. Particle size, for example, is often of little significance, contrary to what might be expected if living membranes contained small holes. Thus, under certain conditions large protein molecules may pass through a given membrane, whereas very small molecules sometimes may not. Again, the molecules of the three sugars glucose, fructose, and galactose, all $C_6H_{12}O_6$, have the same size, yet they are passed through living membranes at substantially different speeds.

Clearly, membranes are highly **selective**; that is, they act as if they "knew" which substances to trans-

mit and which to reject (Fig. 6.17). Moreover, it is now known that active, energy-consuming work is often done by a living membrane in transmitting materials, and that complex chemical reactions take place in the process. Therefore, rather than visualize a passive membrane with small holes, we are led to consider plasma films as dynamic structures, in which entering or leaving particles are actively "handed" across from one side to the other. Fatty components of membranes are thought to contribute particularly to these processes.

OSMOSIS

When a protoplasmic membrane separates one colloid from another, or from a different kind of medium, it often happens that the membrane is permeable to some of the particles present on either side of the membrane and is impermeable to others. If, initially, the transmissible particles are unequally concentrated on the two sides, diffusion will equalize the concentration, as we have seen. What happens when *nontransmissible* particles are unequally concentrated? For simplicity, let us assume that transmissible substances are not present at all and that we deal only with water containing nontransmissi-

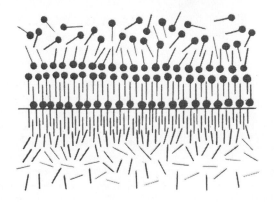

FIG. 6.16. A diagrammatic representation of an interfacial membrane. Where two different colloidal systems meet, the molecular particles become oriented in some regular manner, and this is a major factor in the formation of an interfacial film. In the diagram, the horizontal line separates the two colloidal systems.

FIG. 6.17. Illustrating the selectivity of protoplasmic membranes. Even though different kinds of particles may have the same size, only certain kinds may pass through the membrane.

ble particles. What events occur in such a system? Consult Fig. 6.18:

1. In the initial state, relatively more water molecules are in contact with the membrane X on the A side than on the B side, since fewer of the solid particles occupy membrane space on the A surface than on the B surface.

2. Therefore, more water molecules, on an average, are transmitted through the membrane from A to B than from B to A.

3. As a result, the water content decreases in A and increases in B. Particles in A become crowded into a smaller and smaller volume, and more and more of them therefore take up membrane space on the A surface. On the B side, the increasing water content permits the spreading of the particles into progressively larger volumes, thus reducing particle concentration along the B surface of the membrane.

4. A stage will be reached at which the number of particles along the A surface equals that along the B surface. From then on, the number of water molecules transmitted from A to B equals the number transmitted from B to A. Thereafter, no further *net* shift of water occurs.

This *movement of water is called* **osmosis.**

Note that the extent of osmosis depends on the **concentration differential**, the relative *numbers* of particles in A and B. Actually, it makes no difference whether the particles involved are transmissible or not. If, as normally happens in protoplasm, both kinds are present, transmissible particles on the more concentrated side will eventually diffuse over to the other side until concentrations are equal, but before this equality is reached, transmissible particles still exert a temporary osmotic effect. Nontransmissible particles, not being able to penetrate the membrane, exert a permanent osmotic effect.

If the difference in particle number is great enough (for example, if A contains pure water only and B contains water and a large number of par-

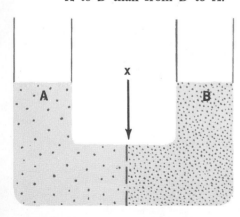

hypotonic   hypertonic

initial state

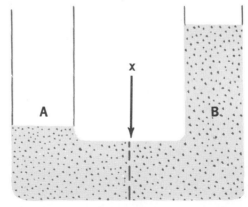

isotonic

end state

FIG. 6.18. Osmosis. In the initial state, because **A** is less concentrated than **B**, water will be pulled from **A** into **B**. This eventually leads to the isotonic end state, where concentrations in **A** and **B** are equal. From this point on, no further *net* migration of water occurs (that is, just as much water moves from **A** into **B** as from **B** into **A**). A semipermeable membrane is represented by x.

ticles), then the A side may dehydrate completely and collapse, while the B side might burst and so collapse also. Since this does not normally happen in living systems, their parts, clearly, must be in general osmotic equilibrium. The concentration of particles must be the same on both sides of membranes, or as often stated, the two sides must be **isotonic** to each other. If the initial concentration on an arbitrary A side is lower than on a B side (as in Fig. 6.18), then the A side loses water. The B medium here is said to be **hypertonic** to A, that is, initially more highly concentrated than the A medium. The B side, having the higher initial concentration of particles, gains water. The A medium is said to be **hypotonic** to the B medium.

Note that the net effect of osmosis is to pull water *into* the region of higher colloidal concentration. Note also that nothing migrates through the membrane except *water* and transmissible particles dissolved in this water.

Many well-known phenomena have an osmotic basis. For example, the laxative action of epsom salt (magnesium sulfate, $MgSO_4$) results from the impassability of this molecule through the gut wall. Consequently, water is pulled osmotically from the body tissues into the gut cavity, softening the feces. In another instance, the drinking of sea water greatly increases the salt concentration of the blood. Water is then pulled from the body tissues into the blood, body protoplasm dehydrates, and thirst is therefore greater than ever. Water containing 0.9 per cent NaCl, or an equivalent total of other particles, is isotonic to human protoplasm. Such a medium is called a *physiological saline* solution and must be used when drugs, glucose, or other substances are injected by physicians.

RESUME   In broad physical terms, protoplasm may be described as a mixed colloidal system, bounded by variously permeable membranes, undergoing localized sol-gel transformations, and being kept in constant internal motion by molecular bombardments, by diffusion displacements, and by osmotic forces. As a result of these properties, living matter is subjected to a continuous physical flux equally as profound as the chemical flux. Indeed, physical changes initiate chemical ones, and vice versa, and from any small-scale point of view, protoplasm is therefore never the same from moment to moment.

Furthermore, the small-scale properties of protoplasm, chemical and physical, materially influence every larger-scale property. As an important case in point, protoplasm does not occur in bulky, continuous masses. Rather, the tendency of the living colloid to form membranes leads to a subdivision of protoplasm into small, discontinuous globules. These have a certain individuality, and they are kept physically separated from one another by their surface membranes. Globules of this sort represent **cells.** We shall examine these universal structural units of protoplasm in the next chapter.

REVIEW QUESTIONS   1. Define ionization, ion, electrolyte, acid, base, salt. Is KCN (see page 132) an acid, a base, or a salt? How does sodium sulfate (Na_2SO_4) dissociate? The magnesium ion is Mg^{++}, and the nitrate ion, already encountered in Chap. 5, is NO_3^-; write the formulas for magnesium hydroxide, nitric acid, and magnesium nitrate.

2. What does the pH of a solution indicate? What would you expect the pH of a solution of NaCl to be? Of HCl? Of NaOH? Compared with pure water, how many more or fewer grams of H^+ ions will there be in a liter solution of (a) pH 5 and (b) pH 10? The pH of human blood is 7.3; what is the actual H^+ ion concentration per liter?

3. What is the general protoplasmic significance of ionization and pH? What are buffers?

4. Review the role of environmental heat in chemical reactions. What is activation energy? How does the external energy requirement differ for exergonic and endergonic reactions?

5. What is an enzyme, and how does it work? Why is invertase ineffective in accelerating the reaction glycerin + fatty acids → fat + water? What kind of enzyme does such a reaction actually require? Review the general operational characteristics of enzymes in protoplasmic reactions.

6. State the law of mass action. How does this law govern the speed, the direction, and the amount of a chemical reaction? Under what conditions is a protoplasmic reaction reversible? Irreversible?

7. What is a colloidal system? How does such a system differ from a solution? What kinds of colloidal systems are possible, and what kinds occur in protoplasm? Review the properties of colloidal systems.

8. Define diffusion, and show how, and under what conditions, this process will occur. What is the biological significance of diffusion?

9. How and where do plasma membranes form? What are the characteristics of such membranes? What roles do they play in biological processes?

10. Define osmosis. Show how and under what conditions this process will occur. Distinguish carefully between osmosis and diffusion. Cite examples of biological situations characterized by isotonicity, hypertonicity, and hypotonicity.

SUGGESTED COLLATERAL READINGS

Substantial additional information on topics dealt with in this chapter may be found in virtually any modern introductory college text of chemistry and of physical chemistry. The student desiring such information is urged to consult such texts, available in all college and most public libraries. The works listed below represent very good sample selections. Many other, equivalent books may be similarly adequate. The article cited last is a good semipopular account on enzymes.

Sienko, M. J., and R. A. Plane: "Chemistry," McGraw-Hill, 1957.

Pauling, L.: "College Chemistry," Freeman, 1950.

Noller, C. R.: "Textbook of Organic Chemistry," Saunders, 1958.

Daniels, F., and R. A. Alberty: "Physical Chemistry," Wiley, 1955.

Maron, S. H., and C. F. Prutton: "Principles of Physical Chemistry," 3d ed., Macmillan, 1958.

Pfeiffer, J. E.: Enzymes, *Sci. American,* vol. 179, 1948.

As a result of the uninterrupted chemical and physical flux within protoplasm, the contents of a living cell are always in actual, often observable motion. New materials enter a cell continuously, wastes and manufactured products leave continuously, and substances in the cell interior are continuously transformed chemically and redistributed physically. Therefore, as cells *function,* such functioning invariably means *change of structure.* And we may note that the concept of structure, quite like that of function, has an important progressive, historical aspect which cannot be dissociated from the dimension of time.

But although cells change with time, certain general compositional features must remain invariant if cells are to be living at all. In this chapter we shall examine the common invariant features of all cells on two levels of organization, the **molecular** and the **microscopic.** We first inquire what kinds of molecules cells are made of, and we then study the microscopically visible structures which are formed by the molecules, and which together add up to a cell.

CELLS: COMPOSITION AND STRUCTURE

Molecular Composition

The gross chemical composition of cells is usually determined by bulk analysis of substantial masses of protoplasm, with relatively little attention to the composition of any individual cell. In this section, we too shall deal with individual cells only by implication and shall be concerned primarily with the average molecular composition of protoplasm in general. As units of protoplasm, cells share this average composition.

Four of the most ubiquitous chemical elements on earth make up approximately 95 per cent of the weight of protoplasm: oxygen, *62 per cent;* carbon, *20 per cent;* hydrogen, *10 per cent;* and nitrogen, *3 per cent.* About 30 other elements contribute the remaining 5 per cent of the weight. Those listed in Table 2 occur in virtually all types of protoplasm.

TABLE 2. The relative abundance of chemical elements in living matter

Element	Symbol	Weight, per cent
Oxygen	O	62
Carbon	C	20
Hydrogen	H	10
Nitrogen	N	3
Calcium	Ca	2.50
Phosphorus	P	1.14
Chlorine	Cl	0.16
Sulfur	S	0.14
Potassium	K	0.11
Sodium	Na	0.10
Magnesium	Mg	0.07
Iodine	I	0.014
Iron	Fe	0.010
		99.244
Trace elements		0.756
		100.00

Trace amounts of others are found only in particular types, and still other elements may become incorporated into living matter accidentally, along with food. All these elements, we recall, are present in the ocean; having originated in water, protoplasm reflects the composition and content of water.

Virtually all the elements occur in the form of

FIG. 7.1. The average overall composition of protoplasm by weight.

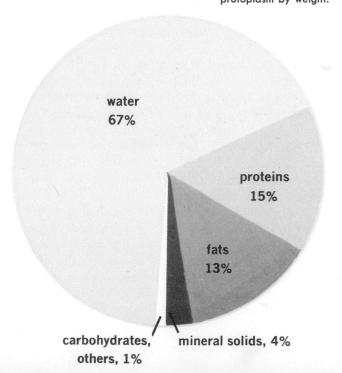

water 67%

proteins 15%

fats 13%

carbohydrates, others, 1%

mineral solids, 4%

compounds. As already noted, protoplasm consists of two great classes of compounds: **inorganic,** or mineral, compounds and **organic,** more or less complex carbon-containing, compounds.

THE INORGANIC COMPONENTS

Directly or indirectly, all inorganic compounds of living matter are of mineral origin; that is, they are supplied in finished form by the external physical environment. **Water** is the most abundant protoplasmic mineral, present in amounts ranging from 5 to 90 or more per cent. For example, the water content of tooth enamel and of certain plant seeds is 5 per cent; of marrowless bone, 25 per cent; of whole bone, 40 per cent; of muscle, 75 per cent; of brain, 80 per cent; of milk, 90 per cent; of a jellyfish, at least 90 per cent. A human being is about 67 per cent water, overall, which is a general average for protoplasm as a whole (Fig. 7.1).

Mineral solids constitute the other inorganic components of protoplasm. They are present in amounts ranging from 1 to about 5 per cent, on an average. A considerable fraction of the minerals may exist in the form of hard bulk deposits, such as bone, teeth, or shells. These are often silicon- or calcium-containing substances. Bone, for example, consists largely of calcium phosphate [$Ca_3(PO_4)_2$]; clamshells consist of calcium carbonate ($CaCO_3$).

All other protoplasmic minerals are in solution, either free or combined with organic molecules. These inorganic constituents exist largely in the form of *ions*. The most abundant positively charged inorganic ions in protoplasm are H^+, hydrogen ions; Ca^{++}, calcium ions; Na^+, sodium ions; K^+, potassium ions; and Mg^{++}, magnesium ions. Abundant negative mineral constituents include OH^-, hydroxyl ions; $CO_3^=$, carbonate ions; HCO_3^-, bicarbonate ions; $PO_4^\equiv$, phosphate ions; Cl^-, chloride ions; and $SO_4^=$, sulfate ions (Fig. 7.2). Note that the mineral compounds of protoplasm, like the elements of which they are made, also are major constituents of the ocean and of rocks and ores; rocks are dissolved by water, water finds its way into the ocean and into soil, and living matter draws its mineral supplies from these sources.

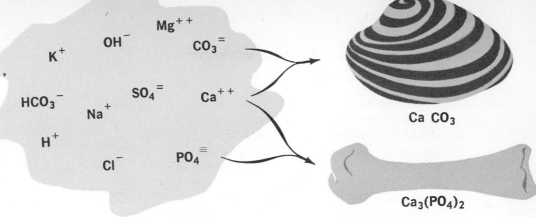

FIG. 7.2. The mineral composition of protoplasm. The principal ions are shown, as well as some of the hard parts formed by some of these ions.

K^+ OH^- Mg^{++} $CO_3^=$

HCO_3^- Na^+ $SO_4^=$ Ca^{++}

H^+

Cl^- $PO_4^{\equiv}$

$Ca\ CO_3$

$Ca_3(PO_4)_2$

THE ORGANIC COMPONENTS

In Chap. 2 we have identified organic compounds as those in which the molecules contain linked carbon atoms. We may now define organic substances more precisely as all compounds of carbon excepting mainly the carbonates and their derivatives. Thus, carbon dioxide (CO_2), carbonate ions ($CO_3^=$), bicarbonate ions (HCO_3^-), and carbonic acid (H_2CO_3) are inorganic. But methane (CH_4) is considered to be an organic molecule, even though it does not contain linked carbon atoms.

Cellular protoplasm contains hundreds of different categories of organic constituents. Most of these we shall not have occasion to refer to at all. Some we shall encounter in special contexts. And a few will demand most of our attention. In abundance and importance, these few form the organic basis of protoplasm, and they are found in all types of living matter. We have already identified them earlier: sugars, polysaccharides, and carbohydrates in general; fats, fatty acids, and glycerin; amino acids and proteins; nucleotides, nucleic acids, and nucleoproteins.

Like mineral compounds, some of these organic substances may contribute to the formation of protoplasmic hard parts. For example, wood, horn, and *chitin*, the external covering of insects and of many other animals, are predominantly organic. More generally, however, organic materials are dissolved or suspended in water, some in ionized, some in nonionized form (Fig. 7.3). Their relative abundance varies considerably in different types of protoplasm. In man, proteins make up about 15 per

FIG. 7.3. The organic composition of protoplasm. The principal organic components are shown, as well as some of the hard parts formed by some of these components.

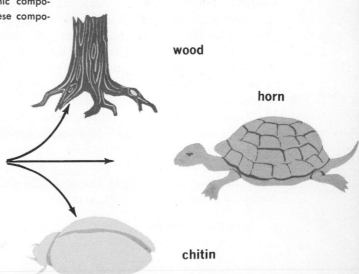

sugars, polysaccharides,
fatty acids, glycerin, fats,
amino acids, proteins,
nucleotides, nucleic acids,
nucleoproteins

wood

horn

chitin

cent of the total weight, fats about 13 per cent, and all other organic constituents together do not exceed about 1 per cent (see Fig. 7.1).

Carbohydrates

As already noted in Chap. 2, carbohydrates are so called because they consist of carbon and of hydrogen and oxygen in a 2:1 ratio, as in water. Sugars and their derivatives are the principal carbohydrates, and **glucose** ($C_6H_{12}O_6$) is probably the most important of the protoplasmic sugars.

As also noted in Chap. 2, it is a general characteristic of organic compounds that even slightly different arrangements of atoms yield different kinds of molecules. In glucose, the H and O atoms are joined to the chain of 6 carbons in a particular pattern:

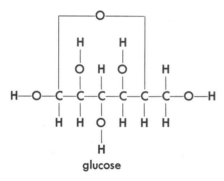

glucose

If the H's and O's are rearranged, the resulting molecule still has the overall atomic formula $C_6H_{12}O_6$, but its properties have become different. The new molecule is, in fact, a different sugar. Depending on *how* the H and OH groups of glucose are rearranged, the resulting new sugar might be **fructose,** fruit sugar, or **galactose,** present in milk, or one of a number of other 6-carbon sugars found in protoplasm, all with the atomic formula $C_6H_{12}O_6$.

Under appropriate conditions, sugars of 6 (or of fewer or more) carbon atoms may combine with one another. For example, one molecule of glucose can join another, like molecule, giving a new 12-carbon sugar: **maltose,** or malt sugar. One molecule of water forms as a byproduct in this reaction:

$$C_6H_{12}O_6 + C_6H_{12}O_6 \rightarrow C_{12}H_{22}O_{11} + H_2O$$
glucose   glucose   maltose

Or glucose can combine with fructose, resulting in the familiar **sucrose,** cane sugar or beet sugar, used daily by practically everyone:

$$C_6H_{12}O_6 + C_6H_{12}O_6 \rightarrow C_{12}H_{22}O_{11} + H_2O$$
glucose   fructose   sucrose

Or again, glucose can unite with galactose, and the result is **lactose,** milk sugar:

$$C_6H_{12}O_6 + C_6H_{12}O_6 \rightarrow C_{12}H_{22}O_{11} + H_2O$$
glucose   galactose   lactose

Because lactose, sucrose, maltose, and other 12-carbon sugars are each composed of two 6-carbon sugars, they are called "double sugars," or **disaccharides.** Glucose and other 6-carbon sugars in turn are called **monosaccharides.**

Two or more disaccharides may combine into even longer chains, producing "multiple sugars," the polysaccharides already referred to in Chap. 2. Among **polysaccharides** important in protoplasm are *cellulose,* which is a chain of about 2,000 united glucose units; *starch,* a chain of 24 to 26 glucose units; and *glycogen,* a chain of 12 to 18 glucose units. Supermolecules of this sort are widespread derivatives of 6-carbon carbohydrates.

Sugars may not only build up into larger molecules but may also break down into smaller ones. Under certain conditions, monosaccharides like glucose, for example, decompose into water and molecules containing 1, 2, or 3 carbon atoms:

$$C_6H_{12}O_6 + 6O_2 \rightarrow 6CO_2 + 6H_2O$$
(six 1-carbon fragments)
$$C_6H_{12}O_6 \rightarrow 2CO_2 + 2C_2H_6O$$
alcohol
(two 1-carbon, two 2-carbon fragments)
$$C_6H_{12}O_6 \rightarrow 2C_3H_6O_3$$
lactic acid
(two 3-carbon fragments)

Such carbohydrate degradation is accompanied by release of energy, a phenomenon treated later in greater detail. At this point we merely note that one of the main functions of carbohydrates in protoplasm is to serve as *energy sources.*

Fats

Like carbohydrates, these are also composed of C, H, and O. We recall from Chap. 2 that a fat is a combination of **glycerin** and **fatty acids.** Glycerin, we have noted, is $C_3H_8O_3$, or

$$
\begin{array}{ccc}
H & H & H \\
| & | & | \\
O & O & O \\
| & | & | \\
H-C-C-C-H \\
| & | & | \\
H & H & H
\end{array}
$$

glycerin

Glycerin is a weak base. When it is dissolved in water, a few of its molecules release up to three OH^- ions.

Fatty acids contain carbon chains of varying length:

The —COOH group always present at one end of such a chain is the **carboxyl** group. This group gives the fatty acid its acid properties; —COOH ionizes into —COO$^-$ and H$^+$.

To form a fat molecule, three fatty acid molecules must be joined to one glycerin molecule. In this union, the three fatty acids each release one H$^+$ ion, the glycerin releases three OH$^-$ ions, and three H_2O molecules thus form as a byproduct (Fig. 7.4).

Being reaction products of acids and bases, fats qualify as salts. Note here that organic salts, formed from organic acids and bases, are called **esters.**

Almost all fatty acids of protoplasm consist of *even-numbered* carbon chains. We shall see why this is so in a later chapter. The physical properties of a fat are determined largely by the nature of its component fatty acids. If the acids are long carbon chains, the fat is likely to be a hard **tallow.** If they are short chains, the fat tends to be a volatile liquid or a semiliquid **oil.**

Chemically related to fats are the **waxes,** in which long fatty acids are joined to certain compounds other than glycerin. Also related to fats are **sterols,** complex ring structures which, as we shall see, form the framework of a number of vitamins and

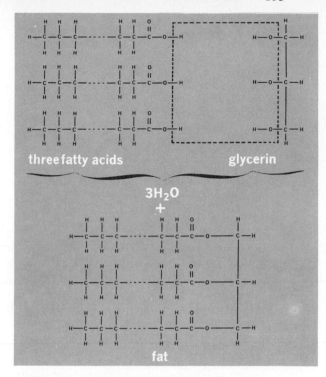

FIG. 7.4. The formation of a fat molecule. Three fatty acid molecules combine with one glycerin molecule, resulting in three water molecules and one fat molecule.

hormones. The general term **lipid** is often used to designate the whole category of fatty, fatlike, and related substances.

The role of fats in protoplasm is manifold. Like carbohydrates, fats are energy-rich molecules. Energy is released by decomposition. Fats can also be transformed into carbohydrates, and vice versa. Fats, like carbohydrates and proteins, may be utilized as starting materials in the synthesis of more complex protoplasmic components. Finally, fats as such are fundamental structural building blocks of protoplasm. For example, they contribute to the framework of bounding membranes, where they probably play an important role in controlling movements of materials into and out of protoplasm.

Proteins

Besides C, H, and O, proteins always contain *nitrogen,* and usually sulfur as well. As noted in

Chap. 2, **amino acids** are the structural units of proteins, represented generally by

$$H-N-R-C \begin{array}{c} O \\ O-H \end{array}$$
$$\quad\ \ H$$

Here —COOH is again the carboxyl group which, as in fatty acids, confers acid properties; —NH$_2$ is the *amino* group; and —R— represents a ring or a chain of carbon atoms holding H, OH, and other components. Amino acids consequently differ according to the nature of their —R— portions. In protoplasm only 23 different kinds of such —R— portions are found; hence there are just 23 different natural types of amino acids. We shall have to inquire later into this curious limitation on the number of amino acid types.

Proteins are long chains of joined amino acids. Consider how varied such chains can be:

1. They may contain any or all of the 23 different types of amino acids.

2. They may contain almost any number of each of these types.

3. The specific sequences in which given amino acids are joined can vary almost without restrictions.

4. The resulting chains can be folded two- and three-dimensionally in virtually any imaginable pattern.

The situation is rather like forming words and sentences from an alphabet of letters. In the English language, 26 different letter symbols can be ordered practically at will to form an infinite variety of combinations. In proteins, the "letter symbols" are 23 different types of amino acids. And unlike real sentences, the protein "sentences" need not remain strung out in straight lines but can be branched and folded in practically any direction and form. Clearly, the number of theoretically possible proteins is astronomical.

Indeed, no two types of protoplasm contain the same types of proteins. This is not the case for carbohydrates or fats. A given complex carbohydrate, for example, is the same whether we obtain it from mushrooms or mangoes, from mice or from men. A given fat, similarly, is the same fat regardless of where we find it. Not so for proteins, however. Even twins have slightly different proteins, and the structural differences between proteins are the greater, the more unrelated two organisms are evolutionally. We say that proteins have a high degree of **specificity**: the proteins of a given protoplasmic unit have a unit- "specific" character, i.e., they are unique for that unit.

Protein specificity is the basis of enzyme specificity, as already noted in the preceding chapter. Some other consequences of protein specificity are well known. For example, transfer of protein from one organism into the protoplasm of another amounts to the introduction of foreign bodies, and disease may result. Thus, the proteins of plant pollen may produce allergy in human protoplasm; blood of one person mixed with blood of another, if not of compatible type, may produce protein shock and death; viruses and bacteria, partly because their proteins differ from ours, may produce many familiar disease reactions. A number of other significant consequences of protein specificity will be encountered later.

As a result of their complicated geometrical make-up, proteins are extremely sensitive to chemical and physical influences. Excessive heat, a change of pH, pressure, electricity, heavy metals, and many other agents produce protein **coagulation;** cross linkages within the folded amino acid chain are broken, the exquisite geometry of arrangement is destroyed, and the molecule collapses (Fig. 7.5). Mild disarrangement is spoken of as **denaturation.** In living protoplasm, a denatured state may sometimes revert to the **native** state, and vice versa. But once coagulated, like boiled egg white, a protein usually cannot be restored to its native form. Protoplasmic death is sometimes a result of irreversible protein coagulation.

Among many functions of proteins, three have fundamental significance. Proteins are among the main structural *building materials* of protoplasm; as noted, proteins function as reaction-accelerating *enzymes;* proteins help in the formation of other organic constituents, *nucleoproteins* in particular.

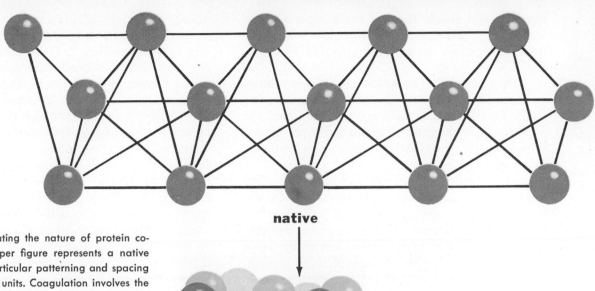

native

coagulated

FIG. 7.5. Illustrating the nature of protein co-agulation. The upper figure represents a native protein, with a particular patterning and spacing of the amino acid units. Coagulation involves the physical disruption of this patterning, as indicated in the lower figure. Note that coagulation does not change the *chemical* composition of the protein, only the physical.

The biochemist today can take the protein complex apart and analyze its atomic composition and its amino acid content. At present, he is also able to link together as many as 30-odd amino acids, producing a molecule with properties vaguely suggestive of those of proteins. But he cannot (yet!) combine hundreds of amino acids into a protein. Apart from immense technical obstacles, our knowledge of architectural patterns in proteins is still wholly rudimentary. Just recently, the internal geometrical structure of a protein was unraveled for the first time. The protein involved in this historic achievement was *insulin*, the hormone of the pancreas. However, a very wide technical gulf still separates knowledge of structure from actual laboratory synthesis. We may ponder nevertheless that, *if*, at some future date, the artificial synthesis of proteins should become possible, then the synthesis of a primitive living system might not be too far off.

Nucleoproteins

We have found in Chap. 2 that these most critical constituents of protoplasm consist of *nucleic acids* and *proteins,* that nucleic acids are made up of many *nucleotides,* and that nucleotides in turn are either *pyrimidine-sugar-phosphate* or *purine-sugar-phosphate:*

$$\left.\begin{array}{l}\text{pyrimidine}\\\text{or purine}\end{array}\right\}\text{-sugar-phosphate} = \text{nucleotide}$$

many nucleotides → nucleic acid

nucleic acid–protein → nucleoprotein

In a nucleotide, the pyrimidine or purine component is usually one of five major kinds; the sugar component can be either of two kinds; and the phosphate component is always the same.

The five principal pyrimidine or purine units are called, respectively, **adenine, guanine, cytosine,**

thymine, and **uracil.** The first two are purines; the last three, pyrimidines. The molecular skeletons of these compounds have been given in Chap. 2, Fig. 2.5.

Thus, depending on which one of these purines or pyrimidines is present in a given nucleotide, five major kinds of nucleotides may be distinguished: adenine-sugar-phosphate, guanine-sugar-phosphate, cytosine-sugar-phosphate, thymine-sugar-phosphate, uracil-sugar-phosphate.

The two possible sugars of nucleotides are called **ribose** and **desoxyribose,** respectively. Both are 5-carbon sugars, and the principal difference between them is indicated by their names: "desoxy"-ribose contains one oxygen atom less than ribose. Therefore, according to the type of sugar present, two kinds of nucleotides may be distinguished: **ribose nucleotide** and **desoxyribose nucleotide.** These two exist in four varieties each, depending on the type of purine or pyrimidine present:

ribose nucleotides	desoxyribose nucleotides
adenine-ribose-phosphate	adenine-desoxyribose-phosphate
guanine-ribose-phosphate	guanine-desoxyribose-phosphate
cytosine-ribose-phosphate	cytosine-desoxyribose-phosphate
uracil-ribose-phosphate	thymine-desoxyribose-phosphate

Note that adenine, guanine, and cytosine occur in both types of nucleotides, whereas uracil is found only in association with ribose, and thymine, only in association with desoxyribose.

A nucleic acid molecule consists of hundreds of joined nucleotides. We shall see in a later chapter *how* nucleotides are probably joined together. Here we may note that, in any nucleic acid molecule, all nucleotides are *either* ribose nucleotides *or* desoxyribose nucleotides, but not both. On this basis, we may distinguish between **ribose nucleic acid, RNA** for short, composed entirely of ribose nucleotides, and **desoxyribose nucleic acid, DNA** for short, composed entirely of desoxyribose nucleotides. As we shall see, RNA is found throughout a cell. But DNA occurs only in the nuclei of cells, where it is a special structural component of genes (Fig. 7.6). Both RNA and DNA carry out vital specific functions, and we may note that it is the DNA type of nucleic acid which may have played the key role

during the origin of life on this planet of ours.

In both DNA and RNA, the structural pattern may vary enormously. A DNA molecule, for example, may contain virtually any number of each of the four types of desoxyribose nucleotides, and the specific sequence of these different nucleotides can vary without known restrictions. The situation is not unlike that in using Morse code to form words and sentences. In the telegraphic code, two different code symbols, dots and dashes, are used in combination to form an infinite variety of patterns. In DNA, there are four "code symbols"—the four different types of nucleotides—which occur in similarly varied combination patterns. Clearly, the number of theoretically possible DNA's is practically unlimited. As with proteins, there are good reasons to believe that nucleic acids are extremely **specific,** i.e., that no two protoplasms have exactly the same kinds. RNA molecules match the complexity and variety of the DNA's.

DNA and RNA are each joined to proteins, forming nucleoproteins. Little is as yet known about the nature of this union. But it should be easy to understand why, inasmuch as proteins contribute enormous complexity and variety of their own, nucleoproteins are the most complicated chemical substances on earth. As we have seen, nucleoproteins were the critical chemicals in the origin of life, and as we shall see later in detail, they have functioned ever since as the principal controllers of all living processes.

We may sum up. Carbohydrates, fats, proteins, nucleic acids, and their various derivatives, together with water and other inorganic substances, and numerous additional organic compounds found specifically in particular types of protoplasm, these are the molecular bricks out of which living matter is made. To be sure, a mere random pile of these bricks does not make a living structure, any more than a mere pile of real bricks makes a house. First and foremost, if the whole is to be living, the molecular components must be organized into a specific variety of larger aggregates, and these in turn into cells.

Accordingly, the microscopic architecture of cells next demands our attention.

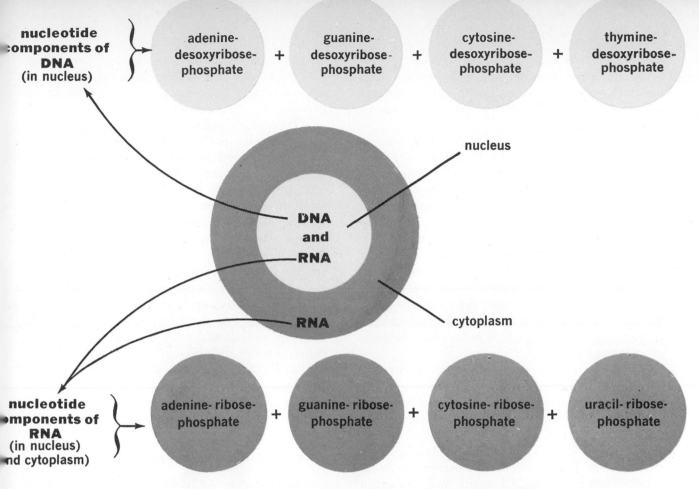

nucleotide components of **DNA** (in nucleus)

adenine-desoxyribose-phosphate + guanine-desoxyribose-phosphate + cytosine-desoxyribose-phosphate + thymine-desoxyribose-phosphate

nucleus

DNA and RNA

RNA

cytoplasm

nucleotide components of **RNA** (in nucleus and cytoplasm)

adenine- ribose-phosphate + guanine- ribose-phosphate + cytosine- ribose-phosphate + uracil- ribose-phosphate

FIG. 7.6. The structure and distribution of DNA and RNA. The kinds of nucleotide units which compose DNA are shown in the top row, and the kinds which compose RNA are shown in the bottom row. The diagram in the middle indicates that DNA occurs only in the nucleus of a cell, whereas RNA occurs both in the nucleus and outside it.

Microscopic Structure

FUNDAMENTAL ARCHITECTURE

The generalization that all plants and animals consist of cells and cell products is known as the **cell theory.** Principal credit for its formulation is usually given to the German biologists Schleiden and Schwann, whose work was published in 1838. But the French biologist Dutrochet had made substantially the same generalization as early as 1824. The cell theory rapidly became one of the fundamental cornerstones of modern biological science and, with minor qualifications, it still has this status today.

Cells came to be recognized early as the "atomic" units of living matter, structurally as well as functionally. In 1831, Robert Brown discovered the presence of nuclei within cells, and in 1839 the Bohemian biologist Purkinje coined the general term "protoplasm" for the living substance out of which cells are made. Virchow in 1855 concluded that *"omnis cellula e cellula"*—new living cells can arise only by reproduction of preexisting living cells. This important recognition of the continuity of life, and thus of the direct derivation of all cells from ancient cellular ancestors, introduced the notion of history into the study of cells. Ever since, cell biology has revolved around three interrelated problems: cell **structure**, cell **function**, and short- and long-range cell **development**. The first of these concerns us here particularly.

Examination of living or killed cells by various kinds of microscopes shows that cells vary considerably in size, ranging in diameter from about $2\,\mu$ to as much as several millimeters and more. However, the order of size of the vast majority of cells is remarkably uniform. A diameter of 5 to 15 μ is fairly characteristic of cells generally. We surmise that, notwithstanding the exceptions, cells can be neither much smaller nor much larger than a certain norm. Too small a size presumably would not provide enough room to accommodate the necessary parts, and too large a size would increase the maintenance problem and at the same time reduce the efficiency of compact operation.

The two fundamental subdivisions of virtually all cells are the **nucleus** and the protoplasm surrounding the nucleus, called the **cytoplasm.** The nucleus is bounded by a **nuclear membrane,** the cytoplasm by a **cell membrane,** also called **plasma membrane** (Fig. 7.7). Most cells contain a single nucleus each. But there are many exceptions. As already noted in Chap. 2, bacteria and blue-green algae do not contain distinct nuclei at all. Conversely, many other single-celled organisms nor-

mally contain more than one nucleus (see Chap. 31). *Binucleate* and *multinucleate* cells are found also with some frequency among multicellular organisms.

There are exceptions too concerning the individuality of cells, normally maintained by the cell membrane. In certain tissues among many young or embryonic organisms, cell membranes at first form boundaries between individual cells. But at a later stage of development, these membranes dissolve, and the tissue becomes a fused, continuous protoplasmic mass, with nuclei dispersed through it. The human heart muscle is one of many pertinent examples. Such a structure, in which cellular individuality has been lost, is called a **syncitium.**

Despite variations in the number of nuclei, or the occasional loss of the structural discreteness of cells, the fundamentally cellular character of living matter is undeniable even in such exceptional cases. And in all other cases the cellular character is unequivocal, for there we deal with distinct bits of protoplasm, each bounded by a plasma membrane and containing one nucleus.

NUCLEUS AND CYTOPLASM

A nucleus typically consists of three kinds of components: the more or less gel-like nuclear sap, or **nucleoplasm,** in which are suspended the **chromo-**

FIG. 7.7. The general structure of cells. The diagram represents a section through a cell, and the photo shows red blood cells of a bird. Note the darkly stained central nucleus of each blood cell. (Photo, General Biological Supply House, Inc.)

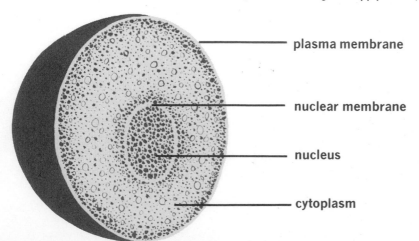

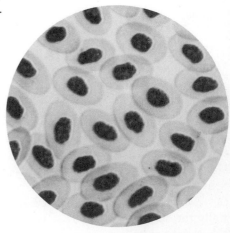

plasma membrane

nuclear membrane

nucleus

cytoplasm

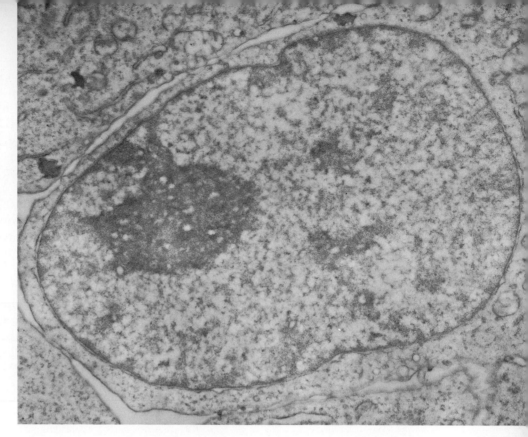

FIG. 7.8. Electron micrograph of a cell nucleus. The whole elliptical structure is the nucleus; cytoplasm is outside it. Note the nuclear bounding membrane. Within the nucleus, the large dark patch is the nucleolus, and the dark speckle is the gene-containing chromatin. (Courtesy of Dr. K. R. Porter, Rockefeller Institute.)

somes, and one or more **nucleoli** (Fig. 7.8). The chromosomes are the principal nuclear structures. Indeed, a nucleus as a whole may be regarded primarily as a protective housing for these slender, threadlike bodies. Chemically, chromosomes consist largely of protein and of nucleoprotein; DNA is the principal nucleic acid of the nucleoproteins, but some RNA is usually also found. Functionally, chromosomes are the carriers of the genes which, as noted on several previous occasions, are the ultimate controllers of all cellular processes. Particular cell types may not contain formed nuclei, as we have seen, and thus they may not contain formed chromosomes; but all cell types contain genes.

Chromosomes are conspicuous only during cell reproduction, when they become thickly coated with additional nucleoprotein. At other times such coats are absent, and chromosomes then are very fine filaments not easily identifiable within the nuclear sap. The exact number of chromosomes within each cell nucleus is an important species-specific trait. For example, cells of human beings contain 48 chromosomes each. Analogously, cells of every other type of organism have their own characteristic chromosome number. A cell rarely contains more than in the order of 100 chromosomes. Hence, since there are several million different species of organisms, many species share the same chromosome number. To be sure, possession of the same *numbers* of chromosomes does not mean possession of the same *kinds*.

A nucleolus ("little nucleus") is a spherical body which also consists largely of nucleoprotein. But the only type of nucleic acid present here is RNA. As we shall see in a later chapter, nucleoli are derivatives of chromosomes, and they appear to play an important role in the control of protein synthesis within cells. Given cell types contain a fixed number of nucleoli per nucleus.

The whole nucleus is separated from the surrounding cytoplasm by the nuclear membrane. This structure, like most other protoplasmic membranes, is constructed mainly of proteins and fatty substances. It governs the vital traffic of materials between cytoplasm and nucleus. Examination with the electron microscope shows that the nuclear membrane is actually a double membrane, the outer one pierced by tiny pores (Fig. 7.9). The functional significance of such an architecture is not yet clear.

If the nucleus, by virtue of its genes, is the control center of cellular functions, then the cytoplasm is the executive center. In it, the directives of the nucleus are carried out. But it should be emphasized at once that such a functional distinction between nucleus and cytopolasm should not be taken too rigorously. Although the nucleus primarily controls, it also executes many directives of the cytoplasm; and although the cytoplasm primarily executes, it also influences many nuclear processes. As we shall see later, a vital reciprocal interdependence binds nucleus and cytoplasm, and experiment has repeatedly shown that one cannot long survive without the other (Fig. 7.10).

Cytoplasm consists of a semifluid **ground substance,** which is in a sol or a gel state at different times and in different cellular regions, and in which are suspended large numbers of various **formed inclusions.** Such inclusions may be shaped into granules, rodlets, filaments, or droplets. Each of these may have various sizes and chemical compositions and may have a variety of functions. Particular cell types often possess unique inclusions not found elsewhere. The following inclusions are widespread among many or all cell types:

Mitochondria. Found universally in all cells, these round or filamentous structures have a predominantly fat-protein composition (Fig. 7.11). In addition to RNA-nucleoprotein, they are known to contain *respiratory enzymes,* that is, enzymes required in energy-producing reactions. Mitochondria are the principal chemical "factories" in which cellular respiration is carried out.

Microsomes. As suggested by their name, these are exceedingly tiny granules, visible under the electron microscope (Fig. 7.11). Present in all cells,

FIG. 7.9. Electron-micrographic close-up of a nuclear membrane. Note the double-layered condition of the membrane. The arrow points to one of the pores of the membrane. (Courtesy of Dr. K. R. Porter, Rockefeller Institute.)

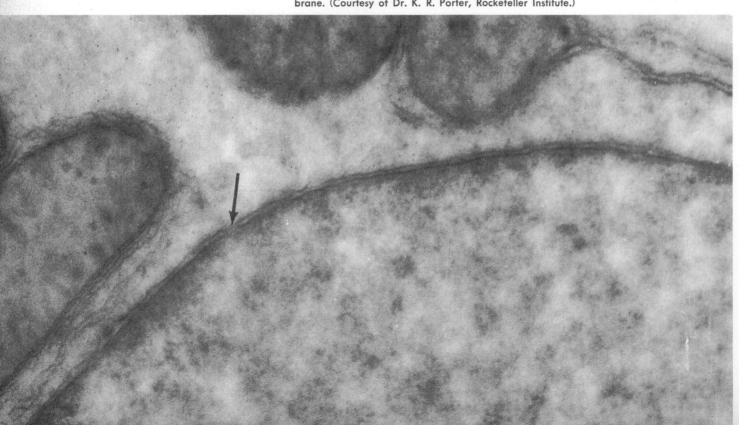

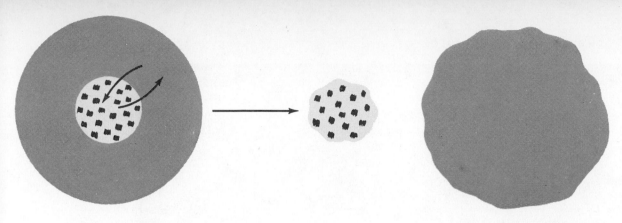

intact cell: living

nucleus and cytoplasm
isolated: nonliving

FIG. 7.10. Diagrammatic illustration of the interdependence of nucleus and cytoplasm. If the nucleus is isolated from a cell, neither the nucleus nor the cytoplasm can survive.

they contain RNA-nucleoprotein and enzymes required in many synthesis reactions. It is believed that microsomes are the principal factories in which cellular protein synthesis is carried out.

Golgi bodies. These probably universal structures may appear variously as droplet complexes or irregular filamentous networks, depending on how the cell has been killed and prepared for study

(Fig. 7.12). Golgi bodies are particularly conspicuous in cells which produce special secretions, such as gland cells. From this, it is believed that the Golgi inclusions play a central role in the manufacture of secretion products.

Plastids. These round or oval bodies are found in plant cells. A plastid may contain pigment, and if the pigment is *chlorophyll*, then the plastid is given

FIG. 7.11. Electron micrograph of cytoplasm, showing mitochondria (sausage-shaped bodies) and microsomes (faint beaded chains). The small black granules are fatty material. The gray background in the photo represents the viscous ground substance in which all cytoplasmic bodies and particles are suspended. (Courtesy of Dr. K. R. Porter, Rockefeller Institute.)

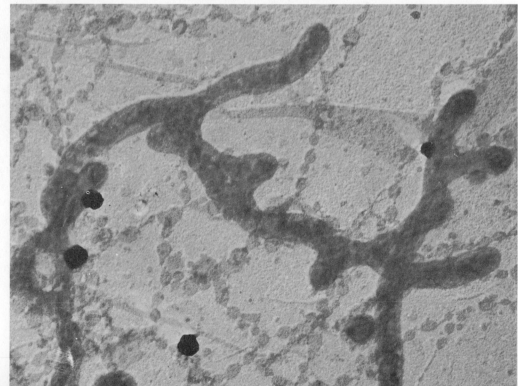

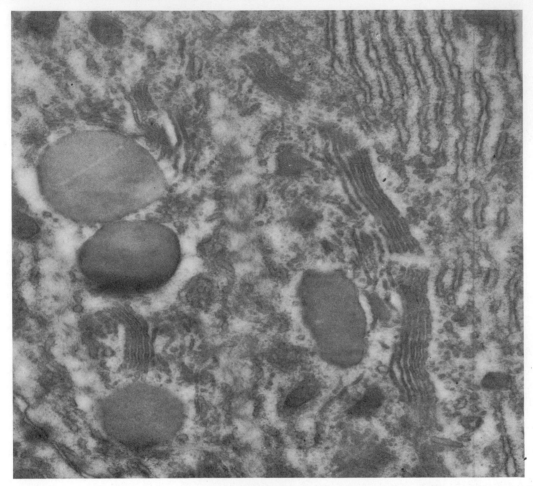

FIG. 7.12. Golgi bodies. In this electron micrograph of a portion of a mucus-secreting cell of the frog, the Golgi bodies appear as bundles of parallel lamellae. The large round bodies are secretory granules. (Courtesy of Dr. K. R. Porter, Rockefeller Institute.)

the name of **chloroplast.** Chloroplasts evidently occur in the *green* cells of plants. In addition to chlorophyll, chloroplasts contain nucleoprotein, enzymes, and all the other chemical machinery for food manufacture; chloroplasts are the factories in which photosynthesis occurs.

Centrioles. In primitive plant cells, and in virtually all animal cells, a single centriole is located just outside the nucleus. As we shall later discover, this small granule functions in cell reproduction.

Apart from the inclusions just listed, cytoplasm generally contains additional **granules** and fluid-filled droplets bounded by membranes, called **vacuoles.** Such cytoplasm granules and vacuoles perform a large variety of functions. They may be vehicles transporting raw materials from the cell surface to interior processing centers (e.g., *food vacuoles*) or finished products in the opposite direction (e.g., *secretion granules*); they may be places of storage (e.g., *starch granules, fat vacuoles, water vacuoles*); they may be vehicles transporting waste materials to points of elimination (e.g., *excretory vacuoles*); or they may be special processing centers themselves.

In addition to all these, cytoplasm may or may not contain a variety of long, thin **fibrils,** made predominantly out of protein (e.g., *contractile fibrils, neurofibrils*). Various other inclusions, unique to given cell types and serving unique functions, may also be present. In general, every function a cell performs, common or not, is based on a particular structure in which the machinery for that function is housed.

Cytoplasm as a whole is normally in motion. Irregular eddying and streaming occur at some times, and at others the substance of a cell is subjected to cyclical currents, a movement known as **cyclosis.** The formed inclusions, as well as the nucleus, are swept along passively in these streams. The specific cause of such motions is unknown, but there is little doubt that they are a reflection of the uninterrupted chemical and physical changes which take place on the molecular level. Whatever the specific causes may be, the apparently random movements might give the impression that nothing is fixed within a cell and that cytoplasm is simply a collection of loose particulate bodies that are suspended in "soup."

But this impression is erroneous, as examination under the electron microscope shows. The ground substance of cytoplasm, which under the light microscope does appear to be a fluid, structureless "soup," actually turns out to be highly structured and organized. A network of exceedingly fine membranes can be shown to traverse the cytoplasm from plasma membrane to nuclear membrane. This network is known as the **endoplasmic reticulum** (Fig. 7.13). Linked to it are the mitochondria, the microsomes, and all the other cytoplasmic inclusions. Thus, little is really "loose" in a cell. When cytoplasm as a whole streams and moves, the endoplasmic reticulum streams and moves too, and the formed inclusions are carried along, still held to the ultramicroscopic network. Evidently, even though the contents of a cell may shift position and the cell as a whole may be deformable, an orderly structural integration of the interior persists nevertheless. Indeed, this is essential if cellular functions are to be orderly and integrated.

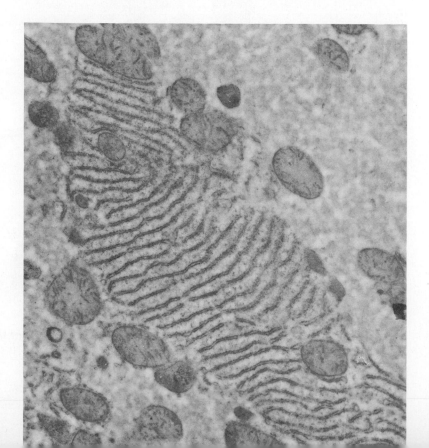

FIG. 7.13. An electron micrograph of a portion of the endoplasmic reticulum of a rat liver cell. Note that the reticulum is made up of an array of double membranes. The oval bodies around the reticulum are sections through mitochondria. (Courtesy of Dr. K. R. Porter, Rockefeller Institute.)

THE CELL SURFACE

The cell as a whole is bounded by a cell membrane. Composed predominantly of protein and fatty substances, this important structure is far more than a passive outer skin. It is an active, highly selective, semipermeable membrane, which regulates the entry and exit of materials into and out of a cell. The membrane therefore plays a critical role in all cell functions, since, directly or indirectly, every cell function necessitates **absorption** of molecules from the exterior and/or **excretion** of molecules from the interior. We shall have occasion in many later contexts to consider some of the specific activities of cell membranes.

In given cell types, additional structures may be present on or around the cell membrane. Such surface structures serve variously in mechanical support, in protection, and in locomotion. For example, plant cells secrete **cell walls** around their plasma membranes. These walls, made of cellulose, are fairly rigid envelopes which maintain cell shape and aid in support against gravity. Plant cells exposed directly to the external air also secrete **cuticles,** in addition to cell walls. Such cuticles are made of wax and other waterproofing materials. Cellulose and wax are not found among animal cells, but in many cases they too surround themselves with walls or cuticles. For example, a coat of **chitin,** a complex organic material, is found in many protozoa and on the skin cells of insects and other invertebrates. Analogously, the surface cells of mammalian skin and hair secrete external coats made of the protein **keratin.** Skeletal **shells,** of lime, glass (silica), or organic substances are among other external covers manufactured by many plant and animal cells (Fig. 7.14).

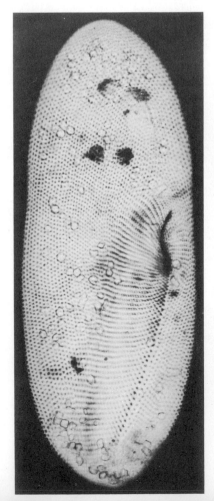

FIG. 7.14. Cell walls in animal cells. Left: the outer covering of the ciliate protozoan *Paramecium,* made of complex, chitinlike organic materials. The dark dots represent tiny holes through which cilia project. Right: siliceous shells secreted around radiolarian protozoa. (General Biological Supply House, Inc.)

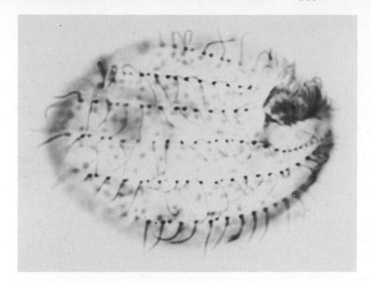

FIG. 7.15. The ciliate protozoan *Tetrahymena*, stained to show the cilia and their arrangement on the body surface. (Courtesy of Dr. Norman Williams, Iowa State University.)

The principal locomotor structures on the surfaces of cells are **cilia** and **flagella** (Fig. 7.15). Both are slender, filamentous projections, and both have similar internal structure. The electron microscope reveals each cilium or flagellum to be a complex bundle of exceedingly fine fibrils. Flagella are usually longer than cilia. A flagellate cell generally carries but one or a few flagella, but a ciliated cell may carry hundreds of cilia. Complex systems of special granules and fibrils, located just under the cell membrane, hold the filaments in place and control their motion. Cilia and flagella are found widely among single-celled organisms, where they are the major means of propulsion and of creating food-bearing currents in the external water environment. Cilia and flagella are also widespread among multicellular organisms. For example, the sperm cells of all but the most advanced plants move by means of flagella. Many embryos, larvae, and small adult animals move by means of ciliated skins. And many animal tissue cells, like those lining the ducts of the breathing and reproductive systems, possess ciliated surfaces (see Chaps. 14 and 25).

The cell surface as a whole maintains overall cell **shape.** If substantial cell walls are present, as in plants, cell shape tends to be more or less rigid. Otherwise, cells are deformable and plastic, but each nevertheless tends to assume a characteristic form. In many cases, such a form is prerequisite for a particular function. For example, muscle cells tend to be elongated, permitting contraction in a longitudinal direction. Nerve cells tend to be drawn out into long fibers, permitting conduction of nerve impulses over considerable distances. In other cases, cell shape as such may be relatively unimportant from a functional standpoint.

If the external environment is reasonably uniform all around a cell and offers little resistance to the expression of shape, then a cell will have a form dictated more or less entirely by the inherent properties of its protoplasm. This is very largely the case, for example, among single-celled organisms, most of which are suspended freely in water or air. A tremendous variety of different shapes is encountered here, each rather unique to a given species. Note, incidentally, that perfectly spherical cell shapes are virtually unknown.

But if the immediate environment around a cell is decidedly nonuniform or does offer resistance to the expression of shape, then the surface configuration of a cell will be affected accordingly.

This is often the case within tissues. For example, if like cells are packed tightly together, so that they make direct contact with one another, then the tissue so formed is called an **epithelium.** Tissues of this type form sheets and layers, as in skin, or compact three-dimensional aggregates, as in liver. Cell shapes in such epithelia are influenced considerably by the pressure of cells on one another. Cuboidal, prismatic, polyhedral shapes, wafer shapes, and other pressure configurations are common here (Fig. 7.16).

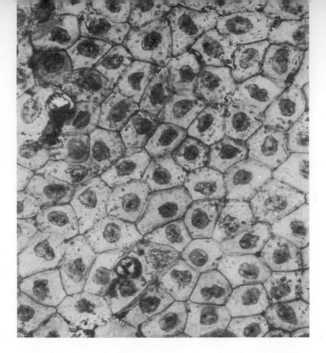

In another general type of tissue, the **connective tissue,** cells are separated from one another by relatively large amounts of intercellular material. For example, blood cells are dispersed in large quantities of fluid plasma. Bone cells are distributed like islands in solid calcium phosphate. The cells of several connective tissues are distributed through meshworks of tough and/or elastic fibers (Fig. 7.17). In tissues of this kind, expression of cellular form is restricted far less than in epithelia. Accordingly, the cells of connective tissues frequently exhibit disk shapes, star shapes, spindle shapes, and others which are determined predominantly by inherent protoplasmic properties (Fig. 7.18).

FIG. 7.17. Connective tissue. This is loose connective tissue, found, for example, under the skin and in many other body regions. Note the cells (small dark dots) embedded in extensive fiber meshworks. (General Biological Supply House, Inc.)

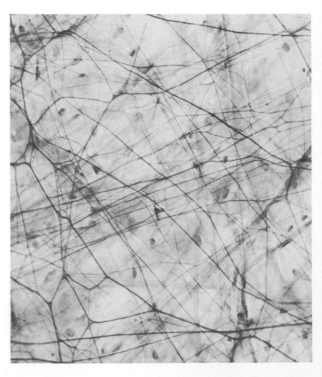

FIG. 7.16. Epithelia. Above: surface view of frog epidermis. Note the close packing of the cells and the angular cell outlines, produced by pressure of cells against one another. Below: section through an epithelium which forms a compact sheet many cell layers thick. (Ward's Natural Science Establishment, Inc.)

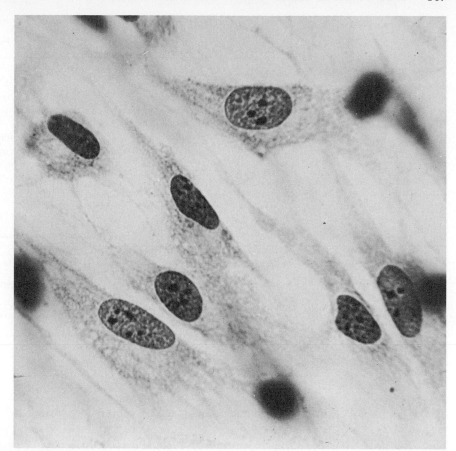

FIG. 7.18. Variations of cell shapes in connective tissues. Right: rat fibroblasts, connective tissue cells which are distinctly spindle-shaped. See also Fig. 3.12. Below: a single pigment cell, developed in connective tissue. Note the many filamentous extensions, characteristic of cells of this kind. (Pigment cell courtesy of Dr. Robert Brenner, Brown University.)

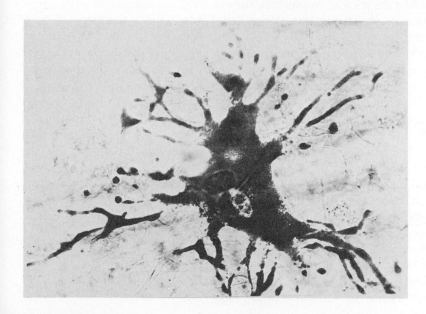

TABLE 3. Some structural components of cells and their correlated functions

Structure	Function
Nucleus	
Chromosomes	ultimate control of cell activities
Nucleolus	control of protein synthesis
Nuclear membrane	traffic control to and from cytoplasm
Cytoplasm	
Mitochondria	site of respiration
Microsomes	site of protein synthesis
Golgi bodies	site of secretion synthesis (?)
Chloroplasts	site of photosynthesis
Centrioles	auxiliary to cell division
Granules Vacuoles	transport, storage, processing centers
Fibrils	contraction, conduction
Surface	
Plasma membrane	traffic control to and from cell
Cell walls Cuticles	protection, support, cell shape
Cilia Flagella	locomotion, current creation

RESUME We have outlined some of the key structural features characteristic of cells generally. As we have seen, certain of the components of the nucleus, the cytoplasm, or the cell surface may be associated directly with well-circumscribed cell functions. Photosynthesis and respiration, for example, are distinct functions performed in distinct cytoplasmic structures. See Table 3 for a summary of such correlations. But many cell functions cannot be localized so neatly. For example, cellular reproduction requires the cooperative activity of many or all of the cell components present. Functions of this kind cannot be referred to any particular part of a cell, but only to the cell as a whole.

Note in this connection that, whereas many cell structures are bulky enough to be visible under the microscope, even more are not visible; individual molecules in a cell "function" no less than larger molecular aggregates. Note also that *each* cellular structure performs a function, and as the structures differ among cells, so do the functions.

Singly and in multiple combinations, and varied in structure by thousands of different specializations, cells form organisms. In nature, only whole organisms reflect the living potential of cells fully; being specialized in at least some measure, cells cannot normally function in isolation. And by virtue of being endowed with life by their component cells, whole organisms are able to exist in particular environments and are able to pursue specialized ways of life in such environments. In other words, organisms vary as their cells vary. We shall examine the nature of these organismic variations in the following two chapters.

1. What is the water content of cellular protoplasm? In this connection, review the biological roles of water, as outlined in Chaps. 2, 5, and 6. Apart from water, what other inorganic constituents occur in protoplasm, and in what forms?

2. What are organic compounds? What principal classes of these occur in protoplasm, and in what relative amounts? Which of them are electrolytes, and which are non-electrolytes?

3. Review the chemical composition and molecular structure of carbohydrates. What are monosaccharides, disaccharides, and polysaccharides? Give examples of each. What kinds of reactions may carbohydrates participate in, and what general roles do they play in protoplasm?

4. Review the chemical composition and molecular structure of fats. How do fats differ from waxes? What are esters? What is the chemical difference between tallows and oils? What general roles do lipids play in protoplasm?

5. What are proteins, and how are they constructed? In what ways do proteins differ from carbohydrates and fats? Discuss fully and carefully. What is protein specificity? How is a coagulated protein different from a native or a denatured protein? Review the general biological roles of proteins.

6. What is the chemical composition and molecular structure of nucleoproteins? In chemical terms, what are DNA and RNA? Where are these found in protoplasm, and what is their relation to nucleoproteins? How are nucleotides related to DNA and RNA? What different kinds of nucleotides occur in protoplasm?

7. What are the structural subdivisions of cells? What are the main components of each of these subdivisions, where are they found, and what functions do they carry out?

8. List cytoplasmic inclusions encountered in all cell types, and inclusions found only in certain cell types. What is cyclosis? How do the cytoplasms of plant and animal cells differ?

9. What structures are found on the surfaces of various cell types? Which of these structures are primarily protective? What do they protect against? What are the functions of other surface structures? How do the surfaces of plant and animal cells differ?

10. What determines cell shape? What is an epithelium? A connective tissue? Give specific examples.

Additional information on the chemical organization of protoplasm may be obtained in the following sources. The first book and the six subsequent articles are excellent semi-popular accounts, and the remaining three books are good standard texts.

Gerard, R. W.: "Unresting Cells," Harper, 1949.

Vallee, B. L.: The Function of Trace Elements in Biology, *Sci. Monthly,* vol. 72, 1951.

Buswell, A. M., and W. H. Rodebush: Water, *Sci. American,* vol. 194, 1956.

Fruton, J. S.: Proteins, *Sci. American,* vol. 182, 1950.

Linderstrom-Lang, K. U.: How Is a Protein Made? *Sci. American,* vol. 189, 1953.

Pauling, L., R. B. Corey, and R. Hayward: The Structure of Protein Molecules, *Sci. American,* vol. 191, 1954.

Thompson, E. O.: The Insulin Molecule, *Sci. American,* vol. 192, 1955.

Noller, C. R.: "Textbook of Organic Chemistry," Saunders, 1958.

Heilbrunn, L. V.: "An Outline of General Physiology," Saunders, 1952.

Tracey, M. V.: "Principles of Biochemistry," Pitman, 1954.

Important original articles on cells and the cell theory are reprinted and annotated in the following, a very good collection in which many other biological subjects are dealt with as well:

Gabriel, M. L., and S. Fogel (eds.): "Great Experiments in Biology," Prentice-Hall, 1955.

The microscopic organization of cells and tissues is discussed in the three standard texts listed first. The fourth book below, a classic, is too advanced for general study but may be consulted for selected readings and references.

DeRobertis, E. D. P., W. W. Nowinski, and F. A. Saez: "General Cytology," 2d ed., Saunders, 1954.

Greep, R. O.: "Histology," Blakiston–McGraw-Hill, 1954.

Maximov, A. A., and W. Bloom: "A Textbook of Histology," 6th ed., Saunders, 1952.

Wilson, E. B.: "The Cell in Development and Heredity," 3d ed., Macmillan, reprinted 1947.

THE
ORGANIZATION
OF PLANTS

PROBABLY THE MOST IMPORTANT STATEMENT WE, as members of the animal kingdom, can make about plants is that without them no animal could continue to exist. Through photosynthesis and other unique manufacturing processes, plants create the oxygen, the usable nitrogen, and the basic organic molecules vital to animal life, as well as to plant life itself. Moreover, plants and plant products provide shelter for countless animals, including man, and, in general, plants transform an otherwise bleak globe of rock and water into an earth inhabitable by animals.

What characteristics put plants into this key position? Specifically, how are plants organized structurally and functionally, and how is this organization adjusted to various environments? To answer this, we first consider the major **patterns of life** among plants as a whole. We then concentrate on the predominant pattern, that of the **green plant,** and examine the factors which affect the particular organization of this plant type. Lastly, we analyze the actual **internal structure** of a green plant in terms of its cells and tissues.

Patterns of Life

The fundamental criteria used to classify living organisms are *evolutionary relationships* and *structural similarities*. Thus, if two or more organisms share a long, common evolutionary history, and if they are therefore rather similar in basic structural features, then they are grouped together in a single category, distinct from other such categories. A species, for example, composed of related and structurally similar individuals, is a well-defined unit of classification. In their turn, related and structurally similar species may be classified into progressively more inclusive units. We shall hear about these in later chapters, but we may note here that the most inclusive units, representing the broad major types of plants and animals, are called *divisions* or **phyla.** A phylum is a group of all those species which, as far as is known, share a common evolutionary ancestry and feature the same basic body organization. As such, the species of one phylum are uniquely distinct from the species of any other phylum.

The particular phyla we shall be concerned with in this chapter are listed in Table 4. Together, they make up the *plant kingdom*. In Chap. 30 we shall discuss the distinctive characteristics and the various subgroups of each phylum. We may note here that the bacteria, and sometimes also the blue-green algae, often are not grouped in the plant kingdom, because their evolutionary history and their relationship to true plants are obscure. However, these two phyla are nevertheless more nearly allied to plants than to animals, and for this reason we shall include them in the present account.

Whatever phylum a plant belongs to, its mode of nutrition, more than any other factor, determines its character. Every plant, like every animal, must supply itself in some way with various inorganic and various organic materials. Such *nutrients* must be used in part as internal sources of energy and in part as building materials for the construction of protoplasm. According to *how* the nutrients are obtained, a plant is either an **autotroph** or a **heterotroph.**

An autotroph may subsist in an exclusively inorganic environment. That is, such an organism draws from its surroundings *only* inorganic nutrients. From some of these, it then manufactures by its own efforts all required organic nutrients. By contrast, a heterotroph must obtain inorganic as well as

a certain minimum of organic nutrients from the environment. It is unable to create organic substances out of inorganic ones. Hence it must procure *prefabricated* organic starting materials, for the manufacture of any other organic substances it may require (Fig. 8.1).

AUTOTROPHS

Autotrophic plants include the largest and most familiar group, the green or **photosynthetic** plants. If bacteria are left out of account, all plants except the fungi are photosynthetic. Directly or indirectly, these green plants create all the organic matter of virtually all living organisms. A second group of autotrophs comprises the **chemosynthetic** organisms, bacterial types which are independent of light.

Autotrophs of all kinds manufacture organic nutrients, or *foods*, according to the following general scheme:

$$CO_2 + H_2O \xrightarrow{E} \text{carbohydrates} + O_2 \uparrow$$

Carbon dioxide and water are absorbed from the environment, and with the aid of an external energy source (E), these inorganic nutrients are transformed into carbohydrates and molecular oxygen. The oxygen is a byproduct, and the carbohydrates are the foods from which all other organic components of protoplasm are then produced.

Photosynthesizers

In *photosynthetic* autotrophs, the external energy source is **light,** and **chlorophyll** is present to trap the energy of light. Thus, photosynthesizers are largely green, although in many cases other pigments are present which obscure, or mask, the color of chlorophyll. The food-producing pattern of green plants may be symbolized as follows:

$$\text{light} \rightarrow \text{chlorophyll}$$
$$CO_2 + H_2O \rightarrow \text{carbohydrates} + O_2 \uparrow$$

At least one group of bacteria is known to be photosynthetic too, namely, some of the **sulfur bacteria** (see also Chap. 2). Certain types of these bac-

---

TABLE 4. The main divisions of the plant kingdom*

Phylum *Schizophyta:* bacteria
Phylum *Myxophyta:* blue-green algae
Phylum *Chlorophyta:* green algae
Phylum *Chrysophyta:* diatoms, golden-brown algae
Phylum *Phaeophyta:* brown algae
Phylum *Rhodophyta:* red algae
Phylum *Mycophyta:* fungi
Phylum *Bryophyta:* mosses, liverworts
Phylum *Tracheophyta:* ferns, seed plants (coniferous plants, flowering plants)

---

* The first, and in many cases the first two, of the phyla listed often are not included within the plant kingdom (see text).

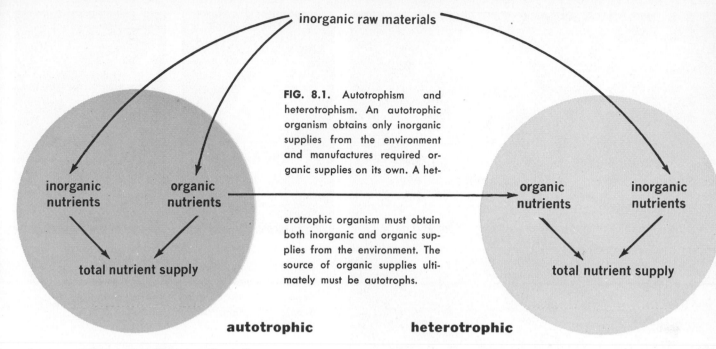

FIG. 8.1. Autotrophism and heterotrophism. An autotrophic organism obtains only inorganic supplies from the environment and manufactures required organic supplies on its own. A heterotrophic organism must obtain both inorganic and organic supplies from the environment. The source of organic supplies ultimately must be autotrophs.

teria are purple in color. Photosynthetic bacteria are distinguished from other photosynthetic autotrophs in that they do not use water, but *hydrogen sulfide* (H_2S), for carbohydrate manufacture:

$$\text{light} \rightarrow \text{chlorophyll}$$
$$CO_2 + H_2S \xrightarrow{\quad\downarrow\quad} \text{carbohydrates} + (S_2 \text{ or } H_2SO_4)$$

Not oxygen, but in some cases free sulfur, in others sulfuric acid, is the byproduct here.

We may note in passing that certain green plants have evolved auxiliary methods of supplementing their photosynthetic nutrition through animal-like bulk feeding. Instances of this are found among tracheophytes, e.g., the insect-catching Venus's-flytrap (Fig. 8.2). Similar examples are provided by a number of green, single-celled, flagellated organisms of the phylum *Mastigophora* (see Chap. 30). These photosynthesize like algae, but they also possess gullets, and when light is too dim or absent, they may feed on bulk food like protozoa. Therefore, these organisms may be described either as protozoalike algae or as algaelike protozoa, and they are classified in neither the plant nor the animal kingdom, or else in both.

Chemosynthesizers

Chemosynthetic autotrophs are nongreen. They are bacteria which obtain energy for carbohydrate manufacture not from light but from a variety of inorganic substances absorbed as nutrients:

$$\text{inorganic nutrients} (+ \text{ oxygen}) \rightarrow E + \text{inorganic byproducts}$$
$$CO_2 + H_2O \xrightarrow{\quad\downarrow\quad} \text{carbohydrates} + O_2 \uparrow$$

As indicated, the energy-yielding reactions are largely processes in which inorganic nutrient molecules are combined with oxygen. The byproducts are excreted, and the energy is used toward carbohydrate manufacture.

Among the best-known chemosynthesizers are the **hydrogen bacteria,** the nonphotosynthetic **sulfur bacteria,** the **iron bacteria,** and the **nitrifying bacteria.** Hydrogen bacteria use molecular hydrogen as nutrient, and they obtain energy by converting the hydrogen into water:

$$H_2 + O \rightarrow H_2O + E$$

Sulfur and iron bacteria use simple compounds of sulfur and iron as energy-yielding nutrients.

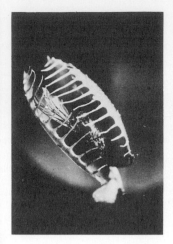

FIG. 8.2. Venus's-flytrap. Left, a group of traps in various states of closure. Right, fly enters a trap and is caught. (Left, Carolina Biological Supply Co.; right, General Biological Supply House, Inc.)

Nitrifying bacteria are of two types. One absorbs ammonia (NH_3) and produces *nitrite* ions (NO_2^-) as byproducts, and the other uses the nitrite ions so formed and produces *nitrate* ions (NO_3^-):

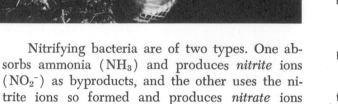

$$NH_3 + O \rightarrow E + NO_2^- \quad \text{nitrite ion}$$
$$NO_2^- + O \rightarrow E + NO_3^- \quad \text{nitrate ion}$$

As noted in Chap. 5, ammonia may be obtained from decaying plants and animals. Some of this ammonia is then transformed to NO_3^-, as above, by the combined activities of the nitrifying bacteria.

Inasmuch as nitrate ions can be absorbed directly by green plants, nitrifying bacteria are a vital link in the global nitrogen cycle; they make possible the return to living matter of some of the nitrogen lost from once-living matter through decay (see Chap. 5). Note, however, that the important product for the bacteria is not nitrate, which is a byproduct, but *E*, energy, which is used toward the manufacture of bacterial carbohydrates. Note, moreover, that some of the **denitrifying bacteria,** which convert nitrates back to ammonia and also to free N_2, may live as chemosynthetic autotrophs too.

HETEROTROPHS

These include all nonautotrophic bacteria and the fungi. As heterotrophs, they must obtain from the environment not only inorganic nutrients but also prefabricated organic ones. They do so either as **symbionts** or as **saprophytes.**

Symbionts

Bacteria and fungi which pursue a *symbiotic* way of life live in intimate physical association with living plant or animal hosts. In some cases, symbiosis takes the form of commensalism or mutualism. For example, as already noted in Chap. 4, commensalistic bacteria live in the alimentary tract of many animals, and *lichens* are mutualistic associations of fungi and algae. But most symbiotic bacteria and fungi are *parasites*, infectious and variously disease-producing. Many of them are more or less familiar to everyone from personal experience.

In all these instances, bacterial or fungal symbionts obtain inorganic and organic nutrients from the protoplasm of their hosts (Fig. 8.3). The nutritional process is exceedingly direct: the symbiont trans-

FIG. 8.3. Symbionts and saprophytes. A symbiont obtains nutritional supplies from a living host organism. A saprophyte obtains required supplies from dead, decaying organisms.

symbiotic (parasitic)   **saprophytic**

fers nutrient molecules from host protoplasm into its own body, by **absorption** through its cell surfaces. Specific food requirements vary greatly. For example, one bacterial parasite may have to obtain a given vitamin or amino acid in prefabricated form, but another may be able to manufacture such a nutrient from other organic starting materials. Biochemical differences of this sort are exceedingly numerous, and they are one reason why a symbiotic bacterium or fungus cannot pick hosts at random. Survival is possible only in hosts in which all required types of nutrients are available.

Saprophytes

Heterotrophic bacteria and fungi which are nonsymbiotic are *saprophytic*. Saprophytes are free-living, and they subsist on *dead* protoplasm or on protoplasmic derivatives: dead plants and animals; dung, sewage, and other elimination products; and protoplasmic materials such as milk, bread, leather, etc. Saprophytes decompose such organic matter chemically and absorb nutrient molecules from the resulting juices (Fig. 8.3). Thus, saprophytic bacteria and fungi bring about **decay**.

As a result of their decay-causing nutritional activities, saprophytes are vital links in global nutrient cycles. For the final decomposition products of decaying organic matter are H_2O, CO_2, and N_2, materials which return to the environment from which living matter obtained them originally (see Chap. 5). In particular, the heterotrophic saprophytes include three of the groups of organisms which contribute to nitrogen turnover (Fig. 8.4). First, decay-causing bacteria and fungi liberate ammonia (NH_3) from decomposing organic matter. Second, some of the *denitrifying* bacteria may live as heterotrophs. As noted, these convert nitrates into ammonia, and ammonia into N_2, gaseous nitrogen which escapes into the atmosphere. And third, compensating for this loss of nitrogen, the heterotrophic *nitrogen-fixing* bacteria may incorporate aerial nitrogen into the structure of complex organic substances (see the nitrogen cycle, Chap. 5).

Figure 8.5 summarizes the ways of life of plants according to their autotrophic or heterotrophic char-

FIG. 8.4. Heterotrophs contributing to nitrogen turnover. Decay causers (largely certain bacteria and fungi) liberate ammonia from dead protoplasm. Denitrifying bacteria produce more ammonia from nitrates and convert ammonia into molecular nitrogen. Nitrogen-fixing bacteria may incorporate molecular atmospheric nitrogen into the structure of their protoplasm.

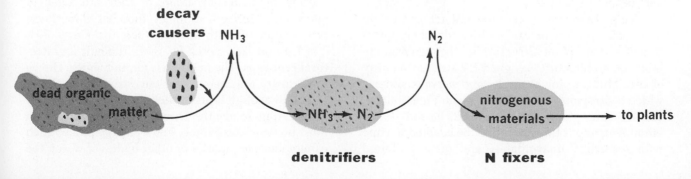

nongreen			green
heterotrophic		**autotrophic**	
Symbiotic:	Saprophytic:	Chemosynthetic:	Photosynthetic:
bacteria	bacteria	bacteria	bacteria
fungi	fungi		algae
			bryophytes
			tracheophytes

FIG. 8.5. The distribution of nutritional patterns among bacteria and plants. Note that most plants are green and photosynthetic.

acter. We now proceed to a more detailed discussion of the predominant way of life among plants, i.e., the way of the *green* plant, or, more precisely, the nonbacterial photosynthetic autotroph.

The Green Plant

As noted, green plants include the various algal phyla, the bryophytes, and the tracheophytes. Two ways of life are broadly characteristic of the group as a whole: the way of the aquatic alga, typified by the microscopic diatom, which drifts passively in the surface waters of the sea; and the way of the terrestrial tracheophyte, typified by the familiar upright tree or herb.

In both environments, required inorganic nutrients are in ample supply. Indeed, the green autotroph is virtually embedded in raw materials. It may therefore absorb nutrients on the spot and need not hunt for them. Thus, active locomotion should not, and in the vast majority of cases actually does not, become necessary.

This absence of a requirement for propulsion affects the entire structural and functional organization of a green plant. Structurally, the organism exhibits an architecture designed for a stationary way of life. Muscles, for example, and nervous systems which control muscles are not present. Functionally, the stationary plant cannot escape its immediate environment, and it therefore must be adapted to cope with recurring, unavoidable, and often profound

changes in local climate. We shall consider here some of these architectural and climatic adaptations of green plants.

ARCHITECTURAL ADAPTATIONS

The Plant Body

A water plant is limited either to a sessile life, anchored to bottom mud or rock, or to a life of passive floating in surface waters. As we have seen in Chap. 5, the required sunlight penetrates only into the top layers of water. Hence shallow regions or shore lines may harbor both attached and floating plants, but in the deep open water of the sea and of large lakes, only floating plants may occur.

Inasmuch as protoplasm is slightly heavier than water, a passive surface existence is possible only if an organism is small enough and light enough to be buoyed up, or if it has expanded surfaces and/or air bladders to keep it afloat. As noted in Chap. 5, floaters meet these simple architectural requirements. Either the plants are microscopic single-celled algae floating by buoyancy alone, or they are algae of many cells, formed variously into flat thin sheets often equipped with air sacs (see also Chap. 30).

Life on land poses far more difficult architectural problems. The medium is air, not water. Hence the primary requirement for terrestrial life is ability to obtain enough liquid water and to guard against evaporating to death. Directly or indirectly, rain must be the water source. For a passive plant which cannot move to puddles or other bodies of water, the only good, relatively steady source of rain water is the ground. Moreover, the ground is the only good usable source of required mineral substances. More or less permanent association with **soil** is therefore mandatory for the vast majority of terrestrial plants.

Certain of the algae have adapted successfully to a terrestrial, ground-associated existence. Indeed, algae, along with bacteria and fungi, have probably led the evolutionary way from ocean to fresh water, and from fresh water to land. But algal life on land, though widespread, is still essentially aquatic; drops of mineral-rich water in soil and in other shaded, moist places simply serve the algal cell in the manner of a tiny pond.

Truly terrestrial living for a green plant clearly requires architectural adaptation to a two-phase environment. Some raw materials can be obtained only from below ground; others, and sunlight, only from above ground. It follows that a portion of the plant must be surrounded by soil, another by air, and a third portion must necessarily interconnect the two, structurally as well as functionally. Unlike an alga, the well-adapted terrestrial plant therefore should possess several *differently* specialized body parts; i.e., it should be complexly multicellular. And the body parts should be structured *vertically*. The familiar subdivision of most tracheophytes into **root, leaf,** and **stem** reflects this requirement. Since soil and air extend horizontally in every direction, a **radial symmetry** around the vertical axis will be of greatest advantage. Cylindrical stems and horizontally balanced leaf and root systems actually predominate.

Surfaces are necessary for the absorption of raw materials. For a given mass of absorbing tissue, the best architectural arrangement consequently is that which offers the largest area. Indeed, roots are most often highly branched, rather than thick and compact; and leaves, similarly, are flat and thin, or needle-shaped. A large surface is also required for illumination by sunlight. However, the sun is not stationary but arcs over the sky every day. A given mass of stationary light-receiving tissue will therefore be illuminated most if it is flat and thin, if it is subdivided into many small plates, and if these are set at many different angles. Foliage is actually so disposed that the largest number of leaves receives the greatest amount of sunshine, for the longest possible period (see Fig. 8.6). Leaves are fairly widely spaced, in largely nonobstructing formations. In many plants, leaves turn toward the sun if the heat is not too great or turn away from the sun if it is too strong. Another well-known adaptation is the ability of plants to grow toward the light, even if they are planted away from it (see also Chap. 19).

However, large surfaces for illumination and absorption also constitute large surfaces for evaporation. To protect against drying out, exposed leaves, and green stems where present, secrete waxy coats which cover the aerial surfaces. These transparent

FIG. 8.6. View of a maple forest, illustrating how the foliage of trees is arranged to provide maximum exposure to sunlight. No one tree completely obstructs the other, and no leaf, similarly, completely obstructs another. (U.S. Forest Service.)

cuticles let sunlight through readily, and they prevent the escape of internal water. But in so doing they also bar the entry of gases from the atmosphere. Yet carbon dioxide and oxygen must be absorbed. The dilemma is resolved by the development of microscopic surface openings, called **stomata** (see below). Distributed in considerable numbers over green tissues, these openings permit absorption of raw materials and permit also a certain amount of evaporation. But the greater part of the tissue is protected by wax, and a large surface is still available for illumination. Waxy surfaces are additionally advantageous in that they allow rain or dew to run off. Thus foliage acts as a gathering system, deflecting water into soil surrounding the plant. Can you think of adaptive reasons why waxy coats are *not* present on roots?

Internal Support and Conduction

An upright body structure on land introduces other design problems. First, an organism without the buoying action of a water environment is affected greatly by gravity. And second, water must be *lifted* from the ground source to the uppermost body parts. Some of the early multicellular plants which colonized the land, i.e., the bryophytes, evidently could not effectively solve these problems. They were, and their descendants today largely still are, small flat ground huggers, not tall and upright. Being spread out along the ground surface, bryophytes circumvent much of the gravity problem and the requirement of lifting water high. But the cost of this conservatism is lack of spectacular success on land. For the dominant land plants today are the tracheophytes, the ferns and seed plants, which did develop an antigravity and a water-lifting mechanism, along with the advantageous vertical body architecture.

The elements of such mechanisms are present in every plant tissue. Cells are *succulent;* that is, the protoplasm contains much water. This water is confined by cellulose cell walls and presses against them. It thus prevents cells from collapsing, just as air prevents an inflated rubber balloon from collapsing. In other words, **turgor** is great. And a closely packed aggregation of turgid cells is both *rigid* and *pliable*. Hence even "soft" plant parts like leaves can maintain their shape well and can resist gravity so long as internal water remains abundant (Fig. 8.7). But if the water evaporates, succulence, turgor, rigidity, and pliability all disappear, and the plant wilts.

This generalized property of plant tissues to resist gravity has become accentuated in tracheophytes through specialization. As we shall see, some of the cells in the stem secrete particularly heavy cellulose walls. These may be further strengthened by impregnation with various materials, for example, inorganic silicon-containing substances, or a manufactured organic substance called *lignin*. A vertical column of such cells becomes a strong, stiff rod, which can maintain its shape even if all internal water is removed. Moreover, if the horizontal cellular cross walls of such a column are removed wholly or partially, a hard cellulose *tube* would remain which could serve ideally in transporting water up and down the stem. In just this manner have tracheophytes developed an antigravity and a water-conducting mechanism; tissue cells give rise to reinforced cellulose tubes which both support and conduct (Fig. 8.8). In the largest tracheophytes, bulk collections of such tubes, cemented to one another in parallel, are well known under the name *wood*.

With wood available for support and conduction, correlated architectural adaptations can be de-

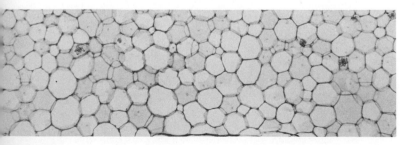

FIG. 8.7. Section through a tissue of a plant (stem pith). Note the close packing of the cells and the angular boundaries. This arrangement is produced by turgor; i.e., the cells are highly succulent, and their water content tends to enlarge them to the maximum. This presses the cells firmly against one another and gives the whole tissue rigidity. (General Biological Supply House, Inc.)

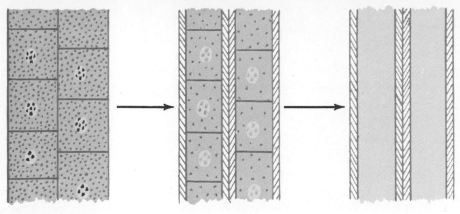

FIG. 8.8. Formation of wood. In columns of cells (tracheids) the vertical parts of the cellulose walls thicken, and the horizontal parts disintegrate. The protoplasm of the cells disintegrates also. Continuous vertical tubes (xylem vessels) are thus formed, which in bulk are called wood.

veloped. For example, a highly branched, radially symmetrical root system will be advantageous not only in providing large absorption surfaces, but also in providing broad, balanced anchorage. The plant also comes to taper upward, the greater weight thus resting on the stronger foundation. And the size of the plant need be limited only by the inherent strength of wood. Wood is, in fact, a more efficient supporting material than animal skeletons; woody plants include the largest organisms of all, living or extinct animals not excepted.

We note how the overall design of the well-adapted tracheophyte has been shaped and molded by the requirements of an autotrophic, stationary way of life in a terrestrial environment. Given soil, sun, and gravity on the one hand, and autotrophism and sessilism on the other, then the general form and architecture of a tree or an herb become almost necessarily the most efficient answer to these specifications. Some tracheophytes, like water lilies and many shore plants, have reverted secondarily to life in water. Yet such plants still reveal their terrestrial origin through their basically land-adapted architecture. As we have seen, algae which live on land analogously still reveal their aquatic origin through a basically water-adapted architecture. It is because of their specific structural adaptations that trees do not grow in the ocean, nor seaweeds in the jungle.

A suitable body design is the first structural requirement for the stationary way of life of the green plant. The first functional requirements are adaptations protecting against potentially lethal changes in local weather.

CLIMATIC ADAPTATIONS

As noted in Chap. 5, the surface waters of the sea do experience "weather," but the climatic changes are not nearly so profound as on land. In winter the water becomes cold, but the salts of the ocean prevent freezing. Only ice could harm the alga; cold merely reduces the rate of metabolic processes. Storms may churn the sea surface at any time during the year, but the scale of such upheavals is far too large to affect the microscopic alga; the organism simply drifts along with any movement of the water. And what on land would be scorching summer heat becomes mild warmth in the sea, not in any way detrimental to the vegetation. The aquatic plant evidently does not require, and it does not possess, special weatherproofing devices.

The situation is far different on land. A rooted terrestrial plant cannot escape heat or ice. Water poses the key problem. In summer the plant is in danger of having too little water, because of increased evaporation. And in winter there is likely to be too much internal water, for water freezes and kills.

Protection against Heat

The summer problem is one of **water conservation.** This problem is solved in various ways. In warm dry climates, for example, the wax cuticles over exposed surfaces may attain considerable thickness. Stomata are often reduced in number. They may be placed preferentially on the undersides of leaves, where shade and somewhat lower temperatures re-

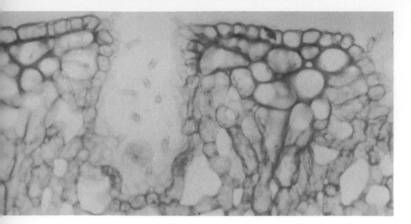

FIG. 8.9. Under desert and near-desert conditions, the stomata of a plant may be located at the bottom of microscopic pits in the leaf surface, as illustrated in this photo. Many desert plants in addition possess very thick wax cuticles (not shown here) secreted by the cells of the leaf epidermis. (Courtesy of J. M. Bell, Polytechnic Institute of Brooklyn.)

duce evaporation, and where dust is not so likely to clog them. Or they may be situated deep in microscopic leaf-surface pits, which provide shade except when the sun shines straight into them (Fig. 8.9).

Under near-desert conditions, the rate of evaporation may nevertheless be too great. Water vaporization can be held down, however, by reducing the *area* of exposed parts. In persistently dry regions, plants may possess fewer leaves (palms) or succulent, bulky, water-storing leaves (as in many ornamental house plants); and stems may grow underground or may be much decreased in size. Or, as in cacti, leaves may be represented merely by thorny spines, and massive stems take over the function of food manufacture (Fig. 8.10).

Through adaptations such as these, plants are able to survive even in the hottest, driest regions,

provided that at least *some* water is available at *some* time. As noted earlier, many terrestrial plants have adapted secondarily to a water habitat; for these, the water-conservation problem is virtually nonexistent.

A summer day may be excessively hot and dry, and the terrestrial plant may droop and begin to wilt. But if the following day brings moisture, conditions within the organism are soon restored to normal. By contrast, winter frost for even an hour is likely to kill. Below the freezing point, water which is not firmly bound in colloidal gels is transformed into ice crystals. Such crystals tear and disrupt the protoplasmic molecular framework. Therein lies the lethal effect of cold.

FIG. 8.10. A variety of cacti—plants adapted to desert conditions. Leaves are reduced to spines, and the green stems have taken over the function of food manufacture and water storage. (General Biological Supply House, Inc.)

Protection against Cold

In response to seasonally recurrent low temperatures, major adaptations have developed in land plants which profoundly affect their whole way of life. On the basis of these adaptations, we may distinguish three groups of tracheophytes: *perennials, biennials,* and *annuals.* The first group includes *woody* plants (ferns, trees, and shrubs) and some of the *herbaceous* forms (soft-stemmed herbs). The second and third groups comprise all other herbaceous plants.

In **perennials,** major portions of the plant body persist through successive winters. Icing up is reduced or prevented altogether. At the approach of winter, such plants excrete a considerable amount of water, and they thereby dehydrate themselves partially. Moreover, large quantities of colloidal gums and resins are manufactured. This loss of water, coupled with increase in the amount of colloid particles, converts much of plant protoplasm into a gel state. As a result, little water remains free inside cells, and freezing is successfully forestalled.

In coniferous evergreens like pines, such winterproofing, or **winter-hardening,** is particularly effective. Even leaves can be retained, and vital processes carry on as in summer, though at a slower pace.

The other woody perennials, called *deciduous* plants (e.g., flowering trees), cannot protect their foliage against the cold. Leaves are shed in the fall, but the rest of the organism lives on. Tiny leaf buds, developed during the preceding summer, blossom forth in the spring as new foliage. In the absence of mature leaves during the cold season, food cannot be produced. However, these woody types accumulate food reserves at other seasons and store them in root and stem.

In herbaceous perennials (e.g., asparagus, dandelion), both leaves and stem die off in the fall, and only the roots survive. Where the root branches join together, just under the soil surface, there is usually a nubbin of stem which survives the winter also, along with the roots. Reserve food in the roots lasts through the winter and suffices in spring for the development of a little green tissue. Thereafter, new stem and leaf systems sprout rapidly. Since they persist only through a relatively short growing season, the aerial portions of these plants never become very extensive. Bulky supporting wood is neither required nor formed, and roots stay relatively small.

The above patterns (Fig. 8.11) give evidence of an adaptive trend among perennials; it is more

FIG. 8.11. The perennial patterns among plants. In one pattern, as in conifers (left), the whole plant survives the winter. In another pattern, as in deciduous plants (middle), foliage is shed in the cold season, but the rest of the plant survives. And in a third pattern, as in herbaceous perennials (right), only the roots and a nubbin of stem survive the winter.

evergreen   **deciduous**   **herbaceous perennial**

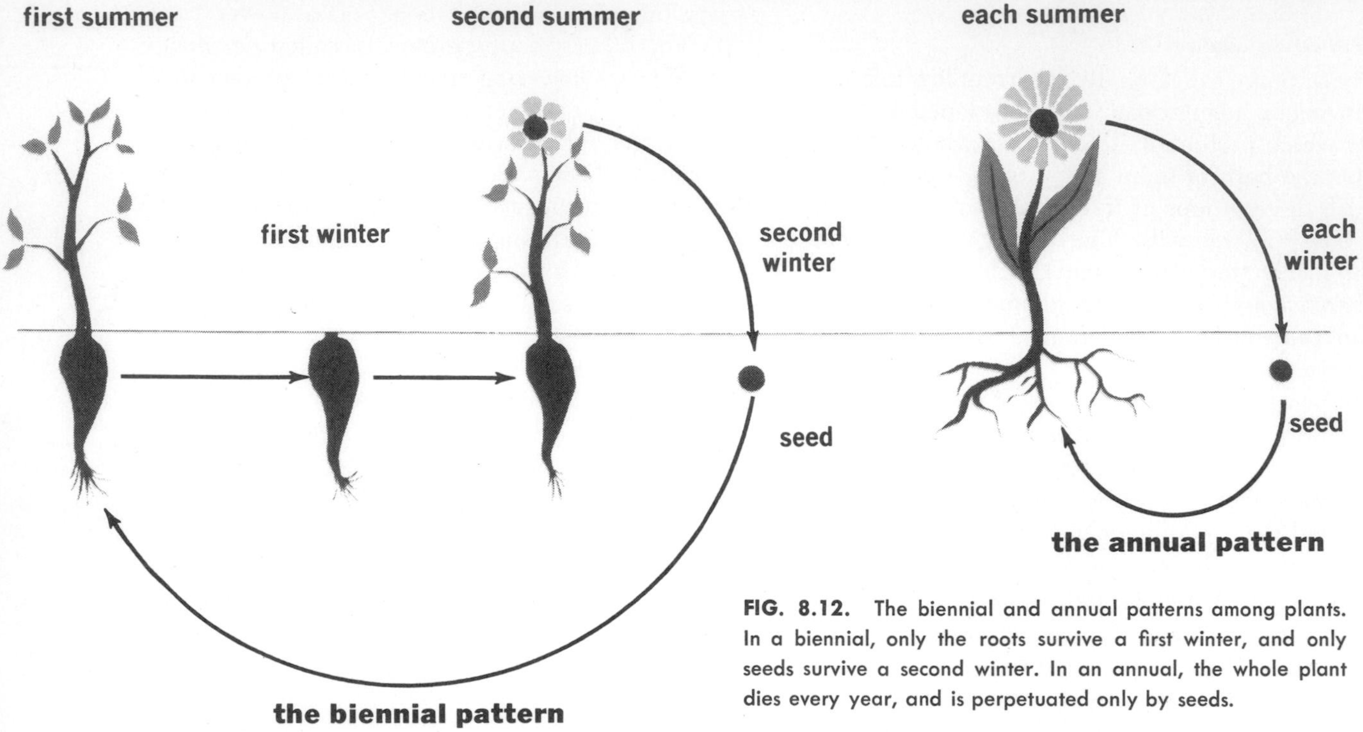

first summer   second summer   each summer

first winter

second
winter

each
winter

seed

seed

the biennial pattern

the annual pattern

FIG. 8.12.   The biennial and annual patterns among plants. In a biennial, only the roots survive a first winter, and only seeds survive a second winter. In an annual, the whole plant dies every year, and is perpetuated only by seeds.

economical to retrench when life becomes difficult than to maintain elaborate aerial superstructures against heavy odds. This trend does not halt here, however. Winter retrenchment goes even farther in biennial and annual herbaceous plants.

In **biennials** (e.g., carrot), leaves and stem die off in a first winter, after procuring extensive food reserves which are stored in bulky roots. The roots survive that winter, and from them develops a new plant in the following spring. This second-year plant flowers, reproduces, and forms seed. At the approach of the second winter, the entire plant dies, roots included. Only the seeds survive, and these subsequently initiate a new 2-year cycle (Fig. 8.12).

The **annual** plant (e.g., wheat, corn) flowers and produces seed every year. The whole plant dies in the fall, and its seeds give rise to a new generation in the following spring (Fig. 8.12).

The immobile land plant, we note, finds several workable solutions to the problem of cold. It may winterproof its whole body, a larger or a smaller part of its body, or it may rely entirely, and most economically, on a handful of hardy cells; seeds, which

often contain as little as 5 per cent water, are even hardier than the hardiest Christmas tree.

Thus, very elegantly, tracheophytes have made the most of their difficult environment. Actually only two climatic extremes can stop the flourishing of the terrestrial plant: glacial temperatures, as at very high altitudes and latitudes, and permanent lack of water, as in some deserts. And where the food-producing green plant cannot live, very little else can live.

Internal Structure

The historic transition from the aquatic algal to the terrestrial tracheophytic way of life has been accompanied, and has been made possible, by a parallel transition from a unicellular to a complexly multicellular body organization. Just how are the many cells of a tracheophyte put together into an integrated, functioning organism?

We begin with a discussion of stems, for more than the leaf or the root, the stem is the distinctive hallmark of the tracheophyte. A violet, a bamboo, and an apple tree are quite obviously different. And of all their differences, those of their stems are the most pronounced.

STEMS: WOODY TYPES

Imagine that the seed of a woody plant has germinated just recently and that a young *seedling* has become anchored in soil. A *shoot* already projects above ground and will later develop into a mature stem. The shoot carries one or more leaves, the **cotyledons,** which have developed within the seed during embryonic stages (Fig. 8.13). Food, photosynthesized or stored by the cotyledons, nourishes the seedling until mature foliage begins to appear. Then the cotyledons shrivel and drop off.

Transformation of the seedling into a tree or shrub involves growth in *length,* growth in *thickness,* and *branching* growth.

In these growth processes, increase of cell number is brought about almost entirely by the repeated division of cells in the **meristem** tissues. These are present in circumscribed regions and are composed of permanently embryonic cells. The new cells formed by division specialize, form adult tissues, and normally do not divide thereafter. Only the meristem cells retain a high division potential.

Growth in Length

One meristem region, the **apical shoot meristem,** is situated at the shoot tip. When an embryonic tip cell divides, one of the daughter cells remains in the space originally occupied by the mother cell; the other daughter cell is pushed ahead. Thus the tip advances, and the shoot grows in length. The youngest part of the plant consequently is at the upper stem terminal; the oldest part, at the stem base.

Newly formed cells below the advancing meri-

FIG. 8.13. Bean seedlings from recently germinated seeds. Note the rootlets, the white shoots (young stems), and on each shoot the two oval cotyledons. A pair of tiny leaves is developing between the cotyledons. (U.S. Department of Agriculture.)

stem tip divide frequently. Just below the tip, therefore, a **zone of division** is found (Fig. 8.14). Soon most of these cells specialize; the zone of division first becomes a **zone of elongation,** then a **zone of specialization,** and new zones of division and elongation appear above it.

FIG. 8.14. The lengthwise development of a growing shoot. The condition depicted in **A** changes to that of **B** after a period of growth. Note how any given zone transforms into that originally below it.

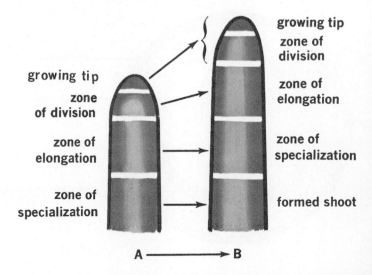

At the level of the specialization zone, a concentric pattern of cellular development is in evidence. From the outside to the center (Fig. 8.15), this development pattern is as follows:

1. Surface cells flatten out and secrete an external waxy coat. A transparent skin, the **epidermis**, arises in this manner. Made of a single layer of cells, this tissue becomes continuous with the epidermis of lower stem levels, laid down at earlier stages. Some of the epidermis cells take part in the formation of stomata, microscopic openings for gas exchange, as on leaves.

2. Cells just underneath the newly formed skin, in the **cortex** of the stem, specialize as a space-filling "packing" tissue, the **parenchyma.** The outer layers of this tissue develop chlorophyll and the metabolic machinery for food production. All the shoot below the specialization zone appears green therefore, and this portion of the shoot aids materially in the nutrition of the young seedling.

3. Still farther inward, we find a single-layered ring of cells which does not specialize but remains permanently meristematic; the advancing tip has left behind a cylindrical tube of embryonic cells. This tissue, the **cambium,** reaches right down to the stem base and is, in fact, continuous with a rather similar cylinder of cells left behind by the oppositely advancing root tip.

4. Cells ringed in by the cambium develop into parenchymal tissue too. These cells do not become green, however, but enlarge, absorb considerable amounts of water, and may store food reserves. This core tissue of the stem constitutes the **pith.**

At any level below the specialization zone the young shoot exhibits this basic cross-sectional pattern.

Increase in length, resulting from divisions of the tip meristem, is termed **primary growth.** Increase in thickness, **secondary growth,** occurs soon after the seedling has germinated. This phase of development requires the activity of the cambium.

Growth in Thickness

Being embryonic, cambium cells divide frequently. Newly formed cells are expelled from the cambial layer: one daughter cell takes the place of the original mother cell within the cambium; the other daughter cell is pushed either to the inside or to the outside of the cambial tube. We may visualize how the cambium as a whole produces now a cylinder of cells adjacent to it on the inside, then a cylinder adjacent to it on the outside. These newly formed tubes push against the tissues already there. The newest inner cylinder tends to compress all earlier ones, as well as the pith parenchyma. Analogously, new outer cylinders displace to the outside all cambium-derived tissues which had formed earlier, and parenchymal cortex and epidermis as well (Fig. 8.16).

Since the base of the shoot is oldest, cambial activity in this region has gone on for a longer period than elsewhere in the stem. The basal part of the stem therefore is thickest, and this head start is never lost. Hence the familiar upward taper of trees.

The cylinders of cells produced by the cambium to the inside and outside develop into *supporting* and *transporting* tissues, called the **vascular tissues** of the plant.

Cells pushed to the *inside* are known as tra-

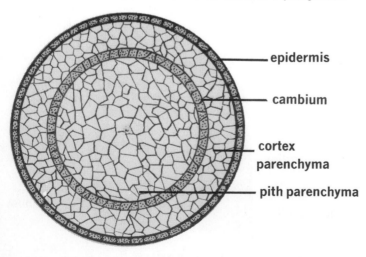

FIG. 8.15.   The basic pattern of cross-sectional specialization of the tissues in a young shoot.

epidermis

cambium

cortex parenchyma

pith parenchyma

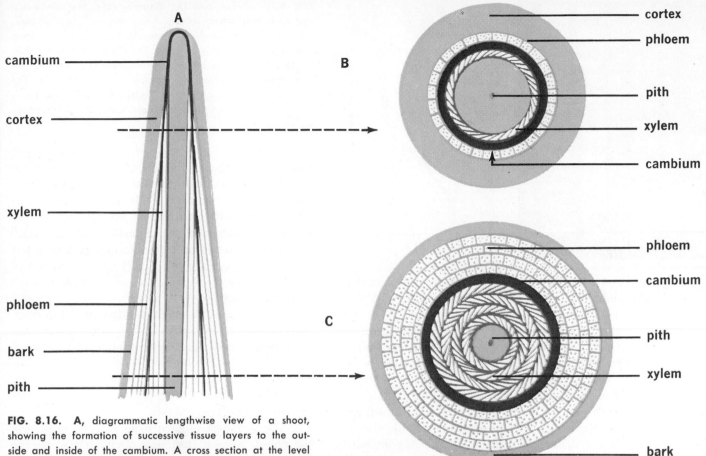

FIG. 8.16. A, diagrammatic lengthwise view of a shoot, showing the formation of successive tissue layers to the outside and inside of the cambium. A cross section at the level of the upper broken line would appear as in **B;** at the level of the lower broken line, as in **C.**

cheids. These secrete particularly heavy cellulose side walls, which also become impregnated with **lignin,** a complex carbohydrate-derived reinforcing substance. However, at a number of points along the surface of a tracheid, lignified reinforcing cellulose is not secreted. Round or oval **pits** are left here, through which water and nutrients may pass easily (Fig. 8.17). Pits develop in such a manner that those of one tracheid are directly apposed against those of an adjacent tracheid. In this way, nutrients may be conducted up or down, or laterally, from one tracheid into the next.

In ferns and conifers, the protoplasm of tracheids soon disintegrates, and only the hollow, pit-

ted cell walls remain. In flowering trees, the top and bottom walls of the tracheids disintegrate in addition. In these plants, therefore, an initial vertical column of tracheids eventually gives rise to a continuous, hollow, nonliving tube of cellulose, called a **xylem vessel** (Fig. 8.18). Such vessels extend uninterruptedly through the length of the stem, and they grow up as the stem as a whole grows up; new sections of tube are added at the upper end when younger tracheids, newly formed by cambium, lose their protoplasm and contribute their cellulose walls.

Viewed in bulk, a large collection of xylem vessels, or of hollow tracheids in ferns and conifers, constitutes **wood.** Its cellulose-lignin composition supports the plant against gravity, and its vertical channels conduct materials absorbed by the roots

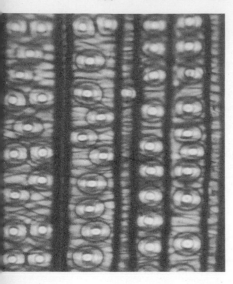 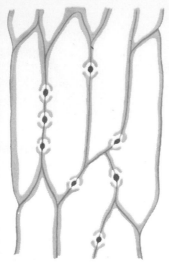

FIG. 8.17. Xylem pits. The diagram shows how pits would appear in longitudinal section. A few tracheids are illustrated, and the thin pit membranes provide lateral pathways from one tracheid to an adjacent one. The thickening in the middle of the pit membrane serves as a stopper, which prevents the membrane from ballooning out too far to either side. The photo depicts a section through the wood of a fir, and shows the xylem pits in surface view. (Photo, General Biological Supply House, Inc.)

into the leaves. The youngest wood is closest to the cambium, i.e., nearest the stem surface; and the oldest wood is closest to the stem core. As more and more xylem vessels develop in the young seedling, they press increasingly against the central pith. Turgid with water, this tissue withstands the pressure. Xylem therefore can only expand outward, and this increases the thickness of the stem.

Cells pushed to the *outside* of cambium form **phloem** tissue. In the development of this tissue, cells in every other vertical column disintegrate partially; that is, the nuclei and some of the cytoplasm break down. Moreover, the top and bottom cellulose walls of these cells develop fine perforations. The perforated cross walls are then known as *sieve*

plates. A vertical column of such sieve-plate-equipped, partially disintegrated cells is termed a **sieve tube.** Alternating with the sieve tubes, and in intimate association with them, are columns of normal cells, called **companion cells.** They probably control the functioning of adjacent, nonnucleated sieve-tube protoplasm (Fig. 8.19). The function of phloem is downward and upward conduction of organic nutrients.

We note that both vascular tissues of the stem, namely, xylem and phloem, develop through the more or less complete disintegration of the protoplasm in vertical columns of cells and the more or less complete retention of the cellulose walls, which form tubes. Hence the designation "tracheophyte," or "tube-possessing" plant.

The youngest phloem is nearest the cambium; the oldest, nearest the outer stem surface. As the diameter of the shoot increases because of the outward expansion of xylem and phloem, the epidermis and the green cortex parenchyma rupture. Older phloem may come to protrude through the fissures. Under the drying influence of air, the parenchymal cells near the stem surface then develop into **cork cambium** (Fig. 8.20). Toward the inside of it, this tissue lays down more cortex parenchyma. Toward the outside, *cork cells* are produced. These secrete a very efficient waterproofing coat, made of a material called *suberin.* Suberin-coated cells constitute **bark.**

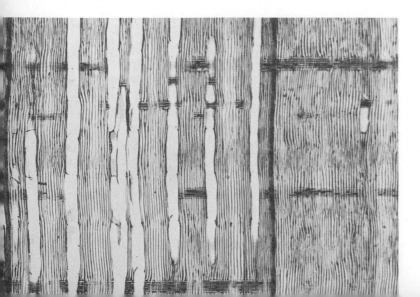

FIG. 8.18. Longitudinal section through wood, showing the xylem channels formed by tracheids. The two dark vertical lines mark out an annual ring. (General Biological Supply House, Inc.)

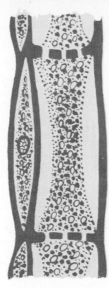

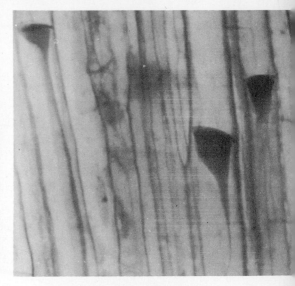

FIG. 8.19. Phloem tissue. In the diagram, note the nucleated companion cell, the sieve plates, and the nonnucleated sieve tube. In the photo, note the vertical sieve tubes, the horizontal sieve plates, and the darkly stained nonnucleated protoplasm of the sieve tubes. Companion cells are out of focus in this high-power view, but they may be seen outlined faintly to the left of the prominent sieve tube near the center of the photo. (Courtesy of J. M. Bell, Polytechnic Institute of Brooklyn.)

As stem girth enlarges, bark ruptures repeatedly. New layers of bark develop from the cork cambium, and older bark on the outside flakes off.

These processes slowly transform the shoot of the seedling into a taller, thicker, tapering woody stem. All the stem up to a level some distance below the zone of specialization is woody. New wood and bark continue to be added at the upper end, behind and in pace with the advancing stem tip. As the stem matures from ground level upward, bark replaces the epidermis and the green cortex tissue of the original shoot. And phloem, cambium, xylem, and pith come to form a concentric pattern interiorly. The advancing tip still remains the primary growth-generating center of the stem. New tissues continuously laid down by this tip at first always repeat the internal arrangement of the original shoot.

In parallel with these events, extensive branching takes place.

Branching Growth

Lateral branching repeats in a different direction of space the pattern of upward growth of the main stem. At more or less regular intervals, the advancing shoot meristem leaves behind surface patches, or disks, of tissue which remain embryonic. These meristematic zones represent **nodes,** and the lengths of stem between them, **internodes** (Fig. 8.21).

Branching growth occurs only at the nodes. **Lateral buds** arise here which grow out at an angle to the main stem. The youngest (uppermost) nodes typically give rise to *leaf buds*. By the time a leaf is mature, the stem has already elongated and new leaf buds have formed at nodes higher up. When mature leaves fall off, e.g., at the approach of winter, a *leaf scar* is left. At such older nodes, *branch stems* may bud off. As these grow out, they usually obliterate the leaf scars at these nodes.

Branch stems grow in length and in thickness like the main stem. Wood and bark develop progressively from the base forward. At the base of the branch, the vascular tissues, phloem and xylem, become continuous with those of the main stem. Branches which angle off nearest to the ground are older, and have grown longer, than branches farther up. Hence the familiar upward taper of the branch system of a tree.

The above pattern of growth is repeated again when secondary branches develop from primary ones. The upper nodes of a young primary branch may first give rise to leaves. Secondary branch stems may form there later. From these, new leaves and tertiary branch stems develop in turn. We note that a small outer branch with its leaves is, in effect, a replica of the original shoot from which the adult tree has grown.

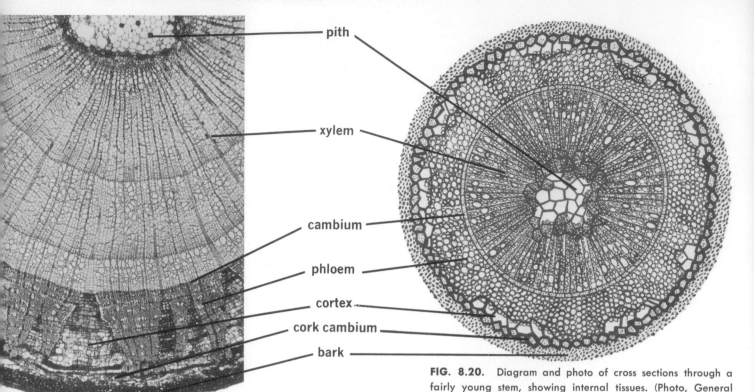

pith

xylem

cambium

phloem

cortex

cork cambium

bark

FIG. 8.20. Diagram and photo of cross sections through a fairly young stem, showing internal tissues. (Photo, General Biological Supply House, Inc.)

The Older Stem

The naked eye identifies only bark and wood when a mature tree trunk is cut across. The microscope, however, reveals the single layer of cambial cells, at the line of juncture between bark and wood, and reveals also that the inner part of "bark" is actually phloem.

Only *young* phloem and xylem are functional. Older phloem tissue ruptures, becomes part of bark, and flakes off. Older xylem vessels, near the pith, become **heartwood.** Its vessels may gradually block up with resins and gums, and conduction through them is then no longer possible. The core of a tree may therefore be hollowed out without interfering with xylem conduction. But the outer, younger wood of a tree, called the **sapwood,** must remain intact if a tree is to remain alive. A tree dies, for example, when it is "ringed," that is, when a cut around the circumference interrupts the vertical continuity of phloem, cambium, and sapwood.

Annual rings are fairly conspicuous in an older stem (Fig. 8.22). Xylem vessels laid down during spring generally have a larger diameter than those formed in summer. In spring, melting snow provides the tree with much water. Wider conducting vessels are then formed which may accommodate the greater flow. The alternation of narrow summer xylem and wider spring xylem is recognizable with the naked eye as concentric dark and light banding —annual rings. The number of rings indicates the age of a tree. Moreover, from the comparative widths of spring and summer rings it is also possible to estimate the amount of rainfall, hence general climatic conditions, during past seasons, as far back in time as the tree has lived.

Trees, shrubs, and woody plants generally are equipped for continuous growth. In temperate climates, however, growth is necessarily at a virtual standstill at recurrent periods. Even if leaves are retained during the winter, even if food is stored in

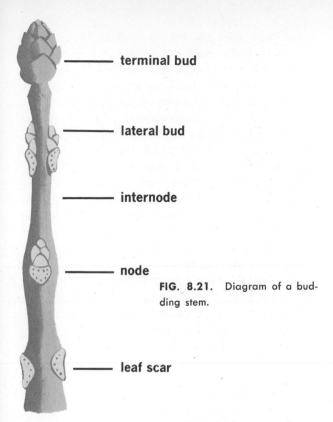

terminal bud

lateral bud

internode

node

FIG. 8.21. Diagram of a budding stem.

leaf scar

STEMS: HERBACEOUS TYPES

The purely woody and purely herbaceous stem types represent structural extremes; a more or less graded series of intermediate "semiherbaceous" types exists.

We may guess what the fundamental difference between the woody and the herbaceous stem might be. A plant equipped with wood and bark is likely to be able to winter over, for wood and bark are not destroyed by cold. But as we have seen, it is just the development of wood and bark which, in the temperate zone, involves an uneconomical expenditure of energy and materials. Therefore, a plant would be adapted more economically to a short growing season if its stem would *not* become woody —if, in other words, *cambial activity would be reduced.* Since the epidermal and cortical tissues would then not rupture, stems would remain green, and the plants would stay smaller. Winter would kill them, but in this very nonexistence during a difficult period would lie a net saving of energy and materials. Roots (as in herbaceous perennials) or seeds (as in annuals) would adequately maintain the protoplasmic succession.

Such a pattern of reduced cambial activity actually distinguishes the herbaceous stem. The pattern is well displayed in the stems of the sunflower, the buttercup, and the corn plant.

the roots, low temperatures reduce the rate of metabolism drastically. And metabolism is a prerequisite for growth. Year after year, therefore, the woody plant in the temperate zone expends energy in extending its phloem, its cambium, and its xylem, in height and in width. Yet for a good part of each year, these tissues hibernate and are nonoperational. But they must still be maintained in good working order. Also, extensive, permanently nonfunctional heartwood bears witness of energy expended in the past which does not yield operational gains in the present.

Does this not suggest a possibility for adaptive improvement? Would not a more economical stem design, better fitted to the realities of the temperate environment, permit a considerable saving of energy? A greater functional economy is, in fact, realized in herbaceous stems.

FIG. 8.22. Portion of a 12-year-old tree trunk, showing annual rings. (U.S. Forest Service.)

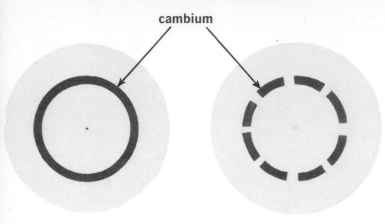

cambium

woody stem **semiherbaceous stem**

FIG. 8.23. Diagram of sections through woody and semiherbaceous stems. In a woody stem, the cambium forms a complete tube. In a semiherbaceous stem, the cambium occurs in circularly arranged strips.

The Sunflower Stem

The early growth of this **semiherbaceous** stem type follows the woody pattern, with one fundamental difference. The advancing shoot meristem does *not* leave behind a *tube* of cambium. Instead, it lays down discrete vertical *strips* of cambium, somewhat like fence posts arranged in a circle (Fig. 8.23). In the sunflower stem, therefore, secondary growth, i.e., formation of phloem and xylem, is considerably restricted. It can occur only in the vicinity of the cambial strips. The xylem vessels formed inside a cambial strip and the phloem formed outside, together with the cambial strip itself, constitute a **vascular bundle.** A cross section through such a stem reveals a structural pattern as in Fig. 8.24. Epidermis and the outer green cortex persist, since growth

FIG. 8.24. Cross section through the stem of a sunflower. Note the circular arrangement of the vascular bundles. In each bundle, xylem vessels are situated toward the center of the stem, and phloem, toward the outside of the stem. (General Biological Supply House, Inc.)

in thickness does not become sufficiently extensive to rupture them. Bark consequently does not form either. Pith parenchyma fills the central portion of the stem, and vascular bundles are arranged circularly in a zone between cortex and pith.

One new type of tissue develops. Capping each vascular bundle on the outside and inside are groups of hollow vertical tubes which resemble xylem vessels. These tubes, called **fiber tissue,** may develop heavier walls than xylem, and their internal diameter is then much reduced. Fiber tissue has a passive supporting function, compensating by its presence for the absence of wood.

In the older, basal portions of aged semiherbaceous stems, the cambial strips tend to grow out to the side, till they join one another and form a complete tube, as in a woody stem. At these basal levels, therefore, the vascular bundles too come to expand till they join, and the condition typical of woody stems is then established; bulk wood and bark develop here. Such stems justify their designation as "semiherbaceous." They are woody at the bottom, green elsewhere.

The significant phenomenon in this stem type

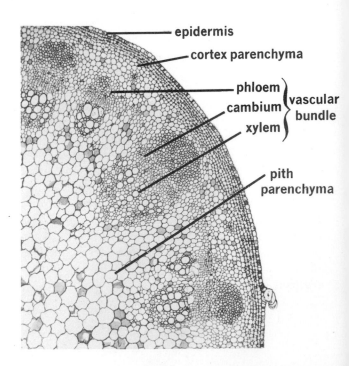

epidermis

cortex parenchyma

phloem
cambium } vascular bundle
xylem

pith parenchyma

is the development of vascular bundles as such, in all but the very oldest stem parts. As we have seen, this development is a result of a first step in cambial reduction. In the buttercup this reduction goes even farther.

The Buttercup Stem

In this wholly herbaceous stem type, vascular bundles are present also (Fig. 8.25). But they are scattered throughout the stem and are not arranged in a neat circle as in the sunflower stem.

Cambium *strips* are again found between xylem and phloem. However, this cambium is *nonfunctional* as a meristem tissue. The cells do not divide, and secondary growth does not occur at all; instead of being formed by cambial activity, xylem and phloem are laid down directly by the apical shoot meristem. Consequently, once the vascular tissues are formed, further increase in the thickness of the bundles cannot take place. Such plants should not develop an upward taper, since the bundles are no thicker at the stem base than at the stem tip. Indeed, many herbaceous stems do not taper. Many, however, do, but this is not a result of phloem-xylem

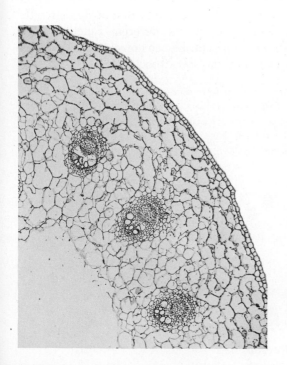

expansion. Rather, the older parenchymal cells toward the base may have retained more water, hence may have enlarged more, than younger cells toward the tip.

Many of these herbaceous plants acquire hollow stems. When, in the early seedling, new cells are produced in the division zone behind the meristem tip, cells divide faster near the surface than near the core. Future parenchyma cells in the center consequently cannot keep up with the growth of peripheral tissues. An axial space appears as a result, and a hollow stem is formed.

We note that, from a standpoint of function, cambial reduction is complete in this stem type. The observation that nonoperational cambium strips nevertheless are still present suggests a historical link with a woody or semiherbaceous ancestry. The buttercup-stem pattern clearly foreshadows the extreme in herbaceous development.

The Corn Stem

In this herbaceous stem type cambial reduction is complete, structurally as well as functionally. As in the buttercup stem, vascular bundles are laid down directly by the apical shoot meristem. But cambium is not formed at all. Vascular tissues are reduced to a minimum. Phloem and xylem vessels are present only in amounts strictly essential as supply lines to leaves and roots (Fig. 8.26).

Many of these plants compensate for the comparative scarcity of supporting xylem and fiber tissue by impregnating parenchymal cells with silicaceous hardening materials. This is the case, for example, in bamboos and cereal grasses.

Summary

We conclude that all significant differences in the organization of stems trace back to differences

FIG. 8.25. Cross section through the stem of a buttercup. Note the spacing of the vascular bundles. In each bundle, the large round spaces present sections through xylem vessels. (General Biological Supply House, Inc.)

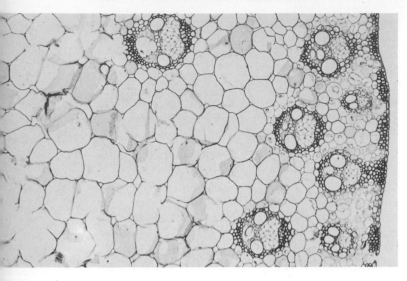

FIG. 8.26. Cross section through the stem of a corn plant. Note the scattered vascular bundles. Only three or four large xylem vessels are present in each bundle. (General Biological Supply House, Inc.)

in the disposition and the activity of the cambium. Maximal cambial activity leads to the woody organization; no activity, to the herbaceous (Fig. 8.27). As noted, the woody stem is primarily an adaptation to environments which permit continuous, year-round growth, such as the tropics and the subtropics. Woody stems are therefore found frequently in perennial plants. The herbaceous stem, on the other hand, is an adaptation to environments permitting only intermittent, seasonal growth, as in the temperate zone. This stem type is found among annuals, biennials, and those perennials in which only

the roots survive during the cold season. Both woody and herbaceous stem types may be found side by side in a given environment, and though both persist, one or the other may be more economically adapted to prevailing climatic conditions. The herbaceous annual succeeds with less expenditure of energy and materials in the temperate zone, and the woody perennial exploits growth opportunities more fully in tropical and subtropical zones.

Structurally and functionally, the stem is the essential intermediary for the rest of the plant. Clearly, successful adaptation of the stem at once implies a parallel success in the adaptation of roots and leaves. What do roots contribute to this overall adaptedness?

ROOTS

On the whole, the principal pattern of root growth is remarkably similar to that of stem growth. However, roots carry out different functions in a different environment. Hence correlated differences in organization may be expected.

FIG. 8.27. Cambium and conducting tissues in different stem types (diagrammatic). Black areas symbolize conducting tissue (phloem toward the stem surface, xylem toward the stem core). Light-gray areas symbolize functional cambium. Dark-gray areas symbolize nonfunctional cambium. Note that reduction of cambium and emphasis on vascular bundles go together.

woody

sunflower

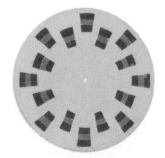

buttercup

corn

FIG. 8.28. Left, a root showing root-hair zone; at lower tip, note thickening formed by the root-cap. Right, a high-power view of a portion of the root-hair zone, showing epidermal cells and individual root hairs. (General Biological Supply House, Inc.)

Growth and Structure

In the young seedling, cells of an **apical root meristem** divide, just as in the stem. As in the stem also, most of the newly formed cells increase the length of the root, and successive zones of division, elongation, and specialization may again be identified. One difference between root and stem is that the apical root meristem pushes some of the newly formed cells *ahead* of it. These outermost cells of the root tip form a **rootcap** (Fig. 8.28). This is an important adaptive device, for as the root tip advances, hard soil grains would soon macerate unprotected meristem tissue. In the presence of a rootcap, however, cap cells wear off instead, and the growing tip is shielded effectively. New cap cells are formed continually by the meristem.

As in the stem, cellular specialization takes place behind the division zone of the root (Fig. 8.29). Surface cells become epidermis. Root epidermis, which absorbs soil water and dissolved minerals, develops neither stomata nor waxy surface coating. Instead, **root hairs** appear. These are delicate finger-like extensions of the cellular protoplasm, providing a tremendous surface area for absorption. Absorbed water soon passes into the cells underneath the epidermis. As these cells swell with fluid they elongate greatly; this generates a push from behind, an important factor in forcing the root tip through soil.

Root hairs persist only for a short while. When an epidermal cell ages its absorptive hair is lost. A distinct **root-hair zone** may therefore be found some distance behind the meristem tip (Fig. 8.28). Ahead of this zone, root hairs have not yet developed; behind it, they have already disappeared. Continued existence of the plant evidently depends on daily extension of its root system, for hair zones must be available at all times.

The root epidermis is underlain by layers of cortical parenchyma. The innermost parenchymal layer is specialized as an **endodermis** (Fig. 8.29). Like the cork cells of bark, endodermal cells manufacture suberin, though not so extensively as cork cells. This substance impregnates the peripheral portions of the endodermal cell walls. Endodermis thus serves as a waterproofed layer which encloses the core tissues of the root. Numerous **passage cells** within the endodermal layer remain soft and unsuberized,

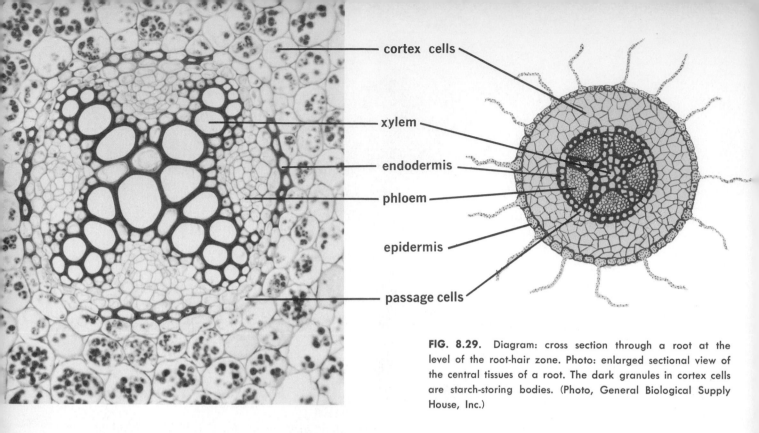

cortex cells

xylem

endodermis

phloem

epidermis

passage cells

FIG. 8.29. Diagram: cross section through a root at the level of the root-hair zone. Photo: enlarged sectional view of the central tissues of a root. The dark granules in cortex cells are starch-storing bodies. (Photo, General Biological Supply House, Inc.)

permitting the unhindered transmission of water from epidermis and cortex to the interior root xylem.

In any root, regardless of which stem type is associated with it, the vascular tissues are aggregated compactly within the endodermal cylinder. Pith is not present, and xylem vessels occupy the central space. In cross-sectional view, the arrangement of these vessels somewhat resembles the spokes of a wheel, the outer ends of the spokes abutting against the endodermal passage cells (see Fig. 8.29). Phloem fills the spaces between the spokes. In woody and semiherbaceous plants, cambium is present between phloem and xylem. Root cambium here may in time produce so much vascular tissue that epidermis, cortex, and endodermis are ruptured. Bark is then formed. In an older woody or semiherbaceous plant, therefore, root merges imperceptibly into stem near the soil-air boundary.

If the plant is wholly herbaceous, root cambium may be present but it may be nonfunctional, or it may not be present at all, as in corresponding stem types. In either case, increase in thickness does not occur, and roots remain nonwoody. The transition to stem is then more abrupt. Near the soil-air boundary, the conducting tubes of the root become segregated into distinct vascular bundles, and these are continuous with the phloem-xylem bundles of the stem.

Types of Roots

Unlike stems, roots do not possess nodes, and branching may occur at any point. A number of patterns may be distinguished (Fig. 8.30). For example, many branch roots may lead off from the stem base in all directions, as in the **fibrous roots** of grasses. Or a single strong **taproot** may penetrate vertically into the ground, and smaller secondary roots may radiate out along its course or at its terminal (e.g., dandelions, carrots). Such roots usually possess extensive cortical parenchyma, an adaptation for food storage. (Slice a carrot across and observe. Note, incidentally, that a potato is a *stem;* that an onion is a concentric system of *leaves,*

FIG. 8.30. Some types of roots. Left, fibrous roots; middle, tap roots; right, prop roots. (Prop roots, Brooklyn Botanical Garden; others, U.S. Department of Agriculture.)

arising from a flat disklike stem; that roots, stems, and leaves may all be adapted for food storage; and that what is pulled out of the ground evidently is not automatically a root.)

Not all roots connect with the stem base; some sprout from anywhere on the stem. Such **adventitious roots** are found, for example, on the horizontal underground stems of a number of seed plants. The banyan tree possesses adventitious roots, which here are called **prop roots;** root branches arch away into the ground from high up on the upright aerial stem. In older corn plants, prop roots are usually encountered too, leading off from the lowest nodes of the stem.

Orchids have **aerial roots,** nowhere in contact with soil. These roots are adapted to absorb rain water directly as it falls. A parasitic aerial root is in evidence in the mistletoe. Equipped with suckers, these roots hold on to the host tree, and water is siphoned off from the host xylem.

These few examples show that roots have adaptive versatility of their own. Being one with the rest of the organism, an adapted root is a prerequisite for an adapted plant. But roots, as well as stems, are largely subservient to the leaves. These are unquestionably the most essential parts of a plant. A single isolated leaf may be put into a glass of water rich in minerals, and when exposed to sunlight, this leaf may survive. But an isolated root or a stem without green tissue soon dies under similar conditions. Root and stem make the functioning of the leaf possible, and thereby they ensure their own persistence.

LEAVES

Everyone is familiar with *needle-shaped, net-veined,* and *parallel-veined* leaf types. In all, the **leaf blades** are connected to stem nodes through **petioles,** woody or green stalks structured essentially like thin stems.

Regardless of whether or not the plant is woody or herbaceous, small aggregations of xylem, phloem, and fiber tissue branch off from the stem and pass

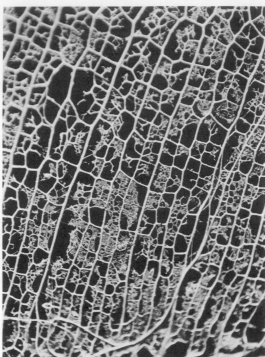

FIG. 8.31. Pattern of the veins in a leaf. A close-up of a portion of the vein pattern is shown at right. (Photos, Brooklyn Botanical Garden.)

uninterruptedly into the leaf as vascular bundles. These are the **veins** of the leaf. Either they ramify in intricate patterns, or they continue in parallel. They provide physical support, and they constitute the upper terminus of supply lines which reach without break from the farthest root tip to the farthest leaf tip (Fig. 8.31).

Cambium generally does not branch away into the leaves. Nor is there a distinct meristem tip. Indeed, leaf growth differs fundamentally from root or stem growth. In the leaf bud, the *whole* leaf is laid down in miniature. Subsequent growth is principally a matter of cell enlargement, boosted now and then by cell division. This takes place in all parts of the leaf simultaneously. If a rectangular grid were drawn on an immature blade, the mesh width of the grid would increase as the leaf grows. But straight lines would remain more or less straight, and the regularity of the grid would be preserved.

An epidermis covers the outside of the leaf (Fig. 8.32). This layer is continuous with the stem epidermis, if present. The epidermal cells of the leaf are transparent, and they are coated with a waxy cuticle of varying thickness. With the exception of cells which form stomata, epidermal cells do not contain chlorophyll.

A **stoma** (plural: stomata) is a free space enclosed by a pair of crescent-shaped, chlorophyll-containing **guard cells** (Figs. 8.32 and 8.33). The walls of these cells are thickest, hence stiffest, on the side which lines the stoma. By virtue of this, a stoma can open or close when turgor increases or decreases within the guard cells. Since these cells are equipped with chloroplasts, they may produce carbohydrates. This increases the concentration of protoplasmic particles. As a result, water from surrounding epidermal cells is drawn osmotically into the guard cells. As these swell they become more turgid, and their thin outer side walls curve out under tension. This pulls the inner thicker side walls apart, and the stoma opens. Conversely, when carbohydrates are being used up, the turgor of

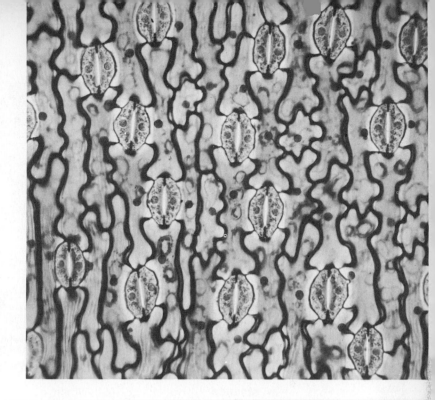

FIG. 8.32. Photomicrograph of the epidermis of a lily leaf, surface view. The dark lines outline epidermis cells. Note the pairs of guard cells enclosing the stomata. (Ward's Natural Science Establishment, Inc.)

guard cells decreases. The elastic cell walls then revert to their original position, and so the stoma closes.

This simple yet extremely efficient automatic control device regulates the rate of gas exchange (oxygen, carbon dioxide, and water vapor) between the atmosphere and the leaf interior. Stomata open wide, moderately, or not at all, in accordance with specific conditions of humidity, temperature, and lighting. For example, on a very dry, hot summer day, the leaf pores are almost fully closed. The rate of photosynthesis in the leaf is then reduced, inasmuch as not enough carbon dioxide can enter. But the evaporation of internal water, a problem of more immediate concern, is held down at the same time. As we have noted earlier, stomata may be present on either or both sides of a leaf, their number per unit of surface area may vary, and they may be placed flush with the leaf surface or may be sunk into pits.

Wrapped in epidermis, **mesophyll** tissue fills the interior of the leaf (Fig. 8.34). This is the chief food-producing tissue of the plant; all mesophyll cells contain chlorophyll. Just underneath the upper epidermis in horizontally placed leaves, and underneath the whole epidermis in most upright and needle-shaped leaves, mesophyll cells are arranged in compact layers, or **palisades.** Elsewhere, mesophyll is **spongy;** that is, it is organized into loose cellular strands and layers. The whole is honey-

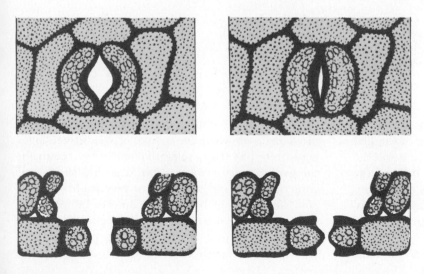

FIG. 8.33. Diagram of leaf epidermis, showing a pair of guard cells. Upper figures, surface view; lower figures, cross-sectional view; left figures, stoma open; right figures, stoma closed.

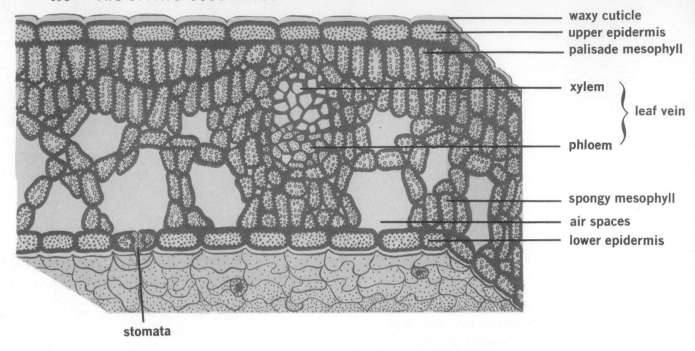

waxy cuticle
upper epidermis
palisade mesophyll

xylem
} leaf vein
phloem

spongy mesophyll
air spaces
lower epidermis

stomata

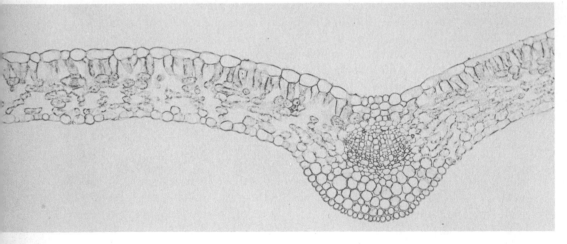

FIG. 8.34. Diagram and photo of section through a leaf. The large vein in photo represents the midrib of the leaf. (Photo, General Biological Supply House, Inc.)

combed extensively with **air spaces.** These connect with one another and lead to the exterior of the leaf through open passages in the palisade tissue and the stomata. This structural arrangement brings the greater part of every mesophyll cell into direct contact with fresh external air. Leaf veins ramify abundantly through the mesophyll, and no green cell is very far removed from these channels.

We have reached the heart of the leaf—indeed,

the heart of the whole plant: the individual mesophyll cell. As we have noted, single green algal cells quite like it are self-sufficient in the ocean. In the evolutionary transposition of such a single cell from ocean to land, the price of survival has been a complicated plant body made up of a billion other cells, carrying out a trillion other reactions, to house it, support it, protect it, supply it, perpetuate it. That price evidently has not been too high. It has been paid gradually through slow evolution, at compound interest in adaptation. The result has been the eminently successful spreading of the autotrophic, photosynthetic way of life.

From the human standpoint, the price has not been too high for yet another reason. Had it not been paid, man would not be here to talk about it. For the chemically creative way of life of the green plant is the crucial prerequisite for the heterotrophic way of life of the animal.

REVIEW
QUESTIONS

1. Define autotrophic nutrition. Review the various autotrophic patterns of life among bacteria and plants. How does chemosynthesis differ from photosynthesis?

2. Define heterotrophic nutrition. Review the various heterotrophic patterns of life among bacteria and plants. Which organisms play a role in global nitrogen turnover? What are the specific contributions of each to the nitrogen cycle?

3. Review the architectural adaptations of green plants. In this connection, contrast aquatic and terrestrial plants. List specific design features of trees that adapt them to land life. What is turgor, how is it maintained, and what is its adaptive role?

4. Review the various climatic adaptations of green plants. In this connection, contrast aquatic and terrestrial plants. How do land plants conserve water? How do they protect against winter cold?

5. What different groups of plants are perennial, biennial, and annual, and what life-cycle patterns define these groups?

6. Show how a woody stem grows in length and in thickness. Make sure that you understand the three-dimensional structure of such a stem. What is the organization of xylem and phloem? How do these tissues develop, and what are their functions? In terms of tissues, what are wood and bark?

7. What is the structure of a woody branch stem? How do such branches form, and where do they give rise to leaves? What is the cross-sectional structure of a mature woody tree trunk? Where in such a trunk are xylem and phloem? What are annual rings, and how do they develop?

8. What is the organization of semiherbaceous and herbaceous stems, and how do these differ from woody stems? How do vascular bundles develop? How does secondary growth occur in herbaceous stems? To which environments are various stem types best adapted?

9. Review the longitudinal and cross-sectional organization of roots. What tissues present in roots are not present in stems? What are the functions of these additional root tissues? Conversely, what structures present in stems are not present in roots? What are the adaptive reasons for this? What are some of the branch patterns of roots?

10. Describe the external and internal organization of a leaf. How does leaf development differ from root or stem development? In what tissues does photosynthesis occur? What is the structure and distribution of stomata, and how do they function? Would you expect stomata to be open or closed at night?

SUGGESTED
COLLATERAL
READINGS

The roles and nutritional processes of bacteria are variously discussed in the following works:

Rahn, O.: "Microbes of Merit," Jaques Cattell Press, 1945.

Grant, M.: "Microbiology and Human Progress," Rinehart, 1953.

Henrici, A. T., and E. J. Ordal: "The Biology of the Bacteria," Heath, 1948.
Lees, H.: "Biochemistry of Autotrophic Bacteria," Butterworth, 1955.
Clayton, R. K., and M. Delbrück: Purple Bacteria, *Sci. American,* vol. 185, 1951.

For additional information on adaptations and the internal structural organization of plants, the following are recommended:

Ward, H.: A Tour of a Tree, in I. W. Knobloch, "Readings in Biological Science," Appleton-Century-Crofts, 1948.
Anderson, E. A.: "Plants, Life, and Man," Little, Brown, 1952.
Daubenmire, R. F.: "Plants and Environment," Wiley, 1947.
Sinnott, E. W., and K. S. Wilson: "Botany: Principles and Problems," McGraw-Hill, 1955.
Wilson, C. L.: "Botany," Dryden, 1952.
Smith, G. M., E. M. Gilbert, G. S. Bryan, R. I. Evans, and J. T. Stauffer: "A Textbook of General Botany," 5th ed., Macmillan, 1953.

9

THE ORGANIZATION OF ANIMALS

IF WE WERE TO SEARCH for a single, unequivocal distinction between *all* plants and *all* animals, we would probably not have too much success. Virtually every fundamental characteristic of plants is represented also among at least some animals, and vice versa. Two of the most nearly universal differences are that plants possess cellulose cell walls, whereas animals do not, and that animals store carbohydrates in the form of glycogen, whereas plants do not. But, as Chap. 30 will show, there are exceptions here too.

Even if it could be found, a rigorous single distinction is not likely to be particularly revealing in any case. For the outstanding feature of plants as a group clearly is that *most* of them photosynthesize and that their whole way of life is conditioned by this. Analogously, the outstanding feature of animals as a group is that their nutritional pattern is entirely heterotrophic and, more especially, that in *most* animals this heterotrophism depends rather typically on active searching for food, i.e., on locomotion.

Thus, we may discuss the characteristically animal organization of living matter by concentrating primarily on two themes, feeding and moving. Specifically, we inquire first how the animal **patterns of life** are conditioned by feeding and moving. We consider next the **architecture** of the animal body, with particular emphasis on motion-associated engineering features, such as form and overall design, muscles, and skeletons. And we conclude with an examination of **locomotion** itself and of the ways in which this distinctively animal activity is carried out.

Patterns of Life

Like plants, animals are classified into phyla. Of the 25 or so phyla recognized within the animal kingdom, about half include the most important and most abundant animal types. From the members of

TABLE 5. Some of the major animal types, as represented by about half of all phyla

Groups	Representative types
Phylum *Sarcodina*	ameboid protozoa, radiolarians, foraminiferans
Phylum *Ciliophora*	ciliate protozoa
Phylum *Porifera*	sponges
Phylum *Coelenterata*	jellyfish, sea anemones, corals, hydras
Phylum *Platyhelminthes*	flatworms, e.g., flukes, tapeworms
Phylum *Nematoda*	roundworms
Phylum *Rotifera*	rotifers
Phylum *Annelida*	segmented worms, e.g., earthworms, leeches
Phylum *Mollusca*	clams, snails, squids, octopuses
Phylum *Arthropoda*	crustaceans, insects, spiders, scorpions
Phylum *Echinodermata*	starfishes, sea urchins
Phylum *Chordata*	tunicates, vertebrates (lampreys, sharks, bony fishes, amphibia, reptiles, birds, mammals)

these major phyla, we may obtain a general idea of the broad diversity of animal life as a whole (Table 5; also Chap. 31).

Being heterotrophs, all animals ultimately depend for food on autotrophs. Consequently, both in space and in time, animal life waxes and wanes in step with plant life. Two large subgroups may be distinguished among animal heterotrophs: **symbiotic** and **free-living** forms.

As among plants, some of the animal symbionts live in mutualistic or commensalistic associations with individuals of other species (see Chap. 4). But most are parasites, on or within specific hosts. Like parasitic plants, animal parasites are sustained largely by *molecular nutrients* absorbed from their hosts (e.g., tapeworms; see Chap. 4). In many cases, however, the animal parasite possesses specialized structures for the intake of cellular materials suspended in the body fluids of the host (e.g., flukes).

Free-living animals variously subsist on any protoplasmic matter available in the environment: living plants and animals, dead plants and animals, and many kinds of protoplasmic derivatives, including in some cases decaying matter. Evidently, free-living animals, on the one hand, may use the same sources of food as parasites; and on the other, the same sources as saprophytes.

However, the distinguishing feature of virtually all free-living animals, and also of most nonparasitic symbionts, is that they are *bulk feeders*; they acquire nutrients not in the form of individual molecules but in the form of bulk protoplasm. In other words, they have mouths and they eat, or **ingest.** They also possess equipment for internal **digestion,** which separates bulk foods into individual molecules. It is these which ultimately sustain even the free-living animal. Bulk foods as available usually contain substances not required or not usable by the animal, and such materials are eliminated, or **egested** (Fig. 9.1).

FIG. 9.1. The pattern of alimentation in free-living, bulk-feeding animals.

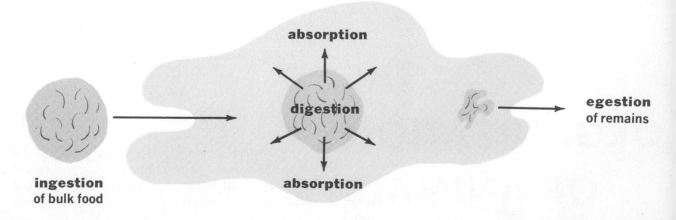

absorption

digestion

absorption

ingestion
of bulk food

egestion
of remains

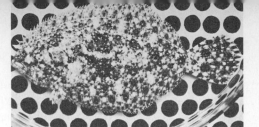

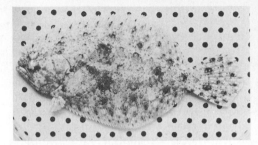

FIG. 9.2. A flounder against four different backgrounds. Note how the animal may adapt its skin pigmentation pattern to the color pattern of the environment. In such cases of adjustable camouflage, information about the environment is communicated to the skin via eyes, nerves, and hormones. Pigment cells in the skin respond to the information by contracting or expanding, thus altering the body coloration. (U.S. Fish and Wildlife Service.)

FEEDING PATTERNS

The most direct consequence of this method of feeding by **alimentation** is the requirement of locomotion. For whereas a plant finds raw materials practically all around it, bulk protoplasm is in strictly limited supply, and its location generally does not coincide with the location of the hungry animal. Therefore, either an animal must move toward food bodily, or it may remain stationary and feed on moving animals which happen to pass by. We may note that numerous animal groups are specialized as permanently or temporarily *sessile* organisms (e.g., sponges, corals). All of them are aquatic, and many of them use their locomotor structures to create currents, which sweep small plants and animals toward them.

Because the supplies of bulk food are limited, animals tend to compete sharply and overtly for available food, and so some become *predators*, some become *prey*; offense and defense are basic expressions of the animal way of life. Correlated with this are variously furtive habits, stealth, cunning, and other forms of *behavior*. We may recognize these too as primary consequences of alimentation and locomotion. Similarly correlated are many structural adaptations, of benefit to either the hunter or the hunted. For example, brute strength, speed, and body colorations which camouflage or warn are exceedingly prevalent, in water as on land. Many animals may even change their body colors according to the colors of backgrounds (Fig. 9.2).

Probably the most universal adaptations to the competitive animal way of life are specializations in eating habits. **Herbivores** are specialized to eat plant food; **carnivores** subsist on other animals; and **omnivores** eat both animal and plant foods, living or dead. In view of its abundance, plant food is easily come by. As a result, more herbivorous animal types exist than any other. Also, since plants do not put up a fight before being eaten, herbivores generally are of more or less gentle disposition and are more adept in defense than in offense.

A plant diet presents its own special problems. Fiber tissue and cellulose cell walls make plants tough and difficult to tear. Pieces of tissue are better cut off or scraped off the plant. The dental equipment of herbivores reflects these conditions; sharp broad cutting teeth predominate in some plant eaters (e.g., cattle, rodents), filelike raspers in others (e.g., the horny *radula* of mollusks; see Chap. 31). Still other herbivores, many insects, for example, are equipped with sucking mouth parts, with which plant juices can be siphoned off. Animals generally cannot digest cellulose; hence plant protoplasm must be freed mechanically from its cellulose envelopes. This may be accomplished well with broad-crowned grinding teeth, e.g., the molars of cattle and elephants (Fig. 9.3), or with modified stomachs, as in birds, where two muscular plates grind against each other like millstones. Herbivores also possess rather long intestines, which provide more time and more surface for the digestion of plant

FIG. 9.3. The photo above shows the grinding surface of a single tooth (molar) of an African elephant. The ridges are enamel; the space between the ridges, dentine. The photo on the left shows the upper jaw of a lion. The pointed teeth are adapted for tearing rather than grinding. (American Museum of Natural History.)

foods. A pound of fresh plant material consists largely of water and cellulose and of correspondingly less usable organic nutrients. Hence herbivores generally eat more, and more often, than other animal types.

In any environment, carnivores are the strongest and fastest animals, equipped to overcome not only herbivores but also smaller carnivores and omnivores. Devices for predatory offense are varied, numerous, and largely familiar: fangs, talons, sharp beaks, and needle-point teeth; poison-secreting stings which immobilize prey (scorpions); spider webs; tentacles with suction cups (squids), or tentacles with sting cells (coelenterates, Fig. 22.7); starfish tube feet which suck patiently, often for days, on the shells of a clam, till the exhausted clam can no longer keep its shells closed (see Fig. 9.26). Fast reflexes, excellent sense organs, and devices like growls, rattles, bioluminescent organs, electric organs, etc., are among the many auxiliary adaptations for a carnivorous way of life. Virtually none of the carnivores kills wantonly, but only when hungry or challenged; it is to the carnivore's advantage to live amidst a thriving population of herbivores. Animal tissue is softer than that of plants and tears fairly easily. Hence a predominance of sharp, pointed teeth among carnivores (Fig. 9.3). Absence of cellulose from animal foods also tends to reduce chewing time and makes for easier digestion and relatively shorter intestines. Nutritive values per pound of animal tissue are greater than in plant foods; hence carnivores generally eat fewer, smaller meals.

Omnivores subsist on whatever nourishment they can find or catch. Many omnivores wait on the scene of battle between carnivore and herbivore, to scavenge among the remains. Others live on minute plant and animal debris in soil or water. A large variety of worms, crabs, lobsters, many types of insects, rats, bears, pigs, and man are among omnivorous animals. Their food-trapping devices, dentition, and alimentary structures combine herbivorous and carnivorous features, as might be expected.

Among protozoa, food catching and eating must be accomplished by single cells. Two principal methods occur. A portion of the cell surface may be constructed as a permanent specialized depression, the **gullet,** into which food is swept by the action of cilia or flagella. Ciliate protozoa like *Paramecium* and *Stentor* eat in this manner (Fig. 9.4). Alternatively,

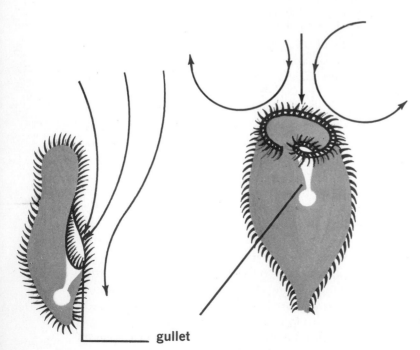

gullet

FIG. 9.4. Feeding currents in *Paramecium* (left) and *Stentor* (right). The cilia of these protozoa create food-bearing currents which sweep toward the gullets of the animals. The general path of the currents is shown by the arrows.

food may be *engulfed,* as in amoebae; the cell sends out fingerlike protoplasmic projections, called **pseudopods,** over, under, and around the sides of food, and the tips of the pseudopods then flow together (Fig. 9.5). Here, as also in gullet feeding, a cytoplasmic vacuole forms around ingested food. Digestive juices are secreted directly into such food vacuoles, and nutrient molecules then pass from them into the cytoplasm. Indigestible materials remain in the vacuoles until they are extruded through some point in the cell surface.

Digestion in protozoa is evidently an **intracellular** process. A similar pattern is encountered also among sponges (see Chap. 31). But most animal groups typically possess specialized alimentary tracts with separate mouth and anal openings. Here digestion is **extracellular;** digestive juices are secreted by gut cells into a gut cavity, where bulk food is broken up directly into molecular components. The gut cells then absorb the nutrient molecules. In some animals, notably the coelenterates and the flatworms, digestion is started extracellularly and is completed intracellularly; amebalike cells lining the gut cavity of these animals engulf partly digested bits of food, and then they finish digestion like protozoa (Fig. 9.6).

OTHER PATTERNS

Once the capacity of locomotion is given, it may be made to serve not only in food catching but also secondarily in numerous other animal activities. For example, locomotion plays a fundamental role in mate selection and reproduction, functions which the motile animal accomplishes far more readily than the sessile plant. Locomotion also is an important factor in protecting animals against environmental dangers, climatic change in particular. For example, as noted in Chap. 4, many animals carry out seasonal north-south migrations. Others remain at given latitudes permanently, yet through locomotion they are able to search out protective forests, caves, or self-constructed shelters like burrows, hives, nests, and houses.

To be sure, locomotion does not make animals

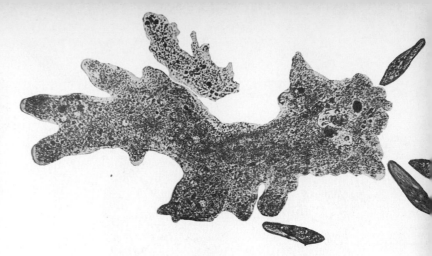

FIG. 9.5. Feeding in amoebae. The large organism is *Pelomyxa,* a multinucleate amebalike form related to the common ameba. Such a common ameba is shown just above *Pelomyxa.* In both, note the pseudopods—protoplasmic extensions which change shape and position rapidly. Food is trapped by such pseudopods. Some paramecia are shown on the right; these are favorite food organisms of *Pelomyxa.* (Carolina Biological Supply Co.)

completely independent of the climate, and environmental temperatures do affect them just as they do plants. Animals other than birds and mammals are designated, rather inappropriately, as being **cold-blooded.** They are not necessarily cold, and they do not necessarily possess blood, but, as in plants, their internal body temperature matches that of the external environment (Fig. 9.7). In such an organism, the rates of internal chemical reactions are high on a warm day, and the animal eats more, moves faster, and in general lives faster than on a cold day. The varying buzzing pitch of houseflies is a familiar indication of the influence of temperature on the tempo of living (see also Chap. 6). In winter, most cold-blooded animals die, but their protected eggs or larvae survive. In this respect they resemble annual plants. Other cold-blooded forms winter over successfully, either in deep water of oceans and lakes or sheltered on land in suitable sites above or below ground.

Birds and mammals maintain a *constant* internal body temperature, regardless of the temperature of the external environment. These animals are designated, again somewhat inappropriately, as being **warm-blooded.** Internal temperature here is

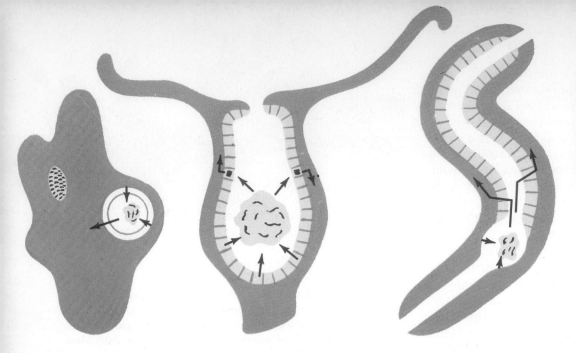

FIG. 9.6. Patterns of digestion in animals. Left, intracellular digestion in protozoa. Enzymes are poured into food vacuoles, and digested foods are absorbed into the cell cytoplasm. Middle, the digestive sac of a coelenterate. In this sac, food is partially digested extracellularly, and small bits of food are then digested intracellularly in the cells lining the sac. Right, extracellular digestion. Foods are digested completely in an alimentary tract, by enzymes secreted from the lining of the tract.

kept constant by regulating devices, which balance heat gain against heat loss. Principal sources of heat gain are food, friction generated by moving parts, and to a variable extent also the heat of the external environment. Fat, fur, or feathers may aid in heat retention. Heat loss results from surface radiation, from evaporation, and from loss of warm body water, as in urination, sweating, and breathing. When food is scarce, as in winter, internal heat production clearly becomes more difficult. Many mammals then *hibernate*, and in this state they are more or less cold-blooded. Heat regulation is tem-

FIG. 9.7. In "cold-blooded" animals, heat is gained or lost according to the temperature of the external environment. The internal temperature therefore matches the external. In "warm-blooded" animals, heat is also gained or lost according to environmental temperatures; but decreased internal heat production compensates for heat gains, and increased internal heat production compensates for heat losses. As a result, the internal temperature is maintained constant, regardless of the temperature of the environment.

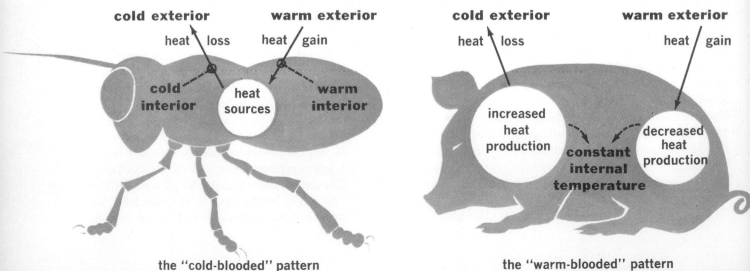

the "cold-blooded" pattern

the "warm-blooded" pattern

porarily suspended, body temperature drops, and food requirements, hence also the need for locomotion, are reduced proportionately (Fig. 9.8).

Hibernating or not, birds and mammals derive an important adaptive advantage from being warm-blooded. They become highly independent of daily and seasonal variations in climate; hence they may compete successfully against cold-blooded forms, which must slow down in every respect on a cold day. Moreover, warm-bloodedness, in conjunction with locomotion, permits the free spreading of mammals and birds between equator and pole, a factor which has contributed greatly to the preeminence of these types.

To summarize, we may note that, because of its dependence on alimentation and locomotion, the animal way of life has led to the exploitation of all conceivable food sources, under vastly varied conditions, in vastly varied environments. This basically is why the animal kingdom is more diversified than the plant kingdom, in numbers of phyla and numbers of species. Moreover, because of alimentation and locomotion, the internal structure of an animal is often far more elaborate than that of a plant.

Architecture

THE PATTERN

All animals, like plants, must possess structural equipment to carry out the fundamental functions of metabolism and self-perpetuation. As might be expected, therefore, animal structure in certain respects matches that of plants. For example, all animals possess **reproductive** structures, as do all plants. Complex multicellular animals possess **circulatory** systems and blood, components which correspond to the nutrient-carrying xylem and phloem of tracheophytes. However, most other gross features of animal structure do not have counterparts among plants. For to make alimentation and locomotion at all possible, the animal organization must include a number of structural systems not needed in plants.

FIG. 9.8. A chipmunk, hibernating in its underground burrow. Note the accumulated store of acorns at the bottom of the nest. (American Museum of Natural History.)

Thus, no plant possesses structures specialized for the collection of environmental oxygen or for the excretion of metabolic wastes. Yet all but the most simply constructed animals possess both: lungs, gills, moist skins, and other specific body parts for breathing; and kidneys, lungs, gills, sweat glands, and other specific body parts for excretion. The reason for this greater structural elaboration of animals lies in the shape of their bodies and, ultimately, in the requirement of locomotion. The light-requiring, stationary plant is built for maximum surface exposure. Practically all its cells are in direct contact with the external environment, and each cell therefore may collect oxygen and excrete CO_2, H_2O, and other wastes on its own. By contrast, the *moving* organism, for obvious mechanical reasons, cannot be built in the ramified shape of a tree but must be constructed far more compactly, for *minimum* surface exposure. Hence in an animal, most cells cannot be in direct contact with the environment; and this necessitates specialized **breathing** and **excretory** systems, operating in conjunction with the internal circulatory system (Fig. 9.9).

Above all, animals do not match plants in structures associated directly with the function of movement. Animals possess **muscles,** and many also feature articulated, movable **skeletons.** And, also unlike plants, animals possess elaborate equipment for in-

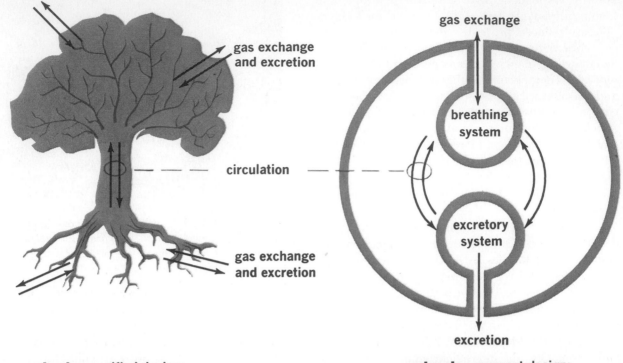

plants: ramified design;
most cells have direct access to environment

animals: compact design;
few cells have direct access to environment

FIG. 9.9. Diagram contrasting the ramified architecture of a plant and the compact architecture of an animal. Because of their respective architectures, the animal does, and the plant does not, require specialized breathing and excretory systems.

ternal coordination. For movement must be controlled, and internal processes as a whole must be readjusted often, in response to rapid changes of external locale brought about by movement. Thus, animals possess systems for **chemical coordination,** such as blood, kidneys, and endocrine glands; and systems for **neural coordination,** such as sense organs, nerves, and brains.

We may emphasize here that neural activities of all kinds, including even the most sophisticated thinking of man, serve fundamentally and primarily toward the control of muscles and of movement in general. In line with this, a close parallelism exists in the degree of nervous and the degree of locomotor development. Sense organs, nerves, and brain centers tend to be greatly reduced in sessile and

slow-moving animals but are highly developed in fast, agile types. For example, the sluggish starfish and sea urchins, though very advanced in other ways, possess but a rudimentary nervous system. So do clams and snails. But their close relatives, the fast squids, possess eyes, nerves, and brains which in structure and functional efficiency match those of vertebrates.

In short, just as the plant body reflects a way of life based on photosynthesis and sessilism, so the architecture of the animal body reflects the way of life based on alimentation and locomotion.

From an engineering standpoint, the important considerations in the design of an animal are overall *form, motion,* and mechanical *support* of form and motion. We now proceed to examine these in detail.

FORM

If living organisms could be "averaged," the average plant would live on land, would be radially symmetrical, and would look something like a pine tree. The average animal, on the other hand, would live in water, it would be bilaterally symmetrical, and it would superficially resemble a worm (Fig. 9.10). Of the two dozen or more animal phyla, about one-third consist entirely of worm-shaped forms. Among them are flatworms, roundworms, hair worms, arrow worms, spiny-headed worms, proboscis worms, segmented worms. Moreover, wormlike animals are included in most of the remaining phyla (see Chap. 31).

We can readily appreciate why this should be so. Locomotion can be accomplished with less effort in water than on land or in the air; friction is greatest on land, support against gravity is least in the air. Unlike the green plant, the animal is independent of sunlight, hence need not remain in surface waters. Nor need the aquatic animal stay microscopic in size, for its locomotor mechanism may serve as an uplifting antigravity device. Added to the abundance of plant food and the general biological benefits of a water environment, these factors have made aquatic life far more attractive to the animal than life on land. We have already noted in Chap. 5 that, of all major animal groups, only a few have terrestrial representatives (snails, various worms, vertebrates, and arthropods).

A gross architecture featuring **bilateral symmetry** and an **elongated shape** is particularly suited for locomotion. Propulsion of any kind necessarily implies that one portion of the organism "goes first" and that another goes last. Mechanical balance will be greatest if the left and right sides are equivalent, that is, if they are mirror images. Resistance by the propulsion medium will be least if the body is elongated in the direction of motion.

Moreover, the forward end enters new environments first. Sense organs for scouting and the chief nerve centers are therefore placed most advantageously at the front; and mouths should be

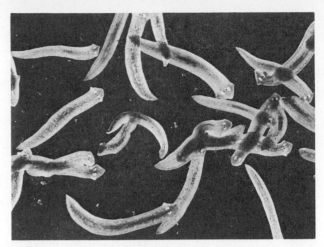

FIG. 9.10. The basic worm shape of the "average" animal is well illustrated by these flatworms, or planarians. (Carolina Biological Supply Co.)

located close to the sense organs. Thus the leading part of the organism becomes **head.** Analogously, elimination products of all kinds are best released at the hind end, where they do not impede forward progression. A general build of this sort is actually standard and nearly universal among *moving* animals (Fig. 9.11).

By contrast, sessile animals, and also many of the very slow movers, face their environment more or less equally from all sides, like plants; and their architecture reflects this. They are, or tend to be, *radially* symmetrical, and a distinct head is usually not present (e.g., corals, starfish). In many sessile forms also, the intestine is looped into a U, which brings the mouth and the anus close together and both openings away from the region where the animal is attached to the ground (e.g., tunicates, Fig. 9.12; see also Chap. 31 for other examples).

How does an animal maintain its shape, and how is it supported internally? Unlike a plant, an animal obtains relatively little mechanical support from the turgor of individual cells. Stiff outer cell walls are not usually present, particularly in the interior cells of the body; and the thin cell membranes withstand only moderate turgor pressure. Hence

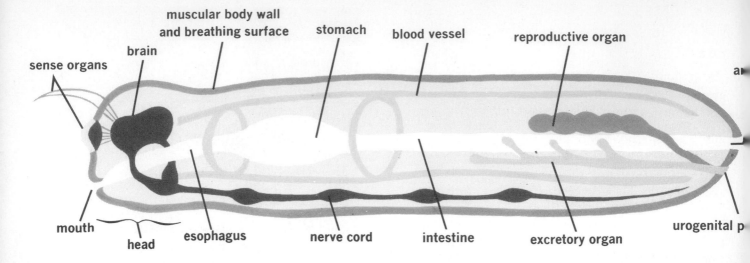

sense organs

brain

muscular body wall
and breathing surface

stomach

blood vessel

reproductive organ

a[

mouth

head

esophagus

nerve cord

intestine

excretory organ

urogenital p

FIG. 9.11.   Diagrammatic representation of the basic structure of a moving animal. This is a hypothetical animal, showing the position and function of various body parts and organs usually encountered in many elongated, worm-shaped types.

whatever inherent rigidity an animal cell possesses is due largely to the semisolid consistency of its colloidal gels. This may suffice to preserve the shape of single cells, but a larger cellular aggregation—a slice of fresh liver tissue, for example—sags badly.

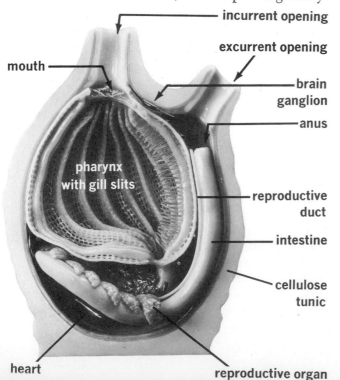

incurrent opening

excurrent opening

mouth

brain
ganglion

anus

pharynx
with gill slits

reproductive
duct

intestine

cellulose
tunic

heart

reproductive organ

The two major types of supporting devices of animals are at the same time the two major locomotor devices: muscles and skeletons. That muscles function not only in motion, but also in support, is well illustrated in animals such as earthworms, which do not possess a skeleton. The same muscles which move such animals also hold them together and maintain their shapes. Moreover, even an animal with a skeleton would sag into a formless mass if muscles did not maintain a taut, firm organization. On the other hand, that skeletons function not only in support but also in locomotion is also clear. A large, heavy animal could neither hold its shape nor propel itself forward by muscles alone, without rigid supports.

FIG. 9.12.   Cutaway model of a tunicate or sea squirt, a chordate animal. This is a sessile marine organism. Food-bearing water is drawn into the pharynx through the incurrent opening, food passes into the U-shaped alimentary tract, and water emerges through the gill slits and the excurrent opening to the outside. More about sessile animals with U-shaped alimentary systems in Chap. 31. (American Museum of Natural History.)

FIG. 9.13. Left: a few fibers of skeletal muscle. Note the cross striations, and the many nuclei within each fiber. Middle: smooth muscle. Note the spindle-shaped cells. Right: heart muscle. Note the branched fibers, the nuclei, the faint longitudinal fibrils within each fiber, and the faint cross striations. (General Biological Supply House, Inc.)

MUSCLES

The beginnings of muscular protoplasm are present even in protozoa, the earliest true animals. In some of them, a few contractile protein fibrils play a considerable role in the maintenance of body shape. Within certain cells of sponges and coelenterates, the number of such contractile fibrils is relatively large, and in all other animals we encounter extensive tissue aggregations of true muscle cells, specialized particularly for contraction. In forms such as mammals, as much as two-thirds of the total body weight is muscle weight.

Three types of muscle tissue may be distinguished: **smooth** muscle, **striated** muscle, and **cardiac** muscle. In the smooth variety, the cells are elongated and spindle-shaped (Fig. 9.13). Contraction of lengthwise intracellular *fibrils* shortens and thickens the cell. Many of such cells may be oriented in parallel, forming a muscular layer. For example, the intestinal wall of vertebrates contains two such layers. In one the cells are aligned longitudinally, and in the other they are placed circularly (Fig. 9.14). Contraction of the one shortens and widens; contraction of the other lengthens and narrows the gut. Contraction of both maintains firmness and a tubular shape. In vertebrates, smooth muscle generally is not connected with the skeleton and is not

under voluntary nervous control. Contractions take place relatively slowly.

Striated, "skeletal," or "voluntary" muscle is made up of syncitial units. Each such unit, a **muscle fiber,** develops through repeated division of a single cell, and in this process the boundaries between daughter cells disappear. The resulting fiber therefore contains many nuclei embedded in a continuous mass of muscular protoplasm (Fig. 9.13). The whole fiber is elongated, and its internal contractile fibrils are aligned longitudinally. Under the microscope these fibrils exhibit cross striations, alternate dark and light bands, hence, the name of this type of muscle tissue. We shall hear more of the internal fine structure of muscle in Chap. 16.

A group of parallel muscle fibers makes up a **muscle bundle.** Such a bundle is enveloped by layers of loose connective tissue. Several bundles form a **muscle,** enclosed within a connective tissue sheath of its own. At either end, a muscle may merge gradually into **tendon,** a tough, nonelastic connective

FIG. 9.14. Cutaway diagram of a section of gut, showing the outer longitudinal and the inner circular layer of smooth muscle.

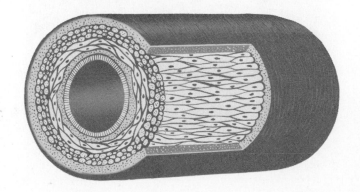

FIG. 9.15. The heavy, rigid, calcareous exoskeleton of snails. (American Museum of Natural History.)

tissue which attaches directly to skeletal parts. Like smooth muscles, striated muscles may be arranged into consecutive layers, each contracting in a different direction (e.g., the layers of the human body wall).

Cardiac muscle composes the bulk of the heart. Like smooth muscle, it is not under voluntary control; like striated muscle, its fibers are syncitial. Indeed, cardiac fibers are themselves fused together in intricate patterns (Fig. 9.13). Consequently, the whole heart thus is a continuous, multinucleate mass of contractile protoplasm.

Living muscles are never completely relaxed. Mild contractions occur all the time, groups of cells or fibers working in relays. A definite **muscle tone** is thereby maintained, and it is through this that muscles preserve body shape and posture and provide structural support in general. Stronger contrac-

tions, above and beyond tonic ones, produce movement of internal organs, or locomotion. We shall see in Chap. 16 how muscular contractions are believed to be brought about.

SKELETONS

As locomotor structures, skeletons clearly cannot operate alone but must be powered by muscles. As supporting structures, skeletons are far more economical than muscles, for they are partly or wholly nonliving, and they may therefore function without perpetual expenditure of energy. Skeletons serve in a third important capacity, that of *protection*.

The solid supports of animals are made of inorganic or of organic substances. Among the former, carbonates and phosphates of calcium and salts containing silicon are particularly widespread. The substances are hard and relatively insoluble, they are easily synthesized, and the necessary raw materials occur abundantly in water and on land. Such **calcareous** and **silicaceous** skeletons may often contain organic materials as well. For example, upon boiling in water, fresh bones of vertebrates yield sticky gelatinous substances rich in proteins. **Horny** skeletons are a third type found widely among animals. Several varieties of horn exist, e.g., the *chitin* of insects, the horny cover of turtles, the skeletal meshwork of bath sponges. All these are made of complex organic materials.

Most animal supports are either **exoskeletons** or **endoskeletons.** In the first case, the supporting material is on the outside of the animal and envelops it partly or wholly. Coelenterates, mollusks, and arthropods are among forms with such exoskeletons. In the second case, the supports are internal, and soft tissues are draped over them. Echinoderms and chordates are the main forms featuring this type of skeleton.

FIG. 9.16. A stag beetle, showing the light, chitinous exoskeleton of insects generally. The parts of such a skeleton are held together by chitinous membranes, permitting movement. (U.S. Department of Agriculture.)

FIG. 9.17. The molting of insects. Left, adult just emerging from cocoon, which has broken open along back. Middle, a moth just emerged from its cocoon. The adult exoskeleton has not yet hardened, and during the ensuing hours the abdomen pumps fluid into the wings. The abdomen thus becomes smaller and the wings larger, as at right. The exoskeleton then hardens. (Left, U.S. Department of Agriculture; others, courtesy of H. Lou Gibson, Rochester, N.Y.)

Exoskeletons

In sessile animals such as corals, and in slow-moving forms such as snails and clams, skeletons are entirely or almost entirely rigid. Made of thick calcareous deposits, the heavy housings afford excellent support and protection in an essentially stationary way of life. Muscularly supported locomotor and ingestive structures may be protruded from openings in the casings (Fig. 9.15).

Rapid locomotion becomes possible only if the skeleton is articulated and nonrigid, and if it is light enough to be carried about with minimum effort. Both conditions are realized in the exoskeletons of insects and other arthropods. These organisms are completely encased in light, horny chitin (Fig. 9.16). This material is divided up into discrete plates, which are articulated together by pliable, chitin-impregnated membranes. Muscles prevent the jointed framework from collapsing, and they also control the bending of the body, and the movement of legs, mouth parts, and the chitinous wings.

Such a constraining envelope clearly precludes continuous growth. Arthropods *molt* from time to time and grow in spurts at these periods. At each molt, the exoskeleton loosens from underlying epidermal tissues and breaks open in one region, usually along the back. The soft, defenseless animal then extricates itself from the old shell and enlarges rapidly during the next few days (Fig. 9.17). Meanwhile, a new and larger exoskeleton is secreted by the epidermal tissues. When the new shell is fully hardened, growth ceases again. In the Crustacea,

the large group of aquatic arthropods which includes shrimps, crabs, and lobsters, periodic molting continues throughout life. Among insects, a last molt transforms the immature, nonflying organism into a winged adult. Adults do not molt thereafter, nor do they grow in size.

The exoskeletal principle reaches its most successful expression in arthropods. Affording structural support and protective armor, as well as great freedom of movement, the chitin skeleton is in large part responsible for the outstanding success of arthropods as a group. But the very principle of exoskeletons entails severe inherent limitations. Most importantly, the larger the encased organism, the less support will central, deep-lying tissues receive. Animals with exoskeletons consequently stay relatively small. Moreover, if the exoskeleton is calcareous, its proportionate weight in a small animal, if not also its external position, restricts motion. And if the housing is horny, it is comparatively less sturdy, since calcium salts are the stronger material. Indeed, larger arthropods like lobsters impregnate their chitin shell with calcium salts. Furthermore, an external housing must be "open" to allow for growth, as in clams, in which case the support and protection are limited. Or, if the shell is all-enveloping as in insects, then the animal must molt at least during early development. In that case, support and protection are periodically lacking altogether.

These various disadvantages largely disappear in endoskeletons. Such an internal framework supports deep as well as superficial tissues. The organism consequently may attain considerable size but

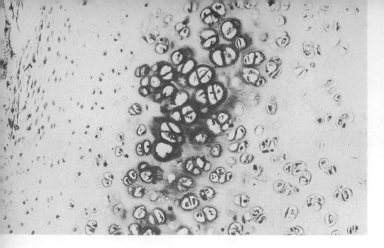
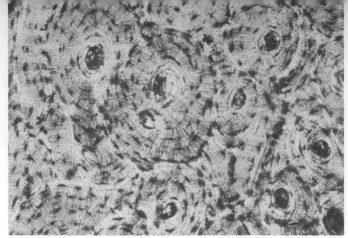

FIG. 9.18. Left, histological section through cartilage. Note the many cartilage-producing cells, surrounded by their own secretions. Right, histological section through bone. Bone-producing cells are located in the dark patches, arranged in concentric patterns. Hard bone substance, light in the photo, surrounds the cells. (Cartilage, General Biological Supply House, Inc.; bone, Ward's Natural Science Establishment, Inc.)

may still be buttressed adequately. Large size permits the development of proportionately large amounts of muscle, which may operate even a relatively heavy calcareous skeleton. The endoskeletal principle evidently combines mobility with large size, good support, and great internal strength. It is not surprising that animals so built have become supreme in their environments.

Endoskeletons

Among animals possessing internal supports (see Chap. 31), vertebrates feature the most elaborate. The vertebrate endoskeleton consists either of **cartilage,** or of **bone,** or of both. Each of these two supporting materials contains calcium salts and organic matter. The chief inorganic constituent of bone is calcium phosphate.

Unlike the skeletons of other animals, secreted by cells which remain outside the solid substance, the vertebrate skeleton is formed by cells which become embedded within their own secretions. As a result, cartilage and bone are not inert throughout but contain islands of cells dispersed through them (see Fig. 9.18). The skeletal fabric of vertebrates consequently possesses "living" qualities, largely absent from the solidly calcified or hornified skeletons

of other animal groups. In these living qualities lies an important advantage. The skeleton not only grows continuously along with the rest of the animal, but it also adjusts better to changing stresses and strains than a completely inert, wholly passive support.

Cartilage is the sole supporting material in primitive vertebrates such as lampreys and sharks. In these, the skeleton remains permanently cartilaginous. In other vertebrates, man included, much of the skeleton is preformed in cartilage during embryonic stages. But these supports are then gradually replaced by bone, in most of the skeleton (Fig. 9.19). Replacement in man is not completed until approximately the twentieth year of life.

The overall construction of the skeleton of a four-footed vertebrate resembles a suspension bridge (Fig. 9.20). An **axial skeleton,** consisting of skull, vertebral column, and rib cage, forms the horizontal part of the bridge. Vertical supports comprise the **appendicular skeleton,** consisting of limbs, pectoral (shoulder) girdle, and pelvic (hip) girdle (Fig. 9.21). Limbs are articulated in sockets formed by the girdle bones, and girdles in turn are attached to the axial skeleton by bony connections, ligaments, and muscles. Individual vertebrae are sepa-

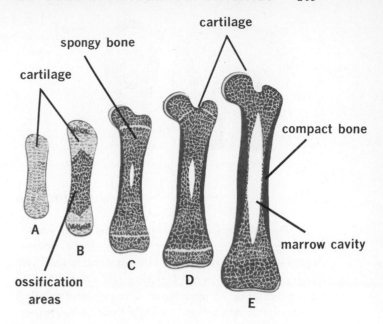

FIG. 9.19. The growth of a bone. **A,** cartilage rod, foreshadowing future bone. **B,** bone-forming cells give rise to three centers of ossification (black areas). **C,** spongy bone replaces all of cartilage, except in regions near joints (white bands); compact bone begins to form at surface of shaft, and marrow cavity in center of shaft. **D,** compact bone (solid black) extensive, marrow cavity enlarging. **E,** mature bone; cartilage layers near joints have been replaced by bone; in shaft, marrow cavity large, and spongy bone largely replaced by compact bone.

rated from one another by disks of fibrous, elastic cartilage, and the vertebral column as a whole is flexible as a result.

The sturdiness of the appendicular skeleton is finely adjusted to body weight. Apart from the inherent strength of the construction material, the strength of a pillar is proportional to the square of its thickness. A column twice as thick as another, made of the same material, is $2^2 =$ four times as strong. But body weight increases with the cube; an animal twice the diameter of another is roughly $2^3 =$ eight times as heavy. We find, indeed, that in comparison with smaller animals larger ones possess *more* than just proportionately thicker legs (Fig. 9.22). Many light, slender-legged mammals are built to walk on their toes, in a manner which adds

springiness to the gait. By contrast, heavy animals generally walk on the whole foot, for greater support.

Virtually by their mere presence, muscles and skeletons produce structural cohesion and mechanical support. By their positive action, they produce movement and locomotion.

FIG. 9.21. Skeleton of a cat, illustrating general skeletal organization of four-footed vertebrate. Note skull, axial skeleton (vertebral column and tail), and appendicular skeleton (limbs and limb girdles). (Ward's Natural Science Establishment, Inc.)

FIG. 9.20. The suspension-bridge principle of the mammalian skeleton. Compare with Fig. 9.21.

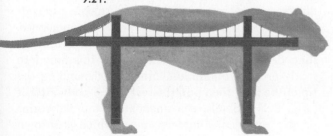

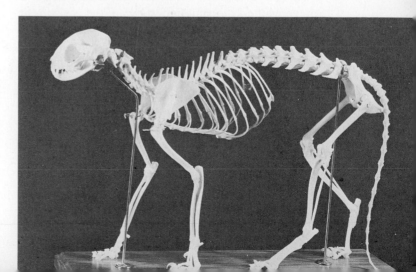

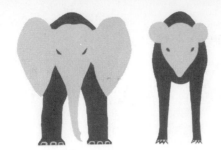

Locomotion

Directly or indirectly, practically every animal function depends in some way on mechanical movement of internal parts, or on locomotion. At the same time, practically every function also *contributes* to the production of movement. For even the simplest form of animal motion is a highly complex, composite activity. Easily observable muscular and skeletal action represents only the final link of a long series of processes. *Power* must be made available through nutrition, digestion, circulation, cellular respiration, and energy transport. Timing, intensity, and direction of movement, rhythmic coordination of different muscles, bodily balance in motion, all these require *control*, primarily through nervous activity. *Maintenance* of the power supply, of the control devices, and of good operating conditions in muscles and skeleton involves virtually every aspect of metabolism and self-perpetuation. This body-wide interplay of processes, of course, functions not only toward locomotion but toward other vital activities as well. However, in so far as they do set the stage for movement and locomotion, they are the basis for an effective exploitation of the heterotrophic, animal way of life.

Four different kinds of animal motion may be distinguished: **ameboid, ciliary, flagellary,** and **muscular** movement. The first not only occurs in the ameba and its relatives but is characteristic also of white blood cells, for example, and of various other cell types in multicellular organisms. In all such cases, the cell extends pseudopods, into which the rest of the cell gradually flows (see above, Fig. 9.5). Similarly, ciliary and flagellary movements are not confined to the protozoa. Flagella propel some bacteria (Fig. 9.23), some algae, and the sperm cells of most animals and of all plants except the seed plants. Cilia move the embryos and larvae of numerous animals, and the adults of some. However, muscular propulsion is the most widespread form. We shall now examine its principal variants.

CREEPING AND WALKING

The basic locomotor process on land, or at the bottom of a body of water, is well known to everyone. The animal extends a part of its body forward, levers that part against the ground, then pulls the rest of the body after it. The two major procedural patterns are *creeping* and *walking,* each with a number of subpatterns.

Invertebrate Patterns

Creeping, or sliding, gliding, and slithering, necessarily results in slow propulsion. For the whole or a major part of the body hugs the ground, and friction between body and ground is rather great. Such friction provides most of the traction and ground leverage. Although this method of moving requires no special locomotor equipment except a muscular flexible body, most creeping organisms have developed one or more ground-gripping devices: suckers, claws, bristles, muscular projections, and others. That many variants of creeping exist is readily appreciated by considering the motion of animals as diverse as earthworms and leeches, snakes, caterpillars, clams, snails, flatworms, or sea anemones. Clams, for example, project a muscular tongue-shaped "foot" from their shell, push this foot into sandy ground, obtain anchorage by expanding the tip of the foot, then pull the rest of the body after it (Fig. 9.24). Snails, sea anemones, and flatworms possess a muscular undersurface, which is thrown into shallow wavelike undulations rippling forward

FIG. 9.23. Electron micrograph of *Proteus vulgaris*, a flagellate bacterium. Note the numerous locomotor flagella. (Society of American Bacteriologists and courtesy of Dr. C. F. Robinow and Dr. J. Hillier.)

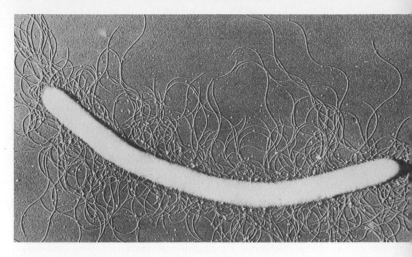

or backward. Sticky mucus, secreted by all these gliding forms, provides traction for the muscular ripples.

Walking, and modifications such as crawling, running, or jumping, become particularly feasible where skeletons can provide *rigid* levers. Set more or less under the body and raising the center of gravity, such levers reduce ground friction and make greater speeds possible. Three groups of animals walk: echinoderms, by means of rigid spines and a remarkable hydraulic system; arthropods and terrestrial vertebrates, both by means of jointed legs.

The hydraulic mechanism of echinoderms is unique in the animal kingdom. The underside of a starfish, for example, is studded with hundreds of small **tube feet** which project through holes in the shell (Fig. 9.25). Each tube foot is a hollow muscular cylinder closed off at the outer end and connecting at the other with a system of tubes in the interior of the animal. Sea water can be pumped in and out of this vessel system through a valve on the upper surface of the animal (see Chap. 31). When the muscular walls of the vessels contract, water in the tube feet is put under pressure. Made rigid in this manner, tube feet are then used as walking levers. The internal structural arrangement is such that each tube foot can be made rigid or flaccid independently of others. Working in relays, groups of tube feet may propel the animal at a slow pace. In starfish and some other echinoderms, the ends of the tube feet may also be used as suction cups, aiding locomotion over hard surfaces.

FIG. 9.24. The locomotion of a clam. Diagrammatic. By successively extending its foot, anchoring it in sand, and then contracting and shortening the foot, a clam may propel itself forward slowly. The net distance covered in one propulsion cycle depends on how far the foot can be extended.

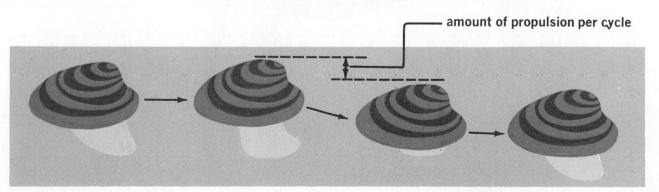

amount of propulsion per cycle

FIG. 9.25. The underside of a portion of a starfish. Note the tube feet and the tiny suction cup at the end of each tube foot. (Courtesy of Woody Williams, Inverness, Calif.)

present at elbow and knee, and lower limb bones are set vertically on the ground. In birds and mammals, the whole limb is placed directly under the body, and pillarlike support is obtained (Fig. 9.27). Strides are longest and speeds are greatest in these animals. The fastest of all land animals is probably the cheetah, a large leopardlike cat which may attain running speeds of about 50 miles per hour over short distances.

In mammalian walking, three of the four legs are generally in contact with the ground. In bipedal apes and in man, the mammalian "suspension-bridge" skeleton is turned upright (Fig. 9.28). Not having been designed for this position originally, it is subjected to new stresses and strains; fallen arches, backaches, and leg weariness in man are common consequences of bipedal locomotion. At rest, two arches and two legs must support a weight which in quadrupeds is distributed over four pillars.

Vertebrate Patterns

Walking by means of legs involves the limb skeleton, as indicated in Fig. 9.26. In the earliest land vertebrates, e.g., salamanders, the limbs jut out from the sides, and elbow and knee joints are rather stiff. Moving in sinuous, serpentine fashion, the animals hug the ground for real support. In later terrestrial vertebrates, limbs are underslung increasingly. Reptiles such as alligators and turtles possess upper limb bones which are still articulated horizontally at the sides, but pronounced bends are

bony
endoskeleton

chitinous
exoskeleton

muscle

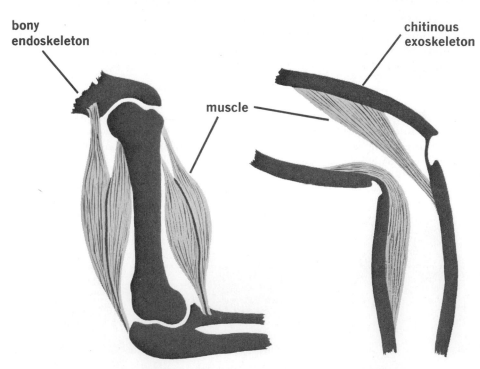

FIG. 9.26. Comparison of skeletal movement in vertebrates **A** and arthropods **B**. Diagrammatic. Note the type of leverage produced by muscles in an endoskeleton and an exoskeleton.

A

B

FIG. 9.27. Comparative positions of limbs in salamanders (left), reptiles (middle), and mammals (right).

FIG. 9.28. The skeleton of man. The mammalian suspension-bridge skeleton is here turned upright. Compare with cat skeleton, Fig. 9.21. (Ward's Natural Science Establishment, Inc.)

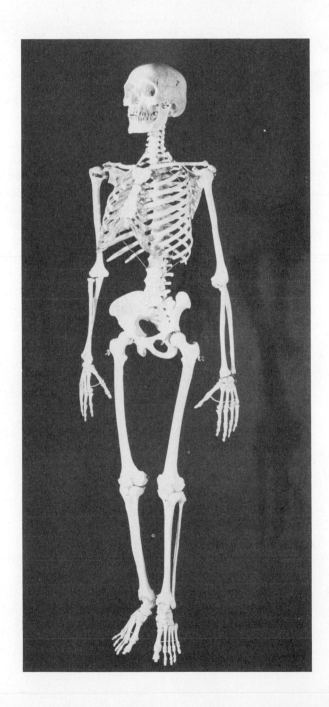

The waist and all the body above it are buttressed by the vertebral column alone, but in quadrupeds the horizontally placed small of the back upholds relatively very little weight.

However, several important adaptations to upright locomotion are in evidence. For example, heel bones are extremely sturdy, supporting most of the weight at rest. The vertebral column is curved like a double S and so cushions walking shocks better than a straight pillar. Individual vertebrae are broadest at the hip, narrowest in the neck, a feature which puts the greater weight on the stronger foundation. Tails, important to quadrupeds as balancers, but obstacles to an upright biped, are virtually absent. Head-supporting ligaments and the muscles of the neck are extremely powerful in quadrupeds but are reduced considerably in bipeds. Head support here derives more economically from the whole body underneath.

Through these adjustments, gradually perfected during recent evolutionary history, bipedal locomotion has become established as a profoundly simplified method of walking. And inasmuch as it has relieved the forelimbs of a locomotor function, it has made possible new roles for hands and fingers, among them the development and use of tools. Evidently, bipedal locomotion was a prerequisite for the emergence of human civilization.

SWIMMING AND FLYING

Although many animals can move in more than one propulsion medium, they are usually most adept in one. A chicken walks better than it flies; a

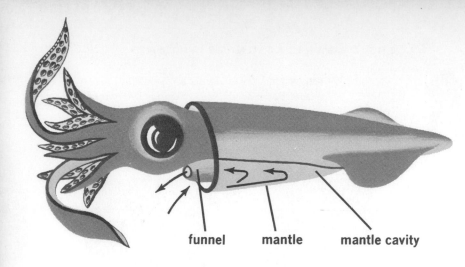

FIG. 9.29. The jet principle of locomotion in a squid. Note the external mantle, the mantle cavity (with arrows), and the funnel, through which water is squirted out, propelling the squid in the opposite direction.

funnel   mantle   mantle cavity

sparrow flies better than it walks. All flying animals have legs which serve at least in take-off and landing, but most habitual walkers and swimmers are permanently confined to the ground or to water. Once successful adaptation to one medium has been achieved, simultaneous adaptation to another becomes not only uneconomical but also unnecessary.

Aquatic Locomotion

The **whip,** the **jet,** and the **paddle** are the three major animal mechanisms for locomotion in dis-

placeable media. All three are encountered in water, but in the thin medium of air, only the paddle is efficient enough to provide lift against gravity.

Whip propulsion occurs in unicellular flagellate organisms, in virtually all aquatic worms, in water snakes, eels, a variety of insect larvae, and in all other elongated animals without obvious locomotor equipment. Jet propulsion has developed to a high degree of efficiency in squids and octopuses. In a squid, for example, water flows freely into a space underneath a muscular surface **mantle** (Fig. 9.29). The free edge of this mantle, at the level of the head, can be contracted so that the interior space is sealed off from the outside, except for an opening in a narrow muscular **funnel.** When the whole mantle contracts, water collected under the mantle is squeezed out through the funnel with great force. The emerging water jet propels the squid in the opposite direction. The funnel may be oriented by muscles, and the squid may thereby control the direction of its spurts. Speeds produced may match those of fish. Squids also possess a pair of horizontally placed fins, which are used for balancing and steering, and for slow, sustained cruising.

The oldest, most familiar, and probably the most widespread method of propulsion is paddling. Among the many paddle mechanisms in water are cilia; fleshy plates; webbed, flipper-shaped, or

FIG. 9.30. The chitinous wings of an insect. Note the stiffening "veins" in the wings. (U.S. Department of Agriculture.)

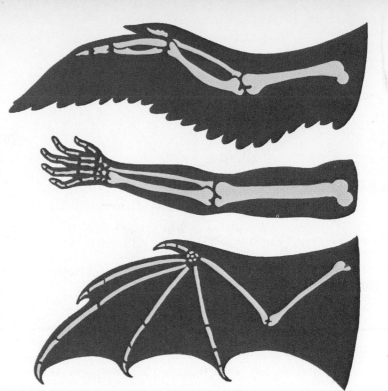

FIG. 9.31. Comparison of limb structure of bird wing (top), human arm (middle), and bat wing (bottom).

feather-shaped legs; lateral fins; tail fins. Fish move primarily by means of their muscular tails and the vertically placed tail fins. Lateral fins serve as balancers and steering devices.

Aerial Locomotion

In view of the physical properties of air, locomotion in this medium calls for much more strenuous paddling than locomotion in water. Only three groups of organisms now living are capable of sustained aerial flight: insects, birds, and bats. Wing structure and the mechanics of flight are different in all three.

Insect wings are thin blades of chitin, reinforced by stiffenings ("veins"), particularly at the leading edges (Fig. 9.30). Two pairs of wings are present in insects. Both pairs may be used for flying (dragonflies, butterflies); or the front pair may be transformed into protective wing covers (grasshoppers, beetles); or the hind pair may be transformed into stalked knobs (houseflies, mosquitoes). Everyone familiar with roast chickens is also familiar with the fleshy and bony components of the bird wing. This forelimb is composed essentially of the same skeletal elements as a human arm. A **humerus** is joined to the pectoral girdle, and a **radius** and an **ulna** are in turn joined to the humerus. Wrist and hand bones are elongated, and only three fingers are present. These various bones are partially fused (Fig. 9.31). The limb as a whole forms the leading edge of the wing, the rest being made up of feathers, avian counterparts of mammalian hair. A relatively small number of long, sturdy flight feathers contribute smooth contours. In bats, the fingers of the hand are elongated enormously, and skin stretched between them forms the wing blade.

Each of these wing types produces lift and push in a different manner. The insect wing describes a path resembling a figure 8. The back-and-down stroke pushes against the air; the forward-and-up stroke cuts the air with the wing edge. This type of wing motion produces propulsion in much the same way as rowing with oars propels a boat. Insect flight is powered by muscles *within* the body, *not* by muscles attached directly to the wings. In flight, insect wings are locked rigidly against the skeleton of the chest, and internal muscles rapidly flatten the chest, now from side to side, then from top to bottom, in a complex cycle.

In birds, the flight feathers of the wings function in the manner of venetian blinds. On the downstroke the "blind" is closed, giving lift and push. It opens on the upstroke, letting air through with a minimum of drag. Flight power is provided by two pairs of enormous chest muscles, the **pectoralis major** and **pectoralis minor** muscles, which form the "white meat" of a chicken. These are anchored at the keel, a bony plate projecting from the breast bone. On each side, the more powerful pectoralis major muscle attaches to the undersurface of the humerus, near the articulation of this wing bone with the pectoral girdle. Contraction of the muscle pulls the wing down. The pectoralis minor muscle is looped to the upper surface of the humerus. Contraction here pulls the wing up (Fig. 9.32).

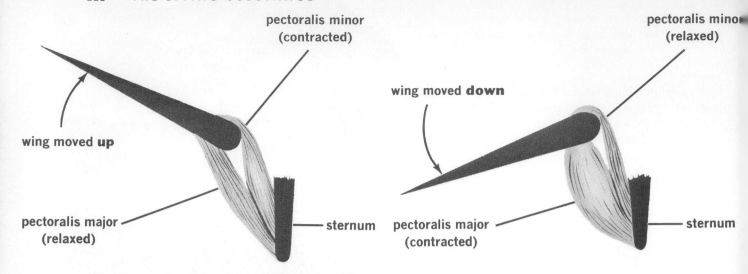

pectoralis minor
(contracted)

wing moved **up**

pectoralis major
(relaxed)

sternum

pectoralis minor
(relaxed)

wing moved **down**

pectoralis major
(contracted)

sternum

FIG. 9.32.   The motion of a bird wing. Left, the *pectoralis minor* muscle is contracted, the *p. major* muscle is relaxed, and the wing is up. Right, the downstroke is
produced when the *p. minor* relaxes and the *p. major* contracts. Both *pectoralis*
muscles are anchored to the keel, a bony plate projecting from the breastbone.

The bat wing gives lift and push on the downstroke, as in birds. In the upstroke, the wing is partially folded and drawn against the side of the body.
The whole cycle of motion closely resembles the
motion of human arms in breast-stroke swimming.
Patterns of muscle action are similar also.

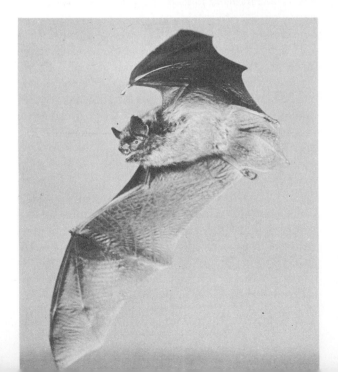

Each group of flying animals possesses important auxiliary adaptations for flight. For example,
light build and relatively small body size characterize all three. In all three also, the neck is rather reduced, for better streamlining. When flying, birds
lock their heads firmly against the neck vertebrae,
and all three flying groups retract their landing
gear.

Various degrees of flight efficiency are encountered. The fastest and most powerful flying is done
by birds, the most agile by insects. Many insects can
stand still in air, a feat matched only by humming-
birds. Cruising speeds of most birds generally do
not exceed 30 miles per hour. A type of South American swift has been clocked at about 75 miles per
hour, a flying speed which may probably be attained
also by falcons. In diving, a falcon may travel at
more than 100 miles per hour. Fast birds are generally rather small, with extremely streamlined bodies
and long slender wings.

Bats control their flying not so much through vision (these animals are nocturnal but they are by no

FIG. 9.33.   Bat in flight. (New York Zoological
Society.)

means blind) as through a unique system of "sound radar." The animal emits pulses of high-pitched sound from its voice box. These pulses are in the ultrasonic range, that is, they cannot be perceived by human ears without instruments. If the sound waves strike an object they bounce back, and this echo is heard by the animal. Time elapsed between emission and reception enables the bat to judge distances. Direction of sound is judged as in man. In free cruising flight (Fig. 9.33), relatively long pauses intervene between successive sound volleys, allowing time for an echo to return from far off before a next pulse is sent out. When a bat approaches an object, the frequency of the pulses increases and remains high till the animal is through a narrow aperture, or is past some obstruction, or has landed. This all-weather flight control easily matches in efficiency and functional elegance anything similar so far invented by man, such as radar or sonar.

To conclude, we stress again that locomotion of any sort is but a means, even though a very crucial means, toward the efficient exploitation of the animal way of life. As we have seen, this way begins with alimentation, and it encompasses all aspects of the internal organization of animals. Survival of this animal organization in turn depends in large measure on the survival of plant organization. Both great patterns of life are based on the structures and functions of cells and, ultimately, on the chemical and physical properties of protoplasm.

Having now examined the molecular, cellular, and organismic make-up of the living substance, we next inquire how this substance is maintained in existence, how it metabolizes and self-perpetuates.

REVIEW QUESTIONS

1. What structural and functional features distinguish most animals from most plants? What are the chief nutritional patterns among animals? How does alimentation influence the general structural and functional organization of animals?

2. Distinguish between herbivores, carnivores, and omnivores. Give examples of each, and show how their alimentary apparatus is adapted to their specific ways of life. Distinguish between intracellular and extracellular digestion. In which animal groups do either or both of these digestive patterns occur?

3. How are animals adapted to cope with climatic changes? Give examples of warm-blooded and cold-blooded animals, and show how they differ with respect to their internal temperature. What is hibernation, and what is its adaptive value?

4. Which internal components of a multicellular animal correspond to equivalent components of a plant? Which are found only among animals? What are the reasons for the greater internal diversification and specialization of animal structure?

5. How does the requirement of locomotion influence the general architecture of an animal? Contrast the basic design of moving and nonmoving animals.

6. What are the functions of muscles? What types of muscular tissue exist, and how are they different? Where is each of these types found in man?

7. What are the functions of skeletons? Distinguish between exoskeletons and endoskeletons. In what animal groups does each of these occur? What are the advantages and disadvantages of exoskeletons? Of endoskeletons? Review the general structure and development of the vertebrate skeleton.

8. What are the main kinds of animal locomotion? What are the main variants of muscular locomotion? How is locomotion accomplished in clams? In echinoderms?

9. Which animals walk? What are some of the skeletal adjustments to bipedal walking in man? What are the main mechanisms of locomotion in water? Give examples.

10. Which animals fly? Describe the wing structures and flight mechanisms of these animals, and describe also some of their auxiliary adaptations for flying.

SUGGESTED COLLATERAL READINGS

An excellent introduction to the patterns of life and the structural organization of animals will be found in the first two books, both beautifully illustrated. The third book is a comprehensive standard text, and the remaining sources listed deal with various aspects of animal organization discussed in this chapter.

Buchsbaum, R.: "Animals without Backbones," University of Chicago Press, 1948.

Romer, A. S.: "Man and the Vertebrates," University of Chicago Press, 1941.

Storer, T. I., and R. L. Usinger: "General Zoology," 3d ed., McGraw-Hill, 1957.

Cott, H. B.: "Adaptive Coloration in Animals," Oxford, 1940.

McLean, F. C.: Bone, *Sci. American,* vol. 192, 1955.

Rodbard, S.: Warmbloodedness, *Sci. Monthly,* vol. 77, 1953.

Lyman, C. P., and P. O. Chatfield: Hibernation, *Sci. American,* vol. 183, 1950.

Milne, L. J., and M. J. Milne: Temperature and Life, *Sci. American,* vol. 180, 1949.

Griffin, D. R.: The Navigation of Bats, *Sci. American,* vol. 183, 1950.

Storer, J. H.: Bird Aerodynamics, *Sci. American,* vol. 186, 1952.

Up to this point, our primary concern has been the "what" of living matter: *What* is the character of the living world as a whole? *What* are the structures and functions of the living substance? In the remainder of this book, we shall continue to heed the what, but our primary concern will be the "how": *How* does the living world come into being, and *how* is it maintained? *How* are the structures developed, and *how* are the functions carried out? In other words, our preoccupation will be more with the **operational** than with the *organizational* nature of living matter.

The operations of protoplasm are circumscribed by two words: metabolism and self-perpetuation. In this sequence of chapters, we deal with the first. Metabolism, we recall, may be described roughly as a group of processes which makes the living machinery run, which transforms an otherwise inert system into an active one. Specifically, metabolism includes, first, **nutrition**; second, the acquisition of oxygen, which is often a phase of breathing but is more generally a phase of **gas exchange**; third, the production of internal energy, or **respiration**, made possible by some of the nutrients and by oxygen; and fourth, the **utilization** of raw materials and of energy, always toward chemical activities such as *synthesis* of new protoplasmic components, sometimes toward physical activities such as *movement* (Fig. 10.1).

Nutrition and gas exchange are auxiliary to the remainder of metabolism. These two activities occur both on the level of the whole organism and on the level of the individual cell. But in either case, they merely support the metabolic work *within* individual cells, namely, respiration and utilization activities. These constitute *cellular metabolism* and, as such, the main

PART

3

METABOLISM

phase of all metabolism. For only if its *cellular* motors are running can the whole organism be alive.

In the seven chapters which follow, it will very often be necessary to discuss metabolic processes and principles in specific relation to particular organisms. In situations of this kind, we shall select the tracheophyte as a representative plant type and the mammal as a representative animal type.

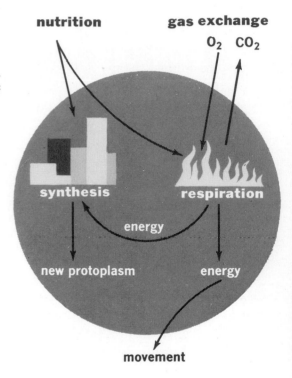

FIG. 10.1. The main component processes and results of metabolism.

NUTRITION MAY BE DEFINED generally as all those events through which necessary and directly usable supplies are delivered to, and into, individual cells. In green plants, nutrition specifically comprises three broad groups of processes: procurement of *inorganic nutrients;* manufacture of *organic nutrients;* and internal *transportation* of both. Inorganic nutrients are absorbed from soil and air and are transported to all cells by the xylem. From some of these materials, and with the aid of sunlight and chlorophyll, green cells manufacture organic nutrients, carbohydrates, through *photosynthesis.* These are distributed to the cells of a plant via the phloem. So supplied with inorganic and organic raw materials, each individual cell may then respire and synthesize (Fig. 10.2).

This chapter deals with the **inorganic nutrients** and the **internal transport** activities of green plants. We shall discuss photosynthesis separately in the following chapter.

The Inorganic Supplies

That plants require water and minerals has been well known since antiquity. What has not been known, and what is not completely known today, is how the plant incorporates these materials into its body. Aristotle believed that roots *eat* soil. What does present knowledge suggest?

SOIL

Before ancestral organisms had invaded the terrestrial environment, the land was bare of soil. But processes making possible its later formation were already under way. A profusion of stones and rock chips, produced by chemical and physical erosion, was steadily fragmented and ground into powder by the milling of rivers, the shear of ice sheets, and the battering impact of coastal surf. Silt was deposited

10

AUTOTROPHIC NUTRITION: SOIL, AIR, AND TRANSPORT

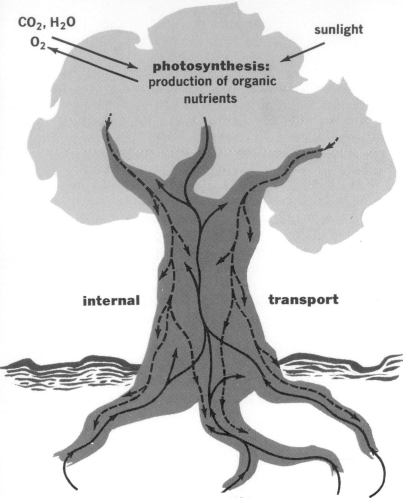

CO₂, H₂O

O₂

sunlight

**photosynthesis:
production of organic
nutrients**

internal   **transport**

**root absorption:
procurement of inorganic nutrients
(H₂O, minerals)**

FIG. 10.2. The general pattern of nutrition in green plants: procurement of inorganic nutrients from soil and air, manufacture of organic nutrients through photosynthesis, and internal transport of both inorganic and organic nutrients.

FIG. 10.3. Hydroponics, the soil-less culture of plants. In the glass jar is a sweet potato growing in water culture. Nutrients are added to the water. (Brooklyn Botanical Gardens.)

in flood plains and along river and ocean shores. Winds spread the dust farther inland. Small rock grains of rough, jagged texture formed **sand**, and even smaller microscopic particles formed **clay**. Sand and clay became the hard mineral fraction of soil.

Its third major component was contributed by protoplasm. Early terrestrial organisms shed their metabolic elimination products into the sand layers, and, upon death, their bodies came to be added as well. Bacteria, carried in by air or water, found sustenance in this material. Decay ensued which transformed the formerly living substance into a variety of complex chemicals, the organic fractions of soil, collectively called **humus**. Acids produced by decay also roughened up the surfaces of rock fragments, and so living organisms contributed to the formation of suitable sand dust.

Humus mixed in with sand and clay constituted soil. Formed first in isolated patches, it provided a foothold for small plants. As these died and decayed, more soil was produced, larger plants could root there, and over the centuries continuous soil layers developed in large areas. At the present time, perhaps a foot of soil, on an average, covers the arable land.

Actually, soil is not an essential medium for plant maintenance. For example, floating aquatic plants do very well without it. Moreover, land plants too can be maintained adequately if their roots are simply immersed in mineral-rich water, called **hydroponic** cultures (Fig. 10.3). Evidently, so long as the environment provides water and minerals at all, it does not matter too much through what medium the plant obtains these materials. On land, soil happens to be the usual and the cheapest, hence the most treasured, large-scale supplier. And it has the additional, very essential property of anchoring plants mechanically, without halting the continuous expansion of root systems.

General references to "soil" are usually references to the **topsoil,** the upper, most valuable layer. Topsoils differ widely in color, according to the types of minerals and humus components contained in them. From the standpoint of plant nutrition, *black soils* generally are the richest. The roots of small plants are embedded entirely in topsoil. Larger plants send their roots into the extensive subjacent layer, the **subsoil.** Here the proportion of clay is high; hence subsoil is relatively dense, and humus is virtually absent. Subsoil is usually underlain by **loose rock,** and this layer extends down to the continuous **bedrock** of the continent (Fig. 10.4).

The quality of topsoil depends on a wide variety of factors. If a soil layer is too thin, or if soil particles

FIG. 10.4. Profile of soil. Note dark topsoil, underlain by light-colored layer of subsoil. Streaked layers of clay lie under the subsoil, and the clay merges into rock near the bottom of photo. (U.S. Department of Agriculture.)

are blown away by wind or washed away by water, plants cannot obtain firm anchorage. Good soils are likely to be found in the lee of the wind, or in areas protected by hedges, trees, and plant cover in general. For as the soil holds the plant, so the plant also holds the soil (Fig. 10.5). In agriculturally impor-

FIG. 10.5. As the soil holds the plant, so the plant also holds the soil. Left: eroded land. Sandy gullies are present, which would enlarge gradually. Right: same landscape as above, after planting and about three years of growth. Erosion has been halted. (U.S. Department of Agriculture.)

tant regions, soil-conserving practices are now widespread. For example, soil erosion by water and wind can be reduced through flood control, through appropriate rain drainage (Fig. 10.6), and through contour plowing (Fig. 10.7).

If the sand particles are too small, or if there is too much clay, the soil is likely to be packed tight, and root growth will be difficult. But if the sand grains are too large, roots slip through the free spaces and plant anchorage is insecure. The **size** of the soil particles is not the only important consideration, however. Smooth round grains leave spaces between them through which water would drain off rapidly. Coarse grains with rough, jagged edges still leave sufficient room for aeration and root growth. However, despite such **texture,** water would be lost by drainage. It is the organic matter, primarily, which endows soil with its spongy, crumbly, water-retaining properties. In a good soil, this water-retaining action of humus is augmented further by the subsoil, which prevents water from seeping away too rapidly.

FIG. 10.7. Aerial view of contour-plowed region. In contour plowing, plow lines are run at right angles to the slope of the land to reduce wind and water erosion. (U.S. Soil Conservation Service.)

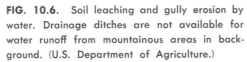

FIG. 10.6. Soil leaching and gully erosion by water. Drainage ditches are not available for water runoff from mountainous areas in background. (U.S. Department of Agriculture.)

WATER AND MINERALS

Soil particles are enveloped by thin films of water. This water is *bound;* that is, electrochemical forces hold the water molecules tightly against the soil molecules. Even relatively dry soil still retains its films of bound water. If there is much water in soil, some of the fluid is bound, but most of it is beyond the range of soil-particle attraction. Held loosely in the spaces between the hard particles, unbound water is the immediate water source for plants (see Fig. 10.9).

Mineral substances are dissolved in soil water. Present largely in the form of ions, soil minerals are normally supplied and replenished in three ways (Fig. 10.8): first, through **chemical dissolution** of the rock particles in soil by water; second, through the **decay** of dead plant and animal protoplasm, which returns to soil the minerals removed by living organisms, which also adds new organic substances, and which thus raises the humus content of soil; and third, through **nitrogen fixation** and **nitrification,** accomplished by bacteria which increase the nitrate (NO_3^-) supply of soil (see Chap. 5).

To prevent nutritional exhaustion of intensively cultivated land, man is often forced to augment these relatively slow natural processes of replenishment. He may do so by various procedures of **soil conservation.** For example, he may add mineral-rich *fertilizers* to soil. He may let soils *rest* for one or more seasons. He may grow crops and, instead of harvesting them, may plow them right back into the ground. Or he may adopt a program of *crop rotation,* whereby different crops are planted in successive seasons, each crop requiring different sets of soil minerals.

Experiments with hydroponic cultures may show what kinds of minerals are needed by different plants and what the cellular functions of these minerals might be. For example, a solution of mixed minerals may be prepared in which a particular ion is not present. If a plant can survive and grow in such a deficient hydroponic, then the missing ion may be concluded to be nonessential in plant metabolism. On the other hand, if the plant dies, or grows poorly, or develops disease, then the missing ion evidently is essential. The nature of the deficiency disease may often indicate the specific normal function of the mineral.

On the whole, the qualitative mineral requirements of plant protoplasm have been found to differ little from those of animal protoplasm. However, detailed quantitative requirements vary greatly, among plants as among animals. The kinds of mineral ions normally required by all plants include, for example, nitrate (NO_3^-), phosphate ($PO_4^{\equiv}$), chloride (Cl^-), carbonate ($CO_3^=$), sulfate ($SO_4^=$); and sodium (Na^+), potassium (K^+), calcium (Ca^{++}), magnesium (Mg^{++}), copper (Cu^{++}), and iron (Fe^{+++}).

ABSORPTION

Soil to Root Hair

All parts of the root epidermis may absorb soil nutrients. Since some 90 per cent of the available root surface is provided by the root hairs (see Chap. 8), most of the absorption occurs there. As noted earlier, root-hair zones advance continuously as the root grows. Therefore, by the time one region of soil is more or less depleted of raw materials, root-hair zones have already advanced to a new region. As individual root hairs grow out from epidermis cells, they drape themselves over a few soil particles, and the cell membrane of the root hair comes into intimate contact with the unbound water surrounding

FIG. 10.8.   Three ways in which soil minerals are replenished.

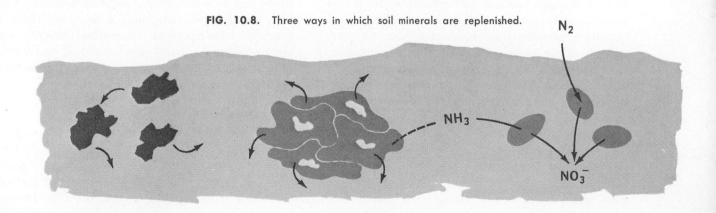

chemical dissolution
of rock grains

decay

nitrification and
nitrogen fixation

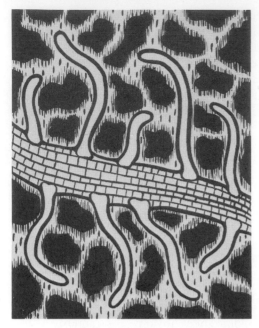

FIG. 10.9. Root hairs and soil (diagrammatic). Solid black areas represent soil grains. Halos of densely placed lines surrounding them represent bound water. Root hairs occupy regions filled with unbound water.

the soil grains (Fig. 10.9). The stage is now set for absorption.

A great deal of water absorption is accomplished through *osmosis*. Protoplasm within a root hair normally contains a higher concentration of dissolved particles than soil water. Osmotic pressure therefore pulls soil water into the root hair. However, a simple test shows that osmotic force cannot be the only agency responsible for water absorption. If it were, then it should be possible by "salting" the soil to stop, or even to reverse, water absorption. For if the soil is made to contain a higher concentration of dissolved particles than root-hair protoplasm, then the plant should *lose* water to the soil. Yet under such conditions the roots still take up water, though less than before (Fig. 10.10). Clearly, osmotic pull normally contributes some absorptive force, but another agency contributes even more. What is that other agency? We do not know, beyond realizing that it is active *absorptive work* done by the living root cell. En-

ergy is required for this work. When the energy-liberating machinery of the cell is stopped with poison, then biological water absorption is stopped too, though osmotic, physical absorption still continues.

The "living" aspect of absorption is also illustrated clearly in the uptake of soil minerals. If the semipermeable root-hair membrane were merely passive, like cellophane, then we should expect ions to *diffuse* from higher to lower concentrations. That is, ions should migrate from the more concentrated root protoplasm into the less concentrated soil water, until the concentrations on each side of the membrane were equal. In other words, root protoplasm should lose ions to the soil. This does not happen. On the contrary, ions migrate from the soil *into* the root, *against* the prevailing diffusion gradient (Fig. 10.10). Here again, energy- and oxygen-consuming work is done by the epidermal cells of the root. Their membranes are selective, moreover. Some ions are passed through readily; others are not.

Thus, Aristotle 2,000 years ago was apparently wrong when he said that roots eat soil—if he meant eating in the customary animal sense. But how does *any* cell "eat"? True, some have gullets; some engulf like amoebae. What about the vast majority of cells, however? How does a bacterium, or a human liver cell, or a cambium cell "eat"? They all *absorb* from their surroundings, whether these surroundings are blood, sap, or water. This absorption is active, selective, energy-consuming, and it does not differ in principle from root-hair absorption. Aristotle was right (or unconsciously prophetic?), if by "eating" he meant *active participation* of the plant in raw-material procurement.

Root Hair to Xylem

What happens to the water and the minerals absorbed into a root-hair cell? The most immediate effect is that the excess water tends to dilute the protoplasm of the cell. Should we not also expect that cell to swell up? We should indeed, but this does not happen to any appreciable extent. For most of the absorbed water and the dissolved materials are removed almost as soon as they enter the cell. The fluid is taken up by the cortex cells immediately adjacent to the root epidermis. This transfer essentially

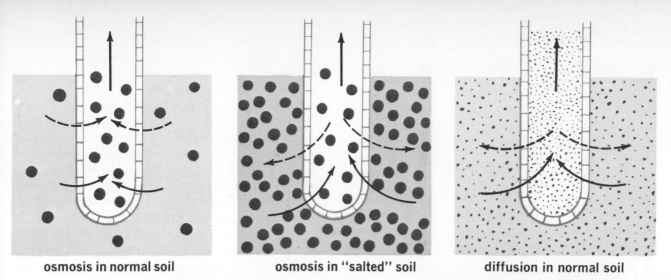

| osmosis in normal soil | osmosis in "salted" soil | diffusion in normal soil |

FIG. 10.10. Left: osmosis in roots. Particle concentrations are greater in root protoplasm than in soil; hence more water moves into root protoplasm from soil than in the reverse direction. Middle: the effect of "salting" the soil. Even if the particle concentration in soil is made greater than in root protoplasm, water still moves into the roots (solid arrows), against the osmotic gradient (broken arrows). This indicates that osmosis is not the only agency in water absorption; active absorption by living root cells is of equal or greater importance. Right: diffusion in roots. Because root protoplasm contains a higher concentration of mineral ions than soil, ions should be expected to diffuse out of roots (broken arrows). Yet ions actually migrate from soil into roots (solid arrows), against the diffusion gradient. This indicates that diffusion cannot be responsible for ion absorption. Active absorption by living root cells is involved instead.

repeats the original process of water absorption. As epidermis cells tend to become more diluted by soil water, concentrations in these cells become lower than in adjacent cortex cells. The latter therefore pull water into them osmotically. Moreover, they also actively absorb water from the epidermal layer. As a result, water which first had been in the soil, and then in the epidermis, is now in the outermost layer of the root cortex. *These* cells then tend to swell up, and their protoplasms tend to become more dilute. But water is now transferred again, into the next inner layer of cortex cells (Fig. 10.11).

In this manner, water and minerals are drawn progressively from cell layer to cell layer, toward the core of the root. Some of these nutritional supplies are retained by the cells along the route, but the

FIG. 10.11. The absorption path within a root. Water and dissolved minerals are absorbed by successively deeper layers of cells. In this manner, supplies eventually reach the xylem vessels.

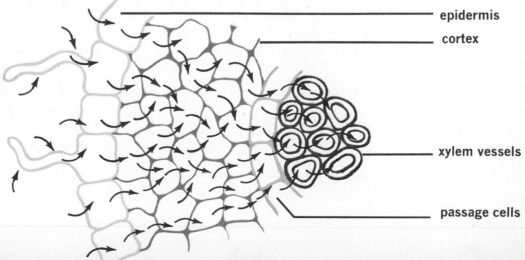

epidermis

cortex

xylem vessels

passage cells

FIG. 10.12. Through their xylem tubes, plants are interposed in the natural land-air-land cycle of water.

bulk soon reaches the root endodermis. We recall the presence of unsuberized *passage cells* in this layer (see Chap. 8). These provide a path into the root xylem. Water and dissolved materials are drawn into the passage cells, and from there they are pushed into xylem vessels.

Pushed is the right word. The water stream from soil to xylem vessel is continuous and uninterrupted, and it is not a stream which trickles lazily by its own weight. Rather, the combined osmotic pressure and the combined absorptive pressure of all root cells are behind the water, and this **root pressure** drives forcefully into the xylem tubes at the root core. As we shall see presently, it is largely this pressure generated by root cells which also drives sap to the crown of even the highest tree.

ATMOSPHERIC GASES

Soil water contains not only mineral ions but also a certain amount of dissolved atmospheric gases (O_2, CO_2). These too are absorbed by the roots along with the water and are transferred into xylem. Small fractions of these gases are retained by the root cells along the conduction pathway, and the remainder eventually reaches the leaf cells.

Whereas the soil represents the exclusive source of minerals and virtually the entire source of liquid water, the air offers a far richer source of gases than the soil. Indeed, photosynthesis requires a much more plentiful gas supply than is provided by the soil water which reaches the leaves; and plants do make ample direct use of the atmosphere.

Chapter 8 has shown that green cells are in direct contact with the external air; stomata and the interconnected spaces in the mesophyll permit free circulation of air through a leaf. Gaseous oxygen, carbon dioxide, and water vapor may therefore be absorbed directly by each leaf cell. Moreover, the gaseous byproducts of metabolism, as well as excess water absorbed by the roots, may be excreted from the green cells into the atmosphere.

We may conclude that, in a tracheophyte, the parts specialized for the procurement of inorganic raw materials are the epidermal root-hair cells and the mesophyll cells of the leaves. The latter also manufacture the organic nutrients, out of the inorganic supply. What makes these localized activities useful to the plant as a whole is *transportation* of the various nutrients from the few points of supply to the many points of utilization.

Internal Transport

XYLEM CONDUCTION

Like other water-containing structures, plants and animals too are affected by the global forces which circulate water in a vast cycle; water on the surface of the earth evaporates, clouds form, rain and snow fall, and surface water is thereby replenished. Inasmuch as they are subjected to water losses through evaporation, all terrestrial plants and animals are interposed in the surface-to-air segment of this cycle. But terrestrial organisms succeed in *delaying* evaporation, and this permits them to retain a necessary reservoir of liquid water for the maintenance of life. Moreover, they exploit this reservoir additionally by making it serve as the vehicle for internal transport.

In the case of terrestrial plants, water is absorbed by the roots, and living energy lifts it high via the xylem channels. Such water as is not retained in the cells is only then allowed to evaporate from the leaves and other exposed surfaces (Fig. 10.12). Minerals stay in the plant since they cannot evaporate.

Push

How is this lifting of water accomplished? It is important here to recognize that, in a healthy plant, xylem tubes are never empty of water. Even before a xylem vessel becomes functional, i.e., at a stage when only a column of newly formed tracheid cells marks the location of a future conducting vessel, protoplasmic water already fills the interior of the cells. Later, when the top and bottom walls of tracheids dissolve and the interior protoplasm disintegrates, the water remains. As the plant grows in length, new tracheids are joined to the top of the xylem vessel. Each added tracheid also adds a corresponding cylinder of water to the column below. Water thus *grows* up, as the plant grows up. No matter how high the plant, therefore, continuous, uninterrupted water columns range from every root-hair membrane, through root cortex and xylem vessels, to every leaf mesophyll membrane.

Upward "transportation" consequently becomes a matter of adding water at the bottom of such columns and withdrawing an equivalent amount from the top, minus the fraction which living tissues incorporate into their substance. As we have seen, root-hair absorption adds water at the bottom and generates **root pressure.** This is the principal force which pushes the water columns up.

Pull

But root pressure is not alone responsible for the lifting of water. A second force, pull from above, is generated by **transpiration,** that is, evaporation of water from the leaves. As water vaporizes from a mesophyll cell, the cell tends to become partially dehydrated, and so the concentration of protoplasmic particles tends to increase. Osmotic pressure there-

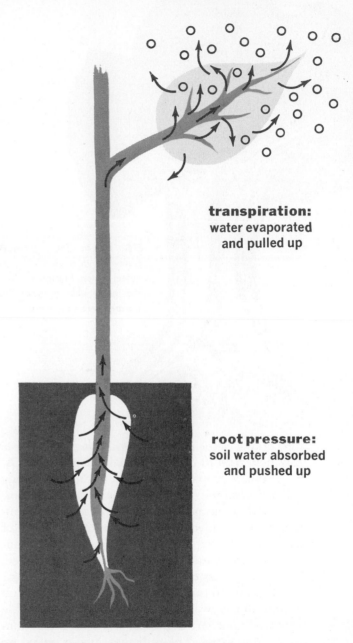

transpiration:
water evaporated
and pulled up

root pressure:
soil water absorbed
and pushed up

FIG. 10.13. Xylem tubes contain continuous columns of water. Root pressure adds more water at the bottom and transpiration removes water at the top through evaporation; hence any given section of a water column in xylem moves upward.

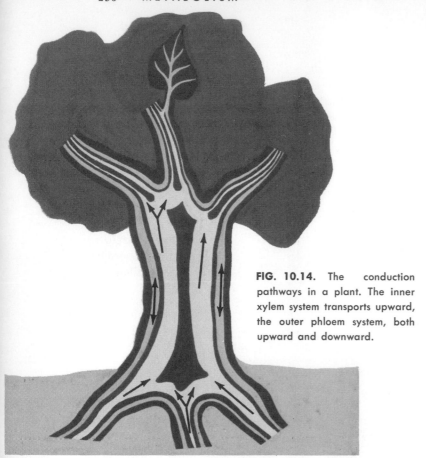

FIG. 10.14. The conduction pathways in a plant. The inner xylem system transports upward, the outer phloem system, both upward and downward.

umns, and an equal quantity (at most) is pulled away from the top by transpiration (Fig. 10.13). Continued over a period of time, water which at first stands at the level of the root is gradually shifted up into the leaves. Water or minerals now entering the roots of a high tree therefore may not reach leaves for several days; and materials now absorbed by mesophyll cells may have entered the roots several days before.

Measurement shows that root pressure generally suffices to drive water right up to the highest leaves of even the tallest tree. This mechanism can be operative when transpiration is not, as in winter when leaves are not present, or under humid conditions, when evaporation from leaves is reduced. Under other conditions, transpiration becomes a potent second force in xylem conduction.

Cohesion

It should be clear that such a mechanism of transport depends on uninterrupted continuity of the water columns. The condition that the transport fluid is water, rather than another medium, greatly facilitates the maintenance of column continuity. For water possesses a high degree of **cohesion.** Individual molecules attract one another rather strongly, and a column of water therefore "hangs together" with appreciable tenacity. If the continuity of water in xylem vessels were broken by emptying them, then these vessels could never again function as water conductors. For neither the roots nor the leaves, nor both together, can raise a whole new column of liquid from the ground to the leaves through air-filled vessels.

As noted in Chap. 8, uninterrupted xylem vessels are not present in ferns and coniferous seed plants, where the horizontal cross walls of the original tracheid cells persist. Transport mechanics are not different here. Pit membranes in the cross walls are permeable to water and mineral ions and present no barrier to continuous flow. In all tracheophytes, pits along the side walls of the xylem channels permit *lateral conduction,* as well as equilibration of flow pressure among adjacent columns of **water.**

fore draws water in from neighboring cells. *These* cells now tend to become partially dehydrated. Osmotic pull is propagated back in this manner, along cell paths leading to xylem terminals. As in roots, osmotic pull is accompanied by active cellular absorption. The combined osmotic and absorptive action of leaf cells pulls water up through the xylem, in quantities commensurate with the amount evaporated. The effectiveness of this pull from above is familiar to everyone. An isolated leaf, or a flower with a stub of stem and a few leaves, survives for a considerable time when put into a glass of water; as water transpires from exposed plant tissues, fluid is pulled up from below.

We note that the two forces which raise sap against gravity are *living* cellular push from below and *living* cellular pull from above. A quantity of water is squeezed into the bottom of the xylem col-

The key point in xylem transport is that the power source lies in living roots and leaves. The nonliving xylem tubes as such are passive, in the same way that a pipeline between two pumping stations is passive. Conduction through phloem is different in this respect. In this system the power source is spread out all along the transportation route.

PHLOEM CONDUCTION

The Transport Process ·

Unlike xylem, phloem is a two-way path (Fig. 10.14). Downward conduction in phloem has long been known to occur; many roots store carbohydrates, which are photosynthesized only in leaf or stem. The occurrence of upward conduction has come to light through grafting experiments. For example, a stem of a tobacco plant grafted to a root of a tomato plant develops normal tobacco leaves, but these are entirely free of nicotine. Conversely, a tomato-plant stem transplanted to a tobacco-plant root produces tomato leaves, but these are full of nicotine. The first graft indicates that only the roots of a tobacco plant synthesize nicotine; the second graft, that the drug is transported upward. And since xylem channels are virtually free of nicotine, upward conduction must occur largely in phloem (Fig. 10.15).

Indeed, most of the organic nutrients of a plant travel in the phloem channel. Photosynthesized carbohydrates and their derivatives migrate from leaves and stem downward; organic storage products and materials manufactured from them travel from roots and stem upward. Some upward conduction of organic substance also occurs in xylem. For example, small amounts of sugar are generally present in this channel. In the case of the sugar maple, this dilute xylem sap is processed into maple syrup.

The driving force in phloem transport is probably generated by the individual phloem units. We recall the composition of such a unit. A living companion cell is adjacent to, and presumably controls the functioning of, a section of sieve tube which contains cytoplasm but not a nucleus (see Chap. 8). The mechanism of phloem transport probably does

FIG. 10.15. If tobacco leaves are grafted onto tomato roots (left), nicotine will be absent from the tobacco leaves. If tomato leaves are grafted onto tobacco roots, the tomato leaves will eventually contain nicotine. Experiments of this sort show that only tobacco roots manufacture nicotine and that this drug is transported upward by the phloem.

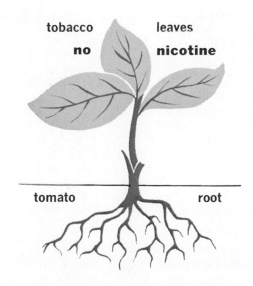

tobacco leaves
no **nicotine**

tomato root

graft shows nicotine is not formed
in leaves, but in roots, of tobacco plant

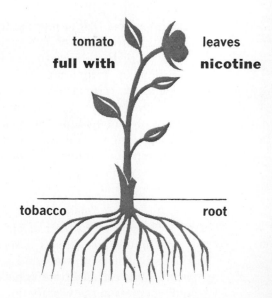

tomato leaves
full with **nicotine**

tobacco root

graft shows nicotine transported
upwards from tobacco root

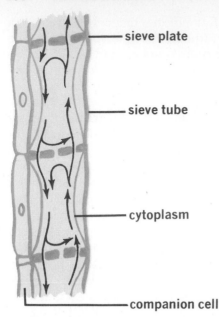

sieve plate

sieve tube

cytoplasm

companion cell

FIG. 10.16. Conduction in phloem units. All materials in the protoplasm of sieve tubes are kept in circulation by cyclotic streaming. Differentials in concentration determine whether or not a given substance will pass through sieve plates from one phloem unit to another.

not differ from that of internal transport in *any* cell. That is, movement of materials may be brought about by cyclosis, by concentration differentials and diffusion in cytoplasm, by sol-gel changes. In phloem, the vertical direction of conduction is imposed by the anatomical arrangement. For absorption of organic materials into sieve-tube cytoplasm, and secretion out of it, are accomplished most easily at the top and bottom perforations, where the barriers are minimal (Fig. 10.16).

Direction of Transport

The two-way aspect of phloem conduction becomes intelligible on this basis. Mesophyll cells in the leaf photosynthesize, and so they acquire relatively high carbohydrate concentrations. Terminal phloem units in the vicinity do not photosynthesize; hence their carbohydrate content is lower. Conse-

quently, diffusion tends to equalize the concentrations, and the terminal phloem units absorb some of the mesophyll-produced carbohydrate. Their own carbohydrate content increases as a result, relative to that of lower phloem units next in line along the conduction path. These lower phloem units now absorb from units above them, and in this fashion nutrient conduction continues downward (Fig. 10.17). Cells along the way may retain greater or lesser amounts of the carbohydrate. But the bulk will be carried into the roots, step by step from one section of sieve tube to the next, under the impetus of the diffusion gradient pointing from the leaves toward the roots.

Alternatively, organic materials may be carried upward, if the concentrations of such materials are high in the roots and lower above. This is the case,

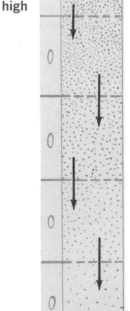

high · · · · concentration

low · · · · concentration

FIG. 10.17. The role of nutrient concentrations in phloem conduction. If a given nutrient is highly concentrated at one end of a phloem channel and less highly concentrated at the other, as shown, then a diffusion gradient will point from the high to the low concentration. The nutrient thus will be translocated in that direction.

for example, in winter and early spring, when leaves are absent and photosynthesis does not take place. Organic nutrients stored in the roots during the preceding summer then travel upward into the food-requiring regions of the stem and the crown.

Like so many other cell membranes, the membranes of phloem cells exhibit selective activity too. If a horizontal disk is cut from a stem, and if this disk is allowed to grow back into its original space in an inverted position, then the stem is intact, but a section of it has reversed polarity. This does not interfere with xylem conduction. But phloem conduction may be impaired. Substances like glucose may still travel downward through the inverted section of stem. Yet materials like auxins, growth hormones manufactured only in apical shoot meristems (see Chap. 19), generally may not. Sieve-tube membranes evidently let some substances through in one direction only.

Phloem conduction, up or down, is slow compared with xylem conduction. In phloem, also, we do not find a distinct flowing sap, as in xylem vessels. The transportation medium, namely, sieve-tube protoplasm, flows and shifts within its cellulose confines only but does not itself flow up or down bodily. Nutrient molecules alone are handed from one unit to the next. For this reason, nutrient conduction in phloem is often spoken of as **translocation,** a more specific designation than "transportation."

Each cell of a plant depends on the conduction channels for some or all of its supplies. Such supplies include raw materials absorbed by roots and photosynthesized in leaves and secretion products manufactured elsewhere in the plant. Evidently, the phloem and xylem channels are likely to transport complex mixtures of many substances.

Internal transport as a whole and procurement of inorganic supplies by roots and leaves not only *contribute* to, but also *depend* on, photosynthesis. For it is this third and most vital nutritional activity which produces the very building materials, and the energy, for the construction of the whole plant, including its roots, its leaves, and its transport tissues.

REVIEW QUESTIONS

1. Define metabolism. What major processes are included under this term? Define nutrition. What are the major nutritional processes of autotrophic plants?

2. What are the components of topsoil? What layers are found under the topsoil? How do soils originate? In what ways do plants depend on soil? What are the attributes of good soils?

3. Review the ways in which soil minerals are replenished.

4. What procedures of soil conservation reduce erosion and aid in soil maintenance? How does man conserve and enrich the mineral content of soil?

5. What are hydroponics, and how do they contribute to our knowledge of the nutritional requirements of plants?

6. What are the specific kinds of inorganic raw materials a plant must obtain? Where, and through what processes, does a plant absorb (*a*) water and (*b*) other minerals?

7. How does a plant obtain atmospheric gases? Review the anatomical pathways by which a plant acquires and transports all the various categories of needed nutrients.

8. What is root pressure, and how is it generated? What is transpiration, and what role does it play in xylem conduction? What kinds of nutrients are transported in xylem, and in which direction?

9. What forces bring about phloem conduction? What kinds of nutrients are carried in phloem, and in which direction? Describe in detail the processes which would bring about the upward translocation of a given nutrient.

10. If a cut length of stem bearing some leaves were put upside down into a glass of nutrient-rich water, how would (*a*) xylem conduction and (*b*) phloem conduction be affected? How has it been proved that phloem may transport in both directions? Can all phloem-transported substances migrate in either direction?

SUGGESTED COLLATERAL READINGS

The last two books listed contain good accounts of all aspects of plant metabolism. The other sources below supplement the discussion of particular topics presented in this chapter.

Kellogg, C. E.: Soil, *Sci. American,* vol. 183, 1950.

Swanson, C. L. W.: Soil Conditioners, *Sci. American,* vol. 189, 1953.

Bennett, H. H.: "Elements of Soil Conservation," 2d ed., McGraw-Hill, 1955.

Dudley, F.: Progress in Soil Science, *Amer. Scientist,* vol. 34, 1946.

Whaley, W.: Research and the Land, *Amer. Scientist,* vol. 38, 1950.

Gilbert, F. A.: "Mineral Nutrition of Plants and Animals," University of Oklahoma Press, 1948.

Hambidge, G.: "Hunger Signs in Crops," American Society of Agronomy, 1941.

Milner, H. W.: Some Problems in the Large-scale Culture of Algae, *Sci. Monthly,* vol. 80, 1955.

Greulach, V. A.: The Rise of Water in Plants, *Sci. American,* vol. 187, 1952.

Bonner, J., and A. W. Galston: "Principles of Plant Physiology," Freeman, 1952.

Meyer, B. S., and D. B. Anderson: "Plant Physiology," Van Nostrand, 1952.

11

AUTOTROPHIC NUTRITION: PHOTOSYNTHESIS

THE FUNDAMENTAL IMPORTANCE of the set of reactions in which CO_2 and H_2O are transformed into carbohydrates and oxygen cannot be overestimated. Carbohydrates produced through photosynthesis constitute the basic raw materials which, directly or indirectly, give rise to all organic components of virtually all plant and animal protoplasm and to virtually all living energy. The only organisms not dependent on photosynthesis are the chemosynthetic bacteria (see Chap. 8), which together amount to probably less than 0.01 per cent of all the protoplasm on earth.

The global impact of photosynthesis is underscored by statistical data. Every year, some 200 billion tons of carbon goes through the photosynthetic process. This makes it the most massive chemical event, and the second most massive event of all kinds, on earth. Only the global evaporation-precipitation cycle of water involves more material. Carbon dioxide is used up in photosynthesis in enormous amounts. If the gas were not replenished through plant and animal respiration and other combustion processes, then the CO_2 content of the entire atmosphere would be exhausted in a few months, and that of the ocean in about 300 years. Oxygen is released through photosynthesis so voluminously that all the O_2 of the present atmosphere could be generated in about 2,000 years, an incredibly short time from a geological standpoint. Finally, the solar energy harvested annually through photosynthesis in the form of carbohydrates amounts to fully one-fourth of the total energy available to man from all sources.

This quantitative and qualitative importance of photosynthesis has been appreciated for a very long time. Research on the nature of the process began in the seventeenth century, when Van Helmont showed that plant growth could not be a result of any soil eating by roots, as Aristotle had believed. Van Helmont planted a willow twig in a measured amount of soil, and after caring for this plant for some years, he found that the weight of the soil had decreased by only a few ounces. But the twig had become a young tree weighing many pounds (Fig. 11.1). Van Helmont therefore concluded that water added to soil, not soil itself, must serve as nourishment in plant growth.

Around the middle of the eighteenth century, Priestley discovered that an animal and a plant sealed together into a glass chamber could survive, although the animal or the plant alone could not survive (Fig. 11.2). He concluded that the plant changed "fixed air" exhaled by the animal into "good air"; or as we would say today, plants take up CO_2 exhaled by the animal, and the animal takes up O_2 released by the plant. Some years later, the Priestley effect was shown to hinge on the presence of light and of living green tissue. Work during the nineteenth century demonstrated that CO_2 and water absorbed by a green plant yielded O_2 and an *organic* endproduct. This endproduct was subsequently identified as a carbohydrate. Thus, not until almost the beginning of the present century could the overall photosynthetic equation be written:

$$CO_2 + H_2O \xrightarrow[\text{chlorophyll}]{\text{light}} \text{carbohydrate} + O_2$$

We know today that the above does not describe the actual photosynthetic reaction. Contrary to what the equation suggests, carbohydrates are *not* formed simply by mixing carbon dioxide and water; the product of such mixing would be only carbonic acid. The above is, in fact, not a proper equation at all but merely a vague statement of *input* and *output*. It indicates what kinds of materials go into photosynthesis and what kinds come out, but it does not, for example, give quantitative information concerning these materials. Moreover, it indicates neither the amount nor the kind of light required, and it does not specify the requirement of living cells with intact chloroplasts. Above all, the statement does not indicate the many intermediate processes now known to occur between input and output.

A consideration of these finer details of photosynthesis is now our objective.

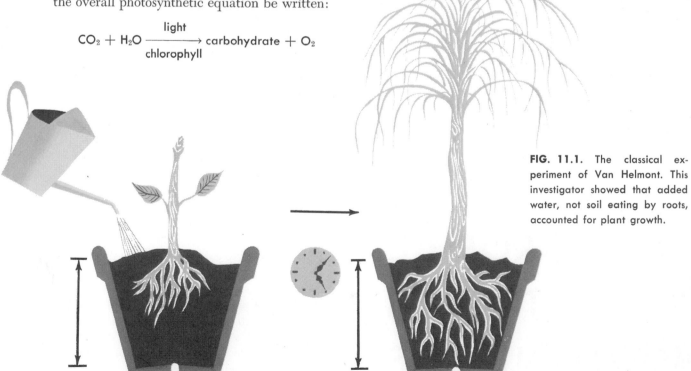

FIG. 11.1. The classical experiment of Van Helmont. This investigator showed that added water, not soil eating by roots, accounted for plant growth.

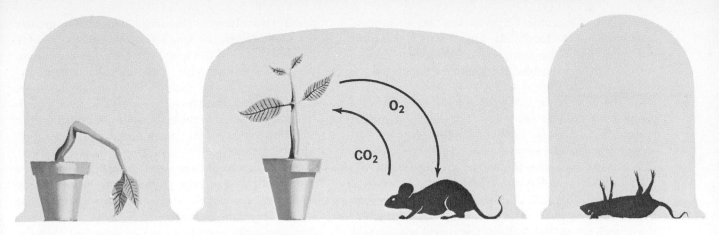

FIG. 11.2.   The classical experiment of Priestley. This investigator showed that a plant and an animal, when sealed into separate chambers, could not survive, but that they could survive if they were sealed into a chamber together.

Light and Chlorophyll

Chlorophyll is perceived as a green substance. This elementary observation tells about the role of the chlorophyll molecule in photosynthesis.

THE MEANING OF COLOR

Color is not an inherent property of an object. It is a subjective impression, dependent entirely on how the eye-brain complex interprets particular light waves received from the object. When we "see

color," the following series of events takes place. An object is illuminated with light waves from a self-luminous source. Depending on the physical and chemical properties of the object, some of the light waves may be **absorbed** into it; some may be **transmitted** through it; and some may be **reflected** from it. If transmitted or reflected waves reach the eye, nerve impulses will travel from the eye to the brain, and the brain will then interpret these impulses as "color" (Fig. 11.3).

It follows that an object which *absorbs* all the light falling on it, and transmits or reflects nothing, would be invisible and would appear as a "hole in

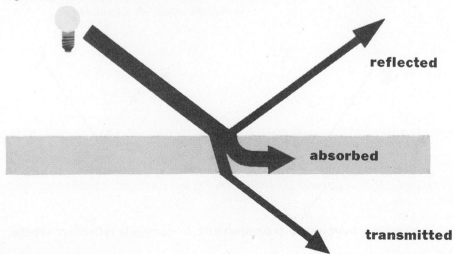

reflected

absorbed

transmitted

FIG. 11.3. Light reaching an object may be partly reflected, partly absorbed, and partly transmitted. Light which is absorbed cannot be seen by an external observer.

space." A black object approaches this theoretical condition most closely. An object which *transmits* all light would be completely transparent and so would also be invisible. And an object which *reflects* all light would appear white (Fig. 11.4).

The subjective nature of color is revealed in a number of familiar situations. For example, certain color-blind persons cannot distinguish red and green objects. The trouble here clearly lies not with the objects but with the visual mechanism of the viewers. Most seeing animals do not even possess visual organs capable of distinguishing between different light waves. These animals may perceive form and shape, but to them the world is a pattern in gray.

Evidently, although we commonly say "chlorophyll is green," we must realize that chlorophyll as such actually has no color of its own. The phrase is a shorthand figure of speech for essentially the following: "The properties of the chlorophyll molecule are such that it absorbs certain light waves and reflects and transmits others. If these reflected or transmitted waves reach the eye, most of us will interpret them as 'green.'"

WAVES AND ENERGY

Light waves of any kind are forms of energy—radiant, electromagnetic energy. The sun emits many electromagnetic radiations other than light, and, like light, each of them is characterized by a

definite **wavelength** and **energy content.** The greater the wavelength, the smaller is the energy content. Electrical waves, the longest of the solar radiations, are the least energetic. Progressively shorter and more energetic are radio waves, infrared waves, light waves, ultraviolet waves, and X rays. So arranged in order of wavelengths, this electromagnetic radiation series forms a continuous **radiation spectrum.**

Just as a radio receiver is sensitive to only a portion of this spectrum, namely, radio waves, so the human eye is sensitive to only a portion, namely, the **visible spectrum,** consisting of light waves. The human eye-brain complex is so constructed that the longest, least energetic light waves are perceived as red color, and the shortest, most energetic, as the color violet. Light waves of intermediate length and energy content are perceived in the various other colors of the rainbow—orange, yellow, green, and blue. Viewed together, the whole spectrum of visible waves is interpreted as "white" light.

We may conclude, therefore, that the light waves which chlorophyll reflects and transmits, and which make chlorophyll appear green to us, have

FIG. 11.4. Complete light absorption by an object makes that object theoretically invisible, or black in practice. Complete light transmission makes an object theoretically invisible too, or transparent in practice. Complete reflection makes an object appear to be of the same color as the light; i.e., if white light is completely reflected, the object will appear white.

complete absorption: **black**

complete transmission: **transparent**

complete reflection: **white**

intermediate length and energy content, and that the light waves which chlorophyll absorbs must be the other components of the visible spectrum, namely, the long red-orange-yellow waves and the short blue-violet waves.

Since light is energy, it can be made to do work, potentially at least. But if light is to do actual work, it must be *absorbed* by a suitable working mechanism. A mechanism which merely reflects or transmits light does not trap the energy of that light, and energy which is not trapped cannot supply power for work. Hence, inasmuch as chlorophyll reflects or transmits "green" waves, we may infer that these can *not* play a role in photosynthesis. On the other hand, chlorophyll does absorb all except the green light waves to greater or lesser degree. We may therefore infer that any or all of these absorbed waves do supply energy for photosynthesis. Indeed, plants exposed exclusively to green light cannot photosynthesize and they soon die. But they grow well when they receive light from any other part of the visible spectrum.

PIGMENTS AND PLASTIDS

From a chemical standpoint, several slightly different types of chlorophyll may be distinguished. So-called chlorophyll *a* occurs in most plants. In addition, chlorophylls *b*, *c*, and *d* are found in different proportions in different plant types (see Chap. 30). All kinds of chlorophyll molecules consist, essentially, of four complex carbon-nitrogen rings, which in turn are combined into a larger ring, the "head" of the molecule. At the center of this head is a single atom of magnesium, held to the smaller rings by side linkages. A "tail" of linked carbons is attached to one of the smaller rings (Fig. 11.5).

It is interesting to note that this structural pattern of chlorophyll is remarkably similar to that of *heme*, the colored component of hemoglobin in animal blood cells. An atom of iron is in the center of heme, in place of magnesium, and some other differences exist. But in major structural respects, the most important plant pigment and the most important animal pigment are intriguingly alike.

In most plants, chlorophyll is concentrated in

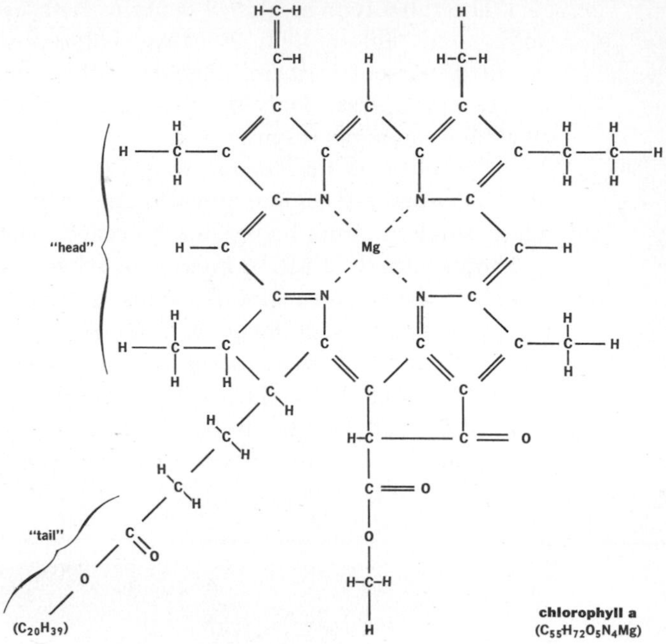

FIG. 11.5. The chemical structure of a molecule of chlorophyll.

plastids, round or oval bodies situated in the cytoplasm of plant cells (see Chap. 7). On the basis of their pigment content, three varieties of plastids may be distinguished.

One does not contain any pigments. Plastids of this kind are found widely in roots and in the colorless tissues of stems and leaves. These bodies function primarily as *starch-storing* centers.

A second type of plastid contains **carotenoid pigments.** These colored substances are of two kinds: the **carotenes,** which vary in color from cream white to turnip yellow, carrot orange, and tomato red; and the **xanthophylls,** which produce the bright yellows of plants, as in buttercups. In different plant species, carotenoid-containing plastids occur in roots, stems, leaves, flowers, fruits, or several of these plant parts together. Carotenoid pigments are widespread also in the animal kingdom (e.g., the yellow hue of egg yolk, butter, and other animal fats), and we may note that they are related chemically to vitamin A (see Chap. 19).

The third type of plastid contains both carotenoids and chlorophyll. Because chlorophyll is uniquely present in them, plastids of this kind are called **chloroplasts**. Only they are green, and only they function in photosynthesis.

The electron microscope shows that a chloroplast is composed of numerous **grana** (Fig. 11.6). These small granular bodies are the functional units in photosynthesis. Each granum consists of a series of protein layers, arranged like coins in a stack. Between every two such layers is a double layer consisting of fatty material, chlorophyll, and carotenoid molecules (Fig. 11.7). The fairly orderly arrangement of these molecules in the diagram may depict actual conditions; the pigment molecules are believed to be positioned with a regularity approaching that of a crystal.

CHLOROPLASTS AND GREEN CELLS

Blue-green algae do not possess chloroplasts. But they do contain individual grana, dispersed throughout the cell. Photosynthetic bacteria contain neither chloroplasts nor grana. The structure of the chlorophyll carriers in these organisms is still obscure.

In chloroplasts, the green pigment largely hides the red-yellow colors of the carotenoids. Different plant types contain different proportions of these pigments, hence the various lighter and deeper

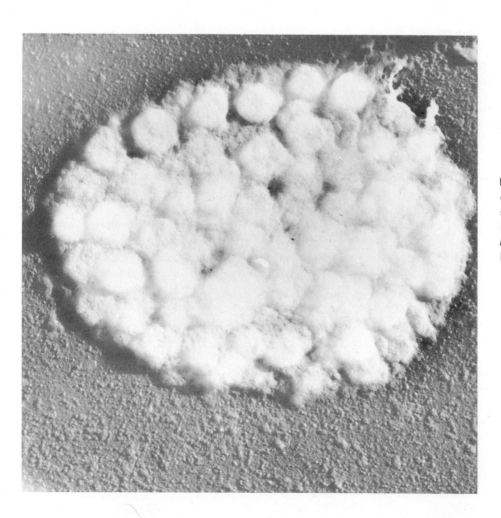

FIG. 11.6. Electron micrograph of a single chloroplast, showing the grana. (Courtesy of R. W. G. Wyckoff, "Electron Microscopy," Interscience Publishers, 1949.)

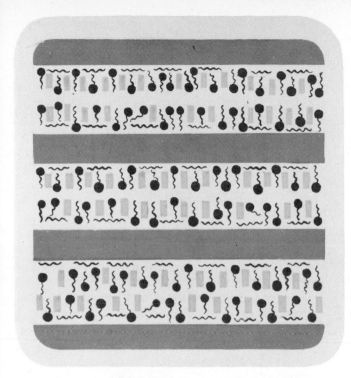

protein

chlorophyll

carotenoid

fatty substances

FIG. 11.7. Diagrammatic representation of the internal structure of a single granum of a chloroplast. Note the layered arrangement of the components.

shades of green in a landscape. In the fall, when the chlorophyll of the leaves disintegrates, the more stable carotenoid pigments become unmasked. These are mainly responsible for the brilliant autumn colors of plants. Many plants at that season also manufacture **anthocyanin** pigments, substances which are not within plastids but are free in cellular cytoplasm. The anthocyanins produce the deep reds, purples, and blues of plants. Some species contain anthocyanins throughout the year, in various body parts (e.g., the deep red of beet roots).

In flowering plants, but not in most others, the production and maintenance of chlorophyll within chloroplasts ordinarily require exposure to light. A young shoot, for example, does not turn green until it is well above the soil surface. In a plant grown in a dark chamber, chlorophyll soon breaks down and the plant loses its green color. In the continued absence of light new chlorophyll is then not synthesized. However, in certain green tissues, chlorophyll may disintegrate even in the presence of light, as a normal process of development. For example, immature fruits are green, and as they ripen the color of chlorophyll in many cases gives way to the brilliant shades of carotenoid and anthocyanin pigments.

Some evidence exists that the manufacture of chlorophyll within cells may be assisted by the carotenoids normally present in chloroplasts. Carotenoids essentially are long chains of carbon atoms, and parts of such chains may form the "tails" of the chlorophyll molecules (see Fig. 11.5).

A green cell may possess from a few up to about 80 chloroplasts. In a mature tree, all the chloroplasts together may provide a surface area for light absorption totaling some 150 square miles. Chloroplasts contain nucleoproteins, as noted in Chap. 7, and these green bodies reproduce within cells. Thus the chloroplast population may keep pace with the growth of the tissues of which they are constituents.

The materials and the machinery for food production are now assembled. Far-off roots have supplied the green cell with water, minerals, and some of the atmospheric gases. Stomata have piped in most of the gases and some of the water. Already deployed in the green cell are the chloroplasts and their grana, which contain the pigments, the enzymes, and the whole chemical machinery required for food production. These materials and structures set the scene for photosynthesis. The play begins when sunlight illuminates this scene.

Water and Carbon Dioxide

THE UNIT REACTION

Photosynthesis is a series of events in which the elements *carbon, hydrogen,* and *oxygen* are joined in such a way that the result is a *carbohydrate.*

We may symbolize the composition of carbohydrates as (CH_2O), which represents the simplest theoretical unit of carbohydrate structure. For example, if six such units were joined together, we would obtain $6 \times (CH_2O) = C_6H_{12}O_6$, a sugar. (CH_2O) as such actually does not play a role in photosynthesis. As we shall see, the simplest real carbohydrates produced are triplets of (CH_2O), namely, $C_3H_6O_3$. However, many of the chemical aspects of photosynthesis can be simplified considerably if a hypothetical (CH_2O) is regarded as the unit product. If necessary, the equations used may later be multiplied by a factor of 3, to bring them more nearly into line with actual events. With these provisions, we may write the following input-output statement for a unit reaction of photosynthesis:

$$CO_2 + H_2O \rightarrow (CH_2O) + O_2$$

Carbon dioxide and water are the chemical raw materials, and molecular oxygen is a byproduct.

What are the sources of the atoms in (CH_2O)? The equation shows readily that the C must come from CO_2. Also, the source of the hydrogen must be H_2O. But what serves as the oxygen source in the manufacture of (CH_2O)? Is it CO_2, or H_2O, or either?

THE OXYGEN SOURCE

The source of oxygen has been discovered experimentally, with the help of an **isotope** of oxygen. Isotopes are variant forms of a chemical element, some found in small quantities in nature, others produced artificially by man. All isotopes of a given element have identical chemical properties but different physical properties. More specifically, the different isotopes of an element differ in mass. Such

FIG. 11.8. Isotopes. Ordinary oxygen is O^{16}, that is, the atomic nucleus is 16 times heavier than the hydrogen nucleus. Isotopic oxygen is *chemically* like ordinary oxygen (i.e., it has the same number of orbital electrons), but it is *physically* different, having a nucleus of mass 18.

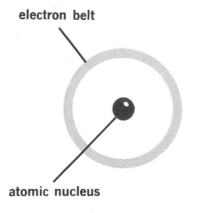

electron belt

atomic nucleus

hydrogen atom:
mass 1

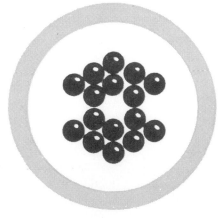

ordinary oxygen atom:
mass 16

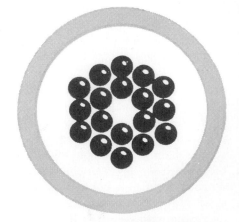

isotopic oxygen atom:
mass 18

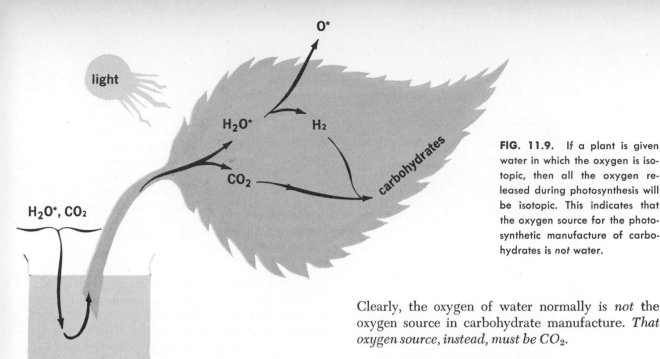

FIG. 11.9. If a plant is given water in which the oxygen is isotopic, then all the oxygen released during photosynthesis will be isotopic. This indicates that the oxygen source for the photosynthetic manufacture of carbohydrates is *not* water.

Clearly, the oxygen of water normally is *not* the oxygen source in carbohydrate manufacture. *That oxygen source, instead, must be CO_2.*

THE FATE OF WATER

In view of this conclusion, the last equation is unbalanced. CO_2 has *two* ordinary oxygens, but only *one* appears in (CH_2O). Moreover, the two O^* atoms in the output (O_2^*) obviously cannot result from the single O^* supplied by H_2O^*. Since nature operates only via balanced reactions, the input clearly must be *two* H_2O^* for every CO_2. We then obtain

$$CO_2 + 2H_2O^* \rightarrow (CH_2O) + O_2^* + H_2O$$

This must be the general balanced form of the input and output in actual photosynthesis. The fates of the various atoms here may be indicated as follows:

$$CO_2 + 2H_2O^* \rightarrow O_2^* + H_2O + (CH_2O)$$

In other words, of the atoms in (CH_2O), the C and the O derive from CO_2, and the H_2 from the water in the input. All remaining atoms of the input form byproducts, namely, molecular oxygen and water. We note that, in normal photosynthesis, water is an output byproduct as well as an input raw material; twice as much water must be supplied as is actually used up (Fig. 11.10).

The finding that water supplies only its hy-

differences of "weight" make it possible to distinguish one isotope from another. In the case of oxygen, the ordinary form of the element is O^{16}; that is, every such oxygen atom has a mass of 16 units. The mass unit is the hydrogen atom, which is the lightest of all atoms and is given the arbitrary mass 1. Thus, ordinary oxygen atoms (O^{16}) are sixteen times heavier than hydrogen atoms. One of the isotopes of oxygen is O^{18}, where each atom has a mass of 18 units. Isotopic oxygen (O^{18}), or simply O^*, in effect is *labeled* oxygen. By virtue of its heavier atoms, it can be traced through any number of chemical reactions. For example, one may artificially prepare water containing O^* instead of ordinary oxygen: H_2O^*. No matter what then happens to this water during chemical reactions, the fate of its labeled, identifiable oxygen can be followed precisely (Fig. 11.8).

Water of this kind has actually been used to determine the oxygen source in the photosynthetic production of (CH_2O). A plant was given H_2O^* instead of ordinary water as raw material. The problem was to find out whether the carbohydrate end-product of photosynthesis then did or did not contain O^*. The results were clear-cut (Fig. 11.9): the O^* of H_2O^* did *not* appear in the carbohydrate but appeared only in the oxygen byproduct:

$$CO_2 + H_2O^* \rightarrow (CH_2O) + O_2^*$$

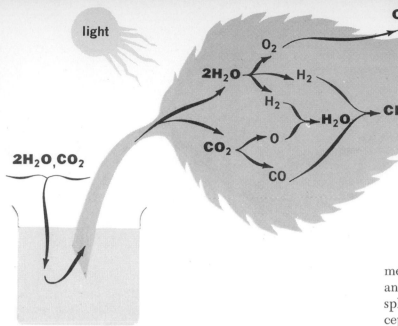

light

O_2

O_2

$2H_2O$ → H_2

H_2

CO_2 → O → H_2O → CH_2O

CO

$2H_2O, CO_2$

FIG. 11.10. The fate of the atoms of the raw materials required in photosynthesis. Water contributes only its hydrogen, and carbon dioxide contributes both its carbon and half of its oxygen, toward carbohydrate manufacture. The byproducts are molecular oxygen and half as much water as entered the photosynthetic process as raw material. Note that the equations in the diagram are balanced.

drogen, and not its oxygen, to carbohydrate manufacture leads to an important inference. Clearly, before water can contribute its hydrogen atoms, these atoms must first be separated from the oxygen. In other words, water must be *split* at some point during photosynthesis:

$$2H_2O \rightarrow 2H_2 + O_2$$
$$\downarrow$$
$$CO_2 + 2H_2 \rightarrow (CH_2O) + H_2O$$

The hydrogen and oxygen of water are known to be joined together very firmly, and a great deal of energy is needed to split them apart. What is the source of this energy?

Another classical experiment has answered this question. Leaves were dried and powdered, and the chloroplasts in this powder were isolated and cleaned. The pure chloroplast preparation was then suspended in water to which certain iron salts had been added, and the whole was illuminated. The result: as soon and as long as the light was on, the chloroplasts actively evolved bubbles of oxygen (Fig. 11.11).

Since such an experiment does not involve living cells, carbohydrate production cannot be expected to occur, and indeed it does not occur. But the experiment does involve light, chloroplasts, and water, and this combination evidently remains functioning. The formation of oxygen bubbles must

mean that water is split into hydrogen and oxygen, and that light energy, via chlorophyll, must do the splitting. The added iron salts serve merely as acceptors, or absorbers, of hydrogen. We may conclude that *the function of light in photosynthesis is to supply the energy required for the splitting of water, and that the function of chlorophyll is to trap this energy and so to make the splitting possible.*

Hence we may conclude further that photosynthesis must consist of two main phases. The first may be termed **photolysis,** that is, the splitting of water by light and chlorophyll. This must be followed by **CO_2 fixation,** that is, the combining of the hydrogen, produced by photolysis, with the carbon and oxygen of CO_2 (consult Fig. 11.12).

We shall now examine each of these two phases in greater detail.

Photolysis

EXCITED CHLOROPHYLL

What happens when light strikes a chlorophyll molecule? We already know that the energy of all but the green light waves is absorbed. The result of this absorption of red-orange and blue-violet light is that the chlorophyll molecule becomes **excited.**

This physical event affects primarily the electrons of the atoms which make up the chlorophyll molecule. All atoms normally possess a given number of electrons, which orbit around the atomic nucleus at given distances. If such an atom absorbs light of sufficient energy, one of the electrons may

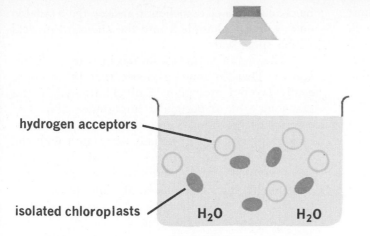

hydrogen acceptors

isolated chloroplasts

H_2O H_2O

in dark: no change

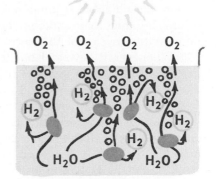

O_2 O_2 O_2 O_2

H_2

H_2 H_2

H_2

H_2

H_2O H_2O

in light: oxygen bubbles out

FIG. 11.11. The functions of light and chlorophyll. Chloroplasts and hydrogen acceptors are suspended in water. In the dark, no change occurs (left). If the light is turned on, oxygen bubbles form (right). This indicates that water is split into H_2 and O in the chloroplasts, with the aid of light energy. Oxygen escapes, and hydrogen is picked up by the hydrogen acceptors.

be displaced from its normal orbit to a new orbit farther away from the atomic nucleus. The atom is then said to be in an "excited," i.e., a more energetic, state (Fig. 11.13).

Red light has just sufficient energy to excite chlorophyll. Blue-violet light is more energetic, but it can be shown to excite chlorophyll to no greater extent than red light. When blue-violet light is absorbed, some of the energy excites chlorophyll, and the excess energy of the light dissipates as heat. We note, in general, that the atoms of which chlorophyll is made trap light energy by becoming excited,

and if we let Ch° stand for "excited chlorophyll," we may write

$$Ch \xrightarrow{\text{light}} Ch*$$

FIG. 11.12. The general pattern of the two phases of photosynthesis, i.e., photolysis and CO_2 fixation. Both phases take place within the grana of chloroplasts.

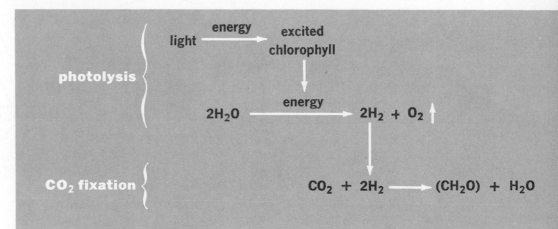

photolysis {

light $\xrightarrow{\text{energy}}$ excited chlorophyll

$2H_2O \xrightarrow{\text{energy}} 2H_2 + O_2 \uparrow$

CO_2 fixation {

$CO_2 + 2H_2 \longrightarrow (CH_2O) + H_2O$

This excited state lasts only an incredibly short time—in order of 10^{-10} sec in the case of chlorophyll. Almost as soon as an electron of an atom has attained a more distant orbit, it jumps back into its normal orbit. The atom may undergo repeated excitation–de-excitation cycles of this sort.

Whenever it reverts from the excited to the normal state, an atom *releases* the energy which it had absorbed to begin with. In the ordinary case, such released energy simply dissipates as *heat*. Under certain circumstances, the released energy may emerge from the atom as a tiny flash of *light*, a phenomenon known as **fluorescence**. Excited chlorophyll is actually known to lose about 1 per cent of its energy through fluorescence. However, neither fluorescence nor energy release in the form of heat produces useful work. Energy so lost is merely dissipated and does not become available for the splitting of water. We may infer, therefore, that a mechanism exists which prevents most of the excitation energy of chlorophyll from being lost uselessly, a

mechanism which somehow transfers the available energy from chlorophyll into the chemical process which splits water.

The precise nature of this mechanism is still unknown. There is some evidence that the orderly, neatly layered arrangement of chlorophyll in the grana may be of particular importance here. For efficient energy transfer into the water-splitting reaction appears to be uniquely associated with the crystallike structure of intact grana. If the internal structure of the grana is destroyed, they no longer mediate photolysis. Similarly, if chlorophyll is extracted from grana, the pigment is no longer effective as a photosynthetic agent.

HYDROGEN LIBERATION

However it may happen in detail, chlorophyll evidently functions as an *energy carrier*. And as the released excitation energy of chlorophyll splits water, de-excited chlorophyll reappears, available

FIG. 11.13. Atomic excitation. If an atom (left) absorbs external energy, one or more of its orbital electrons may jump into an orbit farther away from the atomic nucleus (middle). The atom is then said to be in an excited state. On de-excitation, electrons reattain their normal orbits, and the atom releases the energy it had absorbed originally.

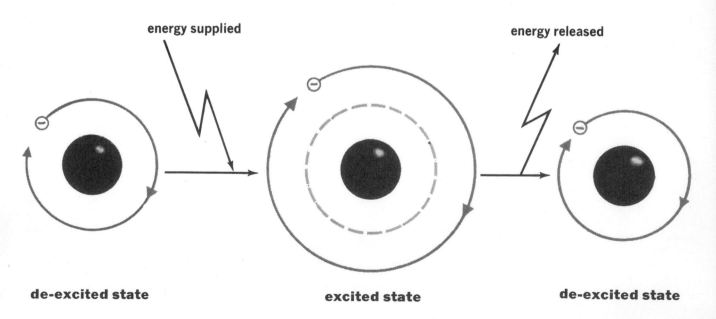

energy supplied   energy released

de-excited state   excited state   de-excited state

to trap and to carry light energy once more. Diagrammatically,

$$\text{Ch} \xrightarrow{\text{light}} \text{Ch*}$$
$$2H_2O \xrightarrow{E} 2H_2 + O_2$$

We may note in this connection that pigments other than chlorophyll indirectly contribute light energy to photolysis. For example, carotenoids absorb blue light (and therefore appear red-orange-yellow to the eye). The energy of this absorbed blue light may be transferred successively to other carotenoid molecules, then to chlorophyll b, and may eventually contribute to the excitation of chlorophyll a. In such serial transfers, chlorophyll a is always the last receiver of energy. Moreover, regardless of which other pigments absorb light, *only* chlorophyll a can transfer energy into the water-splitting reaction; photosynthesis may occur in the absence of carotenoids or chlorophyll b, but it cannot occur in the absence of chlorophyll a.

Water split by photolysis yields oxygen and hydrogen. The oxygen escapes from a chloroplast into the cellular cytoplasm and, if it is not used in plant respiration, passes from there into the atmosphere as a byproduct of photosynthesis. The hydrogen remains in the grana, and here it eventually combines with CO_2 to form carbohydrates, as noted.

But up to the time this combination actually occurs, the hydrogen does not remain "loose." Instead, it joins temporarily with **hydrogen acceptors.** These are normal constituents of protoplasm which, as we shall see in animal metabolism also, play important roles in all cellular reactions in which hydrogen is liberated or captured. In the case of photolysis, certain hydrogen acceptors unite with H_2 immediately as it is produced during the splitting of water. These acceptors then pass on the H_2 to other acceptors, and after a number of such transfers, a last acceptor delivers the hydrogen into the CO_2-fixing reactions. This last acceptor has been identified with certainty. It is a derivative of a nucleotide and is called *triphosphopyridine nucleotide,* or **TPN** for short. As we shall see, this hydrogen acceptor and others quite

like it occur in animal metabolism too. The role of TPN in plants may be depicted diagrammatically as follows:

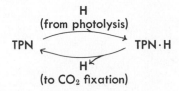

$$\text{TPN} \xrightleftharpoons[\substack{H \\ (\text{to } CO_2 \text{ fixation})}]{\substack{H \\ (\text{from photolysis})}} \text{TPN} \cdot H$$

Note that, as hydrogen is delivered into the CO_2-fixing process, free TPN reappears, available once more to accept newly produced hydrogen.

With the formation of TPN·H, the photolytic phase of photosynthesis may be regarded as completed. The whole pattern of this phase is outlined in Fig. 11.14.

CO₂ Fixation

THE PATTERN

Like the photolytic reactions, those which join hydrogen and CO_2 to yield carbohydrate also do not take place by themselves; energy is required. In photolysis, the source of energy is light. In all other metabolic reactions, CO_2 fixation included, the source of energy is *respiration.*

We shall see in Chap. 15 that respiratory energy is produced by the burning of organic fuels within cells. An interesting consideration arises here. Since respiration requires organic fuels, and since all organic fuels are derived ultimately from the carbohydrates produced through CO_2 fixation, it follows that CO_2 fixation is both a requirement for, and a consequence of, carbohydrate manufacture:

$$\substack{CO_2 + H_2 \\ (CO_2 \text{ fixation})} \xrightarrow{E} \substack{\text{carbohydrates, other} \\ \text{organic substances}} \xrightarrow{\text{respiration}} \substack{\text{new} \\ \text{proto-} \\ \text{plasm}}$$

Put another way, a portion of the harvest of photosynthesis must be funneled back into the harvesting process itself, to make that process possible to begin

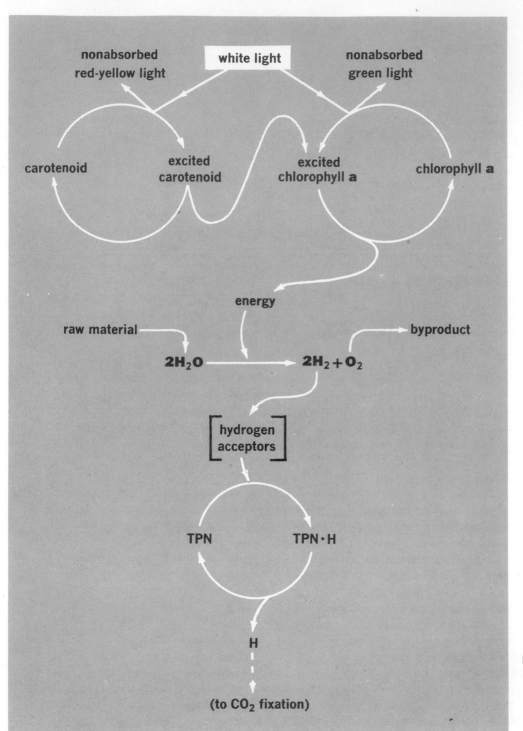

FIG. 11.14. Overall summary of photolysis.

with. Thus, it takes organic materials to get more organic materials.

Just as the use of isotopes has uncovered the occurrence of photolysis, so has this method helped to elucidate the mechanics of CO_2 fixation. Photosynthesizing plants were given artificially prepared C^*O_2. The carbon atom here was an isotope of ordinary carbon. The latter is C^{12}, and the isotope used was C^{14}, two mass units heavier. At successive times during photosynthesis, plants using C^*O_2 as raw material were killed, and their cells were analyzed for substances containing the isotope C^*. Since the plants must have manufactured such substances from the C^*O_2 given initially, this procedure could reveal not only the identity of the photosynthetic endproduct but also the sequence of reactions leading to the formation of that endproduct.

This sequence is now known in virtually complete detail. CO_2 fixation turns out to be a *cycle* of reactions, operating somewhat like an endless belt of an assembly line in a factory. As such a belt moves along, a steady stream of raw materials is funneled to it at one point, and these materials are processed by various workers or machines along the way. A stream of finished products then emerges at another point, and the empty portions of the belt return to the starting point, where they pick up new batches of raw materials. The general pattern of such a cycle, as it applies to metabolic events, is as follows:

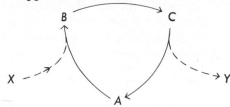

X and Y here are raw material and endproduct, respectively, and A, B, C represent the "endless belt" of chemicals which achieve the transformation of X into Y.

Note that such a cycle could include fewer or more than three reaction steps. Also, more than one raw material could be fed in, at one or at several points, and more than one endproduct could emerge. Note further that C "regenerates" A, an essential requirement if the reaction sequence is to be

a continuously running cycle. As we shall see, many vital metabolic transformations, in animals as well as in plants, occur through such cyclical sequences.

In CO_2 fixation, the reaction cycle consists essentially of three segments, as in the generalized diagram above. CO_2 is fed in between points A and B, hydrogen enters between B and C, and finished carbohydrate emerges between C and A, the segment which also regenerates the starting condition (Fig. 11.15).

Each of these segments consists of not a single but a series of interconnected reactions. As will be seen presently, energy to run the cycle is required in two of the segments. In all segments, each reaction must be catalyzed by a highly specific enzyme. Note in this connection that all reactions to be discussed below, like metabolic reactions generally, are reversible. They may proceed in either direction, and the same enzymes are required in each case (see Chap. 6). However, conditions in cells are normally such that, in certain processes, a given reaction proceeds

FIG. 11.15. The general pattern of the CO_2-fixing cycle. In segment **AB**, CO_2 enters as raw material, and in segment **BC**, hydrogen enters as raw material. Segment **CA** yields the carbohydrate endproduct and regenerates the starting point **A**.

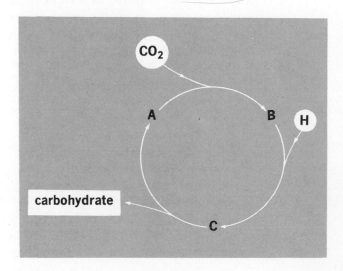

preferentially, or more completely, in just one direction. This preferred direction will be indicated in the equations below.

The chemicals *A*, *B*, and *C*, which form the cycle, all normal constituents of protoplasm, are called **phosphorylated carbohydrates.** Being carbohydrates, their molecules contain carbon atoms linked into chains, to which hydrogen and oxygen are attached. Being phosphorylated, their molecules also possess one or more **phosphate groups.** Such groups are derivatives of phosphoric acid (H_3PO_4). The formula of this acid may also be written as $H—O—PO_3H_2$, and here the $—PO_3H_2$ is the phosphate group. If such a group becomes attached to a carbohydrate, the latter is said to be phosphorylated. For example, in the case of glucose,

$$C_6H_{12}O_6 \; + \; —PO_3H_2 \; \rightarrow \; C_6H_{11}O_6—PO_3H_2 \; (+ H)$$
glucose   phosphate   glucose-phosphate
                 group

Glucose-phosphate is a phosphorylated carbohydrate. Here and in analogous instances, the $—PO_3H_2$ group may be symbolized in abbreviated form, as $—Ⓟ$. Note that, in all phosphorylated carbohydrates, a $—Ⓟ$ group occupies the place normally filled by a hydrogen atom. For example, glucose contains 12 H atoms, but the glucose portion of glucose-phosphate contains only 11. Whenever a carbohydrate *gains* a phosphate group, it *loses* a hydrogen atom at the same time, and vice versa.

Note too that, in plants as well as in animals, carbohydrates generally participate in metabolic processes in phosphorylated form. For example, as we shall see in Chap. 15 in greater detail, sugar eaten by an animal cannot be used as such within cells but must first be phosphorylated. In CO_2 fixation, similarly, phosphorylated carbohydrates are the principal reactants.

SEGMENT AB

The starting substance of the CO_2-fixing cycle is a phosphorylated carbohydrate called **ribulose diphosphate** ($Ⓟ—C_5H_8O_5—Ⓟ$), or **RDP** for short. This compound is a chemical derivative of the 5-carbon sugar *ribulose* ($C_5H_{10}O_5$). In RDP, each end of the carbon chain carries one of the two $Ⓟ$ groups:

ribulose diphosphate

Three molecules of RDP may be considered to start the cycle. These 3 molecules react with 3 molecules of CO_2, the first of the raw materials:

$$3Ⓟ—C_5H_8O_5—Ⓟ \; + \; 3CO_2 \rightarrow$$
$$3Ⓟ—C_6H_8O_7—Ⓟ \quad (1)$$

The endproduct on the right simply incorporates all the atoms present on the left. As a result, the 5-carbon chain of each RDP molecule becomes lengthened into a 6-carbon chain by the addition of CO_2.

The endproduct on the right exists only for an exceedingly short time. It reacts immediately with 3 molecules of water, borrowed from the general protoplasmic supply. "Borrowed" is the right word here, because the water will be returned in a later reaction, as we shall see. Thus,

$$3Ⓟ—C_6H_8O—Ⓟ \; + \; 3H_2O \rightarrow$$
$$3Ⓟ—C_6H_{10}O_8—Ⓟ \quad (2)$$

The new endproduct is again a 6-carbon chain, and it still carries a $Ⓟ$ group at each end. This substance is extremely unstable. It breaks up into two fragments, by a split through the middle of the 6 linked carbons. Each 6-carbon chain thus becomes *two* 3-carbon chains. Since three 6-carbon molecules are being split, six 3-carbon molecules will result:

$$3Ⓟ—C_6H_{10}O_8—Ⓟ \longrightarrow 6C_3H_5O_4—Ⓟ \quad (3)$$

All the six 3-carbon molecules so formed are mutually identical, and each carries one $Ⓟ$ group at one end of the molecule. This compound is called **phosphoglyceric acid,** or **PGA** for short:

phosphoglyceric acid

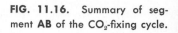

FIG. 11.16. Summary of segment **AB** of the CO₂-fixing cycle.

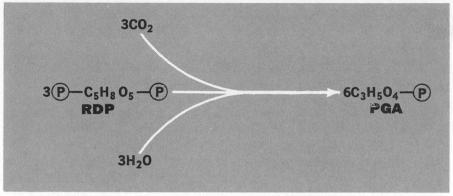

The formation of PGA completes the first segment of the CO₂-fixing cycle. We may summarize the entire segment as in Fig. 11.16. Three molecules of RDP, reacting with 3 molecules each of CO₂ and water, have become 6 molecules of PGA; carbon dioxide has been effectively trapped, or "fixed."

SEGMENT *BC*

In a first reaction here, the phosphoglyceric acid formed in the previous segment unites with hydrogen, the second raw material in CO₂ fixation. As noted above, this hydrogen has been produced by photolysis and has been accepted by TPN. Thus, it is TPN·H which actually participates in the reaction. This is also the first point in the cycle where energy is required; the transfer of hydrogen from TPN·H to PGA necessitates an expenditure of energy. Symbolically,

$$6H_2O \xrightarrow{\text{photolysis}} 6H_2 + 3O_2 \uparrow$$
$$\downarrow$$
$$12\,TPN \cdot H$$
$$\downarrow$$
$$\underset{\text{PGA}}{6C_3H_5O_4} - \text{\textcircled{P}} + 12\,TPN \cdot H \xrightarrow{\text{energy}}$$
$$6C_3H_7O_4 - \text{\textcircled{P}} + 12\,TPN \quad (4)$$

Twelve hydrogen atoms, produced earlier by photolytic splitting of six water molecules, take part in this reaction. In other words, each of the six PGA molecules adds two hydrogen atoms to its structure.

The principal endproduct of the reaction, $C_3H_7O_4$—\text{\textcircled{P}}, undergoes a structural simplification in a subsequent reaction in which it loses a molecule of water. Since this happens in six $C_3H_7O_4$—\text{\textcircled{P}} molecules, six water molecules will appear as byproducts:

$$6C_3H_7O_4 - \text{\textcircled{P}} \longrightarrow 6C_3H_5O_3 - \text{\textcircled{P}} + 6H_2O \quad (5)$$

The H₂O so formed returns to the general supply of protoplasmic water. This more than "pays back" the 3H₂O "borrowed" earlier, in reaction 2 of the cycle. The excess, amounting to 3H₂O, reduces the net water requirement for reaction 4. As noted above, photolysis must split 6H₂O to provide 12 H atoms. Reaction 5 now pays back 3 of the 6 water molecules used up in reaction 4, leaving a net water expenditure of 3H₂O, for every three CO₂ molecules fixed photosynthetically.

With the formation of $6C_3H_5O_3$—\text{\textcircled{P}} in reaction 5, the second segment of the cycle is completed. The compound $C_3H_5O_3$—\text{\textcircled{P}} is **phosphoglyceraldehyde**, **PGAL** for short. Its molecular structure is

$$
\begin{array}{c}
\text{\textcircled{P}} \quad H \\
| \qquad | \\
O \quad O \quad H \\
| \qquad | \quad | \\
H-C-C-C=O \\
| \qquad | \\
H \quad H
\end{array}
$$

phosphoglyceraldehyde

It will be noted that PGAL differs from PGA, which begins segment *BC*, only in that PGAL possesses one less oxygen atom. The events of segment *BC* may be summarized as in Fig. 11.17.

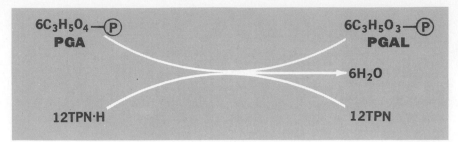

SEGMENT CA

Of the 6 molecules of PGAL just formed, *one* represents the net endproduct of photosynthesis as a whole. Solar energy, grana, chlorophyll, photolysis, CO_2 fixation, all cooperate to yield this final result. A billion years of plant evolution was needed to make that one molecule of PGAL, and on its foundation rests the whole plant kingdom and the whole animal kingdom. We shall discuss the fate and function of this molecule in the next section.

What of the remaining five PGAL's? These undergo a long and intricate series of reactions in which their atoms become reshuffled extensively. Energy is required in these reorganizations, the second place in the cycle where energy must be expended. Also, one additional phosphate group enters the reactions, and this group displaces one of the hydrogens. The final result is the formation of three identical new molecules. We may summarize this sequence as in Fig. 11.18.

As a check of reaction 1 of the cycle will show, the 3 molecules of P—$C_5H_8O_5$—P resulting from segment *CA* are actually not new but are RDP, ribulose diphosphate. We note that the starting point of the cycle has been regenerated. In essence, therefore, the function of segment *CA* is to reorganize five 3-carbon chains (PGAL) into three 5-carbon chains (RDP).

The entire CO_2-fixation cycle is outlined in Fig. 11.19. From this figure, the total input and output may be seen to be

$$3CO_2 + 3H_2O + 12H \rightarrow C_3H_5O_3\text{—}P + 6H_2O$$

or *net:*

$$3CO_2 + 12H \rightarrow C_3H_5O_3\text{—}P + 3H_2O$$

In other words, the three individual carbon atoms supplied as *inorganic* raw material, in the form of

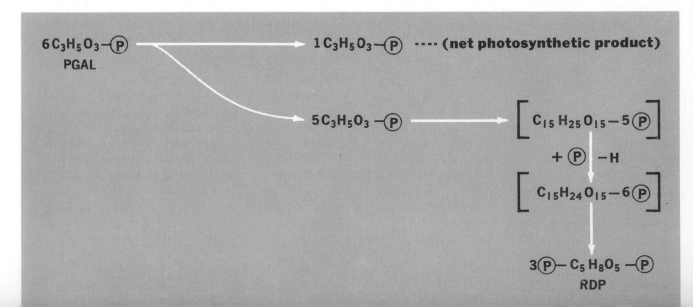

CO_2, emerge bound into a single *organic* molecule, phosphoglyceraldehyde.

THE ENDPRODUCT

The principal endproduct of photosynthesis, phosphoglyceraldehyde, is a *food*. Indeed, a plant nourished artificially with prefabricated PGAL may survive, without photosynthesis and without any other organic supplies.

As PGAL forms in the grana, it does not accumulate to any great extent. For it rapidly undergoes one of three main fates: it may be used directly as a **nutrient** in the cell which produced it; it may be "packaged" for **export** to other cells; or it may be packaged for **storage.**

Phosphoglyceraldehyde is usable immediately as a respiratory fuel. It may happen, therefore, that some of the PGAL just manufactured is burned at once to provide the energy for more CO_2 fixation. PGAL is also usable directly as a building material, and it may contribute to the construction of any of the innumerable protoplasmic components of plant cells. For example, PGAL just produced could be used to build anew, or to repair, some of the chemical machinery required for PGAL production itself—chlorophyll, or TPN, or RDP, or any one of the enzymes taking part in CO_2 fixation.

But a green cell generally manufactures much more PGAL than it requires for its own maintenance. The bulk of the photosynthetic product becomes available for export through the phloem, to root cells, stem cells, and nonphotosynthesizing cells in general. However, PGAL is not exported as such. It is probably too reactive a material. In transit from leaf to root, for example, it would react with other substances long before it could reach its destination. A less reactive "packaged" form of PGAL would clearly be more advantageous. The green cell actually does package PGAL, by converting it to **glucose.**

In this conversion, 2 molecules of PGAL are combined into 1 molecule of glucose. This is a reaction sequence of considerable importance in animal metabolism as well, and we shall later deal with it in some detail. Here we shall merely outline it in

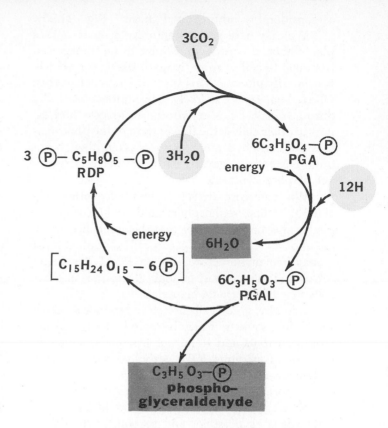

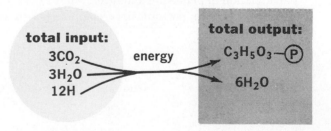

FIG. 11.19. Summary of CO_2 fixation as a whole. The reaction cycle is shown above, and the total input and output are indicated below.

a considerably abbreviated form (Fig. 11.20).

We may note generally, for animals as well as plants, that, if carbohydrates are to be transported from cell to cell or from tissue to tissue, the vehicle is primarily *glucose*. This sugar is less reactive than PGAL, hence is not so likely to be altered chemically during transit. Since conversion to glucose and export to other cells is the fate of most of the photosynthesized carbohydrate, glucose is often, though not quite correctly, regarded as the primary endproduct of photosynthesis.

When glucose arrives in nonphotosynthesizing cells, it is first rephosphorylated to glucose-phosphate, and this food may then be used directly in metabolism. Clearly, the green cells of a plant must in daytime manufacture enough PGAL for themselves and must export enough glucose to all other cells to suffice for a 24-hr period.

Actually, green cells normally produce so much PGAL that some of it may be stored. Storage occurs largely in roots and stem, but leaves too generally store small amounts. Like carbohydrate transport, carbohydrate storage does not involve PGAL as such. In any storage problem, two considerations are paramount. First, the stored material should take up as little space as possible; and second, it should be "out of circulation," that is, relatively unavailable for participation in persisting activities. Since PGAL reacts readily with protoplasmic components in its

vicinity, it would not remain out of circulation for long. Even glucose, though less reactive, would enter metabolic processes fairly rapidly. Moreover, both of these carbohydrates take up considerable molecular space.

Plants have developed ways to "condense" PGAL molecules into more compact, sufficiently unreactive packets. This may take the form of *dehydration synthesis*, i.e., the joining together of two or more molecules, accompanied by a simultaneous removal of water. For example, the green cell may first produce glucose from PGAL as above. Two glucose molecules may then be joined, and one water molecule is removed at the same time:

$$C_6H_{12}O_6 + C_6H_{12}O_6 \rightarrow C_{12}H_{22}O_{11} + H_2O$$

The resulting 12-carbon carbohydrate is **maltose**, malt sugar, a disaccharide (see Chap. 7). Maltose may now be stored as such, or pairs of maltose molecules may be combined and condensed further, until some two dozen glucose units have been joined into a single large molecule:

$$24C_6H_{12}O_6 \rightarrow C_{144}H_{240}O_{120} + 24H_2O$$

This large molecule is **starch**. It is smaller by 24 water molecules than 24 individual glucose molecules, and it is very much less reactive. Hence, it is eminently suitable as a storage form of carbohydrates, and it is actually very common among plants.

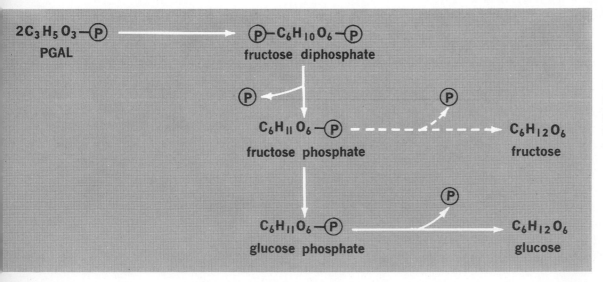

FIG. 11.20. Some of the steps in the metabolic conversion of phosphoglyceraldehyde (PGAL) to glucose. The detailed reaction sequence is given in Chap. 15, Fig. 15.18.

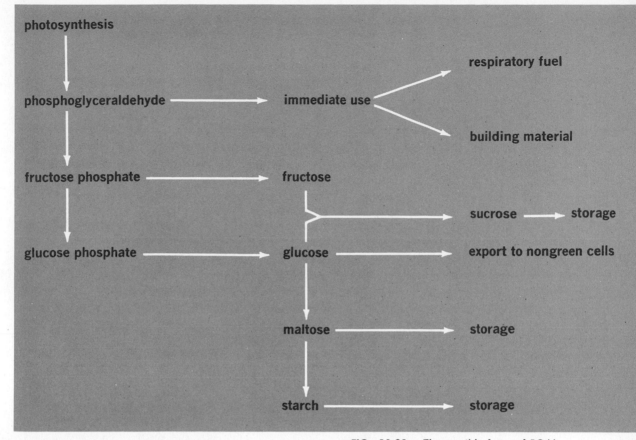

FIG. 11.21. The possible fates of PGAL.

Starches vary somewhat in composition; that is, they may contain more or fewer than 24 glucose units per molecule. The generalized formula for starch may be written $(C_6H_{10}O_5)n$, where n is the number of glucose units per molecule. As will be seen in Chap. 15, starch may also be produced from glucose-phosphate directly, without an intermediate free glucose stage.

Maltose and starch are not the only storage forms of the photosynthetic product. Some plants build PGAL into storage **fats** (e.g., olive oil, castor oil). Others make a variety of storage sugars. For example, PGAL may be converted partly into glucose, partly into **fructose** (see Fig. 11.20). Glucose and fructose may then be combined pairwise into **sucrose,** a disaccharide:

$$C_6H_{12}O_6 + C_6H_{12}O_6 \rightarrow C_{12}H_{22}O_{11} + H_2O$$
glucose   fructose   sucrose

Sugar cane, sugar beets, as well as many kinds of fruits owe their sweetness to stored fructose and sucrose.

Storage syntheses of this sort occur both in green and in nongreen cells. In the latter, imported glucose is the starting material, and nonpigmented plastids often are the sites of storage, as noted earlier in this chapter.

Whenever one of these cells must draw on its stored reserves, the exact reverse of storage synthesis takes place. For example, starch may be converted into glucose by addition of water, or it may be phosphorylated directly and decomposed into glucose-phosphate.

The various possible fates of the photosynthetic endproduct are indicated in Fig. 11.21.

FIG. 11.22. Overall summary of photosynthesis as a whole.

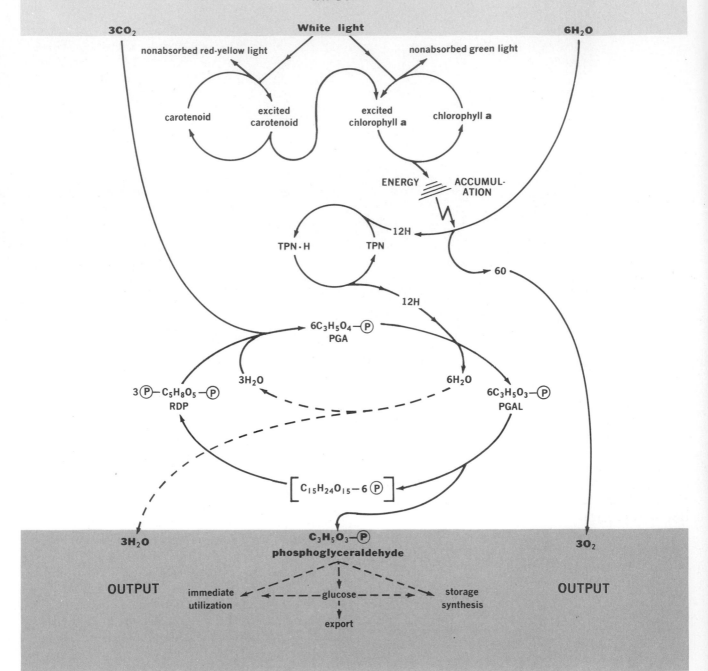

RESUME   The pattern of photosynthesis as a whole is outlined in Fig. 11.22. Since two glyceraldehyde molecules are required to manufacture one glucose molecule, we arrive at the following input-output equation for the production of glucose:

$$6CO_2 + 12H_2O \rightarrow C_6H_{12}O_6 + 6O_2 + 6H_2O$$

or, reduced to the mathematical minimum,

$$6CO_2 + 6H_2O \rightarrow C_6H_{12}O_6 + 6O_2$$

Photosynthesis is a very efficient process. It has been estimated that, of all the light energy absorbed by chloroplasts, some 50 to 60 per cent is recovered as energy built into glucose. However, in terms of light energy absorbed by a given area of land, photosynthesis is markedly less efficient. For example, the energy absorbed by a field of wheat represents only about 2 per cent of the total light energy delivered by the sun; chloroplasts are spread rather thinly over the whole field. Yet this 2 per cent of sunlight, produced by atomic explosions 93 million miles away, constitutes the whole power source which, through photosynthesis, keeps plants and animals alive.

In conjunction with raw-material procurement and internal distribution of nutrients, photosynthesis provides the essential nutritional background against which the metabolism of *individual* plant cells is carried out. We shall see in Chaps. 15 and 16 what such cellular metabolism consists of. The two following chapters examine the animal equivalents of nutrition in plants.

REVIEW
QUESTIONS

1. Distinguish between absorption, transmission, and reflection of light. What physical processes are implied in the statement "chlorophyll is green"? What is the solar radiation spectrum, and what physical attributes distinguish different portions of it? What is the visible spectrum, and how is chlorophyll affected by visible light?

2. What is the general chemical structure of chlorophyll? What are plastids, and what kinds are there? What is the internal architecture of chloroplasts? List the tissues and cell types in which the different kinds of plastids are found.

3. What major classes of pigments are usually found in plants? Where do these pigments occur, and what colors do they produce? What pigments are responsible for the colors of autumn leaves?

4. State the general chemical nature and function of photosynthesis as a whole. Review the sources of the carbon, the hydrogen, and the oxygen atoms which compose photosynthesized carbohydrates. What experiments have demonstrated the derivation of the oxygen in such carbohydrates?

5. What is the function of light and chlorophyll in photosynthesis? What experiments have demonstrated these functions? What are the general events in photolysis and CO_2 fixation?

6. Review the detailed sequence of events in photolysis. How is light energy trapped by chlorophyll and transferred into chemical processes? What is fluorescence? What are the light-trapping functions of carotenoids, and of chlorophylls *a* and *b*? How is photolytically produced hydrogen transferred into CO_2-fixing reactions? What are the net input and the net output of photolysis?

7. Review the general pattern of CO_2 fixation. What are the major steps? What roles do phosphorylated carbohydrates play? What is phosphorylation? What role does energy play in CO_2 fixation?

8. What are the starting materials and the endproducts of each of the three main phases of the CO_2-fixing cycle? For each phase, review the processes which bring about the conversion of starting material to endproduct. What are the net input and output of CO_2 fixation as a whole?

9. What is the principal net endproduct of photosynthesis as a whole? Review the possible fates of this endproduct. What are the main transportation and storage forms of carbohydrates in plants, and how is the photosynthetic endproduct converted into these?

10. Review the detailed reaction sequences of all photosynthesis. What are the net input and the net output of the whole process? Review once more the place of photosynthesis in plant nutrition generally.

SUGGESTED COLLATERAL READINGS

The history of research on photosynthesis is excellently documented by a series of important original articles reprinted in the following. Some of these articles describe key experiments referred to in this chapter.

Gabriel, M. L., and S. Fogel: Photosynthesis, in "Great Experiments in Biology," Prentice-Hall, 1955.

Several good articles on pigments, light, and chloroplasts:

Evans, R. M.: Seeing Light and Color, *Sci. American,* vol. 181, 1949.

Thimann, K. V.: Autumn Colors, *Sci. American,* vol. 183, 1950.

Aronoff, S.: Cholorophyll, *Botan. Rev.,* vol. 16, 1950.

Frank, S.: Carotenoids, *Sci. American,* vol. 194, 1956.

Arnon, D. I.: The Chloroplast as a Complete Photosynthetic Unit, *Science,* vol. 122, 1955.

The following all deal with, or contain accounts of, various aspects of photosynthesis. The most recent chemical knowledge, as outlined in this chapter, began to be recorded in the literature around 1955. Hence publications issued earlier are no longer sufficiently up to date in chemical details. These earlier sources are valuable, nevertheless, in other respects.

Rabinowitch, E.: Photosynthesis, *Sci. American,* vol. 179, 1948.

————: Progress in Photosynthesis, *Sci. American,* vol. 189, 1953.

Franck, J., and W. E. Loomis: "Photosynthesis in Plants," State University of Iowa, 1949.

Bonner, J., and A. W. Galston: "Principles of Plant Physiology," Freeman, 1952.

Hill, R., and C. P. Whittingham: "Photosynthesis," Wiley, 1955.

Calvin, M.: "The Photosynthetic Cycle," University of California Research Laboratories, vol. 2924, 1955.

Aronoff, S.: Photosynthesis, *Botan. Rev.,* vol. 23, 1957.

12

HETEROTROPHIC NUTRITION: ALIMENTATION

To MANY, animal "nutrition" is the same as eating. However, as in plants, nutrition in animals is not completed until inorganic and organic nutrients are delivered into the individual cells of the organism. In this, *eating* is only the first step. Animal nutrition also includes *digestion* of foods, sometimes intracellularly, more often extracellularly, in an alimentary system (see Chap. 9); *egestion* of the indigestible remains; *absorption* of the digested nutrients by the transport system; and *distribution* of the nutrients to all cells. Distribution may occur indirectly via a *liver*, as in vertebrates and some other animal groups, or, where a liver is absent, distribution may be direct from gut to other tissues (Fig. 12.1). These various processes are controlled and coordinated by nerves, by muscles, and in vertebrates also by hormones.

Nutritional events in vertebrates, and in mammals particularly, may serve to illustrate this general pattern in greater detail. In this chapter, emphasis will be on **alimentation,** the process comprising **ingestion, digestion, absorption,** and **egestion.** Nutrient transport and distribution will be dealt with in the following chapter.

Ingestion

THE NUTRIENTS

We have found in previous chapters that a plant cell may survive if it is given water and minerals and if it is supplied with, or is allowed to photosynthesize, organic carbon. From these three categories of nutrients, a plant cell is able to construct all the other components of its protoplasm. But if an animal cell is given only these three types of nutrients, it soon dies. For it requires three additional types of nutrients which, unlike the plant cell, it cannot manufacture on its own.

First, water, minerals, and photosynthesized organic carbon do not provide $-NH_2$, the important amino group present in all proteins and nucleoproteins. Plants are able to make $-NH_2$ out of mineral nitrates (see Chaps. 5 and 16). But even though nitrates are available to animals, they cannot convert these ions into —NH₂. Their cells therefore must be supplied with prefabricated —NH₂, and plants, or other animals which have eaten plants, must be the source of supply.

Second, plants can convert phosphoglyceraldehyde (PGAL), or glucose, or other forms of organic carbon, into all the vitamins they require. Animals cannot do likewise. Most animals do manufacture at least some of the vitamins, although, in many cases, only in inadequate quantities. Specific abilities here vary with the species, but no species is as self-sufficient in this regard as a green plant. Missing vitamins consequently must be supplied in prefabricated form, and plants are again the ultimate source of supply.

Third, unlike plants, animals are unable to convert organic carbon into all 23 kinds of amino acids needed for protein manufacture (see Chaps. 7 and 16). Depending on the species, 8 or 10 kinds, so-called "essential" amino acids, must be supplied prefabricated, and plants are the ultimate supplier here too.

The minimum nutrient supplies to an animal cell therefore must include at least six types of materials: **water, minerals, organic carbon, usable nitrogen, vitamins,** and **essential amino acids.** Evidently, animals cannot survive without plants, which provide four of these six items (Fig. 12.2).

This reduced manufacturing ability of animal cells probably may be explained on an evolutionary basis. Laboratory experiments have shown that the synthesizing capacities of organisms are affected greatly by genetic mutations. If such random hereditary changes occur in an animal, certain metabolic reactions may be blocked, and the manufacturing of given nutrients may then no longer be possible. But the animal may still survive. Being a heterotroph, it may obtain the missing nutrients in prefabricated form, from plants or other animals. Thus, in the course of evolution, different animal species may have developed different deficiencies in synthesizing ability, yet could compensate for this by eating plant-derived foods. Plants under analogous circumstances would die out, for if an autotroph can no longer manufacture a vital nutrient, it has no other means to obtain it. Undoubtedly this happened many times during the long history of plants.

If an animal could obtain all the nutrients it requires in the form of pure, immediately usable molecules, it would not need an alimentary system.

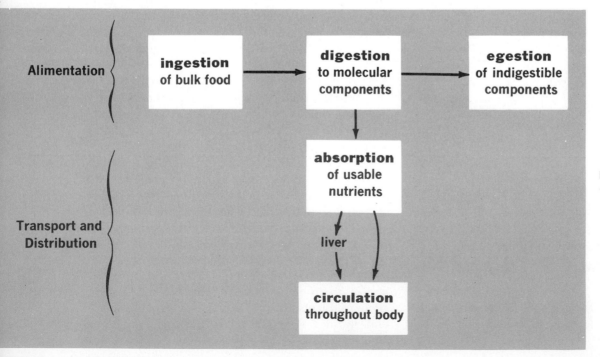

FIG. 12.1. The general pattern of animal nutrition.

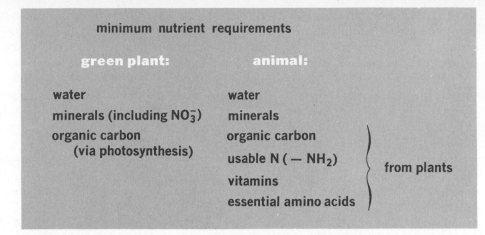

FIG. 12.2. A comparison of minimum nutrient requirements of plants and animals.

minimum nutrient requirements

green plant:

water
minerals (including NO_3^-)
organic carbon
    (via photosynthesis)

animal:

water
minerals
organic carbon
usable N (— NH_2) ⎫
vitamins   ⎬ from plants
essential amino acids ⎭

It could then simply absorb such molecules from the environment, through its cell surfaces. As noted in Chap. 9, this is actually the nutritional pattern in several types of parasitic animals. But, apart from water and the minerals dissolved in water, directly usable nutrient molecules are largely unavailable to free-living animals. What is available to such animals is plant or animal protoplasm in *bulk,* living or dead. And we may note that it is the principal function of an alimentary system to separate bulk foods into individual nutrient molecules directly usable by cells.

This is accomplished by digestion. **Mechanical digestion** first subdivides ingested materials into fine particles suspended in water; and **chemical digestion** then reduces these particles to molecular di-

mensions. In the process, usable molecules become separated out, and more complex molecules are broken up into smaller, usable ones. In this chemical dissolution of bulk foods, *digestive enzymes* secreted by *digestive glands* play important roles (Fig. 12.3).

Digestion produces a food solution in which three groups of substances may be found. First,

FIG. 12.3. Upper figure: if molecular nutrients were available directly, food procurement could be simply a matter of direct absorption through the body surface. Lower figure: since largely only bulk foods are available, animals require an alimentary system; such a system functions toward the procurement of molecular nutrients as shown.

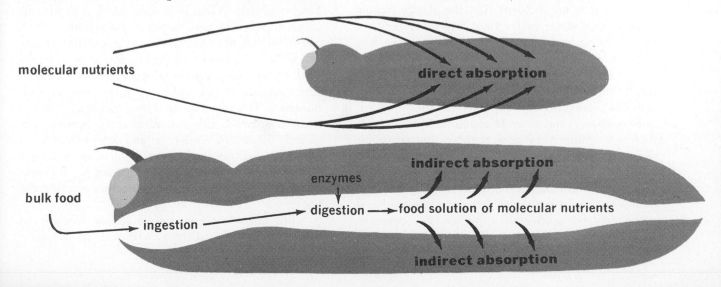

molecular nutrients   direct absorption

bulk food   indirect absorption

ingestion → digestion → food solution of molecular nutrients

enzymes

indirect absorption

there are nutrient molecules which animal cells require but cannot manufacture on their own. These comprise water, minerals, and the four categories of plant-derived substances listed above. Second, there are nutrient molecules which can be manufactured by animal cells but, since eaten food generally supplies them, need not be manufactured. For example, animal cells may manufacture fatty acids from organic carbon, but they may not need to do so if fatty acids are included in eaten food. Utilization of the diverse chemicals contained in bulk foods evidently may lighten the manufacturing effort required of animal cells. And third, the food solution usually contains indigestible or otherwise unusable materials. Plant cellulose, for example, is a common indigestible component of bulk foods. Substances in this last category are egested.

APPETITE AND HUNGER

What prompts us to eat *what* we eat? What makes us decide *how much* to eat? As yet, neither question can be answered fully. The first focuses attention on the nature and control of *appetite* and is much more difficult than the second, which raises the problem of the nature and control of *hunger*.

That we enjoy various nutrient chemicals in preference to any other chemicals undoubtedly reflects the internal need of the body. In many instances, internal need probably also determines our preferences for particular nutrient chemicals. For example, it is no accident that the thirsty animal usually likes water better than any other fluid; or that most animals, especially growing ones, like sugar in one form or another; or that we crave high-calorie foods when we work strenuously, and low-calorie foods when we do not. Fundamental appetites like these probably originated far back in evolutionary history, and animals undoubtedly evolved in such a way that they now register preference for those foods which under given conditions are most suitable.

However, in man in particular, fundamental appetites may be superimposed by, or even displaced completely by, *cultivated* appetites. For example, every newborn likes sweetened water, but many an adult would not touch it. Most of us often eat principally for the taste, rather than for the need. In many such instances, a bodily need may have existed first and may later have become masked by cultivated habit and tradition. For example, do we put lemon juice on fish merely because we have cultivated an artificial taste for it, or because cooked fish is poor in vitamin C and fresh lemon juice is rich in it?

The brain unquestionably plays an important role in appetite control, just as, in mammals, this organ is now known to control the *amount* of food eaten. According to an early popular hypothesis, the stomach was believed to regulate the quantities of food consumed. Muscular contractions of an empty stomach were thought to give rise to sensations of hunger, and a hungry animal was assumed to eat until its stomach was filled. Such filling then was believed to stop the hunger pangs, hence also food intake. But this hypothesis, still widely quoted among nonbiologists, turned out to be untenable long ago. For even after surgical removal of the entire stomach, hunger sensations nevertheless continue to come and go as before. Moreover, a "stomach hypothesis" of hunger control does not account for chronic overeating or undereating.

A better explanation has emerged from experiments which have revealed the existence of special eating-control centers in the mammalian brain. In a brain region known as the *hypothalamus* (see Chap. 21), two such centers have been identified. One is a **hunger center.** When it is stimulated, it sends out nerve impulses to various parts of the body, which cause the animal to eat. The other is a **satiety center** which, when stimulated, makes the animal refuse food. In test rats, tiny electrodes have been used to stimulate one or the other of these centers continuously. The result of such tests has been that the treated animals either overeat and become extremely obese or undereat and starve amidst a plentiful food supply. Evidently, the amount of food a mammal normally eats is determined by the commands the hunger and satiety centers send to the body.

But how do these centers decide whether to send a command "eat" or a command "do not eat"?

Experiments have shown that *blood glucose* is the critical agent which stimulates one or the other of the eating-control centers. As we shall soon see, glucose circulating in the blood is a very sensitive indicator of the hour-by-hour nutritional state of the body. Shortly after a meal, the glucose concentration in the blood tends to rise. Long after a meal, blood-glucose levels tend to fall. If blood reaching the brain contains too much glucose, then the satiety center probably becomes differentially sensitive to this high glucose level and issues the command "do not eat." Conversely, low glucose levels probably stimulate the hunger center differentially, resulting in the command "eat" (Fig. 12.4).

It should be clear that any condition which directly or indirectly influences glucose delivery to the brain, or affects the operation of the brain centers as such, is bound to affect food intake. Dozens of such conditions may actually do so. Proper glucose delivery depends, for example, on normal digestive processes, normal liver function, normal blood circulation, and normal hormone balances, all of which, as we shall see, affect glucose metabolism profoundly. If, through disturbances in any of these functions, the brain receives consistently false information about the actual glucose supplies in the body, then consistent overeating or undereating may result.

Moreover, the brain centers are themselves subject to faulty operation. And they are influenced by a large variety of psychological factors, by reflexes, and by habits of long standing. They are also influenced by inherited genetic constitution which, in the final analysis, governs the detailed operation of the body in all its aspects. Clearly, if the brain centers receive correct information but interpret it incorrectly, or interpret correctly but send out faulty commands, then abnormal food intake may again be the result.

We note that whether or not to eat, a seemingly simple decision, actually is determined by a multitude of interdependent, interacting internal processes. And it is not surprising that, as is well known, practically *any* disturbance of *any* body function leaves its mark on food intake.

Granting now that desired kinds and appropriate amounts of food are being ingested, what happens to such food in its passage through the alimentary canal?

Digestion

THE ROLE OF ENZYMES

Digestion in different parts of the alimentary tract is achieved either by *mechanical* means, or by *chemical* means, or by both.

No matter where they occur, or what foods are involved, all instances of chemical digestion are re-

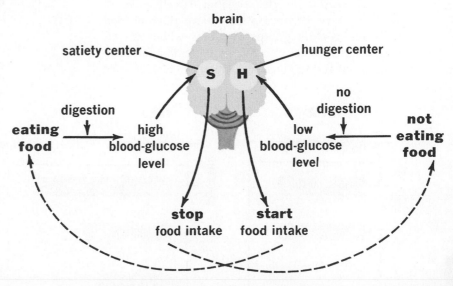

FIG. 12.4. The control of food intake. Desire or lack of desire for food is governed by the satiety (*S*) and hunger (*H*) centers of the brain, which in turn respond differentially to the glucose concentration in blood.

actions of the same common type: **enzymatic hydrolysis.** "Enzymatic" implies that the reaction is accelerated by an enzyme, and "hydrolysis," that the reaction is one of dissolution or decomposition, *water* being the dissolving agent. A generalized digestive reaction may be written

$$\text{food} + \text{H}_2\text{O} \xrightarrow{\text{enzyme}} \text{food components}$$

In most animals, digestive enzymes are extracellular enzymes; that is, they are produced within cells, but they are secreted and function outside cells. This puts them into a special category, for virtually all other enzymes in an organism are intracellular and function within cells. Moreover, digestive enzymes are relatively unusual also in that many of them may act on entire categories of chemicals. For example, digestive *lipase* promotes the decomposition of fat into fatty acids and glycerin:

$$\text{fat} + \text{H}_2\text{O} \xrightarrow{\text{lipase}} \text{fatty acids} + \text{glycerin}$$

Here the lipase may be effective with any kind of fat, regardless of which specific types of fatty acids a fat is composed of. Analogously, certain protein- and carbohydrate-digesting enzymes decompose many *different* kinds of proteins and carbohydrates, respectively. By contrast, most other, intracellular enzymes are highly specific, and each is effective only in reactions involving one particular type of molecule (see Chap. 6).

The reason for this broader effectiveness of some digestive enzymes is that many different food molecules contain groups of atoms which are arranged in the same way. For example, in a fat, fatty acids are linked to glycerin in a certain fashion (see Chap. 7). The enzyme lipase acts specifically on this type of link. Lipase may therefore aid in the digestion of any substance in which such a link is present, namely, *any* fat (Fig. 12.5). In a protein, similarly, various amino acids are joined together by bonds of one particular kind. Digestive proteinases act specifically on such bonds, and because the bonds occur in most types of proteins, proteinases may aid in the decomposition of all of these. In general, we may say that digestive enzymes, like all other enzymes, act specifically on particular chemical bonds; and because certain kinds of bonds are common within broad categories of food molecules, digestive enzymes are broadly effective.

Note, incidentally, that it is never an enzyme itself which accomplishes digestive decomposition. Enzymes only increase the *speed* of digestion or other reactions (see Chap. 6). As pointed out just above, it is *water* which brings about food decomposition, and the function of digestive enzymes is to accelerate the process very greatly. Note further that, like all enzymes, digestive ones too operate best at particular temperatures and pH. As we shall see, appropriately acid, alkaline, or neutral conditions are maintained in the different portions of the alimentary tract where enzymes are at work.

Note, finally, that digestive breakdown of a food molecule is the exact reverse of the synthesis of

FIG. 12.5. Illustrating the group specificity of lipase. This enzyme specifically attacks the bonds between glycerin and fatty acids, regardless of whether the carbon chains of the fatty acids are short, long, or intermediate in length. Hence lipase may digest fats of all kinds. Group specificity of this sort also characterizes several other digestive enzymes.

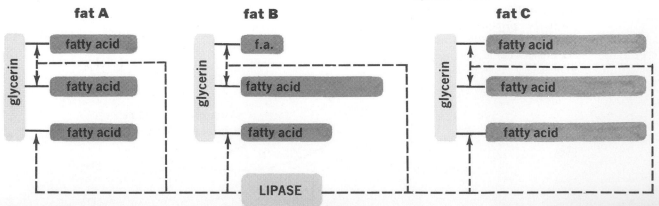

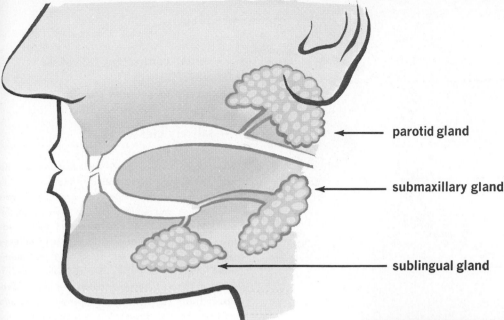

parotid gland

submaxillary gland

sublingual gland

FIG. 12.6. The diagram indicates the location of the salivary glands in man. The photo depicts a section through one of these glands. Note the connective tissue (light areas in photo) which traverses the gland and binds groups of gland cells together. Note also the several small salivary ducts (dark rings). (Photo courtesy of Dr. B. J. Serber, College of Medicine, New York University.)

that molecule. For example, the digestion of fat yields fatty acids and glycerin, and the synthesis of fat requires the joining of fatty acids and glycerin. In general,

$$X + H_2O \underset{\underset{\text{synthesis}}{\text{(enzymatic dehydration)}}}{\overset{\overset{\text{decomposition}}{\text{(enzymatic hydrolysis)}}}{\rightleftarrows}} \text{parts of } X$$

The *same* enzyme promotes the reaction in *either* direction, for, as we have seen in Chap. 6, an enzyme does not determine the direction of a chemical process.

ORAL DIGESTION

In the mouth, tongue and teeth initiate mechanical digestion, and, in man, **saliva** mixed into the food mass initiates chemical digestion.

Saliva is manufactured in three pairs of salivary glands which connect with the mouth by ducts (Fig. 12.6). Salivary secretion is started reflexly.

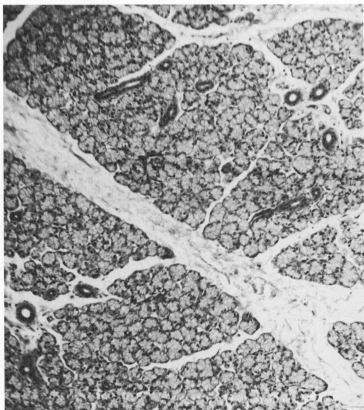

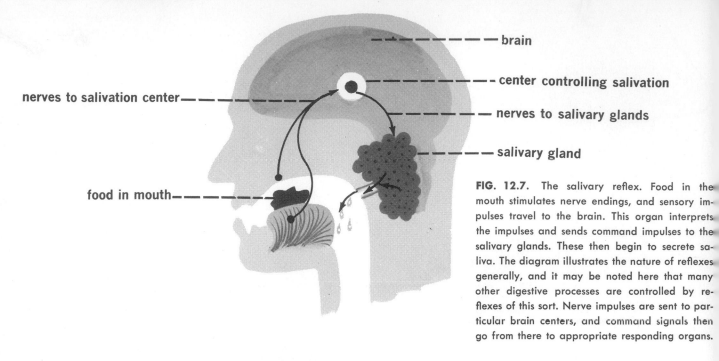

nerves to salivation center

food in mouth

brain

center controlling salivation

nerves to salivary glands

salivary gland

FIG. 12.7. The salivary reflex. Food in the mouth stimulates nerve endings, and sensory impulses travel to the brain. This organ interprets the impulses and sends command impulses to the salivary glands. These then begin to secrete saliva. The diagram illustrates the nature of reflexes generally, and it may be noted here that many other digestive processes are controlled by reflexes of this sort. Nerve impulses are sent to particular brain centers, and command signals then go from there to appropriate responding organs.

That is, when food comes into contact with the tongue and the lining of the mouth, nerve endings are stimulated. These transmit nerve impulses to the brain, and the brain in turn sends impulses to the salivary glands. The latter respond by secreting saliva (Fig. 12.7). As is well known, smell, sight, or mere thought of food may start the flow of saliva. This is brought about by *conditioned reflexes* (see Chap. 21); pleasant past experiences with food here have the same effect as actual food in the mouth. It is also well known that emotions may influence salivation.

Saliva contains water, a variety of inorganic ions, mucus proteins, and two digestive enzymes, **salivary amylase** and **salivary maltase** (Fig. 12.8). The whole mixture is chemically neutral, or very slightly alkaline or acid. From a mechanical standpoint, saliva keeps oral membranes moist and lubricates food for easier passage through the throat. From a chemical standpoint, the two enzymes promote the preliminary digestion of eaten *carbohydrates*. If starch, or glycogen, or other polysaccharides are eaten, salivary amylase accelerates their conversion into disaccharides (maltose) or monosac-

charides (glucose). For example,

$$C_{144}H_{240}O_{120} + 12H_2O \xrightarrow{\text{amylase}} 12C_{12}H_{22}O_{11}$$
starch $\qquad\qquad\qquad$ maltose (malt sugar)

If malt sugar is eaten or is produced as above by oral digestion of polysaccharides, then it may be converted to glucose with the aid of salivary maltase:

$$C_{12}H_{22}O_{11} + H_2O \xrightarrow{\text{maltase}} C_6H_{12}O_6 + C_6H_{12}O_6$$
maltose $\qquad\qquad\qquad$ glucose $\quad$ glucose

Since food does not remain in the mouth very long, and since brief periods of chewing do not always bring saliva into intimate contact with every part of a bite of food, oral carbohydrate digestion usually takes place only to a superficial degree. But saliva mixed into the masticated food is carried along into the stomach, and it is there that most of the digestive action of saliva occurs. Since only amylase and maltase are present in saliva, this fluid does not initiate digestion of foods other than carbohydrates.

FIG. 12.8. The composition of saliva and of gastric juice.

composition of	
saliva (pH ~ 7):	**gastric juice (pH ~ 2):**
water	water
inorganic ions	inorganic ions
mucus proteins	mucus proteins
amylase	HCl (H+ + Cl−)
maltase	pepsin
	rennin
	lipase

FIG. 12.9. In the pharynx, the food channel crosses the air channel. When a person swallows, the larynx is raised up against the epiglottis. This blocks the air channel into the trachea and normally prevents food from going the wrong way. (Model designed by Dr. J. F. Mueller, Ward's Natural Science Establishment, Inc.)

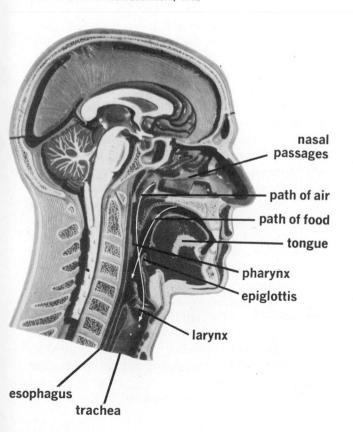

nasal passages

path of air

path of food

tongue

pharynx

epiglottis

larynx

esophagus

trachea

From the mouth proper, food passes into the **pharynx** (Fig. 12.9). This is a cavity where the food channel crosses the air channel which leads from the nasal passages to the windpipe. A slitlike opening into the windpipe, the **glottis,** is formed by a pair of ligaments which may meet along the midline and may close the orifice. Closure is effected during swallowing, when food crosses the air channel—unless one tries to swallow and exercise one's voice at the same time.

The pharynx connects with the **esophagus,** a tube leading to the stomach. A bite of food is moved through the esophagus by the muscles in its walls. When food touches the walls, nerve endings in them are stimulated. Nerve impulses are sent from there to the brain, and returning impulses bring the esophageal muscles into action. These muscles constrict the esophageal tube behind a ball of food, and a wave of constriction then travels toward the stomach, carrying food before it. Such a constriction progressing in wave fashion is called **peristalsis.** The direction of esophageal peristalsis may sometimes be reversed, as in vomiting.

GASTRIC DIGESTION

The stomach is a highly muscular organ located immediately under the rib cage, slightly on the left side (Fig. 12.10). The esophagus enters roughly at mid-region, called the **cardiac** region of the stomach. To the left of this is the pouchlike **fundic** region, and to the right, nearest the intestine, the **pyloric** region.

When balls of food arrive in rapid succession, most of them are pushed into the fundic part, where they are stored temporarily. The cardiac and pyloric portions are the "work regions" of the stomach; they are kept filled only partially. If too much is eaten at one meal, the cardiac and pyloric parts as well as the fundus fill up, and indigestion may result.

The stomach completes mechanical and continues chemical digestion. **Gastric juice** plays a role in both.

Sight, smell, and thought of food, which initiate salivary secretion by conditioned reflex, may at the same time initiate gastric secretion. Moreover, actual food in mouth or esophagus reflexly stimulates the stomach. As a result of these nervous effects, gastric juice is already flowing to some extent even before food has arrived. A more copious flow is produced once food comes into direct contact with the stomach lining. This mechanical stimulation also initiates the production of **gastrin**, a hormone. Stomach cells in contact with food release gastrin, and the hormone is picked up by blood vessels and is dis-

tributed throughout the body. When some of the hormone returns to the stomach and reaches the specialized cells capable of manufacturing gastric juice, these cells are activated. Evidently, gastric secretions may be started and maintained by three types of stimuli, namely, nervous, mechanical, and chemical ones (Fig. 12.11).

Gastric juice is a mixture of water, mineral ions, mucus proteins, *hydrochloric acid* (present in the form of ions, H^+ and Cl^-), and three enzymes, *pepsin, rennin,* and *lipase* (see Fig. 12.8). By virtue of the presence of HCl, the whole is very strongly acid—pH 2, approximately. Different sets of cells in the stomach lining secrete the acid and the enzymes.

Hydrochloric acid macerates food, in the same way any strong acid macerates substances on which it is spilled. Tough fibrous material in plant and animal food is loosened, the cement between cells is eroded, and the food mass literally falls apart. It may be asked why hydrochloric acid does not act similarly on the stomach wall itself. It does, if given the chance. However, the acid is normally produced in appreciable quantity only when food is actually present or is on the way. Second, the mucus proteins of gastric juice coat the stomach lining and protect it. And third, the acid is soon diluted by water in food. But despite these protective factors, hydrochloric acid (and gastric enzymes) may sometimes be secreted to excess. This happens, for example, by continued nervous stimulation of the stomach under chronic emotional stress, when food may not always be present. Portions of the stomach wall may then be eroded, and a gastric ulcer results.

In parallel with acid maceration, the food mass is thoroughly churned and ground by the powerful muscular action of the stomach wall. This action is essentially peristaltic, constricting waves traveling both forward and backward. Also, strong stationary contractions may cut into food at different levels of the stomach. This rather violent combined action of acid and muscular grinding reduces solid food to fairly small particles suspended in fluid. All further breakdown is chemical.

The enzyme **pepsin** is secreted in the form of

FIG. 12.10. The parts of the stomach. Note the peristaltic constriction in the esophagus, pushing food before it.

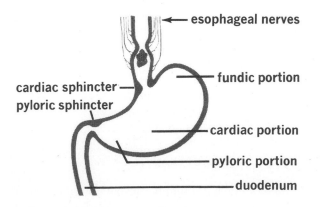

esophageal nerves

fundic portion

cardiac sphincter
pyloric sphincter

cardiac portion

pyloric portion

duodenum

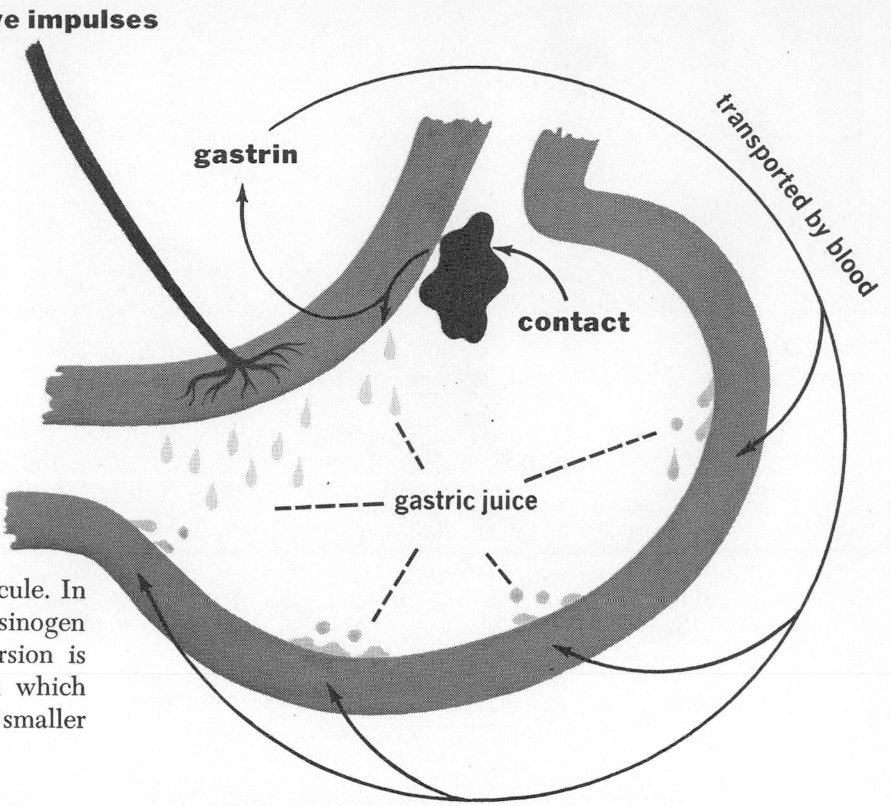

nerve impulses

FIG. 12.11. The three processes by which the stomach lining may be stimulated to secrete gastric juice: (1) by mechanical contact with food; (2) by nerve impulses from the brain; and (3) by the hormone gastrin. Released from the stomach lining by contact with food, gastrin returns via the blood stream to other parts of the stomach, stimulating secretory cells there.

pepsinogen, an enzymatically inactive molecule. In the presence of hydrogen ions from HCl, pepsinogen is converted to active pepsin. This conversion is thought to be an "unmasking" process, in which pepsinogen splits into active pepsin and a smaller molecular fragment:

$$\text{pepsinogen} \xrightarrow{\text{H}^+} \text{pepsin} + \text{fragment}$$

Once a bit of pepsin has so formed, it may itself convert more pepsinogen into pepsin:

$$\text{pepsinogen} \xrightarrow{\text{pepsin}} \text{pepsin} + \text{fragment}$$

Secretion of inactive pepsinogen and conversion to active pepsin in the stomach cavity protect the stomach wall. For if active pepsin were secreted as such, this strong enzyme might digest the very cells which produced it, rather than food.

In the acid medium of the stomach cavity, active pepsin accelerates the breakdown of proteins. Free amino acids are liberated as a result. But during the relatively short time of stomach digestion, pepsin usually cannot act long enough to reduce all proteins in food to amino acids. Many protein molecules are broken up only partially, to compounds known as *proteoses, peptones,* and *polypeptides.* These contain fewer amino acid units per molecule than a whole protein molecule. A good many proteins usually escape peptic digestion altogether, for pepsin may not reach all the food particles present.

Rennin is an enzyme unique to mammals. It acts specifically on *caseinogen,* the protein of milk. Secreted as inactive *prorennin* and converted to the active state by hydrogen ions, rennin splits caseinogen into two smaller proteins, *casein* and *whey.* In the presence of calcium ions (e.g., from milk), casein then coagulates, or *curdles,* and this protein curd subsequently may be digested by pepsin. The entire sequence is

$$\text{prorennin} \xrightarrow{\text{H}^+} \text{rennin}$$
$$\downarrow$$
$$\text{caseinogen} \longrightarrow \text{casein} + \text{whey}$$
$$\downarrow \text{Ca}^{++}$$
$$\text{curd} \rightarrow \text{peptic digestion}$$

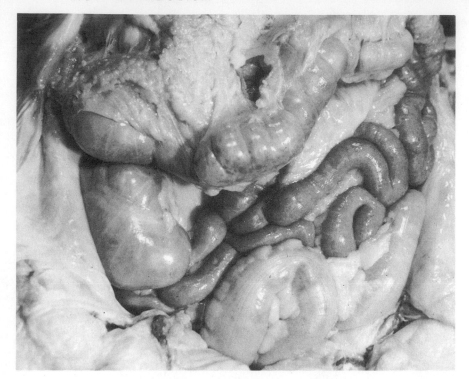

FIG. 12.12. Abdominal dissection, man. A few of the coils of the small intestine are shown in right portion of photo; parts of the thicker large intestine are on left side and just above the small intestine. Note that what appears on the left in the photo is on the right of the body. (Photographic department, Rhode Island Hospital.)

The presence of a special enzyme aiding the digestion of milk is a useful mammalian adaptation. Milk is the first, and for some time the only, food of a young mammal. But milk is a liquid, and its proteins are present in dissolved form. Hence milk would pass through the stomach as quickly as water, and pepsin could not act on it for any length of time. The rennin mechanism, however, coagulates milk, and the now solidified, curdled milk proteins do stay in the stomach long enough to permit appreciable peptic digestion.

Lipase in the stomach digests fats into fatty acids and glycerins. Much of the gastric lipase is not actually produced in the stomach but is regurgitated from the intestine. Gastric fat digestion is particularly superficial. As we shall see presently, thorough breakdown of fats requires bile and an alkaline environment. Neither of these exists in the stomach. Moreover, fats do not mix with water, and lipase, which is present in water, therefore does not readily reach the interior of large drops or tissue masses of fat. Consequently, gastric lipase acts largely on fats which are already divided up into fine colloidal droplets, e.g., the fat in milk, or in cheese, or in mayonnaise.

Since gastric juice does not contain carbohydrases, the only carbohydrate digestion in the stomach is that brought about by saliva, carried down from the mouth. Even this stops fairly soon, for in the highly acid medium of the stomach, salivary enzymes cannot long remain active.

By the time food is ready to leave the stomach, it is a semifluid macerated mass containing some digestion products: a certain amount of glucose, fatty acids, glycerin, peptones, proteoses, and polypeptides. But most carbohydrates, most fats, and a good portion of the proteins in food have so far not been digested.

The openings into and out of the stomach are guarded by **sphincters,** ring-shaped muscles which on contraction close off the connecting tubes (see Fig. 12.10). As food comes from the esophagus into the stomach, the *cardiac sphincter* opens reflexly. While gastric digestion proceeds, both the cardiac and the *pyloric sphincter* are closed. But some 20 to 30 min after a meal is eaten, a first lot of the food in the stomach is already digested and may be ready for passage into the intestine. The pyloric sphincter then opens, letting digested food out, and thereafter closes, until more food is to be expelled into the intestine. In this way, the stomach empties gradually. In man, complete gastric digestion of an average meal may take 3 to 4 hr.

INTESTINAL DIGESTION

The long, much-coiled **small intestine** extends from the stomach to the juncture with the shorter **large intestine,** so called because of its greater diameter (Fig. 12.12).

The uppermost foot or so of the small intestine is the **duodenum** (Fig. 12.13). In this section adjoining the stomach, the most important digestive fluids are mixed with food as it enters. These fluids are **intestinal juice, bile,** and **pancreatic juice.** As they and food are slowly propelled through the length of the small intestine by peristalsis, chemical digestion is carried to completion.

Intestinal juice is secreted by specialized glands in, and just under, the lining of the duodenum (Fig. 12.14). Secretion is started by contact of food with this lining.

Under the influence of HCl carried over from the stomach, the duodenal wall also manufactures **secretins,** a group of hormones. Picked up by blood, these hormones are distributed through the body. Two organs respond to them: the *liver* and the *pancreas.* Stimulated by secretins, liver cells secrete bile. Excess bile produced at other times may have been stored in the gall bladder, an organ which may contract and expel some of its store. Ducts from both liver and gall bladder join into a *common bile duct,* and bile passes through it into the duodenum (Fig. 12.13).

Secretins also stimulate cells in the pancreas (Fig. 12.15). Pancreatic juice flows through a *pancreatic duct* into the duodenum, entering near the opening of the bile duct.

Thus the appearance of food in the duodenum triggers, directly through contact, the secretion of intestinal juice and, indirectly through secretins, the arrival of bile and of pancreatic juice within a short time period. All three fluids are alkaline and, mixed with food, they soon abolish the acidity of the gastric product. All three fluids contain water, inorganic ions, and mucus proteins. In addition, they contribute a number of other agents, as indicated in Fig. 12.16.

Protein Digestion

This is accomplished with the aid of *trypsinogen, chymotrypsinogen,* and the three *peptidases* listed in Fig. 12.16.

Trypsinogen and chymotrypsinogen are inactive enzymes. Their secretion in inactive form protects the pancreas and the pancreatic duct from

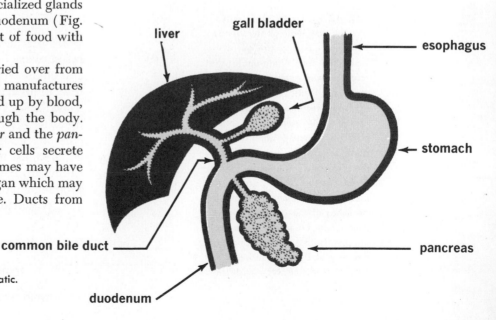

FIG. 12.13.   The duodenal region, diagrammatic.

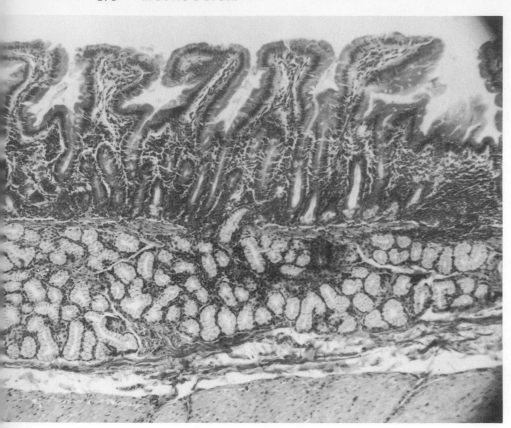

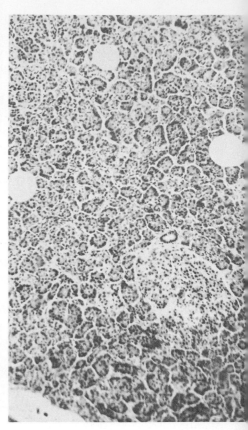

FIG. 12.14. Left: cross section through the wall of the duodenum. The cavity of the gut is toward the top. Underneath the folded inner surface tissues of the gut, note the glandular layer. Its secretion is discharged into the gut cavity and contributes to the composition of intestinal juice. Right: section through the pancreas. The large round spaces in the lower part of the photo are sections through branches of the pancreatic duct. (Duodenum, General Biological Supply House, Inc.; pancreas, courtesy of Dr. B. J. Serber, College of Medicine, New York University.)

being digested. Conversion to the active enzymes takes place in the duodenum. When trypsinogen and chymotrypsinogen arrive in the duodenum, intestinal juice is already flowing; hence **enterokinase** is available. This substance is an enzyme but not a digestive enzyme. It acts on a few trypsinogen molecules and transforms these into active trypsin. Thus enterokinase initiates the formation of **trypsin.** Trypsin in turn now activates all remaining trypsinogen, producing more trypsin, and acts on chymotrypsinogen, producing active **chymotrypsin:**

$$\text{trypsinogen} \xrightarrow{+\text{enterokinase}} \text{trypsin}$$

$$\text{trypsinogen} \xrightarrow{+\text{trypsin}} \text{trypsin}$$

$$\text{chymotrypsinogen} \xrightarrow{+\text{trypsin}} \text{chymotrypsin}$$

Active trypsin and chymotrypsin digest whole protein molecules to proteoses, peptones, and polypeptides, like pepsin in the stomach. Hence, whole proteins which have escaped gastric digestion are now broken up in the intestine.

At this stage, the **amino-peptidase** from the intestinal juice and the **carboxy-peptidase** from the pancreas enter the digestive reactions. These enzymes accelerate the further decomposition of any proteoses, peptones, and polypeptides present in the gut. Amino-peptidase attacks one type of bond in amino acid chains; carboxy-peptidase attacks another. The result of their action is the appearance of *dipeptides*, molecules consisting of only two joined amino acids.

Finally, the **dipeptidase** from intestinal juice reduces all the dipeptides to individual amino acid molecules. Dissolved in the food solution, these are the usable nutrients which the animal body obtains by subjecting eaten whole proteins to step-by-step digestion. The whole sequence of protein digestion is summarized in Fig. 12.17.

Carbohydrate Digestion

Pancreatic and **intestinal amylase** have essentially the same action as salivary amylase. Since food remains longer in the gut and is more finely divided than in the mouth, polysaccharide digestion here is more thorough. Disaccharides form. These, as well as disaccharides eaten as such or produced

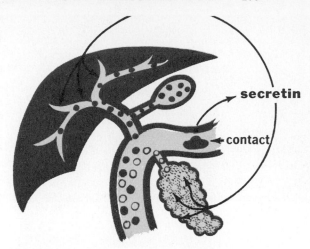

FIG. 12.15. The secretin mechanism. Contact of gastric HCl in food with the lining of the duodenum leads to the secretion of the hormone secretin. This hormone travels via the blood stream to the liver and the pancreas, where it stimulates the secretion of bile and of pancreatic juice, respectively.

by salivary digestion, are converted to monosaccharides by the **disaccharases** of intestinal juice. For example, intestinal **maltase** splits malt sugar into two glucose molecules; **sucrase** (also called *invertase*) splits cane sugar into glucose and fructose; **lactase** splits milk sugar into glucose and galactose. Added

FIG. 12.16. The composition of intestinal juice, bile, and pancreatic juice.

intestinal juice	bile	pancreatic juice
enterokinase	bile salts	trypsinogen
amino-peptidase	bile pigments	chymotrypsinogen
di-peptidase		carboxy-peptidase
disaccharases		amylase
amylase		lipase
lipase		

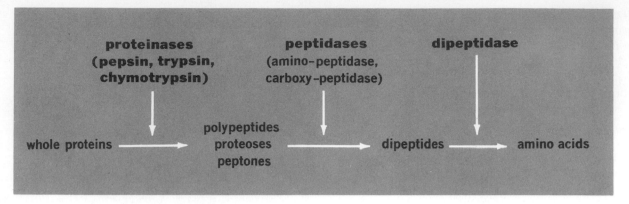

FIG. 12.17. Summary of the pattern of protein digestion.

to whatever glucose has formed by salivary digestion, these and other monosaccharide sugars are the usable nutrients obtained from complex carbohydrates. The whole digestive sequence is outlined in Fig. 12.18.

Note that quite a number of complex carbohydrates cannot be digested by mammals at all. For example, cellulose passes through the alimentary tract unchanged, the molecule being too complex for attack by the amylases. Termites do possess enzymes capable of digesting cellulose, and these animals may therefore subsist on wood or wood products.

Note also that, unlike the proteinases, the amylases are not secreted in inactive form but are immediately active as produced. Protection of the secreting glands and ducts is evidently not required, probably because animal protoplasm generally does not contain more than 1 per cent carbohydrate. Moreover, most of this carbohydrate is accumulated in the interior of cells, where it is beyond the reach of the extracellular, amylase-containing juices which flow by along the cell surfaces.

Fat Digestion

This is accomplished efficiently only in the presence of **bile salts.** Like soap, these complex organic salts reduce the surface tension of fat and so produce a fine colloidal emulsion of fat in water.

Since fat does not dissolve in water, and since fat-splitting lipase *is* dissolved in water, digestion can occur only at the boundary of water and fat. Hence the larger the boundary surface, the more thorough will be digestion. By producing a colloidal suspension, bile salts increase the available fat-water surface tremendously. Even so, only about one-half of all ingested fat is digested chemically. The remainder stays in the form of finely divided whole fat.

Fat which is digested chemically is split by **intestinal** and **pancreatic lipase** into fatty acids and glycerin. These two types of molecules, produced in part also in the stomach, plus the undigested colloidal whole fat, represent the usable nutrients obtained from eaten fat. Bile salts may combine with fatty acids into complexes which are utilized more readily than fatty acids alone.

The sequence of fat digestion is summarized in Fig. 12.19.

Bile pigments have no demonstrated digestive function. They are metabolic wastes, produced in the liver as byproducts of the destruction of red blood corpuscles. Brownish green or greenish yellow in color, bile pigments enter the gut as components of bile. They are eliminated with the indigestible remains, to which they give their characteristic color. Some quantities of bile pigments do not go through the gut but are picked up from the liver and gall bladder by the blood and are transported to the kid-

FIG. 12.18. Summary of the pattern of carbohydrate digestion.

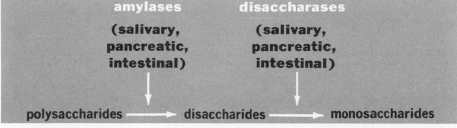

neys. Excreted from there, the pigments are responsible for the characteristic color of urine. When the gall bladder or the bile ducts are blocked by gallstones, bile dams up and cannot reach the intestine. Fat digestion is then impaired. Moreover, bile pigments are absorbed in excessive amounts by the blood and, carried in part into the skin, produce jaundice. In birds, bile pigments may be excreted by being incorporated into the shells of eggs. For example, the blue color of robins' eggs is due to chemically modified bile pigments.

The chemical aspects of digestion as a whole are outlined comprehensively in Fig. 12.20.

Absorption and Egestion

ABSORPTION

As more and more usable nutrients are liberated by intestinal digestion, food becomes increasingly fluid. The resulting solution is kept continuously agitated by two processes.

Peristalsis is one of these. A peristaltic wave may sweep forward for a short distance at some section of the small intestine, then may stop, and another wave may traverse the same or an even longer section. Stationary contractions may occur. Whole loops of the intestine may contract and shift and slide over other loops. Then forward peristalsis may again take place. As these movements proceed all along the gut, they keep food moving and churning and bring it thoroughly into contact with the interior surface of the gut.

This surface is the second agency which keeps the food solution in motion. The inner lining of the gut is greatly folded and is studded with millions of near-microscopic **villi,** fingerlike protrusions which produce a velvety, carpetlike texture. Covering this whole inner surface of the gut is a single layer of cells, the intestinal **mucosa** (Fig. 12.21). By virtue of the folds and the villi, the surface area of the mucosa is exceedingly large. And the villi move continuously from side to side, stirring the food solution and circulating it thoroughly about the mucosal lining.

Agitation of food in the gut is advantageous for two reasons. First, churning mixes and remixes food with the digestive juices, allowing the chemical breakdown of virtually all potential food substances present. Second, agitation brings food into contact with different regions of the intestinal lining, a necessary condition if thorough *absorption* of food is to occur. The large area of the lining clearly facilitates this.

Absorption brings about a transfer of usable nutrients into the transport system, the circulating blood and lymph. A few substances, alcohol, for ex-

FIG. 12.19. Summary of the pattern of fat digestion.

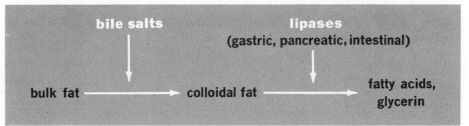

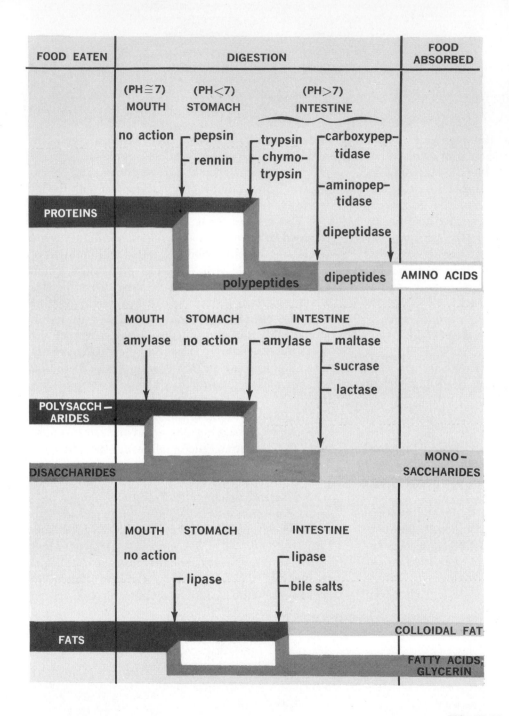

FIG. 12.20. Overall summary of digestion.

FIG. 12.21. High-power view of a portion of the intestinal mucosa. The photo is oriented so that the internal cavity of the gut is toward the top of the page. Note the arrangement of the mucosal cells and their nuclei into a neat single layer, and the fuzzy surface of the mucosa, produced by many short cilialike projections which point into the gut cavity. Note also the several bottle-shaped cells, called goblet cells, which produce mucus. Of the tissues underlying the mucosa as a whole, only a thin layer of connective tissue appears in this photo. (General Biological Supply House, Inc.)

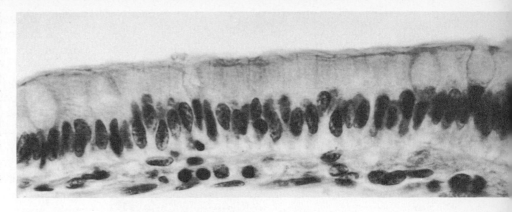

ample, can be absorbed through the stomach wall; but most foods are absorbed through the intestine. Here nutrients must first be passed from the gut cavity into the cells of the mucosa, and these lining cells then must release the food molecules into the deeper parts of the gut wall, where blood and lymph vessels are situated.

In nutrient transfer from the gut cavity into the mucosa, active, selective, energy-consuming membranes are encountered once again: the plasma membranes of the mucosal cells. Passive *diffusion* of nu-

trients into the mucosa plays a role in absorption. But *selective work* by mucosal cells also plays an important part.

This is well illustrated by the different rates with which foodstuffs are absorbed. For example, glucose, galactose, and fructose all have the same molecular size and composition, namely, $C_6H_{12}O_6$. Yet of these three 6-carbon sugars, galactose is absorbed most rapidly, fructose least rapidly. Moreover, sugar molecules containing only 3, 4, or 5 carbon atoms, though smaller than the 6-carbon mole-

FIG. 12.22. The pattern of absorption of molecular nutrients through the intestinal mucosa.

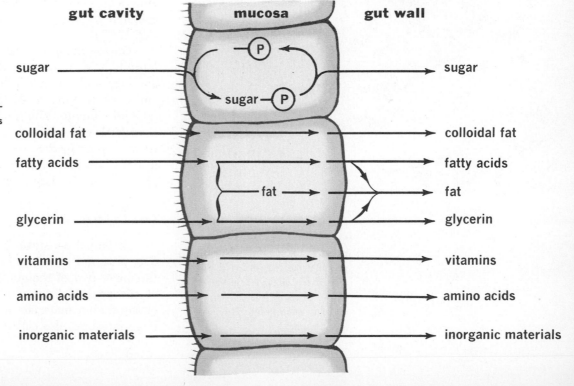

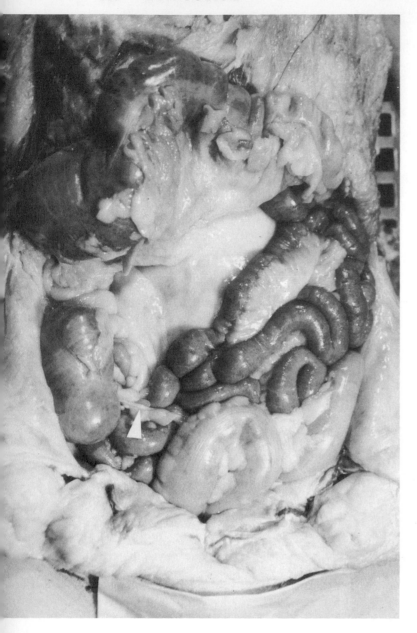

cules, are generally absorbed much more slowly, if at all. Mucosal cells evidently "recognize" and select among the substances present in digested food.

Sugar absorption is accompanied by *phosphorylation;* at the surface membranes of the mucosal cells, phosphate groups are added to the sugar molecules. Monosaccharide-phosphate complexes then enter the cells. Some of these complexes may be used up by the cells themselves, but most of the sugars are soon exported into the deeper tissues of the gut wall. This export is accompanied by *dephosphorylation.* The sugar-phosphate complexes are split apart, and free monosaccharides emerge on the far side of the mucosa. Phosphate groups are retained, however, and may be used again to phosphorylate more sugars absorbed from the gut cavity (Fig. 12.22).

Phosphorylation does not occur in the absorption of other usable nutrients. Water, minerals, amino acids, and vitamins diffuse through the mucosa unchanged. Similarly, colloidal fat droplets, still undigested chemically, as well as fatty acids and glycerin, are passed as such through the mucosa and reappear on the other side. Here some of the fatty acids and the glycerin may recombine immediately into whole fats. This increases the amount of colloidal fat transported away from the gut (see Fig. 12.22).

During the 4- to 8-hr stay of food in the small intestine, this organ absorbs most of the minerals and the usable organic nutrients—monosaccharides, amino acids, fatty acids, glycerin, colloidal whole fat, and vitamins. The small intestine removes relatively little water from the food solution. On the contrary, by pouring digestive juices into the gut cavity, it actually adds water to food. Water is absorbed primarily in the large intestine.

FIG. 12.23. Abdominal dissection, man. The white arrow points to the appendix. Note the pouch of the caecum on the right side of the appendix (to the left as the photo is viewed). (Photographic department, Rhode Island Hospital.)

EGESTION

Intestinal peristalsis occurs in such a way that, over a period of hours, food is slowly shifted into the lower part of the gut. Most of the water, some of the mineral ions, and all the indigestible and unabsorbable materials eventually move into the large intestine, also called the **colon.** The first portion of this section of the alimentary tract is the **caecum,** a blind pouch which, in man and a number of other mammals, carries a terminal fingerlike extension, the **appendix** (Fig. 12.23). In many herbivorous mammals (e.g., rodents), the caecum is extremely large. It serves as a temporary food-storage pouch and provides additional time for digestion, an advantage in a plant-eating animal. At the far end, the large intestine joins the **rectum,** a short tube opening to the outside through the **anus.**

The large intestine has a dual function. First, it is an *absorbing* and *excreting* organ. During the 10- to 12-hr stay of materials in the colon, the bulk of the water and the remaining inorganic nutrients are absorbed. At the same time, many metabolic wastes, and inorganic substances present in the body to excess, are excreted into the colon cavity. We note that, by differentially absorbing from and adding to the materials in the gut cavity, the large intestine aids in maintaining a properly balanced internal composition of the body. That the colon actually does regulate the internal water balance, for example, is indicated by the familiar upset conditions of diarrhea and constipation.

Second, the large intestine initiates *decay* of indigestible and unabsorbable materials. This is brought about by dense, permanent populations of bacteria, which live in the gut as symbionts. These microorganisms obtain food from many of the materials the host cannot digest or absorb, and as a result of the nutritional activities of the bacteria, the substances in the colon undergo rapid decay. Frequently the bacteria release byproducts of their own metabolism, and some of these byproducts may be nutrients usable by the host. Vitamins are among these. Mammals actually obtain an appreciable fraction of their vitamin supply from the intestinal bacteria.

After passing through the large intestine, what is left of the original eaten food is largely *roughage:* tough fibers, gristle, pieces of cellulose, and unmacerated plant tissue, all suspended in more or less reduced quantities of water. Mixed with this are bile pigments, colon excretions, bacteria and bacterial products, and whatever else may have been added or left over in the passage of food through the gut. These **feces** ("dregs") are in a more or less advanced state of decay, and they are ultimately egested as semisolid masses.

The first phase of nutrition, alimentation, is now completed. Water, minerals, and the necessary organic nutrients have been absorbed, have been moved through the intestinal mucosa, and are ready to be transported throughout the body.

REVIEW QUESTIONS

1. Review the general nutritional pattern of animals, and contrast the nutrient requirements of plants and animals. For which materials are animals dependent on plants, and why? What is the basic function of an alimentary system?

2. Review what is known about appetite and hunger control. What role does the brain play in such control?

3. Discuss the chemical aspects of digestion generally. What roles do enzymes play in digestion, and how are digestive enzymes distinct from others? What is the relation between digestion and synthesis?

4. Review the events of oral digestion. What is the composition of saliva, and how is salivary secretion initiated? What mechanical and chemical digestive processes occur in the mouth? Through what processes is food transferred into the stomach? What are the anatomical parts of the stomach, and what are their functions?

5. What is the composition of gastric juice, and by what processes is secretion of this fluid controlled? Review the mechanical and chemical events of gastric digestion. What are the specific functions of HCl, pepsin, and rennin? What are the results of gastric digestion?

6. Which digestive fluids are added to food in the duodenum, and what is the composition of these fluids? Where are the fluids manufactured, and what processes stimulate their secretion? What is enterokinase, and what is its function?

7. Review the specific course of protein, carbohydrate, and fat digestion in the intestine. What enzymes are involved in each case? What are the results of these digestive processes? What is the adaptive reason for the secretion of proteinases in inactive form?

8. What are intestinal villi, and what are their functions? How, and in what form, are different categories of food absorbed into the intestinal wall? What tissue accomplishes absorption? How long does food remain in the small intestine, and in the other parts of the alimentary tract?

9. What are the functions of the large intestine? What is the role of the intestinal bacteria? Do these symbionts live mutualistically, commensalistically, or parasitically?

10. If pure glucose were eaten, where would it be digested? Why are eaten vitamins, or orally administered medicines, not digested in the alimentary tract? Like vitamins, cellulose too is not digested in man; does the body handle vitamins and cellulose in the same way?

SUGGESTED COLLATERAL READINGS

A historical high point in the study of alimentation is spotlighted in the following reprint of the original (1833) book by Beaumont, the father of modern gastric physiology:
Beaumont, W.: "Experiments and Observations on the Gastric Juice and the Physiology of Digestion," Harvard University Press, 1929.

Two standard texts which may be consulted for additional information on most aspects of alimentation are as follows:
Carlson, A. J., and V. Johnson: "The Machinery of the Body," 4th ed., University of Chicago Press, 1953.
Scheer, B. T.: "Comparative Physiology," Wiley, 1948.

Excellent nontechnical articles on nutrition may be found in the following:
Knobloch, I. W.: Nutrition, in "Readings in Biological Science," Appleton-Century-Crofts, 1948.
Various authors: "Food and Life," Yearbook of Agriculture, U.S. Department of Agriculture, 1939.

The following articles are written popularly too and are strongly recommended:
Mayer, J.: Appetite and Obesity, *Sci. American,* vol. 195, 1956.
Remington, R. E.: The Social Origins of Dietary Habits, *Sci. Monthly,* vol. 43, 1936.
Boyd-Orr, I.: The Food Problem, *Sci. American,* vol. 183, 1950.
Weaver, W.: People, Energy, and Food, *Sci. Monthly,* vol. 78, 1954.
Quisenberry, K. S.: The World's Principal Food Plants, *Sci. Monthly,* vol. 79, 1954.

13

HETEROTROPHIC NUTRITION: TRANSPORT AND THE LIVER

LIKE THE TRACHEOPHYTES among plants, most of the larger, compactly built animals possess specialized internal channel systems for nutrient **transport.** These circulatory systems consist of blood and lymph vessels, and the fluids within them serve as the vehicles in which nutrients are carried.

We have found earlier that, in plants, nutrient transport is immediate and direct. From regions of absorption or manufacture, foodstuffs are carried straight to tissue cells for utilization. This is also the pattern in many animals. But in other animals, as for example in all vertebrates, transport is largely indirect. Most of the nutrients absorbed from the gut are first channeled into a **liver.**

We shall here examine this vertebrate pattern of nutrient transport and the vital role played by the liver.

The Transport Pattern

INTESTINE TO LIVER

Representing the largest gland of the body (Fig. 13.1), the liver has been estimated to carry out some 200 separate functions. Many of these are not concerned directly with nutrient transport. But the many which are make the liver the principal receiving station, processing plant, warehouse, distributing organ, and traffic control center, all rolled into one. Liver cells regulate not only what kinds but also what quantities of nutrients are sent out into body tissues. They carry out numerous chemical transformations of incoming materials, and they serve as storage depots for some of them. Through such quartermastering activities, the liver plays a major role in the maintenance of optimal working conditions throughout the body. Indeed, the liver is to bodily metabolic control what the brain is to bodily steady-state control.

The adaptive advantage of an organ such as the liver is evident. No matter when or at what regular or irregular intervals the organism eats, the

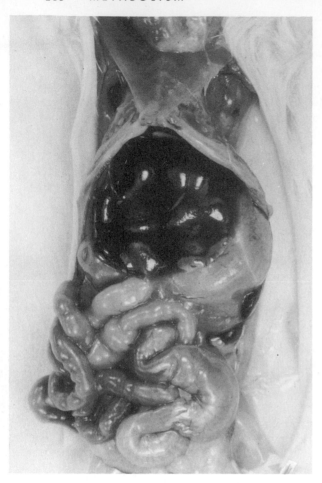

FIG. 13.1. Abdominal dissection, mouse. Note the liver just underneath the diaphragm. The stomach may be seen next to the liver on the left side of the body. The small tongue of tissue on the outer curvature of the stomach is a portion of the spleen. (Courtesy of Dr. Elizabeth Leduc, Brown University.)

Here blood picks up the molecular nutrients already absorbed through the intestinal mucosa: water, minerals, vitamins, monosaccharides, amino acids, and fatty acids and glycerin. It may be noted that colloidal droplets of whole fat, being enormously larger than molecules, cannot enter the blood capillaries in the villi. As we shall see presently, the fat droplets are transported instead by the lymph system.

In their transfer into the blood, molecular nutrients must pass from the intestinal tissues through the walls of the blood capillaries. These capillary walls are exceedingly thin, consisting of a single layer of greatly flattened cells (see Chap. 20). To a great extent, nutrient transfer through such cells is brought about by diffusion. But active absorption by the capillary walls undoubtedly plays a role too. Within blood, the nutrients are carried as dissolved molecules.

Food-laden blood now leaves the intestine. The capillaries in the gut collect into larger vessels, these join and rejoin, and a single very large channel eventually emerges from the whole intestine: the **hepatic portal vein.** This vessel leads directly into the liver (see Fig. 13.2).

Whatever nutrients are not or cannot be transported to the liver in this fashion are collected by the lymph system. Among such nutrients are mainly the colloidal whole fats, but also water, minerals, and variable quantities of other molecular substances, which may have escaped transport by blood.

LYMPH TRANSPORT

The lymph system (Fig. 13.3) compensates for the "leakiness" of the blood circulation. As blood flows in its closed network of vessels, it loses a cer-

liver collects most of the food as it is absorbed from the gut and then releases it into the body, at a pace adapted to the particular requirements of the moment. Hence, whereas the metabolism of other animals reaches peaks just after food has been eaten, the metabolism of animals with livers may remain at a continuously steady level.

A special arrangement of the circulatory pathways ensures that the liver receives nutrients from the gut directly and quickly. Blood is first pumped into the intestine through a few large arteries, which then branch out in the gut wall into extensive networks of microscopic capillary vessels (Fig. 13.2). The gut wall thus contains a rich supply of circulatory channels, and blood reaches into all intestinal villi, where it comes close to the mucosal cells.

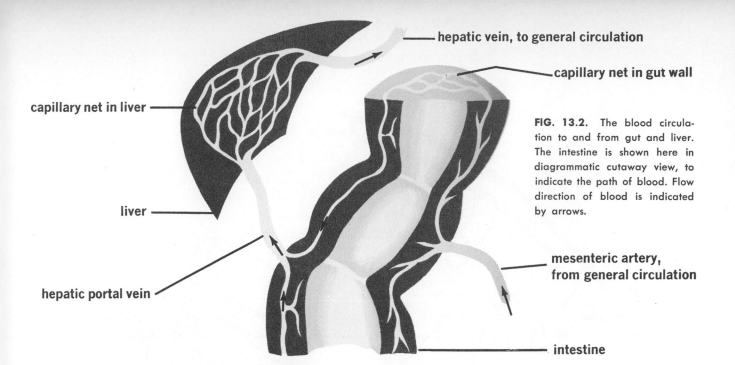

capillary net in liver

liver

hepatic portal vein

hepatic vein, to general circulation

capillary net in gut wall

FIG. 13.2. The blood circulation to and from gut and liver. The intestine is shown here in diagrammatic cutaway view, to indicate the path of blood. Flow direction of blood is indicated by arrows.

mesenteric artery, from general circulation

intestine

tain amount of fluid through the thin walls of the capillaries. This escaped fluid, consisting principally of water, mineral ions, and molecular organic nutrients, is **lymph,** and it is responsible for the moist condition of all body tissues. Note here that a leaky blood circulation is not an instance of faulty engineering. On the contrary, fluid escape from capillaries is an adaptive necessity, for this is how the blood ultimately provides the cells of the body with water and all other necessary supplies.

But blood vessels would soon run dry if fluid losses were not made up. This is where the lymph system comes into play. Tiny lymph capillaries originate in all parts of the body, intestine included, and they pick up any free fluid in the tissues. Lymph capillaries then join into progressively larger, progressively fewer ducts, until a single large channel is formed. This channel empties into a vein in the left shoulder region, and so it returns to the blood all the fluid lost originally.

FIG. 13.3. The pattern of the lymph circulation of the body, diagrammatic. Fluid (lymph) escapes from the blood capillaries into the tissues of the body (large arrow at bottom of figure), and returns via lymph vessels into the blood circulation.

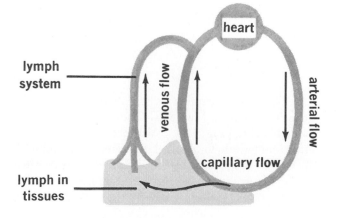

heart

lymph system

venous flow

arterial flow

capillary flow

lymph in tissues

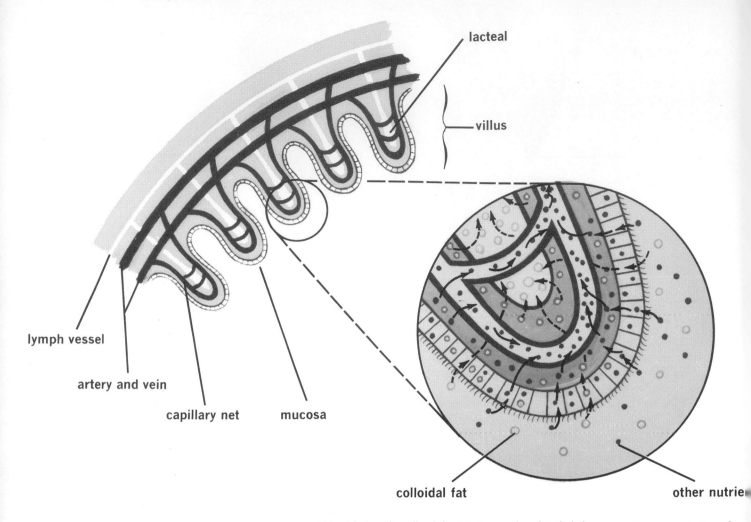

lacteal

villus

lymph vessel

artery and vein

capillary net   mucosa

colloidal fat   other nutrie

FIG. 13.4.   The villi of the intestine and a detailed diagrammatic representation of a single villus. Of the nutrients absorbed through the layer of mucosal cells, whole fats collect in the lacteal of a villus and are transported from there through the lymph system. Other nutrients are picked up by the blood stream.

The lymph capillaries which originate in the intestine are called **lacteals.** One lacteal is situated in each villus (Fig. 13.4). Also present in a villus is intestinal lymph, fluid which has become mixed with the nutrients supplied by the intestinal mucosa. Most of these nutrients enter the blood stream, as noted; but all others, including chiefly the colloidal whole fats, remain in lymph and so pass into the lacteal. After a heavy meal, the lacteals may become milky white from the large quantities of emulsified fat suspended in them. From the lacteals, nutrients are transported through the larger lymph vessels of the body, and eventually into the blood. The whole fats are then carried by the blood into the principal fat-storing regions of the body, as we shall see. Hence the fats largely bypass the liver. But any other nutrients eventually do circulate via the blood into the liver, where they join those already carried in over the more direct route of the hepatic portal vein.

In the liver, the hepatic portal vein breaks up into a very extensive network of capillary channels (see Fig. 13.2). Thus every liver cell comes into contact with incoming blood (Fig. 13.5). The cells absorb blood-borne nutrients, process them, and return the finished products back to the blood in the capillary channels. The channels ultimately join and form larger vessels, and these finally empty into a single large duct, the **hepatic vein.** Blood in this vein carries all liver-processed foods away from the liver, into the general body circulation. In this manner, nutrient supplies reach all parts of the body.

The principal pathways of nutrient transport are summarized diagrammatically in Fig. 13.6. We now inquire what happens to food molecules during their stay in the liver.

Liver Function

We may regard the liver as one side of a vast balance. The other side of the balance is the remainder of the body, and blood serves as carrier, signal mechanism, and general connecting link between the two sides (Fig. 13.7). Nutrients coming or not coming from the gut into the liver may shift the balance one way; nutrients used up or not used up by the body tissues may shift it the opposite

way. These balancing processes operate through chemical equilibria, and they normally adjust in such a manner that the original balance is maintained or, if upset, reattained.

Small fractions of the nutrients from the intestine are likely to be used by liver cells for their own maintenance. What is the fate of the remainder?

CARBOHYDRATES

The body-wide carbohydrate balance may be symbolized as in Fig. 13.8. This figure indicates that, as in plants, **glucose** is the principal compound in carbohydrate *transport.* Glucose is therefore found mainly in the blood. The principal form in which animals *utilize* and *store* carbohydrates is **glycogen.** This polysaccharide is found in all cells, and in so far as it is stored, it is the functional equivalent of starch in plants. Many animal tissues store more glycogen than is required for immediate use. Muscle and skin hold considerable quantities, but the liver is the principal storage depot.

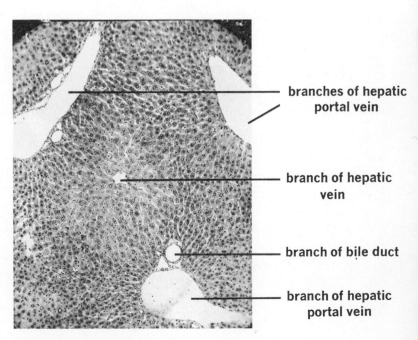

FIG. 13.5. Section through mouse liver, showing a functional unit of the organ. Blood from the intestine arrives through the branches of the hepatic portal vein, passes through the canal-like spaces between the liver cells, and collects in branches of the hepatic vein, from where it is distributed to the body. As blood flows past the liver cells, many vital metabolic exchanges occur. Bile secreted by liver cells collects in the branches of the bile duct. (Courtesy of Dr. Elizabeth Leduc, Brown University.)

branches of hepatic portal vein

branch of hepatic vein

branch of bile duct

branch of hepatic portal vein

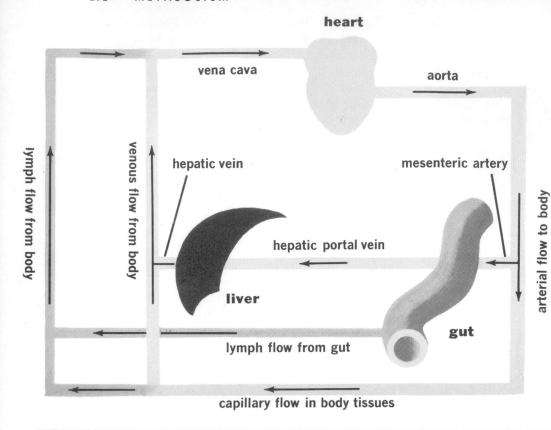

heart

vena cava

aorta

lymph flow from body

venous flow from body

hepatic vein

mesenteric artery

arterial flow to body

hepatic portal vein

liver

lymph flow from gut

gut

capillary flow in body tissues

FIG. 13.6. Summary of the pathways of nutrient transport and distribution.

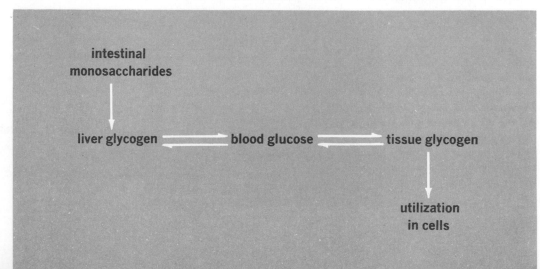

nutrient supply from intestine → liver ⇄ body tissues → nutrient utilization in cells

blood

FIG. 13.7. The general pattern of the nutrient balance in the body and the role of the liver in maintaining this balance.

intestinal monosaccharides

liver glycogen ⇄ blood glucose ⇄ tissue glycogen

utilization in cells

FIG. 13.8. The carbohydrate balance of the body.

Blood-sugar Constancy

The carbohydrate balance above is affected by relative rates of supply and demand. Whenever the rate of carbohydrate supply from the gut exceeds the rate of utilization in the tissues, then a net excess of carbohydrates will accumulate. Such an excess is stored away in the liver as glycogen. Conversely, if intestinal supply does not keep up with tissue utilization, then the liver makes up the deficit by releasing some of its stored glycogen as blood glucose. As a result of such activities, the liver maintains a *constant* blood-glucose concentration, irrespective of the rates of supply and utilization. This is one of the most closely regulated constancies in the body (Fig. 13.9).

Just how does the liver carry out this regulating function? In all cells, those of the liver included,

FIG. 13.9. Blood-glucose balance. If much glucose is supplied to blood from food and little is used, then the blood-glucose concentration will tend to be high (top and left). Under such conditions the liver withdraws glucose and stores it as glycogen, so establishing a normal glucose level (bottom left). On the other hand, if much glucose is used up and little is supplied, then the blood-glucose concentration will tend to be low (top and right). The liver then adds glucose to blood from its glycogen stores, and so reestablishes the normal glucose level (bottom right). Through these actions, the liver maintains a *constant* blood-glucose concentration.

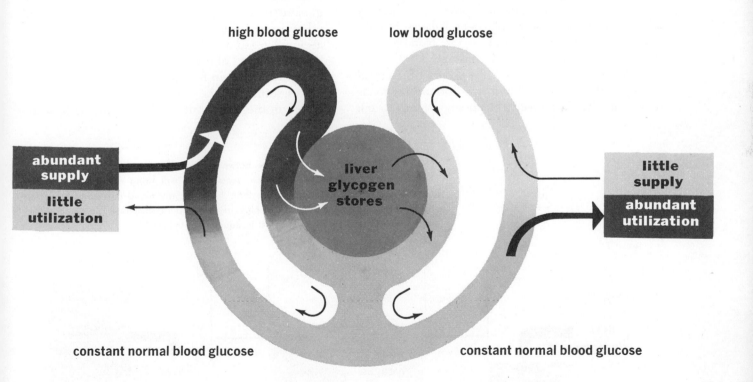

high blood glucose

low blood glucose

abundant supply

little utilization

liver glycogen stores

little supply

abundant utilization

constant normal blood glucose

constant normal blood glucose

blood glucose may be converted into cellular glycogen, and vice versa. As we shall see later in greater detail, this important reversible conversion is a two-step process involving *phosphorylated* glucose, i.e., glucose-phosphate:

$$glucose \rightleftharpoons glucose\text{-}phosphate \rightleftharpoons glycogen$$

This reaction sequence is the key to the carbohydrate-regulating activity of the liver. Liver cells contain stored glycogen, and blood flowing through the liver past the cells contains glucose. The two carbohydrates are in chemical equilibrium. If for any reason the glucose concentration in blood should rise, then the chemical equilibrium will be disturbed. And by the principle of mass action, the glucose excess in blood will be converted into liver glycogen, through the reactions above. Conversely, if for some reason the blood-glucose level should fall, then the chemical balance will shift the opposite way, and liver glycogen will become blood glucose, until the original equilibrium is reattained (Fig. 13.10). In effect, liver and blood are so coordinated that any change in the glucose $\rightleftharpoons$ glycogen balance is automatically counteracted, and so the blood-glucose concentration is maintained constant.

A rise in blood sugar usually occurs after a meal is digested, when blood and lymph transport foods from the gut. Conversely, blood sugar tends to fall during periods of fasting, e.g., during sleep. A fall of blood glucose also tends to occur during strenuous exercise, when muscles and other body tissues use up glycogen at a faster than normal rate. These tissues then become low in glycogen, and, as a result, the blood-glucose $\rightleftharpoons$ tissue-glycogen balance shifts in such a way that blood-glucose levels decrease and tissue-glycogen levels increase (Fig. 13.11). But in this and all similar situations, the liver rapidly counteracts any change of blood-glucose levels by either enlarging or reducing its glycogen stores.

Factors in Sugar Balance

In mammals, and in vertebrates generally, *hormones* play a significant role in these shifting balances. For example, the hormone **insulin,** secreted by specialized cells in the pancreas, promotes the phosphorylation of glucose. Hence it controls the conversion of glucose into glycogen. If, as in a diabetic animal, insulin production is inadequate, then glucose becomes unusable, and the liver and all other tissues cannot manufacture glycogen. Glucose accumulates in the blood, yet the tissues of the body become starved of carbohydrates. Fats and proteins must then make up for the lack of cellular carbohydrates. Much of the unusable blood sugar is excreted in the urine, but the blood-glucose level re-

FIG. 13.10. The reaction balance between liver glycogen and blood glucose. If blood glucose concentrations are low, mass action will bring about more reaction from liver glycogen to blood glucose than the other way round (left), and conversely if blood glucose concentrations are high (right). As a result, blood glucose and liver glycogen will tend to be maintained in equilibrium (middle).

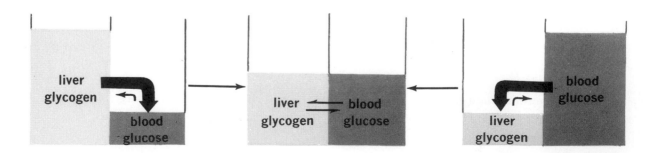

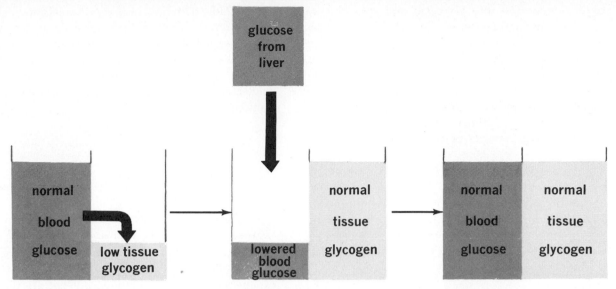

FIG. 13.11. Maintenance of glycogen balance in tissues. If concentrations of tissue glycogen are low, blood glucose will restore the normal concentrations (left). This will lower the concentration of blood glucose (middle), but only temporarily, for glucose supplied by the liver will soon restore the normal concentration in blood (right).

mains abnormally high nevertheless. Conversely, if too much insulin is produced, glucose will be converted to liver and tissue glycogen to such an extent that the blood-glucose level drops drastically. The brain is particularly dependent on glucose, and when the glucose supply in blood becomes abnormally low, "insulin shock" and eventually death may ensue.

The hormone **adrenalin,** secreted in the core of the adrenal gland, acts in exactly the opposite fashion. It promotes the dephosphorylation of glucose; hence it speeds up the conversion of glycogen into glucose. Adrenalin is secreted particularly during intense emotional or physical stress. The hormone then causes a large-scale conversion of liver glycogen into blood glucose, appropriately at a time when the body tissues require a great deal of fuel. As we shall see later, many other hormones affect carbohydrate balances as well.

What happens if, in a healthy animal, the liver and all body tissues hold glycogen to capacity, all current carbohydrate needs are satisfied, yet still more sugar is being supplied by the gut? Internal carbohydrate saturation may actually be reached rather rapidly, since even at peak storage, the carbohydrate content of the body does not exceed 1 per cent of the total weight. If sugars supplied by food exceed the internal capacity, then a small fraction of the excess may be excreted in urine. This occurs, for example, right after a heavy meal. But the bulk of any carbohydrate excess goes to the liver, where it is *converted into fats.* This explains why even a nonfatty diet may produce increased layers of body fat, particularly if over a long period of time more food is eaten than the body requires.

Conversely, if an animal subsists on reduced food intake, or undergoes outright starvation, then the internal glycogen stores will soon be greatly diminished. Yet, up to a point, the blood-glucose level and the carbohydrate supply to the tissues may still remain normal. For under such conditions the liver draws on the fat of the body and converts as much of it as required into glycogen and into glucose.

One major function of the liver thus emerges. Through glycogen storage and blood-glucose control and, whenever necessary, through interconversion of carbohydrates and fats, this organ ensures that all cells of the body receive an adequate glucose supply. This supply does not depend on any particular pattern of mealtimes, and it is geared to the changing requirements of the tissues.

AMINO ACIDS

A body-wide equilibrium exists, as outlined in Fig. 13.12. Just as for carbohydrates above, if the rate of amino acid supply from the intestine exceeds the rate of utilization in the tissues, then an amino acid excess will develop.

Amino Acid Excess

This is the usual situation. Amino acid requirements are greatest in young, growing animals, in pregnant females, and in animals in which extensive tissue repair is under way, as after disease. In all such cases, protein synthesis and growth proceed at a very high rate, and large quantities of amino acids are utilized in the cells. But even here, more amino acids are usually eaten than are required. In healthy adults, where processes of growth and structural replacement occur at a much reduced rate, amino acid requirements are reduced correspondingly.

Unlike carbohydrates, excess amino acids are not stored. Some tissues may accumulate more protein than they require, and such proteins in a sense may be considered to represent amino acid reserves, available to the body when food supplies are deficient. But specialized storage of amino acids, comparable to the storage of carbohydrates, does not occur. What then happens to the usual excesses of these acids? The bulk of them is transformed chemically, through reactions taking place in the liver.

The first step in this transformation is **deamination.** As the term implies, the amino group ($-NH_2$) is split away from the remainder of an amino acid molecule. An enzyme, *deaminase,* promotes the reaction:

$$NH_2-R-COOH \xleftrightarrow{\text{deaminase}}$$

$$\text{amino acid}$$

$$-NH_2 + -R-COOH \longleftrightarrow NH_3 + \text{keto acid}$$

$$\text{ammonia}$$

The separated $-NH_2$ group ultimately appears as free **ammonia** (NH_3). This is a toxic material. The remainder of the amino acid molecule, which has contributed one H atom toward the formation of ammonia, becomes a **keto acid.** What are the fates of these two endproducts?

In many animals, aquatic ones in particular, ammonia is carried from the liver to the kidneys by blood and is excreted as such in urine. In other animals, free ammonia is first changed into less toxic substances, and the latter are then excreted in urine. In insects and birds, for example, ammonia is combined with certain other organic molecules and is made into **uric acid.** This acid is then carried to the kidneys for excretion. Mammals dispose of ammonia in a different way. The compound is combined in the liver with carbon dioxide, abundantly available as a byproduct of respiration. The result of this combination is **urea.** This substance is then carried by blood to the kidneys, where it is excreted.

Urea production by combination of NH_3 and CO_2 in the liver occurs through a *cyclical* sequence of reactions. This is called the **ornithine cycle.** As indicated in Fig. 13.13, three amino acids, normally present in the liver, form the "endless belt" of this

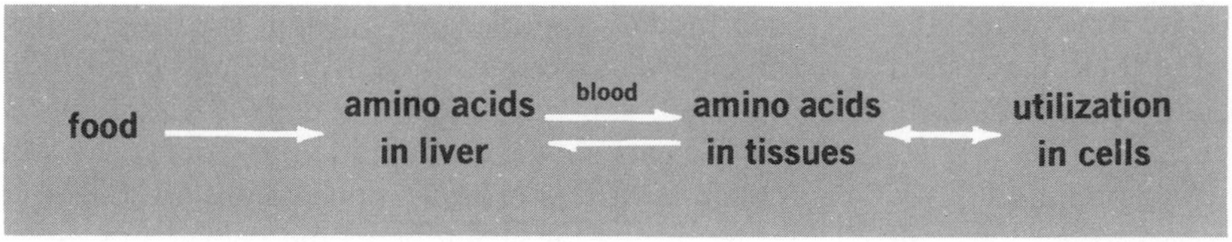

food $\longrightarrow$ amino acids in liver $\xrightarrow{\text{blood}}$ amino acids in tissues $\longleftrightarrow$ utilization in cells

FIG. 13.12. The amino acid balance of the body.

cycle: *ornithine*, *citrulline*, and *arginine*. Ornithine first reacts with 1 molecule of ammonia and 1 molecule of carbon dioxide, yielding citrulline. This amino acid then combines with another molecule of ammonia, forming arginine. Arginine finally splits into two fragments, in a reaction requiring the enzyme *arginase*. One of these fragments is urea, the other is ornithine, and the starting point of the cycle is thereby regenerated.

Keto acids are the second product of deamination. These acids are not excreted but are salvaged; they are converted to *fats* and *carbohydrates* by liver cells. Fats and carbohydrates so formed are treated indistinguishably from all other fats and carbohydrates; i.e., they may be stored as liver and tissue glycogen, or they may be added to the fat pool of the body. Clearly, an animal may become fat not only by eating too many carbohydrates or fats but also by consuming too many proteins or other amino acid–supplying substances. In short, too much food of any kind will make an animal obese.

Deamination into ammonia and keto acids is the fate of most excess amino acids. But some are not deaminated. Instead, they are used in liver cells as starting materials in the production of a number of special compounds. For example, blood normally contains a permanent population of free protein molecules. Some of these blood proteins are enzymes. Others play a role in blood clotting, as we shall see. Still others establish immunity against infectious agents (see Chap. 20). Many of these blood proteins are manufactured in the liver, and the raw materials here are nondeaminated amino acids.

Amino Acid Deficiency

The assumption so far has been that food provides a net excess of amino acids. What happens when the opposite is the case? Much of the answer is contained in the deamination reaction. To reiterate,

$$\text{amino acids} \xrightleftharpoons[\text{}]{\text{deaminase}} NH_3 + \text{keto acids}$$

$$\qquad\qquad\quad \updownarrow \qquad\qquad \updownarrow$$

$$\qquad\qquad -NH_2 \qquad \text{fats, carbo-}$$
$$\qquad\qquad \text{pool} \qquad\quad \text{hydrates}$$

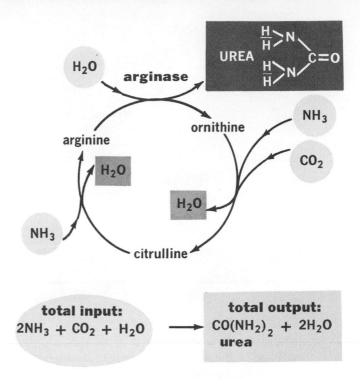

FIG. 13.13.   The ornithine cycle.

total input:
$2NH_3 + CO_2 + H_2O$

total output:
$CO(NH_2)_2 + 2H_2O$
urea

Note that this is a reversible reaction: proceeding to the right, amino acids are broken up; proceeding to the left, they are synthesized. Under the usual conditions of amino acid excess, mass action operates in such a way that the breakup reaction to the right occurs to a far greater extent than the reverse reaction. But if the protein content of eaten food is so low that a deficiency of amino acids develops, then some of this deficiency may be made up by the liver, through the reverse of deamination, that is, amino acid synthesis by *amination* of keto acids.

In such a synthesis, some ($-NH_2$)-containing substance may be the source of the required ammonia; and eaten or stored carbohydrates and fats may be transformed into the necessary keto acids. But whereas all kinds of keto acids may be converted to fat or carbohydrate, these latter substances cannot be converted into all kinds of keto acids. We recall (Chap. 12) that, of the 23 types of naturally occurring amino acids, 8 or 10, the misnamed "essential"

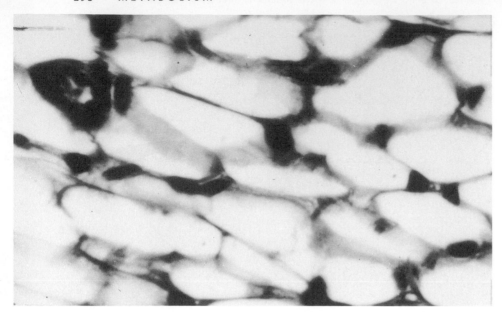

FIG. 13.14. High-power view of a section through adipose tissue. The dark-stained nuclei of these fat-storing cells have been pushed toward the cell boundaries, and fat fills the cell interiors (white spaces). (Courtesy of Dr. B. J. Serber, College of Medicine, New York University.)

ones, cannot be manufactured by animals. This is actually an inability of animals to manufacture 8 or 10 kinds of keto acids. And unless these are supplied steadily by food, in fully prefabricated form and in appropriate quantities, an animal will die of malnutrition. Clearly, an adequate diet must contain daily doses of protein, or equivalent foods which supply essential amino acids, or at least the corresponding keto acids.

On the other hand, all other types of keto acids *can* be produced in the liver, even if food does not provide them, so long as carbohydrate or fat is available as raw material. Such acids may then be combined with ammonia, and the resulting 13 or 15 types of amino acids may reduce an existing deficiency.

A second major regulating function of the liver is now in evidence. Through deamination and synthesis, the liver balances the external amino acid supply against the internal demand and gears the distribution of these acids to the varying requirements of the tissues. Moreover, through the associated processes of urea production and blood-protein manufacture, the liver also carries out vital protective functions and so contributes significantly to maintaining a steady state in the body.

FATS, FATTY ACIDS, AND GLYCERIN

Fats are the animal storage food *par excellence*. All cells may store some fat, but certain cells are specialized for this to a very high degree. They form extensive **adipose tissues** which, when viewed with the naked eye, have the appearance of continuous, homogeneous masses of fat. The fatty rind on steak is an example. Each cell in such tissues contains one or more large fat vacuoles, which may fill practically the entire cellular space (Fig. 13.14). Adipose tissues, also called *fat depots*, occur in more or less circumscribed body regions: under the skin, around the heart and the kidneys, and particularly along the membranes which envelop the intestine and the other abdominal organs. The latter depots are principally responsible for the girth of many an abdomen.

We recall that colloidal droplets of whole fat are absorbed from the gut into the lymph system and, bypassing the liver, are carried from there into the blood stream. As blood then circulates throughout the body, most colloidal fats are taken up directly by the fat depots. Some colloidal fats also enter the liver, reached in this manner by a rather roundabout route. A more direct path to the liver is taken by the fatty acids and the glycerin absorbed from the gut. As we have seen, these digestion products of fat enter the liver via the hepatic portal vein.

The liver is an important fat depot. It not only receives fats, fatty acids, and glycerin but, as noted earlier, it also manufactures fats from excess carbohydrates and amino acids. The total fat content of the liver is in balance with that of the other fat depots of the body. If liver fat increases too much, the excess is sent via the blood to the other depots. Conversely, the other depots make up any deficiency in liver fat. In these redistributions, fat is transported either as whole fat or as fatty acid and glycerin.

The tissues of the body are supplied either by the liver or by the other fat stores. Consequently, the overall fat balance of the body is maintained by a three-cornered equilibrium, as shown in Fig. 13.15. The healthy animal generally eats just enough that, over fairly long periods of time, a net increase or decrease of the body fat does not occur.

We already know that an animal could survive if it were fed a carbohydrate-free diet which contained a compensating amount of fat. The liver could then transform fat into the required carbohydrates. What would happen in the converse situation, where an animal is on a fat-free diet but eats a proportionately larger amount of carbohydrates? Such an animal could probably not survive. To be sure, liver and depot fat would be kept at normal levels, through fat manufacture from carbohydrates. The fat requirements of tissue cells would be satisfied similarly. Yet health would be impaired nevertheless. For certain fatty acids, *linoleic acid,* for example, cannot be manufactured by many animals. Such acids must be supplied by food in fully prefabricated form, and in this respect they are quite like the es-

sential amino acids and most vitamins. We may here speak appropriately of **essential fatty acids.**

OTHER NUTRIENTS

Specialized storage of water and of mineral ions does not occur, beyond such quantities of these substances as form part and parcel of the normal working machinery of the body. Some water is synthesized as a secondary product in many metabolic reactions, but much more water is lost by evaporation, egestion, sweating, and urination. Inorganic ions are lost in this manner also. Food must compensate for these losses. Any food eaten is likely to contain considerable quantities of water and at least some of the necessary ions. A diversity of foods generally ensures a balanced ion supply. The distribution of water and inorganic ions absorbed by the gut does not involve the liver in any special manner. Like all other cells of the body, liver cells merely absorb portions of these substances from the blood and use them for their own maintenance.

But the liver *is* involved especially in the distribution of several vitamins. Some vitamins absorbed from the gut are transported directly to tissue cells. However, others are taken up and collected by the liver and are released as the tissues require them. Vitamins A and D are in this category. The livers of fish store particularly large quantities of these vitamins, hence the nutritive value of, for example, cod liver oil. In certain instances, the liver also manufactures vitamins from nonvitamin precursors. The pigment carotene, present in many plant and animal foods, is not a vitamin. But when carotene reaches the liver, it may be transformed into active vitamin A (see Chaps. 11 and 19).

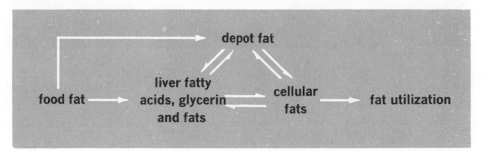

FIG. 13.15. The fat balance of the body.

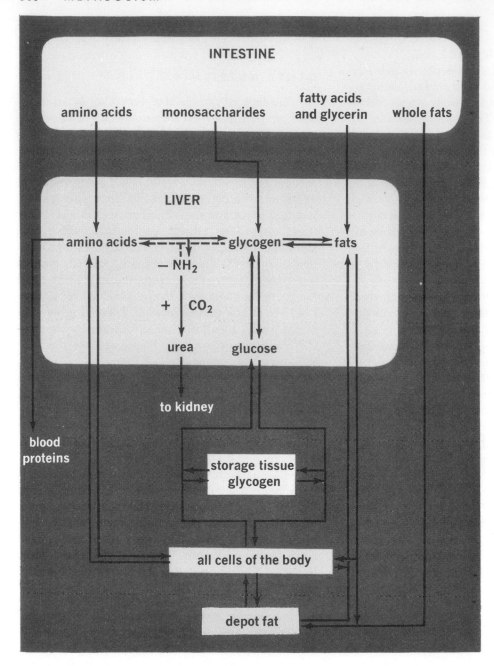

FIG. 13.16. The overall pattern of liver function, food distribution, and nutrient equilibria.

In addition to these many storing and food-processing activities, the liver also performs numerous other, not necessarily nutritional, functions. In this context, the synthesis of blood proteins has already been mentioned. Moreover, other manufacturing processes are also carried out in which various kinds of nutrients, not just amino acids, serve as raw materials. Bile manufacture is an example. Special liver products also include compounds which, like hormones, are vital for the maintenance of tissue cells, but which are not available in food. It may be noted in this connection that the occasional inclusion of liver in the diet has long been known to be beneficial generally, and indeed necessary in certain diseases.

The whole pattern of liver function and nutrient transport is outlined schematically in Fig. 13.16. We may note, in conclusion, that among the nutrients delivered to individual cells are glucose; 23 different kinds of amino acids; fats, fatty acids, and glycerin; water and mineral ions; vitamins; and various special organic compounds. Being so supplied through the digestive and absorptive agency of the intestine, the regulative agency of the liver, and the transportive agency of blood, the animal cell, like the plant cell, may now see to the main business at hand: survival, based on the liberation of energy and the synthesis of new protoplasm.

REVIEW QUESTIONS

1. Describe the blood circulation through the intestine. Which food materials are carried away from the intestine by blood?

2. Describe the pattern of the lymph circulation in the body as a whole. What is the function of this circulation, and what is the composition of lymph? What is the arrangement of the lymph vessels in the intestine? Which foods are carried away from the intestine by lymph?

3. By what pathways do foods reach the liver? What is the pathway and destination of colloidal fat? By what pathways do processed foods leave the liver?

4. What is the broad, general function of the liver, and what is the adaptive advantage of this organ? What happens to carbohydrates reaching the liver? Discuss fully. What happens if carbohydrate supplies are exceedingly excessive?

5. By what processes is the constancy of the blood-glucose concentration maintained? Discuss several specific situations in which the blood-glucose level tends to change, and show how such tendencies are counteracted by the liver.

6. By what reaction sequence is glucose converted to glycogen? What are the effects of insulin and adrenalin on these reactions? How does diabetes affect carbohydrate metabolism?

7. What is deamination? When, and where, does it occur, and what are the results of this process? In which form do various animals eliminate nitrogenous wastes? Review the ornithine cycle.

8. Can the liver manufacture carbohydrates and fats from derivatives of amino acids? Conversely, can the liver manufacture amino acids from carbohydrates or fats? Discuss fully. Can the liver manufacture essential amino acids?

9. Describe the interplay between liver, fat depots, and body tissues in fat metabolism. Can an animal survive if fats are substituted for carbohydrates in its diet? Can an animal similarly survive in the converse situation?

10. Describe the role of the liver in the internal distribution of water, mineral ions, and vitamins. Suppose that an animal were not given any food for a considerable length of time. What specific progressive changes would then occur in the body-wide balances of carbohydrates, fats, and proteins?

SUGGESTED COLLATERAL READINGS

Supplementary information on the topics discussed in this chapter may be obtained from any of the five standard texts cited first. These five are listed in order of increasing comprehensiveness. The sixth source below is a reprint of an original article by one of the early founders of modern experimental biology.

Carlson, A. J., and V. Johnson: "The Machinery of the Body," 4th ed., University of Chicago Press, 1953.

Heilbrunn, L. V.: "An Outline of General Physiology," Saunders, 1952.

Scheer, B. T.: "Comparative Physiology," Wiley, 1948.

Prosser, C. L., F. A. Brown, D. W. Bishop, T. L. Jahn, and V. J. Wulff: "Comparative Animal Physiology," Saunders, 1950.

Fulton, J.: "Textbook of Physiology," Saunders, 1950.

Bernard, C.: On the Mechanism of Formation of Sugar in the Liver, in M. L. Gabriel and S. Fogel, "Great Experiments in Biology," Prentice-Hall, 1955.

14

GAS EXCHANGE

MOST PLANTS AND ANIMALS are *aerobes;* that is, their cells require oxygen for the liberation of energy. Also, carbon dioxide is a byproduct of energy liberation, and this gas must be eliminated from the organism. Therefore, if a cell is to respire, it must not only be nourished with foods. It must, in addition, be provided with oxygen, and it must be rid of carbon dioxide.

In organisms in which individual cells are in direct contact with the external environment, exchange of respiratory gases is accomplished readily. Oxygen simply diffuses into each cell, and carbon dioxide diffuses out. But in many organisms, notably in complexly and compactly constructed animals, most cells are not in contact with the external environment. Gas exchange here requires specialized structures for the collection and elimination of respiratory gases, i.e., a **breathing** system. Moreover, the gases must be ferried to and from individual interior cells, and this is achieved by a **transport** system, usually the blood circulation. The functioning of such systems in exchanging and transporting O_2 and CO_2 forms the subject of this chapter.

Breathing

PLANT AND ANIMAL PATTERNS

Recognized by man as *the* unfailing sign of life, breathing is only the first complicated step in the seemingly simple process of carrying atmosphere to and from the deepest recesses of the body. We may define **breathing** as an exchange of respiratory gases between a whole organism and the physical environment. This function evidently is a means to an end. It prepares the way for internal **gas transport,** to and from individual cells. Gas transport, in turn, is but a means. The end here is gas exchange through the surfaces of cells. And the end of that, finally, is **respiration,** that is, production of energy within individ-

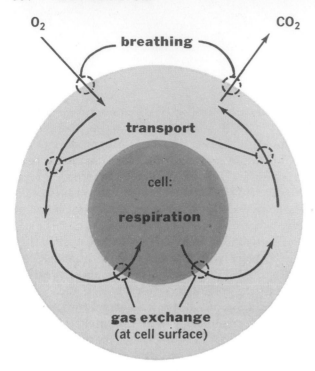

O_2 CO_2

breathing

transport

cell:

respiration

gas exchange
(at cell surface)

FIG. 14.1.   The component processes of gas exchange. The outer circle represents an organism; the inner circle, an individual cell. Breathing proper occurs at the organism-environment boundary. Respiratory gases are transported to and from cells, and cells exchange gases with the internal transport medium. Respiration takes place within cells.

ual cells. It should be clearly kept in mind, therefore, that breathing, gas transport to and from cells, and gas exchange through cell surfaces are but *auxiliary* functions of respiration. An *organism* breathes; but only a *cell* respires (Fig. 14.1).

Gas Exchange in Plants

A plant evidently does not breathe like an animal. Yet gas exchange with the physical environment must occur in a plant nevertheless. As already noted in Chap. 10, oxygen may enter into a plant over various routes. Stomata admit air into the leaves, and so leaf cells have direct access to gaseous oxygen. The gas diffuses through cell surfaces and dissolves in protoplasmic water. Some of this oxygen is carried into the phloem channels along with water, and stem and root tissues may be supplied in this fashion. Oxygen also enters the plant through the roots, dissolved in soil water. Root cells may retain some of the gas, and the remainder reaches xylem vessels. Stem and leaf tissues therefore may obtain oxygen over that path. If the stem is green, stomata on its surface provide a third entry point for

air. And if the stem is woody, any crack in the bark will do similarly. Finally, green tissues produce oxygen as a byproduct of photosynthesis, still another source of this respiratory gas.

Respiratory CO_2 may diffuse straight into the environment from plant cells exposed directly to soil or air. Deeper-lying cells may release CO_2 into the xylem or phloem, and the stomata may then pass the gas into the atmosphere. In green tissues, respiratory CO_2 may be used as a raw material in photosynthesis (Fig. 14.2).

In effect, exchange of respiratory gases in plants is predominantly direct, for much of the living tissue is in immediate contact with the external environment. Gas diffusion to and from deeper cells, and a certain amount of transport by xylem and phloem, accomplish the rest. Since much of the deeper substance of a plant is nonliving xylem in any case, the gas requirement in these regions is zero. Plant tissues in general are likely to require less oxygen than equivalent amounts of animal tissues; plants do not maintain muscles; hence their metabolism is on the whole less intense.

Gas Exchange in Animals

Five different gas-exchange patterns are encountered among animals (Fig. 14.3). First, several types of animals are so built that, as in plants, most of their cells are in immediate contact with the external environment. Protozoa, sponges, coelenterates, and flatworms are among these. In such animals, **direct exchange** of gases with the environment serves adequately.

More compactly built animals possess specialized gas-collecting and gas-transporting systems. In terrestrial arthropods like insects, such systems are formed by **tracheal tubes.** These hollow tubes origi-

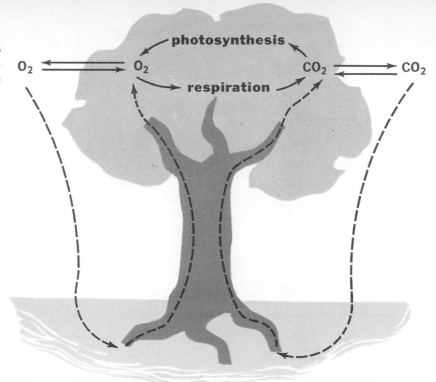

FIG. 14.2. The pattern of gas exchange in plants. The main sources and transport pathways of oxygen and carbon dioxide are indicated in the diagram.

photosynthesis

O_2 ⟵ O_2 respiration CO_2 ⟶ CO_2

nate at the body surface of the animal and lead into the interior. There they branch extensively, microscopic branch terminals reaching into all tissues. In effect, air is here piped from the outside to all interior cells, and gas exchange then can take place even deeply within the animal.

In most other animals, the internal gas-transporting system is blood, and the gas-collecting apparatus is a thin membrane. This membrane is usually one cell layer thick, and it is exposed on one side to external air or water, on the other to blood vessels. Oxygen is absorbed into blood, and carbon dioxide released from it. Three principal variants of this pattern are encountered, namely, **skin breathing, gill breathing**, and **lung breathing.** Earthworms, for example, breathe exclusively through their thin, moist skins. Frogs use their skins too, but, in addition, frog tadpoles possess gills, and frog adults, lungs. In fish, water enters through the mouth and returns to the outside past the gills, situated on the sides of the head. As water flows by the gills, the gill membranes exchange gases. Many differently constructed types of gills are found in different aquatic animals, but the principle of operation is the same as in fish.

Lungs occur chiefly among terrestrial vertebrates. We shall examine the pattern of lung breathing in some detail, and as an illustrative example we shall use the specific pattern in man.

FIG. 14.3. The five principal patterns of animal breathing. From left to right: direct diffusion of gases through the cell surface (e.g., protozoa); tracheal tubes (insects); skin breathing (e.g., earthworms); gill breathing (e.g., fishes); and lung breathing (e.g., man). The surface for gas exchange in all but the insect is indicated in light gray.

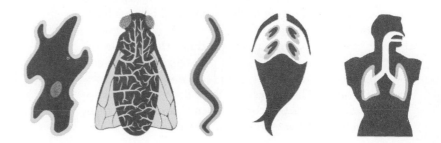

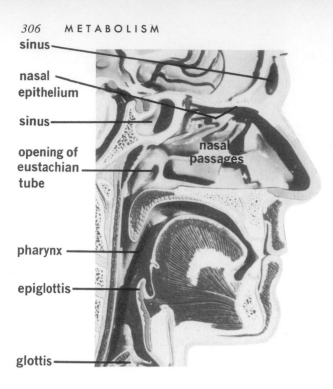

sinus

nasal epithelium

sinus

opening of eustachian tube

nasal passages

pharynx

epiglottis

glottis

FIG. 14.4. The nasal passages, and the upper parts of the breathing system. (Model designed by Dr. J. F. Mueller; photo, Ward's Natural Science Establishment, Inc.)

tear ducts into the nose (Fig. 14.5). Near the entry of the nasal passages into the pharynx, another two openings, one on the right, the other on the left, lead into the **eustachian tubes.** These pass into the middle-ear cavities. This connection permits the equilibration of air pressure between the external atmosphere and the middle ear, a space which is closed off from the outside by the eardrum (see Chap. 21).

Nasal passages, head sinuses, tear ducts, and eustachian tubes are lined with a continuous single layer of epithelial cells. Mucus secreted by them moistens the exposed surfaces. The epithelial cells in the nasal passages are ciliated, and some of these cells are specialized as odor receptors. Nerves lead from them to the nearby brain, where impulses are interpreted as smell.

Air passing through the narrow spaces of the nasal pathways is warmed and moistened; is freed of dust by the ciliated cells, which act as a filtering screen; and is smelled. As everyone is uncomfortably aware, inflammation of the passages, as in a cold

FIG. 14.5.   The tear apparatus, diagrammatic.

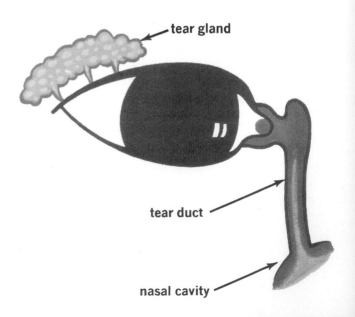

tear gland

tear duct

nasal cavity

THE BREATHING SYSTEM

Several familiar organs form the air channels of the breathing apparatus: **nose** and **nasal passages,** **pharynx, larynx** (or Adam's apple), **trachea** (or windpipe), and **lungs.**

The Upper Tract

The nasal passages are narrow winding pathways leading past intricately grooved and ridged walls (Fig. 14.4). Along the walls are found a number of paired openings. Some of these connect with the head **sinuses,** hollow air-filled cavities within some of the skull bones. For example, one large sinus is present in each of the two frontal bones which form the forehead.

Another pair of openings admits the contents of the **tear ducts** into the nasal passages. Tears are secreted continuously by glands in the outer corners of the eyes. The lymphlike fluid flows over, and so moistens, the surface of the cornea, then collects in the inner corners of the eyes and runs through the

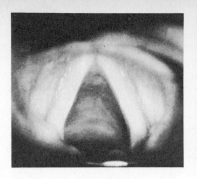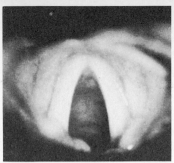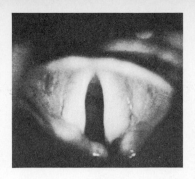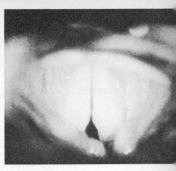

FIG. 14.6. The vocal cords of man. The view is from above, looking into larynx and trachea. From left to right: sequence of vocal-cord positions during the transition from quiet breathing to voicing. (Bell Telephone Laboratories, Inc.)

or in hay fever, blocks air transmission to greater or lesser degree. The tissues swell up and obliterate the pathways. Increased secretion of mucus adds to the discomfort. Smelling is impaired. Tears overflow from the eyes, since the fluid cannot easily drain off into the blocked nasal chambers. And in severe cases, the inflammation may spread into the head sinuses, the middle-ear cavities, the throat, and the pathways leading from the throat to the lungs. Breathing by mouth under such conditions introduces relatively unwarmed, dust-laden, and un-smelled air.

As has been noted in Chap. 12, the air and the food channel cross in the pharynx (see Fig. 12.9). The esophagus is more or less collapsed in the absence of food, but some air may pass into it nevertheless. Most of the air enters the *larynx* through the **glottis,** a slit which can be closed or opened to varying degrees. The larynx consists of a number of cartilages. Held together by membranes, and movable relative to one another by muscles, these cartilages enclose a hollow, cylindrical chamber. Attached to the inner surfaces of this chamber is a pair of horizontally placed fibroelastic ligaments, the **vocal cords.** These run from front to back in the laryngeal cavity, leaving an air passage in the mid-plane (Fig. 14.6).

Voice Production

Sound is produced when air is expelled past the vocal cords through the glottis. The shape of the glottal opening and, as in a violin string, the length and tension of the vocal cords determine tone pitch. The shape of the larynx may be changed at will by muscles, and this in turn alters the tension of the cords. Taut ligaments vibrate rapidly and produce a highly pitched sound. Also, notes are the higher, the shorter and thinner the vocal cords, and the narrower the glottal slit. The volume of the sound produced depends on the force of the air blast and on the amplitude with which the cords vibrate.

A third characteristic of voice, tone quality, is influenced by the size and shape of the resonating cavities: chest, pharynx, mouth, and nasal passages. That tone quality changes as the position of lips, tongue, jaws, and cheeks is changed is familiar to everyone. Tone quality is altered also during a cold, or when the nose is pinched, or when sound is produced on inhalation, rather than on exhalation as is normal. During puberty in males, the chest cavity and larynx enlarge, and the vocal cords lengthen. The voice "breaks" as the individual learns to control his modified sound equipment. Deeper tones than in females are produced thereafter. The vocal cords may thicken or scar during disease, or they may become encrusted with mucus during a cold, and a rasping voice is the result.

Most mammals make sounds of some sort. The giraffe is a notable exception. In birds, the only other vertebrate group with extensive, conspicuous voice capacity, sound is not produced in the larynx but in a **syrinx.** This voice box is located at the lower, not the upper, end of the windpipe.

The Lower Tract

The larynx is continuous with the trachea. This tube is prevented from collapsing by C-shaped rings of cartilage set horizontally into its wall. As in the

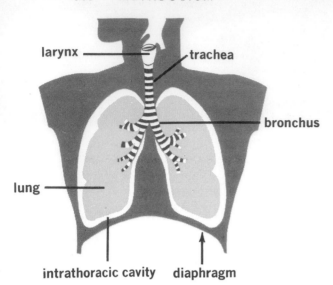

larynx

trachea

bronchus

lung

intrathoracic cavity   diaphragm

the diaphragm below, against the cavity holding the heart along the mid-plane of the chest, and against the rib cage at the top and along the sides. The inner membrane covers the lung itself. Except for openings which admit the bronchi and the blood vessels to the lungs, the intrathoracic cavities are sealed off from the rest of the body. This feature is essential in breathing.

THE BREATHING PROCESS

Air is moved through the breathing system by action of the **diaphragm,** the **rib muscles,** or both. The diaphragm produces what is called **abdominal breathing,** and the rib muscles, **chest breathing.**

The diaphragm separates the chest cavity from

FIG. 14.8. An alveolus of the lung, surrounded by capillaries and connective tissue.

microscopic branch of bronchiole

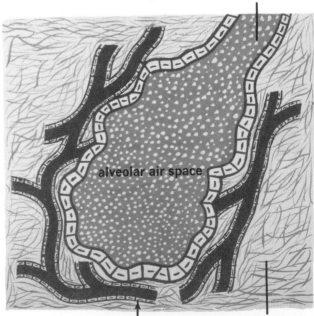

alveolar air space

blood capillary   connective tissue

larynx, the inner lining of the trachea is a ciliated, mucus-secreting layer of cells. The cilia beat upward, carrying mucus, dust, and occasional bits of food which "went the wrong way" into the pharynx. Air forced out as a cough facilitates the process.

At its lower end, the trachea divides into two **bronchi,** tubes having a smaller diameter than the trachea but the same structure otherwise (Fig. 14.7). Each bronchus subdivides after a distance into **bronchioles,** and each of the latter, in turn, branches repeatedly. Cartilage supports are not present in these smaller ducts. Also, their walls become thinner as they branch. Only the inner ciliated lining layer and some connective tissue containing elastic fibers are carried forward into the microscopic terminations of the branch system. Each such terminus is a raspberry-shaped sac made of a single layer of thin flat cells. This is an **alveolus** (Fig. 14.8). The sum of all alveoli constitutes the lung. The alveoli are held together by connective tissue, which carries nerves and a dense network of blood capillaries. The left and right parts of the lung are sculptured into lobes, their number corresponding to the number of main branches arising from the bronchi.

The lung on each side is situated in an **intrathoracic space,** which is bounded by two **pleural membranes.** The outer of these membranes lies against

ABDOMINAL (DIAPHRAGMATIC) BREATHING

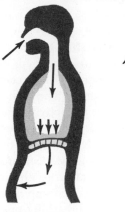

inspiration

expiration

CHEST BREATHING

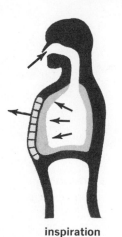

inspiration

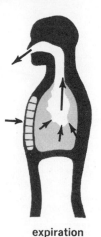

expiration

FIG. 14.9. The essential events in abdominal breathing and chest breathing.

the abdominal cavity; stomach and liver lie directly underneath it. In relaxed condition, this thin muscular partition is dome-shaped. When it is contracted, the upward curvature of the dome disappears, and the diaphragm flattens out. Such contraction pushes liver, stomach, and intestine downward and outward and so forces the belly out. Hence the designation "abdominal breathing." A flattening out of the diaphragm also enlarges the chest cavity, and this is the effective event in **inhalation** (Fig. 14.9). As a result of the enlargement, the pressure in the sealed intrathoracic space falls. This lowered pressure sucks the lung alveoli wide open. Air pressure within the alveoli consequently falls also, but this decrease is rebalanced instantly by air rushing in through the nose or mouth.

When the diaphragm relaxes, it resumes its original dome shape. The belly is pulled back, and the chest cavity, together with the intrathoracic space, reattains its former volume. Pressure within the intrathoracic space is then no longer lowered, and no further suction is therefore exerted on the alveoli. As a result, the elastic fibers which cover the alveoli recoil, and air is pressed out from the lungs in an **exhalation.**

Breathing movements carried out by the rib cage have the same effect on the lungs as the above. Ribs are hinged to the vertebral column along the back, and to the breastbone, or *sternum,* along the front. Attached between successive ribs are two layers of muscles, which raise or lower the rib cage. When the chest is raised, the thoracic cavity expands and, through suction on the alveoli, inhalation occurs. A lowering of the chest results in exhalation (Fig. 14.10). Chest breathing may enlarge the intrathoracic spaces much more than abdominal breathing; hence the former may produce deeper breaths than the latter.

Evidently, the mammalian method of breathing is a pressure mechanism. This knowledge has made possible procedures of "artificial respiration," often employed when injury or disease has incapacitated the automatic internal controls which maintain breathing normally. In artificial respiration by hand, or in "iron lungs," the chest is subjected to intermittent external pressure, which forces air into and out of the lungs just as does normal breathing.

In view of the importance of pressure, effective breathing clearly depends on the structural wholeness of the intrathoracic space. If the chest wall is pierced by a wound, external air enters the cavity on that side, and the diaphragm or the rib muscles

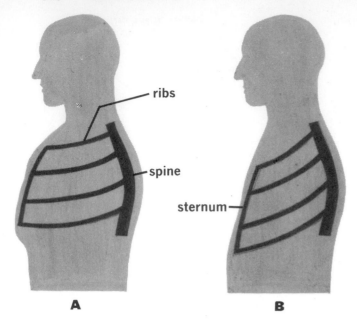

FIG. 14.10. The positions of the rib cage in inhalation **A** and exhalation **B** during chest breathing.

then can no longer exert suction on the lung. Hence the lung stays collapsed. In some diseases (e.g., tuberculosis), it is often desirable to rest one of the lungs. This is done by injecting air into one of the intrathoracic cavities, and the lung on that side collapses and becomes nonfunctional. The procedure may have to be repeated from time to time, for the injected air is gradually absorbed and removed by the blood circulation.

THE CONTROL OF BREATHING

What maintains the bellowslike breathing movements year after year, without interruption, until life ebbs away? And what adjusts these movements in rate and depth to changing requirements? Breathing is maintained and regulated by a **breathing center** in the brain. This center is located in the **medulla oblongata,** the hind portion of the brain near the juncture of skull and neck (see Chap. 21).

The Normal Cycle

The breathing center responds to two kinds of incoming stimuli, one nervous, the other nonnervous. The nonnervous stimulus is *carbon dioxide,* present in blood at all times as a byproduct of cellular respiration. Blood-borne CO_2 accelerates the activity of the breathing center. The higher the CO_2 concentration, the greater the activity, and vice versa. This activity consists in sending nerve impulses to the breathing muscles, i.e., the diaphragm or the rib muscles. Special nerves conduct such impulses. For example, a pair of large **phrenic nerves** innervates the diaphragm. When impulses from the breathing center reach the breathing muscles, these contract, the chest cavity enlarges as a result, and the lung alveoli are sucked open. Air is then inhaled (Fig. 14.11).

The very stretching of the alveoli now stimulates special sets of nerves which originate in the alveolar walls. These nerves conduct impulses from the inflated lung to the breathing center. When such impulses arrive there, the center is *inhibited.* That is, the impulses override and suppress the stimulating effect of blood-borne CO_2. Consequently, the center ceases to send signals to the breathing muscles, and this prevents inhalation from going too far. For in the absence of signals from the brain, the breathing muscles relax. And as they do so, the chest cavity becomes smaller, the lung alveoli recoil to their original state, and air is exhaled (Fig. 14.11).

After the alveoli have recoiled they are no longer stretched, and the nerve endings in their walls therefore are no longer stimulated. Hence impulses cease to be sent to the breathing center, and the center consequently ceases to be inhibited. In the absence of inhibition, blood-borne CO_2 can again exert its effect. The breathing center now resumes its impulse transmission to the breathing muscles, and a new inhalation begins. The whole cycle is outlined schematically in Fig. 14.12.

Blood-borne oxygen also has an effect on the breathing center, but this effect is much less powerful than that of CO_2, and it probably plays only a minor role during normal breathing. We may conclude that a basic breathing rhythm is maintained

FIG. 14.11. The control of inhalation **A**, and of exhalation **B**. In **A**, CO_2 in blood stimulates the breathing center to send impulses to the diaphragm, leading to inhalation. In **B**, impulses from the inflated lung inhibit the breathing center, leading to exhalation.

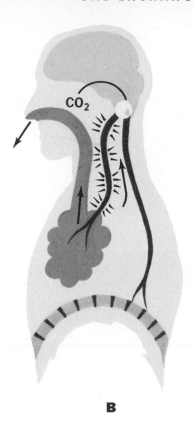

B

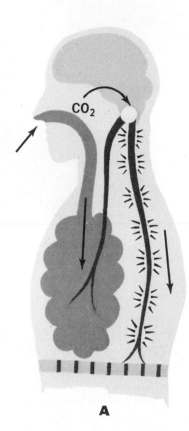

A

by alternating, automatically self-renewing effects on the breathing center, produced largely by nervous inhibitions and carbon dioxide stimulations.

Variations in Rhythm

It should follow that, as the inhibitions and stimulations vary, so should the breathing rhythm. This is the case. As is well known, both the rate and depth of breathing can be altered easily. For example, an exercise of will, or powerful sensory and emo-

tional experiences, may affect breathing greatly. These are nervous influences, relayed to the breathing center over many different and often indirect nerve paths.

Carbon dioxide produces modifications of the breathing pattern too. When the CO_2 concentration in blood is high, the *rate* of breathing is proportionately high, and vice versa. High CO_2 concentrations build up whenever the rate of CO_2 production through respiration is greater than the rate of CO_2 removal via the lungs. This is the case, for example, at the start of strenuous physical work, when intensified energy production in cells liberates increasing amounts of CO_2. By speeding up breathing under such conditions, CO_2 hastens its own removal through the lungs. Faster breathing at the same time increases the oxygen supply, just when the tissues require more oxygen. It will be found later that CO_2 also speeds up the heart;

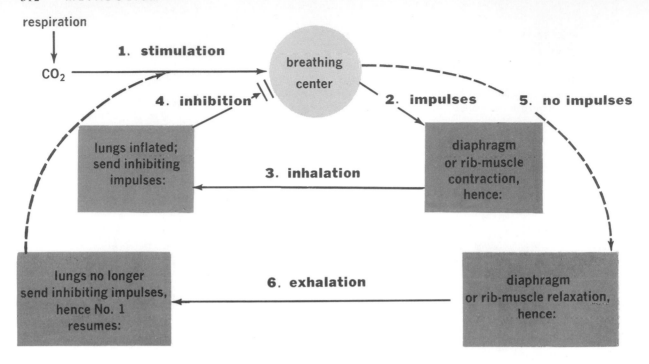

respiration

CO_2

1. stimulation

breathing center

4. inhibition

2. impulses

5. no impulses

lungs inflated; send inhibiting impulses:

3. inhalation

diaphragm or rib-muscle contraction, hence:

lungs no longer send inhibiting impulses, hence No. 1 resumes:

6. exhalation

diaphragm or rib-muscle relaxation, hence:

FIG. 14.12. Summary diagram of breathing control. An arrow tipped with a transverse double bar, as in 4, designates inhibition.

hence more rapid circulation aids additionally in increasing the speed of gas exchange.

The concentration of CO_2 in blood becomes extremely high when breathing is deliberately stopped altogether. But the accumulating gas then soon stimulates the breathing center so strongly that a resumption of breathing is *forced,* even against the most intense will. An animal cannot commit suicide by holding its breath.

Conversely, when the CO_2 concentration in blood is low, the breathing center is stimulated rather weakly, and breathing slows down. This is the case during sleep or rest, when respiration and CO_2 production are minimal. The extreme here is the **overventilated** condition, produced, for example, when breathing is intentionally made as deep and as rapid as possible. Carbon dioxide may then be exhaled so fast that abnormally little of the gas reaches the breathing center. A similar lack of

CO_2 and of oxygen may develop in the rarefied atmosphere at very high altitudes. Under conditions of this sort, the breathing center may temporarily cease to operate altogether, and a "blackout" may ensue. Breathing will remain stopped until the CO_2 concentration has again built up to a high enough level to stimulate the center adequately.

Breathing has been described above as a means to an end. The most immediate end is the procurement of additional oxygen and the removal of excess carbon dioxide. Fresh atmospheric air as inhaled contains some 20 per cent oxygen and 0.03 per cent carbon dioxide. Exhaled air includes only 16 per cent oxygen, but some 4 per cent carbon dioxide. Evidently, a fifth of the available oxygen has been retained in the body, and more than 100 times the amount of carbon dioxide has been expelled. What happens to the one, and where does the other come from?

Gas Transport

THE PATHWAY

Inasmuch as blood is the transport medium of the respiratory gases, an intimate association between circulation and breathing may be inferred. Indeed, the heart is virtually embedded in lung, and millions of blood capillaries ramify over the lung alveoli. Blood and air here approach each other very closely. Moreover, as we shall see later, the same region in the medulla oblongata which contains the breathing center also contains centers controlling heartbeat and circulation.

If blood is rich in oxygen, it is called **arterial** blood; if it is rich in CO_2, it is called **venous** blood. An **artery** is a blood vessel leading *away* from the heart; a **vein**, a vessel leading *to* the heart. Note that the designation "artery" or "vein" does not depend on the kind of blood carried but rather on the direction of blood flow within the vessel.

In all body tissues, cellular gas exchange takes place; cells take up oxygen from, and add carbon dioxide to, the blood. Here, therefore, blood becomes venous. This CO_2-rich blood then travels to the heart, entering this organ via a vessel called the **vena cava** (Fig. 14.13). From the heart, venous blood is pumped through a pair of short **pulmonary arteries** into the nearby lungs. These arteries branch into extensive networks of capillaries, spread over

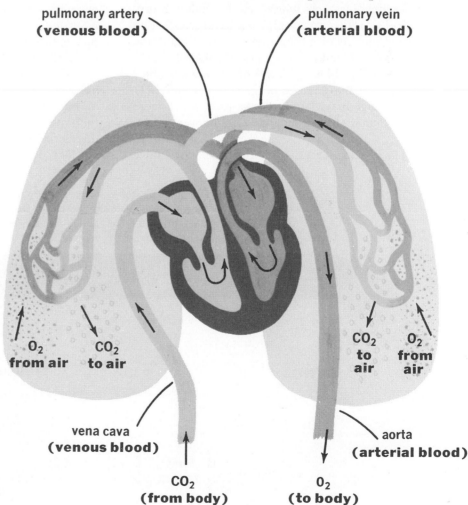

pulmonary artery (venous blood)

pulmonary vein (arterial blood)

FIG. 14.13. The pulmonary circulation. Arterial blood is shown in dark gray, venous blood in light gray. Note that the left side of the body appears on the right in this diagram, and the right side of the body on the left. Anatomical drawings are usually oriented as if observer and subject were face to face.

O_2 **from air** CO_2 **to air**

CO_2 **to air** O_2 **from air**

vena cava (venous blood)

aorta (arterial blood)

CO_2 **(from body)**

O_2 **(to body)**

the lung alveoli. Pulmonary gas exchange takes place here; CO_2 leaves the blood, and O_2 enters. Thus blood becomes arterial. This O_2-rich blood now collects in a pair of **pulmonary veins,** which lead back to the heart. Redistributed from the heart via the **aorta** throughout the body, blood supplies new oxygen to tissue cells and is ready to carry off new carbon dioxide. That is the general pattern. How is it realized in detail?

THE EXCHANGES

The transfer of oxygen from the lung alveoli into the blood, and the reverse transfer of carbon dioxide, are governed primarily by diffusion. This is one of the very few instances where active cellular absorption and secretion do not play a role. The wall of an alveolus consists of a thin, single layer of cells, and the wall of a blood capillary also consists of such a layer (see Fig. 14.8). Neither of these walls offers resistance to the passage of gaseous O_2 and CO_2. Gas exchange may therefore take place much more rapidly than if absorption and secretion were necessary.

The specific direction in which the gases move is determined by the prevailing pressure gradients, or **tension gradients,** between blood and lung. Specifically, atmospheric air in the lungs contains only a little CO_2, but the venous blood which flows into the lungs from the body is virtually saturated with the gas. Hence the pressure, or tension, of CO_2 in blood is greater than that in the alveoli, and a tension gradient points *out* of the capillaries. Carbon dioxide therefore moves in that direction, or, better, more CO_2 molecules diffuse out of the blood than into it. As a result, blood ceases to be venous (Fig. 14.14).

The pressure pattern is the reverse with respect to oxygen. Blood flowing into the lungs from the body is oxygen-poor, for the tissues have removed much of the gas. But the air in the alveoli contains a maximal amount of O_2. Hence a tension gradient points *into* the blood, and more O_2 molecules diffuse into the capillaries than in the reverse direction. As a result, blood becomes arterial.

These interrelations explain why breathing is inefficient at high altitudes. In rarefied air, the atmospheric oxygen pressure is greatly reduced, and the pressure differential between lung and blood is therefore low. Oxygen diffusion consequently does not take place as readily. We may similarly under-

FIG. 14.14. The exchanges of respiratory gases between the lungs and blood and between the body tissues and blood. Oxygen enters the blood in the lungs and leaves in the tissues. Carbon dioxide enters in the tissues and leaves in the lungs.

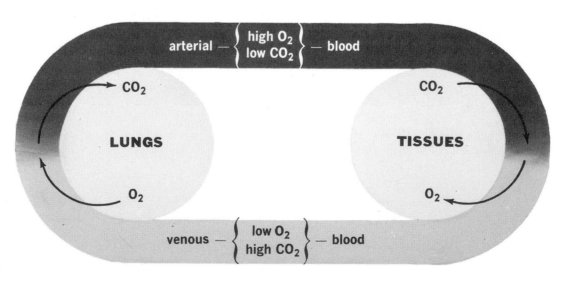

stand why the close atmosphere of an unventilated, overcrowded room makes breathing difficult. The CO_2 tension in the room is high, approaching that in blood. Hence CO_2 cannot easily leave the blood.

Just as in the lungs, cellular gas exchange in the body tissues is also governed by tension gradients (see Fig. 14.14). Cells continuously use up oxygen in respiration, and the tension of this gas in cellular protoplasm is therefore low. The tension in arterial blood is higher, however; hence O_2 diffuses from blood into tissue cells. Blood consequently ceases to be arterial. At the same time, since respiratory CO_2 is produced in cells steadily, the CO_2 tension within tissue cells is high. But arterial blood has low CO_2 tensions, and the gas therefore diffuses from tissue cells into blood. This makes blood venous.

How are respiratory gases carried in blood?

THE VEHICLE

Oxygen Transport

Transport of respiratory gases requires a medium containing water, a number of inorganic ions, and red blood corpuscles.

The corpuscles owe their red color to **hemoglobin.** This complex pigment, customarily symbolized as Hb, consists of two parts, *heme* and *globin.* Heme resembles chlorophyll structurally, but as has been noted in Chap. 11, it contains iron rather than magnesium. Heme is the active, functionally significant fraction of hemoglobin. Globin is a protein, which probably serves mainly as a carrier of heme.

Hemoglobin has the capacity of forming a loose chemical combination with oxygen:

$$Hb + O_2 \rightleftharpoons HbO_2$$

By the principle of mass action, this reversible reaction will shift to the right when O_2 is present in excess. As we have seen, this is the case in the lung capillaries, and HbO_2, or **oxyhemoglobin,** forms there.

Oxygen is carried in blood largely in the form of HbO_2. A little oxygen also *dissolves* in the water of blood, in the same way as all atmospheric gases dissolve in water. Indeed, blood contains dissolved

CO_2 and N_2 as well. When the external air pressure suddenly falls, as during rapid ascents into high altitudes or up from great depths, then the dissolved gases may fizz out of the blood in the form of bubbles. Dangerous "bends" may result. The effect here is rather like removing the cap of a bottle of soda; gases then fizz out too.

When oxyhemoglobin reaches the tissues, the reaction above shifts to the left. Cells are oxygen-poor relative to the blood, and the conditions of mass action therefore are such that HbO_2 "unloads" its oxygen. Free Hb forms again, and the free O_2 is taken up by the tissues (Fig. 14.15).

It may be noted that hemoglobin may transport not only oxygen but also *carbon monoxide:* $Hb + CO \rightleftharpoons HbCO$. This union is achieved much more easily than the union with oxygen. Hence, if carbon monoxide is present in the atmosphere, Hb becomes HbCO in preference to HbO_2. This means that little oxygen can be transported to the tissues, which consequently cannot respire. Therein lies the poisonous effect of carbon monoxide.

Carbon Dioxide Transport

Of the CO_2 released from tissue cells, a small fraction dissolves physically in blood water, as already noted. Another small fraction combines with hemoglobin and is transported to the lungs in the form of $HbCO_2$. But the bulk reacts with water chemically and forms bicarbonate ions (HCO_3^-):

$$CO_2 + H_2O \rightleftharpoons \underset{\substack{\text{carbonic} \\ \text{acid}}}{H_2CO_3} \rightleftharpoons H^+ + \underset{\substack{\text{bicarbonate} \\ \text{ion}}}{HCO_3^-}$$

Inasmuch as tissue cells constantly add CO_2 to blood, this reaction proceeds to the right in the tissues. Most of the CO_2 is therefore transported to the lungs in the form of HCO_3^-. In the lungs, the conditions of mass action are reversed: CO_2 escapes into the alveoli, the reaction consequently shifts to the left, and more free CO_2 is released for exhalation (Fig. 14.15).

We may note that the *rapid* conversion of CO_2 and H_2O into HCO_3^- and H^+, as above, requires an enzyme, **carbonic anhydrase.** This enzyme occurs only within red blood corpuscles. Hence HCO_3^- is formed mostly in these corpuscles. After they are formed, bicarbonate ions largely diffuse out of the corpuscles and are carried to the lungs in the fluid component of the blood.

Inasmuch as bicarbonate ions are electrically negative, we might expect that, as they leave the red corpuscles, the corpuscles would not remain electrically neutral. But it has been found that, for every bicarbonate ion which diffuses out from a red corpuscle, a chloride ion (Cl^-) diffuses in. Chloride

ions are normally present in blood water. This exchange, called the **chloride shift**, preserves the electrical neutrality of the red corpuscles. In the lungs, these processes take place in reverse. Chloride ions move out of red corpuscles, and bicarbonate ions move back in. The enzyme carbonic anhydrase then promotes the rapid re-formation of free CO_2, and this gas diffuses from the blood into the lung alveoli (Fig. 14.16).

Note too that the reaction between CO_2 and

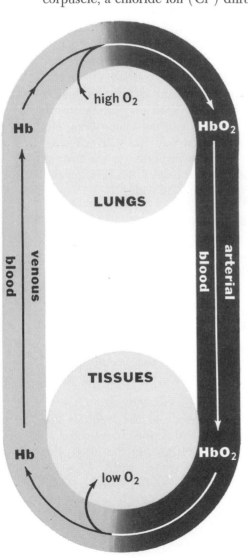

O₂ transport

FIG. 14.15. The transport of respiratory gases in blood. Oxygen is carried in the form of oxyhemoglobin (HbO_2), carbon dioxide in the form of bicarbonate ions (HCO_3^-).

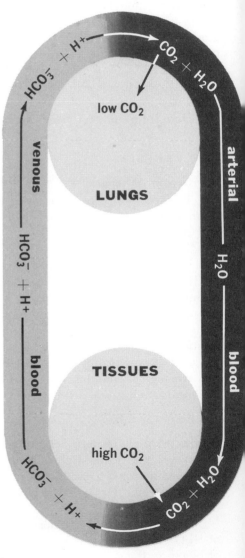

CO₂ transport

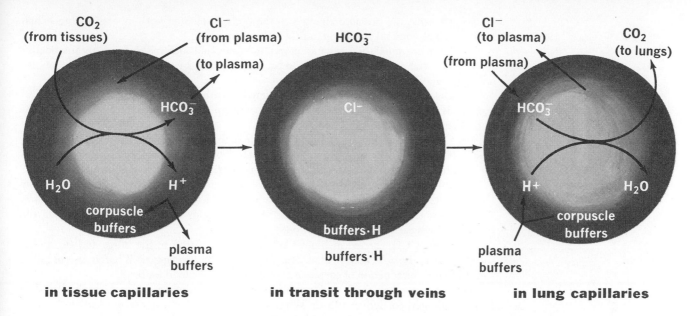

FIG. 14.16. The chloride shift in red corpuscles. In tissue capillaries (left), CO₂ reacts with water in the corpuscles. Bicarbonate ions appear, and as these diffuse into the plasma, chloride ions diffuse into the corpuscles. Hydrogen ions are also formed, and these are buffered (middle). In the lungs these processes occur in reverse, resulting in the liberation of gaseous CO₂ (right).

H_2O yields not only bicarbonate ions but also hydrogen ions (H^+). This ion lowers the pH, and blood therefore might be expected to become considerably more acid whenever it transports CO_2. However, this does not happen, since blood is strongly *buffered* (see Chap. 6). Among the substances which act as buffers are various inorganic ions, as well as blood proteins, including hemoglobin. These buffers unite with H^+ as it is formed, and the resulting combinations remain more or less nonionized. Hence the amounts of free H^+ are

greatly reduced, and pH does not change appreciably. In the lungs, the conditions of mass action are such that the buffers release H^+, and CO_2 and H_2O are reformed (see Fig. 14.16).

The processes auxiliary to cellular metabolism are now completed. Every cell of a plant or an animal has been supplied with oxygen, has been rid of carbon dioxide, and has already been provided with food. Hence it is ready to produce energy and to synthesize new protoplasm.

REVIEW QUESTIONS

1. Distinguish between breathing and respiration. How does gas exchange occur among plants? What are the principal patterns of gas exchange among animals?

2. Describe the structural organization of the breathing system in man. How is sound produced, and how can sound be varied in pitch, volume, and quality? What is an alveolus, and what is its relation to the lung? What chest structures surround the lungs?

3. Describe the pressure changes in the body associated with inhalation and exhalation in (*a*) abdominal breathing and (*b*) chest breathing.

4. How are inhalation-exhalation cycles controlled and maintained automatically? Review here the role of CO_2 and of the brain, and show by what sequence of events inhalation comes to alternate with exhalation.

5. Describe the processes through which breathing rate increases when physical exercise is begun and decreases at the onset of sleep. What is overventilation, and what is its effect?

6. Describe the pattern of blood circulation through the body. Where, specifically, does venous blood become arterial, and arterial blood become venous? In the circulation through the lungs, which blood vessels contain arterial and which contain venous blood?

7. By what processes does arterial blood become venous, and vice versa? Show what factors govern these changes, and describe the actual changes in lungs and tissues.

8. How is oxygen carried in blood? What reactions occur in the lungs and in the tissues? Why is carbon monoxide poisonous?

9. How is CO_2 carried in blood? What reactions occur in the lungs and in the tissues? What is the role of red blood corpuscles in CO_2 transport? What is the chloride shift? What is the function of carbonic anhydrase, and of blood buffers?

10. How are breathing and gas transport affected during ascent to high altitudes? How is nitrogen carried in blood? Why is breathing difficult in an unventilated room? What happens when a person holds his breath for a long time? How may artificial respiration restore breathing processes?

SUGGESTED COLLATERAL READINGS

Any of the five texts cited at the end of Chap. 13, especially the first, may again be consulted to advantage for additional information on breathing and gas transport. Various comparative aspects of these topics are described in the following sources:

Baldwin, E.: "An Introduction to Comparative Biochemistry," Cambridge, 1949.
Buchsbaum, R.: "Animals without Backbones," University of Chicago Press, 1948.
Williams, C. B.: Insect Breathing, *Sci. American*, vol. 188, 1953.
Fox, H. M.: Blood Pigments, *Sci. American*, vol. 182, 1950.

NUTRITION AND GAS EXCHANGE make cellular metabolism possible. Cellular metabolism in turn makes possible nutrition, gas exchange, and indeed life itself.

Whatever the organism, plant or animal, and whatever the pattern of nutrition and gas exchange, the pattern of cellular metabolism is always the same: with or without the aid of oxygen, and with organic nutrients as fuel, cells respire; that is, they *produce* energy. Such energy may then be *used* within the cell that produced it, toward cellular maintenance and self-perpetuation. Energy **production** is the subject of this chapter; energy **utilization**, that of the next.

The Pattern of Respiration

FUEL AND ENERGY

Respiration may be defined as the liberation of chemical energy from organic molecules within living cells.

The last part of this definition, "within living cells," means largely *mitochondria*. The main phases of respiration take place in these specialized components of the cell cytoplasm. Virtually all complex cellular processes occur in distinct "factory" locations, and we have seen this to be so, for example, in photosynthesis. We may now note it to be the case also in respiration. To the mitochondria present in every cell flow all the necessary raw materials, and from them emerges usable energy. The electron microscope reveals that mitochondria have a complicated fine structure (Fig. 15.1). Much of the chemical machinery of respiration has been shown to be located along the walls of the internal mitochondrial partitions.

Concerning the remainder of the definition above, "liberation of chemical energy from organic molecules," we may note that, directly or indirectly, the energy content of organic molecules represents

15

CELLULAR METABOLISM: RESPIRATION

FIG. 15.1. Electron micrograph of a single mitochondrion of a liver cell. Note the double bounding membrane and the internal membranous partitions. The chemical components of the respiratory machinery are situated along the membranes. (Courtesy of Dr. K. R. Porter, Rockefeller Institute.)

stored solar energy. It is the sun which, through photosynthesis, makes possible the formation of primary organic molecules. All other organic materials are derived secondarily from these.

In photosynthesis, several inorganic molecules are *combined* into organic ones. In other words, the sun's energy is stored in the form of bond energies, which hold the atoms of a molecule together. Hence the locked-in energy may be released if, for example, the bonds between the atoms are broken. As much energy will then be liberated as was expended originally in making the bonds (Fig. 15.2). Bonds need not always be broken outright to release energy. If they are merely weakened, then a fraction of the locked-in energy may be liberated too. Not all bonds contain the same amount of energy. The carbon-to-carbon bonds of organic moecules are particularly good sources, and we may note that respiration typically includes a breaking or a weakening of carbon-to-carbon bonds in fuel molecules.

A similar process is very familiar from the nonliving world: burning. Fuels burned in a stove are principally wood, coal, oil, or "gas," and these too are organic materials containing stored solar energy. Energy liberation here is also a matter of breaking bonds. The principle involved is precisely the same as in respiration, and respiration, indeed, may properly be regarded as a burning. If this is so, why does respiration not produce the high temperatures of a fire?

For two reasons. First, a fire is *uncontrolled* combustion, in the sense that *all* the bonds within a fuel molecule may be broken simultaneously. A maximum amount of energy may then be released all at once. Such sudden, explosive release generates the high temperatures of a fire. Respiration, on the other hand, is *controlled* combustion. Energy is extracted from one bond at a time. If a fuel is respired completely, the total energy yield is the same as if it were burned in a stove, but in respiration the energy is liberated bit by bit, bond by bond. Hence temperatures stay low. Enzymes exercise the necessary control. Respiration is a series of enzymatic reactions, and biological combustion cannot take place any faster than the controlling enzymes will permit.

Second, the energy liberated in a fire is *free* energy—largely heat, and to some extent light. But in respiration only very little of the liberated energy escapes as heat, and practically none as light. Instead, most of it is "packaged" directly into new *chemical* energy. As we shall see, fuel energy creates *new* chemical bonds, and it is in this form that metabolic energy is used in protoplasm. Since chemical bonds are not "hot," temperatures stay low during respiration (Fig. 15.3).

ENERGY LIBERATION

Oxidation

How is the chemical energy of a bond extracted? As we shall see, there are several ways. One of the most important, in respiration as in a fire, is *withdrawal of hydrogen* from the fuel, or **dehydrogenation:**

$$\text{fuel} + A \rightarrow \text{fuel fragments} + H_2A + E$$

In this general equation for combustion, A is a **hydrogen acceptor.** If such an acceptor is available, hydrogen can be withdrawn from a fuel. The carbon bonds of the fuel may break as a result, bond energy (E) is thereby released, and the hydrogen can be

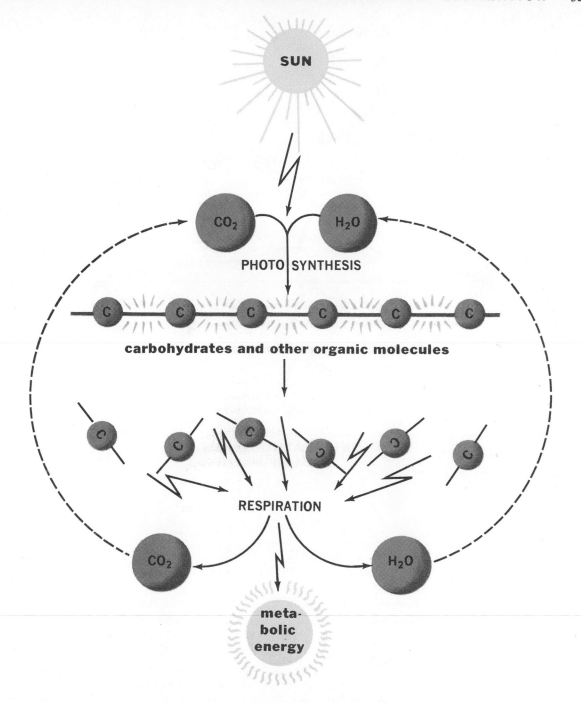

FIG. 15.2.   The source of respiratory energy. The ultimate source is the sun, some of whose energy is trapped by photosynthesis into organic molecules. Respiratory energy results from a breakdown of these molecules.

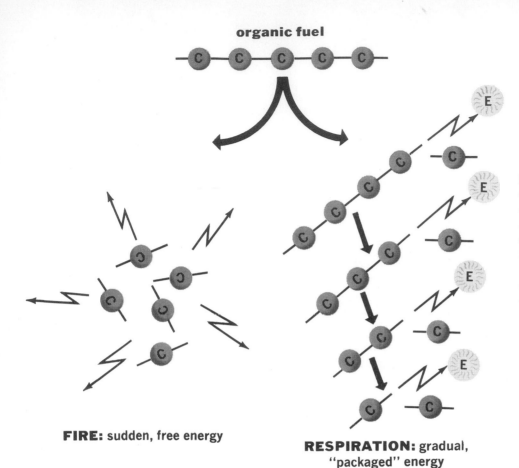

organic fuel

FIRE: sudden, free energy

RESPIRATION: gradual, "packaged" energy

FIG. 15.3. Comparison of a fire and respiration. In a fire, organic molecules are decomposed all at once, yielding sudden, free energy (left). In respiration, bonds of organic molecules are broken one at a time, yielding energy gradually. Moreover, this energy does not become free, but is "packaged" into other chemicals (right).

collected and held by the acceptor (Fig. 15.4).

Many different substances can and do serve as hydrogen acceptors. One which serves in fires, and in a major form of respiration, is atmospheric *oxygen*. Combustion in the presence of oxygen thus takes the general form

$$\text{fuel} + O_2 \rightarrow \text{fuel fragments} + H_2O + E$$

Water is a byproduct.

Note that hydrogen acceptors *do not start* combustion. They merely serve to collect and to remove the hydrogen "wastes." Note also that dehydrogenation is more or less synonymous with **oxidation,** whether oxygen or any other hydrogen acceptor is involved; in losing hydrogen, a fuel is said to become oxidized.

If it is not the hydrogen acceptor that starts combustion, what is? In a fire, the starter is *heat*. We must supply an initial amount of heat (by friction as in lighting a match, or through an electric spark, for example) to ignite the fuel, that is, to achieve a first dehydrogenation. Such activation energy, applied from the outside, agitates the atoms of a fuel molecule to such an extent that hydrogen atoms begin to break loose. Enough energy is thereby released to initiate a self-sustaining chain

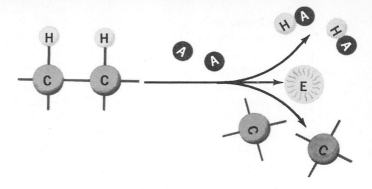

FIG. 15.4. Illustrating the role of hydrogen acceptors. Carbon chains break, energy is released, and the liberated hydrogen joins the acceptors **A**.

reaction. Adjacent fuel molecules become agitated, *their* hydrogen atoms break loose, more energy is thereby released, new fuel molecules become agitated, etc.

In living protoplasm, respiration actually never starts, because it never stops. It is always under way, unceasingly. The "fire" of life was lit when life first originated, and since then it has been handed down from parent to offspring, without interruption. The continuing dehydrogenations are maintained not by heat but by enzymatic reactions. Special enzymes promote hydrogen removal from fuels, and special enzymes also act as primary hydrogen acceptors. As we shall see, these reactions themselves require energy. Hence, to maintain them, some of the energy obtained as a result of respiration must be funneled back to sustain the respiration process itself (Fig. 15.5).

The Fuels

What are the organic fuels in protoplasm? Anything that contains breakable carbon bonds—which means *any* organic constituent of protoplasm: carbohydrates, fats, proteins, their various derivatives, vitamins, other special compounds, and indeed all the innumerable substances which together make up protoplasm. Like a fire, respiration is no respecter of materials. Anything that can burn will burn, and in protoplasm this is the very substance of protoplasm itself. Respiration does not distinguish between the expendable and the nonexpendable. For example, an amino acid which is an important structural member of the framework of protoplasm, or is part of an enzyme, may be burned just as readily as an amino acid which has just arrived as a food.

However, if a fire is fed much of one fuel but little of another, more of the first is likely to be burned. Indeed, under normal conditions, a cell receives a steady enough supply of foods to make *them* the primary fuels, rather than the structural parts of a cell. Also, some kinds of materials burn more easily

than others, and some are more accessible to the fire than others. On this basis, foods, carbohydrates and fats in particular, are again favored as fuels, and the finished components of a cell tend to be spared. Yet the sparing is relative only. The formed parts of a cell *are* burned gradually, including even those which make up the burning apparatus itself, i.e., the mitochondria.

But if protoplasm itself burns away, how can it remain intact and functioning? Only by continuous construction of new protoplasm, offsetting the continuous destruction through respiration. Note that these two processes go on side by side, at all times: destructive energy metabolism and constructive synthesis metabolism. One is in balance with the other, and foods serve both as fuel for the one and as building materials for the other. We say that the components of protoplasm are continuously "turned over," that is, existing parts are continuously replaced by new ones. Protoplasm, we note, is never quite the same from instant to instant (Fig. 15.6).

FIG. 15.5. Some of the energy resulting from respiration must be funneled back into respiration, to sustain that process.

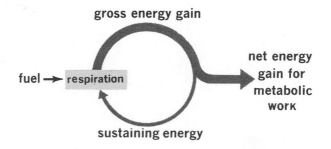

The Energy Gain

What of the energy liberated in respiration? If it were to pass freely into the surroundings, it would become more or less useless metabolically. Evidently, an energy-trapping device is required. Such a device exists and is present in all cells. It consists of a group of chemicals collectively known as *adenosine phosphates*. Every cell contains at least two types of these: **adenosine diphosphate, ADP** for short, and **adenosine triphosphate, ATP** for short. As these names indicate, as many as three phosphate groups may be attached to an adenosine molecule. A molecule of ADP can be transformed into one of ATP by the addition of a third phosphate group, a process which requires energy. Conversely, ATP may become ADP by loss of one phosphate group and energy:

$$ADP + phosphate + E \rightleftharpoons ATP$$

Proceeding to the right, this reaction symbolizes the energy-trapping process of respiration. Energy liberated from a fuel molecule becomes incorporated into ADP and phosphate, and ATP is formed. Hence ATP is the chief endproduct of respiration. This important substance is also the energy vehicle; that is, it emerges from the mitochondria and diffuses to all locations within a cell where energy must be utilized. In utilization, the above reaction proceeds to the left: ATP breaks down, energy is released and used, and ADP and phosphate reappear (Fig. 15.7).

In summary, therefore, respiration as a whole consists of three correlated events. First, a fuel molecule is oxidized, which means most often that hydrogen is removed from it. This hydrogen becomes attached to an appropriate acceptor, and if the acceptor is oxygen, water forms. Second, as a result of oxidation, the carbon-to-carbon bonds of the fuel molecule may be broken. Smaller fuel fragments then form, and these may be oxidized and broken up in turn, until the original fuel has been degraded completely into 1-carbon fragments. These always appear in the form of CO_2. Third, also as a result of oxidation, energy is released. A little of this energy escapes as heat, indicating that respiration is not 100 per cent efficient. However, most of the energy does not become free in this manner but is harvested by the ADP-ATP system. We may symbolize these three events as in Fig. 15.8.

This is the general pattern. What are the details of each of its three main components?

FIG. 15.6. Destruction of protoplasm by respiration normally is offset by simultaneous construction of protoplasm by synthesis. See also Fig. 16.12 for a more comprehensive illustration of this.

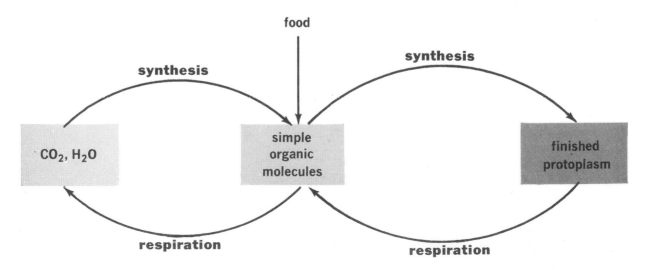

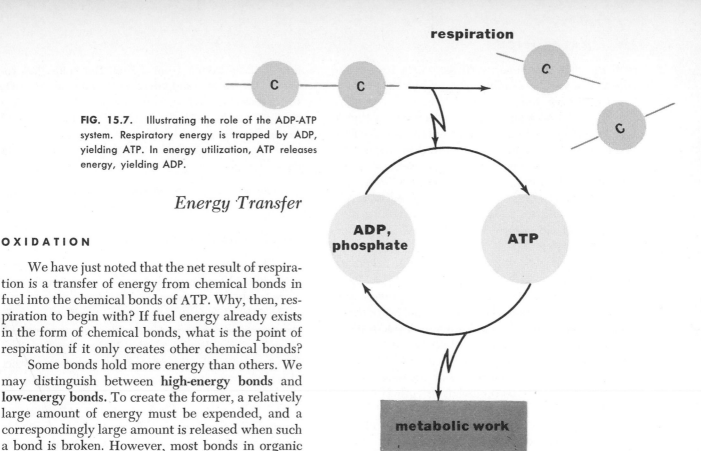

respiration

FIG. 15.7. Illustrating the role of the ADP-ATP system. Respiratory energy is trapped by ADP, yielding ATP. In energy utilization, ATP releases energy, yielding ADP.

ADP, phosphate

ATP

metabolic work

Energy Transfer

OXIDATION

We have just noted that the net result of respiration is a transfer of energy from chemical bonds in fuel into the chemical bonds of ATP. Why, then, respiration to begin with? If fuel energy already exists in the form of chemical bonds, what is the point of respiration if it only creates other chemical bonds?

Some bonds hold more energy than others. We may distinguish between **high-energy bonds** and **low-energy bonds.** To create the former, a relatively large amount of energy must be expended, and a correspondingly large amount is released when such a bond is broken. However, most bonds in organic fuel molecules are of the *low*-energy type. For example, any of the carbon-to-carbon, carbon-to-hydrogen, carbon-to-nitrogen, or carbon-to-oxygen links we have dealt with so far are low-energy bonds. If one of these is broken, only a little energy is released.

A critical dilemma now arises. On the one hand, available fuels provide only bond energies of low intensity. But on the other, very concentrated, intense packets of energy are needed for the synthesis of protoplasmic components, for muscular contraction, and for metabolic work in general. Fuels, as it were, provide energy of popgun intensity, but metabolic work requires cannons. What is needed, clearly, is an energy-*intensifying* process, one which would

FIG. 15.8. The three main phases of respiration: breakdown of fuel, hydrogen transfer from fuel, and energy transfer from fuel.

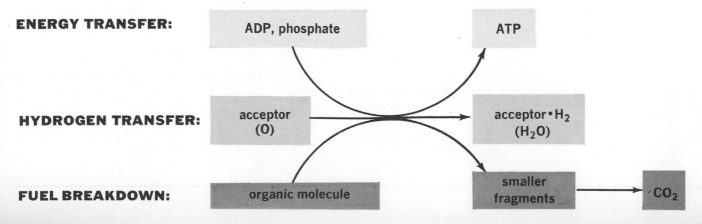

ENERGY TRANSFER: ADP, phosphate → ATP

HYDROGEN TRANSFER: acceptor (O) → acceptor·H₂ (H₂O)

FUEL BREAKDOWN: organic molecule → smaller fragments → CO₂

pool the many low-energy packets of a fuel molecule into a smaller number of high-energy packets.

Respiration does just that. It first concentrates the low bond energies of fuel and creates within a fuel molecule one or more high-energy bonds. This is the crucial event in oxidation, and in respiration as a whole. Then these high-energy bonds are transferred from fuel into the structure of ATP, a substance which is a high-energy carrier. Clearly, respiration accomplishes more than merely making new bonds out of old ones; it makes high-energy bonds out of low-energy bonds. And through ATP it supplies energy of uniformly high intensity to all points of utilization.

The creation of high-energy from low-energy bonds is achieved essentially by *internal reorganizations* of a fuel molecule. Each such molecule is characterized by a specific pattern of atoms, hence a specific pattern of bonds between the atoms. If a chemical change occurs, some of the atoms may change position, others may be removed, still others may be added. Whatever happens, the arrangement of the atoms will change, and the pattern of the bonds will therefore change also. Many changes of this sort do not affect the content or distribution of the bond energies. But some do. And it may then happen that the original bond energies of the molecule become redistributed in such a way that one of the bonds comes to hold a great deal of energy, whereas others hold even less than before. In effect, a high-energy bond will have been created at the expense of several low-energy bonds (Fig. 15.9).

If a molecular reorganization occurs which does redistribute the energy so that a high-energy bond is created, then we say that an **oxidation** has taken place. As already noted, the most important type of oxidative change is a **dehydrogenation**, that is, a removal of hydrogen from a fuel. But note that removal of water (**dehydration**), removal of CO_2 (**decarboxylation**), and numerous other chemical changes can be oxidative too and may likewise lead to the formation of high-energy bonds. In sum, respiration includes oxidative reactions of the following general type:

$$\left.\begin{array}{l}\text{fuel with}\\\text{low-energy bonds}\end{array}\right\} \xrightarrow{\text{oxidation}} \left\{\begin{array}{l}\text{fuel with}\\\text{high-energy bonds}\end{array}\right.$$

PHOSPHORYLATION

The principal high-energy bond in metabolism is the **phosphate bond,** that is, the bond which joins a molecule to a phosphate group ($-PO_3H_2$, or $-Ⓟ$). We have already encountered such $-Ⓟ$ groups earlier, e.g., in Chap. 11. Note that not all phosphate bonds are of the high-energy variety. For example, glucose-phosphate and many other phosphorylated compounds dealt with previously are low-energy combinations. But the properties of the phosphate bond are such that it can contain a great deal of energy, much more than is needed simply to hold $-Ⓟ$ to a molecule. In that case, the phosphate bond in effect stores *extra* energy; i.e., it is a high-energy bond. To distinguish the high-energy bond, we use the symbol $\sim$. Thus, we may have either

$$\text{fuel}-Ⓟ \qquad \text{low-energy phosphate bond}$$

or

$$\text{fuel}\sim Ⓟ \qquad \text{high-energy phosphate bond}$$

A low-energy phosphate bond may be converted into a high-energy phosphate bond if more energy becomes concentrated in it. As noted above, such energy enrichment of a bond may be achieved by oxidation. Hence we may have

$$\text{fuel}-Ⓟ \xrightarrow{\text{oxidation}} \text{fuel}\sim Ⓟ$$

Clearly, before such a reaction can take place, "fuel

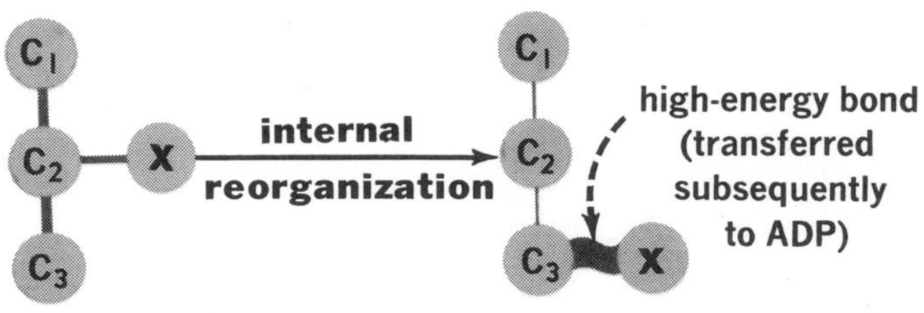

FIG. 15.9. Through internal reorganization of the atoms of a molecule, a high-energy bond may be created. Such a reorganization is an oxidative change.

FIG. 15.10. The four ways in which phosphate bonds may be transferred or changed: low-energy transfers; creation of high-energy bonds; high-energy transfers; and degradation of high-energy bonds.

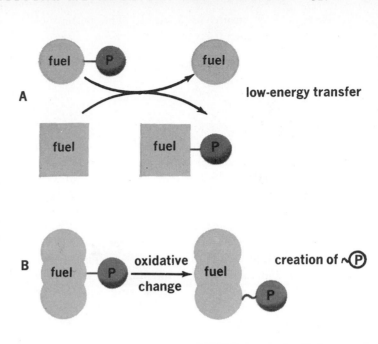

—℗" must be available as a starting material. In other words, the addition of a low-energy —℗ group to a fuel molecule, or **phosphorylation,** will be an important preliminary toward the creation of high-energy bonds. Respiration actually includes such preliminary phosphorylations, and the creation of high-energy bonds proceeds according to the following general sequence of events:

$$\text{fuel} \xrightarrow{\text{phosphorylation}} \text{fuel—℗} \xrightarrow{\text{oxidation}} \text{fuel} \sim ℗$$

PHOSPHATE TRANSFERS

The phosphorylation of a fuel obviously requires a phosphate donor, that is, a substance which may contribute —℗ groups. One group of such donors includes phosphoric acid (H_3PO_4) and inorganic ions derived from phosphoric acid. These substances are supplied by the external environment as mineral nutrients, and they are the ultimate source of all phosphates in protoplasm. Either phosphoric acid or its ions may phosphorylate an organic molecule. For example, if we rewrite H_3PO_4 as $H—O—PO_3H_2$, we note that phosphoric acid contains $—PO_3H_2$, or a —℗ group. This group may become transferred to an organic molecule by chemical reaction, resulting in phosphorylation.

Once an organic molecule is so phosphorylated, its —℗ may then be transferred in turn to various other organic molecules. In many such cases, a **low-energy transfer** occurs; that is, the low-energy value of the —℗ bond does not change. For example, if *M* and *N* symbolize two molecules, then we may have (see also Fig. 15.10):

$$M—℗ + N—H \rightleftharpoons M—H + N—℗$$

Note again that a molecule which loses —℗ gains one H atom, and vice versa (see Chap. 11).

In a particularly important series of cases,

high-energy transfers take place. This occurs between organic molecules which possess $\sim ℗$ groups and the ADP-ATP system which harvests respiratory energy. For example, a fuel molecule may have been phosphorylated and oxidized and possesses a ~ⓟ group as a result. The pattern of phosphate transfer then is

fuel ~ ⓟ   fuel residue

ADP   ADP~ⓟ═ATP

ADP becomes ADP~ⓟ, or ATP, by accepting ~ⓟ from fuel. Through this type of transfer, some of the energy of a fuel becomes incorporated into ATP. We shall see below that ~ⓟ groups are created in substances other than fuels, through energy derived ultimately from fuels. In all such cases, ~ⓟ groups may be transferred to ADP as above, resulting in the formation of ATP (see Fig. 15.10). Note here that *only* through ATP can energy become available for useful metabolic work within cells. Any other substance possessing ~ⓟ groups cannot contribute its energy to metabolic work directly; ATP always must be the intermediate energy carrier.

ATP is not only a carrier and potential donor of a high-energy bond but is also a carrier and potential donor of a phosphate group. Indeed, like phosphoric acid, ATP is a major phosphorylating agent in cells. It may react with a fuel molecule and donate its third phosphate, and energy, to the molecule. ATP thereby becomes ADP again. For example, glucose is normally phosphorylated by ATP:

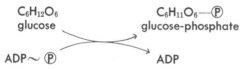

$C_6H_{12}O_6$ $C_6H_{11}O_6$—ⓟ
glucose   glucose-phosphate

ADP~ ⓟ   ADP

Two points should be noted here. First, as above, the fuel which gains a —ⓟ group loses an H atom. This atom is incorporated into ADP and is usually not specially indicated when ADP is written in symbolic form. Second, the high energy of the transferred phosphate bond is not preserved; ~ⓟ is detached from ATP, but —ⓟ is attached to the glucose. Like many phosphorylated fuels, glucose-phosphate is a low-energy combination. Yet ~ⓟ supplies more energy than is needed to produce this combination. In every such case, any excess energy of ~ⓟ dissipates as heat. Heat losses of this sort are unavoidable. Many phosphorylations, such as that of glucose, can be achieved only by ATP, even though not all the energy supplied by ATP is being used (see Fig. 15.10).

In sum, we note that the bond energies of phosphate groups may be affected in four different ways (see Fig. 15.10):

1. —ⓟ to —ⓟ, **low-energy transfer,** as in phosphate exchange by two molecules
2. —ⓟ to ~ⓟ, **creation of high bond energy,** as in respiratory oxidation
3. ~ⓟ to ~ⓟ, **high-energy transfer,** as in the harvesting of energy by ADP → ATP
4. ~ⓟ to —ⓟ, **loss of high bond energy,** as in phosphorylation of glucose by ATP

As we shall see, all four types of changes play vital roles in respiration.

ATP AND PHOSPHAGENS

As noted previously, ATP is the principal end-product of respiration. This carrier leaves the mitochondria and diffuses to all parts of a cell where energy must be utilized. In utilization, ATP reconverts to ADP, and so the energy of ~ⓟ becomes available for metabolic work. The ADP formed at the same time is then free to accept more ~ⓟ from fuels. Clearly, a relatively small amount of ADP-ATP, "turning over" repeatedly, suffices for a great deal of respiration (see Fig. 15.7).

In most cells, the ADP-ATP turnover suffices to meet the energy demands of all metabolic activities. But some cells are alternately highly active or virtually inactive. This is particularly true of muscles, which may burst into intense activity at any time. During given periods, therefore, more ATP may be required in a muscle than respiration may be able to create. Conversely, during rest, fuel oxidation in muscles may produce more ~ⓟ than the entire ADP-ATP system can hold. Muscles and a few other animal tissues are able to cope with such excess supplies or demands. They possess a device which can *store* high-energy phosphate bonds, beyond the storage capacity of ATP.

This device operates through either of two chemicals. One of these is **creatine,** a nitrogen-containing organic substance found largely in the muscles of vertebrates. The other is **arginine,** an amino acid already encountered in the earlier discussion of urea production in the liver (see Chap. 13). Apart from its other functions, this acid plays the same role in the muscles of most invertebrates as creatine plays in vertebrates. We may describe this role as follows:

$$\left.\begin{array}{c}\text{creatine}\\ \text{or}\\ \text{arginine}\end{array}\right\}\quad\underset{\underset{\text{ATP}\qquad\qquad\text{ADP}}{\longrightarrow}}{}\quad\left.\begin{array}{c}\text{creatine}\sim \textcircled{P}\\ \text{or}\\ \text{arginine}\sim \textcircled{P}\end{array}\right\}=\text{phosphagen}$$

In other words, creatine or arginine may accept $\sim\textcircled{P}$ from ATP and so become a **phosphagen.** Conversely, a phosphagen may donate $\sim\textcircled{P}$ to ADP and so revert to creatine or arginine.

The adaptive value of this reaction in muscle is clear. If, during rest, fuels supply more $\sim\textcircled{P}$ than can be harvested as ATP, then the reaction above proceeds to the right; ATP unloads $\sim\textcircled{P}$ into phosphagen and becomes ADP. This ADP is now free to collect more $\sim\textcircled{P}$ from fuel. Conversely, if the demands of $\sim\textcircled{P}$ exceed the supply from fuel, the phosphagen stores may be drawn on. The reaction above then proceeds to the left, and phosphagen becomes an energy and phosphate source for the production of additional ATP. Like fuel, a phosphagen cannot provide energy for metabolic work directly. It too can function only via ATP.

The whole pattern of phosphorylation, oxidation, and energy transfer is summarized in Fig. 15.11.

FIG. 15.11. The general pattern of the energy relations in respiration. Phosphorylation is followed by oxidation, and the high-energy bonds so created are transferred into ATP. This compound may then energize metabolic work. The energy of ATP may also be stored temporarily in phosphagens.

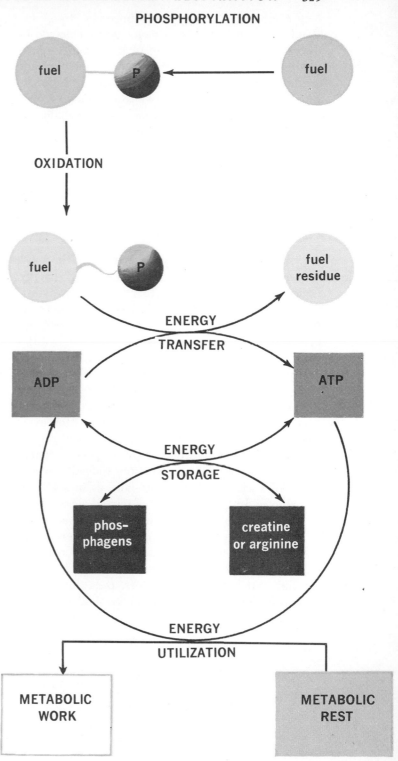

Note that useful energy never becomes "free." Instead, it is conducted from molecule to molecule in discrete packets, in the form of high-energy phosphate bonds. Note also that all transfer reactions are fundamentally reversible. But the steady expenditure of energy during metabolic work imposes a one-way direction, so that fuels continue to be oxidized, and ATP continues to be formed.

Hydrogen Transfer

THE PATTERN

As noted above, dehydrogenation is the most common oxidative change which creates high-energy bonds in a fuel (consult Fig. 15.8). Whenever hydrogen is to be removed from a fuel molecule, two conditions must be fulfilled. First, specific **dehydrogenases** must be present. These enzymes control the extraction of hydrogen, and each different fuel generally requires its own specific dehydrogenase. Second, a specific **hydrogen acceptor** must be present. Atmospheric oxygen is an excellent acceptor. Yet fuels do not deliver H to oxygen directly. Moreover, oxygen may not always be available.

Fuels release hydrogen only to special organic acceptors of complex construction. Indeed, a whole series of such acceptors exists and, as in a bucket brigade, hydrogen from fuel is passed successively from one acceptor to the next, in fixed sequence. When oxygen is available, this gas functions as the last acceptor in the series; and H_2O then forms as a byproduct of respiration. If we let A, B, C, etc., stand for different hydrogen acceptors, then the pattern of H transport to oxygen may be symbolized as follows:

We may ask at this point why a succession of carriers is required at all. Could not hydrogen be passed on to oxygen directly? Indeed it could, and that this is so can be demonstrated readily in the test tube. When such a test-tube experiment is performed, hydrogen and oxygen are found to combine explosively. We should not conclude, however, that a similarly direct combination in cells would lead to explosion of cells; the quantities of gases involved here at any moment would probably be far too small to cause damage. The important conclusion is, rather, that the combination of hydrogen and oxygen is an *energy-yielding* process. And this undoubtedly explains the adaptive value of the succession of hydrogen carriers in cells. If hydrogen were to combine directly with oxygen, any energy released would appear suddenly, all at once. Most or all of it would then dissipate as heat and would become useless metabolically. But with a succession of carriers, the energy can be freed little by little; and this energy becomes useful. For when one carrier passes hydrogen to another, the carrier is in effect *dehydrogenated*. This is an oxidative change, and it yields usable energy trapped as ATP.

We have found in the preceding section that oxidation of a fuel creates fuel~ⓅP and that the ~Ⓟ is then transferred to ADP and harvested as ATP. Now we note that, if oxidation of a fuel is achieved by removal of hydrogen from it, then the transfer of the liberated hydrogen via H carriers to oxygen yields a great deal of energy too; and this energy is harvested. In this, creation of high-energy phosphate bonds and formation of ATP again play critical roles. The details of these processes are just beginning to be unraveled by research, but the general pattern is already clear. If A and B are hydrogen carriers as above, then the pattern is (see top column next page)

A—H ⟶ B

A ⟵ ⟶ B—H

dehydrogenation
energy
⟱

—Ⓟ ⟶ ~Ⓟ ⟶ ATP

ADP

It can be shown that, with every transfer of two hydrogen atoms through the entire carrier series to oxygen, 3 molecules of ATP are formed.

Thus, there are actually *two* sources of ~Ⓟ, hence of ATP, in respiration. One is the conversion of fuel —Ⓟ into fuel ~Ⓟ by oxidation, as outlined earlier. The other is the creation of ~Ⓟ during hydrogen transfer away from fuel (Fig. 15.12). This second source is, in principle, like the first, for a hydrogen carrier too may be regarded as a "fuel," which becomes oxidized as it loses hydrogen to an-

other carrier. Of the two sources of ~Ⓟ, the second is the more important. As we shall see below, far more total energy is obtained by the formation of ATP during hydrogen transfer than by the immediate formation of ATP during oxidation of the original fuel.

Which compounds are the specific hydrogen carriers, and how do they function?

THE FIRST H CARRIERS

Two substances serve as the first acceptors when hydrogen is removed from fuel: **diphosphopyridine nucleotide,** or **DPN** for short, and **triphosphopyridine nucleotide,** or **TPN** for short. We have already encountered TPN earlier, in the discussion of photosynthesis. There too it functioned as a hydrogen carrier, delivering H derived from water and other carriers into the carbohydrate-manufacturing cycle. In respiration, the function of TPN is roughly the reverse:

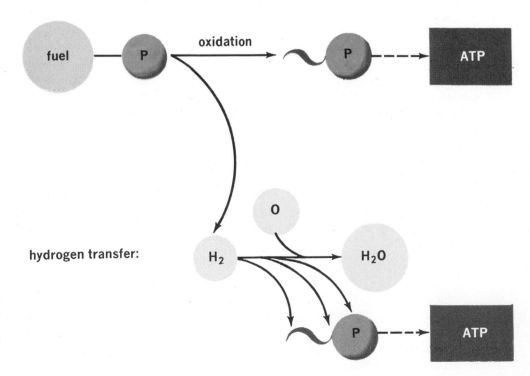

FIG. 15.12. The two sources of ATP in respiration. One source is oxidation of fuel, and a second is hydrogen transfer from fuel to oxygen.

$$\text{H}_2\text{O} \xrightarrow[\text{sun}]{\quad} \text{H}_2 \rightarrow \text{other carriers} \rightarrow \text{TPN}\cdot\text{H} \rightarrow \text{carbohydrates}$$

(common form of photosynthetic H transport)

$$\text{H}_2\text{O} \leftarrow \quad \text{H}_2 \leftarrow \text{other carriers} \leftarrow \text{TPN}\cdot\text{H} \leftarrow \text{organic substances}$$

(one form of respiratory H transport)

This scheme implies, as it should, that the respiratory energy of fuel molecules ultimately derives from solar energy which has split water. Thus, in the sense that the energy trapped by photosynthesis may subsequently be released by respiration, the two processes may be regarded as the reverse of each other. But in every other sense this does not hold. For example, carbohydrates are always the endproduct of photosynthesis, but only sometimes the starting materials of respiration. Oxygen may not be available, and water is then not a byproduct of respiration, as we shall see. The "other carriers" are not the same in respiration and photosynthesis. And TPN itself, always the last H carrier in photosynthesis, is only sometimes the first carrier in respiration.

Some fuels release hydrogen specifically to TPN; others, specifically to DPN. Indeed, in many reactions we shall discuss, it is DPN, not TPN, which must be available as the hydrogen acceptor. DPN and TPN are closely related. They differ only by one phosphate group, and in cells one may be converted into the other: $\text{DPN} + -\textcircled{P} \rightleftharpoons \text{TPN}$. Both DPN and TPN are manufactured in part from nucleoprotein derivatives, in part from one of the B vitamins, namely, **nicotinic acid.** Here is the reason why this vitamin is essential for life, and why it must be produced by plants and eaten by animals. Each of their cells requires nicotinic acid as a vital building material in the construction of DPN and TPN.

We may describe the respiratory functions of DPN and TPN as follows:

DPN/TPN   (DPN/TPN)·H

dehydrogenase

oxidation

fuel—$\textcircled{P}$ fuel~$\textcircled{P}$, dehydrogenated

The subsequent fate of DPN·H or TPN·H depends on whether or not oxygen is available to a cell. Recall that in Chap. 2 we have referred to two forms of respiration: oxygen-dependent **aerobic respiration** and oxygen-independent **anaerobic respiration,** or *fermentation*. Fermentation is the more primitive form, but aerobic respiration is the more common form. We assume for the present that conditions are *aerobic* and that oxygen is in ample supply.

AEROBIC TRANSPORT

The Formation of Water

Like the exhaust pipe leading away from a motor, the hydrogen "exhaust" of respiration leads from DPN/TPN through a series of other hydrogen carriers. Actually, such successive transfers do not involve whole hydrogen atoms. Hydrogen *ionizes* into two components. One is the familiar H^+ ion, which, in the language of atomic physics, is simply the positively charged nucleus of a hydrogen atom (Fig. 15.13). Spinning around this nucleus in a whole atom is a negatively charged electron (e^-). This electron is the second component resulting from ionization of an H atom:

$$\text{H} \rightarrow \text{H}^+ + e^-$$

Hydrogen transfer in biological systems involves only the electron. At the start of a transfer sequence, hydrogen ionizes. The electron so liberated is then carried through to the end of the sequence. There the electron rejoins its H^+, which had been "waiting" in the meantime, and the whole hydrogen atom is recreated:

Hydrogen transfer therefore is actually **electron transfer,** and this, we may note again, is an energy-yielding process. For simplicity of description, we shall continue to assume that whole H atoms, not just their electrons, are being transferred.

The carrier required specifically just after DPN or TPN is a derivative of another component of the vitamin B complex: **riboflavin,** or vitamin B_2. Riboflavin is converted in cells into a *flavoprotein*. The properties of this vital substance are such that it specifically accepts hydrogen from DPN or TPN. For example,

Free DPN reappears, available now to accept new hydrogen from fuel.

Flavoprotein in turn passes hydrogen on to a succession of five carriers, which together represent the **cytochrome system.** All five members of this system are variants of a single substance, namely, **cytochrome.** This is a red, iron-containing pigment, structurally related to the red, iron-containing *heme* of hemoglobin in blood. Heme is an oxygen carrier; cytochrome is a hydrogen carrier. Iron in the diet

evidently makes not only for healthy gas exchange, but also for healthy respiration in the cells of all organisms.

The five variants of cytochrome have been called cytochromes a, a_3, b, c, and c_1. Their role and sequence of action in hydrogen transport may be symbolized as follows:

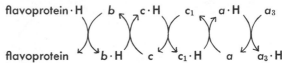

Free flavoprotein reappears at the start of this chain, available now to accept more H from $DPN \cdot H$ or $TPN \cdot H$. Cytochrome $a_3 \cdot H$ appears at the other end of the series, and the cytochromes in the middle successively accept and hand on hydrogen from one to the other.

Cytochrome a_3 is the penultimate carrier in the entire transfer series, for the next, and the last, is atmospheric oxygen:

$$2 \text{ cytochrome } a_3 \cdot H \qquad 2 \text{ cytochrome } a_3$$
$$\text{oxygen} \qquad H_2O$$

The pattern of hydrogen transport as a whole is summarized in Fig. 15.14.

Conditions for H Transport

Several observations may be made concerning the transport reactions above. First, as everywhere else in metabolism, each of the reactions here must be catalyzed by a specific enzyme. We may note too

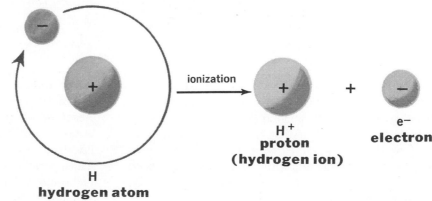

FIG. 15.13. Ionization of a hydrogen atom yields a hydrogen ion and an electron.

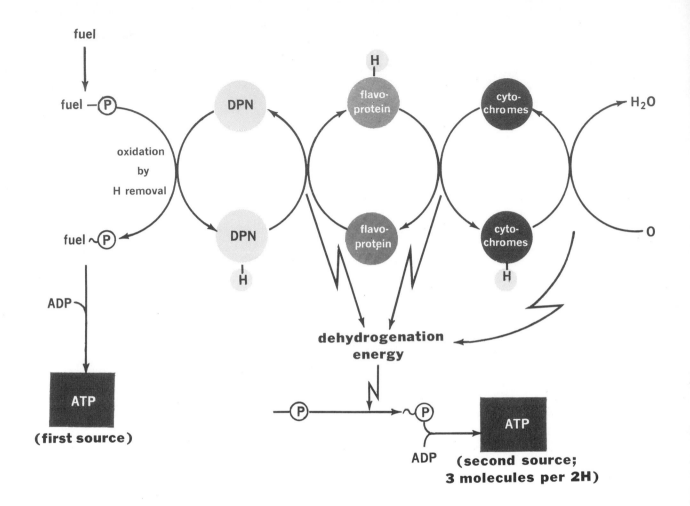

FIG. 15.14. Summary of aerobic hydrogen transfer.

that vitamin E and vitamin K are known to be required in the reactions. However, it is not yet known what specific roles these vitamins play.

Second, it is clear that relatively small quantities of the hydrogen carriers suffice to transport comparatively large quantities of hydrogen. For each carrier molecule functions cyclically and may be used repeatedly.

Third, if any one of the reactions is stopped, the whole transport system becomes inoperative, and the energy it normally supplies cannot be obtained. Reaction blocks may occur in a number of ways. For example, *inhibitor* substances of various kinds may interfere specifically with given transport reactions. Thus, potassium cyanide specifically inhibits the cytochrome system, and this is why cyanide is such a violent poison. Another form of reaction block is produced if one of the carriers is in deficient supply.

A consistently riboflavin-deficient diet, for example, would soon impair the reactions in which flavoprotein is a participant.

Any such reaction barrier introduced into the transport sequence will act like a "roadblock" and will lead to an accumulation of hydrogen back of the barrier. For example, if the cytochrome system is blocked, flavoprotein cannot get rid of its hydrogen. All available flavoprotein then will soon hold H to capacity, and none will be free to accept more H from DPN·H or TPN·H. Therefore, DPN·H and TPN·H cannot get rid of their own hydrogen, and free DPN/TPN will no longer become available to accept more hydrogen from fresh fuel. Respiration will be effectively stopped.

Experimental use of reaction blocks has been one of the principal methods of elucidating the normal pattern of hydrogen transport. For example, after the experimental production of a riboflavin deficiency in a test animal, one would find that the amount of hydrogen-holding cytochrome molecules decreases, whereas the amount of (DPN/TPN)·H increases. One would conclude, then, that DPN/TPN and the cytochromes are a part of the H-transport system and that DPN/TPN must function before flavoprotein, the cytochromes after. Blocking techniques of this sort are employed quite generally whenever the components of a sequence of metabolic reactions are to be identified.

ANAEROBIC TRANSPORT

The Pattern

Cyanide poisoning or vitamin B deficiencies are not particularly common hazards in the life of an organism, and most organisms on earth would probably survive quite well even without special protective adaptations against such contingencies. But there is one ancient hazard affecting H transport which all living matter has had to cope with ever since it originated. That is the unavailability of atmospheric oxygen. Lack of oxygen is a reaction barrier of the same sort as cyanide poisoning or vitamin deficiencies. The consequence is a damming up of

hydrogen all the way back to DPN/TPN, with the further consequence that respiration as a whole becomes blocked.

The earliest organisms lived in an environment which did not provide free oxygen at all (see Chap. 2). Yet these organisms survived. Today, certain bacteria, presumably direct descendants of the first living things, cannot use oxygen even though the gas may be available. Such organisms are **obligate anaerobes.** Various other organisms are **facultative anaerobes;** that is, they may or may not use oxygen and survive either way. The fungus yeast is an example. Most living organisms are **obligate aerobes;** that is, they must have oxygen if they are to survive. However, such aerobes very frequently may not be able to obtain enough of the gas. For example, during strenuous activity, energy requirements and respiration rates may become so high that even maximum breathing rates cannot meet the oxygen demands of the cells.

Whenever oxygen supplies are inadequate, or whenever hydrogen transport to oxygen is otherwise blocked, organisms may respire in a way which does not require oxygen. This is *anaerobic respiration,* or *fermentation,* the ancient original form of energy production. As already noted in Chap. 2, fermentation capacity has been inherited by all organisms. Under conditions of oxygen deficiency, this anaerobic type of respiration may become a substitute or a subsidiary source of energy.

The principle of anaerobic hydrogen transport is relatively simple: when the exhaust pipe of an engine is stopped up, the engine may still continue to operate if an alternative outlet for the waste gases is available. Oxygen is the normal outlet for hydrogen, and if oxygen is unavailable, a final acceptor other than oxygen is used.

This alternative acceptor functions directly after (DPN/TPN)·H. Whenever DPN·H, for example, cannot unload hydrogen to flavoprotein, it unloads to the alternative acceptor. Thus free DPN becomes available again, and energy release from fuel can continue.

The alternative hydrogen acceptor is **pyruvic acid** ($C_3H_4O_3$). As we shall see shortly, this acid is produced normally during the respiratory breakdown of carbohydrates. If oxygen is amply available, pyruvic acid is merely one of the intermediate steps in the combustion of carbohydrates. In other words, it is a fuel which, in the presence of oxygen, may be burned further to CO_2 and H_2O. But pyruvic acid has the property of combining readily with hydrogen. And if DPN·H cannot use its normal hydrogen outlet to flavoprotein, pyruvic acid is used instead. The acid then ceases to be a fuel and becomes a hydrogen carrier.

When pyruvic acid combines with hydrogen, the result is the formation of *lactic acid* in animals and some bacteria, and of *alcohol* and CO_2 in plants:

$C_3H_4O_3 + 2H \longrightarrow (C_3H_6O_3) \longrightarrow C_3H_6O_3$ (in animals
pyruvic   lactic   and
acid   acid   certain
                                                   bacteria)

$\longrightarrow C_2H_6O + CO_2$ (in plants)
         alcohol

Different enzymes promote these reactions in plants and animals, hence the difference in the endproducts.

With these reactions, anaerobic respiration comes to a halt. The overall pattern is outlined in Fig. 15.15. Since only carbohydrates normally yield pyruvic acid directly, fermentation will be most efficient when carbohydrates are available as fuels. Other types of fuels may be sources of pyruvic acid also, but, as we shall see, lengthier reaction sequences are required to produce it, and the acid is consequently formed more slowly. Indeed, anaerobic respiration is predominantly carbohydrate-dependent.

The Energy Gain

The energy gained anaerobically is far less than that gained aerobically. First, with the path to oxygen blocked, the ATP normally created by H transfer to oxygen cannot be realized. Second, anaerobic combustion stops at the pyruvic acid stage, and the potential energy still contained in pyruvic

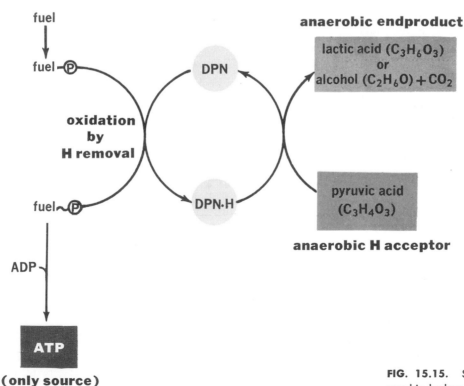

FIG. 15.15. Summary of anaerobic hydrogen transfer.

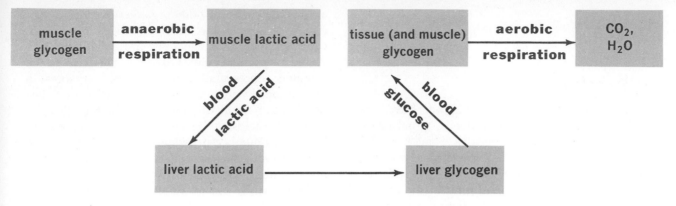

FIG. 15.16. The pattern of utilization of lactic acid, formed in muscle by fermentation. Through the steps shown, the acid is eventually respired aerobically, and its energy is obtained.

acid therefore remains unused and locked in lactic acid or alcohol.

Nevertheless, fermentation energy alone does suffice to sustain the life of the obligate or facultative anaerobes among bacteria and fungi. The alcohol and CO_2 produced by most of these organisms are excreted into the environment. Through beer and wine, man has known longer about these excreted fermentation products than about the organisms which give rise to them.

In obligate aerobes, on the other hand, the energy gain from fermentation alone is too small to sustain life. If hydrogen transport to oxygen is blocked completely, cell death will occur quickly, even though fermentation is under way. However, fermentation may suffice to *supplement* aerobic respiration when energy demands are high. For example, during intensive physical activity among animals, the oxygen supply to the cells may be insufficient despite faster breathing, and an **oxygen debt** will be incurred. Fermentation then proceeds in parallel with aerobic respiration, and more energy so becomes available. Lactic acid will accumulate as a result, particularly in the muscles, which bear the burden of physical work. At such times also, the energy stored in phosphagens is likely to be used up.

Muscular fatigue is associated with increasing accumulation of lactic acid. When the amount of acid becomes very high, fatigue may become so great that intense activity can no longer be maintained. During an ensuing rest period, faster breathing at first continues; the oxygen debt is being repaid. The extra oxygen helps to burn away the accumulated lactic acid. This occurs in the following manner. Lactic acid diffuses from the muscles into the blood, and the blood carries the acid to the liver. This organ then converts the acid into glycogen, which may be stored or sent back to the muscles and other tissues via blood glucose. In either event, glycogen is eventually burned aerobically to CO_2 and H_2O (Fig. 15.16).

Thus, like alcohol in plants, lactic acid is a potential fuel which, via reconversion to carbohydrates, may be burned completely. The energy contained in the endproduct of fermentation is therefore not permanently lost to the animal. It is harvested during the aerobic conditions of a rest period, when the oxygen supply is high relative to cellular requirements. The phosphagen energy stores may then be replenished too. With the gradual disappearance of lactic acid from the muscles, fatigue disappears, breathing slows down, and a normal oxygen-energy balance is then reestablished.

These accounts of energy transfer and hydrogen transfer set the stage for a discussion of the third aspect of respiration: the actual combustion of fuels.

Fuel Combustion

THE PATTERN

In the course of reorganizing internally and thereby acquiring high-energy bonds, a fuel molecule becomes changed chemically. Sometimes the change is not great, and the basic structure of the molecule is not affected. But sometimes the oxidative change may bring about a splitting of the carbon skeleton of the molecule. High-energy bonds may form regardless of whether a molecule splits or not, but when a split does occur, fragments with shorter carbon chains result. These are still energy-yielding fuels. Sooner or later, they in turn may be split into still shorter chains. Eventually, fragments will arise which contain but a single carbon atom each.

This final 1-carbon breakdown product emerges from respiration in the form of CO_2. Carbon dioxide represents the end condition of all metabolic fuels, and when a fuel has been degraded this far, all extractable energy has already been extracted. Complete degradation of a fuel to CO_2 can occur only in the presence of oxygen.

If we follow the sequence of fuel breakdown backward, then the next-to-last fuel fragment should consist of *two* linked carbons. This is the case. The fundamental molecule representing the 2-carbon stage in respiration is **acetic acid** ($C_2H_4O_2$). In other words, progressive breakdown eventually transforms all fuels to acetic acid, and this 2-carbon acid then transforms to 1-carbon CO_2.

The manner in which the acetic acid stage is reached differs for different types of fuels. For example, many carbohydrates are first broken up into 3-carbon compounds. Carbohydrates often contain whole multiples of 3 carbons. As noted, photosynthesis yields a 3-carbon endproduct, and more complex carbohydrates are built up from such units. This holds for glucose and all other 6-carbon sugars, for 12-carbon disaccharides, and for polysaccharides such as starch and glycogen. As we shall see, when any of these are used as respiratory fuels, the original 3-carbon units reappear in the course of breakdown. Many other organic substances, glycerin, for example, are 3-carbon molecules to begin with. All such C_3 compounds are eventually converted to **pyruvic acid** ($C_3H_4O_3$). This acid is the common representative of the 3-carbon stage in respiration. Pyruvic acid subsequently loses 1 carbon in the form of CO_2 and so becomes acetic acid.

Fatty acids and related molecules consist of long, even-numbered carbon chains. These do not break up into 3-carbon units but become 2-carbon units directly. Other fuels are 2-carbon molecules to begin with, and all such C_2 compounds eventually appear as acetic acid. Amino acids break down partly to pyruvic acid (which subsequently becomes acetic acid), partly to acetic acid directly. This holds also for many other organic substances which may happen to be used as fuel.

Thus, the overall pattern of aerobic fuel combustion may be likened to a tree with branches, or to a river with tributaries (Fig. 15.17). A broad main channel is represented by the sequence pyruvic acid → acetic acid → carbon dioxide. Numerous side channels lead into this sequence, some funneling into the 3-carbon pyruvic acid step, others into the 2-carbon acetic acid step. The side channels themselves may be long or short, and each may have smaller side channels of its own. In the end, the flow from the entire system drains out as 1-carbon carbon dioxide.

The various sequences in this pattern are series of metabolic reactions. All are fundamentally reversible, but they proceed in a preferred direction during respiration. As usual, each reaction requires specific enzymes and, among mammals, often also specific hormones.

Carbohydrates are among the chief respiratory fuels, and they play a particular role in anaerobic respiration. Their combustion may advantageously be examined first.

CARBOHYDRATE BREAKDOWN

The general pattern of this sequence consists of two phases. In a first series of reactions, complex carbohydrate fuels in cells are degraded into smaller

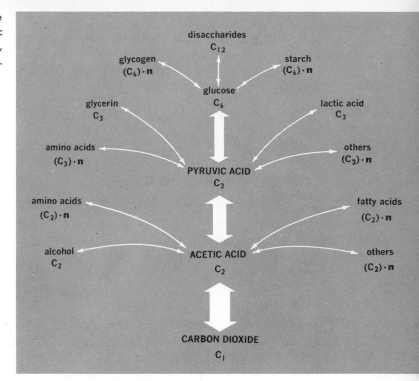

FIG. 15.17. Some of the main pathways in the aerobic combustion of fuels. Pyruvic acid, acetic acid, and carbon dioxide form a main sequence, which other pathways join, as branches of a tree.

fragments. Preliminary low-energy phosphorylations occur at the same time, and energy is here *expended*. These reactions may be said to represent a **preparatory phase.** In a subsequent series of reactions, high-energy phosphate bonds are created by oxidation, and energy is then *harvested*. More energy is gained here than has been expended earlier. This may be called the **oxidative phase.**

The Preparatory Phase

The starting material in carbohydrate breakdown may be taken to be glucose, or glucose derivatives such as starch in plants or glycogen in animals. The first preparatory reaction is the phosphorylation of these carbohydrates to **glucose-phosphate.** ATP is the phosphate and energy donor, 1 molecule of ATP being expended for every 6-carbon unit.

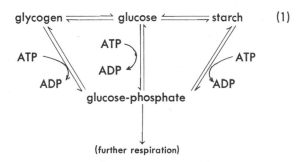

(1)

Note that glycogen and starch may first become glucose before they are converted to glucose-phosphate. Such transformation to free glucose occurs, as in digestion, by the addition of water. But glycogen and starch may be phosphorylated directly into glucose-phosphate, and the free glucose stage is then bypassed. This is the usual event in respiration. Whatever pathway is followed, it should be remembered that one molecule of either glycogen or starch yields a dozen or more molecules of glucose-phosphate, at the expense of a corresponding number of ATP molecules.

The diagram above illustrates that glucose-phosphate may be an intermediate in the reversible conversion of glycogen into glucose:

glycogen $\rightleftharpoons$ glucose-phosphate $\rightleftharpoons$ glucose

We have already referred to this in Chap. 13, in connection with the role of the liver in carbohydrate transport throughout the body. The hormones **insulin** and **adrenalin** were then noted to influence this conversion. Specifically, insulin was found to promote the phosphorylation of blood glucose, hence its utilization as tissue glycogen. We may appreciate now how this is so. By being converted into glucose-phosphate, blood glucose may be drawn directly into cellular respiration. Or it may first be stored as cellular glycogen, which may become glucose-phosphate later and serve as fuel then. Note that **estrogen,** a sex hormone, promotes the phosphorylation of glucose also and that still other hormones may affect this important reaction as well.

Whatever the source of glucose-phosphate, the respiratory fate of this fuel is always the same. It first undergoes a series of internal rearrangements which transform it into **fructose-phosphate**. This conversion does not change the low energy values of the phosphate bonds:

$$C_6H_{11}O_6-\text{P} \xrightarrow{\text{rearrangement}} C_6H_{11}O_6-\text{P} \qquad (2)$$
$$\text{glucose-phosphate} \qquad\qquad \text{fructose-phosphate}$$

When free fructose is a respiratory fuel, it enters the reaction sequence at this point. With the aid of ATP, fructose may become fructose-phosphate, and the latter adds indistinguishably to the fructose-phosphate formed from glucose, starch, or glycogen:

This scheme also shows how cells may convert fructose into glucose, or vice versa.

Fructose-phosphate next becomes **fructose-diphosphate**. The —P group of fructose-phosphate is situated at one end of the carbon chain, and another low-energy phosphate group is now added to the other end of the molecule. ATP is again the phosphorylating agent:

In gaining a second —P group, fructose-phosphate also loses an H atom to ADP.

If an imaginary line is drawn through the fructose-diphosphate molecule between the third and fourth of its 6 carbons, then the two halves will be noted to contain mirror-image carbon skeletons. This is significant in what happens next. Fructose-diphosphate *splits* between its third and fourth carbons, and *two 3-carbon fragments* are thereby formed. These undergo slight internal rearrangements and become two identical molecules: **phosphoglyceraldehyde**. This transformation still does not change the energy values of the phosphate bonds:

$$\text{P}-C_6H_{10}O_6-\text{P} \longrightarrow 2C_3H_5O_3-\text{P} \qquad (4)$$
$$\text{fructose-diphosphate} \qquad \text{phosphoglyceraldehyde}$$

phosphoglyceraldehyde

Phosphoglyceraldehyde, **PGAL** for short, will be recognized as the principal organic endproduct of photosynthesis. We now find it to be an intermediate in the combustion of sugar. PGAL evidently interconnects the reaction sequence of photosynthesis with that of carbohydrate respiration:

We note that PGAL just photosynthesized may be used at once as respiratory fuel, via further reactions to the *right;* or it may be converted into fructose, glucose, or starch, via the reactions to the *left.* As a check of Fig. 11.21 on page 261 will show, these reactions to the left actually have already been referred to in the discussion of the fates of photosynthesized PGAL. We conclude that the formation of complex carbohydrates *from* PGAL is the exact reverse of the respiratory breakdown of complex carbohydrates *to* PGAL.

A last preliminary phosphorylation occurs next. PGAL already possesses one —$\circled{P}$ group, joined to one end of the molecule by a low-energy bond. Another —$\circled{P}$ group is now added to the other end of the molecule. The phosphorylating agent here is inorganic phosphoric acid (H_3PO_4 or H—O—$\circled{P}$), drawn from the mineral supply of the cell:

$$2C_3H_5O_3-\circled{P} + 2H-O-\circled{P} \rightarrow 2\circled{P}-C_3H_6O_4-\circled{P} \quad (5)$$

PGAL   phosphoric   diphosphoglyceric
              acid   acid

The whole H—O—$\circled{P}$ molecule is added to PGAL. With the formation of this endproduct, called **diphosphoglyceric acid,** the preparatory phase of combustion is completed, and the oxidative, energy-yielding phase now begins.

The Oxidative Phase

Diphosphoglyceric acid first undergoes an oxidative change which raises the low-energy —$\circled{P}$

$\Rightarrow\circled{P}$—fructose—$\circled{P} \leftrightharpoons 2$ PGAL $\rightarrow$ (further respiration)
                 $\uparrow$
           photosynthesis

bond, just added in reaction 5, to a high-energy level. This oxidative change is a *dehydrogenation:* 2 atoms of H are withdrawn and are immediately accepted by DPN, which must be present:

$$2\circled{P}-C_3H_6O_4-\circled{P} \qquad 2\circled{P}\sim C_3H_4O_4-\circled{P} \quad (6)$$

diphosphoglyceric
acid

4DPN   4DPN·H

The principal endproduct, $\circled{P}\sim C_3H_4O_4-\circled{P}$, now transfers its $\sim\circled{P}$ to ADP:

$$2\circled{P}\sim C_3H_4O_4-\circled{P} \qquad 2C_3H_5O_4-\circled{P} \quad (7)$$

                         phosphoglyceric acid

2ADP   2ATP

In this reaction, the molecule which loses the $\sim\circled{P}$ group gains an H atom from ADP. Two molecules of ATP are created, and these *pay back* the 2ATP expended earlier, in preparatory reactions 1 and 3. As yet there has been no *net* gain of energy.

The other endproduct, $C_3H_5O_4-\circled{P}$, is already familiar. It is **phosphoglyceric acid, PGA** for short. In photosynthesis, as we have seen, PGA adds hydrogen from TPN·H and energy from ATP and becomes PGAL (see Chap. 11). In respiration, we now find that PGAL loses hydrogen to DPN and energy to ADP and so becomes PGA. The two sequences are virtually mirror images:

glucose $\rightleftharpoons$
starch $\rightleftharpoons$ glucose—$\circled{P}$ ⇌==⇌ 2PGAL $\underset{\text{photosynthesis}}{\overset{\text{respiration}}{\rightleftharpoons}}$ 2PGA
glycogen $\rightleftharpoons$

(further respiration)

(photosynthesis)

In short, photosynthesis and carbohydrate combustion *share* the reversible sequence PGAL $\rightleftharpoons$ PGA. A PGA molecule may contribute to photosynthesis, and carbohydrate production generally, by reacting to the left in the scheme above, or, by reacting to the right, it may contribute to further energy production.

Oxidation now continues; an oxidative *dehydration* occurs, in which PGA loses not hydrogen alone, but hydrogen and oxygen in the form of water. A new high-energy bond is created at the same time:

$$2C_3H_5O_4-\circled{P} \rightarrow 2H_2O + 2C_3H_3O_3\sim\circled{P} \quad (8)$$

PGA   phospho-enol-
                            pyruvic acid

Since water appears rather than hydrogen alone, hydrogen acceptors are not required here. The principal endproduct, $C_3H_3O_3\sim\circled{P}$, is called **phospho-**

enol-pyruvic acid. This substance transfers its $\sim\!\textcircled{P}$ to ADP:

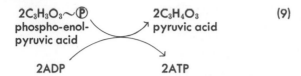

$$2C_3H_3O_3\!\sim\!\textcircled{P} \qquad\qquad 2C_3H_4O_3 \qquad\qquad (9)$$

phospho-enol-pyruvic acid → pyruvic acid

2ADP → 2ATP

Two additional molecules of ATP are created, and these represent the *net* energy gain of the reaction sequence up to this point. The $\sim\!\textcircled{P}$ group lost from phospho-enol-pyruvic acid is replaced by a hydrogen from ADP, and $C_3H_4O_3$, **pyruvic acid,** is formed. This compound no longer carries any phosphate groups.

The whole reaction sequence so far is summarized in Fig. 15.18. On balance, the total input is seen to be 1 molecule of free glucose, 4 molecules each of ADP and DPN, and 2 molecules each of phosphoric acid and ATP. The total output consists of 2 molecules each of pyruvic acid, ADP, and water, and 4 each of ATP and DPN·H. The *net* input-output therefore is:

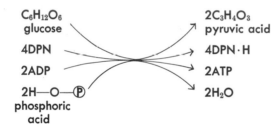

$C_6H_{12}O_6$ glucose → $2C_3H_4O_3$ pyruvic acid

4DPN → 4DPN·H

2ADP → 2ATP

$2H\!-\!O\!-\!\textcircled{P}$ phosphoric acid → $2H_2O$

Altogether, four phosphorylations have occurred (reactions 1, 3, and 5). Two of the $-\!\textcircled{P}$ groups have been supplied by phosphoric acid, the other two by ATP. Each of these four phosphates sooner or later has acquired a high-energy bond, and four ATP molecules have been formed. Two of these pay back for the ATP expended, and two are net gain. The fate of the atoms in glucose may be described by the equation

$$C_6H_{12}O_6 \rightarrow 2C_3H_4O_3 + 4H$$

Thus the net loss of atoms from glucose amounts to 4H, and these are held by DPN.

If respiration occurs under *anaerobic* conditions,

pyruvic acid must now serve as the final hydrogen acceptor:

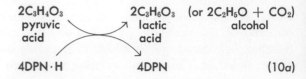

$$2C_3H_4O_3 \qquad 2C_3H_6O_3 \quad \text{(or } 2C_2H_5O + CO_2)$$

pyruvic acid → lactic acid   alcohol

4DPN·H → 4DPN   (10a)

Carbohydrate combustion in this case stops with the formation of lactic acid in animals, or alcohol and CO_2 in plants. The two ATP gained represent the net energy yield of the entire process.

But if conditions are *aerobic*, two desirable consequences supervene. First, the four hydrogens held by DPN may be passed on to oxygen, a transfer which, as noted earlier, yields three additional ATP molecules per 2H, or 6ATP total. Second, since pyruvic acid need not serve as a hydrogen carrier, it may be burned further. Most of the energy of the original glucose is actually still untapped. As we shall see, complete combustion of pyruvic acid will supply many more ATP molecules than have formed thus far.

With the production of pyruvic acid, the special sequence of carbohydrate combustion may be regarded as completed. For, as has been noted above, 3-carbon pyruvic acid is also a key stage in the combustion of many other types of fuels.

PYRUVIC ACID TO ACETIC ACID

The Pattern

Fats, proteins, and most other classes of protoplasmic compounds may contribute to pyruvic acid formation. In each such case a separate breakdown sequence exists, yielding greater or lesser net amounts of energy. We shall not discuss these sequences in as detailed a fashion as that for carbohydrates but shall merely indicate general patterns.

When cellular fats are used as respiratory fuel, they are first degraded to fatty acids and glycerin, as in digestion. Glycerin, a 3-carbon unit, is then transformed into phosphoglyceraldehyde, PGAL. This compound becomes pyruvic acid via reactions already discussed above for carbohydrates. Protoplasmic fatty acids bypass the pyruvic acid stage and

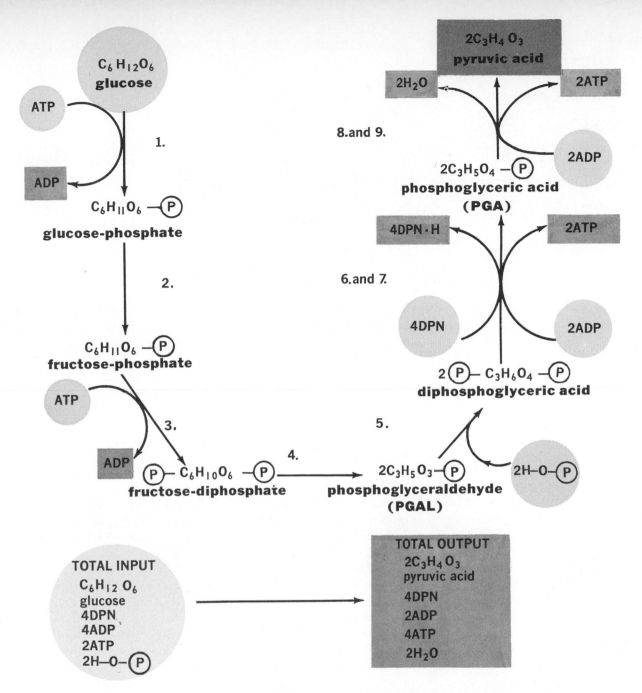

FIG. 15.18. The conversion of glucose into pyruvic acid. The main steps of the conversion are shown in the reaction sequence, and an input-output summary is given separately.

split up directly into 2-carbon units. These then convert to acetic acid. The general pattern is outlined in Fig. 15.19. It should be clear that this pattern also describes metabolic pathways by which carbohydrates may be converted into fats, and vice versa.

Cellular protein fuel first breaks down into its

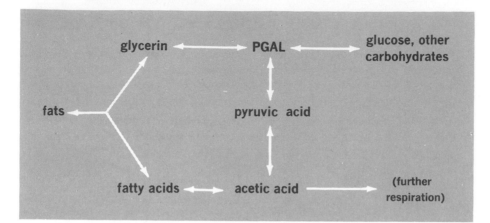

FIG. 15.19. Some of the major pathways in fat metabolism.

amino acid components (NH₂—R—COOH), again as in digestion. Next, the amino acids are deaminated. This removal of the —NH₂ groups resembles deamination in the liver, except that only in liver cells is —NH₂ transformed into urea. In other cells, amino groups detached from amino acids are attached to various other organic compounds. New amino acids or other nitrogenous substances may be formed in this way. The deaminated remnants of the original amino acids finally undergo reactions which convert them either into pyruvic acid or into acetic acid.

The following generalizations may be made here. All nonessential amino acids, i.e., those which animal cells *can* synthesize, as well as certain of the essential amino acids, tend to form carbohydrate derivatives like pyruvic acid. They are said to be **glucogenic,** potentially "glucose-producing." The remaining essential amino acids are said to be **ketogenic,** that is, potentially keto-acid-producing. Keto acids subsequently convert to acetic acid and fatty derivatives generally. The pattern is outlined in Fig. 15.20. Note that some of the arrows in the degradation of essential amino acids must be unidirectional for animals, as shown.

Protoplasm contains, or temporarily possesses, many other substances which either are 3-carbon units to begin with, such as lactic acid, or may become 3-carbon units by one reaction pathway or another. In all such cases, pyruvic acid is likely to be one stage of the pathway. Of the substances which can become pyruvic acid, one of the most important

is *acetic acid.* The reverse pathway, pyruvic to acetic, is the channel by which 3-carbon compounds are degraded into 2-carbon compounds during respiration.

This degradation is an oxidative, energy-yielding process. The oxidative change which creates a high-energy bond in pyruvic acid is a combined *dehydrogenation* and *decarboxylation:* both hydrogen and CO_2 are extracted. At least four consecutive reactions occur, and they require a whole battery of acceptors and carriers. DPN must be present to accept hydrogen; ADP must be present to accept energy; and phosphoric acid must be present to donate a —Ⓟ group to the unphosphorylated pyruvic acid.

Moreover, at least three additional substances are required. One of these is a derivative of **thiamine,** or vitamin B_1. This vitamin is an essential building material with which cells construct an enzymelike substance. The substance somehow aids in the removal of CO_2 from pyruvic acid and perhaps may be a temporary CO_2 carrier. If vitamin B_1 is in deficient supply, the conversion of pyruvic acid to acetic acid is impaired, and respiration as a whole may therefore be blocked. Under such conditions, the unusable pyruvic acid accumulates in cells, and in animals it eventually seeps into the blood. Pyruvic acid is then excreted in urine.

The proper functioning of thiamine in cells requires the presence of **magnesium ions** (Mg^{++}). These metal ions therefore are a fifth essential in the breakdown of pyruvic acid.

And a sixth is a compound called **coenzyme A,** or **CoA** for short. In the construction of CoA in cells, yet another component of the vitamin B complex is a vital building material: **pantothenic acid.** Joined to other protoplasmic constituents, including, in particular, the sulfur-containing H—S— group, the vitamin pantothenic acid is made into CoA. The latter may be represented symbolically as H—S—A. This important reaction ingredient functions as a special carrier. It combines with pyruvic acid and holds on to what is left of the acid after hydrogen and CO_2 have been extracted from it.

The Process

Given the six types of materials above, the following processes may take place. In a first reaction, pyruvic acid joins with CoA:

$$C_3H_4O_3 + H—S—A \longrightarrow C_3H_5O_3—S—A$$
pyruvic   CoA
acid
$$\text{(1) [10b]}$$

In a second reaction, the endproduct loses CO_2, presumably under the influence of thiamine. It also loses hydrogen, which is accepted by DPN. At the same time, since these extractions are oxidative, a high-energy bond is created. In this case, energy is concentrated into the *sulfur* bond which holds the endproduct above together:

$$C_3H_5O_3—S—A \qquad\qquad CO_2 + C_2H_3O\sim S—A$$

thiamine, Mg^{++}

2DPN $\qquad\qquad\qquad$ 2DPN·H $\qquad$ (2)

Carbon dioxide escapes into the cellular protoplasm. The product $C_2H_3O\sim S—A$ contains a 2-carbon C_2H_3O group, which is the remnant of the original pyruvic acid. This atomic combination is called the *acetyl* group. The endproduct above may therefore be designated as **acetyl~CoA.**

In a third reaction, acetyl~CoA reacts with phosphoric acid (H—O —ⓅP), and the acetyl group from the one is exchanged with the —ⓅP group of the other. Acetic acid is now one of the endproducts:

$$C_2H_3O\sim S—A \qquad\qquad C_2H_4O_2 \qquad (3)$$
acetyl~CoA $\qquad\qquad$ acetic acid

H—O—ⓅP $\qquad\qquad$ ⓅP $\sim$ S—A

We note that the high-energy bond of sulfur be-

FIG. 15.20. Some of the major pathways in protein metabolism. Note that animals cannot make essential amino acids but that plants can (broken arrows).

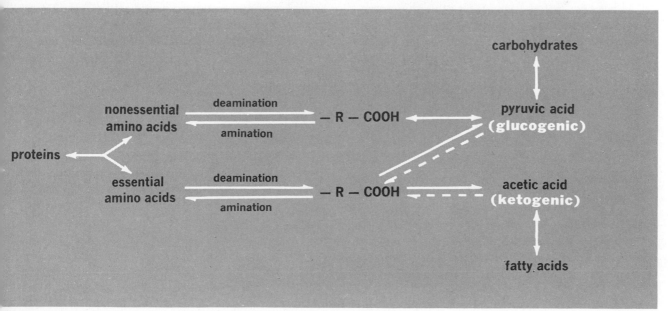

comes linked to phosphate and that the combination $\textcircled{P}{\sim}S{-}A$ in effect now contains a high-energy phosphate bond. In a final reaction, this high-energy phosphate is transferred to ADP, yielding ATP, while ADP releases an H atom to $-S-A$, regenerating the original CoA:

$$\textcircled{P}{\sim}S{-}A \qquad\qquad H{-}S{-}A \qquad (4)$$
$$\text{CoA}$$
$$\text{ADP} \qquad\qquad\qquad \text{ATP}$$

The entire conversion of pyruvic acid to acetic acid is summarized in Fig. 15.21. Note that CoA emerges from the whole process in exactly the same form as it enters. Note too that the input here includes, in hidden form, a molecule of water. For in reaction 1, CoA ($H{-}S{-}A$) contributes an H atom to the input, and in reaction 3, phosphoric acid ($H{-}O{-}\textcircled{P}$) contributes $H{-}O{-}$ to the input. We may therefore write an arithmetical summary of the fate of pyruvic acid as follows:

$$C_3H_4O_3 + H_2O \longrightarrow C_2H_4O_2 + CO_2 + 2H$$
pyruvic   acetic
acid   acid

ACETIC ACID TO CO₂

As has been noted, many fuels other than pyruvic acid may become 2-carbon acetic acid. Chief among these are the fatty acids and the keto acids formed from some of the essential amino acids. In addition, many compounds which are 2-carbon units to begin with may convert to acetic acid also.

In all such conversions, it has been found that the common endpoint actually is not acetic acid itself but, rather, *acetyl~CoA*. As we have seen above, pyruvic acid first becomes acetyl~CoA, and the latter then becomes acetic acid. Therefore acetyl~CoA represents an intermediary in acetic acid formation, and this same intermediary is formed when other fuels are decomposed into 2-carbon units. For example, when a fatty acid chain decomposes into 2-carbon units, these immediately join with CoA and become acetyl~CoA. Acetic acid as such then may or may not form. We may write generally

$$\text{pyruvic acid}$$
$$\text{keto acids} \qquad\qquad \text{other C}_2 \text{ units}$$
$$\text{fatty acids} \rightleftharpoons \textbf{acetyl}{\sim}\textbf{CoA} \rightleftharpoons \text{acetic acid}$$
$$\downarrow$$
$$\text{(further respiration)}$$

And note that it is acetyl~CoA, rather than acetic acid itself, which undergoes further respiratory change. For simplicity, however, we shall nevertheless continue to regard acetic acid ($C_2H_4O_2$) as the key 2-carbon fuel.

The oxidative degradation of acetic acid repre-

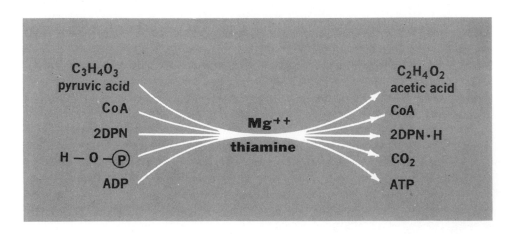

FIG. 15.21. Summary of the conversion of pyruvic acid into acetic acid.

FIG. 15.22. Some of the main steps of the citric acid cycle.

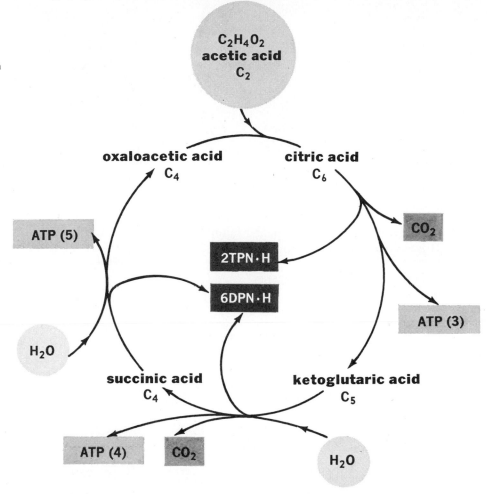

sents the last phase of respiration. This phase has the form of a cycle of reactions. Acetic acid is funneled in at one point of the cycle, its 2 carbons emerge at other points as CO_2, and the starting condition is eventually regenerated. The whole sequence is known as the **citric acid cycle,** a name taken from one of the participating substances.

The energy harvested in this cycle is far greater than that gained in all previous reactions together. Per molecule of acetic acid, about one dozen new ATP molecules arise, partly through oxidative decarboxylations and dehydrogenations. However, most of the new energy derives from hydrogen trans-

fers to oxygen, as outlined earlier in this chapter. In the reactions below, we shall indicate in parentheses the net total ATP yield, formed both by fuel oxidation and by hydrogen transfers.

The complete cycle consists of nine steps. DPN is required at certain of these, TPN at others. Water is sometimes a raw material, sometimes an endproduct; and with each turn of the cycle, a net total of two water molecules is expended. In much abbreviated form, the reaction sequence is as follows (see also Fig. 15.22). The starting material is a 4-carbon compound called **oxaloacetic acid.** It reacts with acetic acid (more precisely, acetyl~CoA) and

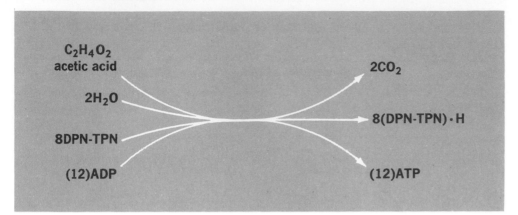

FIG. 15.23. Input-output summary of the citric acid cycle.

yields **citric acid,** a 6-carbon compound familiar as the acid component of lemon juice:

$$C_4H_4O_5 \ + \ C_2H_4O_2 \longrightarrow C_6H_8O_7 \qquad (1)$$
oxaloacetic   acetic   citric
acid   acid   acid

Citric acid next undergoes four successive reactions, which include a dehydrogenation and a decarboxylation. The final result is energy, CO_2, hydrogen held by TPN, and a 5-carbon compound called **keto-glutaric acid.** In summary,

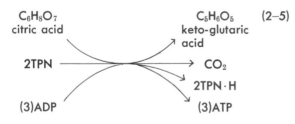

Dehydrogenation and decarboxylation now occur again, yielding more energy, more CO_2, more hydrogen (here held by DPN), and a 4-carbon compound called **succinic acid.** Water is a raw material in this sequence:

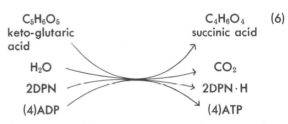

Succinic acid finally undergoes three reactions which include two successive dehydrogenations. More energy is obtained, and oxaloacetic acid is regenerated. Water is again required. In summary,

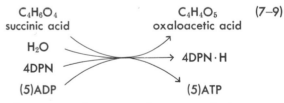

The net total input and output of the entire cycle are shown in Fig. 15.23. And the arithmetical summary of the fate of acetic acid is given by the statement

$$C_2H_4O_2 + 2H_2O \longrightarrow 8H + 2CO_2$$
acetic
acid

RESUME   With the complete conversion of fuel to CO_2, combustion has reached its endpoint. What is the overall tally? We may illustrate by considering glucose as the starting fuel, and by tracing the fate of its carbons, hydrogens, and oxygens.

As we have seen, the net conversion of 1 molecule of free glucose to pyruvic acid is described by the equation

$$C_6H_{12}O_6 \rightarrow 2C_3H_4O_3 + 4H \qquad \text{(see page 342)}$$

Two ATP, net, is obtained from glucose breakdown as such, and since each 2H transported to oxygen yields 3ATP, the total *aerobic* energy gain up to the pyruvic acid stage is 8ATP.

Next, *two* pyruvic acid molecules are transformed into acetic acid, according to the equation

$$2C_3H_4O_3 + 2H_2O \longrightarrow 2C_2H_4O_2 + 4H + 2CO_2 \qquad \text{(see page 346)}$$

The energy yield here is 2ATP from fuel oxidation, plus, again, 6ATP from the transport of 4H to oxygen. The total is 8ATP once more.

Finally, in *two* turns of the citric acid cycle, one for each of the two acetic acid molecules,

$$2C_2H_4O_2 + 4H_2O \longrightarrow 16H + 4CO_2 \qquad \text{(see page 348)}$$

Here the net energy yield from both fuel oxidation and hydrogen transport is 12ATP per turn of the cycle, or 24ATP for two turns.

If we now add the three equations above, we obtain

$$C_6H_{12}O_6 + 6H_2O \longrightarrow 6CO_2 + 24H$$

The 24H has been transferred to atmospheric oxygen, yielding water. Twelve oxygen atoms are required to accept 24H, and 12H$_2$O then forms. Hence we have

$$C_6H_{12}O_6 + 6H_2O + 6O_2 \longrightarrow 6CO_2 + 12H_2O$$

Or, reduced to the arithmetical minimum,

$$C_6H_{12}O_6 + 6O_2 \longrightarrow 6CO_2 + 6H_2O$$

This is the familiar input-output statement for the complete combustion of glucose. But it should be amply clear that this statement is not an equation, for glucose does not react directly with oxygen at all. A lump of sugar exposed to the oxygen of air merely remains sugar and does not change into CO_2 and water. The statement also does not indicate the major endproduct, namely, the energy yield of 40 molecules of ATP for each molecule of glucose burned aerobically. This contrasts sharply with the yield of only 2ATP when glucose is burned anaerobically.

If a fuel other than glucose is used, different quantities of oxygen are likely to be required, and different amounts of CO_2, water, and ATP will be produced. Whatever the fuel, more ATP is always gained than expended, and it is this net gain which makes the long and complicated reaction sequences of vital adaptive value.

The entire pattern of respiration is outlined in Fig. 15.24. In cells, these metabolic processes take place exceedingly fast. For example, a glucose molecule is estimated to be burned completely within a single second. Considering the number of reactions, reactants, enzymes, carriers, and the like, such speed is truly impressive. In mammals, moreover, respiratory rates are greatly influenced by the thyroid hormone **thyroxine**. This hormone accelerates respiration in proportion to

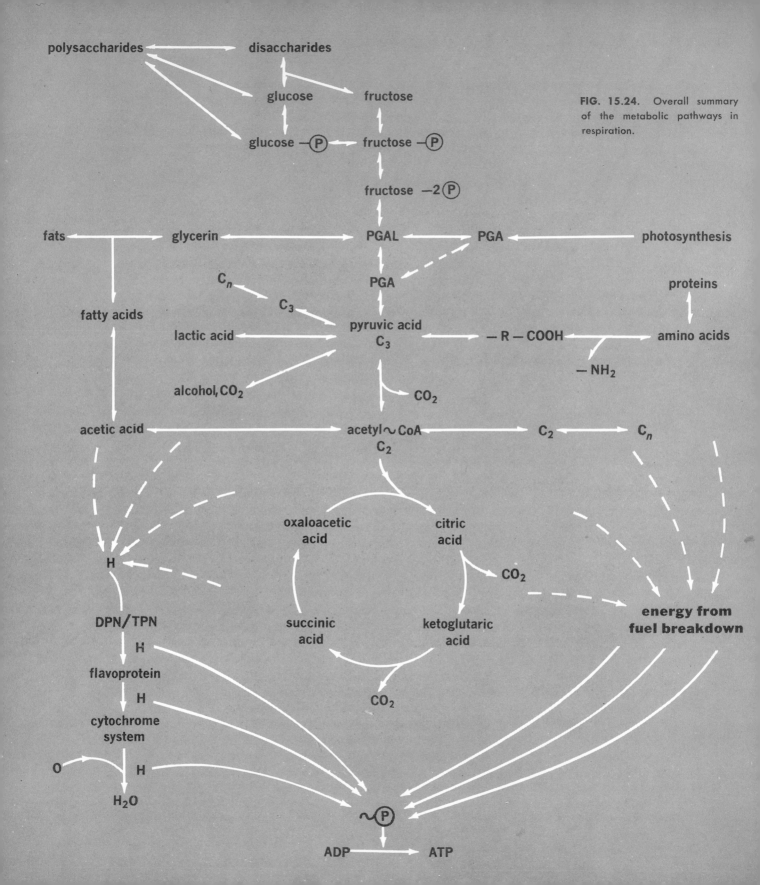

FIG. 15.24. Overall summary of the metabolic pathways in respiration.

its concentration. How this effect is achieved, and what particular reactions are influenced, is still more or less completely unknown. Most organisms are not mammals, and their respiration is not under thyroxine control. Nevertheless, respiratory breakdowns still occur extremely rapidly. Very efficient enzyme action provides part of the answer. The remaining part of the answer undoubtedly lies in the close, ordered proximity of all required ingredients in the submicroscopic recesses of the mitochondria. Just as a well-arranged industrial assembly line turns out products at a great rate, so do the even better-arranged mitochondria.

The fate and function of their chief product, ATP, is our next subject.

REVIEW QUESTIONS

1. Contrast a fire with respiration. What is common? What is different? Which materials are fuels in respiration? What three general types of events occur in respiration?

2. What is oxidation? What happens to the atomic pattern of a molecule during oxidation? What is the result of oxidation in terms of bond energies? What different kinds of oxidative changes occur in respiration?

3. Describe fully the role of phosphates in respiration. What is the ADP-ATP system, and how does it function? What different kinds of energy changes may occur in phosphate bonds, and what role does each play in respiration?

4. What and where are phosphagens? Describe their functional relation with the ADP-ATP system. Review the entire pattern of how energy is harvested from fuel molecules, and how it may be stored.

5. What is dehydrogenation? Where does it occur, and what role does it play in respiration? In what general way is hydrogen transferred to oxygen? Review the pattern of ATP formation during this transfer. To which specific carriers is hydrogen first transferred from fuel?

6. Distinguish between aerobic and anaerobic respiration. In which organisms, and under what conditions, does either occur? Review the specific sequence of carriers in (*a*) aerobic H transfer and (*b*) anaerobic H transfer. How and where may transfer in (*a*) become blocked, and what happens then? What endproducts are formed in (*b*), and what are the subsequent fates of these?

7. What is the general significance of pyruvic acid, acetic acid, and CO_2 in the respiratory breakdown of fuels? Review the chief steps in the breakdown of carbohydrates to pyruvic acid. (*Note:* Chemical formulas need not, and indeed should not, be memorized; the important thing is to *understand* what kinds of changes occur, how one step leads to the next, and what, in *words*, these steps are.)

8. What happens to pyruvic acid if conditions are (*a*) aerobic and (*b*) anaerobic? How much ATP is gained, in either case, during the conversion of glucose into pyruvic acid, including energy harvested during H transfer?

9. Which classes of foods break down to pyruvic acid during respiration, and which to acetic acid? Describe the steps of these breakdowns.

10. What ingredients must be present if pyruvic acid is to be converted to acetic acid? What is coenzyme A, pantothenic acid, and thiamine, and what are their specific functions?

11. Review the reaction sequence in the conversion of pyruvic acid to acetic acid, and describe particularly the total input and output. How much ATP is gained, including energy harvested during H transfer to oxygen?

12. What is acetyl~CoA, and what is its function? Review the steps of the citric acid cycle. What is the total input and output of this cycle? How much ATP is gained, and what are the sources of this gain?

13. Review and summarize the overall fate of 1 molecule of glucose during complete respiratory combustion. What is the total net input here, and what is the total net output? What happens to the individual atoms of glucose? What is the total ATP gain, and how much is gained during each of the main steps of breakdown?

14. Make a list of all the vitamins which play a role in respiration, and show for each what its specific role is. Correlate this list with Fig. 15.24. Similarly, list the hormones known to play a role in respiration.

15. Review the general and the specific interrelations of respiration and photosynthesis. In what sense are the two processes the reverse of each other? What reversible reactions are shared in common? Make a large diagram which incorporates Figs. 15.24 and 11.22 and which thus interconnects the events of respiration and photosynthesis.

SUGGESTED COLLATERAL READINGS

Several popularly written articles dealing with various aspects of respiration are as follows:

Siekevitz, P.: Powerhouse of the Cell, *Sci. American,* vol. 197, 1957.

Zamecnik, P. C.: The Microsome, *Sci. American,* vol. 198, 1958.

Stumpf, P. K.: ATP, *Sci. American,* vol. 188, 1953.

Green, D. E.: Biological Oxidation, *Sci. American,* vol. 199, 1958.

Green, D. E.: Enzymes in Teams, *Sci. American,* vol. 181, 1949.

Green, D. E.: The Metabolism of Fats, *Sci. American,* vol. 190, 1954.

Levine, R., and M. S. Goldstein: The Action of Insulin, *Sci. American,* vol. 198, 1958.

Three reprints of important original articles, all found in M. L. Cabriel and S. Fogel, "Great Experiments in Biology," Prentice-Hall, 1955:

Buchner, E.: Alcoholic Fermentation without Yeast Cells.

Keilin, D.: On Cytochrome, a Respiratory Pigment Common to Animals, Yeast, and Higher Plants.

Warburg, O.: The Enzyme Problem and Biological Oxidations.

Three books containing excellent accounts of respiration, arranged here in order of increasing difficulty with respect to the chemical aspects:

Gerard, R. W.: "Unresting Cells," chaps. 5, 6, and 7, Harper, 1949.

Moore, J. A.: "Principles of Zoology," chap. E-2, Oxford, 1957.

Baldwin, E. B.: "Dynamic Aspects of Biochemistry," 2d ed., Cambridge, 1952.

I N WHAT CELLULAR PROCESSES must energy be expended? In all processes which contribute to the maintenance and self-perpetuation of a cell.

Such processes include physical as well as chemical ones. Probably the most important physical role of energy is to produce *movement*, of whole cells or their components. Subsidiary physical roles are the production of heat, of light, and of electricity. The chief chemical roles of energy are maintenance of respiration itself and, above all, maintenance of activities associated with the *synthesis* of new protoplasmic parts. Such parts must be manufactured to offset the combustion and the wear and tear of existing ones, to make possible protoplasmic repairs after injury, to maintain growth, and to permit reproduction. Under the heading of energy utilization, therefore, two major subtopics are the **physical uses** and **chemical uses** of energy.

How much energy must be expended by a cell for physical and chemical activities? The answer here varies, according to the varying intensities of cellular activity. But while a cell lives, its activities are never zero. Hence if life is to continue, at least a basic minimum quantity of energy is required under all conditions. Clearly, a discussion of energy **requirements** forms a third major subtopic. We shall deal with it first.

The Energy Requirement

CALORIES, ATP, AND OXYGEN

Every energy requirement of living organisms must be met by respiration: demand must be balanced by supply. So far, the supply of energy has been measured in terms of ATP molecules. Utilization, on the other hand, is measured in terms of mechanical work, chemical work, and many other forms of activity. Evidently, before comparative statements can be made about supply and demand, a common yardstick should be available.

Such a yardstick is *heat*. This is the cheapest and most usual form of energy. All other forms of energy

16

CELLULAR METABOLISM: ENERGY UTILIZATION

can be converted into heat, and any energy quantity may therefore be expressed as a **heat equivalent.** Two or more of these equivalents may then be compared directly. The unit of measurement here is the **Calorie.** One Calorie (or **Cal**) is defined as that quantity of heat which would raise the temperature of one liter of water (about four-fifths of one quart) by one degree centigrade. For example, to raise the temperature of a liter of water from the freezing point to the boiling point would require 100 Cal.

What is the energy content of a metabolic fuel expressed in heat equivalents? To determine this, one simply burns the fuel in a laboratory furnace and measures the total heat given off. By such means, it is found that, for example, 1 g of glucose, or of carbohydrates generally, contains 3.8 Cal. A gram of protein liberates roughly the same amount of heat, namely, 4 Cal, and a gram of fat yields about 9 Cal. Table 6 lists the heat equivalents, or "caloric values," of some common foods.

These values show how much energy is *potentially* available in given quantities of fuel. In cells, does all this energy become *actually* available in the form of ATP? In other words, how efficient is respiration? How much of the energy content of fuels can be harvested as useful chemical energy? We know from the preceding chapter that cellular combustion of, for example, 1 molecule of glucose yields 40 molecules of ATP. It can be shown that, when all the molecules in 1 g of glucose are burned in cells, the total amount of energy trapped as ATP is equivalent to 2.5 Cal. Since 1 g of glucose contains an energy potential of 3.8 Cal, as noted, the efficiency of respiration is 2.5/3.8, or 67 per cent (Fig. 16.1).

This is a most remarkable efficiency level. The very best man-made machines can use barely 40 per cent of the energy potential of fuel. In respiration, the 33 per cent of fuel energy not stored as ATP represents unavoidable energy loss through heat dissipation. But even this energy is not entirely wasted, as we shall see.

We note that if an organism is supplied with 100 Cal, through the medium of a slice of bread (see Table 6), for example, then ATP energy equivalent to about 67 Cal will become available for cellular metabolism. How far does such an amount of energy go toward support of life? To answer this, we must know the rate of energy expenditure of an organism under specified conditions of activity.

To assess this expenditure, could one not simply determine the energy content of all the food photosynthesized or eaten during a stated period? No, because all this food is normally not used toward energy production. An indeterminable fraction may be stored, another fraction may be used in protoplasmic construction rather than in respiration, and some food may also be eliminated unused. Moreover, an organism very often manufactures or eats more food, or less food, than actually needed. Clearly then, the amount of energy supplied by food is not a reliable measure of energy requirements.

A much better measure is **oxygen consumption.** Atmospheric oxygen is not stored, it is used specifically in respiration only, and it is inhaled in amounts geared precisely to actual requirements; as we have seen in Chap. 14, breathing rates are proportional to respiration rates. Furthermore, one can easily determine how much fuel may be burned with the aid of a given quantity of oxygen. For example, 1 l of oxygen will support complete combustion of 1.25 g of glucose.

Therefore, to determine the energy requirement

TABLE 6. Caloric values of some common foods

1 "complete" ice-cream sundae	500
1 glass of milk	200
1 tablespoon mayonnaise	100
1 boiled egg	75
1 doughnut	200
1 slice of bread	100
1 plain cookie	50
1 teaspoon sugar	20
1 frankfurter	100
1 broiled lamb chop	100
1 small slice roast beef	100
1 strip crisp bacon	30
1 average serving navy beans	300
1 boiled medium potato	100
1 average serving peas	50
1 average serving plain lettuce	10
1 banana	100
1 small apple	50
1 medium tomato	20
1 cherry	10

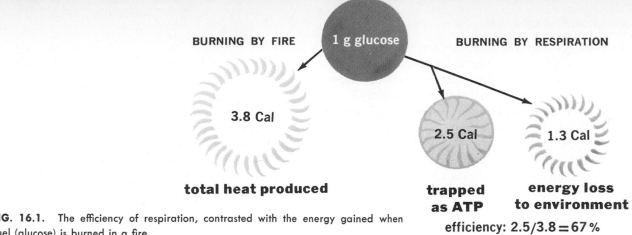

BURNING BY FIRE   1 g glucose   BURNING BY RESPIRATION

3.8 Cal

2.5 Cal   1.3 Cal

total heat produced   **trapped as ATP**   **energy loss to environment**

FIG. 16.1. The efficiency of respiration, contrasted with the energy gained when fuel (glucose) is burned in a fire.

efficiency: 2.5/3.8 = 67 %

of an organism, it is necessary to specify, first, the activity to be carried out by the organism; second, the period of time during which this activity is to be maintained; and third, the amount of oxygen consumed during this period.

BASAL METABOLISM

Most actual measurements of energy requirements have been made on man, but the same procedures apply in principle to any organism, plant or animal. The conditions chosen are often those of *basal* metabolism, that is, when body activity is reduced to a minimum. The test subject is at complete physical and mental rest, as during quiet sleep, and the digestive system is empty. Oxygen consumption is then measured over a given period of time. Under such conditions, the energy that is expended by the test subject represents his **basal metabolic rate, BMR** for short. It indicates the energy necessary *just* to remain alive during complete rest or sleep: the energy required to maintain minimum breathing and heartbeat, minimum activity of brain, liver, kidneys, and all other vital organs, and minimum respiration and chemical syntheses in all cells.

Many years of testing have shown that, under basal conditions, a human adult consumes on an average about 14 l of oxygen per hour. Since 1 l burns 1.25 g of glucose, and since 1 g of glucose yields 3.8 Cal, the energy expenditure will be 14 × 1.25 × 3.8, or 66.5 Cal. In other words, a slice of

bread of 100 Cal will supply just enough effective energy to keep an adult alive during 1 hr of sleep.

BMR values vary widely. A growing child expends more energy per pound of tissue than a nongrowing adult. A male metabolizes slightly more intensely than a female. If the temperature of the environment is low, more energy is expended toward maintenance of constant body temperature. A short, thin person possesses a large skin area in proportion to his volume, and he uses more energy to offset the greater heat loss through surface radiation and evaporation. Because of such variables, BMR determinations in practice are rather more complicated than implied above, and much more than oxygen consumption must be measured.

BMR in fact varies not only with age, sex, weight, height, season, and climate. It also varies with race and, above all, with the state of health of the organism. During disease, BMR values may become abnormally low or high, and this may sometimes be a clue to the nature of the disease. An abnormal BMR usually indicates that the utilization or the combustion of foods is somehow defective. This is the case in diabetes, for example, where insulin production is inadequate and glucose utilization is impaired. Or respiration within cells could be impaired as a result of vitamin B deficiencies, or because of improper functioning of the thyroid gland. Indeed, BMR measurements are made frequently when diseases of this sort are suspected.

Conditions are not basal when the body is active. Energy requirements then are greater, in proportion to the intensity or the amount of activity. Thinking, speaking, sitting, eating, walking, chopping wood, or merely keeping one's eyes open, all raise the energy requirement beyond BMR levels. Table 7 lists the requirements of various kinds of activities. It will be noted that profound thinking (sedentary work) comes cheap in terms of energy. This does not mean that brainwork is valued low in the scheme of nature. On the contrary, animals have become so adapted that cerebration, like heartbeat and other essential processes, is guaranteed even if only a minimum of energy is available.

From the figures in Table 7, *daily* energy requirements may be calculated. For example,

	College student	Lumber-jack
8 hr sleep, at 70 Cal per hr	560	560
12 hr sedentary work, at 100 Cal	1200	
2 hr walking and light work, at 200 Cal	400	
2 hr athletics, at 500 Cal	1000	
8 hr heavy work, at 500 Cal		4000
8 hr sedentary occupation, at 100 Cal		800
Daily total	3160 Cal	5360 Cal

The requirement of the college student could be satisfied by a little over 1 lb of butter a day: 1 lb butter = 454 g fat → about 4100 Cal; and at 67 per cent efficiency, 4100 Cal provide about 2750 Cal. But it should be clear that such an intake would not represent an adequate diet. Additional food is needed for protoplasmic synthesis, and this, as well as respiration itself, requires a wide *variety* of foods, from minerals and water to vitamins and essential amino acids. The caloric value of a diet is only *one* aspect of adequate nutrition.

The energy expended daily by an organism sustains both the chemical and the physical metabolism of all cells. Among animals, physical requirements use up a particularly large share of the available energy, for the energy cost of internal and external *movement* is high. Largely because of movement, energy requirements are comparatively far greater in animals than in plants. How is the energy of foods and ATP translated into movement, and into physical work in general?

Physical Functions of Energy

MUSCULAR CONTRACTION

As outlined in Chap. 9, muscular contraction is the basis of the most widespread form of movement in living systems. Muscular contraction also ranks among the most important activities of cells generally, for few animal functions exist that do not include it. For example, it is the muscular system which maintains breathing, heartbeat, blood pressure, posture, and shape, even during "inactive" periods like sleep. Moreover, muscles are quantitatively the most conspicuous components of animals. For example, in an animal such as man, as much as one-third of the body is muscle. A proportionate amount of all available energy therefore must be expended to keep muscles contracting.

The Contractile Units

The functional units of all kinds of muscles are long, thin, intracellular filaments called **myofibrils.** Each muscle cell or muscle fiber contains many of such myofibrils, aligned in parallel and extending in the same direction as the long axis of the whole cell or fiber (Fig. 16.2). In striated muscles (see Chap. 9), the myofibrils exhibit alternate dark and light crossbands, visible under the microscope. When such a muscle contracts, only the dark bands become shorter. The total contraction is the sum of all the individual contractions of the dark bands.

The electron microscope shows that each myofibril is actually a bundle of many long, ultrathin,

TABLE 7. Caloric requirements during various activities, performed continuously for 1 hr

Basal activity (sleep)	70
Sitting at rest	100
Walking (leisurely)	200
Moderately active work (carpentry)	250
Walking down stairs	350
Sawing wood	450
Swimming	500
Very fast running	600
Walking up stairs	1100 (!)

parallel filaments. These are composed principally of four kinds of materials: water, inorganic ions, ATP, and a protein called **actomyosin.** Together, these form the basic contraction apparatus.

That this is so has been demonstrated dramatically by experiment. With appropriate procedures, actomyosin can be extracted from muscle and can be fashioned into artificial fibers. These may be put into a water bath containing inorganic ions, and some ATP may then be added. When this is done, it is found that, as soon as ATP reaches an actomyosin fiber, the latter contracts violently! Indeed, such fibers may lift up to 1,000 times their own weight, just as a living muscle may do. And it is also found that, in a contracted fiber, ATP is no longer present, but that ADP is present instead.

Such experiments suggest how contraction may be brought about in a living muscle. The process is far from being fully understood, but from available data a preliminary hypothesis of the main events may be formulated. It is known, for example, that muscle activity is at least a two-step cycle, involving alternate **extension** and **contraction.** The action pattern in many ways resembles the stretching and releasing of a rubber band. Thus, when a rubber band is stretched, energy is supplied from the outside, and the stretched band then is rich in *potential* energy.

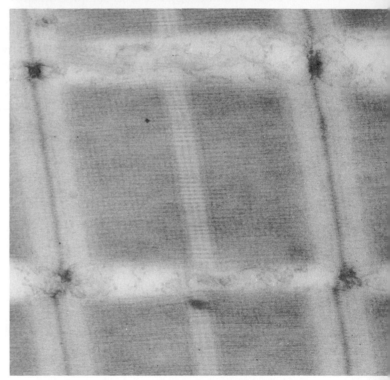

FIG. 16.2. The structure of skeletal muscle. A whole muscle fiber is shown at the top. Note here the cross striations, the internal longitudinal myofibrils, and the many nuclei, which appear as dark patches. The bottom photo is an electron micrograph of a few individual myofibrils. Note that each myofibril in turn consists of bundles of still finer fibrils. These latter are the functional units of the contraction apparatus. Note again the prominent cross striations. (Top, General Biological Supply House, Inc.; bottom, courtesy of Dr. K. R. Porter, Rockefeller Institute.)

FIG. 16.3. The basic contraction-extension cycle of muscle activity.

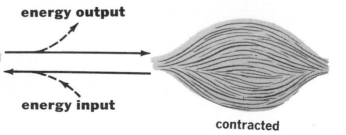

extended

contracted

When released, the band snaps together, and, in this, the potential energy becomes actual and is spent in the mechanical work of contraction. Similarly in muscle. External energy must first be put into a muscle to extend it, and this energy is spent subsequently during contraction. Like a rubber band, muscle is shorter and thicker when contracting, longer and thinner when extending (Fig. 16.3).

The Energy Cycle

The energy donor in muscle contraction is ATP. Experiments indicate that ATP is associated intimately with actomyosin, and indeed the two are present as an actomyosin-ATP complex. Moreover, ATP appears to be not only an energy donor but also a necessary *structural* part of the contraction mechanism; ATP makes actomyosin supple and elastic and *able* to contract at all. When ATP separates from actomyosin, as, for example, after death, during rigor mortis, muscle becomes rigid and stiff.

In contraction, the ATP of actomyosin-ATP yields up its energy, and actomyosin-ADP thereby forms. To extend and "recharge" a muscle, new energy must be supplied from the outside. Respiration is the ultimate source of this energy; but it is not the immediate source. Fast though combustion of muscle glycogen is, it is far too slow to supply the ATP required by an active muscle. A glycogen molecule in muscle may burn within a second, but in that second the wing muscle of an insect may contract up to 100 times and use up energy far faster than could be supplied directly by fuel combustion.

It is here that the phosphagen stores of muscle serve their special function. As will be recalled from Chap. 15, phosphagens are $\sim$ⓅⓇ donors present particularly in muscle. During periods of relative muscular inactivity, fuel combustion in muscle may supply more energy than needed. High-energy phosphates from fuel are then transferred via ATP into phosphagens, which are present in much larger quantity than ATP itself. Conversely, during intense activity, fuel combustion in muscle may be too slow relative to energy requirements, and the energy stored in phosphagen is then transferred back into ATP. Thus, in recharging a muscle, phosphagen interacts with contracted actomyosin-ADP, energy is transferred, and actomyosin-ATP is reformed. The muscle extends at the same time and so becomes ready to contract again. These energy relationships are summarized in Fig. 16.4.

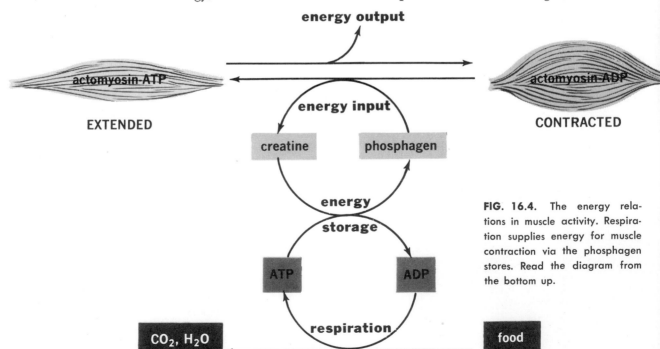

FIG. 16.4. The energy relations in muscle activity. Respiration supplies energy for muscle contraction via the phosphagen stores. Read the diagram from the bottom up.

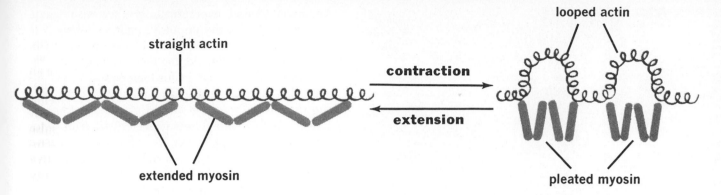

FIG. 16.5.   A symbolization of the molecular mechanics of muscle activity. Contraction may be imagined to occur through a pleating of myosin molecules, which would shorten the continuous actin fibril. The scheme is still hypothetical in many particulars.

The Contraction Cycle

What mechanical processes take place when a muscle contracts and extends? This aspect of muscle activity is as yet known very inadequately. Actomyosin can be decomposed chemically into two protein fractions, *actin* and *myosin*. According to one view, actin may be a continuous fiber running through the whole length of a muscle cell. At intervals along such a "rope," short sections of myosin may be attached. This protein is envisaged to consist of chains of molecules which can be pleated accordion-fashion, so that a pull or push on the ends would elongate or shorten the chain (Fig. 16.5). Muscle contraction would occur when the "pleats" of myosin fold together. The actin fiber would then loop out where myosin is attached, and this would shorten and thicken the whole muscle cell. Extension of muscle would involve a stretching out of the myosin pleats and a lengthening of the actin fiber.

What would cause a pleating and unpleating of myosin? Here again, answers are still hypothetical and speculative. Three bits of information are probably significant. First, it is known that muscle contraction begins by a *nerve impulse* (Fig. 16.6). Second, it is known that inorganic ions are attached to myosin and that myosin therefore carries electric surface charges. These charges may be arranged so that the outside of a myosin fiber is either electro-

positive or electronegative, and the inside the opposite. For example,

So charged, myosin would be electrically neutral as a whole, but it would possess an **electrical potential** over its surface.

Third, it is known that actomyosin, and probably the myosin fraction in particular, functions as an enzyme. Specifically, actomyosin is an **ATP-ase**, an enzyme which splits ATP into ADP and $\sim$Ⓟ. Several kinds of ATP-ases are known to occur in different tissues, and whenever ATP becomes ADP or vice versa, as in respiratory reactions, a particular ATP-ase is known to be at work. In muscle, ATP-ase is found also. And either this enzyme is so closely linked with actomyosin that available techniques cannot separate the two, or it is, in fact, identical with actomyosin itself. Evidently, the actomyosin-ATP complex possesses not only built-in potential energy in the form of ATP but also the necessary built-in enzyme which may make this energy available.

The following events might then take place during muscle contraction. Initially, because of their electric charges, myosin fibers would be kept in an

FIG. 16.6. The structural connection between nerve and muscle. Individual nerve fibers terminate at individual muscle fibers by means of motor endplates, shown in the photo as aggregations of small dark granules. Nerve impulses are delivered to muscles via such endplates. (Ward's Natural Science Establishment, Inc.)

extended, unpleated state. For if charged myosin were to fold, the like charges on the outside would be brought very closely together. And since like charges repel each other, electric repulsion would cause a restretching of the fiber. In effect, myosin would be maintained in a stretched state so long as the electric potential over its surface were in existence. A nerve impulse now arrives. This probably has at least two consequences.

First, directly or through unknown intermediary processes, the impulse apparently neutralizes or reduces the electric potential of myosin. The plus and minus charges may somehow be permitted to combine pairwise through the myosin surface. That muscular contraction is accompanied by a reduction of electric potentials in muscle is well known and can

be demonstrated experimentally (see also Chap. 21). And second, the impulse might somehow "activate" the enzymatic capacities of actomyosin. In an extended, resting muscle, the actomyosin-ATP complex exists without change for long periods. This implies that actomyosin is enzymatically inactive during that time. Now, the arrival of a nerve impulse must somehow bring about an activation of actomyosin. However this may be achieved, the active enzyme then splits ATP, and so the potential energy of actomyosin-ATP becomes actual.

This energy, together with the reduction of electric potentials in myosin, may make possible a forceful pleating of the myosin fibers. We may reiterate here that the actual details and sequences of events after nervous stimulation are unknown. But it is known generally that nerve impulse, reduction of electric potentials, energy release, and muscle contraction do go together.

Conversely, muscle extension and recovery may be brought about by a rebuilding of electric potentials on myosin. This would stretch the fiber by electric repulsion. At the same time, new energy is supplied by phosphagen, ATP is re-formed, and actomyosin must once more become inactive as an enzyme. How such inactivation is achieved again is not known. The whole contraction cycle, evidently still hypothetical in many particulars, is summarized in Fig. 16.7. Duplicated trillions of times in all the contractile units of the muscular system, cycles of this sort take place fast enough to propel a cheetah at 50 miles per hour, and powerfully enough to permit many animals, man included, to lift objects weighing more than the animals themselves.

Fatigue

Muscular activity clearly can continue only as long as the energy stores of phosphagen last. For if all phosphagen has been exhausted, actomyosin-ATP cannot be regenerated, and muscle becomes fatigued. As noted in Chap. 15, fatigue is associated with comparative oxygen lack, fermentation, and lactic acid accumulation. Muscle can contract in the complete absence of oxygen so long as fermentation alone can maintain the phosphagen stores, and so long as lactic acid concentrations are not excessive.

Indeed, muscle normally probably respires anaerobically as well as aerobically, and any lactic acid formed can be carried off by blood as fast as it appears. Lactic acid tends to accumulate only during intense activity, and increasing fatigue then brings the activity to a halt sooner or later. Aerobic combustion of muscle glycogen subsequently continues at a rapid pace, and depleted phosphagen stores are replenished. At the same time, as outlined in Chap. 15 (Fig. 15.16), lactic acid slowly diffuses into the blood, becomes liver glycogen, and returns to muscle and other tissues as blood glucose.

OTHER PHYSICAL FUNCTIONS

Muscular motion is not the only form of movement among living systems. As we have seen

(Chap. 9), ciliary, flagellary, and ameboid movements are widespread too. In all these, ATP again appears to be the common energy source. But the action cycles here are understood even less well than those of muscular contraction. Some evidence suggests that the beat of cilia and of flagella is produced by alternate contraction and relaxation of ultrafine protein filaments. If so, a machinery essentially like that of muscle may conceivably be involved. Contractile protein fibrils energized by ATP also may play a role in the movements of chromosomes during cell division (see Chap. 23).

But the energizing of *mechanical* cell functions is not the only physical role of ATP. Production of **heat**, of **light**, and of **electricity** is an additional household task of many a cell type, and ATP is the energy donor here too.

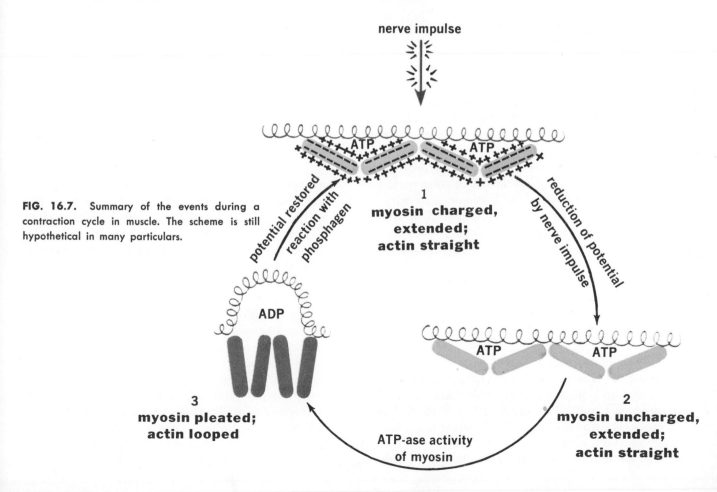

FIG. 16.7. Summary of the events during a contraction cycle in muscle. The scheme is still hypothetical in many particulars.

nerve impulse

ATP   ATP

potential restored
reaction with
phosphagen

reduction of potential
by nerve impulse

1
myosin charged,
extended;
actin straight

ADP

ATP   ATP

3
myosin pleated;
actin looped

2
myosin uncharged,
extended;
actin straight

ATP-ase activity
of myosin

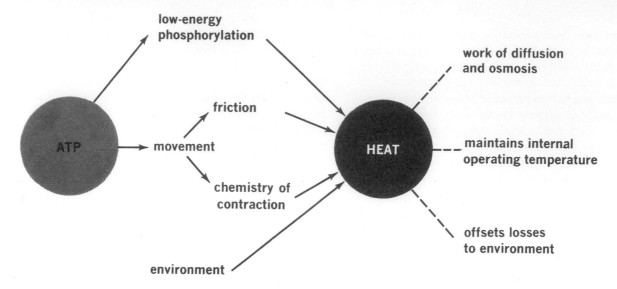

FIG. 16.8. The principal sources and functions of heat in organisms.

Heat Production

One source of heat has already been referred to in the last chapter: if the high-energy phosphate of ATP is used in low-energy phosphorylations, then any excess energy of $\sim$ⓟ becomes heat. Another source is ATP-energized movement, muscular or otherwise. For friction of moving parts generates heat. Moreover, ATP is not used with 100 per cent efficiency in the production of movement. For example, muscular contraction is accompanied by a loss of energy, and this energy dissipates into the body in the form of heat.

Added to whatever heat is supplied by the external environment, ATP-derived heat maintains body temperature and offsets heat lost to the environment by evaporation and radiation; creates tiny convection currents within cells, and so assists in diffusion and osmosis in and among cells; and provides adequate operating temperatures for enzymes and all other functional parts of cells. As noted in Chap. 9, heat production in birds and mammals is balanced dynamically against heat loss, and a constant protoplasmic temperature is thereby maintained. But constant or not, heat is an essential requirement of every acting system, and if ATP served no other function than heat production, it would still be among the most vitally necessary components of protoplasm (Fig. 16.8).

Bioluminescence

Living light is emitted by virtually all major groups of organisms. Bacteria, fungi, algae, and practically all animal phyla include marine or terrestrial representatives which are bioluminescent. Evidently, the capacity to produce light has developed several times independently during evolution. Yet the essentials of the light-generating mechanism appear to be alike in all cases.

This mechanism consists of at least six components: water, inorganic ions, oxygen, ATP, and two groups of substances called, respectively, **luciferin** and **luciferase.** These last differ in composition in different species. Luciferin and the enzyme luciferase are the principal light-generating elements. They can be extracted from light-producing cells, and they are nonluminous on their own. If ATP is added to luciferin, a luciferin-ATP complex is formed. If, in the presence of ions and oxygen, a solution of luciferase is now added, the mixture

FIG. 16.9. The general pattern of light production in bioluminescent organisms.

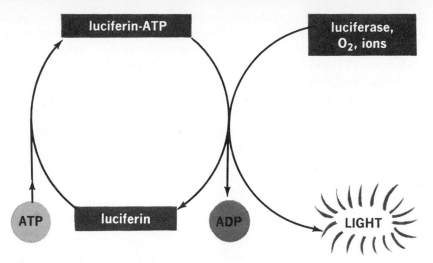

emits a flash of light. At the same time, oxygen is used up, and ATP becomes ADP. If more oxygen and more ATP are added, a new flash of light is generated. Light production evidently is an oxygen-requiring, ATP-dependent process (Fig. 16.9).

Bioluminescent bacteria and fungi may stay lit up continuously, but most animal light producers flash discontinuously (Fig. 16.10). The emission of a flash here depends on nervous stimulation of specialized cells in the light-producing organs (see Chap. 5, Fig. 5.8). The light emitted by different organisms may be of any wavelength in the visible spectrum, that is, to the human eye it may be red, yellow, green, or blue. Little or no nonvisible radiation is generated. The actual wavelength of the emission is probably determined by the particular chemical make-up of luciferin. In some cases, two or more kinds of luciferin may occur in a single organism, and such an organism then may light up in several colors. In all cases, the available energy is spent very efficiently, for little heat is lost during light production. Hence the frequent designation of living light as "cold" light. Also, the unit intensity of the light is remarkably great. It compares favorably with that of modern fluorescent lamps.

Bioelectricity

Bioelectricity is a byproduct of all protoplasmic processes in which ions play a part. In other words,

electricity is as common throughout the living world as table salt. However, certain eels and rays are highly specialized in their capacity to produce electricity. These fish possess *electric organs,* composed mainly of modified muscles. The component cells are disk-shaped, noncontractile, and they are piled into stacks. Assemblies of this sort have the appearance and the function of storage batteries connected in series.

FIG. 16.10. Test-tube culture of bioluminescent bacteria. The continuous light they emit is strong enough to illuminate a portion of a printed page. (Carolina Biological Supply Co.)

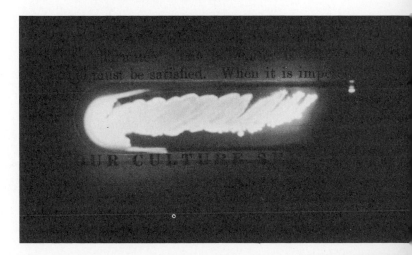

The details of operation here are understood less well than those of light production. However, it is known that the generation of electricity depends on ATP and a substance called **acetyl-choline.** This chemical will be encountered again later, for it functions widely as a key agent in the transmission of nerve impulses. It also functions in the generation of bioelectricity. This event is apparently accompanied by a splitting of acetyl-choline into separate acetyl and choline fractions. The two are then recombined into acetyl-choline, with energy from ATP:

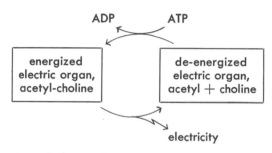

As in light production, the efficiency of energy utilization is remarkably great. So also is the intensity of the electricity generated. An electric eel may deliver a shock of up to 400 volts, enough to kill another fish, or to jolt a man severely, or to light up a row of electric bulbs wired to a tank into which such an eel is put. Nervous stimulation of the electric organ triggers the production of electricity.

It is still unknown just how the chemical energy of ATP is actually converted into light energy or electrical energy. But that ATP is the key is clearly established, and this versatile compound emerges as the source of all forms of living physical energy, usual or unusual (Fig. 16.11). Indeed, ATP is even more versatile, for it is also the source of all living *chemical* energy.

Chemical Functions of Energy

THE PATTERN OF SYNTHESIS

Breakdown of organic compounds leads to a net build-up of ATP, through respiration. Breakdown of ATP leads either to physical activity as discussed above, or to a net build-up of organic compounds, through chemical *synthesis*. Figure 16.12 outlines this basic balance of energy and materials, which governs the overall metabolism of all cells.

Synthesis of protoplasm and breakdown occur simultaneously, all the time. As already noted in the last chapter, breakdown may affect any proto-

FIG. 16.11. General summary of the functions of ATP.

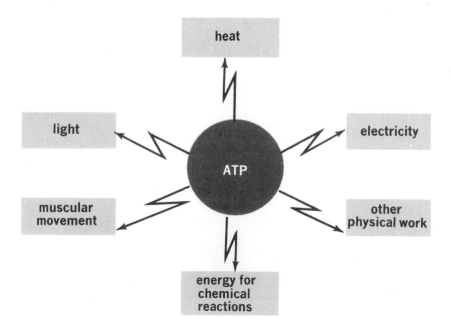

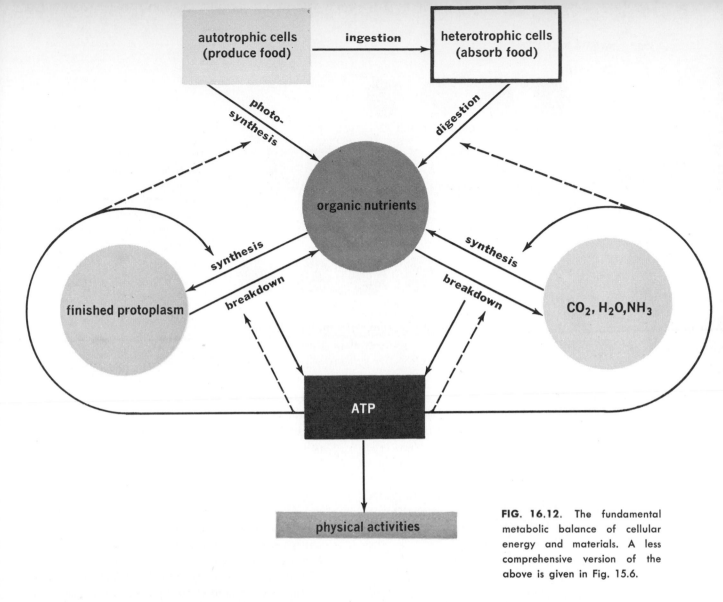

FIG. 16.12. The fundamental metabolic balance of cellular energy and materials. A less comprehensive version of the above is given in Fig. 15.6.

plasmic constituent regardless of composition or age. A protein just synthesized through long reaction sequences, and at great expense of energy, is as likely to be destroyed as a glucose molecule already present for days. A certain *percentage* of all cellular constituents is decomposed every second, and which constituents actually make up this percentage is largely a matter of chance.

Such randomness applies also to synthesis. Regardless of the source of materials, a certain percentage of available molecular components is synthesized every second into finished protoplasm. If synthesis and breakdown are exactly balanced, the

net character of a cell may remain unchanged. But continuous **turnover** of energy and materials occurs nevertheless, and every brick in the building is sooner or later replaced by a new one. Thus the house always remains "fresh."

Synthesis and breakdown cannot sustain each other in a self-contained, self-sufficient cycle, even when the two processes are exactly balanced. For energy dissipates irretrievably through physical activities and through heat losses in chemical reactions. And materials dissipate through elimination, evaporation, and friction. Just to maintain a steady state, therefore, a cell must be supplied continuously

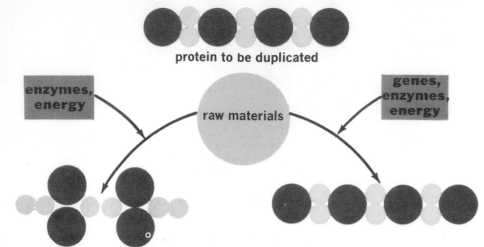

protein to be duplicated

enzymes, energy

raw materials

genes, enzymes, energy

new protein does not match original: gene-control absent

new protein does match original: gene-control present

FIG. 16.13. Illustrating the requirement of specificity control in protein synthesis. Without gene control, the structural pattern of new proteins would not match the pattern of preexisting proteins.

with energy and raw materials: solar energy, CO_2, and water in the case of photosynthesizing cells, and in the case of all other cells, condensed packages of these three, namely, organic nutrients. Very often, moreover, the rate of supply of such materials must exceed the rate required for mere maintenance, for net synthesis may exceed net breakdown: in growth, in repair after injury, and in many specialized secreting cells, which manufacture materials for export to other cells.

With certain important exceptions, synthesis reactions generally are the exact reverse of breakdown reactions. Almost invariably, they *require* ATP rather than yield it. And whereas energy-yielding breakdown revolves largely around carbohydrates and fats, protoplasm-yielding synthesis revolves largely around proteins and fats.

PROTEIN SYNTHESIS

Protein synthesis is the key to cellular maintenance and self-perpetuation, for proteins are the most important organic components of cell structure and cell function. Not only do they make up the skeleton of the protoplasmic framework, but they also serve as enzymes and, in the form of nucleo-

proteins, as the fundamental regulators of cellular characteristics. The very nature of a cell depends largely on its proteins, and the kinds of proteins a cell contains are themselves traits regulated by proteins, namely, nucleoproteins.

Specificity and Genes

What sets protein synthesis apart from most other syntheses is the condition of **specificity,** already referred to in Chap. 7. Glycogen, for example, is more or less always the same, no matter where or when it is found. To synthesize it in cells, the essential requirement is only glucose or a glucose derivative, energy, and an enzyme capable of linking glucose molecules together. Proteins, however, are decidedly not the same everywhere or at any time. The proteins, and especially the nucleoproteins, of two cell types or organisms are never identical. Moreover, the development of a cell, or of an organism, is largely a story of *changing* protein composition. Proteins are *source-specific* as well as *time-specific*.

Therefore, more is needed for the synthesis of a protein than for the synthesis of any other type of compound. Energy, amino acid raw materials, and enzymes capable of linking amino acids together are the first requirements. But this cannot be all. For the enzymes are capable merely of *combining* amino acids, and they do not regulate the **pattern** of the combinations. A protein formed without pattern control would be neither source-specific nor time-specific, and it would not have the same properties as the cellular protein which is to be replaced or duplicated. Since faithful copying of preexisting proteins is essential for the maintenance of cell character, protein synthesis evidently requires another ingredient, in addition to energy, amino acids, and enzymes. It requires an agent which controls the pattern of amino acid linkage, an agent, in short, which confers specificity.

As indicated in Fig. 16.13, the ultimate guardians of specificity in a cell are nucleoproteins, in particular the **genes,** carriers of hereditary characteristics. We shall see in Chap. 18 how these vital nucleoproteins function. Here we shall simply take their specificity-controlling role for granted. Note that protein *breakdown,* like the breakdown of any other compound, can occur without immediate participation of genes. For the precise patterns of breakdown are relatively unimportant, so long as breakdown is accomplished in *some* way. Pattern becomes important only in *building.* That is why protein synthesis is not necessarily the reverse of protein breakdown. And that is also why the synthesis of most other protoplasmic components *is* essentially the reverse of their breakdown and does not require direct gene action. For, no matter in what sequence an enzyme links 12 glucose molecules together, the result will be the same glycogen. All glucose molecules are alike, and any sequence of joining them will yield the same product.

Amino Acid to Protein

All proteins existing on earth trace back to amino acids manufactured by plants. In the general structure of an amino acid (NH_2—R—COOH), the —R—COOH part is prepared in plant cells from carbohydrate and fatty starting materials, as outlined in the preceding chapter (Chap. 15, Figs. 15.20 and 15.24). Out of hundreds of theoretical possibilities, plants produce just 23 different kinds of —R—COOH's. Why only 23? Why these particular

23? The answers are unknown. If the first living system on earth had contained other amino acids, life today might be radically different from what it is.

Plant cells manufacture the amino fraction (NH_2—) from nitrate ions which are absorbed as mineral nutrients (see Chap. 5). Once produced, NH_2— and —R—COOH may be combined into amino acids. Animal cells may make such combinations also, but they can manufacture neither the NH_2— groups nor the 8 or 10 essential —R—COOH groups. These components must enter animal food chains from plants, in prefabricated form. Nonessential —R—COOH groups may be constructed in animals as in plants, from carbohydrate and fatty starting materials (see Chap. 15).

Given 23 varieties of amino acids, every plant or animal cell—but no biochemist as yet—is capable of synthesizing proteins. This function is performed largely, if not exclusively, in the **microsomes,** extremely fine granules dispersed abundantly throughout the cytoplasm of a cell (see Chap. 7). Again we find an important biochemical activity being carried out in specialized "factory" locations. The microsomes contain all the necessary chemical equipment for protein synthesis, including, as we shall see, the crucial specificity-controlling agents.

Disregarding this problem of specificity control for the time being, the chaining together of amino acids is the reverse of protein digestion. Whole proteins become individual amino acids by progressive *hydrolysis,* that is, addition of water (see Chap. 12); and amino acids become whole proteins by progressive *dehydration,* or removal of water:

Two amino acids joined as above form a *dipeptide;* and the —CO—NH— group here is called a

peptide link. Several dipeptides may subsequently combine into *peptones, proteoses,* and *polypeptides,* and a number of these ultimately give rise to a whole protein molecule (Fig. 16.14).

If this linking process is indeed the reverse of digestion in the gut, the same enzymes which accelerate digestion should also be effective in cellular synthesis. This is the case. Proteinases such as pepsin, trypsin, or chymotrypsin speed up the reaction in either direction, but conditions of energetics and mass action in the alimentary tract are such that the breakdown reaction is favored. Within cells, the proteinases are called **cathepsins,** and they are very similar to, or perhaps the same as, the alimentary ones. In cells, however, energetics and mass action

permit the synthesis reaction to occur as readily as the reverse. After death, on the other hand, ATP is no longer formed, synthesis therefore cannot occur, and cathepsins then digest cellular proteins rather than build them.

Protein synthesis appears to be an "all or none" phenomenon. It can take place only if all required amino acids are available in a cell simultaneously. If the acids arrive a few at a time, construction cannot proceed part way and later continue to completion. This is probably correlated with the structural complexity of the compounds formed. If the building blocks were all alike, stepwise synthesis might be possible, since the blocks could be used interchangeably. But the building blocks are not alike,

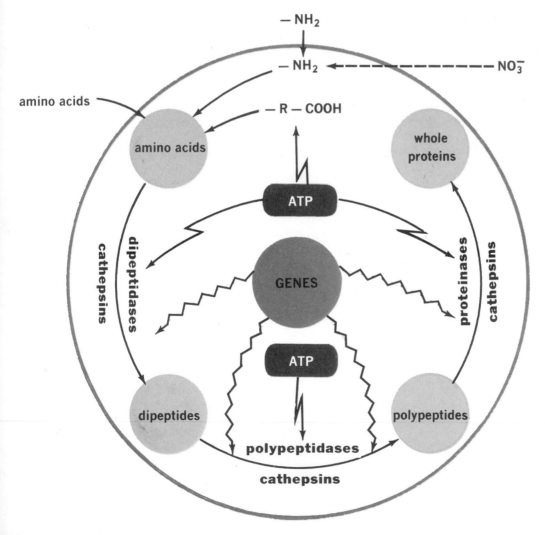

FIG. 16.14. The pattern of protein synthesis in cells. Amino acids are either supplied as food or are synthesized from simpler raw materials directly within a cell. These acids are then built up into whole proteins, with energy from ATP, the catalytic action of enzymes, and the pattern control of genes.

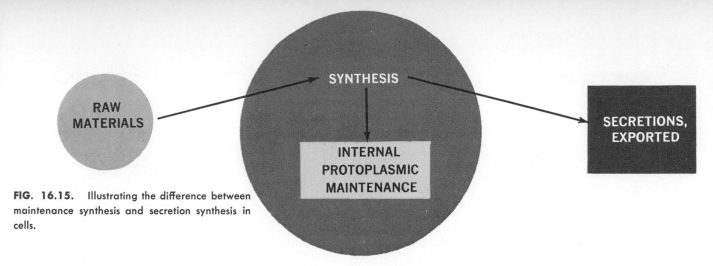

FIG. 16.15. Illustrating the difference between maintenance synthesis and secretion synthesis in cells.

and, as everyone knows, a single missing screw of a particular type may well prevent the assembly of a complex machine.

Finished proteins add to, or replace parts of, cellular components. For example, by virtue of its particular specificity, a protein may become incorporated into fibrils, membranes, mitochondria, chloroplasts, or indeed any other cellular structure. Alternatively, the properties of a newly formed protein might be such that it may come to function as a particular enzyme, or as a raw material in the synthesis of protein-containing complexes, e.g., nucleoproteins, hemoglobin, certain hormones, and many other vital compounds.

OTHER SYNTHESES

Maintenance Syntheses

The synthesis of polysaccharides and fats has already been discussed. For, read in reverse, the respiratory reactions outlined in the preceding chapter describe such syntheses adequately. Moreover, the same enzymes, vitamins, and other reaction aids function at the same steps in the reversed sequences. Like proteins, fats and carbohydrates too become part of the structural and functional make-up of cells. In addition, they also serve importantly as storage materials and, together with proteins, as source materials for the construction of the innumerable other compounds of protoplasm.

A cell actually contains comparatively few proteins, carbohydrates, and fats as such. For most protoplasmic chemicals are direct or indirect derivatives of these three categories of substances. The manufacture of such derivatives occurs largely through special reaction sequences, and the details in most cases still require experimental analysis.

But although the synthetic processes are poorly known, the products are known fairly well. Some of these products occur in all cells, and we have encountered a few of them in foregoing chapters: ADP, DPN, creatine, cytochrome, and others. Some syntheses are restricted to specific, variously specialized cell types. A good example of this is the production of chlorophyll, and of pigments in general, in particular cell types only. Characteristic synthesis products of certain tissues, plant tissues especially, have often proved to be useful to man—rubber, quinine, caffeine, nicotine, to mention only a few. It is still largely unknown what functions, if any, such substances might have in the very cells in which they are manufactured. Since such compounds are not formed universally in all cells, they cannot be of general significance in metabolism. In some cases at least, they probably represent unique waste products, retained in the cells of organisms which do not possess specialized excretory systems.

Secretion Syntheses

Many syntheses benefit not primarily the cells in which they occur, but other cells or body parts to which the products are exported. These are *secretion* syntheses, important both in plant and animal maintenance (Fig. 16.15). *Every* cell is a secreting cell to some extent, for, at the very least, it exports metabolic wastes. But many cells in addition manufacture specialized secretions, and these may have a variety of roles. For example, they may be **nutri-**

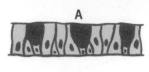

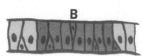

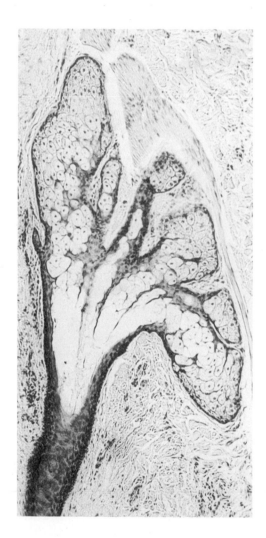

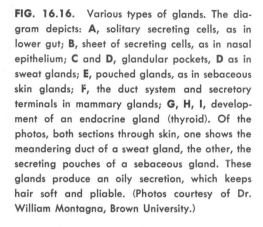

FIG. 16.16. Various types of glands. The diagram depicts: **A**, solitary secreting cells, as in lower gut; **B**, sheet of secreting cells, as in nasal epithelium; **C** and **D**, glandular pockets, **D** as in sweat glands; **E**, pouched glands, as in sebaceous skin glands; **F**, the duct system and secretory terminals in mammary glands; **G, H, I**, development of an endocrine gland (thyroid). Of the photos, both sections through skin, one shows the meandering duct of a sweat gland, the other, the secreting pouches of a sebaceous gland. These glands produce an oily secretion, which keeps hair soft and pliable. (Photos courtesy of Dr. William Montagna, Brown University.)

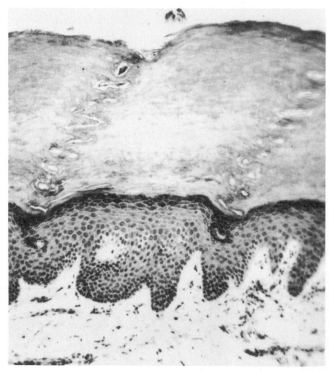

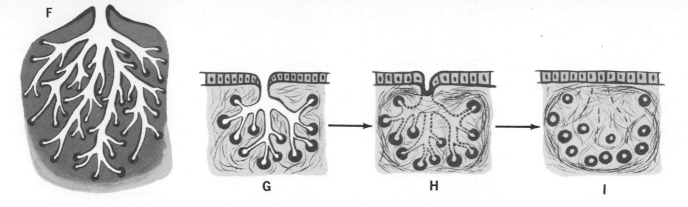

tive (e.g., glucose secreted by photosynthesizing cells), **digestive** (e.g., enzymes poured into the gut), **excretory** (e.g., urea secretion by liver), **regulative** (e.g., hormones secreted by given plant and animal cells), **supportive** (e.g., secretion of cellulose in plants, bone substance in animals), **reproductive** (e.g., aromatic attracting scents secreted by plants and animals), or variously **protective** (e.g., secretion of irritants and poisons by plants and animals, including the secretions of antibiotics by soil organisms). Indeed there are few plant or animal functions that do not require secretions of some sort.

Secreting cells in animals are generally more highly specialized than in plants. They are **gland** cells, and often they are aggregated into distinct glandular tissues or organs (Fig. 16.16). The **exocrine** glands empty their products into a free space or a duct. And the ductless **endocrine** glands secrete into the blood. Animal *hormones* are the products of endocrine glands. All other secretions are manufactured in exocrine glands.

Added to materials synthesized and used *within* a given cell, secretions received from *other* cells complete the list of ingredients required for the manufacture of cellular protoplasm. This total multitude of chemicals, built up at the expense of ATP, then maintains and perpetuates the body of a cell. But it must not be imagined that newly constructed compounds just happen to arrange themselves into new protoplasm. If the proteins, fats, and other components were merely mixed together in water, the result would be a complex but lifeless soup. As we have already noted in Chap. 7, **omnis cellula e cellula**—all cells arise from preexisting cells; all life arises from preexisting life. New protoplasmic constituents become "protoplasm" only if older protoplasm provides the framework; the house may be added to, and its parts may be replaced or modified, but an altogether new house cannot be built. That apparently occurred only once during the history of the earth.

RESUME We have completed the discussion of metabolism. Viewed from afar, this whole complex of functions rides on a powerful energy beam emanating from the sun. Our ultimate energy donor plays via photosynthesis into all the organic matter of plants and animals, radiates into ATP through respiration, and, still strong, so energizes life's process. Man's every thought actually represents a bit of the sun.

Viewed close up, metabolism is a staggering multitude of reactions and shifting chemical equilibria, of matter conversions and energy conversions, of spinning atoms and vibrating molecules. Yet when all is done, the outcome, unfailingly in each of billions of organisms and trillions of cells, is far from random. Rather, it is a highly ordered, efficient set of processes, oriented toward continued nutrition and gas exchange on the one hand, and toward continued production of energy and new protoplasm on the other (Fig. 16.17).

What creates this remarkable orientation, and what maintains it? The specific answer is processes of **control,** and the general answer, processes of **self-perpetuation.** Metabolism is one half of life; self-perpetuation is the other. The system which only metabolizes is but an inanimate machine, and an uncoordinated machine at that. To ensure internal coordination, to allow it to meet the impact of the external environment, and therefore to make it a *living* system, it must perform the processes of self-perpetuation. These make orderly metabolism possible—but they are themselves made possible by this metabolism.

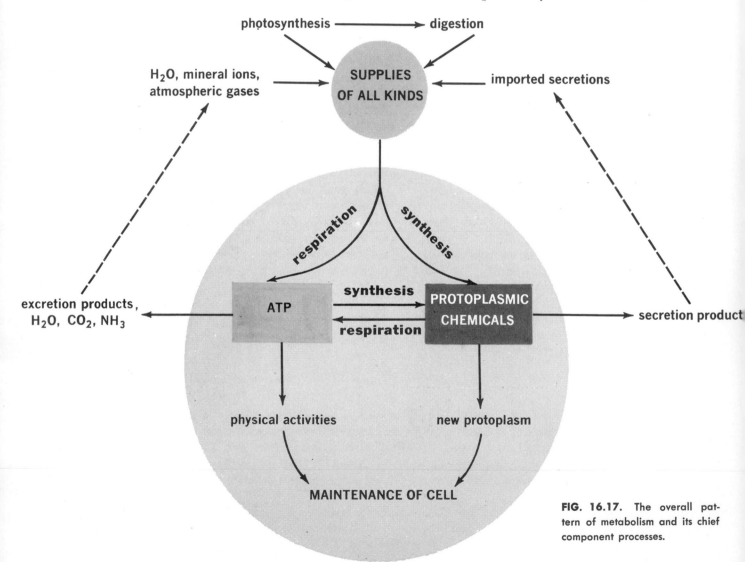

FIG. 16.17. The overall pattern of metabolism and its chief component processes.

REVIEW
QUESTIONS

1. Define Calorie, heat equivalent, BMR. Why are requirements and expenditures of protoplasmic energy often expressed in Calories? What is the "caloric value" of a given food? How much of the energy of a food is trapped by respiration, and what happens to the rest?

2. What is the relation between measurement of oxygen consumption and measurements of BMR? What is the actual rate of oxygen consumption in man? What variables affect BMR? With the help of Tables 6 and 7, work out a 24-hr diet suitable for you personally and adequate from the standpoint of both energy and food variety.

3. Describe the internal fine structure of a muscle. What, and where, is actomyosin? In what respects are the contractions of a muscle and of a piece of rubber alike?

4. What are the roles of ATP in muscle? In what specific ways is the ATP supply maintained? Describe the energetic aspects of a unit cycle of muscle activity.

5. Describe the nervous, chemical, mechanical, and electrical events which, according to current hypotheses, may conceivably occur during a unit cycle of muscle activity.

6. Describe the ways in which organisms produce heat, light, and electricity. What are the properties of bioluminescence and bioelectricity, as compared with nonliving forms of these energies?

7. Describe the basic balance of synthesis and breakdown in living organisms. How does protein specificity influence the ingredients required for protein synthesis? What are the ingredients? By what general sequence of processes, and where, does protein synthesis occur?

8. Describe the specific sequence of reactions through which acetic acid in cells could be synthesized into (a) fats and (b) glycogen or starch. If necessary, consult Chap. 15, Fig. 15.24.

9. What are the various possible functions of proteins, fats, and carbohydrates synthesized in cells? What are secretion syntheses? What is a gland, and what is the difference between exocrine and endocrine glands?

10. Review and summarize the broad components of metabolism as a whole, and review again the general relation between metabolism and self-perpetuation.

SUGGESTED
COLLATERAL
READINGS

The texts listed at the end of Chap. 13 contain accounts of various topics dealt with here. These texts may profitably be consulted for additional information on, for example, energy requirements and protoplasmic synthesis. On synthesis, see also the book by Baldwin, cited last at the end of Chap. 15. Of the readings suggested below, the first is a reprint of a famous classical paper.

Lavoisier, A., and P. Laplace: Memoir on Heat, in M. L. Gabriel and S. Fogel, "Great Experiments in Biology," Prentice-Hall, 1955.

Johnson, F. H.: Heat and Life, *Sci. American,* vol. 180, 1949.

Szent-Gyorgyi, A.: Muscle Research, *Sci. American,* vol. 180, 1949.

Hayashi, T., and G. A. W. Boehm: Artificial Muscle, *Sci. American,* vol. 187, 1952.

Katchalsky, A., and S. Lifson: Muscle as a Machine, *Sci. American,* vol. 190, 1954.

Harvey, E. N.: The Luminescence of Living Things, *Sci. American,* vol. 179, 1948.

Harvey, E. N.: Luminescent Organisms, *Am. Scientist,* vol. 40, 1952.

WE RECALL THAT SELF-PERPETUATION comprises three groups of processes: first, those which maintain the **steady state** of protoplasmic units and adjust and coordinate their internal operations; second, processes of **reproduction,** which extend the operations of protoplasmic units in space and in time; and third, processes of **adaptation,** which mold and fit the long-term character of protoplasmic units to the character of specific environments. Through self-perpetuation, living matter in the global aggregate becomes potentially indestructible.

Adaptation is contingent on reproduction, and reproduction is contingent on steady-state control. All three components of self-perpetuation operate on all levels of the living organization, and cellular self-perpetuation is prerequisite for the persistence of all higher levels. Consequently, maintenance of steady states within cells becomes the foundation of self-perpetuation as a whole.

Our plan of procedure for this first series of chapters is therefore clear. We begin with a discussion of the broad **patterns** of steady-state maintenance, and examine here the principles of control and the kinds of controls encountered on various levels of protoplasmic organization. We then concentrate specifically on cellular steady states. In that context we inquire into the role of **genes**, which are the most important controlling agents, and into the roles of other cellular controllers, such as **vitamins** and **hormones.** Lastly, we deal with steady-state controls on higher levels of organization. Here we concern ourselves particularly with the coordinating functions of **blood,** and of the **circulatory system,** the **excretory system,** and the **nervous system.**

PART 4

SELF-PERPETUATION: THE STEADY STATE

ANY EXTERNAL OR INTERNAL CONDITION which tends to upset the normal, smooth operations of a system may be regarded as a **stress.** In a living system, *external* stresses are often produced by the environment: by enemies, injurious agents, lack of food, change of temperature, and innumerable other physical, chemical, and biological conditions. *Internal* stresses arise continuously as a result of the very operations of the system itself: fuels are used up, concentrations change, parts age and wear out, waste products accumulate, etc. In so far as *any* external or internal change, usual or unusual, affects living matter, any such change also becomes a more or less significant stress. Actually, the living system is under stress all the time.

The problem of maintaining a steady state, therefore, is to counteract or to relieve stress. The requirement for this is, first, ability to *recognize* stress when and where it exists, and second, ability to *react* to such stress in self-preserving fashion. What is needed, in other words, is ability to recognize a **stimulus,** and ability to carry out an appropriate **response** to that stimulus. So long as a system recognizes stimuli, and reacts to them with fitting responses, it exercises **control.** And it may then remain intact and functioning, despite stresses which would otherwise upset its internal coordination.

In this chapter, we examine the nature of control mechanisms in general and survey the particular control systems in operation within cells, tissues, organs, and organisms.

Principles of Control

COMPONENTS OF CONTROL SYSTEMS

In a system composed of many parts acting cooperatively, as in protoplasm, steady state will be preserved if the parts may continue to act in harmony despite stress. If a stimulus should change the action of one part, then, in response, the action of all

17

THE PATTERN OF CONTROL

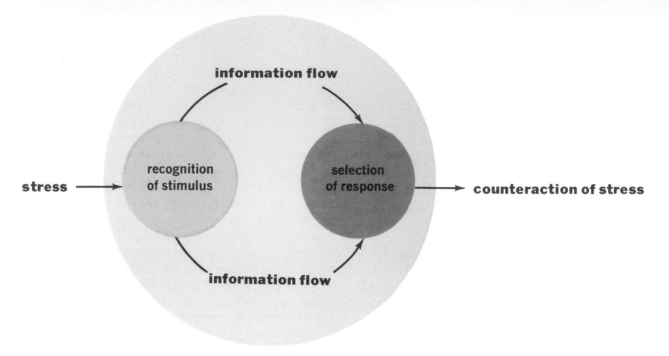

FIG. 17.1.   The general pattern of maintenance and control of steady state.

other parts should change too, in such a way that the total action of the system still remains integrated and coordinated.

To achieve such persisting internal coordination, a first fundamental requirement is continuous and rapid flow of **information** among the parts of the system. Each part must be kept informed of what other parts are doing, so that, if a stimulus affects one part, other parts may receive notice of it. Moreover, if the system is capable of responding to a stimulus in more than one way, a second fundamental requirement is ability to make **selections**. A simple system designed always to give the same response is not required to select. But where several response possibilities exist, ability to decide among them clearly is crucial. For choice of inappropriate responses leads to unsteady, not steady, states (Fig. 17.1).

Thus, "control" ultimately becomes a matter of information and of selection. These terms imply messages or signals of some sort, message carriers, senders, receivers, transmission pathways, relays, switches, channel selectors—in short, all the components of a communications system. Indeed, in one form or another, communications systems are found wherever steady states are maintained. In protoplasm, we find them within cells and between cells, within organisms and between organisms, on all levels of organization.

All such protoplasmic communications operate on a common pattern. An initial stimulus irritates, or *excites*, a receiving device, called a **receptor**. Excitation of this receptor causes the emission of a signal, which is transmitted over a **sensory pathway** to an interpreting and response-selecting device, the **modulator.** This component sends out an appropriately chosen command signal, over an appropriately chosen **motor pathway.** The signal leads to an **effec-**

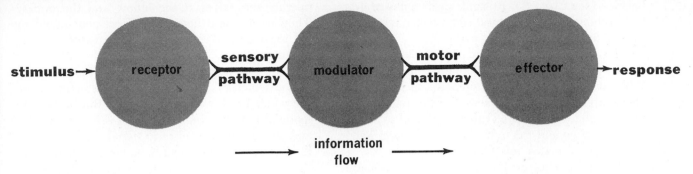

stimulus→ receptor

sensory
pathway

modulator

motor
pathway

effector

→response

information
flow

FIG. 17.2. The pattern of the control components in protoplasm.

tor, a device which executes the commands. This is the response which counteracts the original stimulus (Fig. 17.2).

We may illustrate the operation of such a system by means of a mechanical model. Suppose that the water level of a flow tank, as in Fig. 17.3, is to be maintained in steady state. That is, despite possible variations of inflow or outflow (e.g., if an ob- struction develops in one of the pipes, or if someone resets the speed of inflow or outflow), the water level is to stay at a predetermined height. Such a system is an **open system,** since materials are continuously entering and leaving; and the problem is to maintain a *dynamic equilibrium.* In these respects the model corresponds closely to living entities, which also are open systems maintained in dynamic

FIG. 17.3. Illustrating the difference between an open and a closed system. Continuous flow characterizes the open system, and if a balanced condition is attained the equilibrium is dynamic. Nothing enters or leaves the closed system, and if an equilibrium is attained it is static.

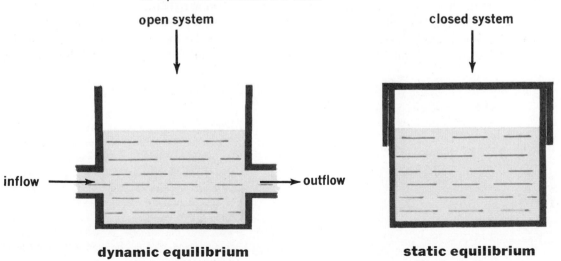

open system

closed system

inflow → → outflow

dynamic equilibrium

static equilibrium

balance (see Chap. 5). By contrast, in a **closed system** nothing enters or leaves, and balance is a *static equilibrium* (Fig. 17.3).

To establish a dynamic equilibrium in our model, we must install an automatic control device. Without help from external agencies, such a mechanism ought to be able to "sense" any change in water flow, and, by means of valves, it should so re-adjust the inflow and the outflow that the water level in the tank remains relatively constant.

We have equipped our tank with automatic controls in Fig. 17.4. An air-filled float *R* functions as receptor. Inasmuch as it moves up or down with the water, it senses changes of water level. Any up or down motion of *R* is communicated via a rod *sp*, the sensory pathway, to the modulator *M*. Here the sensory message—up or down motion of *sp*—is interpreted, and appropriate commands for response are sent out. Imagine *M* to be a simple electrical trigger mechanism. It might be so built that any upward motion of *sp* trips a switch which makes an electric current of certain strength and duration flow through the wires *mp*. Similarly, any downward motion of *sp* would reverse the switch position, and another electrical impulse, of different strength and duration, would be produced. Indeed, possible switch positions might be more numerous, and each might cause the flow of a current of unique characteristics. These electrical impulses are the command signals, transmitted over the motor pathways *mp* to the two effectors *E*. The effectors are engines which

operate the valves at the inflow and the outflow. They are so built that each different command signal received makes them move the valves into different positions.

Imagine now that for some external reason the inflow decreases. The outflow is still as before; hence the water level will begin to drop. But at once the modulator *M* will be informed of this change via *R* and *sp*. Appropriate electric signals will now go to the effectors, and the inflow valve will open more, the outflow valve close more. As a result, before the water level can drop very far, net inflow will increase, and the water will rise back to normal. This new change of level will again be communicated to the modulator, new signals will go out to the effectors, and the valves will be returned to their original position.

If at this point the inflow is still reduced, the control device will go into action once more, precisely as above. Clearly, by readjusting as often as necessary, the device is capable of maintaining a steady state despite changes in the "environment."

PROPERTIES OF CONTROL SYSTEMS

Energy Requirements

Our model illustrates a number of features common to control systems, protoplasmic ones included.

First, internal *operating energy* is needed to make the system work. In the model, energy is required for the transmission of electric signals and

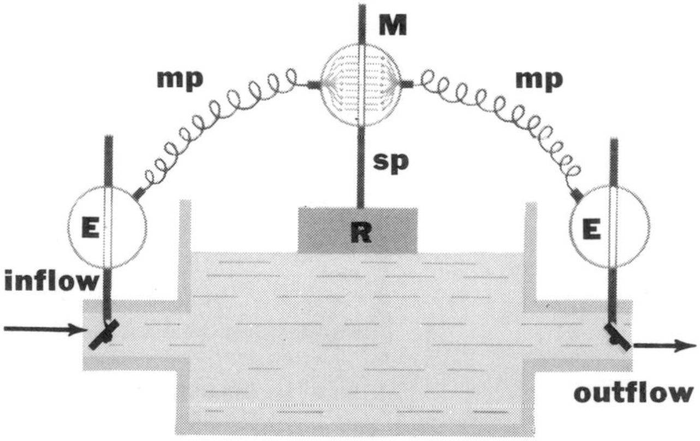

FIG. 17.4. Model of a steady-state maintaining device. **R**, receptor; **M**, modulator; **E**, effector; **sp**, sensory pathway; **mp**, motor pathway. If the system is adjusted as described in the text, then any change of inflow or outflow will bring about signals through **R→sp→M mp→E**. Valve positions will then be adjusted in such a way that the change of inflow or outflow is counteracted, and the original water level in the tank is reestablished.

for the motors which move the valves. Signal transmission itself can be accomplished on little energy. Indeed, the sensitivity of the whole device can be made desirably great if the float and the rod *sp* are built very light, so that they move easily, and if the modulator sends signals on a minimum of energy. On the other hand, the effectors will be the more useful, the more powerful they are, that is, the faster and the more forcefully they can respond, even against the push of the flowing water. The effectors therefore should have available an ample supply of energy—certainly more than they receive from the modulator in the form of signal energy. Consequently, an **amplifier** should be built into the effector to increase the power of the incoming signal energy to a level sufficient to move the valves. Protoplasmic controls are designed on just this principle. That is, receptors, modulators, and connecting pathways are highly sensitive and operate on a minimum of energy supplied by ATP. And the effectors work on amplifier energy supplied by comparatively large amounts of ATP.

Feedback

Another common feature of control devices is that response to a stimulus is not a sudden, single event, but a stepwise, repeated one. In our model, a small, initial change in valve position will produce a small, initial change in water level. The receptor immediately signals to the modulator that a certain adjustment has been carried out. Accordingly, the modulator then cues the effectors to continue, to stop, or to reverse operations. The resulting effector action is essentially a new stimulus, which is again communicated back via the receptor to the modulator. Continuous information thus passes from sensory to motor component and from motor back to sensory component. Many such cyclical passages of information, each contributing a small effector action, are usually required before a total response to a stimulus can be achieved. Indeed, the control device is not at rest even then. For in the absence of environmental stimuli, the receptor in effect signals "no change" to the modulator, the modulator sends "no adjustment required" to the effector, and the effec-

tor then informs the receptor of "no operation."

In such unceasing cyclical passages of information, we note that a response is "fed back" into the sensory end of the regulating device as a new stimulus, informing of the degree of counteraction already accomplished. The new stimulus in turn, fed into the modulator, informs of the degree of counteraction yet to be carried out. **Feedback** is to the motor-sensory segment of the cycle what modulation is to the sensory-motor segment. Both feedback and modulation control the direction, the amount, and the duration of adjustment. In protoplasm, as elsewhere, control activity becomes *effective* control only if appropriate feedbacks are operative. Without feedback, the modulator would never become aware of what the effector has been doing; hence it would never be able to send out "correct" new commands. The general pattern of the control cycle is outlined in Fig. 17.5.

Overshoots

Feedbacks and continuous cycles of information account for yet another common property of control systems: they function essentially by **trial and error,** by "hunting" for the correct equilibrium condition. Refer again to our model in Fig. 17.4. Suppose that the inflow changes so as to cause an initial drop in water level. Depending on the sensitivity of the apparatus, a given number of seconds may elapse before the valves are brought into corrective positions. By that time, the water level may be down 1 in., say. Now the water begins to rise, but again there will be a time lag of some seconds before the effectors receive the new command to return the valves to normal. But by that time, the water may already have risen somewhat *above* the correct level. Fresh signals to reverse valve positions a bit will now be forthcoming, and by the time that action is executed, the water may be down again *below* the appropriate level.

Most controls **overshoot** in this fashion, and they undergo *hunting oscillations* to either side of the equilibrium state. Clearly, it will be important that such oscillations either become smaller and smaller till they subside or else continue at constant

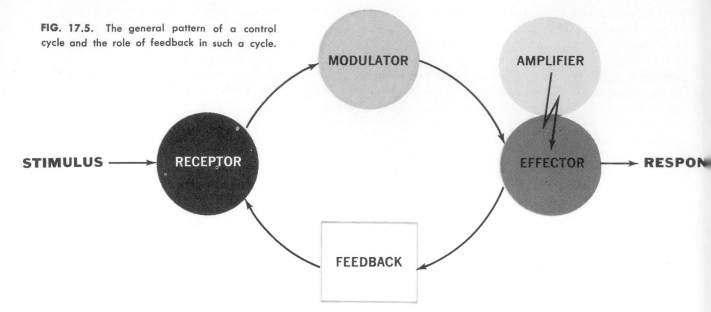

FIG. 17.5. The general pattern of a control cycle and the role of feedback in such a cycle.

amplitude. Poorly adjusted control devices often produce ever increasing hunting oscillations, in which case "steady" state, of course, will not be maintained. The zigzagging locomotion of a drunk walking toward a stated object is a familiar example of this. Under the influence of alcohol, nervous control over locomotion becomes loose and imprecise, and increased hunting oscillations occur. Normally, such oscillations are so small, and they subside so rapidly, that straight-line locomotion is possible.

Errors

Control mechanisms have inherent limits of efficiency. If they are overloaded, that is, if they must work too fast or too hard, they may become "neurotic." They may make **errors** in sensing stimuli, or in interpreting signals, or in selecting and executing responses. Extreme overloading may cause internal structural breakdowns, which may make the device inoperative altogether. In protoplasm, functional or structural failures of control systems result in **disease**. Disease itself is a stress stimulus to other, still intact regulating devices, and repair or circumvention of the diseased condition may ensue.

What kinds of control systems are found in living matter?

Protoplasmic Controls

The regulating devices of protoplasm are organized into a hierarchy, in accordance with the hierarchy of protoplasmic levels of organization. Cells contain complete internal control systems made up of molecules. Tissues contain control systems made up of cells. Organs contain control systems made up of tissues, etc. In such an order, the response of one level may be a component of the regulating activity on the next higher level. For example, the effector activity of a cell may serve in tissue control. Or the cell as a whole may function as receptor, in which case its response represents a sensory signal on the tissue level. Or the cell may function as modulator, which makes its response a motor signal on the tissue level. Or the cell may function as effector, and its response then constitutes a feedback signal on the tissue level. In like manner, effector activity of a whole tissue may serve in organ control. These interrelations are generalized in Fig. 17.6.

It follows from this that controls among protoplasmic molecules are the foundations of all protoplasmic control.

MOLECULAR CONTROL

Regardless of how a cell is stressed, the stress stimulus usually affects one or more metabolic processes. For example, changes in nutrient supplies, waste accumulation, injury, pH change, temperature change, sol-gel transformations, or indeed any other physical or chemical stimuli are likely to influence a cell either by *accelerating* or by *decelerating* particular metabolic reactions. Also, regardless of how a cell responds, the response is ultimately *produced* by metabolic processes. For whatever the effector action of a cell may be, acceleration or deceleration of respiration, or of chemical activities such as synthesis, or of physical activities such as movement, is likely to be involved.

Steady-state maintenance in a cell therefore becomes largely a matter of controlling cellular *metabolism*. The duration, speed, and amount of every reaction must be suitably geared to the duration, speed, and amount of every other reaction. And to maintain such coordination, every accelerated reaction must eventually be decelerated back to normal, and every decelerated reaction must be accelerated back to normal.

Acceleration

Actually, a metabolic reaction is itself the simplest and most basic kind of control system. Molecules function as receptors, modulators, and effectors, and the water in which a reaction takes place serves as sensory and motor pathway. For example, consider the reaction

$$\text{glucose} \overset{\textbf{enzymes}}{\rightleftharpoons} \text{glycogen}$$

When this reversible reaction is in chemical equilibrium, it is also in dynamic equilibrium or steady state; no net change occurs. The totality of glucose molecules in a cell, called a *glucose pool*, may now function as receptor. For example, if additional glucose arrives in the cell as food, this will be a stimulus "sensed" by the glucose pool as an increase in concentration. By mass action (see Chap. 6), the reaction to the right will now outbalance that to the left, and more glycogen will be formed. The *glycogen pool* then is the effector, and the increase of glycogen concentration is the response. For as glycogen accumulates at the expense of glucose, the glucose pool decreases back to normal—and the original stimulus is thereby removed. The extra glycogen, in turn, may represent a new stimulus in the cell, initiating other reactions and new responses.

Note that the designations "receptor" and "effector" are not fixed. If a cell were to acquire additional glycogen rather than glucose, then the glycogen pool would be the receptor, and the glucose pool the effector. Note further that, in either case, the function of the modulator is performed by the *enzymes*. Mass action notwithstanding, it takes a specific enzyme to "interpret" a specific stimulus

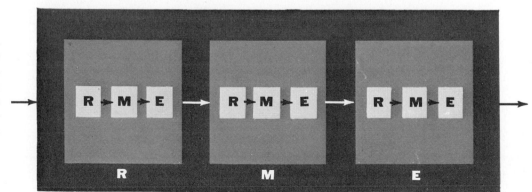

FIG. 17.6. Illustrating the protoplasmic hierarchy of control systems. **R,** receptor; **M,** modulator; **E,** effector. The entire control apparatus of one level (within a rectangular box) is a component of the control apparatus on the next higher level.

R or M or E

and to direct the specific response. Because it *is* specific for a particular reaction, an enzyme cannot interpret various different stimuli, but only one. And it cannot select among several possible responses but must promote the same response every time. Yet inasmuch as it functions like a "clearing center" for incoming and outgoing chemical information, every enzyme is a fundamental modulator in reaction control.

Four other kinds of reaction modulators occur in cells: *vitamins, hormones, inorganic substances,* and, above all, *genes.* These too accelerate specific metabolic reactions. For example, we have seen in Chap. 15 that the conversion of pyruvic acid to acetic acid requires, in addition to enzymes, a B vitamin, magnesium ions, and in mammals also the hormone thyroxine. We may now note that practically *all* metabolic reactions appear to require enzymes *plus* various other agents. Virtually each protoplasmic reaction analyzed closely has been found to depend on a whole battery of accelerators.

In addition to at least one enzyme, one or more vitamins, hormones, and inorganic materials are usually required as well. Moreover, there is now little doubt that every metabolic reaction depends ultimately on gene action.

We shall examine later how these five classes of substances differ in function. Here we note their functional similarities: they are essentially enzyme-*like* in their activities. Thus, like enzymes, genes, vitamins, hormones, and inorganic substances are specifically necessary for specific reactions; small quantities of them suffice; and they do not become part of the endproduct but are recoverable intact and unchanged after the reaction. In short, they all function more or less like catalysts. And in the language of control systems, they function as information relays, or as modulators (Fig. 17.7). They share with enzymes the property of being differentially sensitive to single sensory messages only and of promoting the same reaction responses every time, without freedom of choice.

FIG. 17.7. The molecular modulators within cells.

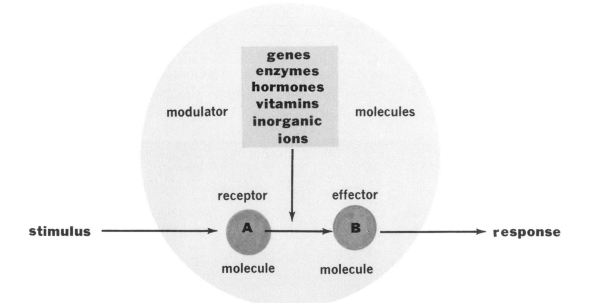

Being active in the manner of catalysts, these molecular modulators all tend to *accelerate* reactions. How, then, are reactions decelerated or inhibited? Steady-state maintenance clearly requires both.

Deceleration

Deceleration occurs in three major ways. One way is based on the **reversibility** of most metabolic reactions. For example, glucose $\rightleftharpoons$ glycogen. As we have seen in earlier chapters, the hormone insulin accelerates glycogen formation. But adrenal hormones accelerate glucose formation, hence decelerate glycogen formation: *a reaction can be inhibited by accelerating the opposite reaction.* We shall find that this principle holds not only on the molecular level but also in steady-state control on any other level. Brakes and accelerators are present together and hold one another in mutual check. The net reaction they allow to occur is a restrained compromise between *excitation* and *inhibition.* Any change in the quantities of the modulators, or in the concentrations of the reactants, will change the balance between excitation and inhibition. And the reaction will then speed up in one direction, hence slow down in the other.

A second deceleration method is based on **competition among modulators** for reactants. For example, glucose can become either glycogen or pyruvic acid, as we have seen (Chap. 15). Either step requires specific modulators (M_1, M_2):

$$\text{pyruvic acid} \xleftarrow{\quad M_1 \quad} \text{glucose} \xrightarrow{\quad M_2 \quad} \text{glycogen}$$

M_1 and M_2 in this case *compete* for available glucose. If M_1 has a competitive advantage, for example, by combining more easily with glucose or by being present in larger amount, then glycogen synthesis will be decelerated, and pyruvic acid formation will be speeded up. Here again the modulators hold one another in check, and the net reactions are quickly adjusted when any part of the balance shifts.

A third method of deceleration depends on **competition among reactants** for modulators, the converse of the above. This may occur where given

protoplasmic reactions are so alike that the same modulator may promote them. For example, the same cathepsins could transform amino acids into either protein *A* or protein *B*:

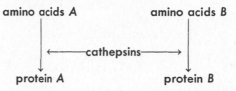

The reactants on the *A* side here compete with those on the *B* side for the required enzymes. Hence, whenever concentrations or other conditions favor one reaction, the other would be inhibited. We may therefore appreciate how competition for a limited quantity of modulator in a cell may crowd out one reaction at the expense of another.

We may note here in passing that chemical competition is often the cause, as well as the cure, of disease. For example, disease may be caused by a poison, which competes either with a normal modulator or a normal reactant and so crowds out an essential reaction. Cure may then be effected by reversing the abnormal competition, that is, by injecting normal modulators or normal reactants in sufficient quantities to crowd out the disease reaction (see Fig. 6.10, page 139).

Modulator Interaction

Control of molecular metabolism may now be envisaged as follows (consult Fig. 17.8). In a given sequence of reactions, each separate reaction is influenced by several kinds of modulators. Some promote the reaction in one direction (M_1, M_2, M_3), and others promote it in the opposite direction (M_4, M_5). Some modulators compete for reactants (M_4, M_6), and such modulators act **antagonistically**. Similarly, some reactants compete for modulators, e.g., *B* and *B'* compete for M_7. Other modulators are mutually reinforcing in their activity (M_4, M_5), and these are said to act **synergistically**.

Depending on the specific balances between all modulators and all reactants at any moment, the whole sequence, or parts of it, will proceed one

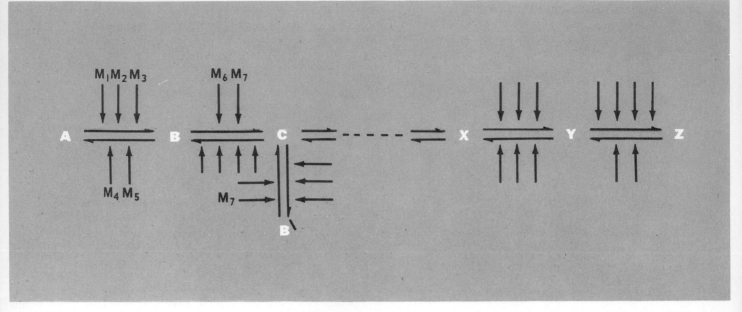

FIG. 17.8. The general pattern of control of molecular metabolism. **A, B, C, . . . X, Y, Z** symbolize molecular reactants, and **M₁, M₂,** etc., symbolize molecular modulators. Some of these modulators act synergistically and reinforce each other in their action. Others act antagonistically. Also, just as modulators may compete for reactants, so reactants may compete for modulators. Each step of a reaction sequence is controlled by a battery of modulators, and the net reaction is a resultant of the various modulator effects.

way or the other for certain lengths of time, in certain amounts, and at certain rates. The overall result of such multiple excitations and inhibitions is a steady state, a dynamic equilibrium. When, now, a stimulus affects any part of the sequence, then the balance between the excitations and inhibitions shifts automatically; and so, like ripples in a pond traveling away from a center of disturbance, the reaction sequence will undergo "hunting oscillations," until a steady state is reattained.

We may ask here why multiple controls for each reaction are required to begin with. Would not a single modulator suffice? Possibly it might, but there is safety in numbers. Multiple controls re-

duce the chance of error, and if one modulator becomes inoperative, the reaction may not be stopped completely. Multiple controls provide desirable **redundancy,** or repetition. If one wishes to make sure that information is received exactly as sent, then one repeats the message several times. Just so, chemical messages in metabolism are highly redundant, as are protoplasmic messages in general, as we shall see.

SUPRAMOLECULAR CONTROL

All other protoplasmic controls are based on the molecular controls of metabolism. In the cell, molecules are variously aggregated into comparatively large formed structures, and these, by virtue of the control functions of their component molecules, carry out specific higher-level control functions of their own.

Cellular Controls

Many molecular aggregates within cells, visible under the microscope, serve as receptors. For example, pigmented granules absorb light and form excellent photoreceptors. Long filaments are sensitive to displacement, to pressure, to touch, and they may therefore serve as receptors of mechanical stimuli. Other formed microscopic structures may be sensitive to particular classes of chemicals, and they may function as chemoreceptors. Note that a cell does not necessarily possess receptors for all possible kinds of stimuli. For example, magnetic energy is generally not receivable as a stimulus.

Formed bodies also function as modulators. Of these, the cell nucleus is the most complex. Through its genes it ultimately controls all cytoplasmic activities. Complex modulators in the cytoplasm include, for example, the mitochondria, the microsomes, and the plastids of green plant cells. As we have seen in earlier chapters, these play vital specific roles in specific stimulus-response sequences.

Complex cellular effectors are equally varied. Many contribute to the numerous physical and chemical responses necessary in the *internal* maintenance of a cell. Others link a cell to its *external* environment. For example, some produce light, as in bioluminescent cells, or electricity, as in the cells of animal electric organs. Some bring about cell movement, and some absorb or secrete various substances through the cell surface.

We may note here that *every* microscopic formed body present in a cell contributes to at least one control process on the cellular level, just as every protoplasmic chemical contributes to control on the molecular level. Moreover, a given microscopic structure may have multiple control functions. It may serve as receptor in one instance, as modulator in another, as effector in yet a third. For example, the cell membrane is a receptor when it "recognizes" a glucose molecule, but it is an effector

when it allows that molecule to pass through. The cell nucleus has been referred to above as a modulator, which indeed it often is. But it may also serve as receptor—it receives many stimuli from the cytoplasm; or it may be an effector—it executes many responses. Clearly, functional labels are not fixed. How one designates a structure participating in several control processes depends largely on which of these processes one wishes to emphasize. Such multiplicity of function is evident not only in cellular controls, but in all supracellular ones as well.

Moreover, the cellular level is the lowest on which we encounter modulators capable of distinguishing between *various* sensory messages and of *selecting* among various response possibilities. For example, the cell membrane is *selectively* permeable. Functioning as a modulator, it may interpret the chemical nature of *different* kinds of molecules in contact with it, and it may "decide" how fast and to what extent each such molecule is to be passed through. Similar selectivity is displayed by other complex control components within a cell, and also by all supracellular control systems.

How does this crucial capacity of making decisions arise? The answer is not yet clear. But note that a complex cellular modulator contains within it different *molecular* control systems, many of them, and each capable of a single response. It is therefore likely that the number of decisions a complex modulator may make is correlated with the number of different molecular unit systems of which it is composed.

Supracellular Controls

The response of a cell as a whole may be propagated by direct contact to adjacent cells, or it may be transmitted more widely by the internal transport system—sap in plants, blood in animals. If one cell stimulates others in the manner of a chain reaction, a whole tissue, organ, or organism may eventually be drawn into a larger response. Steady-state regulation of this kind is still essentially cellular. Although more than one cell is involved, receptors, modulators, and effectors beyond those present in the individual cell do not exist.

This form of functional control constitutes the

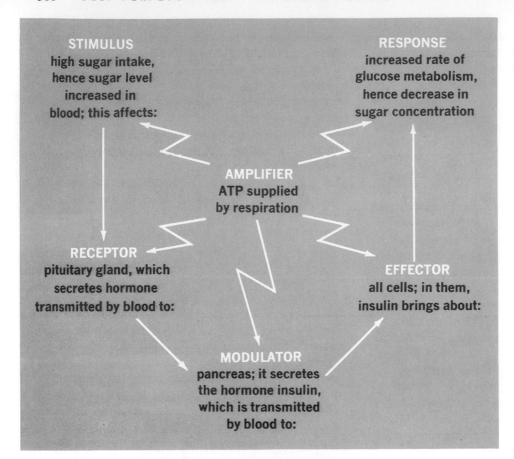

FIG. 17.9. An example of organismic steady-state control.

highest pattern in most plants, and in certain primitive sessile animals, notably sponges. For example, if a living sponge is prodded with a stick in one region, that region may contract. Slowly and in ever widening circles, areas surrounding the original irritation also contract, until the sponge as a whole responds. Other responses to internal or external stresses, here as in plants, may propagate in similar fashion.

Plants and sponges, being immobile, encounter far fewer environmental changes than fast-moving animals, which enter new environments in rapid succession. Such animals therefore must be able to make correspondingly rapid adjustments of their internal environment. Indeed, superimposed on

steady-state mechanisms based on the cell, complex animals possess supracellular regulating devices not present in plants or sponges. Whole specialized tissues, organs, and organ systems serve here specifically as receptors, modulators, or effectors. As above, a given structure may function in more than one of these capacities.

A most important supracellular mechanism involves the blood as sensory and motor pathway. Change in any one part of the body is signaled to all other parts via the blood. A battery of modulators and effectors may be called into action as a result: heart, blood vessels, skin, kidneys, liver, endocrine and other glands, muscles, to mention a few. Their specific operation, to be discussed systematically later, counteracts the original change. For example, see Fig. 17.9.

Probably the most familiar, and the most complex, control device is the nervous system. Sense organs, in the skin and within the body, are receptors. A brain is the chief modulator. Muscle-bone systems and glands function as effectors. And nerves serve as sensory and motor connecting paths. Transmission of information through such a sequence of specialized neural structures, energized along its length by ATP, constitutes a *reflex*. Two examples are given in Fig. 17.10.

Reflexes are the basis of nervous steady-state control. They may, and often do, act in concert with other control mechanisms, for example, the hormone-producing endocrine system, the circulatory system, the digestive system, and many others. Most situations requiring control actually are regulated by a multiplicity of devices, and the nervous system often is one of them.

Again we may note that, just as every molecule and molecular aggregate serves in some control function on intracellular levels, so also *every* tissue, organ, and organ system serves in some control process on higher levels. As pointed out above, the control systems of various levels are arranged in an integrated hierarchy. And it is important to keep in mind that the molecular reaction is maintained in steady state by the totality of reactions in a cell; the cellular reaction, by the totality of reactions in a tissue; the tissue reaction, by the total organ reaction; and the organ reaction, by the body as a whole.

In Chap. 3, we compared the hierarchical organization of living matter with a pyramid of cards. We now find that the analogy holds also for the hierarchical organization of protoplasmic control systems. For in a pyramid of cards, one level controls the steady state of other levels. Take away a top card and the perfection of the pyramid is destroyed, but the lower levels persist. Just so may impairment of heart, brain, liver, kidney, or other high-level controls mar organismic perfection. But individual cells live on as long as *cellular* steady state is preserved. When the brain of a frog is de-

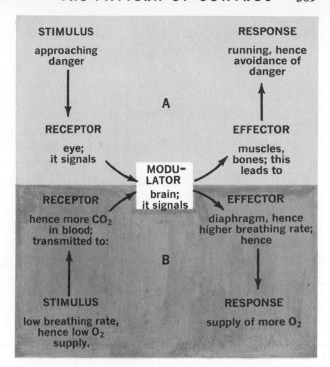

FIG. 17.10. Two further examples of organismic steady-state control, reflexes being involved in both cases.

stroyed experimentally, we no longer deal with a whole living frog, but we do not deal with a dead frog either. A "spinal" frog jumps and swims, yet it is capable neither of higher sense perception nor of voluntary motor activity, and it eventually dies of starvation. However, its life could be maintained if it were fed artificially and if it were shielded from influences which a functional frog brain would normally counteract.

Take away a bottom card from the pyramid, and the whole structure topples. Just so does impairment of molecular and cellular control functions—gene action, for example—produce body-wide disease, or death. This is of considerable practical significance, since it is on the whole much easier to correct a faulty brain, kidney, or other organ than to tinker with gene molecules.

RESUME   The general conclusion emerges that every part of protoplasm is controlled *by* all other parts and at the same time contributes *to* the control of all other parts. And since every structure, large or small, so functions in steady-state maintenance, "controlling" becomes a very major component of "living." Recognizing the stimuli of the environment, and actively responding to them, is even more characteristic of "being alive" than metabolizing. Indeed, control is the crux of self-perpetuation, and, as we shall see, reproduction and adaptation are special forms of control. Without control, life becomes nonlife.

Conversely, nonlife became life when the first control mechanism came into existence. That, as we have seen, was the nucleoprotein molecule, the gene. All evolution ever since may be looked upon as a progressive development of more varied and more efficient control mechanisms. These were capable of counteracting more environmental stresses; hence they permitted the extension of life in each environment for longer periods. The controls developed in man are one culmination of this. Through exquisitely sensitive receptors, such as eyes and ears; through refined modulation, such as learning and thinking; and through versatile responses, such as speaking, writing. and using tools for building and manufacturing, the human organism has become one of the best controlled, remarkably able to resist the stresses of the most varied environments.

This outlines the broad pattern of protoplasmic control. We now refocus our attention on the individual cell and discuss the critical agents around which all self-perpetuation ultimately revolves: the genes.

REVIEW QUESTIONS

1. In general terms, what kinds of processes take place in the execution of control activities? What general function do such controls serve in the maintenance of life? What is the role of information flow in the maintenance of steady states?

2. What are the structural components of every control system in protoplasm? What specific role does each such component play in the maintenance of dynamic equilibria?

3. Review the functional properties of control systems. How is the energy requirement distributed among control components? What is feedback, and what is its significance in control activities?

4. What is the significance of trial and error in control activities? What happens when control systems are overloaded? Interpret the temperature-regulating action of a home thermostat in terms of a control system, and indicate the specific roles of feedback and trial and error. Do likewise for the temperature-regulating systems of mammals and birds.

5. Describe the hierarchical organization of the controls in protoplasm. How does interference with control at any level affect the controls of (*a*) lower and (*b*) higher levels?

6. In what sense does a molecular reaction constitute a control system? What kinds of substances may serve as molecular modulators? What functional characteristics do these have in common?

7. Review the ways in which molecular reactions may be decelerated. Give examples. Show how disease may sometimes be a result of chemical competition. Distinguish

between antagonistic and synergistic control components. What is the significance of redundancy in control activities?

8. For each microscopic body usually present in cells (as listed in Chap. 7, Table 3), describe a cellular activity in which that body functions as (*a*) receptor, (*b*) modulator, (*c*) effector, and (*d*) sensory or motor pathway.

9. Review the general pattern of protoplasmic control on supracellular levels. What is a reflex? Which parts of a plant or an animal do *not* participate in control activities?

10. Interpret the automatic alternation of inhalation and exhalation in breathing, as outlined in Chap. 14, in terms of control activity. What parts of the breathing system serve as receptors, modulators, effectors, and transmission paths, and what are the stimulus, the feedback, and the response? How does the breathing system respond to external stress, and what is the result of overstress?

SUGGESTED COLLATERAL READINGS

Control systems of biological importance are discussed in detail in subsequent chapters, and appropriate readings will be found in these later contexts. See, however, the first three sources cited below. The remaining articles listed here provide excellent background information on control operations in general.

Cannon, W. B.: "The Wisdom of the Body," Norton, 1932.

Gerard, R. W.: The Dynamics of Inhibition, *Sci. American,* vol. 179, 1948.

Brown, F. A.: Biological Clocks and the Fiddler Crab, *Sci. American,* vol. 190, 1954.

Nagel, E.: Self-regulation, *Sci. American,* vol. 187, 1952.

Tustin, A.: Feedback, *Sci. American,* vol. 187, 1952.

Brown, G. S., and D. P. Campbell: Control Systems, *Sci. American,* vol. 187, 1952.

King, G.: What Is Information? *Sci. American,* vol. 187, 1952.

Walter, W. G.: An Imitation of Life, *Sci. American,* vol. 182, 1950.

18

GENES AND SPECIFICITY

L IFE BEGAN after the first nucleoproteins had been formed. Creation of this original life took billions of years, for it had to occur by physical and chemical chance; there was no blueprint to follow. But after nucleoproteins were on the scene, creation of new life could become a very rapid process. Today it takes only 20 min to create a new bacterium, only 22 months to create a new elephant. This tremendous acceleration is made possible by nucleoproteins, more specifically, by genes, the modern descendants of the first nucleoproteins. Present in every cell, genes do provide a blueprint, a recipe, not only for the creation of life, but also for its maintenance. Through genes, creation and maintenance cease to be matters of chance but become matters of controlled planning.

Like modulators generally, genes *store information*. When they receive appropriate sensory messages from cellular receptors, they transmit their information to cellular effectors. Specifically, this information consists of chemical instructions on how to build *proteins*—how to build particular kinds, *specific* proteins. Through this, as this chapter will show, genes control *all* metabolism and *all* self-perpetuation, including themselves.

We begin with an examination of **gene structure**, the basis of **gene function**.

Gene Structure

DEFINITION

We recall from Chap. 7 that the nucleus of a cell consists of an external membrane and a semifluid nuclear sap, and that two kinds of structures are suspended in this sap: one or more spherical bodies, called **nucleoli,** and a number of elongated, filamentous bodies, the gene-containing **chromosomes** (Fig. 18.1).

We recall also that the number of chromosomes per nucleus is an inherited trait, constant for each species. A fertilized egg of an organism possesses a given number of chromosomes, inherited from the parents, and all the cells which arise from this egg in the development of an adult inherit that same number of chromosomes. Human cells, for example, usually contain 48 chromosomes. In most organisms the number is even at least at one stage of the life cycle, and in very many of these, it is even for a substantial part, or virtually the whole, of the life cycle. Thus, alternative conditions notwithstanding, a largely even, fixed number of chromosomes houses the genes.

No one has ever knowingly seen one gene. This is not primarily because it is too small, but primarily because it is not a uniquely definable object. We may say, in general, that *a gene is a unit of length within a chromosome.*

But at least three different, more or less equally acceptable definitions of "unit" are possible. A gene may be (1) that minimum part of a chromosome which controls a single metabolic reaction in a cell; or (2) that minimum part of a chromosome which, when it mutates, i.e., changes structurally in some permanent way, alters just one trait of a cell; or (3) that minimum part of a chromosome which, in the nucleus of a reproductive cell, can transfer, or "cross over," to a neighboring chromosome. The significance of the events here referred to will become clearer later. For the present we merely note that a "gene" may be defined either as a **unit of biochemical action,** or as a **unit of mutation,** or as a **unit of crossing over.**

And these units usually are not identical. Any one of them may be shorter or longer than any other, and this itself may vary for different genes. We conclude, therefore, that the term "gene" does not refer to any specific, fixed piece of a chromosome but rather to an *operational concept.* Just as the unit of physical length varies according to whether we define it in inches or in centimeters or in ells, so does the chromosome unit vary according to the experimental methods we use to measure it. Henceforth, when we refer to a "gene" without further qualifications, we shall keep in mind that we are making a rather vague reference to *some* section of a chromosome.

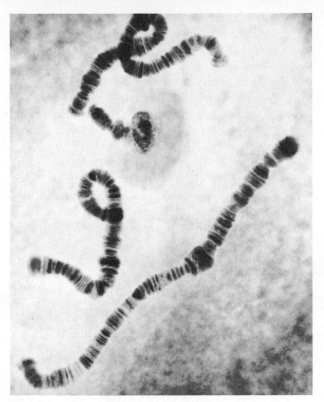

FIG. 18.1. Chromosomes. In this stained preparation of insect chromosomes, characteristic crossbands are clearly visible. Such banding is found in all chromosomes studied. From D. F. Poulson and C. W. Metz, *J. Morph.,* vol. 63, 1938.)

COMPOSITION

However carefully we must qualify the definition of a gene, we need not qualify similarly in considering the chemical composition of a gene. The whole chromosome is an integrated unit, and for chemical analysis it does not matter too much just exactly where one gene ends and the next one begins.

Genes, like whole chromosomes, consist largely of nucleoproteins. And as outlined in Chaps. 2 and 7,

nucleoprotein $\rightarrow$ nucleic acid $+$ protein

A considerable body of information now available shows fairly clearly that it is largely, or entirely, the nucleic acid component, not the protein component, which endows chromosomal nucleoprotein with the properties of genes. For example, it is possible to isolate nucleic acids from one kind of microorganism and to transfer them experimentally into another. The result is that the recipient acquires genetic traits of the donor. This is not the case when the protein fraction is similarly transferred (Fig. 18.2). The functioning of genes therefore must be explained primarily in terms of the structure of nucleic acids.

About this structure much has already been said in Chaps. 2 and 7. To recapitulate briefly,

nucleic acid $\rightarrow$ many nucleotides

nucleotide $\rightarrow \left\{ \begin{array}{l} \text{purine or} \\ \text{pyrimidine} \end{array} \right\} +$ sugar $+$ phosphate

We recall that the 5-carbon sugar of a nucleotide may be either *ribose* or the related *desoxyribose*, which differs from ribose by the absence of one oxygen atom. We have noted this to be the basis of distinction between ribose nucleic acid, or **RNA**, and desoxyribose nucleic acid, or **DNA**. *The nucleic acids of genes are invariably DNA.*

We also recall that desoxyribose nucleotides occur in four varieties, according to the kinds of pu-

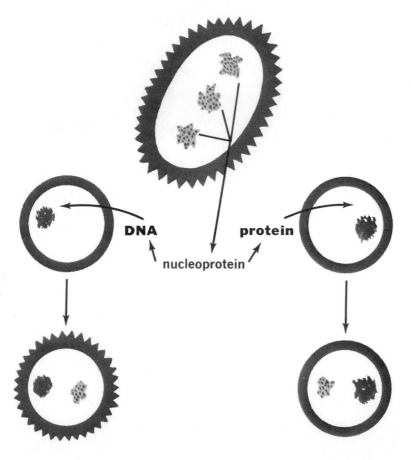

transformation by DNA   **no transformation by protein**

FIG. 18.2. Bacterial transformation. The nucleoprotein of a rough-coated bacterial type is extracted, and separate DNA and protein fractions are prepared. If a smooth-coated bacterial type is allowed to absorb the DNA fraction, it will change into a rough-coated type. But it will remain smooth-coated if it absorbs only the protein fraction. Experiments of this sort show that the nucleic acid part, not the protein part, of nucleoproteins is of genetic importance.

rines or pyrimidines they contain. The four varieties are adenine-desoxyribose-phosphate, guanine-desoxyribose-phosphate, thymine-desoxyribose-phosphate, and cytosine-desoxyribose-phosphate. The central problem concerning nucleic acid structure now is to determine how numerous nucleotides of each of the four kinds are joined to form DNA.

ARCHITECTURE

The best available evidence tends to indicate that DNA in genes is a *double chain of nucleotides,* one chain parallel to the other. In each single chain, nucleotide molecules appear to be united in such a way that the phosphate group of one molecule links to the sugar molecule of the next and that the purines and pyrimidines stick out laterally. If we symbolize a nucleotide molecule as *P—S—B, P* for phosphate, *S* for sugar, and *B* for purine or pyrimidine, then in a single chain,

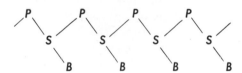

The evidence further suggests that two such single chains are linked into a double chain by the two sets of *B*'s, which are held together pairwise by comparatively weak bonds:

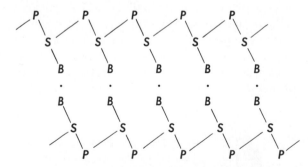

As noted, *B* stands for either adenine or guanine, or for either thymine or cytosine. The first two are purines; the last two, pyrimidines. Which are

joined to which, in a double chain as above? Purines are larger molecules than pyrimidines (see also Chap. 2):

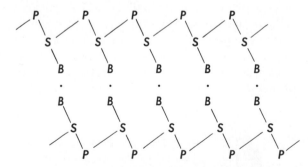

pyrimidine
skeleton
(thymine, cytosine)

purine skeleton
(adenine, guanine)

Therefore, if a —*B·B*— combination in a double chain as above consisted of two pyrimidines, it would be smaller than if it consisted of two purines. Actually, all —*B·B*— combinations are of the same overall size; in a double chain, one *B* of a pair is always a pyrimidine, the other, a purine. Any such two together take up the same amount of space, and the *P—S—P—S* chains to which they are attached are therefore parallel.

Specifically, four different —*B·B*— combinations occur in DNA, as outlined in Fig. 18.3. Note that *adenine is always paired with thymine, guanine with cytosine.* The chemical properties of these purines and pyrimidines, and the space available between the parallel *P—S* chains, are such that only combinations shown in Fig. 18.3 can be formed.

But there is apparently no limit to the number of times each of these combinations can occur in a long double chain. Nor, apparently, are there restrictions as to their sequence. Thus, *A·T, T·A, G·C,* and *C·G* may be regarded as an alphabet of four symbols, and "words" of any length may be constructed by using these symbols as often as desired, and in any order. Evidently, the possible number of compositionally different DNA's is practically unlimited. This is reminiscent of the situation in proteins, where an alphabet of 23 amino acids gives rise to a virtually unlimited number of different complexes.

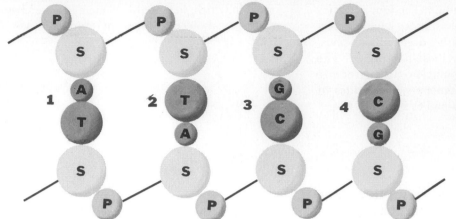

FIG. 18.3. The four kinds of purine-pyrimidine pairs found in a double chain of DNA. **P**, phosphate; **S**, sugar (desoxyribose); **A**, adenine; **T**, thymine; **G**, guanine; **C**, cytosine. Each of the four possible pairs (**A·T, T·A, G·C, C·G**) may occur very many times, and the sequence of the pairs may vary in unlimited fashion.

A final architectural characteristic of DNA is that its double chain is probably not straight, but *spiraled* (Fig. 18.4).

It is to be noted that these various organizational features of DNA are not yet established conclusively. The structure as outlined must be regarded as little more than a preliminary working model, and indeed it is designated as the **Watson-Crick model**, after the investigators who proposed it. It still leaves many problems unsolved. To cite just one, how and where is DNA joined to protein to form nucleoprotein?

The model does answer many other questions, however. For example, it may explain the observation that, whereas all genes contain DNA, not all DNA is found in genes; chromosomes contain much DNA which is inert genetically. This is undoubtedly a result of varying DNA *specificities*. Just as proteins are specific by virtue of particular combination patterns among their amino acids, so, according to the Watson-Crick model, may DNA's be specific by virtue of particular combinations of

their four-symbol alphabet. Certain combinations make up DNA *without* genetic effect, others *with* such effect. Moreover, different DNA specificities undoubtedly account for the observation that, although all genes contain DNA, genes are far from alike. Each organism contains sets of functionally different genes, and the sets of one species differ functionally from those of every other species.

Above all, the Watson-Crick model may explain how a gene might operate.

Gene Function

Considerable uncertainty still exists about the ways in which genes actually exercise control over cellular activities. Nevertheless, a good tentative working hypothesis may be formulated today, based in part on present knowledge of gene structure and in part on researches dealing with the interrelations between the nucleus and the cytoplasm of a cell.

FIG. 18.4. A DNA double chain is spiraled as shown in this diagram. The two spirals symbolize the —**P**—**S**—**P**—**S**— chains, and the connections between the spirals represent the purine-pyrimidine pairs.

NUCLEO-CYTOPLASMIC INTERRELATIONS

That the nucleus is vital for cytoplasmic survival has been known for a long time. The first pertinent experiments, now classical, were done on amoebae. These large-celled protozoa are readily cut into halves, so that one half is with nucleus, the other without. The results show that a nucleated half carries on in every respect like a normal ameba. But a nonnucleated half invariably dies. Surprisingly, death here is not instantaneous. An ameba without nucleus may persist for as long as a month, and at first it may even move and feed. But it never grows, it never reproduces, and soon it cannot digest or metabolize food (Fig. 18.5). Evidently, nuclear effects are fundamentally long-range effects, a conclusion confirmed also by other experiments.

Just as survival of the cytoplasm depends on the nucleus, so does survival of the nucleus depend on the cytoplasm; a naked isolated nucleus dies sooner or later. Inasmuch as the cytoplasm is the site of food management, respiration, and synthesis, a nucleus freed of cytoplasm undoubtedly succumbs from lack of energy and raw materials.

Gene function therefore must be viewed against a background of *cyclical* interactions between nucleus and cytoplasm. The nucleus, its genes comparable to a "policy-making" board of directors, supervises the long-range activities of the cytoplasm. The cytoplasm in turn executes nuclear directives, and this includes feeding and caring for the nucleus (Fig. 18.6).

Is there a special director gene for every single cytoplasmic function to be carried out? This is not likely on general grounds. A nucleus is estimated to contain in the order of a few thousand genes. But the cytoplasm probably performs in the order of several tens or hundreds of thousands of separate chemical and physical activities. Therefore, a single gene probably controls numerous cytoplasmic processes.

As we shall see below, such control of many events is achieved largely through one major gene function: control of **protein synthesis.** As noted in Chap. 16, protein manufacture occurs in the microsome granules of the cytoplasm, and in this process genes serve as *specificity*-conferring agents. They ensure that any new proteins formed contain a particular, specific sequence of amino acids

FIG. 18.5. When an ameba is bisected, only the nucleated half continues to live. The enucleated half eventually dies.

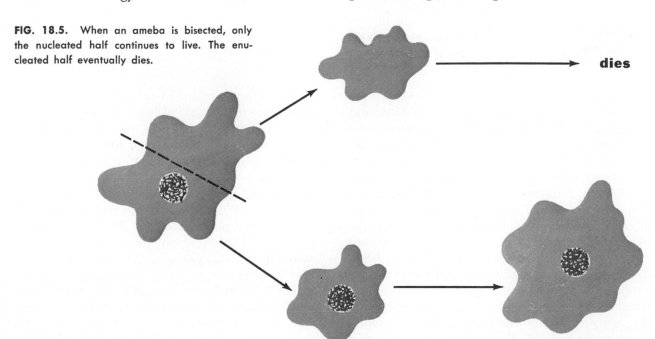

dies

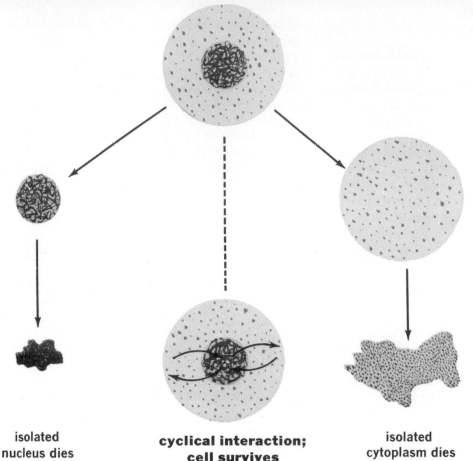

FIG. 18.6. The pattern of interdependence of nucleus and cytoplasm. When nucleus and cytoplasm are isolated from each other, both die (left and right). Normally, nucleus sustains cytoplasm, and cytoplasm sustains nucleus, in cyclical interaction (middle).

**isolated
nucleus dies**

**cyclical interaction;
cell survives**

**isolated
cytoplasm dies**

and so have a particular, specific architectural configuration. We may understand therefore why gene control is long-range control; when genes are removed, specific proteins built earlier still persist, and as long as the supply lasts, life may continue.

Protein synthesis takes place in the microsomes, but genes are in the nucleus. Clearly, some kind of functional connecting link must exist between nucleus and cytoplasm. Microsomes happen to be especially rich in *ribose* nucleic acid, *RNA*. The presence of this substance in these particular granules, and its chemical similarity to the DNA found in genes, suggest the striking possibility that the connecting link between genes and microsomes might be RNA. To test the validity of such a

hypothesis, in principle at least, one would have to show (1) that RNA is indeed intimately associated with protein synthesis; (2) that RNA actually does originate in the nucleus; and (3) that the specificity of cellular proteins is in some direct way traceable first to RNA, and from RNA in turn to the DNA of the genes. What does available evidence indicate?

That protein synthesis and RNA go together is now substantiated amply (Fig. 18.7). In many secreting cells, for example, the secretion products are proteins (e.g., enzyme-secreting digestive glands). It can be shown readily that when secretion synthesis occurs at a rapid pace, the RNA content of the microsomes is high. Conversely, RNA decreases when secretion synthesis does. Analogous evidence has been obtained from experiments on nonnucleated amoebae. As noted, such individuals may persist for considerable periods. Analysis shows that during this time the protein content of the amoebae slowly decreases; new proteins are apparently not synthesized. In parallel with this decline, the RNA content declines also. These two changes are here related directly to the absence of a nucleus. Evidence of the most direct kind is now available also. It can be shown that RNA extracted from cells may promote protein synthesis in the test tube!

Thus, there can be relatively little doubt that RNA in the microsomes plays a vital role in protein synthesis. It is, in fact, extremely likely that RNA is the immediate, "on-the-spot" specificity-conferring agent. If so, RNA itself would have to be specific, differently so for different RNA molecules. These RNA specificities in turn would have to originate in the genes. Does cytoplasmic RNA actually have a nuclear origin?

In all probability, yes. It can be shown, for example, that nuclear DNA contributes parts of its own substance toward the manufacture of cytoplas-

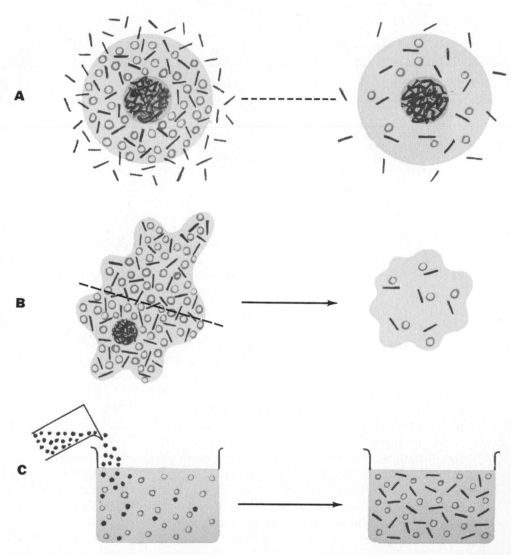

FIG. 18.7. Evidence that RNA is required for specific protein synthesis is of three kinds. **A,** left: secretion of much protein by a cell (rods) is correlated with a high RNA content (circles); right: low protein content and low RNA content go together, similarly. **B,** in an enucleated cell such as an isolated half of an ameba, a gradual decrease in protein content (rods) is accompanied by a corresponding decrease in RNA content (circles). **C,** in test-tube experiments, RNA extracted from cells is found to promote the conversion of amino acids (light circles) into specific proteins (rods).

A

B

C

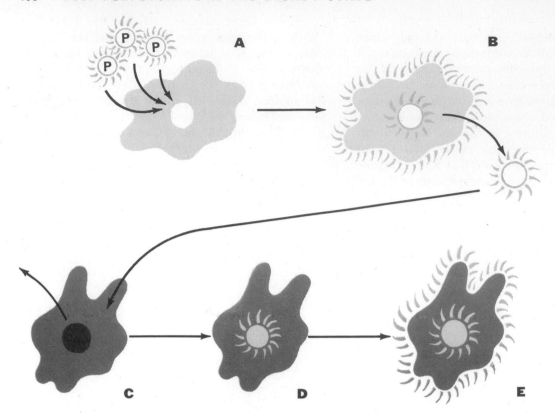

FIG. 18.8. An ameba is made radioactive with phosphates (**A, B**), and the nucleus is used to substitute for the nucleus of an untreated ameba **C**. The radioactivity of the implanted nucleus then spreads into the cytoplasm (**D, E**), indicating that radioactive phosphate passes from the nucleus into the cytoplasm. Since RNA is the principal phosphate-containing derivative of the nucleus, the experiment suggests the nuclear origin of cytoplasmic RNA.

mic RNA (Fig. 18.8). Two amoebae may be used to demonstrate this. One ameba is put into a medium containing radioactive phosphate. Some of this phosphate will be absorbed and will be used as a raw material in the construction of the numerous phosphate-containing protoplasmic chemicals. DNA is among these. In a "radioactive ameba," therefore, the nucleus will eventually contain DNA in which at least some of the phosphate is radioactive. The second ameba is not made radioactive, but, through delicate surgical operations, its nucleus is removed. The experiment now consists in transplanting the radioactive nucleus of the first ameba into the non-radioactive, nonnucleated second ameba. One thus obtains an animal in which no component except the transplanted nucleus is radioactive.

But it soon becomes apparent that this radioactivity does not remain confined to the transplanted nucleus. It spreads into the originally nonradioactive cytoplasm, and analysis shows that it is particularly the phosphate of cytoplasmic RNA which becomes radioactive. Evidently, nuclear DNA contributes phosphate to cytoplasmic RNA. This is a good indication that RNA has a nuclear origin.

Other important evidence revolves around the *nucleolus.* As noted earlier, each nucleus contains at least one of these round, fluid-filled bodies. Three kinds of data have been assembled about them. First, nucleoli can be shown to be direct products of chromosomes. At certain times, certain chromosomes bud off material which collects into nucleoli (see Chap. 23). Second, nucleoli contain large amounts of RNA, and indeed these bodies may be regarded as specialized storage sites for RNA. And third, at certain times nucleoli discharge their contents into the cytoplasm.

The view has therefore been put forward that RNA is manufactured in the chromosomes by, or in association with, the genes; that, in the process, RNA somehow acquires the particular specificities of genetic DNA; and that variously specific RNA's then accumulate in the nucleoli, from where they eventually reach the cytoplasm and the microsomes. Note that neither this path of RNA nor this role of the nucleoli is established conclusively. Yet most biologists today do subscribe to the general hypothesis that RNA is manufactured in the nucleus, that

it mirrors the specificities of DNA, and that it somehow passes into the cytoplasm, where it confers gene-derived specificity on proteins under construction (Fig. 18.9).

On the basis of this hypothesis, the all-important directing role of a gene would reduce to a single, fundamentally passive function, namely, *to allow its specificity to be copied.* A gene would serve rather like an important original "text," carefully preserved in the "library" of the nucleus, and available as the authoritative master document from which expendable duplicates may be prepared. This analogy is in line with what we already know of genes as modulating components of control systems. Like other controlling agents, a gene is an information carrier, a repository of a message. Transferred via RNA, this message informs cytoplasmic effectors how to link which amino acids together.

Just *how* are such specificity transfers accomplished?

FIG. 18.9. Illustrating the functional connection between DNA and RNA and the transport pathway of RNA from nucleus to cytoplasm.

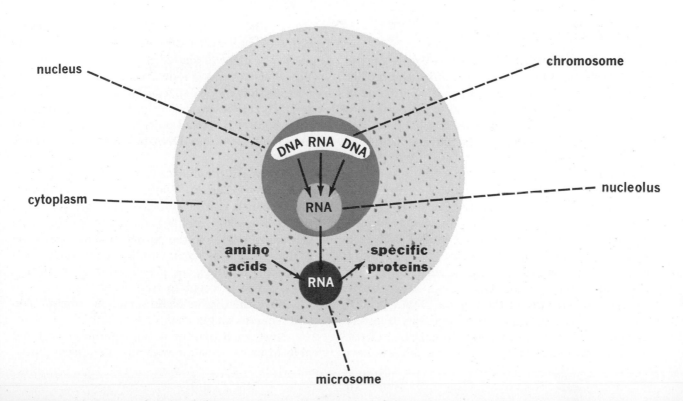

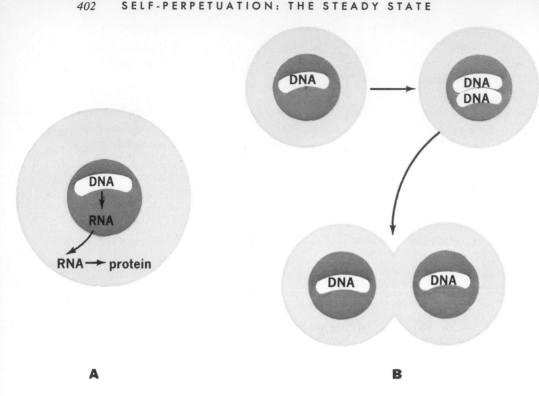

FIG. 18.10. The two kinds of specificity transfers. **A,** transfer from DNA to RNA and protein. **B,** transfer from DNA to new DNA, at the time of chromosome duplication.

A

B

SPECIFICITY TRANSFERS

Presumably, transfer of specificity from genetic DNA in the nucleus to nongenetic RNA, and further transfer from RNA to proteins being constructed in the microsomes, occurs continuously during the life of a cell. However, just before a cell reproduces, another type of transfer occurs: the specificities of existing DNA are passed on to *new* DNA, manufactured in the nucleus at that time. For just before cellular reproduction, the entire set of genes present in a cell is duplicated precisely. One set is then incorporated into each of the two new cells formed by the division of the original mother cell (see Chap. 23). The production of two gene sets out of one requires new DNA, and since the gene sets are identical, newly formed DNA must have exactly the same specificities as the original DNA.

Consequently, two kinds of specificity transfers must be explained: first, transfer from DNA to RNA and protein, and second, transfer from DNA to new

DNA (Fig. 18.10). How either is actually accomplished is still rather obscure today. Such answers as may be given are based, directly or indirectly, on the Watson-Crick model of DNA structure. In terms of this model, specificity transfer from DNA to DNA can be explained quite well, but transfer from DNA to RNA and protein cannot be envisaged as readily. How may DNA-to-DNA transfers come about?

We recall the double-chain nucleotide pattern which, according to Watson and Crick, depicts DNA structure. For example, consider the DNA model illustrated in Fig. 18.11. The specificity of this model resides in the particular sequence of the purine-pyrimidine pairs. Duplication of such a pattern, with simultaneous preservation of specificity, is envisaged to occur in three steps.

First, the double chain somehow "unzips" into two separate, single chains (Fig. 18.12).

Next, each pyrimidine and purine, now freed of its former association with a pyrimidine or purine

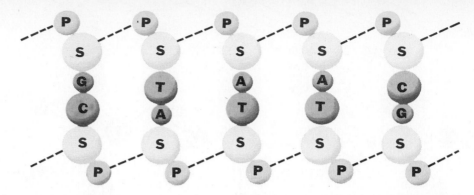

FIG. 18.11. This and the four following figures illustrate the process of DNA duplication, as envisaged today on the basis of the Watson-Crick model. In this diagram, a portion of a sample DNA molecule is shown. It is to be duplicated with preservation of specificity. **P,** phosphate; **S,** sugar; **A,** adenine; **T,** thymine; **G,** guanine; **C,** cytosine.

partner, may reassociate with a new identical partner, drawn from the pool of raw materials supplied by the cytoplasm. For example, every adenine (*A*) in a nucleotide chain may attach to its free bond a new thymine molecule (*T*), if such a molecule is available as raw material. Analogously, every thymine, guanine, or cytosine projecting from a nucleotide chain may reexpress its particular chemical affinity for a given partner and combine with *A*, *C*, or *G*, respectively, from the raw-material supply (Fig. 18.13).

Newly attached purines and pyrimidines in turn are capable of combining with desoxyribose sugar (*S*), and this sugar finally has affinity for phosphate (*P*). If, therefore, *S* and *P* are available as raw materials too, new nucleotides may be built up progressively, in "correct" association with each preexisting nucleotide chain.

This process need not necessarily occur stepwise. For example, if available raw materials should include the whole nucleotide *P—S—T*, in already prefabricated form, then this nucleotide may at-

FIG. 18.12. The first step of duplication may be an "unzipping" of the double DNA chain into two single chains.

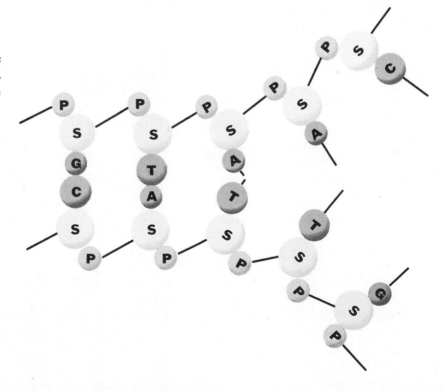

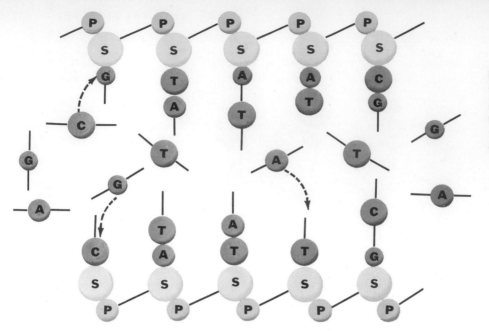

FIG. 18.13. Each single chain then attaches to its purines and pyrimidines appropriate A's, T's, G's, and C's, available in the raw-material supply. Thus A's attach T's, T's attach A's, etc.

FIG. 18.14. Newly attached purines and pyrimidines in their turn then link up with desoxyribose sugars available as raw materials, and these sugars subsequently link up with available phosphates. In addition to such stepwise attachment of new DNA components, whole nucleotides may attach to single DNA chains in a block, if such nucleotides occur in the raw-material supply.

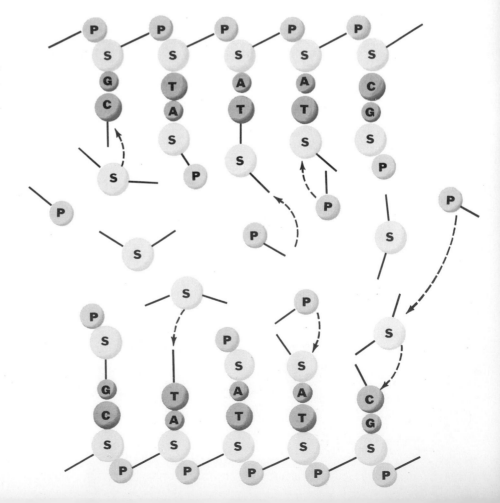

tach as a finished complex to an *A* projecting from a nucleotide chain. Other preformed blocks of components may be similarly available as raw materials, and these too may attach as wholes (Fig. 18.14).

In this manner, new nucleotides may be built up gradually wherever free bonds are available on a preexisting chain. The third and final step then requires only a linking up of the newly attached nucleotides, to form new chains (Fig. 18.15).

The overall result: *one* DNA double chain has given rise to *two* double chains, and these are identical to each other, as well as to the original "mother" chain. DNA thus has reproduced, and specificity has been preserved. Note that all DNA always incorporates the old and the new. One of its two nucleotide chains preexists; the other is newly manufactured.

This duplication process is as much a hypothetical model as the Watson-Crick structure itself. To what extent it describes the actual process of gene duplication is quite unknown. But because it does show how gene duplication *might* occur, and because a better model is not available, it is widely accepted as a reasonable approximation of actual events. It should be remembered here that, according to Watson and Crick, DNA is normally spiraled. Hence duplication of a spiral would produce two intertwined spirals, and these would have to unwind before they could separate. This may or may not happen in actuality.

The basic idea underlying this duplication model is often referred to as the **template hypothesis.** Each single nucleotide chain of DNA serves as a *template,* or blueprint, or master pattern, according to which a new, *matching* nucleotide chain is manufactured. Some such template principle is envisaged to be involved also in all other specificity transfers. For example, during the manufacture of RNA in the nucleus, the DNA of a gene could be the template according to which an RNA with

FIG. 18.15. The final event is the linking together of the newly attached P's and S's, forming new —P—S—P—S— chains. Thus two DNA double chains have been created out of one, with the aid of appropriate raw materials.

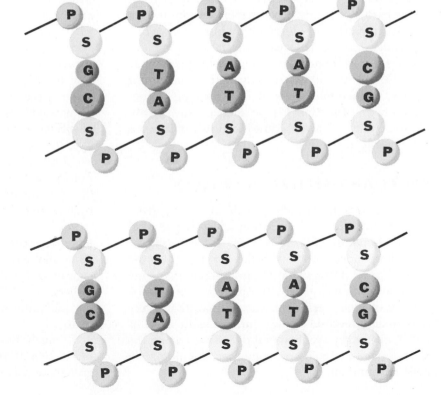

matching specificity is being built up. This RNA eventually reaches the microsomes, where it may in turn serve as template, guiding amino acid linkage in a specific, gene-determined sequence. How this might occur in detail remains a problem for future research.

A finer conception of the structure and function of genes emerges in any case. A whole chromosome may be regarded as a single supermolecule, consisting fundamentally of a very long and perhaps completely continuous DNA double chain. Specificities along this chain vary as the sequences of purine-pyrimidine pairs vary. Just before cell reproduction, the entire chain serves as a supertemplate, and two identical chromosomes are formed from the one. At other times, shorter sections of the chain function as subtemplates, and correspondingly short RNA's are built with matching specificities. The actual length of such subtemplates would vary. Moreover, a given section of the DNA chain serving as subtemplate in one case could partially overlap with a section serving as subtemplate in another case. As noted earlier, various experimental techniques enable us to mark and identify certain sections along a chromosome, and we call such sections "genes." But we do not know how many subtemplates may be included wholly or partially within one of our "genes," hence our difficulty of defining "gene" uniquely in a functional sense. Hence also the conclusion that a "single gene" controls numerous cytoplasmic processes.

GENES AND SELF-PERPETUATION

By governing specific protein synthesis, genes play so strategic a role that they ultimately control the whole nature and the very life of every cell.

First, since proteins make up more of the formed solid framework of protoplasm than any other constituents, genes determine the basic **architecture** of every cell. This means, too, that every normal architectural change during the life cycle of a cell, and every architectural difference among the cells of one or of different organisms, are ultimately gene-determined.

Second, by controlling the nature of proteins, genes control the nature of *enzymes,* all of which are proteins. Since practically every metabolic reaction in a cell requires at least one enzyme, genes thus determine what kinds of **metabolic processes** are possible in a cell. Nutritional reactions, respiratory reactions, motion-producing reactions, synthesis reactions of all kinds, all are enzyme-dependent, hence gene-dependent.

Third, by so governing the whole metabolic character of a cell, genes also govern its entire self-perpetuative character. In steady-state regulation, genes represent one of five categories of modulating agents, as we have noted in the preceding chapter. But whereas enzymes, vitamins, hormones, and inorganic substances control metabolic reactions directly, genes control them indirectly, by exercising control over the other controllers.

More specifically, genes regulate enzyme action via control over enzyme-protein synthesis. Genes regulate hormone action, first, by determining which cells are to manufacture which hormones, and second, by determining which hormones, and what quantities of them, are to be admitted into every cell through the plasma membrane. Genes regulate vitamin action by controlling the manufacture of these modulating agents within cells and again by regulating surface absorption in cells which do not synthesize vitamins on their own. Control of surface absorption also accounts for gene control over the inorganic constituents of cells.

Lastly, the genes of a cell govern one another. For by controlling metabolic synthesis, they direct the production of the sugars, the purines, the pyrimidines, the proteins, and all other components required in the construction of a gene. Each gene, moreover, serves as its own blueprint in the synthesis of another, identical gene. In sum, many agents control metabolism, but genes control these controllers, as well as themselves. This makes them the ultimate maintainers of **steady state** (Fig. 18.16).

Fourth, by governing synthesis in general, and production of new genes in particular, genes direct growth, development, and the **reproduction** of cells.

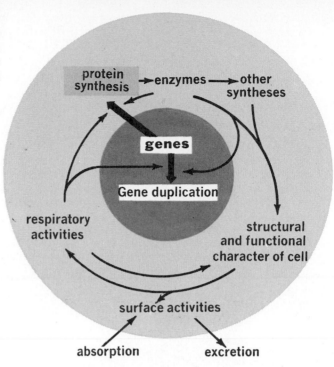

FIG. 18.16. The controlling role of genes in metabolism and steady-state maintenance. The principal action of genes is control of their own duplication and control of protein synthesis, via RNA. Through this, genes exert secondary and tertiary effects, as shown.

By being exchanged among cells and pooled within cells, as we shall see, genes become the basis of **sex**. By duplicating and being transmitted to offspring cells, genes become the basis of **heredity**. Moreover, through one final property, genes become the key to **evolution**.

This final property is *mutability*, the capacity to mutate. As already noted in Chap. 2, genetic nucleoproteins are among the most stable of all organic compounds. Indeed, unless an information carrier were relatively stable, it would cease to be useful as a repository of important information. In addition to the inherent chemical stability of genes, several safeguards exist which ensure that the specific genetic messages are not lost or altered.

One such device is the nucleus itself. Kept in that structure as in a vault, genes are less subject to the destructive effects of the unceasing metabolic mill churning away in "open" cytoplasm. And when gene action is required, genes do not move to the place of action themselves but send expendable copies of themselves in the form of nongenetic RNA. Another safeguard is redundancy; genetic information is stored in more than one place. Each cell of most organisms ordinarily contains *two* complete sets of genes, one set having been inherited originally from the mother of an organism, the other from the father. Hence the even number of chromosomes in most species. Moreover, each cell *type* is usually represented by *many* like cells; hence even if some cells die, the genes of the remaining cells still possess the specific information characteristic of that cell type.

Yet despite inherent stability, protected existence, and redundancy, structural change is bound to occur. For genes are no more exempt from the modifying impact of the environment than any other component of the earth. As we shall see later, a variety of physical and chemical agents may affect and alter gene structure and therefore gene specificity. Such new specificities will be stable and will be passed on into all subsequent gene duplicates. Protein synthesis will be affected accordingly, and, as a result, cell traits will become changed. **Mutations** of this sort may probably arise also during the process of gene duplication, for, like any other process, gene duplication is probably not error-free. If an occasional error occurs during the formation of new nucleotide chains, then an imperfect copy will in effect be a mutated copy (Fig. 18.17).

Whatever the cause, gene mutations bring about stable changes in cell character, and unless such changes produce lethal effects at once, they will be preserved and transmitted to offspring cells. Mutations in reproductive cells therefore may lead to offspring *organisms* exhibiting altered traits, and as we shall see in a later chapter, this is the basis of evolution.

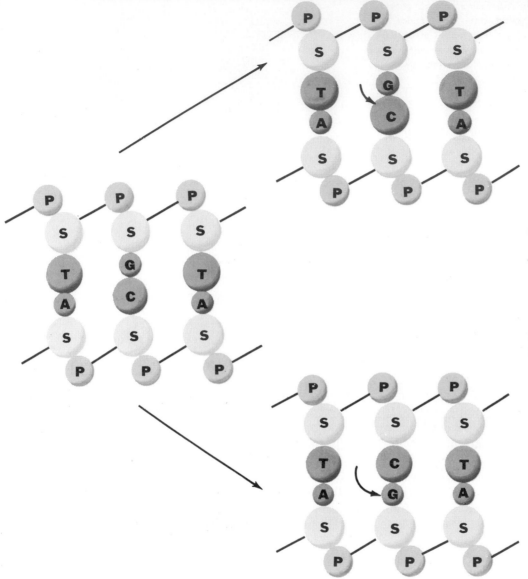

FIG. 18.17. It is possible that errors may occur on occasion when DNA molecules reproduce (e.g., on lower right, inverted position of **C·G** pair). Imperfect copies so formed would be stable, mutated copies, and the mutations would be transmitted to subsequent generations of the molecules.

In summary, therefore, we find that genes serve in just one *primary* role: they allow their specificities to be copied. Three indirect *secondary* roles emerge from this: genes control protein specificities; genes control the specificities of new genes; and, to the extent that gene stability is imperfect, genes may change their specificities. Through these three secondary activities, genes indirectly carry out *tertiary* functions which encompass every aspect of living. For by controlling all metabolism and all self-perpetuation, genes govern cell structure, cell function, and cell development. And by controlling

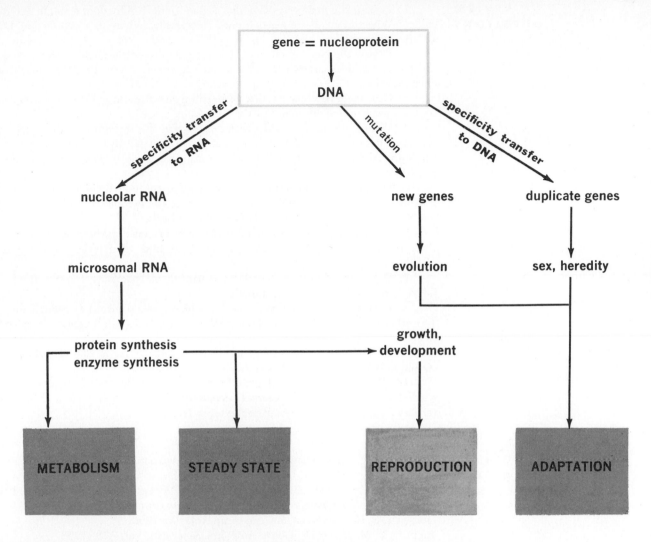

FIG. 18.18. Overall summary of the pattern of gene action. Through their primary action of transferring their specificities, genes control celluar metabolism and all phases of cellular self-perpetuation.

cells, genes govern the life of all organisms, hence the survival of the whole living world. Genes started life, genes still continue it, and, by their failure or absence, genes ultimately end it.

The whole pattern of gene function is sum-

marized in Fig. 18.18. We now examine the functions of other agents which, directed by genes and carrying out genetic commands, play important subordinate roles in the steady-state regulation of cells.

1. In what different ways may one define "gene"? Why does a single definition not suffice? Where in a cell are genes found? Be specific. Where in a cell do (*a*) DNA and (*b*) RNA occur?

2. Review the kinds of chemical components present in nucleoproteins, and specify the particular kinds present in genetic nucleoproteins. How do DNA and RNA differ chemically?

3. Describe the Watson-Crick model of gene structure. What probably accounts for the specificities of different DNA's?

4. What experimental evidence indicates that the nucleus and the cytoplasm of a cell cannot survive in isolation but must interact cyclically? What appears to be the fundamental function of genes? In what sense may gene function be considered to be passive?

5. Describe experimental evidence indicating (*a*) that RNA is manufactured in the nucleus, (*b*) that nuclear RNA is transferred into the cytoplasm, and (*c*) that cytoplasmic RNA plays a role in the control of protein synthesis.

6. What two kinds of specificity transfers do genes participate in, and when do these transfers occur? What is the template hypothesis, and what is it designed to explain?

7. Review in detail the possible mechanism of specificity transfer from DNA to DNA, based on the Watson-Crick model.

8. Review the pattern of processes by which genes control (*a*) cellular metabolism; (*b*) other cellular controllers, including other genes; and (*c*) all aspects of self-perpetuation.

9. How is the stability of genes safeguarded? What is the importance of gene stability? What is the effect of alterations in gene structure?

10. Review the pattern of gene function as a whole. Which function may be regarded as primary? Which indirect secondary functions derive from this, and which tertiary functions result in turn from the secondary ones?

The following are excellent popular articles on various aspects of gene structure and function:

Crick, F. H. C.: The Structure of the Hereditary Material, *Sci. American,* vol. 191, 1954.
Mirsky, A. E.: The Chemistry of Heredity, *Sci. American,* vol. 188, 1953.
Horowitz, N. H.: The Gene, *Sci. American,* vol. 195, 1956.
Ingram, V. M.: How Do Genes Act? *Sci. American,* vol. 198, 1958.
Taylor, J. H.: The Duplication of Chromosomes, *Sci. American,* vol. 198, 1958.
Beadle, G. W.: The Genes of Men and Molds, *Sci. American,* vol. 179, 1948.
Gamow, G.: Information Transfer in the Living Cell, *Sci. American,* vol. 193, 1955.
Gale, E. F.: Experiments in Protein Synthesis, *Sci. American,* vol. 194, 1956.
Danielli, J. F.: On Transplanting Nuclei, *Sci. American,* vol. 186, 1952.

The following are annotated reprints of important original papers, all collected in M. L. Gabriel and S. Fogel, "Great Experiments in Biology," Prentice-Hall, 1955:

Avery, O. T., C. M. McLeod, and M. McCarthy: Studies on the Chemical Nature of the Substance Inducing Transformation of Pneumococcal Types.
Muller, H. J.: Artificial Transmutation of the Gene.
Beadle, G. W., and E. L. Tatum: Genetic Control of Biochemical Reactions in *Neurospora.*
Horowitz, N. H.: On the Evolution of Biochemical Syntheses.

WHENEVER A COMPONENT of a protoplasmic control system becomes abnormally overactive or underactive, *unsteady* state, or disease, is likely to follow. Inasmuch as abnormal functions often give clues to normal functions, diseases are sometimes produced deliberately, by experimental means, in attempts to study the normal roles of particular control components.

The functioning of cellular controllers has been investigated extensively by this means. For example, the action of given genes has been analyzed by the production of genetic deficiencies in cells, that is, experimental alteration, or complete removal, of chromosome sections in which the genes under study are located (see Chap. 27). Similarly, enzyme functions have been elucidated by use of enzyme inhibitors. Specific instances of this have already been mentioned in Chap. 15. Or again, by withholding inorganic substances from a cell, nutritional deficiencies may be produced which may reveal the normal roles of the deficient agents.

Above all, the experimental production of deficiencies, and also of excesses, has provided the bulk of our knowledge about **vitamins** and **hormones**. Some of the information obtained about these two classes of cellular controllers is described in this chapter.

19

CELLULAR CONTROL: VITAMINS AND HORMONES

Vitamins

Most cell types synthesize at least some vitamins. Plant cells produce all they require, but animal cells generally do not manufacture enough, or not all necessary kinds. Insects, for example, may synthesize all except the B vitamins. A few rodents, apes, and man cannot manufacture their own vitamin C, but other animals can.

These differences between various animal species, and between animals as a whole and plants, are probably a result of mutation and evolution.

Originally, all organisms undoubtedly were able to produce all vitamins on their own. If a random mutation subsequently prevented a green plant from synthesizing one or more of the vitamins, that plant could not have survived, since these missing nutrients could not be obtained in any other way. But a similarly affected animal still could obtain prefabricated vitamins heterotrophically. That mutations may indeed destroy vitamin-synthesizing capacity can be demonstrated experimentally.

More than 30 compounds are known to possess the properties of vitamins. That is, they are required in very small amounts, and their prolonged absence produces deficiency diseases and impairment of metabolic processes in cells. As noted above, the normal roles of vitamins have become known largely through study of vitamin deficiencies. In such studies, careful distinction is made between the *clinical* and the *biological* effects of deficiency. For example, it has been known for some time that thiamine deficiency in man may lead to *beriberi*. This is a clinical result; beriberi is a disease characterized grossly by nervous and muscular paralysis. The implication might be that thiamine normally plays a special controlling role in nerve and muscle cells only. Actually, however, thiamine and, indeed, *all* vitamins are probably required in *all* cells, plant or animal. In the case of thiamine, we already know that this vitamin is essential in the conversion of pyruvic to acetic acid in *all* cells (see Chap. 15). It happens that the gross effects of a deficiency may show first, or most pronouncedly, in a particular group of cells—nerves and muscles, for example. But such clinical results are merely the visible secondary consequences of deeper effects of deficiency, influencing all cells universally. It is these which are of basic biological significance. Clearly, clinical results are the beginning, not the end, of vitamin studies.

When first investigated, vitamins were given letter designations in alphabetical order. Later, virtually every vitamin so labeled was found to consist of not one but of several, often related substances. Letters with subscripts then came into use. Today, the tendency is to refer to a new vitamin by its chemical name only. Many vitamins therefore do not have a letter designation, and some have both letter and chemical labels.

Vitamins as a whole may be classified as **fat-soluble** or **water-soluble.** The first group includes vitamins A, D, E, and K; the latter, vitamins B and C. In animals, all fat-soluble vitamins require bile for proper absorption from the gut, and whenever fat digestion is impaired, or when fats are rigidly excluded from the diet, vitamin deficiency develops easily. Water-soluble vitamins frequently pass into cooking water and into the water surrounding canned food; hence such juices should not be thrown away.

FAT-SOLUBLE VITAMINS

Vitamin A Group

These closely related substances are derivatives of the pigment **carotene** synthesized by plants. As noted in Chap. 11, carotene is present in the chloroplasts of leaves. It is also found in carrots and in other red-orange-yellow plant parts, e.g., tomatoes, squash, sweet potato. Egg yolk, butter, and cream are among animal products rich in carotene. Spinach contains more carotene than an equal weight of egg yolk. Among yellow foods, depth of color is a fair indicator of comparative carotene content.

In plant cells and in the liver of animals, 1 molecule of carotene is split into 2 molecules of vitamin A by enzymatic hydrolysis:

$$\underset{\text{carotene}}{C_{40}H_{56}} + 2H_2O \rightarrow \underset{\text{vitamin A}}{2C_{20}H_{30}O}$$

The vitamin is stored in the liver to a considerable extent. Fish livers and their oils are particularly rich sources of the finished vitamin. Fish obtain carotene through food chains originating with algae.

One specific cellular function of vitamin A is known; the compound plays an essential part in the chemistry of vision (see Chap. 21). Unavailability of the vitamin leads to night blindness. Among its other, less clearly understood functions, it ensures proper growth of bones and teeth enamel and of nerve tissue; and it prevents drying and cracking of exposed, normally moist membranes, such as the membranes in the eyes, the breathing system, the alimentary tract, and the urogenital tract. Probably through this action, it reduces the incidence of infectious diseases. Indeed, vitamin A is sometimes called the "anti-infection vitamin." But such a designation might apply equally well to many another vitamin.

The specific role of vitamin A in plants is relatively unknown.

Vitamin D Group

Some 10 related compounds are included here. Two of these, D_2 and D_3, are particularly potent. Chemically, the D vitamins are derivatives of **sterols,** compounds containing rings of carbon in a particular pattern. More will be said about such sterols in the next section. In man, precursors of the D vitamins are present in skin, and these vitamins by and large are the only ones that man can manufacture in sufficient quantity on his own. The precursors are converted into active vitamins by irradiation with ultraviolet light, hence the designation of the D vitamins as "sunshine vitamins." The active vitamins may be stored in the liver. Good external sources of D vitamins are fish-liver oils and dairy foods. In general, foods rich in vitamin A are also rich in vitamin D.

The specific mode of action of these controllers is obscure, but their area of action is fairly well established. They regulate reactions involving calcium and phosphorus, particularly in the complex processes of bone formation and bone maintenance. In the cells of the gut, these vitamins probably balance calcium and phosphorus absorption against excretion of these elements into the gut cavity. The vitamins thus maintain an optimum supply of Ca and P within the body, and they subsequently regulate the deposition of these raw materials as bone and tooth substance.

Deficiency of the D vitamins leads to *rickets*. Among the symptoms of the disease are softening and bending of bones, beading of ribs, erosion of teeth, and elimination of calcium and phosphorus in large quantities. Conversely, continued overdoses of vitamin D may produce abnormal thickening of bones and some calcification of soft tissues.

Vitamin E Group

Several very closely related compounds fall into this category. These vitamins are relatively unstable. However, they are so widely distributed in both plant and animal foods that a deficiency is not likely to arise on any normal diet. The chemical nature of the E vitamins is known.

These controllers are often called "antisterility vitamins," because deficiency can be shown to lead to permanent infertility in male rats and to premature births, and to death of embryos, in pregnant female rats.

Experiments have indicated that vitamin E is required during human pregnancy at a particular stage of embryonic development, i.e., at a time when eyes are formed. For vitamin-E-deficient embryos often exhibit a characteristic abnormality in eye development. Among other results of vitamin E deficiency are injury to the nervous system and muscular atrophy.

Within cells, the E vitamins appear to be required in hydrogen transfer during aerobic respiration (see Chap. 15). What particular role the vitamins play here is still unknown.

Vitamin K Group

A few related compounds of known structure are so classified. They occur widely in food and are synthesized by intestinal bacteria. The vitamins are known best for their role in blood clotting; that is, deficiency leads to failure of the clotting mechanism.

For this reason, vitamin K is now often given before surgery, particularly surgery on bile ducts blocked by gallstones. Vitamin K is dissolved in the fatty portions of food; hence bile is required for its proper absorption from the gut cavity. Therefore, if the bile duct is blocked, an individual is likely to be vitamin-K-deficient, and his blood-clotting mechanism will be impaired. Ingestion of the vitamin (along with bile salts) before an operation may forestall severe surgical hemorrhage.

Just how the K vitamins function in clotting is still unknown. Their participation in respiratory hydrogen transfer has been noted (Chap. 15).

WATER-SOLUBLE VITAMINS

Vitamin B Group

Included here are **thiamine** (B_1), **riboflavin** (B_2 or vitamin G), **nicotinic acid** ("niacin"), **pyridoxine** (B_6), **biotin, vitamin B_{12}, pantothenic acid, folic acid, choline.** These vitamins are not particularly related in chemical structure or in biological function. They are grouped together largely because they tend to occur together in food. Most of these vitamins have been identified chemically, and many can be synthesized in the laboratory. The B vitamins are present in natural foods of all types, particularly rich sources being whole-grain products, yeast, peas, beans, and nuts among plant foods, and liver, egg yolk, and meat among animal foods. Intestinal bacteria synthesize many of the B vitamins.

Precise cellular functions are known for thiamine, riboflavin, nicotinic acid, and pantothenic acid, as we have seen in the account on respiration (Chap. 15). The metabolic roles of pyridoxine and choline are also understood fairly well. Pyridoxine contributes to the formation of an enzyme required in amino acid metabolism, and choline is a source of a particular group of atoms ($-CH_3$, the "methyl" group) in chemical transformations. Biotin is probably required in the formation and utilization of carbon dioxide, and folic acid and vitamin B_{12} play a role in the metabolism of nucleotides.

A more or less well-defined disease is associated with lack of each of the B vitamins. In animals, mild thiamine deficiency, for example, produces fatigue, weakness, and lassitude. More severe thiamine starvation over a period of weeks may result in *beriberi*, a disease characterized by nervous and muscular paralysis and atrophy. These symptoms disappear when thiamine is administered. American diets generally contain enough thiamine to preclude beriberi, but not always enough to prevent milder deficiency symptoms. Grain products made from refined flour are notoriously thiamine-poor; the refining procedure removes a rich source of most of the B vitamins. Millers then sometimes put thiamine back into the flour, in an "enriching" process.

Riboflavin deficiency leads to loss of hair, growth failure, and eye disorders (Fig. 19.1); niacin deficiency, to *pellagra*, a disease of the skin and the nervous system; vitamin B_{12} and folic acid deficiencies, to anemia; choline deficiency, to bone deformities (in chickens) and internal hemorrhages; and pyridoxine and pantothenic acid deficiencies, to growth failure, anemia, lowered resistance to infections, and nerve and skin disorders. Administration of the appropriate vitamin usually relieves the disease.

Vitamin C

This compound is **ascorbic acid,** chemically related to monosaccharide sugars. It is widely synthesized in plants, particularly rich sources being citrus fruit, cabbage, and tomatoes. Most animals—but not man—manufacture it, as has been noted. Ascorbic

FIG. 19.1. Some effects of riboflavin deficiency. Top: riboflavin-deficient rat. Pronounced loss of hair, sickly appearance. Weight 63 g. Bottom: same rat as above, 6 weeks later, after riboflavin-rich diet. Recovery complete. Weight 169 g. (Bureau of Human Nutrition and Home Economics.)

acid is one of the least stable vitamins. Cooking destroys it, and in fresh and canned foods, much of the vitamin diffuses out into the food juices.

The cellular role of this vitamin is still poorly understood. A catalytic function in respiratory reactions is indicated, particularly in the oxidation of certain amino acids. It may be noted that ascorbic acid, like other vitamins which participate in respiratory reactions, is generally found in the mitochondria of cells. Vitamin C additionally controls a phase of synthesis metabolism, and its absence here leads to the best-known deficiency symptoms. The vitamin apparently regulates the manufacture of the "cementing" substance which binds cells together. When this function is impaired, *scurvy* results. Blood vessels begin to "leak," and hemorrhages may occur in any part of the body. Connective tissues no longer bind efficiently, and teeth, for example, loosen from their sockets. In more advanced stages, bones may weaken, muscles degenerate, and death ultimately supervenes. Mild deficiencies of vitamin C may not lead to an outright scorbutic condition, but they may nevertheless impair energy metabolism sufficiently to produce lassitude and to cause fleeting rheumatismlike pains in limb joints.

The functions of the vitamins discussed here are summarized in Table 8. To a variable extent among animals, adequate supply of vitamins depends directly on adequate nutrition. In all animals and all plants, the supply of hormones, on the other hand, hinges primarily on internal secretion.

Hormones

Substances secreted by a cell, carried in the body fluids, and used by another cell are called **humoral agents.** For example, carbon dioxide may serve as a humoral agent. Most organisms possess a large variety of humoral agents, many of them of complex construction, and many serving in steady-state regulation. One group of such agents is found in plants, and numerous others play important roles in all animals. Strictly speaking, the term "hormone" is reserved for those humoral agents which are secreted by distinct, specialized **endocrine glands.**

TABLE 8. The principal vitamins and their functions

Name	Source	Chief functions	Effects of deficiency
Vitamin A	leaves, yellow foods, carotene, liver	chemistry of vision; membrane integrity	night blindness; infectious diseases; bone, nerve abnormalities
Thiamine (B$_1$)		pyruvic acid →acetic acid	beriberi
Riboflavin (B$_2$)		aerobic H transfer	hair loss; growth failure
Nicotinic acid		DPN precursor	pellagra
Pantothenic acid	grain products, yeast, beans, nuts, liver, eggs, meat	coenzyme A precursor	anemia; growth failure; hemorrhages; bone disorders; nerve, skin disorders; infectious diseases
Folic acid		nucleic acid metabolism	
Vitamin B$_{12}$			
Biotin		CO$_2$ metabolism	
Choline		fat, protein metabolism	
Pyridoxine (B$_6$)			
Vitamin C	citrus fruits, tomatoes	amino acid combustion; synthesis of cell "cement"	scurvy
Vitamin D	liver, fish oils	Ca and P regulation	rickets
Vitamin E	most foods	aerobic H transfer	sterility; eye abnormalities; nerve, muscle disorders
Vitamin K			failure of blood clotting

Two animal groups are known to possess such glands, the insects and the vertebrates. It is therefore somewhat inappropriate to refer to "plant hormones," even though this is customary, and the term "animal hormone" has rigorous significance only for insects and vertebrates.

Humoral agents of all kinds, hormones included, provide a transition from cellular to higher-level steady states. As we shall see, they regulate reactions within cells, but they also control the total reactions of whole organs and organisms.

PLANT HORMONES

Auxins

The best-known plant hormones, or humoral agents, are called the **auxins.** They are secreted by shoot meristem tissue, and their central function appears to be the regulation of water metabolism in plant cells.

Through this, the auxins also control many responses of plants to stimuli from the external environment. As a result, the hormones are to behavior control of plants more or less what the nervous system is to behavior control of animals. The most potent auxin is **heteroauxin,** or, in chemical terms, *indole acetic acid.*

The net result of the presence of auxin in a cell is increased absorption of water, paralleled by cell enlargement. This growth apparently involves much more than a simple swelling due to water inflow. It includes, for example, enzymatic softening of the cellulose cell wall, stretching of the wall, deposition of more cellulose, and hardening of this larger envelope. The auxins evidently regulate many sets of reactions. Indeed, the growth effect of auxin is probably merely one indirect expression of its effect on water metabolism and, through this, on all aspects of cellular metabolism generally.

Auxin exerts different effects when present in different concentrations. It stimulates metabolism and growth at medium dosages, but it inhibits when present either in very low or in very high concentrations. This is a widespread characteristic of many protoplasmic components, in plants as well as in animals. That one and the same substance should have diametrically opposite effects at different concentrations can be understood, in general terms, on the basis of chemical equilibria. Too much or too little of a substance, or of a process, is likely to upset delicate balances. This is probably at the root of many commonly known phenomena. For example, in moderate doses X rays may produce cancer, but in large doses they may destroy cancer. Alcohol in moderate doses exhilarates, but it depresses when present in excess. And even food is beneficial only in moderate amounts: too much or too little shortens life.

Low, high, and intermediate are not fixed terms applying equally to all plant cells. Hormone concentrations which are intermediate—hence stimulating —for stems are high—hence inhibiting—for roots (Fig. 19.2). We may say generally that each tissue

FIG. 19.2. The effect of auxin, at different concentrations, on plant root and stem.

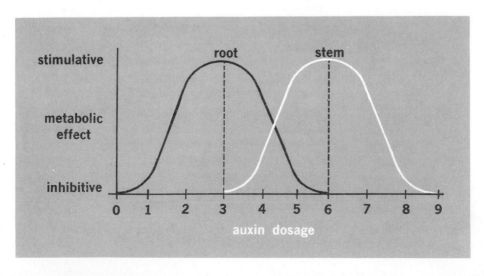

FIG. 19.3. This plant was illuminated only from the top left. Note the bending of the stem in the direction of the light source. (Courtesy of W. G. Smith, Jr., and Boyce Thompson Institute for Plant Research.)

is uniquely sensitive to given concentrations of hormone. This applies also to animal tissues and animal hormones. Moreover, individual metabolic processes within a cell are probably differentially sensitive to various concentrations.

Behavior Control

Much of plant behavior is a consequence of (1) the destruction of auxin by light and (2) the ready diffusibility of the hormone from cell to cell. Suppose that an upright shoot is illuminated only on the left side and is kept in comparative darkness on the right. Much of the hormone secreted on the left side of the shoot tip is destroyed before long by light. But on the right side, the auxin persists. Hence, shoot-tip cells on the left do not grow so much as those on the right. The tip consequently bends over to the left. In other words, the plant acts as if it were "aware" of the position of the light and grows toward it (Fig. 19.3).

A plant in an open field is illuminated more or less equally from all sides. Some auxin is therefore destroyed on all sides, and the shoot grows straight up. But it does not grow as much as if it were kept in darkness. Let an onion or a potato sprout in a dark cellar, and another one on a window sill; observe the size difference of the sprouts after a few days. Of course, in the prolonged absence of light, growth cannot continue indefinitely. A dark-grown plant will die after stores of food reserves are exhausted. Under normal field conditions, plant growth is a compromise between stimulation by light, via photosynthesis, and inhibition by light, via auxin destruction.

If a shoot is planted horizontally, illumination comes predominantly from above. The lighted side here grows less, and the shoot therefore bends upward. This behavior is reinforced by *diffusion* of auxin. In the horizontal plant, any hormone escaping destruction by light soon seeps toward the lower dark side. There it accelerates growth, hence promotes the upward bending of the plant (Fig. 19.4). In an upright plant, diffusion carries undestroyed auxin into the roots, where the hormone regulates growth into the earth.

Responding to auxin in this manner, plants exhibit simple forms of behavior called **tropisms.** Stems are said to be *positively phototropic* and *negatively geotropic;* that is, they grow toward light and away from the earth's center. Roots, on the other hand, are *positively geotropic* and *negatively phototropic.*

FIG. 19.4. Top: a plant placed horizontally into soil soon bends and grows vertically. Like the phototropic growth response of plants, this geotropic response is brought about by auxin. Bottom left: tomatoes grown without hormone application. Bottom right: tomatoes formed after flowers were sprayed with plant hormones. Note the striking growth-promoting effect of the hormones. (Courtesy of P. W. Zimmerman, A. E. Hitchcock, and the Boyce Thompson Institute for Plant Research.)

Other control functions of auxin do not always involve growth. But like growth control, all such other functions probably trace to regulation of water metabolism also. Here may be mentioned the prevention of premature shedding of leaves and the dropping of fruits; the initiation of fruit development by auxins released from pollen; and the control of fruit ripening. Although the mechanisms of control in most of these instances are still relatively obscure, the very fact of auxin involvement has been turned to important horticultural advantage. For auxin can be extracted and can be applied to economically significant plants in the form of sprays or salves. Moreover, some 30 other substances have been found which do not occur naturally in plants, but which are auxinlike in their effects. Such artificial hormones may be applied to plants in lieu of auxin.

For example, by judicious use of hormone sprays, the rate of fruit ripening and the time of fruit drop can be adjusted to some extent. Thus, if a fruit-bearing branch is moderately constricted at its base, auxin diffusion out of the branch is partially prevented. The accumulating hormone, and probably also the accumulating sugars, may produce larger fruits. Auxin applied to flower pistils before fertilization initiates fruit development, and such fruits will be seedless. In this manner, seedless tomatoes, squash, watermelons, and other fruits may be produced. Auxins are also used as weed killers. Certain hormone concentrations are only mildly stimulative or are indifferent to lawn grass but are overstimulative to many weeds. Sprayed weeds then metabolize so intensely that they almost literally burn themselves out and die. In effect, the hormone is inhibitive.

ANIMAL HORMONES

The true hormones of insects and vertebrates vary greatly in chemical composition. Some are proteins, some are amino acids, some are sterols, some are other simple or complex kinds of compounds. A few can be synthesized in the laboratory, a few have a known chemical structure, and the remainder are known only through their clinical effects. Such effects become evident through hormone deficiency (e.g., undersecretion, excision of the secreting cells) or through hormone excess (e.g., oversecretion, injection of hormone).

Insect hormones are essentially *growth* promoters. They initiate and control the development of larvae, the transformation of larvae into pupae, and the final transformation of either larvae or pupae into adults. Beyond these very basic developmental functions, little is known about the cellular, metabolic roles of the hormones. In vertebrates, on the other hand, the cellular functions of hormones may be circumscribed rather well, although the precise reactions in which hormones play parts cannot yet be pinpointed as well as for many vitamins. For example, there is no doubt that the thyroid hormone promotes respiration, but what specific reaction or reactions are affected is still obscure. The account below will be confined to vertebrate hormones in general, and to the hormones of mammals in particular.

Just as all cells probably require all vitamins, so also all mammalian cells probably require all hormones. The term "sex hormone," for example, is somewhat misleading. True, sex hormones are manufactured in sex organs, and they contribute to their proper functioning. As we now know, however, these hormones also contribute to the functioning of practically every other organ in the body. It happens that the effect of deficiency or excess of a given hormone may show first, or most obviously, in a particular group of cells. We may infer from this that, in these cells, the hormone probably regulates a specialized function. We may, for convenience, *name* the hor-

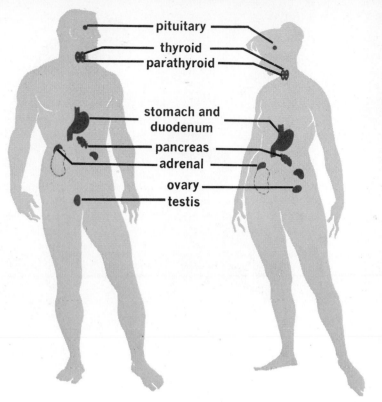

FIG. 19.5. The endocrine system.

mone according to this function, but we cannot conclude this role to be its only one, or even its most fundamental one.

Apart from their other controlling functions in cells, many hormones have an additional special function; they control the manufacture and secretion of one another. Thus, many endocrine glands cannot secrete their hormones unless they are stimulated to do so by other hormones, from other endocrine glands. The entire endocrine organ system (Fig. 19.5) in effect functions like a board of directors, in which the members hold one another in close mutual check. The output of each gland is controlled, wholly or partially, by the output of one or more other glands. And as a result, the overall output by all glands is carefully balanced. This is essential, for whereas one hormone may accelerate a given cellular process, another hormone may inhibit the same process. Hence, unless the amounts of hor-

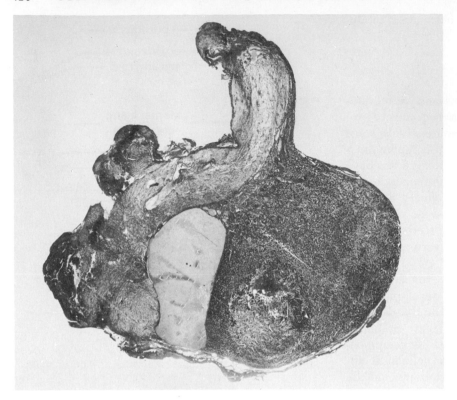

FIG. 19.6. Longitudinal section through a human pituitary gland. The right side of the photo points in the direction of the face; the left side, in the direction of the back of the head. Note the anterior lobe in the right part of the gland and the intermediate and posterior lobes in the left part. The posterior lobe continues dorsally as a stalk which joins the whole gland to the brain. (Courtesy of Dr. B. J. Serber, College of Medicine, New York University.)

mones are continuously readjusted relative to one another and relative to the requirements of the moment, flexible control over cellular processes would not be possible.

If the system of endocrine glands is like a board of directors, then the pituitary gland probably qualifies as chairman of the board.

Pituitary Hormones

Situated approximately in the dead center of the head, the bean-sized pituitary gland is made up of three parts: **anterior lobe, intermediate lobe,** and **posterior lobe** (Fig. 19.6). Each of these is a complete endocrine gland in its own right. Their cells are uniquely specialized, and they secrete distinct hormones. A short stalk of tissue from the posterior lobe attaches the whole gland to the brain.

Anterior lobe. This is the part of the pituitary which exercises control over other endocrine glands. The anterior lobe secretes a set of **tropic hormones** required specifically to activate other endocrine

glands. For example, the rate of manufacture of thyroid hormone depends on the supply of *thyrotropic hormone* from the pituitary. Analogously, production of sex hormones in the gonads (testes and ovaries) is controlled by *gonadotropic hormones.* Another tropic pituitary hormone is *adrenocorticotropic hormone, ACTH* for short. This substance stimulates the cortex (the outer layers) of the adrenal glands.

In exercising such tropic effects, the anterior lobe does not act autonomously but is itself governed by the very glands it stimulates. This is a good illustration of the "checking" process referred to above, which balances the output of various endocrine glands. For example, as more and more thyrotropic hormone is secreted by the anterior lobe, more and more thyroid hormone will be released by the thyroid gland. But once the concentration of thyroid hormone has reached a certain level in the blood, that hormone has an *inhibitive* effect on the anterior lobe. It stops or reduces further secretion of thyrotropic hormone. And by this very action, it stops or reduces further secretion from the thyroid gland. Hence the concentration of thyroid hormone also does not rise further. Conversely, if the amount of thyroid hormone in the blood is low, the anterior lobe will be inhibited rather weakly, and correspondingly much thyrotropic hormone will be secreted. The thyroid gland will therefore be stimulated strongly, and more thyroid hormone will be produced. Evidently, the two glands and their two hormones form an automatic, organ-level control system with built-in feedback. Sex hormones control their own secretion rate analogously, as do the adrenocortical hormones (Fig. 19.7).

In addition to producing the tropic hormones, the anterior lobe also manufactures other hormones. These do not have any demonstrable function as endocrine stimulators but act primarily as metabolic regulators. In this category are the **lactogenic hormones,** which play a role in the control of milk production in mammals. Injection of these hormones stimulates mammary secretions, and hormone deficiency reduces them. Note, however, that removal

of milk by suckling young is at least as essential for continued lactation as is the presence of the hormones. Either hormone deficiency or milk accumulation may alone lead to cessation of milk flow.

Another anterior-lobe secretion is a **growth hormone.** In the young, this hormone maintains growth rates of cells generally. *Gigantism* and *dwarfism* are the results of hormone excess and deficiency, respectively. Most circus giants and dwarfs are of this "pituitary" type; that is, their growth was abnormally accelerated or retarded during early youth, often as a result of pituitary tumors. When the growth hormone reaches excessive concentrations in the adult, tissues which still can grow are stimulated to do so. Characteristic overgrowths are then produced, particularly in parts of the skeleton. The coarse-featured condition known as *acromegaly* is a result.

The anterior lobe exerts very definite, demonstrable effects on carbohydrate, protein, and fat metabolism in cells. Some of these effects are direct, produced by specific pituitary hormones such as the growth hormone. Others are indirect, produced via

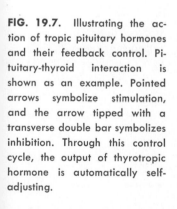

FIG. 19.7. Illustrating the action of tropic pituitary hormones and their feedback control. Pituitary-thyroid interaction is shown as an example. Pointed arrows symbolize stimulation, and the arrow tipped with a transverse double bar symbolizes inhibition. Through this control cycle, the output of thyrotropic hormone is automatically self-adjusting.

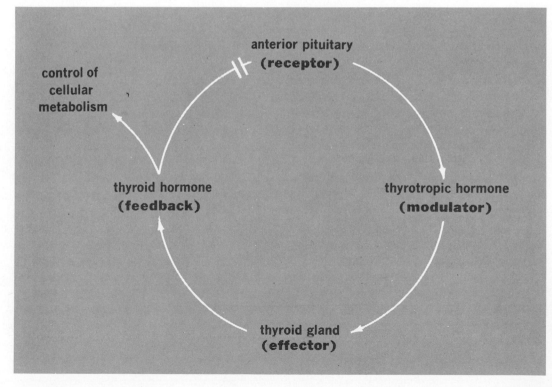

tropic hormones and stimulation of other endocrines. We shall discuss some of these relationships below. See also Fig. 19.8.

All the anterior-lobe hormones are proteins. Active but crude pituitary extracts have long been used in research and medicine, and purified, crystalline hormones are now available also. Most vertebrates manufacture very similar, and in some cases identical, hormones, and those of one species are effective when injected into another. Cattle, sheep, and pigs are the sources of most commercial hormone preparations, those of the anterior lobe included.

Intermediate lobe. This part secretes **intermedin,** a hormone functioning most conspicuously in vertebrates which possess adjustable skin pigmentation. In a frog, for example, the hormone brings about an expansion of pigment cells and consequent dispersal of their pigment granules. This lightens skin color. Intermediate-lobe extracts from any mammal, when injected into a frog, exert the same effect. Mammals evidently possess intermedin, but whether, in the absence of adjustable pigment cells, the hormone intermedin has a function is still unclear.

Intermedin illustrates that a control apparatus can be inherited from early ancestors even though the most conspicuous object of control—adjustable skin-pigment cells—is not inherited.

Posterior lobe. Several hormones with distinct effects can be isolated from this gland. Some regulate the excretion of water, a function which adrenal hormones also perform (see below). Water balance in the body thus is closely controlled by at least two different groups of hormones, integrated in their actions. Other hormones of the posterior lobe stimulate the contraction of smooth muscles, particularly those in the blood vessels and in the uterus. Through this effect on blood vessels and through its control of water balance, the posterior lobe influences blood pressure decisively. The effect on the smooth muscles of the uterus may play a particular role during the process of childbirth, when strong labor contractions expel the infant from the womb. Posterior-lobe hormones are sometimes used by obstetricians to facilitate births.

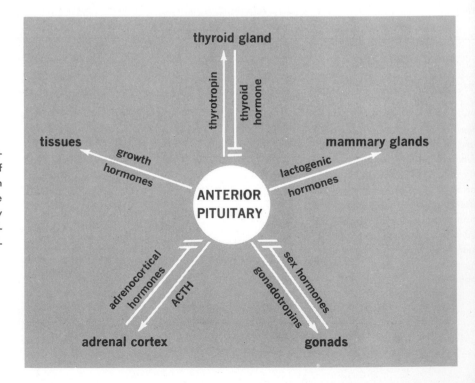

FIG. 19.8. Summary of the secretions of the anterior lobe of the pituitary. Arrows tipped with transverse double bars symbolize known inhibitory feedbacks by which the secretion rate of pituitary tropic hormones is adjusted.

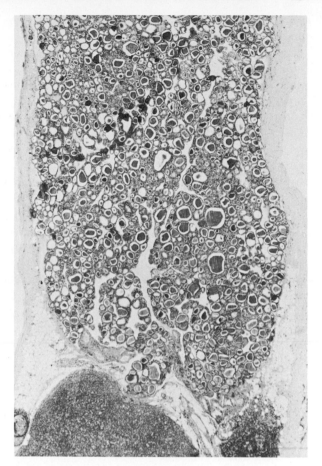

FIG. 19.9. Section through a thyroid gland. The round spaces filled in part with dark material are the regions where thyroid hormone accumulates before being transported away by blood. (Ward's Natural Science Establishment, Inc.)

Thyroid Hormones

The much-studied thyroid gland is a two-lobed organ lying along the trachea, just underneath the larynx. Secreting cells are arranged into single-layered hollow spheres, which are held together by connective tissue (Fig. 19.9). The space within the spheres is a storage depot for thyroid secretion.

This secretion is called **thyroglobulin.** It consists of *globulin,* a protein, which probably serves as a carrier, and of a functionally active hormone fraction, **thyroxin.** Thyroxin is one of the 23 naturally occurring amino acids ($C_{15}H_{11}O_4I_4N$). Its potency as a hormone is in some way associated with its four I atoms. If two of them are removed or substituted by other atoms, potency is sharply reduced. If all four I atoms are removed, potency disappears altogether. Being an amino acid, thyroxin is not digested in the gut, hence can be administered by mouth. A protein hormone would be digested in the gut; such hormones must be injected.

As already noted on several earlier occasions, the cellular function of thyroxin (or of thyroglobulin) is known in general terms: the hormone accelerates respiration. But what particular reaction or reactions are affected is not established as yet.

The clinical effects of thyroxin probably are secondary consequences of its respiratory role. When the iodine content of the diet is low, or when the cells of the thyroid gland are defective, a thyroxin deficiency is likely to develop. If this occurs during early youth, *cretinism* may be the result. In this disease, growth is stunted, even though pituitary growth hormone may be secreted normally; mental development is retarded severely; sexual development is delayed or does not take place at all; and

body weight increases, since little food is burned in cells but much is stored as fat. In the adult, thyroxin deficiency leads to *myxedema.* This is characterized by reduction of mental and bodily vigor, loss of sex drive, loss of hair, and abnormal thickening of the skin, as if much water had accumulated in it (i.e., "edema").

Thyroxin deficiency may be accompanied by thyroid enlargement, or *goiter.* Here the number of thyroid cells increases, and more hormone may then be secreted by the enlarged gland. This may, or may not, suffice to compensate for an original hormone deficiency. If it does, body functions will be normal, but a *simple goiter* will be in evidence. And if it does not, cretinism in the young and myxedema in the adult may develop in spite of, and in addition to, the goiter. Goiter, cretinism, and myxedema may all be relieved by the administration of adequate amounts of thyroxin from an external source.

The thyroid gland may also enlarge when hormone production is originally normal. This may happen, for example, through a tumor. Goiter of this type does not compensate for deficiency. On the contrary, it leads to the manufacture of excess hormone, over and above normal requirements. As might be expected, the effects of thyroxin excess are virtually the reverse of those of deficiency. Greatly speeded-up cellular respiration liberates so much heat that the affected individual feels hot all the time. Despite ravenous food consumption, so much is burned that body weight may decrease. Whereas the myxedemic mammal is sluggish, the hyperthyroid individual is under constant nervous tension, highly irritable by stimuli, yet unable to perform sustained work because of lack of fuel reserves. In man, hyperthyroidism does not produce excessive growth. But in frog tadpoles and other amphibian larvae it does; thyroid excess greatly accelerates metamorphosis into adults.

As noted above, the secretion of thyroid hormone is regulated via thyrotropic hormone from the pituitary. Much of the pituitary influence on metabolic rate is probably due to this thyroid stimulation.

Parathyroid Hormones

The parathyroid glands are tiny, paired, cellular aggregations either located near, but outside, the thyroids (e.g., rabbit) or embedded within the thyroids (e.g., dog, man; Fig. 19.10). Thyroidectomies (removal of the thyroids) in dogs and rabbits therefore produce partly different results. This has been the clue which has led to the discovery of the parathyroids.

The hormone of these glands is known only through its effects. Called **parathormone,** it must be injected whenever it is administered. It is probably a protein, subject to intestinal digestion. The basic function of parathormone is control of calcium metabolism in cells and, as a corollary, maintenance of a constant calcium level in the blood. If the hormone is in abnormally low supply, even if vitamin D is amply available, blood calcium may be deposited in

abnormal quantity in bones, leading to a lowering of blood calcium concentrations and to a thickening of bones and calcification of joints. Low blood calcium has another drastic effect. Lack of these ions makes muscles and nerves hyperirritable; the slightest stimulus may throw the whole body into convulsive twitching. Sooner or later, such attacks completely exhaust the organism and prove fatal.

Symptoms are reversed when parathormone is present in excess. Calcium is then withdrawn from bones, and the skeleton weakens. Blood calcium rises, and the ions may be excreted in large quantities. Moreover, nerves and muscles become hypoirritable, and an individual becomes unresponsive to stimuli.

Adrenal Hormones

As their name indicates, "adrenal" glands are situated "at the kidneys," more precisely, one atop each kidney. An adrenal gland consists of two structurally distinct parts: an outer **cortex,** made up of many layers of cells, and a **medulla,** occupying the

FIG. 19.10. Diagram of the structural relation of the thyroid and parathyroid glands in man. Parathyroid tissue is shown embedded within thyroid tissue.

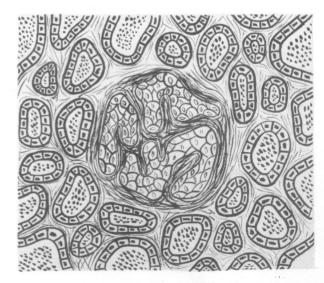

core of the organ (Fig. 19.11). Each of these parts is a separate endocrine gland, and each produces different hormones.

Adrenal cortex. More than 100 different compounds are known to be produced by this structure. Most of these adrenocortical hormones are related chemically, and the basis of their structure is a **sterol** skeleton. This chemical term refers to a framework of carbon atoms arranged as follows:

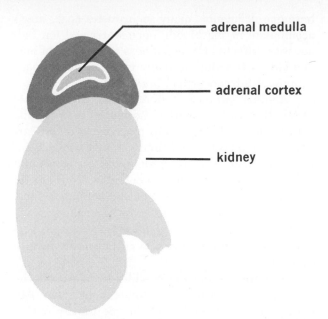

FIG. 19.11. Diagram indicating the position and general internal structure of the adrenal gland.

Hydrogen, oxygen, fatty acids, and many other atomic groupings are attached to these carbons, forming side chains and saturating the unfilled bonds. The number of possible compounds based on the sterol structure evidently is large. Sterols are constituents of virtually every cell, and most of these compounds are inert from an endocrine standpoint. For example, one of the most common sterols is cholesterol, responsible sometimes for gall and kidney stones and for hardened arteries. Some sterols are precursors of the D vitamins, as we have seen. And some, manufactured in specialized cells, are hormones. Adrenocortical and sex hormones are of this type. Often the chemical differences between two sterol hormones are exceedingly slight, yet the biological difference may be very pronounced.

Since adrenocortical secretions contain complex mixtures of many sterols, the specific function of a given one has, in many cases, not yet been separated from that of the others. **Cortisone** is the best known of the adrenal sterol hormones. Adrenocorticotropic hormone (*ACTH*) from the pituitary is necessary for the production of all cortical compounds.

Insufficiency of adrenocortical hormones results in *Addison's disease*. Its most conspicuous symptoms include a characteristic bronzing of the skin, muscular weakness, low blood pressure, and digestive disturbances. These abnormalities have been traced to a wide range of upsets in metabolic processes within cells, involving water, inorganic ions, carbohydrates, fats, and amino acids. From such observations, cellular functions of adrenocortical hormones have been deduced in general terms.

For example, adrenocortical hormones control the water balance of cells, a function carried out jointly with hormones from the posterior lobe of the pituitary, as noted.

Adrenocortical hormones promote the retention of sodium and chloride ions and the excretion of potassium ions. Hormonal insufficiency therefore leads to a lowering of sodium and chloride and to a rise of potassium in the blood and the body tissues.

Adrenocortical hormones regulate the excretion of metabolic wastes from the kidneys. In cases of hormone deficiency, many such wastes (e.g., urea) accumulate in the blood. Since water and ion balances are affected by the kidneys too, control of normal kidney function probably is one of the primary actions of adrenocortical hormones.

Another primary action affects carbohydrate metabolism: adrenocortical hormones promote the conversion of glycogen into glucose. As noted earlier, insulin directly, and thyroxin indirectly, have a contrary effect. Evidently, blood-glucose levels and carbohydrate metabolism generally are held in steady state by sets of antagonistic hormones. Inasmuch as the pituitary controls the adrenal cortex via ACTH, and the thyroid gland via thyrotropic hormone, the pituitary influences carbohydrate metabolism also.

The adrenal cortex, in addition, influences the sex organs and is in turn influenced by them. Abnormal hormone production in one usually entails abnormal production in the other. In view of the chemical similarity of the two groups of sterol hormones, this may not be too surprising. Indeed, the adrenal cortex produces compounds which more or less duplicate the effects of sex hormones. Before puberty, that is, before adult sex hormones are produced, a boy is very distinctly different from a girl, not only in the nature of the sex organs as such, but in characteristics associated with sex generally. Such differences are produced and maintained by adrenal hormones. After puberty, sex hormones secreted by the gonads intensify the sexual differences, and the production of adrenal sex hormones declines. Adrenal tumors sometimes lead to a resumption of cortical sex-hormone production, with abnormal intensification of sexual characteristics.

Adrenocortical hormones exert still other effects. Most of these probably trace also to cortical control of water, ion, and carbohydrate metabolism, to sterol metabolism, or to the influence of the adrenal cortex on other endocrine organs. By virtue of these widely divergent functions, the adrenal cortex constitutes one of the most important regulators in the body.

Adrenal medulla. The hormone produced by this gland is **adrenalin,** a relatively simple compound which can be synthesized in the laboratory. The adrenal medulla is largely under control of the nervous system. Indeed, the connection between this gland and the nervous system goes even deeper. The gland develops from the same embryonic tissue from which the nervous system develops; and certain nerves regulate cellular functions by releasing adrenalin (see Chap. 21).

When injected into the body, adrenalin raises blood pressure; increases heart rate; promotes conversion of liver glycogen to blood glucose; inhibits the peristaltic movements of the gut; stimulates the tiny muscles which attach to hairs and feathers, appendages which are raised as a consequence (producing "goose flesh" in man); dilates the pupils of the eye; increases muscular power and resistance to fatigue; and also promotes faster coagulation of blood.

Most or all of these effects are collectively sometimes called the **alarm reaction.** It is produced normally when an organism is under great emotional stress, or when it makes ready to exert a supreme effort, or when it gets set to battle an adversary. In such situations, adrenalin is released in increased quantity from the adrenal medulla. This secretion pattern and the above effects suggest that adrenalin functions primarily during danger or emergency, quickly preparing the organism for increased effort. This view is strengthened by the results of surgical removal of the adrenal medulla. The organism then cannot adjust rapidly to emergencies.

Sex Hormones

As already noted, these are produced in matured ovaries and testes, under the influence of pituitary gonadotropic hormones. Several male and several female sex hormones are manufactured and, just as in the adrenal cortex, all are sterols. We may refer to male hormones collectively as **androgens,** i.e., "male-producing," and to female hormones as **estrogens,** i.e., "estrus (menstrual cycle)-producing." The most potent androgen is **testosterone,** and the most potent estrogen, **estradiol.** Much of the detail concerning secretion and the specialized functions of sex hormones will be discussed in Chap. 25. Here we may examine the general role of these compounds.

They maintain, first, **primary sex characteristics**, namely, the structural and functional integrity of the male and female reproductive systems. They maintain, second, **secondary sex characteristics**, namely, all the features other than sex organs which differentiate male from female. Among these are different growth and distribution patterns of hair; voice differences; differences in physical strength, endurance, and muscular development; skeletal differences, as in the hip region; differences in the amount of fat under the skin; mammary development in females; sexual differences in skin coloration and plumage among fish, birds, and other vertebrates (Fig. 19.12). Sex hormones also maintain sex urge; they decisively influence mental vigor and mental development; and they stimulate blood circulation. Evidently, they affect the body as a whole.

Pituitary or gonadal insufficiency, or castration, leads to a decline of these various functions and to atrophy of the reproductive system. Injection of androgens into males, and of estrogens into females, intensifies the sexual character of the organism. Conversely, continued injection of androgens into females, and of estrogens into males, tends to reverse sexual characteristics in the direction of the opposite sex. In a few vertebrates, but not in man, a functional female can be produced in this manner from a male. Sperm-producing testes then become egg-producing ovaries, and other parts of the reproductive system change correspondingly; and vice versa. But in most vertebrates, injection of the opposite hormone merely deemphasizes the original sexual

FIG. 19.12. Secondary sex characteristics of vertebrates, and their differences in males and females. Top: bobwhites. Male at left, female at right. Note differences in color pattern of plumage. Middle: pintail ducks. Drake at left, hen at right. Note differences of body size and of plumage pattern. Bottom: moose. Male at right, female at left. Note difference in body size, and absence of antlers in female. See also Fig. 4.7 for another example. All such sex differences are controlled and maintained by hormones, and they are instances of polymorphism, more specifically, of sexual dimorphism. (Top to bottom, courtesy of E. P. Haddon, R. G. Schmidt, J. M. Greany, U.S. Fish and Wildlife Service.)

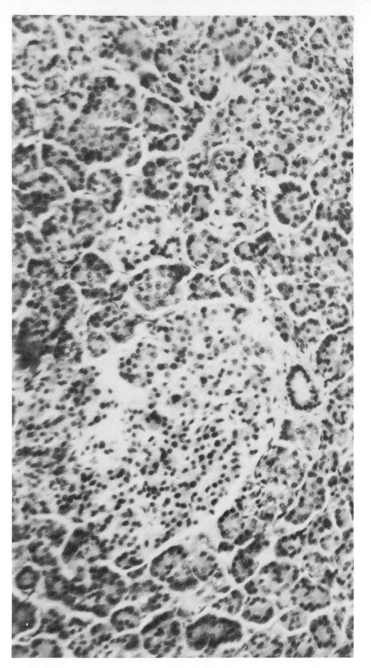

FIG. 19.13. Section through the pancreas. The round, lighter-colored tissue area, somewhat off center in the photo, is an insulin-secreting islet of Langerhans. (Courtesy of Dr. B. J. Serber, College of Medicine, New York University.)

traits. For example, an estrogen-injected human male would acquire a more highly pitched voice, would accumulate increased quantities of subcutaneous fat, would develop broader hips, and would perhaps change toward other secondary sexual traits characteristic of females. Yet sex organs would remain male, though they would atrophy and become nonfunctional. In many ways, the results here duplicate those of castration.

Both sexes normally produce *both* androgens and estrogens. The compounds are only slightly different chemically, and *both* kinds are probably manufactured in testes as well as in ovaries. In an extreme case, mares actually secrete very much more androgen than estrogen, yet the horses are, and remain, female. These observations illustrate the general principle that it is the relative quantitative *ratio* of hormones, not their absolute amount, which is of importance. Thus, so long as a definite ratio of male and female hormone is present, regardless of which is more abundant in absolute terms, the cells of a female will respond differentially to female hormone, the cells of a male, to male hormone. When this quantitative balance is upset, cellular processes will swing more toward maleness or toward femaleness. Normal sex-hormone balances actually differ slightly for different individuals, and this probably accounts for the various degrees of masculinity and femininity widely in evidence.

Other Hormones

Various other endocrine secretions have already been discussed in earlier contexts. For example, the roles of the hormones **gastrin** and **secretin** have been described in the account on digestion (Chap. 12). We have also dealt with **insulin,** the protein hormone manufactured in the "islets of Langerhans," groups of endocrine cells embedded within the pancreas (Fig. 19.13). Unlike pancreatic digestive juice, insulin does not have access to the pancreatic duct; blood is its only exit path. As noted in Chap. 13, the result of insulin deficiency is *diabetes,* a condition in which utilization of blood glucose is impaired. Insulin excess, on the other hand, produces so much liver and muscle glycogen, at the expense

TABLE 9. The principal endocrines and their hormones

Gland	Hormones	Chief functions	Effects of deficiency or excess	Gland	Hormones	Chief functions	Effects of deficiency or excess
Pituitary, anterior lobe	thyrotropic gonadotropic ACTH	stimulates thyroid stimulates gonads stimulates adrenal cortex		Adrenal cortex	cortisone, other sterol hormones	controls metabolism of water, salts, carbohydrates, fats, proteins; inhibits ACTH secretion; duplicates sex-hormone functions	Addison's disease
	growth	promotes cell metabolism	dwarfism; gigantism; acromegaly				
	lactogenic	stimulates milk secretion					
Pituitary, mid-lobe	intermedin	controls adjustable skin-pigment cells		Adrenal medulla	adrenalin	alarm reaction	inability to cope with stress
Pituitary, posterior lobe	at least five distinct fractions	controls water metabolism; blood pressure; kidney function; smooth muscle action	excessive water excretion	Pancreas	insulin	glucose → glycogen	diabetes
				Testis	testosterone, other androgens	promote cell respiration; blood circulation; maintain primary and secondary sex characteristics, sex urge; inhibit gonadotropic secretions	atrophy of reproductive system; loss of secondary sex characteristics
Thyroid	thyroxin	stimulates respiration; inhibits thyrotropic secretion	goiter; cretinism; myxedema	Ovary	estradiol, other estrogens		
Parathyroid	parathormone	controls Ca metabolism	nerve, muscle abnormalities; bone thickening or weakening				

of glucose, that blood-glucose levels fall abnormally.

The kidneys produce a hormone called **renin,** which regulates blood pressure. Two other organs at one time were thought to have endocrine functions: the **pineal** body and the **thymus** body. The pineal is situated on a stalk between the two halves of the brain. In some vertebrates, for example, the lamprey and the reptile *tuatara* (see Chap. 31), the pineal is usually extremely large. Its stalk carries it as far as the head skin, and the skin at that point is transparent. The pineal here is actually a third functional eye situated on top of the head. In most vertebrates, optic functions of the pineal are not in evidence, and the organ is quite small. Removal of this

body has no demonstrable effect whatsoever; hence an endocrine function may probably be ruled out.

The thymus body lies in the neck and the upper chest regions. In some mammals it persists throughout life, but in man and in others the organ gradually decreases in size during youth and disappears altogether at the time of puberty. Removal of the organ at any stage of life does not produce demonstrable effects. As in the case of the pineal, therefore, an endocrine function of the thymus is unlikely. And what other function the organ might have is also unknown.

The functions of the principal hormones discussed here are summarized in Table 9.

RESUME   Three points may be reemphasized. First, vitamins are universal, as we have seen, but hormones are not. Plant hormones, insect hormones, and vertebrate hormones are unique to these respective organisms. This is not to say that estrogen, for example, or thyroxin may not be found in protozoa or in some other animal or plant group. Indeed, many hormone compounds do occur very widely among plants and animals. But, so far as is known, such compounds do not *function* as specific hormones. Wide occurrence probably indicates that certain chemicals are fairly usual products of cellular metabolism and that, through evolutionary specialization in some organisms, many of such chemicals have become components of specialized control mechanisms. It may be significant in this connection that elaborate hormonal controls are found in insects and vertebrates, the very groups which have the most advanced evolutionary status among animals.

Second, this account of vitamin and hormone functions shows well how highly redundant the control of cellular processes may be. Consider, for example, on how many controllers the specialized functioning of bone cells depends: vitamins A, riboflavin, choline, pyridoxine, C, and D; pituitary growth hormone, thyroxin, parathormone, and cortisone; calcium and phosphorus, which must maintain a balance between free calcium and phosphate ions on the one hand, and precipitated calcium phosphate on the other; a host of enzymes, most of them not yet identified; and quite a number of genes, as genetic experiments indicate. These regulate only the *specialized* function of bone cells. The list does not include controllers required additionally in the maintenance of housekeeping functions in bone cells, on which specialized activities depend. Analogous lists could be drawn up for any other cellular activity. This confirms our earlier generalization that cellular activities are intricate sequences of reactions, each reaction controlled by one or more specific accelerators and by one or more specific inhibitors. Acting tropically, antagonistically, or synergistically, these controlling agents maintain a steady state, and when any one of them is in deficient or excessive supply, an abnormal end result will be the outcome. Moreover, the nature of the abnormality will vary in one and the same body part, according to which of the underlying reactions is impaired.

Finally, as noted, hormones lead to a consideration of steady-state controls on supracellular levels. Such higher-level controls operate on the same basic principles as the cellular controls: a balancing of excitations against inhibitions in essentially reversible processes; and mutual checks among controlling agents, through tropic, antagonistic, and synergistic interactions. To be sure, the controlling agents here are no longer molecules and cells, but tissues and organs.

As pointed out in Chap. 17, supracellular controls are most elaborate in advanced animals. In these, the body fluids interconnect all body parts and maintain them in steady state relative to one another. Here also the circulatory and excretory systems regulate the properties of the body fluids, and the nervous system exercises general supracellular control in addition. These tissue- and organ-level controls will be the subjects of the next two chapters.

REVIEW
QUESTIONS
1. What is a vitamin? Different animals must be supplied with different vitamins. Why? How did these differences probably arise?

2. Distinguish between clinical and biological effects of vitamin or hormone deficiencies. Which vitamins are fat-soluble, and which are water-soluble?

3. Review the food sources and the chemical nature of the principal vitamins. As far as is known, what are the cellular functions of each of the principal vitamins? What are the clinical effects of deficiencies of these vitamins?

4. Define "humoral agent." Define "hormone." In what groups of organisms is each of these found? Where in a plant are auxins produced, and what appears to be their primary function? What derivative functions result from this?

5. Describe the role of auxins in plant growth and growth behavior. How do shoots grow toward light regardless of their original orientation? Similarly, how do roots grow in the direction of the earth's center? What are tropisms? In what processes other than growth do auxins play a role?

6. How do given endocrine glands control the activity of other endocrine glands? Show how the activity of the adrenal cortex is regulated by the pituitary, and vice versa.

7. Review the general chemical nature of the principal hormones. What determines whether a medicinal hormone preparation must be injected or may be taken orally?

8. What are the specific hormones produced by the various endocrine glands? As far as is known, what are the primary cellular functions of each of these hormones? In each case, what are the clinical effects of (*a*) hormone deficiency and (*b*) hormone excess?

9. Inasmuch as both sexes produce both male and female sex hormones, how can the sexes remain distinct? What is the effect of injecting male hormone into a female, and vice versa? Distinguish between primary and secondary sex characteristics. What specific features are grouped into the latter category?

10. By three specific examples involving vitamins and hormones, illustrate the high degree of redundancy of control processes within cells. In what respect are hormones both cell-level and tissue- and organ-level controllers?

SUGGESTED
COLLATERAL
READINGS
Classical original papers by famous biologists are reprinted and annotated in the sections on Auxins, Vitamins, and Hormones in M. L. Gabriel and S. Fogel, "Great Experiments in Biology," Prentice-Hall, 1955. The following additional articles are strongly recommended for further information on humoral agents in plants:

Salisbury, F. B.: Plant Growth Substances, *Sci. American,* vol. 196, 1957.

Schocken, V.: Plant Hormones, *Sci. American,* vol. 180, 1949.

Audus, L. J.: Growth Substances and Plant Development, *Endeavor,* vol. 14, 1955.

Thimann, K. V.: The Physiology of Growth in Plant Tissues, *Am. Scientist,* vol. 42, 1954.

Kraus, E. J.: The Significance of Growth Regulators in Agricultural Practice, *Am. Scientist,* vol. 42, 1954.

Jacobs, W. P.: What Makes Leaves Fall, *Sci. American,* vol. 193, 1955.

Biale, J. B.: The Ripening of Fruit, *Sci. American,* vol. 190, 1954.

Greulach, V. A.: Plant Movements, *Sci. American,* vol. 192, 1955.

Naylor, A. W.: The Control of Flowering, *Sci. American,* vol. 186, 1952.

On animal hormones, consult any of the following:

Zuckerman, S.: Hormones, *Sci. American,* vol. 196, 1957.

Beach, F. A.: "Hormones and Behavior," Hoeber, 1947.

Funkenstern, D. H.: The Physiology of Fear and Anger, *Sci. American,* vol. 192, 1955.

Constantinides, P. C., and N. Carey: The Alarm Reaction, *Sci. American,* vol. 180, 1949.

Li, C. H.: The Pituitary, *Sci. American,* vol. 183, 1950.

Levine, R., and M. S. Goldstein: The Action of Insulin, *Sci. American,* vol. 198, 1958.

Heilbrunn, L. V.: Calcium and Life, *Sci. American,* vol. 184, 1951.

Milne, L. J., and M. J. Milne: How Animals Change Color, *Sci. American,* vol. 186, 1952.

Williams, C. B.: The Metamorphosis of Insects, *Sci. American,* vol. 182, 1950.

CELLS ARE IN STEADY STATE relative to their environments. Within a multicellular organism, this environment consists of other cells and, in most animals, also of body fluids, namely, **blood** and **lymph.** Lymph fills all the spaces between cells and cell layers, and, as noted in Chap. 13, this fluid originates in the bloodstream. Blood itself comes close to most cells, for tiny blood capillaries ramify through all tissues. Single flat cells compose the walls of the capillaries, and these walls are the only barriers which separate blood and tissue cells.

The body fluids are major controllers of steady states within tissues and organs. Tissues reflect the conditions prevailing in blood and lymph, and vice versa. In their turn, the body fluids are controlled by two organ systems, the **circulatory system** and the **excretory system.** The first is more than a network of channels. It also regulates the *physical* attributes of the fluids it carries, such as pressure, distribution, and rate of flow. Likewise, the excretory system is more than an eliminating apparatus. It is made up of many screening stations, which regulate the *chemical* attributes of the body fluids: the system continuously checks and adjusts the composition of the fluids circulating through it.

The nature of blood and lymph, and the operations of the circulatory and excretory systems, are the subjects of this chapter.

Blood and Lymph

The expression that a certain personality trait "is in one's blood"; phrases like "hot blood," "bad blood," "blue blood"; and race doctrines based on hypothetical blood differences all trace back to primitive notions of ancient and medieval philosophers. They believed that blood, together with "phlegm," "yellow bile," and "black bile," constituted four "humors" which, mixed in various proportions, determined the nature of man. We know today that the gall bladder and its bile can be removed surgi-

20

THE BODY FLUIDS

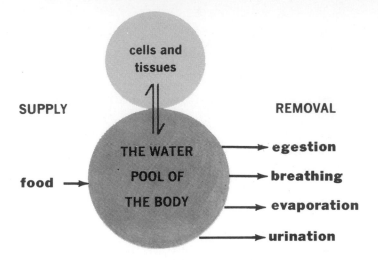

FIG. 20.1. The water balance of the body. Under normal conditions, supply and removal are adjusted for maintenance of a constant water content within the body.

cally, that blood can be drained off and replaced by blood from another person, yet the nature of man changes not one whit. Moreover, in the healthy person, blood is always maintained at a constant temperature of 37°C; blood is always subjectively red if the viewer is not color-blind; and from one race to another, blood chemistry differs no more than between extremes within a given race. The nature of man, and of animals generally, is determined in part by genes and in part by environment, not by blood.

Blood is a tissue. It is composed of loose **cells** and of **plasma,** a fluid in which the cells are suspended. Approximately half of the blood of a mammal is cellular, the other half plasma. All body tissues affect the momentary composition of blood, by adding wastes and withdrawing nutrients. Four structures in particular regulate the long-term composition: the liver; the marrow of long bones; and the lymph nodes, which control the cellular content; and the liver, the kidneys, and probably also the lymph nodes, which control the composition of plasma.

BLOOD PLASMA

Overall Composition

The main constituent of plasma is water. Its source is food and metabolic water excreted by cells into the body fluids. The supply of water is carefully counterbalanced by excretion, through lungs, sweat glands, and kidneys. The total water content of the body, hence blood volume, is thereby maintained constant (Fig. 20.1).

Blood water has many functions. From this store, cells draw their own protoplasmic water. Oozing out from capillaries as the main constituent of lymph, blood water envelops all tissues of most anials, in the same way that ocean water enveloped the cells of their primitive ancestors. By its very presence in a certain quantity within a closed channel system, blood water contributes importantly to blood pressure. After extensive blood loss through wounds, one of the foremost requirements is restoration of blood volume, that is, restoration of water.

Blood water is the transport vehicle for all other plasma components and for blood cells. Dissolved or suspended in blood water, apart from cells, are two groups of substances. One consists of materials normally maintained at *constant* concentrations. This group includes inorganic ions; plasma proteins; and other organic materials, which might be nutritional raw materials in transit to cells, such as glucose, or waste products in transit to the kidneys.

The second group of plasma constituents consists of substances which fluctuate more or less widely in concentration, depending on body activity. In this category are a number of foods in transit; urea and other waste products in transit; hormones in transit; and many other substances. Our present concern is a discussion of the constant plasma components.

Constancy of plasma components is achieved by balancing supply against removal. Supply may take the form of absorption from the gut, or release by tissue cells, or manufacture and release by the liver. Removal may involve liver storage, excretion from kidneys and a variety of other organs, or absorption by tissue cells. In each case, too high or too low a concentration of a given substance in the blood is the critical stimulus for its own removal or replenishment. As we have seen, for example, a moderately high blood-glucose level stimulates liver cells to lower it, by storing the excess as glycogen. A still higher level similarly stimulates not only liver but also muscles. And a very high concentration leads to glucose excretion from the kidneys. We note that the differential sensitivity of these control organs to actual supply and demand of a given compound brings about a steady state in blood.

Inorganic Ions

These are balanced through ion supply in food, through turnover in tissue cells, including such specialized tissues as bone, and through excretion. The functions of inorganic ions in blood point up the vital importance of ion balance. Like all other particles in plasma, inorganic ions contribute to the **osmotic pressure** of blood. This pressure is adjusted to the osmotic pressure within tissues. And when either blood or the tissues acquire greater concentrations of particles, then water is pulled osmotically one way or the other. For example, if, through intake of much salt water, the ion concentration of blood should rise, then the tissues would become dehydrated. Conversely, if, through intake of too much tap water, the ion concentration should fall, then the tissues would become overly hydrated. Short-term fluctuations of this sort occur frequently, as a consequence of normal metabolism.

Another function of the ions is **pH control** and pH balance between blood and tissues. Any small change of pH is readjusted to normal by the buffering action of the inorganic ions (see Chap. 6). Most important in this respect are the positively charged sodium (Na^+), potassium (K^+), calcium (Ca^{++}), and magnesium (Mg^{++}) ions; and the negatively charged phosphate ($H_2PO_4^-$, $HPO_4^=$, $PO_4^{\equiv}$), chloride (Cl^-), bicarbonate (HCO_3^-), carbonate ($CO_3^=$), and sulfate ($SO_4^=$) ions. Over half of the total ion content of blood represents sodium chloride, common table salt.

Ion pairs like $HPO_4^=$ and $H_2PO_4^-$, and $CO_3^=$ and HCO_3^-, are particularly significant buffers in blood. For example, if H^+ ions should accumulate in abnormally large quantities, then carbonate ions ($CO_3^=$) could combine with H^+, forming HCO_3^-. Carbonate concentrations would thereby decrease, bicarbonate concentrations would increase, and the free H^+ ions would have been "taken out of circulation." Analogously, $HPO_4^=$ could combine with H^+ and become $H_2PO_4^-$. The reverse reactions would occur when blood tends to become too alkaline. Original ion balances may subsequently be restored by the kidneys, through excretion of ions present in relative excess.

In addition to these physicochemical effects, inorganic ions also exert important biological effects. For example, we have noted earlier that calcium ions regulate the sensitivity of nerves and muscles. Since both of these tissues are in contact with blood or lymph, the concentration of blood calcium is evidently of enormous significance. Earlier contexts have also referred to specific biological actions of most other inorganic ions in the body, and those that are in the body are also in plasma.

Plasma Proteins

Some of these proteins are known to be manufactured in the liver, destroyed in the liver, and held at constant concentrations by the liver. The origin of others is still unknown. Since all plasma proteins are particles, and since most of them are ionized, they contribute importantly to osmotic balance and pH balance. In addition, they perform other functions.

One type of blood protein, **fibrinogen,** has long been known to play a major role in blood clotting (see below). Another group of blood proteins includes a large variety of enzymatically active agents. A few of these, for example, **prothrombin,** are also essential in blood clotting. Others are enzymes such as are found in tissue cells generally. Their functions in blood are largely obscure. A third type of blood protein has been called **albumin,** because it resembles egg albumen chemically. Albumins are excreted in certain kidney diseases. Physicians test urine routinely for protein content, as a check on kidney function.

A fourth group of plasma proteins, the **globulin** fraction, plays two known major roles: globulins are the cause of **blood-type** differences, and they serve as defensive **antibodies.**

That bloods of different individuals may differ in type has been known for some time. Where type differences exist, the plasma globulins of one individual act as foreign bodies when introduced into another individual, and the foreign globulins may cause the blood cells of the recipient to *clump.* Clumped blood cells clog narrow blood capillaries and may cause death. Therefore, before a blood transfusion is made, it is essential to establish blood compatibility. Type differences evidently are of major clinical significance. Biologically, they are merely one further expression of the general phenomenon of protein specificity, i.e., of protein differences among all organisms.

An antibody is a protein which confers immunity against infectious agents. When a foreign protein is introduced into the blood of an organism, for example, by bacterial infection, then there soon appears an antibody in the blood which specifically "combats" the foreign protein. Such antibodies are globulins. Where are antibodies manufactured? This is not certain, but lymph nodes and liver are likely guesses. What does "combating" mean? As far as can be ascertained, it means the combining of the antibody with the foreign protein, thus preventing the latter from acting in a damaging manner. This combination is thought to be a "lock-and-key" process, rather like the combination of an enzyme with a reactant. The molecular configuration of the antibody

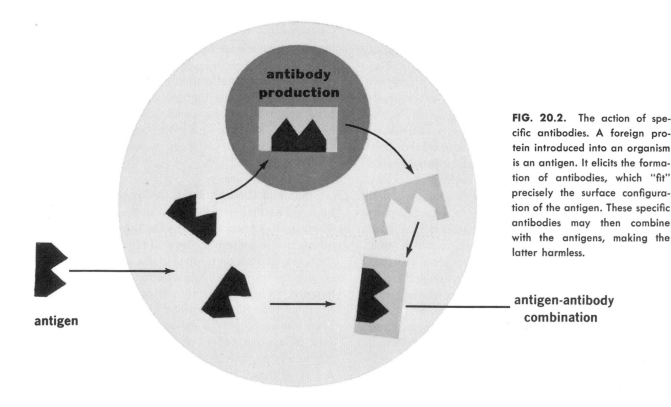

FIG. 20.2. The action of specific antibodies. A foreign protein introduced into an organism is an antigen. It elicits the formation of antibodies, which "fit" precisely the surface configuration of the antigen. These specific antibodies may then combine with the antigens, making the latter harmless.

antigen

antibody production

antigen-antibody combination

nonvirulent agent

A

virulent agent

B

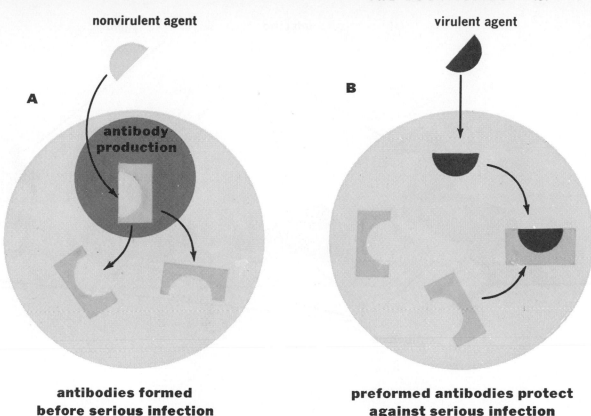

antibody production

**antibodies formed
before serious infection**

**preformed antibodies protect
against serious infection**

FIG. 20.3.   The principle of active immunization. **A,** nonvirulent agents are introduced into an organism, and specific antibodies are formed. **B,** when virulent forms
of the foreign agents should later infect the organism, specific antibodies are already
present to combat the infection.

apparently is such that it "fits" into the configuration of the foreign protein; the antibody is specific (Fig. 20.2). How does specificity arise? Do cells which manufacture antibodies take "samples" of invading proteins, make closely fitting "molds," and then synthesize large quantities of globulins on the mold patterns? Does DNA or RNA play a role here? Such questions cannot be answered as yet.

A large area of preventive and curative medicine is based on specific antibody production. In vaccination procedures, an individual is injected with nonvirulent strains of disease-producing bacteria, or with bacteria made harmless previously by killing them. Specific antibodies against these in-

jected bacteria are then synthesized in the body. In this manner, **active immunity** is established, for periods up to several years or often throughout life. If virulent bacteria invade during such periods, the combating antibodies are already present, and the disease may be expressed only in mild form, or not at all (Fig. 20.3).

In many cases, active immunity arises without vaccination. Infectious agents producing hardly noticeable attacks of disease invade continuously and bring about the development of antibodies against them. These disease organisms thus "build up immunity," and when their more virulent relatives invade, the protective antibodies are already deployed.

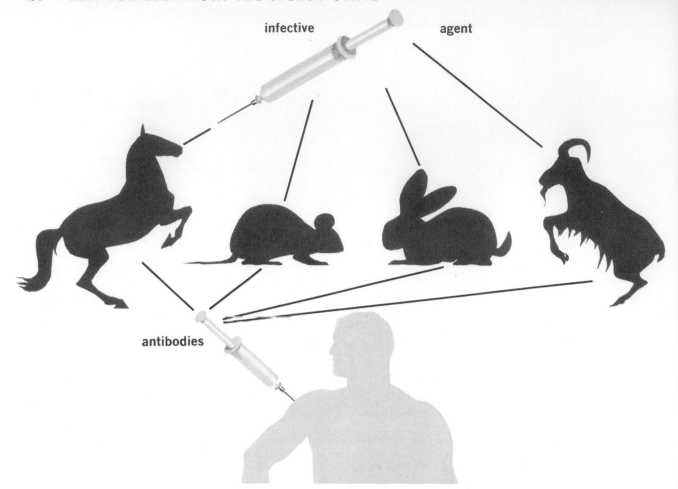

infective   agent

antibodies

FIG. 20.4.   The principle of passive immunization. Various animals may be infected and allowed to manufacture specific antibodies against the infectious agent. Blood serum of these animals, containing the antibodies, may then be used to protect man against the same infectious agent. Immunity here is not permanent, since human tissues do not produce the antibodies on their own.

When a virulent disease is contracted, short-term **passive immunization** can often combat it; previously prepared, ready-made antibodies may be injected. Such antibodies are obtained from rabbits, sheep, horses, guinea pigs, and other mammals. The mammal is exposed to a given infectious agent, and globulins manufactured by the mammal against the agent are withdrawn and are used to immunize man (Fig. 20.4). Diphtheria antitoxin is an example of

such an "immune globulin" conferring passive immunity.

There are, unquestionably, many types of compounds in plasma which are unidentified so far. But even those we have dealt with here reveal the many ways in which plasma contributes to body-wide steady-state maintenance. Plasma constitutes a sensory and motor path interconnecting all cells of the organism. It represents a modulator contributing to

TABLE 10. The principal constituents and functions of blood plasma*

Components	Functions
1. Water	maintains blood volume, pressure; forms lymph; water supply of cells; vehicle for other constituents
2. Inorganic ions	maintain osmotic balance, pH balance, act as buffers; CO_2 transport to lungs; varied biological actions
3. Plasma proteins	all aid in osmotic and pH balance;
fibrinogen	participates in blood clotting;
prothrombin	participates in blood clotting;
albumins, enzymes	functions obscure;
globulins	basis of blood types; act as antibodies
4. Glucose, other organic materials	in transit to and from cells
5. Urea, CO_2, O_2, foods, hormones, vitamins, and others	in transit to and from cells

* Categories 1 through 4 are maintained at *constant* concentrations; materials in category 5 occur in variable concentrations.

the physical and chemical constancy of all tissues. And it is a receptor of infectious stimuli, and a defensive effector against them. All this is in addition to the purely transportive functions of plasma, namely, delivering nutrients and collecting wastes; and in addition also to the function of plasma as lymph, through which it provides a proper operating environment for all cells. The main constituents and functions of plasma are summarized in Table 10.

BLOOD CELLS

Three kinds of cellular components are found in blood: **red corpuscles, white blood cells,** and **blood platelets** (Fig. 20.5).

Red Corpuscles

The major function of these blood constituents is the transporting of respiratory gases (see Chap. 14). In the adult vertebrate, red corpuscles are manufactured in the red marrow at the ends of long bones (e.g., ribs, arms, legs). Liver and spleen are the production sites in the embryo, before bones mature. After the skeleton is fully formed, and blood-cell production is initiated in it, the spleen becomes principally a blood-storing organ. It may contract, and like a sponge squeeze reserve blood into the circulation. The liver becomes the organ where red corpuscles are destroyed.

Production in bone marrow is geared to destruction in the liver. The controlling signal is the amount of oxygen carried by blood (Fig. 20.6). Low oxygen content stimulates bone marrow to produce red corpuscles at a faster rate. At the same time, the liver is inhibited from destroying corpuscles at too fast a rate. Hence when inhaled air contains too little oxygen for extended periods, as at high altitudes, then more blood corpuscles are manufactured. An adequate quantity of gas thus may still be delivered

FIG. 20.5. Human red blood corpuscles. Note absence of nuclei. A white blood cell (nucleated) is shown in center on left, and a few blood platelets in center on right. (General Biological Supply House, Inc.)

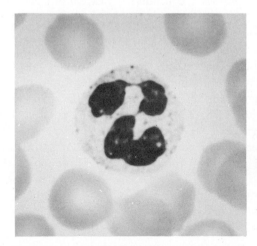
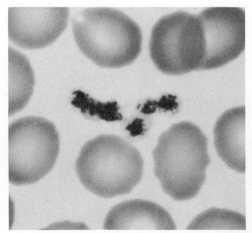

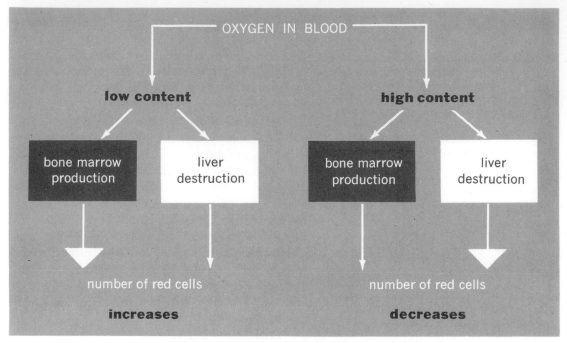

FIG. 20.6. Control of red corpuscle number. Production in bone marrow and destruction in liver are geared to each other by the oxygen content of blood.

to the tissues by this greater number of corpuscles. A persistently high oxygen concentration in blood has the opposite effect on liver and bone marrow. Through this mechanism, the number of red corpuscles is adjusted to oxygen requirements. Since requirements and the atmosphere normally remain fairly constant, the number of corpuscles is constant also.

When the number of corpuscles, their hemoglobin content, or both, are reduced significantly, the result is *anemia*. This may be brought about by excessive corpuscle destruction in an abnormal liver or by extensive blood loss through wounding. In the latter case, production in bone marrow soon makes up the loss. Anemia may also arise as a result of inadequate production of corpuscles, for example, when marrow cells are defective, or when the iron content of the diet is low.

In man, each cubic millimeter of blood, roughly the volume of a pinhead, contains over 5 million red corpuscles. It has been estimated that every *second*

some 10,000 corpuscles are manufactured and an equal number are destroyed. Red corpuscles arise from generating tissue in bone marrow by cell division. The new cells specialize and mature and are then expelled into the blood stream (Fig. 20.7a and b). In mammals, but not in other vertebrates, maturation of a red corpuscle involves the disintegration of the cell nucleus. Thus, corpuscles in the mammalian blood stream are enucleated "bags of chemicals." A mature corpuscle in man may exist for about 120 days, but the corpuscle may be destroyed at any prior time by the liver.

Destruction in the liver is nonselective. So many corpuscles are broken up per second, regardless of whether they are "young" or "old." The iron fraction of disintegrated hemoglobin is returned to the iron pool of the body, and some of it may find its way back to bone marrow, for reutilization in hemoglobin synthesis. The remainder of destroyed hemoglobin is largely excreted in bile and urine (see Chap. 12).

White Cells

These are so called because they do not contain hemoglobin but are transparent and colorless. Whereas red corpuscles are quite uniform in size and appearance, white blood cells are not. Two groups may be distinguished, **leucocytes** and **lymphocytes,** each consisting of a number of subgroups. These various types are distinguished on the basis of cell structure, size, origin, and function. All white cells possess nuclei, but they normally do not divide.

Leucocytes (Fig. 20.7*c*) are manufactured in red bone marrow, probably by the same generating tissue which also gives rise to red corpuscles. Lymphocytes (Fig. 20.7*d*) are formed in lymphatic tissue, principally the lymph nodes found along the path of lymph vessels. Lymphocytes reach the blood stream via the lymph channels. Altogether, white blood cells are much less abundant than red corpuscles. A cubic millimeter of human blood contains about 8,000 white cells. This is a fairly constant number under normal conditions. It is not known where white cells are destroyed or by what mechanism the rates of production and destruction are controlled.

Cancer of the bone marrow may result in *leukemia,* characterized by uncontrolled, abnormally rapid formation of white cells. Other diseases too may raise the white-cell count excessively or may lower it to abnormal levels. The number of white cells increases temporarily during infectious diseases, and this points up the function of these blood constituents.

To greater or lesser degree, all white cells, but leucocytes particularly, are capable of ameboid locomotion. Like amoebae, they extend pseudopods into which the rest of the cell flows. By this means, they are able to squeeze through blood capillary walls, passing in between neighboring cells in the walls (Fig. 20.7). Once out in the tissues, they migrate toward sites of infection, and there they engulf and digest bacteria, in the same way an ameba engulfs and digests food. How do white cells find the bacteria? Bacteria excrete metabolic wastes, and as these diffuse away from the site of infection, their concentrations decrease. White cells are believed to be sensitive to varying concentrations of bacterial waste. They are guided somehow to move *into* higher concentrations, just as amoebae are thought

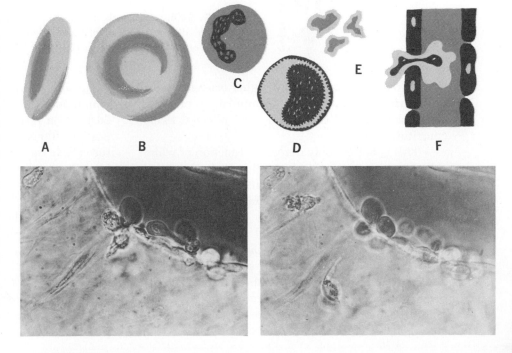

FIG. 20.7. Diagram: **A** to **E,** the cellular components of blood. **A, B,** red blood corpuscle, side and face views; **C,** leucocyte; **D,** lymphocyte; **E,** platelets; **F,** a white blood cell migrating through a capillary wall. Photos: the migration of blood cells through capillary walls. In each photo, a blood-filled capillary is in upper-right portion. In photo at left, two white blood cells have just penetrated through the capillary wall into surrounding tissues, and a red corpuscle is about to penetrate through the wall. In photo at right, the white cells have migrated farther into the tissue, and the red corpuscle is halfway through the capillary wall. (Photos courtesy of Dr. Robert Brenner, Brown University.)

A   B   C   D   E   F

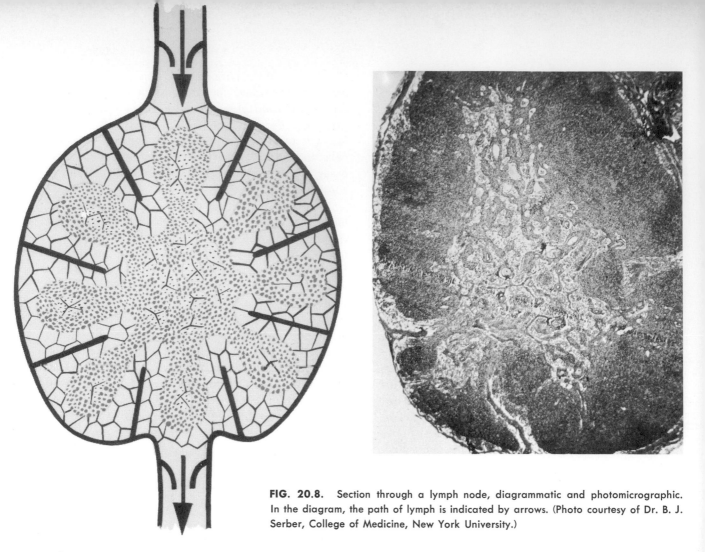

FIG. 20.8. Section through a lymph node, diagrammatic and photomicrographic. In the diagram, the path of lymph is indicated by arrows. (Photo courtesy of Dr. B. J. Serber, College of Medicine, New York University.)

to find food by migrating into higher concentrations of diffusing food molecules. Accumulations of white cells, bacteria, and the debris from infected tissue constitute **pus**.

This is not the only defensive function of white cells. Lymphocytes, for example, are *pluripotent* connective tissue cells, specialized to perform several different functions in succession (see Chap. 3). They contribute importantly to scar-tissue formation after injury, to sealing off a surface wound against new bacterial invasions, and to allowing the wound to heal underneath the scar. Lymphocytes also accumulate in great number where healing processes are under way in the interior of the body. Here they may contribute to scar tissue or may become part of regenerated connective tissue.

Many lymphocytes are retained within the lymph nodes in which they are manufactured (Fig. 20.8). As a result of this, lymph nodes become important "filters." As lymph passes through the nodes, the cells in the nodes pick out and engulf bacteria or other foreign bodies which may have chanced into the body fluids. Among coal miners, for example, tiny particles of coal frequently get into the body fluids through the lungs. This coal dust is strained out by the lymph nodes and remains there permanently.

Platelets

These are not cells in the usual sense but are probably cell *fragments*. They are tiny bits of protoplasm surrounded by a membrane, and nuclei are often absent (Figs. 20.5 and 20.7*e*). About one-quarter million of these bodies are found in each cubic millimeter of human blood. The origin of platelets is obscure, as is the control system which keeps their number constant. They are probably manufactured predominantly in red bone marrow. A certain fraction is believed to be formed in the connective tissue which binds the lung alveoli together.

Platelets are essential in blood clotting. This self-sealing mechanism of the circulatory system is brought into action whenever platelets encounter obstructions which rupture them. In most cases, such obstructions are the rough edges of torn blood vessels. External clotting then occurs. But air bubbles in blood (e.g., when dissolved gases effervesce) or roughness of the inner surfaces of blood vessels, produced, for example, by solid deposits, as in hardened arteries, may suffice for the rupturing of platelets. An internal blood clot may then form.

The clotting process is exceedingly complex, and the complete sequence of events is not yet established. However, an abbreviated, simplified account may be given to indicate what takes place (Fig. 20.9). Among the materials oozing out from ruptured platelets is an enzymatically active substance, **thrombokinase,** also called *thromboplastin.* This substance interacts with two components of blood plasma: calcium ions and prothrombin—one of the plasma proteins referred to earlier. Prothrombin is an inactive precursor of the catalyst **thrombin.**

Thrombokinase, in the presence of calcium ions, converts prothrombin to thrombin. Thrombin subsequently reacts with fibrinogen, another of the plasma proteins. As a result of the reaction, fibrinogen becomes **fibrin,** an insoluble protein. Fibrin constitutes the blood clot. It is a yellowish-white meshwork of coagulated protein, in which blood corpuscles are trapped. Hence the redness of the clot. As noted in Chap. 19, vitamin K is required at some step in the clotting reaction. Moderate heat speeds clotting time; cold slows it.

Clotting can be prevented when any of the ingredients are missing or are made inoperative. For example, fibrinogen can be withdrawn fairly easily from whole blood or plasma. This procedure is often used in storing blood or plasma for transfusion. Plasma minus fibrinogen is called **blood serum.**

Clotting can also be prevented by precipitating out the calcium of blood. Leeches, fleas, bedbugs, and other blood feeders secrete **hirudin** and mix it with ingested blood. Hirudin is a clotting inhibitor enabling leeches, for example, to store uncoagulated blood in their digestive tracts for as long as 6 months.

Finally, clotting will be impossible when blood platelets are defective. In one type of (hereditary) disease, platelets are missing altogether. In another, platelets have thickened membranes which prevent their rupturing. In either *bleeder's disease,* the slightest wound can be fatal.

The functions of the cellular components of blood are summarized in Table 11. Through anti-

FIG. 20.9. The main features of the clotting reaction.

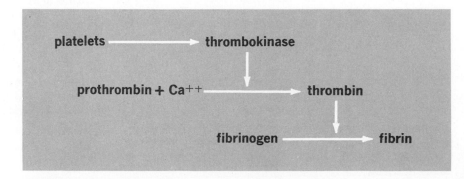

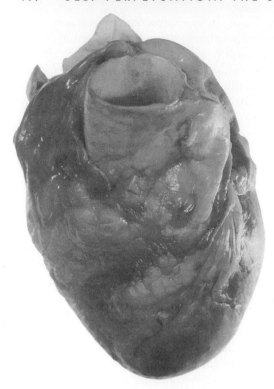

FIG. 20.10. The human heart. The large blood-vessel stump is the aorta. The auricles are partly hidden by the aorta. The size of your fist is very nearly the actual size of your heart. (Institute of Pathology, Rhode Island Hospital.)

TABLE 11. The cellular constituents of blood and their functions

Component	Origin	Amount per cubic millimeter	Functions
Red corpuscles	red marrow (adult) liver, spleen (embryo)	5 million	transport of O_2, CO_2
White cells		8,000	
Leucocytes	red marrow		engulf bacteria, foreign bodies; aid in wound healing
Lymphocytes	lymph nodes		
Platelets	red marrow, lungs	250,000	release thrombo-kinase, aid in blood clotting

bodies, through white cells, and through clotting, blood forms the first line of internal defense. However, this control function of blood, as well as its other functions in transport and tissue maintenance, can be exercised only if blood *circulates*. Consequently, as tissue functions are dependent on blood, so blood functions in turn are dependent on the circulatory system.

Circulation

This composite activity is carried out by the heart, the blood vessels, and the lymph vessels. As noted earlier, these organs represent more than a pumping station and a system of pipes. To be sure, their basic function is to provide pathways for body fluids and to keep these in motion. But they also regulate the speed and force of motion and the distribution of the moving fluids.

It should be kept clearly in mind that, from the standpoint of individual tissue cells, the important parts of the circulatory system are the capillary vessels. It is through them, and only through them, that circulating body fluids sustain the life of cells. Vital exchanges of information and of materials between blood and tissue cells occur only in the microscopic capillaries. But to make such exchanges possible, structures like heart and large blood vessels become necessary adjuncts.

THE COURSE OF CIRCULATION

Contrary to popular belief, the heart is not situated on the left. In man, the organ lies in the midplane of the chest, directly underneath the breastbone. But it is tilted somewhat, the lower tip projecting over to the left (Fig. 20.10). This is where the beat of the heart is most readily discernible.

To each of the four chambers of the heart, the right and left **auricle** and the right and left **ventricle**, connects one large blood vessel (Fig. 20.11). The **aorta** leaves the left ventricle, and its branches supply all parts of the body with arterial blood. Venous blood collects from all body regions and returns through the **vena cava** into the right auricle.

The right auricle connects with the right ventricle through the **tricuspid valve,** an opening equipped with three flaps which lets blood through from auricle to ventricle, but not in the reverse direction (Fig. 20.12). Venous blood collected in the right ventricle leaves this chamber via the **pulmonary artery,** a vessel leading to the lungs. Here blood is oxygenated, and arterial blood returns through the **pulmonary vein** into the left auricle (see also Chap. 14, Fig. 14.13).

A **bicuspid,** or *mitral*, valve, equipped with two flaps, separates the left auricle from the left ventricle. Like the tricuspid on the right, the mitral valve also opens into the ventricle only. The valve flaps are prevented from letting blood pass in the wrong direction by strands of tissue resembling parachute strings, which attach to the free edges of the valve flaps on one end, and to the ventricle walls on the other. The tricuspid and mitral valves together

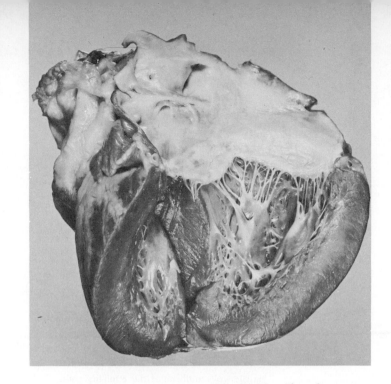

FIG. 20.12. The heart cut open to show the interior of the left ventricle. Note the strands of tissue attached to the two flaps of the bicuspid valve. These strands prevent the valve from opening into the auricle (white area above the ventricle). (Institute of Pathology, Rhode Island Hospital.)

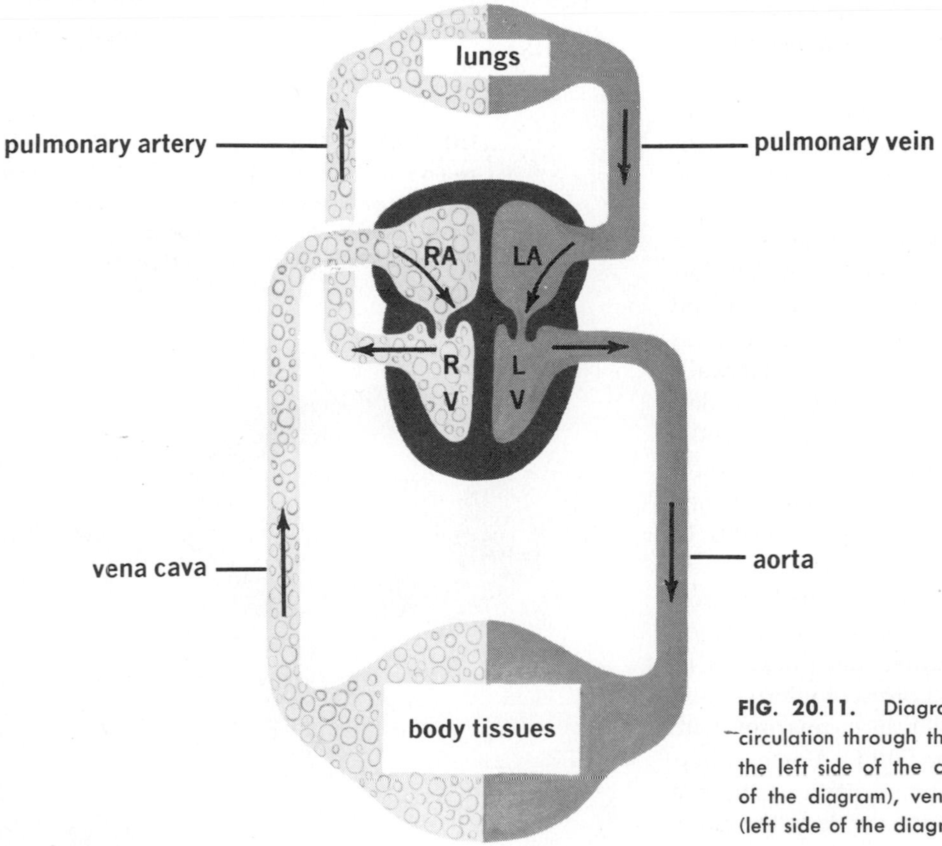

lungs

pulmonary artery

pulmonary vein

RA   LA

R
V   L
V

vena cava

aorta

body tissues

FIG. 20.11. Diagram of the course of blood circulation through the body. Arterial blood is in the left side of the circulatory system (right side of the diagram), venous blood in the right side (left side of the diagram).

FIG. 20.13. Diagram of a cross section **A**, and a surface view **B**, of blood capillaries. In the cross section, note how few cells are needed to form a tube. In the surface view, note the characteristic wavy outlines of the capillary cells.

may be referred to as the auriculo-ventricular valves, or **A-V valves.**

Smaller valves are situated where the aorta and the pulmonary artery leave the left and right ventricle, respectively. These valves *open away* from the heart and close toward it.

Note that the left chambers of the heart are not connected directly with the right chambers. The left handle arterial blood only; the right, venous blood only. Inasmuch as the auricles pump blood only as far as the ventricles, relatively thin muscular walls suffice. But the ventricles, the left one in particular, pump blood into the farthest parts of the body. These chambers possess proportionately thick walls.

The heart and the entire vessel system are lined with a single continuous layer of smooth flat cells. In blood and lymph capillaries no other cells are present (Fig. 20.13). But in the larger channels, muscle and fibrous elastic tissue envelop the lining layer. The wider a vessel, the sturdier and thicker is its wall. Arteries, which bear the brunt of internal fluid pressure, are particularly thick in comparison with veins or lymph vessels (Fig. 20.14). For example, the outer diameter of the human aorta at the exit from the left ventricle is about as wide as the diam-

eter of one's thumb, and the inner diameter, about as wide as one's little finger. By contrast, the outer diameter of the vena cava near the right auricle may be as wide as a thumb or even wider, but the inner diameter is at least as great as the width of the middle finger.

Large veins and lymph vessels are equipped with internal valve flaps at more or less regular intervals (Fig. 20.15). These flaps open toward the heart and close away from it. Body fluids in these vessels are normally under low forward pressure, and the valve flaps prevent the fluids from flowing backward.

THE MECHANICS OF CIRCULATION

The heart is a pressure pump. It generates pumping force on contraction, or **systole,** and it rests during muscular relaxation, here called **diastole.** A complete heartbeat consists of one systole and one diastole, the whole beat lasting about 0.8 sec in a normal human adult at rest. On an average, therefore, 72 beats take place per minute.

FIG. 20.14. Section through an artery and two veins. Note the thicker wall of the artery and the presence of many elastic fibers (dark wavy lines) in this wall. (Courtesy of Dr. B. J. Serber, College of Medicine, New York University.)

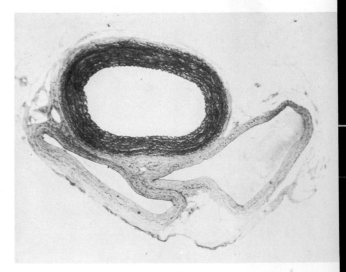

A heartbeat starts with the contraction of the auricles (Fig. 20.16). These chambers gradually fill with blood returning via vena cava and pulmonary vein. When they are full, their muscular walls contract. The ventricles are relaxed at that time. As the auricles contract, blood cannot flow backward, because incoming blood presses steadily *into* the auricles. Therefore, the only path open to auricular blood is through the A-V valves, which lead into the ventricles. These chambers now fill as the auricles empty. The auricular phase of the heartbeat lasts about 0.1 sec. The auricles then relax for the remaining 0.7 sec of the cycle, slowly refilling during this interval in preparation for the next beat (Fig. 20.17).

As soon as the auricles have relaxed, the ventricles, by this time full with blood, contract in their turn. Their thick walls generate much more pressure than the walls of the auricles. Also, ventricular systole lasts longer, namely, some 0.3 sec. The contraction rapidly builds up to a peak, is held at peak, then subsides. As the contraction peak is reached,

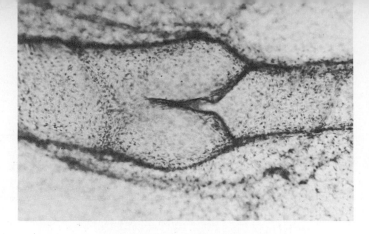

FIG. 20.15. Longitudinal section through a lymph vessel, showing an internal valve. Such valves prevent backflow. Valves very much like this are present also in the larger veins. (General Biological Supply House, Inc.)

FIG. 20.16. The pumping action of the heart. In the left figure, the auricles are shown contracting, forcing blood into the relaxed ventricles. The A-V valves are open, but the pressure of blood closes all others. In the right figure, the ventricles contract, forcing blood into the pulmonary artery and the aorta. The auricles are relaxed at the same time, filling with blood in preparation for the next beat.

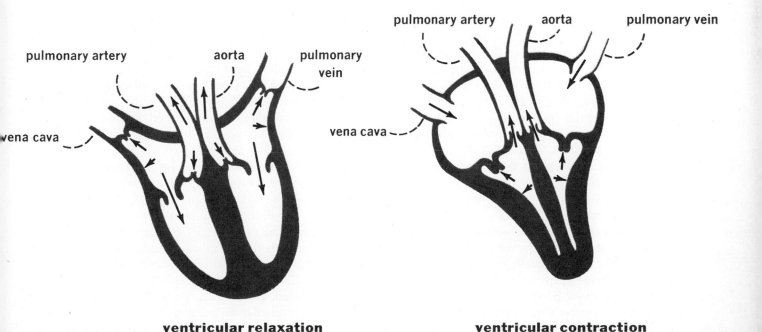

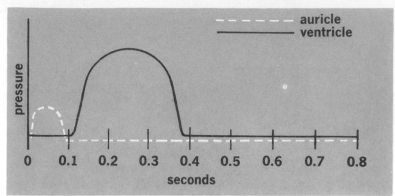

FIG. 20.17. The time relationship between auricular and ventricular beats. Note that the auricles contract and generate pressure when the ventricles are relaxed, and vice versa. Note also that the whole heart is relaxed for half the time of a beat.

blood is forced against all ventricular openings, including the A-V valves. But as blood slaps against the A-V flaps, these snap shut and prevent backflow into the auricles (see Fig. 20.16). This impact of blood against the valve flaps produces the **first heart sound,** which can be felt or heard as "the" heartbeat. When the A-V valves are defective, the flaps may not close tightly, and some blood then does flow back into the auricles. This can be heard with a stethoscope and is described as a "heart murmur." Slight murmurs do not impair the efficiency of the heart significantly.

The only way blood can leave the ventricles, normally, is via the aorta on the left and the pulmonary artery on the right. The exit valves into these vessels open as blood presses against them with great force. The sudden quantity of fluid now rushing out dilates portions of the exit arteries adjacent to the heart. But the arterial walls are elastic and snap back into position, thereby adding to the pressure of blood. Most of the blood is thus forced forward, where the open paths lead to the lungs and to all body tissues. But some blood tends to press back into the ventricles. This snaps the exit valves shut, and blood then cannot flow in this direction (see Fig. 20.16). The impact of blood in closing the exit valves generates the **second heart sound,** fainter than the first.

Note that even the ventricles rest more than half the time (see Fig. 20.17). Note also that no part of the heart actually is ever empty but is only more distended or less distended, with blood under greater or lesser pressure. This differential pressure alone determines the position of the heart valves, hence the course in which blood can flow.

Arterial blood "flows" in rhythmic spurts, according to the rhythm of the heart. As each spurt of fluid impinges on the walls of arteries, it gives rise to **pulse** vibrations. Feel for your neck pulse with the left hand, and for your left wrist pulse with the right hand; notice the time difference between the pulses, as a result of the different distances of neck and wrist from the heart.

With increasing distance from the heart, arterial spurts become less and less forceful. By the time blood is through capillary vessels and has reached veins, it no longer spurts but flows in a continuous, even stream. The heart here produces very little direct push. Venous blood keeps moving slowly by the push of blood from behind and by contraction of skeletal muscles which squeeze the veins. The valves in the veins impose the right direction on venous return. In view of the architecture of the mammalian body, particularly the upright human body, much venous flow takes place against gravity, a condition which diminishes the already low forward pressure of venous blood. When one stands upright for long periods, blood tends to accumulate in the legs; leg muscles may compress the leg veins very little, and venous return becomes sluggish. This contributes to fatigue and leg weariness, since metabolic wastes are not carried off fast enough.

Breathing facilitates the return of blood to the heart. The same negative pressure which sucks air into lungs during inhalation also enlarges the auricles somewhat and sucks blood into them.

The pressure of lymph is even lower than that of blood. Here again, push of lymph from behind and muscular activity provide the major forces which return lymph to the blood circulation.

Evidently the pressure of blood is an important index of heart and circulatory efficiency. What controls blood pressure? What, indeed, controls heart rate, heart force, and the proper timing of auricular and ventricular contractions?

THE CONTROL OF CIRCULATION

Heart muscle (see Chap. 9, Fig. 9.14) possesses inherent contractility. When isolated in an artificial nutrient medium, a piece of heart muscle may contract and relax in a slow, fairly regular rhythm. In the body, this inherent rhythm of the heart is adjusted in strength and in rate by control systems. Some of these operate on a nervous, some on a chemical and physical basis.

Heart Rate

It is clear that if the heart beats too slowly, even if forcefully, fuel and waste-material exchange in tissues and lungs will occur at an inadequate pace. And if the heart beats too rapidly, its pumping action will be inefficient.

The main nervous regulating center of heart rate is located in the medulla oblongata, the same general region of the hindbrain which also houses the breathing center. Two pairs of nerves lead from a **heart-rate center** to the heart (Fig. 20.18). Impulses through one pair accelerate heartbeat; impulses through the other slow it. The accelerator nerves travel through the spinal cord for some distance, emerge in the chest region, and innervate the heart. The inhibitory nerve fibers pass from the heart-rate center into the large **vagus nerves.** One vagus nerve on each side leaves the hindbrain and runs through the neck alongside the trachea. Some vagus branches then lead to the heart, others to a variety of organs (e.g., stomach; see Chap. 12).

Both the accelerator and inhibitor nerves terminate in the wall of the right auricle, at a small patch

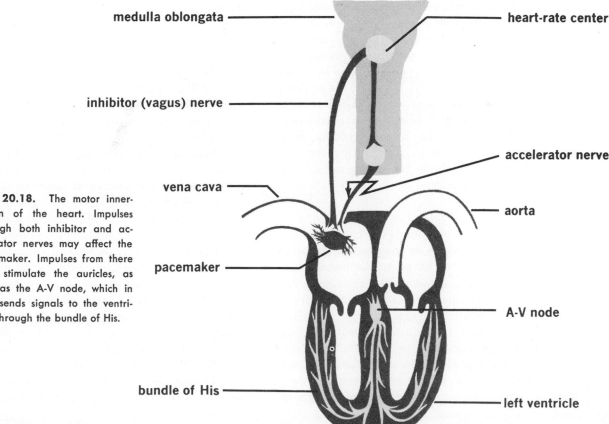

FIG. 20.18. The motor innervation of the heart. Impulses through both inhibitor and accelerator nerves may affect the pacemaker. Impulses from there then stimulate the auricles, as well as the A-V node, which in turn sends signals to the ventricles through the bundle of His.

medulla oblongata — heart-rate center

inhibitor (vagus) nerve

accelerator nerve

vena cava — aorta

pacemaker

A-V node

bundle of His — left ventricle

of specialized tissue called the **pacemaker,** or *sinus node* (see Fig. 20.18). When the pacemaker is stimulated, a wave of contraction spreads out from it through both auricles. Auricular contraction in turn stimulates a second patch of tissue, the *A-V node,* situated in the wall which divides the left and right sides of the heart. At the A-V node originates a bundle of modified heart muscle, the **bundle of His,** specialized for impulse conduction. The strands of this bundle radiate away through the walls of both ventricles. Thus, auricular contraction stimulates the A-V node, and impulses transmitted from there through the conductive strands initiate ventricular contraction (see Fig. 20.18). The time required for stimulus transmission from pacemaker to A-V node ensures that the ventricles contract a fraction of a second *after* the auricles.

The pacemaker is the immediate regulator of heart rate, and the heart rate center in turn controls the action of the pacemaker. Heart rate, like so many other processes in the body, is a restrained compromise between acceleration and deceleration. Experiments show that inhibitory signals via the vagus nerves allow a more flexible adjustment of heart rate than accelerator signals. For example, it can be demonstrated that a speeding up of the heart is specifically associated with a *decrease* of impulse frequency through the vagus nerves; the heart beats faster primarily because the "brake" has been eased, not because acceleration has been stepped up. Similarly, a slowing of the heart is primarily a result of increased braking via the vagus nerves, not a result of decreased acceleration.

Stretch Reflexes

The heart-rate center sends out brake or accelerator signals in response to specific sensory nerve impulses which affect it. Of particular interest here are impulses originating within the circulatory system itself. Produced partly as a result of heartbeat, such impulses constitute neural feedback signals to the heart-rate center, through which heart rate controls "itself," automatically.

In the walls of the vena cava, the aorta, and the *carotid* arteries, a pair of vessels branching away from the aorta into the head, there are found endings of sensory nerves which lead to the heart-rate center (Fig. 20.19). When these blood vessels become distended by large quantities of blood, their walls stretch, and this stimulates the nerve endings. When the heart-rate center receives impulses from the vena cava, the center *accelerates* the heart. Impulses to the center from the aorta, the carotid artery, or both, bring about a *slowing* of the heart.

Suppose that a person begins strenuous work. His muscles vigorously compress many veins, and venous return to the heart increases. This distends the vena cava pronouncedly. A *stretch reflex,* as just described, now increases heart rate, just when the tissues require more fuel and oxygen. Also, a heart beating more rapidly can handle the larger quantities of incoming blood by pumping them out faster. But the increased outflow dilates the walls of the aorta and the carotid arteries. Stretch reflexes now originate here, and these *slow* the heart; that is, they prevent it from beating *too* rapidly (Fig. 20.20).

Through these controls, heart rate is adjusted automatically to the volume of blood which the heart must handle. Moreover, any excessive speed-up produces signals forcing a slowdown. Similarly, if the heart should slow down, the aortic and carotid walls would be stretched less, reflex inhibition of the heart would decrease, and heart rate would increase back to normal.

Stretch reflexes are not the only nervous controls of the heart. In all probability, *any* stimulus producing sensory nerve impulses anywhere in the body affects the heart-rate center, hence heart rate. All nerve tracts in brain and spinal cord are interconnected, and it is therefore not surprising that impulses passing into, or originating in, these regulating organs are also transmitted to the heart-rate center. Bad dreams, fear, hate, and virtually all other emotions; pain stimuli, pressure stimuli, visual stimuli; and other environmental changes communicated via nerves—all are well known to influence heart rate, sometimes increasing it, sometimes decreasing it.

Nonnervous Controls of Rate

In addition to nervous control, heart rate is also decisively regulated by many nonnervous agencies.

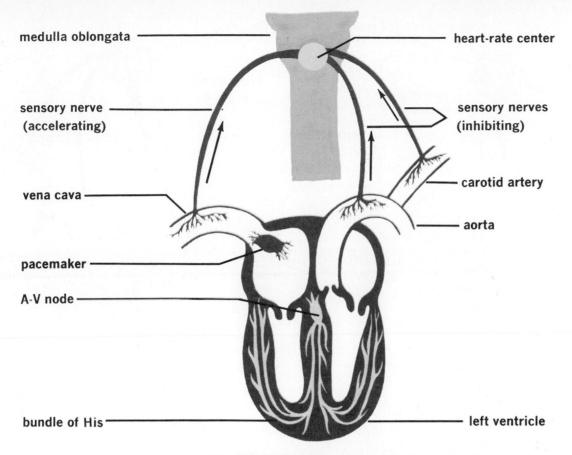

FIG. 20.19. The sensory innervation of the heart. The heart-rate center receives messages through sensory nerves which originate in the vena cava, the aorta, and the carotid artery. In response to such messages, the center then may send appropriate command signals to the pacemaker, as per Fig. 20.18.

Most of these act on the heart muscle, specifically the pacemaker, directly. Like any other metabolic process, heartbeat is affected by temperature—high temperature speeds, low temperature slows. The effect of pH is pronounced—relative acidity speeds, relative alkalinity slows. Since carbon dioxide lowers the pH of blood, this compound increases the rate of the heart when it is present in high concentrations. High CO_2 concentrations also speed up breathing (see Chap. 14). Hence fast breathing and a fast heart usually go together. The inorganic ions in blood exert pronounced effects on heart rate. So do

hormones. For example, the action of adrenalin under severe emotional or functional stress has already been mentioned. Analogously, thyroxin, insulin, sex hormones, pituitary hormones, and others all influence heart rate decisively.

Indeed, there is hardly an internal process which does not have a specific effect on the heart. Some processes act more strongly, some less strongly; some accelerate, some inhibit. All these influences act simultaneously, and at any given moment, the actual rate of the heart is determined by the resultant of these many effects.

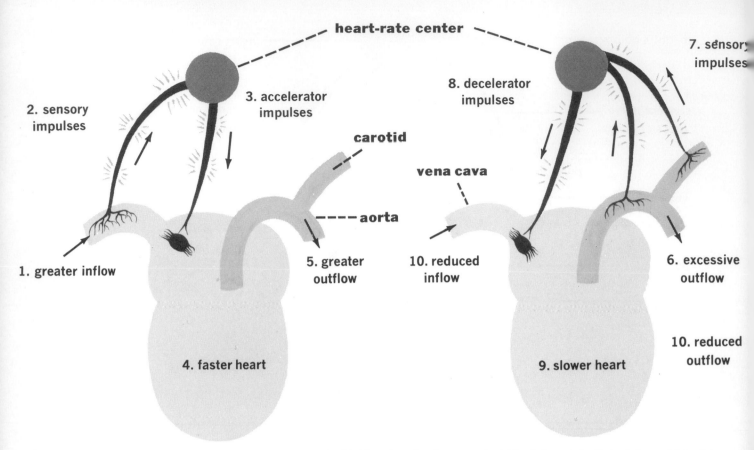

FIG. 20.20.   Stretch-reflex control of blood flow. Left: if the inflow of blood into the heart increases, outflow will increase too, through reflex acceleration of the heart (1 to 5). Right: if the outflow rate is excessive, inflow and outflow will quickly be reduced, through reflex deceleration of the heart (6 to 10).

Blood Pressure

If blood pressure becomes too high, thin vessels, and the thin-walled auricles of the heart, might burst. And if blood pressure becomes too low, blood would not possess sufficient momentum to circulate.

Even in the absence of a pumping mechanism, a quantity of fluid filling a confined space is under a certain pressure. The larger the volume of fluid, and the smaller the available space, the greater will be the pressure. Blood pressure therefore depends on three major factors: blood **volume**, blood **vessel space**, and, obviously, the **force** of the heartbeat. A

careful distinction should be made between heart *force* and heart *rate*. The heart may beat fast, but feebly; slowly, but forcefully; fast and forcefully; or slowly and feebly.

As already noted, blood volume is adjusted through fluid intake and fluid loss. This is a long-range control and, except for contractions of the spleen which put stored blood into circulation, is involved very little in second-to-second regulation of blood pressure. On the other hand, the force of the heart, and the space within blood vessels, can be varied instantly. These are the significant factors in rapid adjustments of blood pressure.

If the heart is healthy and properly nourished, then the main determinant of the force of its beat is the *amount* of blood received and pumped out in a given span of time. This is a curious but little-understood phenomenon characteristic of all muscle. The greater the work load of a muscle and the more it is thereby stretched, within limits to be sure, the stronger is its contraction. For example, when the heart fills slowly and receives only little blood per beat, then its contraction will be weak. But when blood fills the ventricles quickly and to capacity, then the pumping action will be powerful, and blood pressure will increase correspondingly.

The heart fills with much blood when venous return is great. As we have just seen above, a stretch reflex originates under such conditions from the wall of the vena cava, and heart rate is raised. Venous return evidently affects *both* heart rate and blood pressure. The adaptive value of this is clear. During exercise, for example, a heart which is merely fast could not supply the tissues with extra fuel and oxygen, if its beat were feeble. But high rate combined with great force does put the necessary drive behind blood to service the tissues adequately. We shall presently encounter other interrelations between heart rate and blood pressure.

The space available within blood vessels is adjusted by contraction and relaxation of the muscles in the vessel walls. *Vasoconstriction* reduces the diameter of blood vessels; *vasodilation* increases it. Vasoconstriction and vasodilation together are referred to as **vasomotion.** These muscular activities are controlled by a **vasomotor center** in the brain, located again in the medulla oblongata, close to the breathing and heart-rate centers. Nerves lead from the vasomotor center to all blood vessels (except the capillaries, which do not possess muscles). Experiments show that changes in the caliber of a blood vessel are brought about primarily by variations in the activity of constrictor muscles. Dilator muscles play a lesser role. Consequently, a vessel ordinarily narrows as a result of more impulses from the vasomotor center to constrictor muscles. The vessel widens when fewer impulses reach these muscles (Fig. 20.21).

Vasoconstriction in all parts of the body raises overall blood pressure, and vasodilation lowers it. Vasomotion may also occur in limited regions of the body, leading to a rise or fall of the local blood pressure only. Actual events are controlled by the vasomotor center, which, like the heart-rate center, acts in response to nervous and chemical cues.

FIG. 20.21. The pattern of vasomotion. Vasoconstriction occurs when a blood vessel receives many constrictor impulses from the vasomotor center and few dilator impulses. Vasodilation occurs when constrictor impulses are few and dilator impulses many.

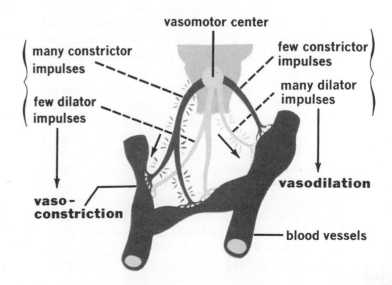

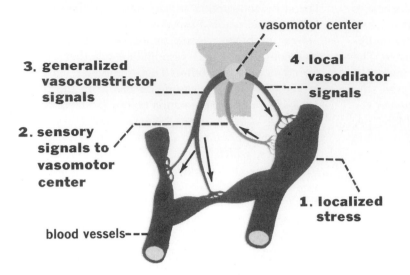

3. generalized vasoconstrictor signals

vasomotor center

4. local vasodilator signals

2. sensory signals to vasomotor center

1. localized stress

blood vessels

FIG. 20.22.   The vasomotor effects of localized stress. Generalized vasoconstriction and localized vasodilation follow through the numbered events shown. Sensory nerves in light gray, motor nerves in black.

Vasomotion

Nervous cues to the vasomotor center are as numerous as those affecting heart rate. Virtually any nervous signal transmitted into the brain is likely to have an effect on the vasomotor center also. For example, pain, emotions, and stresses generally all tend to increase blood pressure, through body-wide vasoconstriction. At the same time, in specific parts of the body in which stresses are to be counteracted, the local blood pressure often falls, through regional vasodilation. For example, when an organism sustains a wound, overall blood pressure rises, but the wounded area swells, through local vasodilation. The adaptive advantage of this is clear. A rise of overall blood pressure produces a state of readiness, which enables the organism to combat stress more effectively. And a local vasodilation in the stressed region itself permits more blood to flow into that region; hence more nutrients and oxygen become available (Fig. 20.22).

Like heart rate, blood pressure too is normally prevented from varying excessively. The stretch reflexes discussed above play a role here as well. Some sensory nerve fibers from the aorta and the carotid arteries lead into the vasomotor center. When these

arteries distend greatly under the pressure of blood spurting out from the heart, i.e., when blood pressure is high, body-wide vasodilation is ordered by the vasomotor center. A high blood pressure is thus brought back to normal. Conversely, when the aorta and carotid arteries distend very little or not at all, vasoconstriction increases and blood pressure is made to rise. In this manner, stretch reflexes provide an important gearing of heart rate, heart force, and blood pressure (Fig. 20.23).

The chief chemical cue to which the vasomotor center responds is, as in the case of the breathing and the heart-rate center, carbon dioxide in the blood. If blood reaching the vasomotor center carries a high concentration of CO_2, then the center transmits constrictor signals throughout the body. Blood pressure therefore rises. Conversely, low CO_2 concentrations bring about a generalized fall of blood pressure. We already know that CO_2 also affects heart and breathing rates. Evidently, intensive CO_2 production by highly active tissues neatly keys the whole circulatory machinery to increased efforts, and such tissues will then be serviced at an augmented pace.

Carbon dioxide also has a direct, local effect on vasomotion, apart from its effect on the vasomotor center. In tissues where much CO_2 is produced, the gas acts directly on the blood vessels in the vicinity and *dilates* them. Carbon dioxide thus aids in increasing the blood supply to stressed tissues (Fig. 20.24). During arm exercises, for example, blood vessels in the arm dilate, through the local direct action of the CO_2 produced here. But elsewhere in the body blood vessels constrict, through the generalized effect of CO_2 on the vasomotor center. Hence overall blood pressure is raised, and greater quantities of blood are allowed to flow through the arm.

Adrenalin and many other drugs influence blood pressure decisively. Adrenalin produces

FIG. 20.23.   The gearing of heart rate and blood pressure. If the inflow of blood into the heart increases, outflow increases also (as already shown in Fig. 20.20); but at the same time, blood pressure also increases, through reflex constriction of blood vessels (1 to 5). But if blood pressure should become too high, the pressure will quickly be lowered, through reflex dilation of blood vessels; at the same time, outflow rate will also decrease (6 to 10). Compare with Fig. 20.20.

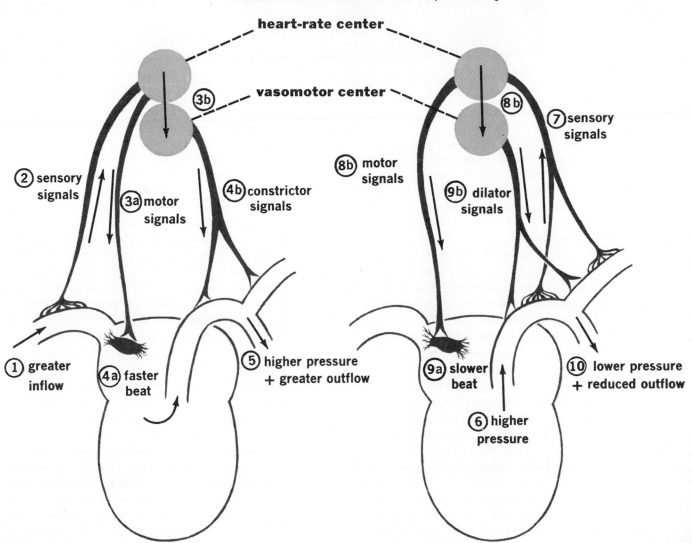

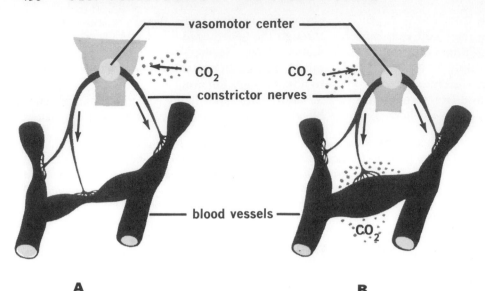

vasomotor center

CO_2 CO_2

constrictor nerves

blood vessels

CO_2

A   **B**

FIG. 20.24. Vasomotor control by carbon dioxide. **A,** generalized vasoconstriction as a result of stimulation of the vasomotor center by CO_2. **B,** CO_2 produced locally overrides the general vasoconstriction ordered by the vasomotor center, and brings about a local vasodilation.

vasodilation in skeletal muscles, but vasoconstriction elsewhere. During states of emergency, this reinforces the action of CO_2. Both CO_2 and adrenalin elevate overall blood pressure but dilate vessels in arms, legs, chest, etc., body regions usually involved in counteracting an emergency.

Blood Distribution

We note that vasomotor control, both nervous and chemical, not only regulates blood pressure as such but also the *distribution* of blood. This is immensely significant, in emergencies as well as under normal conditions. For example, it is well known that, after a meal, an animal tends to be somewhat sluggish. The whole alimentary system becomes active and produces large amounts of carbon dioxide. Blood vessels in the alimentary system dilate, but those in skeletal muscles tend to constrict. As a result, blood flows freely through gut and liver, where it is particularly needed at the time, but flows in lesser quantity through the peripheral muscles of the body. Hence the disinclination to do physical work. If one were to undertake strenuous exercise under such conditions, muscle cramps would be likely to arise. Conversely, an empty digestive system facilitates blood flow through muscles, and this

is why athletes do not eat immediately before they exert themselves physically.

Other distributive adjustments of blood flow are familiar to everyone. For example, temperature affects the caliber of blood vessels. Cold constricts; hence on a cold day blood flow through the skin is reduced, and excessive heat loss by skin radiation is prevented. High temperature has the opposite effect. When one ascends in an elevator, inertia tends to pull blood into the legs. On descending, blood tends to rush into the head. The vasomotor control system quickly counterbalances these tendencies, by constricting or dilating blood vessels in the upper or lower body regions, pushing blood *in* the direction of body motion, *against* the direction of inertia.

We may summarize. Like all controls, circulatory ones too are interlocking and interdependent in action. A change in heart rate, for example, may produce changes in blood pressure, in venous return, in the force of the heart, in breathing rate, in the distribution of blood, and eventually in heart rate itself. If one condition of circulation is altered, all others are altered also. Circulatory adjustments illustrate once again that the action of control systems is such as to produce a "right" response to a given stimulus, and that built-in feedbacks impose restraints which prevent responses from going too far in direction, strength, and duration. The various interrelations of circulatory controls are illustrated in Fig. 20.25.

Proper maintenance and control of physical circulation is one requirement if blood is to service the tissues adequately. A second requirement is maintenance and control of proper chemical conditions in blood, despite changes produced continuously by actively metabolizing tissues. This requirement is met by the excretory system.

Excretion

As blood aids in steady-state control of tissues, so the excretory system aids in steady-state control of blood. The excretory system regulates the water content and the blood volume of the body, the pH and the osmotic pressure of blood, and blood chemistry in general. Moreover, through its water-balancing activities, it is also a major regulator of body

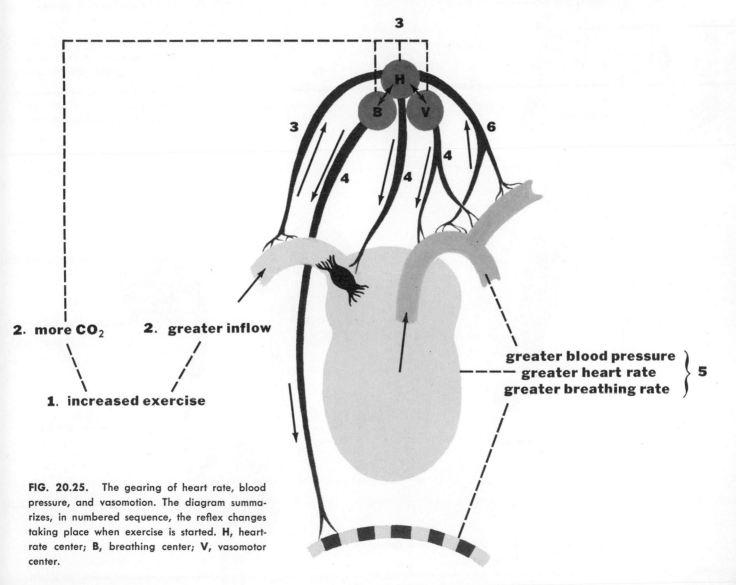

FIG. 20.25. The gearing of heart rate, blood pressure, and vasomotion. The diagram summarizes, in numbered sequence, the reflex changes taking place when exercise is started. **H**, heart-rate center; **B**, breathing center; **V**, vasomotor center.

2. more CO_2

2. greater inflow

1. increased exercise

greater blood pressure
greater heart rate   5
greater breathing rate

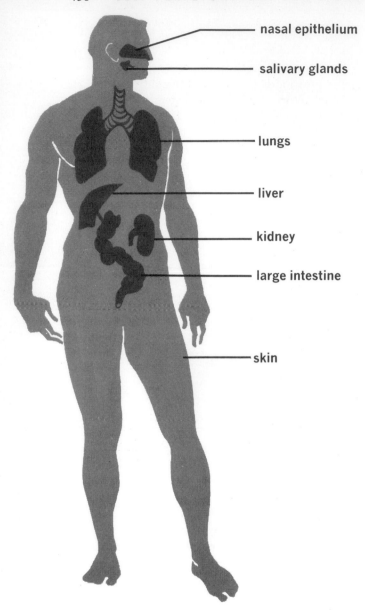

nasal epithelium

salivary glands

lungs

liver

kidney

large intestine

skin

FIG. 20.26. Some of the component organs of the excretory system.

temperature. Recall here the importance of water- and salt-balancing functions in marine and fresh-water organisms (see Chap. 5).

The organs composing the excretory system are shown in Fig. 20.26. We have discussed the excretory action of many of these organs in various earlier contexts. For example, the lungs contribute to elimination of excess water and carbon dioxide. The sweat glands aid in regulating water balance and, to some extent, inorganic ion balance. The large intestine makes a further contribution to ion balance. The liver excretes many diverse materials via bile. And the nasal epithelium, the salivary and the other digestive glands, indeed all the organs with direct access to the exterior of the body, either directly or via the alimentary tract, contribute importantly to excretion.

But the kidneys exercise the major excretory control. When the kidneys are inoperative, all the above organs together are inadequate to prevent death from excretory failure. As noted in Chap. 19, kidney function is itself controlled by a number of hormones.

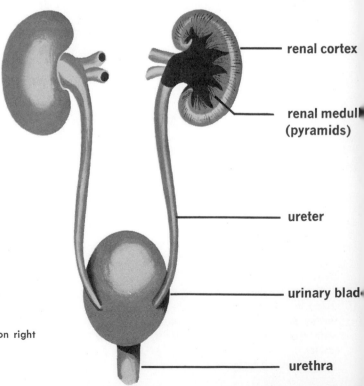

renal cortex

renal medul (pyramids)

ureter

urinary blad

urethra

FIG. 20.27. The renal system. Kidney on right is shown in section.

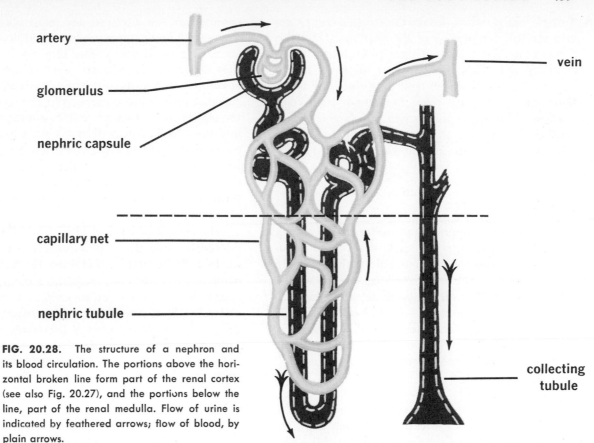

artery

vein

glomerulus

nephric capsule

capillary net

nephric tubule

collecting tubule

FIG. 20.28. The structure of a nephron and its blood circulation. The portions above the horizontal broken line form part of the renal cortex (see also Fig. 20.27), and the portions below the line, part of the renal medulla. Flow of urine is indicated by feathered arrows; flow of blood, by plain arrows.

KIDNEY STRUCTURE

The structure of the mammalian kidney is complex in detail but relatively simple in principle. Each kidney consists of an outer **renal cortex** and an inner **renal medulla** (Fig. 20.27). Located partly in the cortex and partly in the medulla are many thousands of **nephrons**, the operational units of the kidney (Fig. 20.28).

The most conspicuous component of a nephron is a tube, called the **nephric tubule.** At one end, this tubule enlarges into a **nephric capsule,** a structure resembling a hollow ball which has been pushed in on one side until the whole becomes a double-layered cup. At the other end, the nephric tubule leads into a **collecting duct,** which receives the output of

many neighboring nephric tubules. There are many collecting ducts in a kidney. All of them eventually join, forming a wide vessel, the **ureter** (see Fig. 20.27). This channel carries urine into the **urinary bladder.** A final duct, the **urethra,** connects the bladder with the outside.

Between the nephric capsule and the entrance into the collecting duct, the nephric tubule is variously coiled and looped. As might be expected, a nephron is in extensive contact with the blood circulation. A large **renal artery** enters the kidney in the region where the ureter leaves, branches out repeatedly into many smaller arteries, and one of these leads to each nephron (see Fig. 20.28). Dipping into the hollow of the nephric capsule, the small artery breaks up into a dense ball of capillaries, called a **glomerulus.** The capillaries then rejoin into a single vessel, which leaves the capsule and passes into the tubular portion of the nephron. Here this blood vessel branches out once more into a dense capillary net. This net envelops all parts of the nephric tubule. Near the collecting duct, the capillaries lead into a small vein, and many such veins from neighboring nephrons join into larger vessels. All these eventually form a single channel, the **renal vein,** which leaves the kidney where the renal artery enters.

KIDNEY FUNCTION

The standard operating procedure of the kidney might be compared to the work of a pair of hypothetical fish inspectors stationed along the bank of a river. One has a net with which he collects all the fish passing by. The other examines each fish: dead or defective ones he throws away; healthy ones he puts back into the river. Moreover, if there are too many fish altogether, or too many of a particular kind, he may even throw healthy ones away.

Filtration

In the kidney, the river is the blood stream. The man with the net is the capsule of each nephron. Here blood is **filtered** through the walls of the glomerular capillaries and the adjacent wall of the capsule (Fig. 20.29).

Filtration requires force. This force is blood pressure. By its agency, every blood component which *can* go through the glomerular and capsular walls will be pressed into the upper cavity of the nephric tubule. Only two groups of blood constituents normally can *not* pass through this filter: blood cells and plasma proteins. All other components do pass through, without change of concentration. Within the cavity of the nephric capsule will therefore be found blood minus cells and proteins—*lymph;* or, as lymph in this space is commonly called, **capsular urine.**

Capsular urine passes into the tubular portion of the nephron. The cells composing this tubule represent the second fish inspector of our analogy. These cells share with root-hair cells of plants, mu-cosa cells of the intestine, and many others the distinction of being more or less a riddle to us. We know in general terms what they do, but not how they do it. Tubule cells are finely selective in their action. On one surface they **reabsorb** from passing capsular urine a picked group of substances. And on the other surface they secrete these substances back into the blood stream, through the adjacent blood capillary walls (see Fig. 20.29). Whatever is not reabsorbed into the blood in this manner constitutes urine, specifically, **bladder urine,** since it is carried through the collecting ducts and the ureters into the bladder.

In man, all 5 or 6 qt of blood in the body are filtered through the kidneys once every 45 min or so. In a 24-hr period, therefore, the kidneys filter about 150 qt of liquid. Yet in the same period, only about 1½ qt of urine, on an average, is actually excreted by the normal adult. This means that tubule cells reabsorb 99 per cent of the water in capsular urine and leave only 1 per cent as urine. As might be expected, more urine is excreted when the fluid intake is large, less when it is small.

Reabsorption

During the reabsorption of water from capsular urine, some materials dissolved in it are, and some are not, reabsorbed too.

For example, capsular urine contains glucose, in the same concentration as in blood. Under normal conditions, all the glucose in capsular urine is reabsorbed into the blood, and none escapes into bladder urine. We have noted that glucose is excreted only when present in excessive quantities. Presumably, tubule cells then cannot reabsorb this carbohydrate fast enough. Glucose is said to be a **high-threshold substance;** a high concentration must be present in blood and capsular urine before it will be excreted in bladder urine. Among other high-threshold materials are amino acids, fatty acids, glycerin, vitamins, hormones, in short, all the essential nutrients and other usable supplies in transit to cells. These are the "healthy fish" of our analogy.

On the other hand, some substances in capsular urine are always left in urine by the tubule cells.

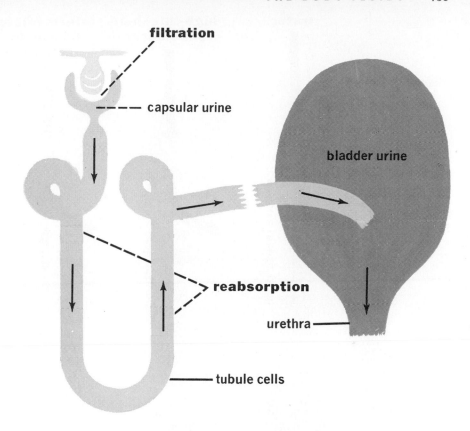

filtration

— capsular urine

bladder urine

reabsorption

urethra —

— tubule cells

FIG. 20.29. Illustrating the operation of a nephron. Through filtration of blood, capsular urine is formed, and through reabsorption of various components present in capsular urine, bladder urine is formed.

Urea, pigmented blood-breakdown products, and other outright wastes are among these. Since such materials are excreted even when they are present in low concentrations, they are referred to as **low-threshold substances.** These become highly concentrated as water is withdrawn from capsular urine. Bladder urine contains some seventy times more urea, for example, than an equal volume of capsular urine.

Finally, there are **intermediate-threshold substances,** which tubule cells sometimes do and sometimes do not reabsorb, depending on whether these materials are or are not in proper balance in blood. Most inorganic ions and many organic substances belong to this category. High salt intake, for example, will probably be followed by excretion of sodium and chloride ions, if these ions were already in adequate supply. But if the supply was low originally, tubule cells would retain these inorganic ions.

Tubule cells evidently possess exquisite discriminatory powers. They are not only capable of distinguishing one type of molecule from another, but they are also sensitive to concentrations of materials in blood and are able to readjust these concentrations. By now rejecting, now reabsorbing given substances, they are the final arbiters of blood composition (Fig. 20.30).

Note that, as urine becomes more concentrated by withdrawal of water, the osmotic pull of urine becomes greater. But despite this force, which tends to draw water *from* blood *into* urine, tubule cells nevertheless transport more water from *urine* to *blood*.

The kidneys clearly are much more than expellers of waste. Indeed, what is or is not "waste" is determined from moment to moment principally by

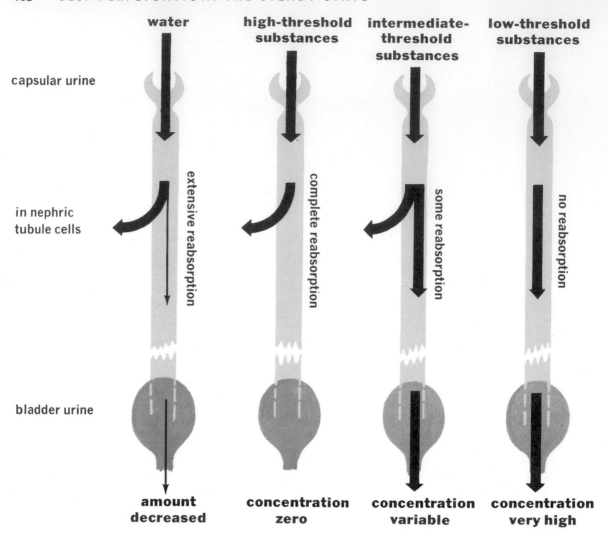

FIG. 20.30. The selective action of the cells of a nephric tubule. Water is reabsorbed to a very large extent; high-threshold substances like glucose are reabsorbed more or less completely; low-threshold substances like urea are not reabsorbed at all; and intermediate-threshold substances like many mineral ions are reabsorbed in part, depending on the amount already present in blood.

the kidneys. In this, their function of **retention** is at least as vital as their function of excretion. It may be appreciated why examination of urine will reveal not only how well the kidneys function, but also how well steady state is maintained in the body as a whole.

Urine emerges from the kidneys continuously. The wall of the bladder stretches as urine accumulates, and at a certain stage of stretching, sensory nerve endings in the wall are stimulated. A reflex initiates contraction of the muscles in the bladder wall, and the organ then empties to the outside.

RESUME   Excretion, circulation, blood, lymph, and their many control mechanisms are means to an end. They enable *cells* to maintain steady states, and thereby they enable the whole body to maintain steady states.

But body fluids, and the numerous substances carried by them, are not the only agents exerting external control over individual cells. As must have become abundantly apparent from this and earlier chapters, the nervous system is at least as influential. In animals, nerve endings, no less than body fluids, form part of the immediate environment of cells. And cells exchange information and materials with nerve endings just as they do with blood or lymph. A discussion of the nervous system clearly is essential in any discussion of steady-state controls.

REVIEW QUESTIONS

1. Review the composition of blood plasma and the functions of each group of components. How, specifically, may ions in plasma act as buffers? Give examples.

2. What are antibodies? When, where, and how are they produced? Distinguish between active and passive immunity. Why does passive immunity not give as lasting protection against infection as active immunity?

3. What cellular components occur in blood, and what are the functions of each? By what processes is the number of red corpuscles maintained relatively constant? What role do lymph nodes play in internal steady-state control? Review the reaction pattern of blood clotting.

4. Name the principal parts of the heart and the principal blood vessels, and review the general course of blood circulation. What structural features distinguish arteries, veins, lymph vessels, and capillaries?

5. Review the events during a complete heartbeat, with attention to durations, pressure patterns, valve positions, direction of blood flow, and heart sounds. How is blood moved through veins and lymph vessels?

6. Describe the nervous controls of the heart. How are control signals transmitted through the heart itself? Which motor signals accelerate the heart, and which decelerate it? Describe stretch reflexes which (*a*) accelerate and (*b*) decelerate the heart. Through what specific processes is the heart (*a*) speeded up when physical exercise is begun and (*b*) slowed down during rest or sleep? What nonnervous agencies affect heart rate?

7. What three major factors control blood pressure, and what governs each of these factors? Describe the action of the vasomotor center. What nervous and chemical agencies affect this center, and how?

8. What is the interrelation between vasomotion, heart rate, and breathing rate? Suppose that physical exercise is begun; describe the specific processes leading simultaneously to (*a*) increased heart rate, (*b*) increased breathing rate, (*c*) increased blood pressure, and (*d*) redistribution of blood within the body.

9. What are the overall functions of the excretory system? What organs compose this system, and what is the excretory function of each? Describe the general structure of the kidney and its associated ducts, and the specific structure of a nephron.

10. Review in detail the process of urine formation. What are the roles of filtration and reabsorption, and where and how does each occur? What are high-threshold substances? Give examples. Construct a table showing how bladder urine differs from blood and capsular urine with respect to (*a*) the kinds of substances present and (*b*) the concentrations of substances present.

SUGGESTED COLLATERAL READINGS

Any of the five texts listed at the end of Chap. 13, especially the first, offers excellent background reading on topics covered here. Of the articles cited below, the first is about, and the second by, the discoverer of the blood circulation in man. The remaining titles additionally supplement the subject matter of this chapter.

Kilgour, F. G.: William Harvey, *Sci. American,* vol. 186, 1952.

Harvey, W.: On the Motion of the Heart and Blood, translation of original (1616) Latin, in T. S. Hall, " A Source Book in Animal Biology," McGraw-Hill, 1951.

Surgenor, D. M.: Blood, *Sci. American,* vol. 190, 1954.

Ponder, E.: The Red Blood Cell, *Sci. American,* vol. 196, 1957.

Wood, W. B.: White Blood Cells vs. Bacteria, *Sci. American,* vol. 184, 1951.

Fox, H. M.: Blood Pigments, *Sci. American,* vol. 182, 1950.

Burnet, M.: How Antibodies Are Made, *Sci. American,* vol. 191, 1954.

Boyden, A. A.: The Blood Relationships of Animals, *Sci. American,* vol. 185, 1951.

Wiener, A. S.: Parentage and Blood Groups, *Sci. American,* vol. 191, 1954.

McKusick, V. A.: Heart Sounds, *Sci. American,* vol. 194, 1956.

Page, I. H.: High Blood Pressure, *Sci. American,* vol. 179, 1948.

Smith, H. W.: The Kidney, *Sci. American,* vol. 190, 1954.

21

NERVOUS COORDINATION

Nervous activity is based on *reflexes*. These are the functional units of the nervous system. A reflex is routed through a *reflex arc*, which, like any other control apparatus, consists of five components: receptor, sensory pathway, modulator, motor pathway, and effector.

The neural receptors are specialized cells, which may or may not be housed in elaborate organs such as eyes or ears. Receptors translate the energy of incoming stimuli into nerve impulses, and these are transmitted over sensory nerve fibers to the modulators, namely, brain and spinal cord. Their activity produces nerve impulses which travel over motor nerve fibers to the effectors. These are predominantly muscles and glands, and they translate the motor impulses they receive into explicit responses.

Effector functions of muscles and glands have already been discussed in various earlier contexts. In this chapter, therefore, we concentrate primarily on the **neural pathways**, the **neural receptors**, and the **neural centers**.

The Neural Pathways

The mammalian nervous system consists of two subdivisions, the **central nervous system** (**c.n.s.**) and the **autonomic nervous system** (**a.n.s.**). Brain and spinal cord house the neural centers of both. The c.n.s. largely controls voluntary, conscious activities, and the a.n.s., involuntary, unconscious ones. But the c.n.s. and a.n.s. are highly interdependent, and, as we shall see, they form a unified, intimately coordinated functional complex.

Regardless of whether reflex activity occurs in the c.n.s. or the a.n.s., the internal working material of the entire nervous system is always the same: nerve cells, which produce and transmit nerve impulses. These properly demand our first attention.

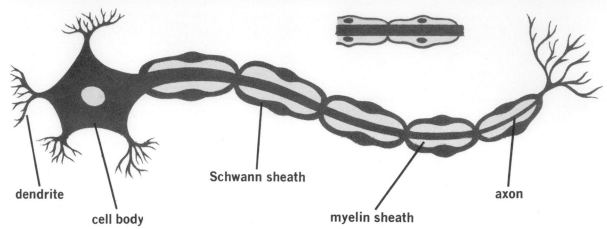

Schwann sheath

dendrite

cell body

myelin sheath

axon

FIG. 21.1.   The structure of a neuron. Dendrites may be longer than those shown. Upper inset: a length of nonmyelinated axon.

NERVE CELLS

A nerve cell, or **neuron,** typically consists of a star-shaped **cell body,** containing the nucleus, and of one or more long or short filamentous outgrowths, called **nerve fibers,** which extend away from the cell body (Figs. 21.1 and 3.11). Nerve impulses normally originate at the terminal of one of the fibers, travel toward the cell body, traverse it, then lead away from the cell body through another of its fibers. Nerve fibers in which impulses travel toward the cell body are termed **dendrites;** those carrying impulses away from the cell body, **axons.** A neuron characteristically possesses only a single axon, but it may have one or several dendrites.

By and large, neurons are comparatively huge cells. Dendrites and axons may be as much as a yard or more long, or they may be relatively short.

Long nerve fibers, but not the cell bodies or the shorter fibers, are enveloped by one or by two sheaths. Most of the long fibers of the central nervous system are surrounded directly by a layer of noncellular fatty material, the **myelin sheath.** This sheath in turn is enveloped by what is called the **Schwann sheath,** which is made up of a single layer of thin flat cells. In most nerve fibers of the autonomic nervous system, only a Schwann sheath sur-

rounds the axon, while myelin sheaths are absent.

Myelin sheaths probably increase the speed of nerve-impulse transmission. It can be shown that myelinated fibers of the c.n.s. may conduct impulses at speeds of about 100 yd per sec, whereas nonmyelinated a.n.s. fibers at most conduct at about 25 yd per sec. The suggestion has been made that the accelerating effect of the fatty myelin layer results from an insulating action; a myelin envelope would be to a nerve fiber what a rubber envelope is to an electricity-conducting metal wire.

The Schwann sheath maintains the continued existence of the nerve fiber it envelops. It is known to supply nutritive materials to the fiber, and it also plays a critical role in fiber regeneration. For example, if an axon is cut, the part which is disconnected from the cell body degenerates (Fig. 21.2). If now the cut ends of the Schwann sheath heal together, the intact axon stump slowly grows out, into the reconnected Schwann tube. A complete new axon eventually regenerates, replacing the degenerated portion. This is not the case when the cut ends of the Schwann tube do not, or cannot, heal together. For example, if a section of nerve fiber is destroyed entirely and the sheath ends consequently are too far apart, then the axon stump still grows out. But this may occur in an uncontrolled, randomly oriented

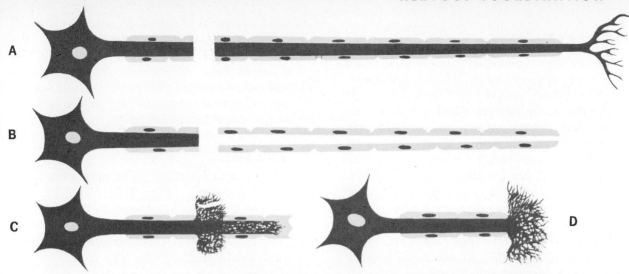

FIG. 21.2.   The role of the Schwann sheath in neuron regeneration. **A,** cut axon. **B,** axon on far side of cut has degenerated. **C,** if a Schwann sheath is present, a new axon grows into it. **D,** if a Schwann sheath is not present, new axon growth is random and disoriented.

manner, and the axon may never reach the tissue it should have innervated (see Fig. 21.2d).

Neurosurgeons may sometimes save a shattered nerve fiber by rerouting the disconnected portions over a shorter path, so that the ends of the Schwann sheaths meet and can heal together.

Individual neurons are placed end to end, form-

ing long neural pathways. The axon fiber of one neuron connects functionally with a dendrite of the next. But there is never a structural connection. Fiber terminals come exceedingly close to one another, yet a microscopic gap, a **synapse,** still separates them (Fig. 21.3). We shall soon see how nerve impulses are transmitted across such synapses.

FIG. 21.3.   Neurons arranged end to end form extensive neural paths. A synapse, or gap, separates one neuron from the next structurally, but not functionally.

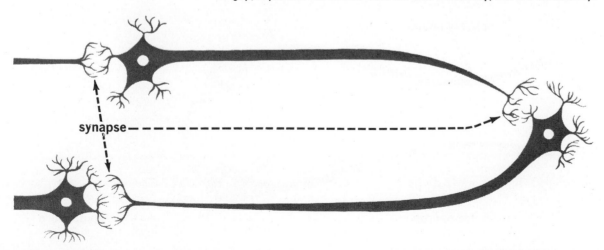

REFLEX ARCS

The minimum number of neurons in a reflex arc is two: one **sensory neuron,** which transmits impulses from a receptor organ to either brain or spinal cord, and one **motor neuron,** which relays the impulses sent out by brain or spinal cord to an effector organ. Most reflex arcs consist of more than two neurons. One or more additional **interneurons** may be located within brain or spinal cord, between the end of the sensory and the beginning of the motor neuron. In the entire nervous system, interneurons are actually the most abundant, for they make up the bulk of the brain and the spinal cord (Fig. 21.4).

Sensory neurons leading to, and motor neurons leading from, brain and spinal cord are collected into discrete bundles, which traverse the body like the cables of telephone trunk lines. Such bundles of neuron fibers are called **nerves.** Connective tissue holds the fibers of a nerve together (Fig. 21.5). The nerve illustrated in the last figure is a **mixed nerve,** so called because it contains both sensory and motor fibers. In certain nerves only sensory fibers are present, and these are called **sensory nerves.** Analogously, some nerves contain motor fibers only, and they are referred to as **motor nerves.** Nerves are also classified as **cranial** or **spinal,** according to whether they connect with the brain or the spinal cord.

The c.n.s. and the a.n.s. each possess their own set of nerves. Each set connects with distinct c.n.s. or a.n.s. centers in brain and spinal cord, and each of the two subdivisions of the nervous system thus possesses its own reflex pathways.

C.N.S. Reflexes

The familiar knee-jerk reflex may serve as an illustrative example (Fig. 21.6). The knee is tapped, and this stimulus, processed by receptor organs in the kneecap tendon, elicits a nerve impulse in a sensory nerve fiber. This fiber joins others from the knee region, and together they form part of a spinal nerve which passes through the thigh and connects to the spinal cord at hip level. Just outside the spinal cord, this spinal nerve divides into two fiber bundles. These attach to the cord at slightly different points. One of the bundles contains all the sensory fibers *from* the knee region; the other, all the motor fibers *to* the knee region. The cell bodies of the sensory neurons are located outside the spinal cord, in a nodular thickening called a **ganglion.** Any collection of neuron cell bodies found outside brain or spinal cord is a ganglion. Note that the cell bodies

FIG. 21.4.   The pattern and the components of a reflex arc.

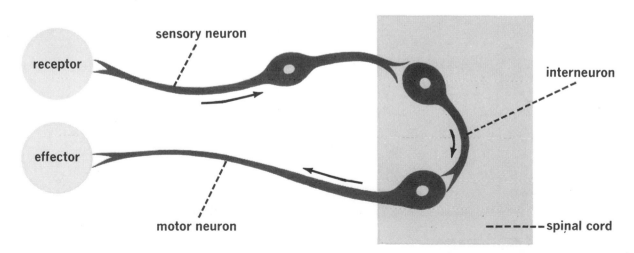

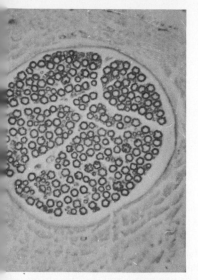

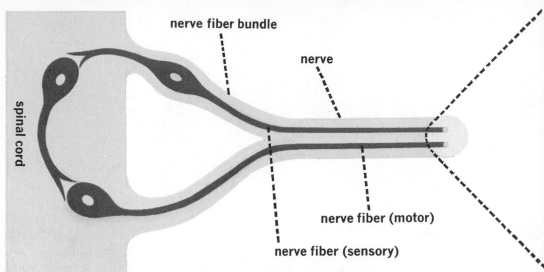

nerve fiber bundle

nerve

spinal cord

nerve fiber (motor)

nerve fiber (sensory)

FIG. 21.5. The structure of a nerve. Many sensory fibers, motor fibers, or both, traveling together constitute a nerve. The photo inset shows what such a nerve looks like in cross section. In this particular section, note that each nerve fiber is enveloped by a myelin sheath (the dark rings). (Photo courtesy of Dr. Mac V. Edds, Brown University.)

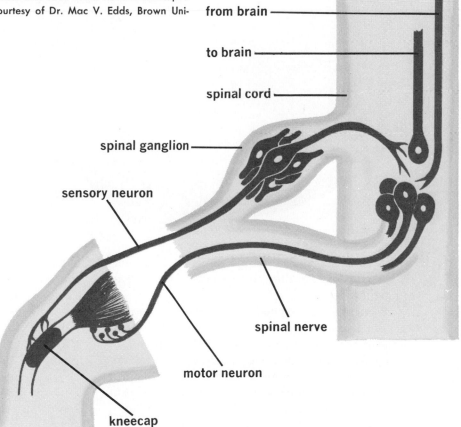

from brain

to brain

spinal cord

spinal ganglion

sensory neuron

spinal nerve

motor neuron

kneecap

FIG. 21.6. A reflex arc in the central nervous system. The knee-jerk reflex is illustrated.

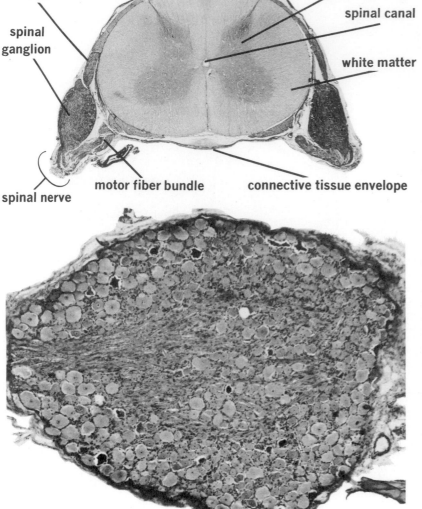

sensory fiber bundle

spinal ganglion

spinal nerve

motor fiber bundle

gray matter

spinal canal

white matter

connective tissue envelope

FIG. 21.7. Top: cross section through mammalian spinal cord. Note the spinal nerves, each dividing into two fiber bundles. The motor bundle connects with the cord ventrally, and the sensory bundle passes through a spinal ganglion and connects with the cord dorsally. The spinal cord itself is a dense meshwork of neurons, the cell bodies of which are aggregated around the center, forming so-called gray matter. The axons and dendrites of these neurons are collected around the gray matter, forming white matter. The central spinal canal contains lymphlike spinal fluid. Bottom: enlarged view of a section through a spinal ganglion. Note the many nerve fibers, some seen in cross section, some in longitudinal section. (Ward's Natural Science Establishment, Inc.)

of the motor neurons of this spinal nerve are *within* the spinal cord, and they consequently do not form a ganglion.

Evidently, the spinal nerve which connects knee and spinal cord is a mixed nerve. This holds for all the 31 pairs of spinal nerves of the c.n.s. found in mammals. These nerves are attached to the spinal cord at more or less regular intervals, and they innervate most of the skeletal musculature in chest, arms, abdomen, and legs. As above, the sensory and motor fibers of each of these nerves connect to the

spinal cord at separate points, and the cell bodies of the sensory fibers form 31 pairs of **spinal ganglia** (Fig. 21.7).

In our example, therefore, nerve impulses originating at the knee travel first through a dendrite, then through a cell body situated in a spinal ganglion, and finally through an axon into the spinal cord. The spinal cord itself may be envisaged as a dense meshwork of neurons, interlinked by synapses. Axons entering the spinal cord terminate at such synapses, and neural pathways from there lead up as far as into the brain, down, and laterally. Thus, hundreds of *possible* pathways are available within the spinal cord into which an incoming nerve impulse from the knee might be channeled. Yet only a limited, selected number of pathways are actually used. Such path selection constitutes the principal control activity of the spinal cord.

Specifically, an impulse from the kneecap tendon is normally relayed over two principal paths. It is transmitted up into the brain, and this produces *awareness* of the knee-tapping stimulus. Simultaneously, the impulse is channeled into motor neurons originating close by at hip level. The long axons of these motor neurons emerge from the spinal cord and form part of the spinal nerve which innervates the knee region (see Fig. 21.6). Motor impulses travel through the thigh, and there the motor fibers branch away from the spinal nerve and lead to muscles. In response to the motor impulses, the muscles in the front part of the thigh contract, and those in the hind part relax. As a result, the leg kicks out.

This completes the knee-jerk reflex. Note that the leg response is accompanied by, but does not depend on, conscious awareness of the knee-tapping stimulus. The leg would kick out even during sleep, or if the brain were destroyed. It is a general characteristic of c.n.s. reflexes that they become conscious, but consciousness is not a necessary condition for their completion. However, consciousness may bring about additional responses, superimposed on the leg response. For example, if the knee should be tapped too violently, one is likely to cry out, get up, or run away, or one may attempt to suppress any such expressions of pain or annoyance. In general, consciousness may initiate new reflexes which modify the original response, and the total response, different in different individuals, then adds up to complex subjective *behavior*. Reflex modification is an important function of c.n.s. centers in the brain, and varied conscious behavior is a direct result.

The knee jerk is one of many **spinal reflexes,** so called because the basic neural path leads through spinal nerves and spinal cord. C.n.s. activity also includes numerous **cranial reflexes,** executed by the brain and the cranial nerves. Such reflexes too usu-

ally become conscious. Twelve pairs of cranial nerves are found in mammals, some mixed like the spinal nerves, others purely sensory or purely motor. As Fig. 21.8 and Table 12 indicate in detail, these nerves innervate structures in the head, the neck, the chest, and the abdomen. Like spinal reflexes in the c.n.s., cranial ones too serve largely to control skeletal, voluntarily movable muscles.

A.N.S. Reflexes

Reflexes in the a.n.s. generally do not become conscious, regardless of whether they are routed through the brain or the spinal cord. And they regulate the functioning of body parts which are not under voluntary control: smooth muscles, the heart, and most glands and other internal organs.

Some *sensory* pathways of the a.n.s. have already been described in earlier contexts. For example, the stretch reflexes which regulate heart function involve sensory neurons from the vena cava and the aorta to the heart-rate center in the brain (see Chap. 20). Heart control is a purely autonomic, involuntary function, and the heart-rate center, together with the nerve fibers to and from it, are part of the a.n.s. Similarly, every other internal organ which is not controllable by force of will is innervated by sensory a.n.s. fibers leading to a.n.s. centers in brain or spinal cord.

Two distinct sets of a.n.s. centers exist. As noted in Chap. 17, control of any kind is a dual process, involving excitation as well as its opposite, inhibition. That this is the case for nervous controls too is shown particularly well by the two sets of a.n.s. centers. One of these brings about excitations and accelerations of internal organs, and the other, inhibitions and decelerations. Correspondingly, there are also two sets of a.n.s. *motor* fibers, and each organ is innervated *doubly*. We have already found this to be so for the heart, for example, where certain motor fibers accelerate and others inhibit. Similarly, the diameter of blood vessels is under the control of distinct vasoconstrictor *and* vasodilator nerves (see Chap. 20). In general, the net activity of any organ under a.n.s. control is a resultant of a given degree of acceleration by one set of motor nerves and a given degree of inhibition by another set of motor nerves.

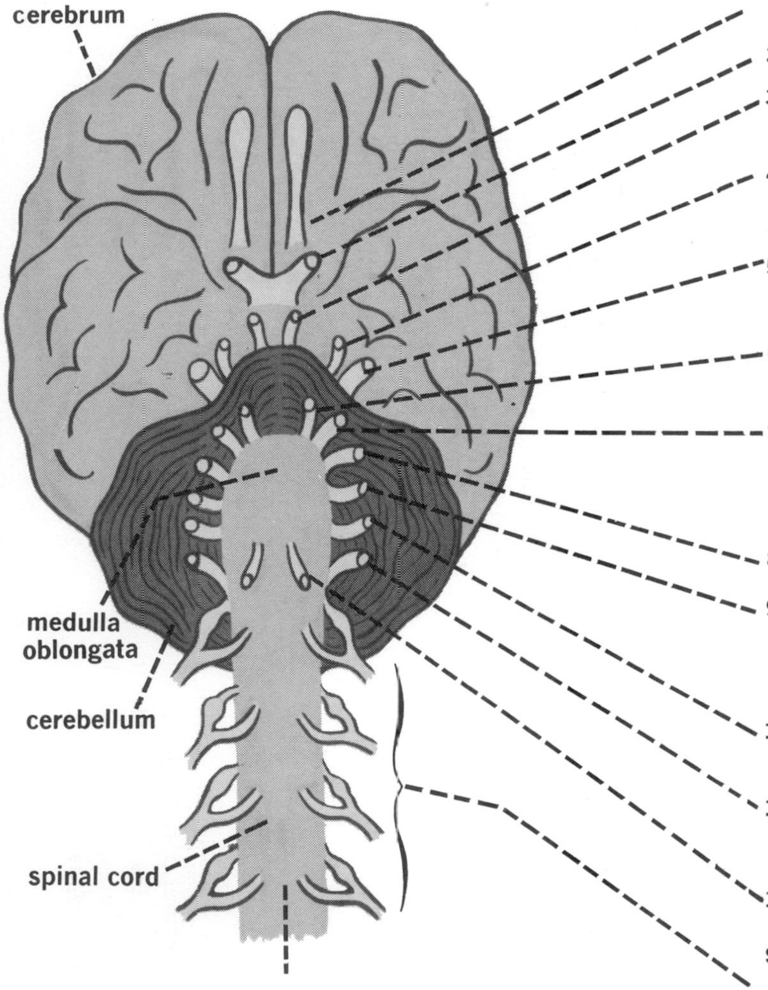

TABLE 12.

The nerves of the central nervous system

Name	Type	Innervation
1. Olfactory	sensory	from nose
2. Optic	sensory	from eye
3. Oculomotor	motor	to muscles of eyeball
4. Trochlear	motor	to muscles of eyeball
5. Trigeminal	mixed	from and to face, teeth
6. Abducens	motor	to muscles of eyeball
7. Facial	mixed	from taste buds to salivary glands and facial muscles
8. Auditory	sensory	from ear
9. Glosso-pharyngeal	mixed	from and to pharynx, from taste buds to salivary glands
10. Vagus	mixed	from and to chest and abdomen
11. Spinal accessory	motor	to shoulder muscles
12. Hypoglossal	motor	to tongue
Spinal nerves (31 pairs)	mixed	from and to muscles in arms, legs, and trunk

cerebrum

medulla oblongata

cerebellum

spinal cord

FIG. 21.8. Diagram of the underside of brain and anterior part of spinal cord, showing the origin of the cranial nerves and a few of the spinal nerves. The names and functions of these nerves are given in the table.

The two sets of a.n.s. centers are located in what are called the **sympathetic** and **parasympathetic** portions of the a.n.s. (Fig. 21.9). Sympathetic centers are grouped together in the middle part of the spinal cord, roughly between shoulder and waist levels. Parasympathetic centers are situated above and below the sympathetic ones, i.e., in the deeper parts of the brain, in the medulla oblongata, and in the neck and hip portions of the spinal cord.

A given internal organ receives motor fibers from some part of the sympathetic system *and* from some part of the parasympathetic system. Therefore, every organ is regulated from two control centers, the one excitatory, the other inhibitory. In some cases the excitatory center is in the sympathetic system; in other cases it is in the parasympathetic system. For example, the center which accelerates the heart is sympathetic, and the center which slows the heart is parasympathetic. The dual a.n.s. motor controls of a number of other organs are illustrated in Fig. 21.10.

This figure also shows that the motor paths of the *sympathetic* system are made up not of single neurons, but of at least two neurons each, one following the other. The first motor neuron leaves the sympathetic portion of the spinal cord and may terminate just outside the cord in a ganglion, one of the **sympathetic chain ganglia.** These ganglia form two chains, one along each side of the spinal cord. Many sympathetic motor neurons from the spinal cord terminate in these ganglia and synapse here with a second set of motor neurons. These last innervate the organs of the body. For example, an accelerator path to the heart begins with a motor neuron, which emerges from the sympathetic portion of the spinal cord and leads to a chain ganglion. Here this first neuron synapses with a second motor neuron, and the latter then leads to the heart. The motor pathways from the spinal cord to the chain ganglia are called **preganglionic fibers;** and the motor pathways from the chain ganglia to the organs are called **postganglionic fibers.**

In some cases, preganglionic fibers do not terminate in the chain ganglia but extend farther, to other ganglia located in various parts of the body. Postganglionic fibers then originate there. This is the

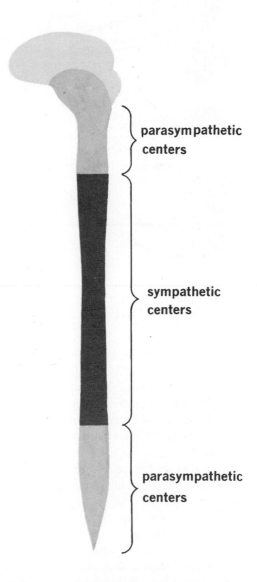

parasympathetic centers

sympathetic centers

parasympathetic centers

FIG. 21.9. Diagram showing the location of sympathetic and parasympathetic a.n.s. centers in brain and spinal cord. Each subdivision receives its own sensory nerves and sends out its own motor nerves. A given a.n.s.-controlled organ therefore is innervated by two sets of motor nerves, one originating in sympathetic centers, the other in parasympathetic centers.

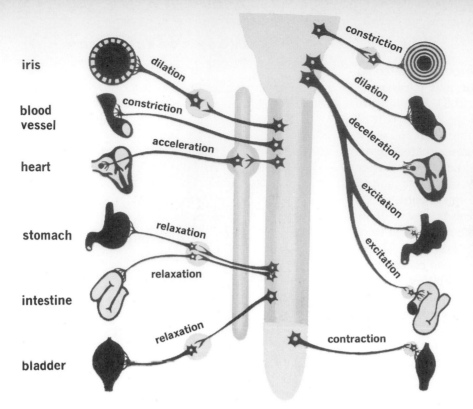

iris

blood vessel

heart

stomach

intestine

bladder

dilation
constriction
acceleration
relaxation
relaxation
relaxation

constriction
dilation
deceleration
excitation
excitation
contraction

SYMPATHETIC   **PARASYMPATHETIC**

FIG. 21.10. Some of the motor pathways of the autonomic nervous system. Column to the left of spinal cord represents sympathetic chain ganglia. Each neural path shown occurs pairwise, one on the left and one on the right of the body. Similarly, sympathetic chain ganglia occur to both the left and the right of the spinal cord. For simplicity, however, only one side is indicated in each case.

case, for example, in the sympathetic motor paths to stomach and intestine (see Fig. 21.10). Note that, in the vicinity of the spinal cord, sympathetic motor fibers, and indeed also sensory fibers, travel together with the fibers of the mixed spinal nerves of the c.n.s. The anatomical interrelations here are shown in Fig. 21.11.

The motor paths of the *parasympathetic* system do not lead through the chain ganglia. But they do travel through other ganglia, present along the way to given organs (see Fig. 21.10). Moreover, parasympathetic fibers too may run together with c.n.s. nerves. For example, the parasympathetic inhibitory fibers to the heart utilize the pathway of the vagus nerve (see Chap. 20), which is a cranial nerve of the c.n.s.

A.n.s. and c.n.s. are closely interconnected not only anatomically but also functionally. Many familiar observations bear this out. For example, visual experiences, which are c.n.s.-controlled, may affect heart rate, which is a.n.s.-controlled. A frightening sight may initiate a c.n.s. reflex from the eyes to the

visual center in the brain, and from there to the muscles of the legs. This might lead to running, and to deliberate, conscious avoidance of the frightening sight. At the same time, heart rate increases and blood pressure rises. Evidently, impulses coming into the visual center from the eyes are relayed also via interneurons to the heart-rate center. It is this kind of interconnection between c.n.s. and a.n.s. centers which produces an adaptive total response. For voluntary running could not be long sustained without an appropriate involuntary adjustment of the body circulation (Fig. 21.12).

Indeed, a frightening sight is likely to bring into play many additional a.n.s. reflexes as well: vasomotion and breathing will be affected, adrenalin output will increase, sweat glands will be activated, the alimentary system will be inhibited, and in fact the whole body will tend to rally into a state of emergency. We may note, in general, that a.n.s. and c.n.s. are geared together so intimately that any reflex in one system is likely to initiate one or more concurrent reflexes in the other.

The above outlines the structural arrangements of the neural pathways. How do these pathways function? What is a nerve impulse, and how is it transmitted?

NERVE IMPULSES

The precise nature of a nerve impulse is still unknown. We may say, in general, that an impulse is a sequence of metabolic reactions propagated along a nerve fiber. After an impulse has passed, the reaction balance returns to the original state, readying the fiber for a new impulse. These processes consume oxygen and energy.

Accompanying the chemical changes are electrical phenomena. Indeed, the intriguing resemblance of the nervous system to a meshwork of electrical wires conducting electrical currents has been the basis of many attempts to explain nervous activity. Moreover, just as one can measure currents in wires by galvanometers, voltmeters, ammeters, and the like, so this same electrical equipment can be used on nerves. But nerve impulses are not simply electrical impulses. What travels some 100,000 miles per sec in a wire travels at most about 100 yd per sec in a nerve fiber. Nerve impulses are neither purely electrical nor purely chemical, and at present they may best be described as **electrochemical** events.

FIG. 21.11.   The anatomical interrelations of spinal c.n.s. and a.n.s. nerve fibers. Note that a given fiber bundle or nerve connecting with the spinal cord contains sensory fibers of both c.n.s. and a.n.s., motor fibers of both c.n.s. and a.n.s., or both sensory and motor fibers of both c.n.s. and a.n.s. Sensory fibers of all kinds always enter the spinal cord dorsally, and motor fibers of all kinds always leave the cord ventrally.

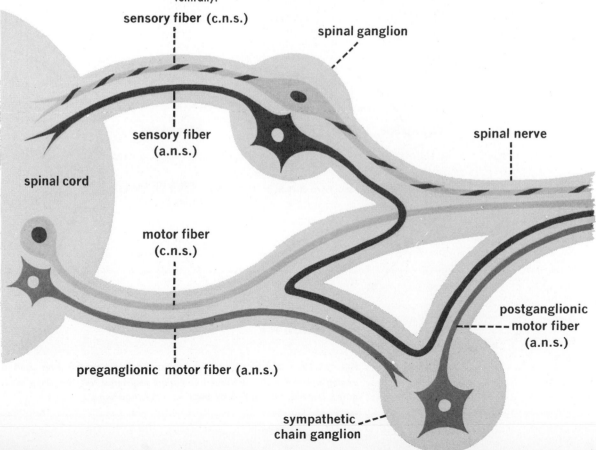

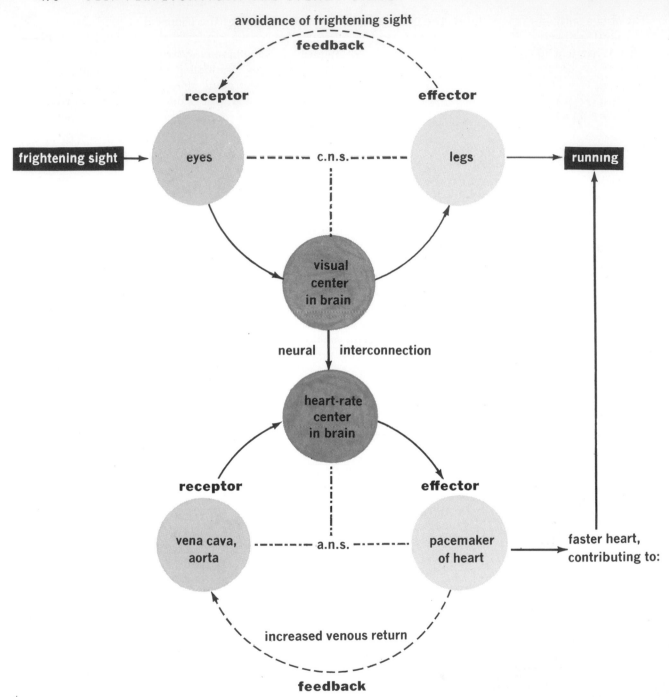

FIG. 21.12. The functional interconnection between the c.n.s. and a.n.s. In the example shown here, a sense perception registered via the c.n.s. leads to coordinated responses controlled by both the c.n.s. and a.n.s.

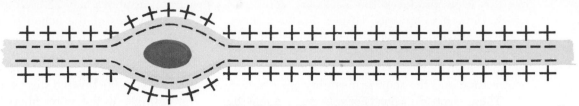

FIG. 21.13. The polarization of an inactive, resting neuron. The positive charges on the outside and the negative charges on the inside produce an electrical potential across the cell membrane.

Transmission in Fibers

Before a nerve fiber can transmit an impulse, it must be stimulated *adequately*. Whereas every environmental change represents a stimulus, not every such change represents an adequate stimulus. To be adequate, a stimulus must be at least of minimum strength, or **threshold intensity.** Too weak a stimulus will not activate a nerve fiber. Further, to be adequate, a stimulus must reach threshold intensity fast enough. If the build-up to the required intensity occurs too slowly, a nerve fiber, again, will not be activated. Stimulation evidently depends on an appropriately **high rate** of environmental change. Finally, to be effective, a stimulus must last long enough; i.e., it must be of at least **minimum duration.**

Once it is stimulated adequately, a neuron will "fire," that is, transmit an impulse from the point of stimulation over its fibers. Under normal conditions within the body, stimulation occurs at a dendrite terminal, and an impulse then travels through the cell body to an axon terminal.

Whatever else an impulse may be, it is known that it is a **wave of electrical depolarization** sweeping along a nerve fiber. It can be shown that a resting, nonstimulated neuron is electrically positive along the outer side of its surface membrane, and electrically negative along the inner side (Fig. 21.13). These electric charges are carried by inorganic ions, attached to the two sides of the neuron membrane. As a result, an *electrical potential* is maintained across the cell membrane, and the membrane is said to be **polarized** electrically. In some ways this resembles the polarization believed to be maintained in the actomyosin units of muscle (see Chap. 16).

Polarization, and indeed the integrity of a neuron membrane, appear to depend on *semipermeability;* the membrane is so constructed that it prevents the positive and negative ions from coming

together. If semipermeability were destroyed, the membrane would depolarize; that is, the positive and negative ions *would* join. Conversely, if depolarization were to occur, membrane semipermeability would be abolished.

When a nerve impulse sweeps along a nerve fiber, local depolarization and simultaneous destruction of semipermeability actually do occur at successive points of the fiber membrane. As this happens at any one point, an avenue is created through which positive and negative ions of an adjacent point may meet (Fig. 21.14). In other words, the

FIG. 21.14. The passage of an impulse through a nerve fiber produces a local depolarization and destruction of the permeability properties of the fiber membrane, propagated in a wavelike manner through successive portions of the fiber. After an impulse has passed a given region, the original polarization and membrane characteristics reappear.

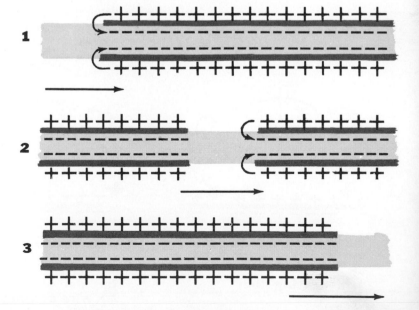

impulse itself produces the necessary conditions which allow it to advance farther. In this manner, it travels wavelike along a fiber. Some short time after an impulse has passed a given point, the membrane at that point recovers; that is, both the polarization and the semipermeability are restored.

These electrical aspects of transmission may be demonstrated experimentally. For example, it is possible to expose a nerve of a test animal and to connect a galvanometer to this nerve with fine wires, as shown in Fig. 21.15. When the nerve is then stimulated, the needle of the galvanometer is deflected, in one direction as the impulse passes the first wire contact, and in the opposite direction as it passes the second. This indicates that electrical changes occur during impulse transmission. Moreover, the test reveals that the particular portion of the outer fiber surface which carries the impulse at any given moment is electrically less positive than the remainder of the fiber surface. This is what should be expected if an impulse were to cause local depolarization, i.e., reduction or removal of the outer positive charge. The current flow accompanying impulse transmission is called the action current, or the **action potential,** of a nerve fiber. Apparatus as above may be used to measure the varying intensities of the action potentials of different fibers and also the different speeds of impulse transmission.

In some nerve fibers, impulses are fired continuously, in fairly rapid succession. This is the case, for example, in the motor fibers from the heart-rate center to the heart. Adjustment of heart rate is brought about by "frequency modulation": impulses are sent uninterruptedly, and when heart rate is to change, the frequency of the impulses is varied. In other cases, a fiber is normally at rest and carries impulses only when an effector response is to be brought about. For example, in fibers to many glands, impulses are sent only as long as the glands are to secrete.

What happens when an impulse reaches an axon terminal? How does it jump across the gap of the synapse to the dendrite terminal of a neighboring neuron?

Transmission across Synapses

Synaptic transmission appears to be a chemical process. In certain cases, it can be shown that, when an impulse reaches an axon terminal, the terminal

FIG. 21.15. The action potential of a nerve impulse. Left: resting fiber, connected to galvanometer by wire contacts. Middle: impulse passes first wire contact, which becomes electronegative relative to second contact. Hence current flows through galvanometer from right to left, as indicated by deflected galvanometer needle. Right: impulse passes second wire contact. Current now flows in opposite direction, the second contact being electronegative relative to the first. Current flow accompanying an impulse represents the action potential of that impulse.

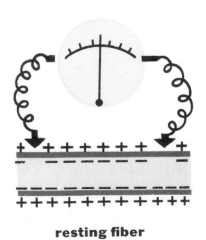

resting fiber

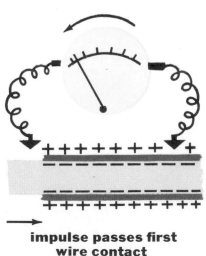

impulse passes first wire contact

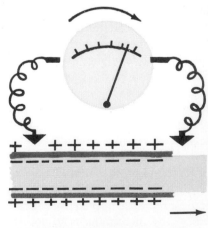

impulse passes second wire contact

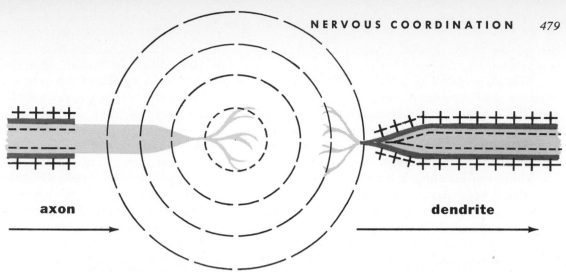

FIG. 21.16. Diagram of a neural synapse, showing the release and local spreading of hormones from the axon terminal of one fiber to the dendrite terminal of another. Impulses are transmitted across synapses by such chemical means.

acts like a miniature endocrine gland; it secretes minute amounts of a hormone. This hormone diffuses through the synaptic gap, some of it eventually reaches dendrite terminals of adjacent neurons, and the hormone here affects a dendrite in such a way that a new impulse is initiated in it (Fig. 21.16).

Two different hormones are known to play a role in synaptic transmission. One is **adrenalin,** or a substance very similar to adrenalin in chemical structure and biological effect. This hormone is secreted by the axon terminals of the postganglionic fibers of the sympathetic a.n.s. Because they produce adrenalin, these fibers are often said to be **adrenergic.**

The preganglionic fibers of the sympathetic system, all fibers of the parasympathetic system, and possibly the nerve fibers of the c.n.s. secrete a second type of hormone, namely, **acetyl-choline.** We have already encountered this substance in Chap. 16, as a participant in the generation of bioelectricity in specialized electric organs. We may now note that, like adrenalin, it brings about impulse transmission across many neural synapses. Acetyl-choline-secreting fibers are said to be **cholinergic.**

In synapses formed by cholinergic fibers, an enzyme is present which splits acetyl-choline into acetyl and choline fractions and so makes the hormone ineffective. This enzyme is **choline esterase.** Its adaptive advantage is clear. If it were not present, acetyl-choline would linger in the synapse and would stimulate dendrites repeatedly. Hence if two impulses came into a synapse in rapid succession, acetyl-choline produced by the first would still be effective when the second produced a hormone of its own. The impulses would therefore merge into each other, and the result would be one long drawn-out response, not two sharply distinct responses. Choline esterase prevents the merging of impulses. There is just time for acetyl-choline to stimulate dendrites once, and the hormone is destroyed immediately thereafter.

An equivalent enzyme cannot be demonstrated in the synapses formed by adrenergic fibers. Adrenalin does have a lingering effect, and this contributes to the comparative slowness and sustained quality of responses produced by the sympathetic part of the a.n.s.

The consequences of synaptic impulse transmission by chemicals are far-reaching. First, diffusion takes much longer than impulse conduction within a fiber. Hence a complete reflex, involving many synapses, lasts longer than would be expected on the basis of impulse speeds within fibers alone.

Being "slow on the uptake" is largely a result of delays at synapses.

Second, nerve fibers as such rarely fatigue, but synapses get tired fairly easily. When they are operating intensely, axon terminals may temporarily exhaust their hormone-secreting capacity, and synaptic transmission then slows even more or stops altogether for the time being.

Third, synapses impose a one-way direction on neural pathways. A nerve fiber can be stimulated artificially at either end or in the middle, and impulses then travel backward, forward, or in both directions. But only axon terminals are specialized to secrete hormones, and only dendrite terminals are sensitive to these hormones. Hence the unidirectional conduction of impulses.

Fourth, different types of impulses within fibers presumably release different concentrations of hormone from axon terminals. If a given terminal secretes only relatively small amounts of hormone, it may not be able by itself to activate an adjacent dendrite. But if each of several axons at a synapse produces subthreshold amounts of hormone at the same time, then the total might suffice to start an impulse in an adjacent dendrite. **Synaptic summation** of this sort probably plays an important role in normal nervous activity.

The first nerve impulse in a reflex arc is normally produced by a sensory receptor organ. How is a receptor constructed, and how does it function?

The Neural Receptors

We do not see with our eyes and do not hear with our ears. Nor do we see or hear with our brain. Seeing, hearing, "sensing" in general require the operational integrity of a sensory receptor *and* of a sensory neural path *and* of a neural center, which interprets the signals received.

Mammals possess many more than the familiar five senses of vision, hearing, smell, taste, and touch. They also sense pain, pressure, heat, and cold. They sense the position of their limbs, the mechanical equilibrium of their bodies, and the motion of their bodies, all without looking. They possess a genital sense, and they experience distinct sensations when tickled, when a limb "falls asleep," when the skin "stings" or "burns," when they are hungry, thirsty, or sleepy. These are only some of the numerous senses which penetrate into the conscious. And in probably more than an equivalent number of senses, conscious awareness is lacking. For when a blood vessel dilates under pressure, sensing is involved also.

A separate type of receptor structure probably does not exist for each of these senses. Only about a dozen different kinds of receptors are demonstrable. They mediate different sensations when stimulated singly and when a varied group of them is stimulated together. Receptors are often classified as **exteroceptors** and **interoceptors**, i.e., structures receiving information either about the outside world or about the interior of the body. All are alike in that they translate specific stimulus energies into specific nerve impulses.

We first discuss receptor types distributed widely throughout the body.

DISPERSED RECEPTORS

Structural Types

The simplest type of neural receptor is a free nerve ending. The hairlike dendrite terminals of sensory neurons may carry a series of nodular thickenings or may be bunched together like balls of twine, but beyond such structures other functional parts are not present. This is probably the most widespread kind of neural receptor. Relatively simple sensory endings of this sort relay a.n.s. signals from many internal organs, as well as a large variety of c.n.s. signals. For example, muscle sense and tendon sense (by which we feel the position of body parts) and the sense of pain are mediated by plain or variously nodulated and coiled sensory endings (Fig. 21.17a).

Moreover, comparatively simple nerve endings represent one type of receptor for touch stimuli. Each hair in the skin is surrounded at its base by a net, or *plexus*, of sensory fiber terminals (Fig. 21.17b). When a hair is bent, the position of the hair base changes slightly, and this stimulates the fiber plexus. The resulting nerve impulses are interpreted as touch.

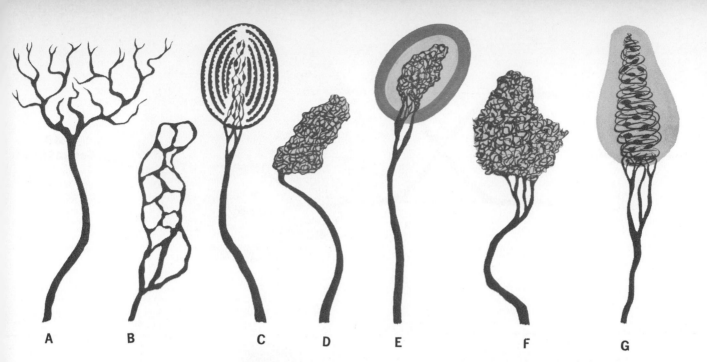

FIG. 21.17. Some types of neural receptors in the skin. **A,** free nerve ending (pain). **B,** nerve plexus surrounding hair (touch). **C,** Pacinian corpuscle (pressure). **D,** organ of Ruffini (pressure). **E,** organ of Krause (cold). **F,** end organ of Ruffini (warmth). **G,** Meissner's corpuscle (touch).

Touch stimuli are received additionally by sense *organs* located in the skin. These are tiny structures made up of many specialized cells (not neurons), innervated by sensory fiber terminals (Fig. 21.17g). Here it is the organ, not the fiber terminal, which translates stimulus energies into nerve impulses. Touch organs may be clustered together relatively densely, as in finger tips, palm, and lips, or they may occur sparsely, as on the back.

In addition to touch organs, the skin also contains tiny organs sensitive to heat, to cold, and to pressure. Together with the numerous touch organs and pain fibers in the skin, these make up what are called **cutaneous receptors.** They vary in relative distribution and in number. It is estimated that the human skin contains some 4 million pain receptors, half a million pressure receptors, 150,000 cold receptors, and 16,000 heat receptors.

Functional Properties
Very little is known about the mechanism by which specific stimuli, affecting either the tiny organs or free nerve endings, produce nerve impulses. In all probability, stimulus reception is brought about primarily by environmental *change* as such. For when the altered situation persists unchanged for a time, a sense dulls, or "adapts." For example, we soon become relatively insensitive to the pressure of clothes, to a persistent odor, or a taste. Ease of adaptation varies, pain probably being most difficult to adapt to. On the other hand, odor perception dulls very easily. We cannot judge our own body odors, for example. We live with them constantly, and we are continuously adapted to them.

Sensations depend on stimulation of *appropriate* receptors. For example, the feeling of pressure is contingent on impulses emanating from pressure points; *only* pressure receptors are able to register pressure stimuli. A complex stimulus may affect more than one kind of receptor, in which case a composite sensation is perceived. For example, simultaneous impulses from heat and pain receptors may give rise to a burning sensation. Similarly, when one enters a hot shower, both hot and cold receptors may be affected, and one may feel hot and cold at the same time. Ice on the skin may produce sensations of burning, through simultaneous stimulation of cold, heat, and pain points.

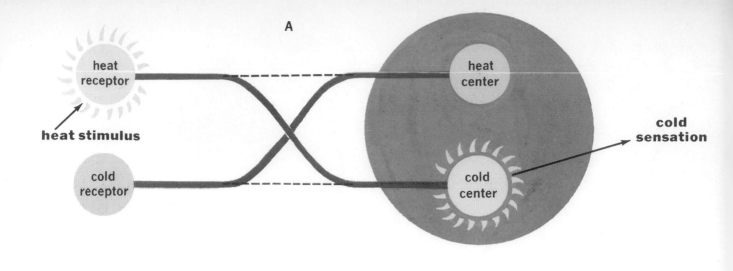

A

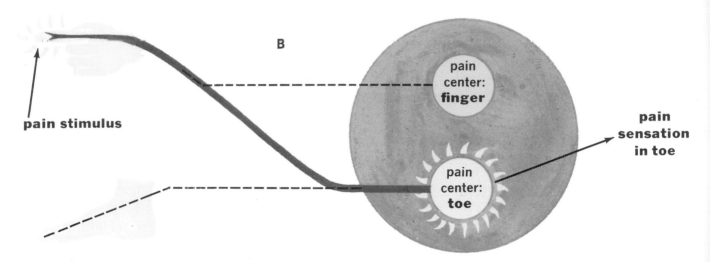

B

FIG. 21.18. **A,** if the neural paths from receptors to interpreter centers are switched experimentally as shown, then a heat stimulus will be interpreted as a cold sensation. This indicates that the quality of a sense perception depends on the central connections of the neural pathways. **B,** if the neural paths from receptors to interpreter centers are switched experimentally as shown, then a pain stimulus applied to a finger will be interpreted as a pain stimulus applied to a toe. This indicates that correct localization of a sense perception depends on correct central connections of the neural pathways.

It can be shown dramatically that the different kinds of sense perceptions depend not so much on impulse differences as on the different *central connections* of fibers coming from various types of receptors into the brain and spinal cord. For example, it is possible to cut a fiber from a heat receptor and a fiber from a cold receptor and to let the cut ends reinnervate the sense organs, but in switched order. The fiber from the heat receptor then terminates in the cold center of the brain, and the fiber from the cold receptor terminates in the heat center. Under such conditions, the organism feels hot every time the cold receptor is stimulated, and cold every time the heat receptor is stimulated

(Fig. 21.18*a*). Evidently, the quality of a sensation is determined not by the receptor, nor by the type of nerve impulse sent by the receptor, but by the neural centers. The sensation depends on which of various centers receives signals.

Furthermore, correct *localization* of a stimulus hinges on the central connections too. If pain fibers from finger tip and big toe were switched as above, then a needle prick on the big toe would prompt immediate examination of the finger for blood, and vice versa (Fig. 21.18*b*). We may note that the anatomical distribution of receptors throughout the body is matched virtually point for point in the anatomical distribution of neural centers. Each receptor has its neural center, and so long as the structural relationships are preserved, impulses will be correctly interpreted as coming from particular body regions and particular receptors.

We may qualify this generalization in one respect. It is a fairly common experience that pain originating in an internal organ is often sensed as if it originated at some remote skin area, or at another distant internal region. For example, pain stimuli actually affecting the liver may be "referred" to the shoulder region. Pain in the uterus may be erroneously thought to originate in forehead, chest, and palm of hand. Similarly, an ache in one tooth is often thought to come from the whole side of the head. In all such cases of **referred pain,** pain fibers

originating in different body regions lead into the same general area in the brain or spinal cord. Impulses arriving through one of the fibers may stimulate a greater or lesser portion of that area, as if impulses actually arrived over more than one pain fiber. As a result, pain sensations may be diffuse and may be referred to numerous body regions.

All receptor types discussed so far agree in that their distribution is body-wide. The most familiar receptors, on the other hand, are confined to specific body regions. In this category of localized receptors are the sense organs of the tongue, the nose, the eye, and the ear.

TASTE AND SMELL

The Tongue

Our reduced tasting ability when the nose is blocked with a cold reveals that smell is an integral component of "taste." The receptors on the tongue are affected by chemicals in *solution,* and the receptors in the nasal epithelium, by *vapors* of chemicals. Our sensory judgment about a substance is keenest when impulses from both tongue and nose reach neural centers.

Clusters of elongated ciliated cells, set into depressions in the tongue, form **taste buds** (Fig. 21.19). Sensory fiber terminals from each of the bud

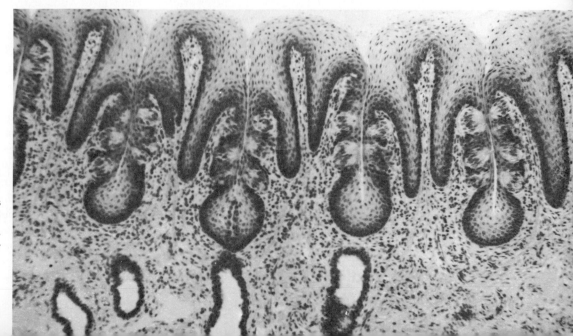

FIG. 21.19. Section through the tongue, showing taste buds. The buds are located at the ends of deep narrow channels leading into the tongue from the surface. (General Biological Supply House, Inc.)

sweet   sour   salty   bitter

FIG. 21.20.   Diagrams of the tongue, showing the distribution of taste buds for the four taste sensations.

cells lead into the brain. Taste buds are distributed all over the upper tongue surface, and although structural differences among buds cannot be demonstrated, well-known functional differences exist; the four primary taste sensations, *sweet, sour, salty,* and *bitter,* arise through stimulation of buds at different regions of the tongue. Bitter substances primarily affect buds located at the back of the tongue; sweet substances, buds in the forward part of the tongue; and sour and salty materials are tasted predominantly along the tongue edges (Fig. 21.20).

Here, as in other sense perceptions, it is the central connections that matter. Certain chemicals exist which, when applied to the tongue tip, produce a sweet sensation; but when the same chemicals are applied at the back of the tongue, they produce a bitter taste. Evidently, chemicals to which we are sensitive do not possess "inherent" taste but only have the property of stimulating this or that taste bud. And depending on which of the tongue areas sends impulses to its unique brain connections, a given subjective taste sensation will be registered.

Therefore, to say that "sugar is sweet" erroneously implies an objective property of sugar. Sweetness is a subjective sensation, and the only pertinent objective property of sugar is its capacity to stimulate certain taste buds. In different individuals, one and the same sugar may produce qualitatively and quantitatively different sensations of sweetness. At least one substance is known which one person may not taste at all, but which might taste sweet to an-

other, bitter to a third, salty to a fourth, and sour to a fifth. This substance is *phenylthiocarbamide.* Individually different reactions of this sort trace back to differences in heredity.

Taste buds are highly sensitive receptors. Quinine, for example, a substance normally producing a bitter taste, generally can be sensed in concentrations as low as 1 part in 2 or 3 million parts of water.

A large variety of composite tastes are built up from different combinations and intensities of the four basic tastes, from smell, and from other sense perceptions initiated in the mouth. For example, both a hot meal and a cold meal affect the same taste buds if the two meals are alike chemically. But the hot meal vaporizes more, hence smells more; and it also stimulates heat receptors in the lining of the mouth and on the tongue. The hot and the cold meals consequently taste differently.

The Nose

Varied as taste sensations are, odor perceptions are even more diversified. Attempts to establish basic odors, from which all others can be derived, have met with relatively little success. A fairly adequate scheme can be constructed on the basis of four primary odors, *rancid, vinegary, fragrant,* and *burnt,* each classified in various intensities.

Part of the ciliated lining in the upper nasal passages is the receptor tissue for the sense of smell in vertebrates. Sensory fibers lead into the **olfactory**

lobe of the brain, relatively small in man but large in other vertebrates. Man is a comparatively poor smeller, but in most other vertebrates, the sense of smell is as well developed, and has the same outstanding importance, as vision in man.

As among taste buds, structural differences among the cells of the nasal epithelium cannot be detected. Moreover, it is virtually impossible to determine which receptor cells in the nose mediate perception of what odors. Are there as many functionally different types of receptor cells and central fiber connections as there are different odors? Probably not. Is each receptor cell capable of emitting as many different types of impulses as there are different odors? Again, probably not. When the perception of one odor dulls by adaptation, perception of other odors is usually not dulled. This suggests that functionally distinct receptor cells and central connections do exist to some extent, each receptor cell perhaps being able to emit different impulses for a small group of different odors. Paradoxically, our understanding of smelling mechanisms is much less satisfactory than that of the manifestly more complex visual and auditory mechanisms.

VISION

The human eye is among the most efficient light receptors developed during evolution. Insect eyes possibly are better adapted for the detection of motion, and many birds may focus on five horizon points at once without moving their heads. But the human visual apparatus probably registers color more clearly than that of any other animal, and human eyes are virtually as sensitive as eyes can possibly get; two or three photons suffice to stimulate, a photon being the smallest unit of light.

The Eye

The eye is made up of three coats (Fig. 21.21): an outer **sclera**, fibrous in man, cartilaginous in many other mammals; a middle **choroid**, a layer which is pigmented black, and which carries blood vessels to and from the eye; and an inner **retina**, the actual light-receptor tissue. In many mammals, a thin film of whitish, greenish crystalline material coats the choroid layer. This material reflects light, and in the dark it makes the eyes of these animals shine and glow.

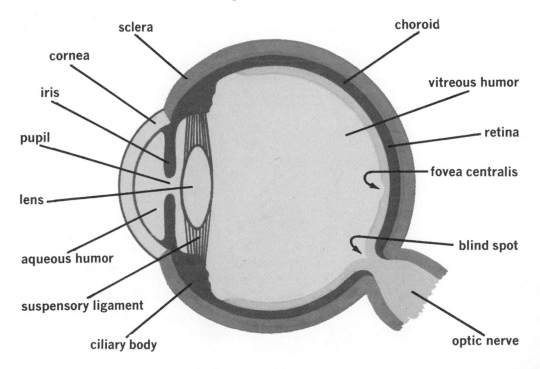

FIG. 21.21. The structure of the eye.

sclera

cornea

iris

pupil

lens

aqueous humor

suspensory ligament

ciliary body

choroid

vitreous humor

retina

fovea centralis

blind spot

optic nerve

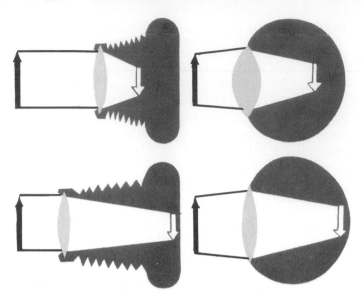

FIG. 21.22. Focusing in camera and in eye. Upper figures: images fall short of photographic film and retina. Lower figures: camera is focused by changing the lens-film distance, and eye is focused by changing the curvature of the lens.

FIG. 21.23. Focusing when object changes distance. Left: far object, flat lens. Right: near object, curved lens. Lens curves out when the muscles of the ciliary body contract.

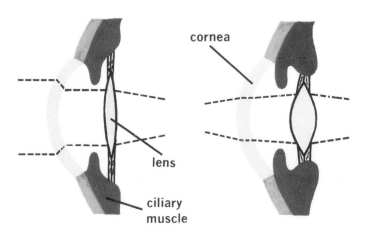

cornea

lens

ciliary muscle

In the front part of the eye, the three coats are modified structurally. The sclera merges into the transparent **cornea.** The choroid coat continues as the sometimes pigmented **iris,** which encloses the **pupil,** and as a ring-shaped muscle, the **ciliary body,** to which the **lens** is attached by ligaments. The spaces between lens and cornea are filled with the fluid, lymphlike **aqueous humor;** and the space between lens and retina contains a glassy, jellylike material, the **vitreous humor.**

Functionally, the eye resembles a photographic camera, with one major difference. A camera is focused by varying the distance between lens and film. The eye is focused by adjustment of the curvature of the lens, the lens-retina distance remaining fixed (Fig. 21.22). A beam of light passes through the cornea, through the pupil, into the lens. The pupillary opening corresponds to the diaphragm of a camera; it enlarges or becomes smaller, regulating the amount of light admitted into the eye. This control mechanism is set into operation by light itself. Intense light initiates a reflex via retina, the autonomic nervous system, and a set of circularly arranged muscles in the iris. These muscles contract, and the pupil becomes smaller. Conversely, low light intensity reflexly produces contraction of a set of iris muscles arranged like the spokes of a wheel, and the pupil of the eye then enlarges (see Fig. 21.10).

The lens focuses an object onto the retina. When a far-off object is viewed, and when the eye is at rest, the lens is fairly flat. As an object moves nearer, the lens curves out increasingly (Fig. 21.23). Lens shape is controlled by the ciliary body. When this muscular ring is relaxed, the ligaments holding the lens are taut, and the lens is flat. Conversely, when the ciliary muscle contracts, the lens ligaments relax, and the lens, an elastic structure, is then allowed to curve out. The ciliary muscle is under reflex control. A blurred image on the retina elicits reflex impulses to the ciliary body, which contract or relax that body more, until the image is no longer blurred. The adjustment reflex then ceases, and a focused image so reaches the retina. Note that the image of an object is projected on the retina in an inverted position.

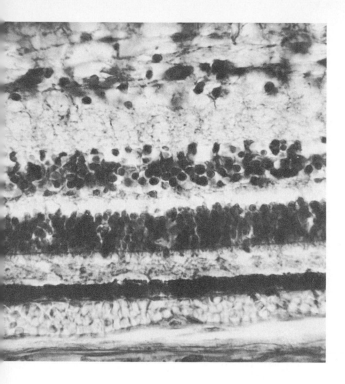

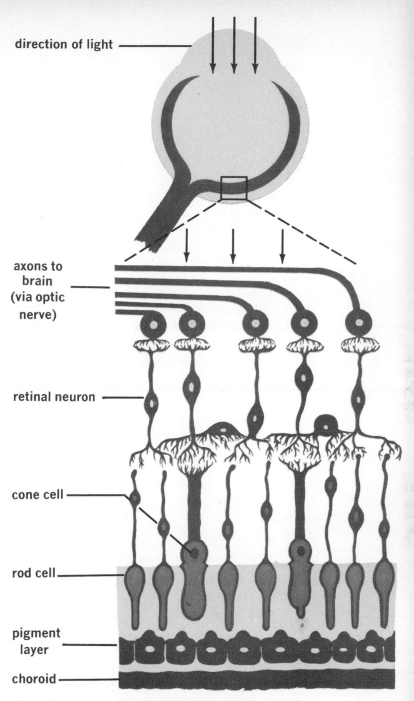

direction of light

axons to brain (via optic nerve)

retinal neuron

cone cell

rod cell

pigment layer

choroid

FIG. 21.24. The diagram illustrates the retina in section, greatly simplified. Note that the neuron layers of the retina are toward the inside of the eye, and that light must pass through these layers before it reaches the photosensitive rods and cones. The photo shows a cross section through a portion of the human retina. The layered structure is clearly in evidence. Dark round bodies are cell nuclei. (Photo courtesy of Dr. B. J. Serber, College of Medicine, New York University.)

The Retina

This tissue is made up of several layers of neurons and of one layer of **rods** and **cones.** These are the receptor cells which translate light energy into nerve impulses (Fig. 21.24). Note that the rod and cone layer is adjacent to the choroid coat.

Hence light must pass through the neuron layers before it reaches the rods and cones. These light-receiving cells connect functionally with the neurons of the retina. The neurons synapse among one another in intricate ways, and nerve fibers from the whole inner surface of the retina eventually collect in one region and form the **optic nerve** to the brain.

Where this nerve leaves the eye, somewhat off center, it interrupts the continuity of the rod and cone layer, and of the choroid and sclera. This is the *blind spot,* so called since visual images cannot be formed at this point (see Fig. 21.25).

Rods and cones are distributed unevenly in the retina. In the center of the retina is a tiny depression, called the **fovea centralis** (see Fig. 21.21). In this area only cones occur. Neurons are absent here, and the cones are exposed to light directly. Cones are responsible for color vision and for the perception of sharp, bright images. Indeed, the fovea is the area of most acute vision. Cones are distributed less densely through other parts of the retina, and at the retinal periphery cones do not occur at all. Rods, on the other hand, are particularly abundant here. Rods are sensitive to dim light, and they serve predominantly in the detection of motion; we notice a moving object well when we view it out of the corners of our eyes. Away from the retinal periphery, rods are distributed more sparsely, and they are not present at all in the fovea centralis.

The chemical basis of light reception in rods is relatively well known. Rod cells contain a photosensitive pigment called **visual purple.** When light strikes it, the pigment is bleached through a photochemical reaction, and two endproducts are formed. One is a substance called **retinene,** which is linked to a protein fraction. The other endproduct is *energy,* which stimulates an optic neuron and produces a nerve impulse (see Fig. 21.26). In the dark, and with the aid of respiratory energy, the retinene-protein complex may be reconverted into visual purple. Alternatively, retinene-protein may first be transformed into a vitamin-A–protein complex, which may regenerate visual purple in turn (see Fig. 21.26). In very intense light, visual purple may be destroyed faster than it can be formed. Vision

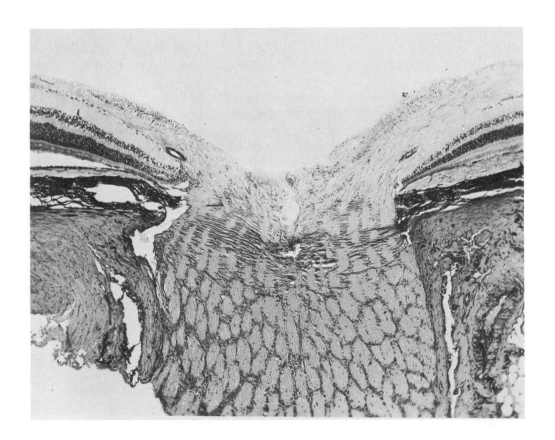

FIG. 21.25. Section through the blind spot. The retina is toward the top of the photo. Note the neuron layers at the surface of the retina and the merging of the neuron fibers at the depression of the blind spot, forming the optic nerve. This thick nerve leads downward in the photo. (Ward's Natural Science Establishment, Inc.)

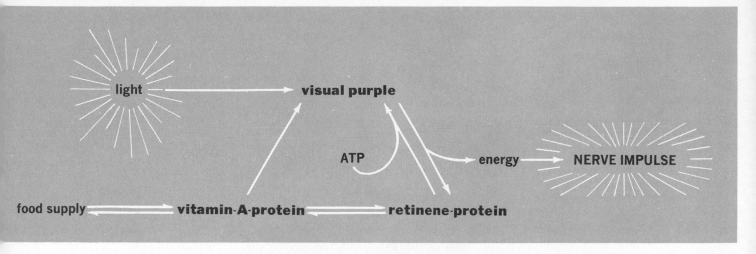

FIG. 21.26.   The pattern of the chemistry of rod vision. Note that visual purple may be regenerated either from retinene-protein or from vitamin A—protein.

then may become impaired (e.g., snow blindness). We may also appreciate how vitamin-A deficiency would interfere with vision.

Light-initiated chemical reactions which produce impulses take place in cone cells too, but processes here are understood less well. The photosensitive pigment **iodopsin** is known to be present in cone cells. Are there different cones for each color? Probably not. Any color, including white, can be produced from various combinations and intensities of three primary colors, namely, red, green, and blue. Most theories of color vision presuppose that three functionally different cone types exist, one for each primary color. Indeed, color television is based on an analogous principle.

Impulse Interpretation

An external object is "pictured" on the retina as a series of points, like the points of a newspaper photograph. Each point corresponds to a rod or a cone. Impulses from these points are transmitted into the brain according to the following pattern.

All fibers from the left sides of *both* eyes lead into the left half of the brain; and all fibers from the right sides of both eyes lead into the right half of the brain (Fig. 21.27). In each brain hemisphere there is a circumscribed region, the **optic lobe,**

FIG. 21.27.   The nerve fiber tracts from eye to brain. An object in the left field of vision registers on the right halves of both retinas, and impulses are transmitted into the right half of the brain.

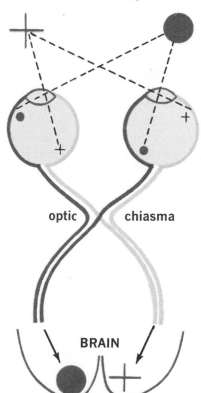

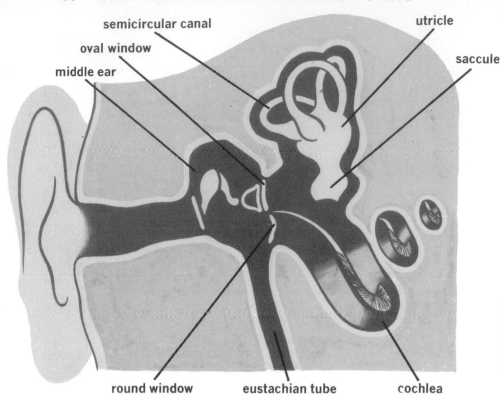

semicircular canal

oval window

middle ear

utricle

saccule

round window   eustachian tube   cochlea

FIG. 21.28. The gross structure of the ear. Note ear bones in the middle-ear cavity, and attachment of semicircular canals to utricle.

where fiber tracts from the eyes make synaptic connections with the neurons of visual centers. It can be shown that for each group of rods and cones there exists a corresponding group of interpreter neurons in the optic lobes. In other words, the "point picture" of an object on the retina is duplicated more or less faithfully in the optic lobes, by impulses from specific rods and cones to their correlated interpreter neurons. Stimulation of the latter registers as vision.

It should be clear that the left half of every external field of vision produces images in the right halves of both eyes. Similarly, the right half of what can be seen is focused onto the left halves of both retinas (see Fig. 21.27). Therefore, in view of the fiber patterns from eyes to brain, the right half of a field of vision registers in the left half of the brain, and the left half of a vision field registers in the right half of the brain. The left and right optic

lobes are not directly continuous. Yet interpreter activity normally is such that the "left" picture of the external world is joined smoothly to the "right" picture. Moreover, both halves of the picture are sensed right side up, even though the retinas receive inverted images. Left and right pictures sometimes fail to join smoothly, as under the influence of alcohol, in which case one "sees double."

Why is an inverted retinal image not also "seen" as an inverted picture? The answer is that the optic centers in the brain have learned to give visual experiences correct orientations. Our recognition of up, down, and sideways is based ultimately on sensing the direction of gravitational pull. Muscles and ears play an important role in this, as the next section will show. Hence, even if we imagined that retinal images actually arrived in the optic lobes in an inverted position, gravity perception would teach us, shortly after birth, to associate the bottom part of a picture with the idea of "up," the upper part with the idea of "down." In outer space there would be no such gravity orientation, and any visual or gravitational notions of "right-side-upness" would become meaningless.

How does an impulse arriving in an optic neuron in the brain produce a conscious sensation of light? How indeed does any other sense become conscious? Answers to this cannot be given as yet. However, it is known that an immense number of more or less direct neural paths lead from vision-interpreting centers to virtually all other centers in the brain and spinal cord. Consequently, a tremendous number of reflexes can be initiated through the receptor cells in the eyes, and it is this which makes the sense of vision so important to man.

THE EAR

This organ houses receptors for three senses: the sense of **static body balance,** the sense of **dynamic body balance,** and the sense of **hearing.**

The **outer ear** carries sound to the *eardrum,* a membrane which separates the cavity of the **middle ear** from the outside (Fig. 21.28). The connection of this cavity with the mouth, via the eustachian tube, has already been referred to (see Chap. 14). Three tiny middle-ear bones, **hammer, anvil,** and **stirrup,** moved by the smallest muscles in the body, form an adjustable bridge from the eardrum, across the middle-ear cavity, to the **inner ear.** The latter is an intricate system of canals and spaces, surrounded by bone and filled with lymphlike fluid. These chambers are closed off from the middle ear by two membranes. One is stretched across a so-called **round window,** and one across an **oval window.** The stirrup bone of the middle ear is anchored to the membrane of the oval window.

The inner ear consists of three functional and structural divisions: a chamber consisting of two parts, the **utricle** and the **saccule;** the **semicircular canals;** and the **cochlea,** a structure coiled like a snail shell. These tunnels and cavities are interconnected.

Balance

The receptors for *static body balance* are located in the *utricle* and *saccule.* At several places along the walls of the chambers, there are clusters of specialized cells. Sensory nerve fibers lead off from one side of these cells, and tiny hairs project from the other. The tips of the hairs of such a cell cluster attach to a tiny **ear stone,** a calcium-containing body (Fig. 21.29). When the stone is in a certain position, it pulls on some of the hairs more than on others, and this stimulates the cells to which the hairs are connected. Nerve impulses from these hair cells to the brain register the particular position of the ear stone. When the head is tilted, or when the balance of the body as a whole is changed, then gravity acts on all the ear stones and shifts them in a given manner. This pulls different sets of hair cells, and different sets of impulses to the brain inform of the change in balance. Reflex signals from the brain then ensure that equilibrium is not lost.

This sense permits recognition of up, down, side, front, and back, even when visual stimuli and sensory impulses from muscles fail to provide such recognition. A blindfolded mammal with inoperative ear-stone mechanisms has difficulty in remaining

FIG. 21.29. Upper figure: a receptor organ for static balance, showing hair cells and ear stone (diagrammatic). Lower figures: position of the receptor organs in relation to the head, and the effect of tilting the head.

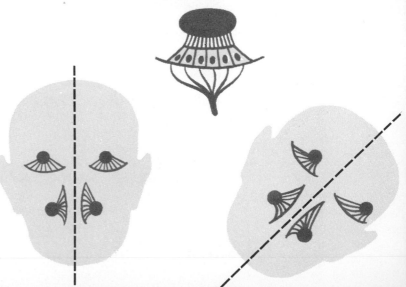

upright; and when its position is abnormal, it does little to correct this position.

The sense of movement and of *dynamic body balance* is mediated by the *semicircular canals*. There are three in each ear, looping from the utricle back to the utricle. The canals are placed at right angles to one another, in the three planes of space (see Fig. 21.28). At one end of each canal is an enlarged portion, and in it is found a cluster of hair cells, rather similar to those described above. However, there is no ear stone, and the hairs are longer.

When the head is moved, the semicircular canals move with the head. But the fluid in the

canals "stays behind" temporarily, as a result of its inertia, and "catches up" with the head only after the head has stopped moving. This lag in fluid motion bends the hairs of the receptor cells, producing nerve impulses. Depending on the direction and intensity of fluid motion in the three pairs of canals, different impulse patterns are transmitted to the brain. Every straight-line motion or rotation of the head, or of the body as a whole, produces a distinct impulse pattern, hence a distinct sense perception (Fig. 21.30).

Mammals, which pursue a more or less two-dimensional way of life, are relatively unaccustomed to up-and-down motion. Indeed, such motion initiates reflexes via the semicircular canals leading to well-known symptoms of dizziness, nausea, and gastric upsets. Seasickness is produced in this way, as is the discomfort experienced when one rides in an elevator. Lying flat on a ship, or bending one's head in an elevator, reduces the upsetting sensations, since the head is then in the same relative position to the direction of motion as in walking. The sense of balance may also be affected by rapid temperature change in the environment. For uneven cooling or warming of the fluid in the semicircular canals may produce currents which may stimulate the receptor cells. Sensations of motion or of dizziness may then be experienced, even if the head does not move.

Hearing

The functioning of the cochlea as the receptor for the sense of hearing is understood fairly well today. The internal space of the cochlea is partitioned into canals by membranes running the length of the cochlear coils. One of these membranes, the **basilar membrane**, supports rows of hair cells, the actual receptors (Fig. 21.31). Nerve fibers lead from them to the brain. The hairs make contact with the **tectorial membrane**, a fold of tissue which overhangs the receptor cells. Basilar membrane, hair cells, and tectorial membrane together constitute what is called the **organ of Corti.**

Sound waves set the eardrum into vibration. This motion is communicated via the middle-ear bones to the oval window. As the membrane at this

FIG. 21.30.   The semicircular canals of the left ear. The top of the diagram is anterior, and the right side is toward the midplane of the head. The three canals are set at right angles to one another, and therefore only the horizontal canal reveals its curvature in such a view. Both ends of each canal open into the utricle. One end of each canal is enlarged into a chamber, and in it are present the hair cells which function as receptors for the sense of dynamic balance. Arrows indicate motion of internal fluid when the head is moved.

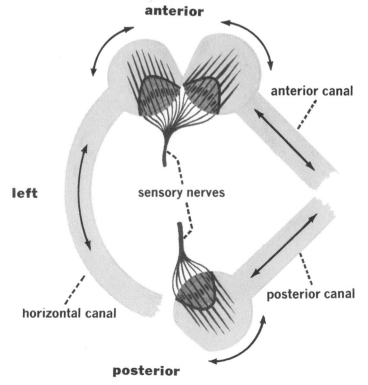

anterior

anterior canal

left

sensory nerves

posterior canal

horizontal canal

posterior

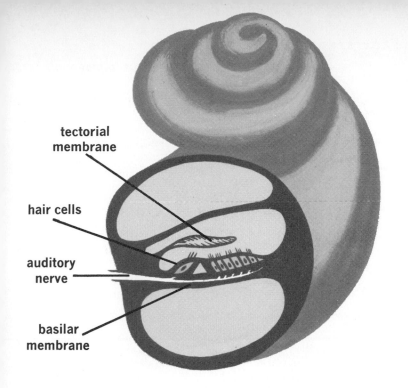

tectorial
membrane

hair cells

auditory
nerve

basilar
membrane

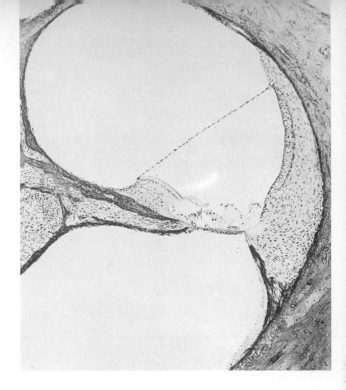

window vibrates, it sets the fluid of the inner ear into vibration also. Since fluid is practically incompressible, the membrane over the round window bulges outward every time the membrane over the oval window bulges inward, and vice versa. The round window thus serves as a pressure compensator (Fig. 21.32).

The fluid of the inner ear, including the cochlear fluid, now vibrates in harmony with external sound waves. What takes place next involves the basilar membrane particularly. This membrane contains strands of tough connective tissue fibers, stretched transversely across the cochlear tube. At the base of the cochlear coil these fibers are shortest, and at the tip of the coil they are longest. The fibers may vibrate at different rates or frequencies according to their different lengths. In this respect they resemble the tone strings of a piano.

These basilar fibers are set into vibration by the cochlear fluid. As the fluid vibrates at a given frequency under the impact of external sound waves, it sets into motion those basilar fibers which vibrate at the same frequency. This is a selective *resonance* effect. In a similar way, a string of a piano may be set into resonating vibrations if a corresponding sound is produced nearby with a tun-

FIG. 21.31. The cochlea. The diagram shows the coils of the cochlea and a cochlear cross section with the parts of the organ of Corti. A section through this organ is illustrated also in the photo. The tectorial and basilar membranes, and the hair cells, are clearly visible. (Photo, Ward's Natural Science Establishment, Inc.)

FIG. 21.32. Pressure of the stirrup bone on the oval window sets the basilar membrane into vibration (serpentine line). The round window bulges out, compensating for the inward pressure of the oval window.

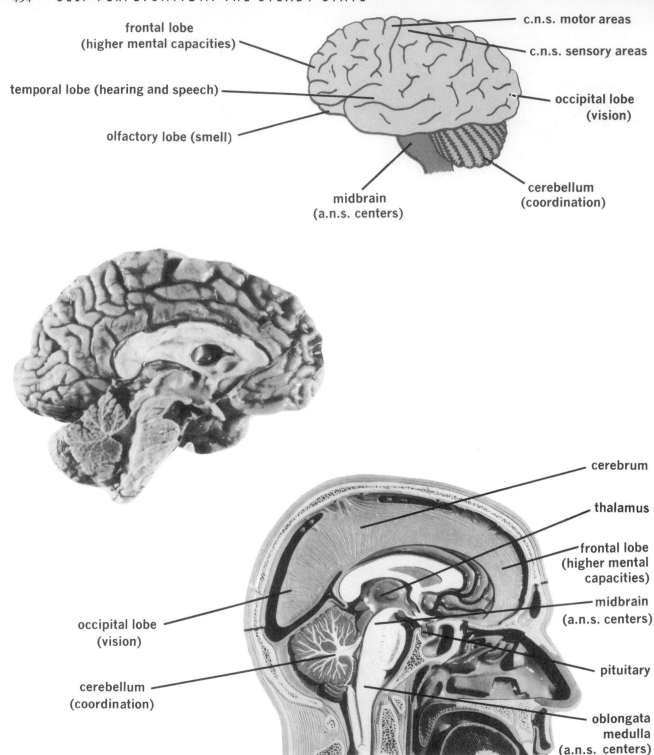

frontal lobe
(higher mental capacities)

c.n.s. motor areas

c.n.s. sensory areas

temporal lobe (hearing and speech)

occipital lobe
(vision)

olfactory lobe (smell)

midbrain
(a.n.s. centers)

cerebellum
(coordination)

cerebrum

thalamus

frontal lobe
(higher mental
capacities)

midbrain
(a.n.s. centers)

occipital lobe
(vision)

pituitary

cerebellum
(coordination)

oblongata
medulla
(a.n.s. centers)

ing fork, for example, or by striking an appropriate key on another piano.

In the ear, therefore, different external sound patterns first produce different vibration patterns in the cochlear fluid. This in turn then produces vibrations in particular sets of basilar fibers. As a result, the hair cells attached to the vibrating basilar fibers move up and down. And as these cells touch against the overhanging tectorial membrane, their hairs are bent and nerve impulses are initiated. Each different sound pattern thus gives rise to a different pattern of nerve impulses.

The impulses are transmitted via the auditory nerves into the **temporal lobes** of the brain, where the hearing centers are located. Here the nerve fibers from the hair cells in the cochlea make individual connection with separate neurons, and each of these interprets a different pitch. For example, a high-frequency sound wave selectively produces nerve impulses in hair cells attached to the short basilar fibers; and the particular neurons in the hearing center which receive these impulses interpret them as a highly pitched sound. If these portions of the hearing centers should be injured, deafness to high sounds would result. Analogously, selective deafness to low sounds is known to occur.

Although animals such as dogs hear a wider range of sounds and are probably more sensitive to sound than man, the ear of man is unsurpassed in distinguishing tones of only slightly different pitch and tones of widely different quality. As an interpretive sense, and as an important adjuster of speech, hearing has acquired a human importance second only to vision.

FIG. 21.33.   Top: the left half of the brain, viewed from the outside. The functions of the various labeled parts are indicated in parentheses. Middle: the left half of the brain, viewed from the inner cut side. The various parts and their functions are indicated in the model shown at the bottom. (Middle photo, Rhode Island Hospital; bottom photo, detail of model designed by Dr. Justus F. Mueller, Ward's Natural Science Establishment, Inc.)

That the neural centers are as essential in sense perception as the neural receptors has become clear in this section. The centers of brain and spinal cord also are essential in producing effector responses. What is known about the ways in which the brain and spinal cord carry out their modulating functions?

The Neural Centers

STRUCTURAL FEATURES

The normal roles of many parts of the brain and the spinal cord have been discovered by observing the effects of accidental or experimental damage to those parts. In a newer, more precise method, selected points in brain or spinal cord may be stimulated electrically with needle electrodes. The resulting responses of the test animal may then provide clues to the control functions of the stimulated areas. By such means, distinct subdivisions in brain and spinal cord have been identified, and the location of a large number of neural centers has been pinpointed.

In the brain (Fig. 21.33), the deep central portions and the medulla oblongata contain most of the cranial a.n.s. centers. Situated dorsal to the medulla oblongata is the **cerebellum,** which is the chief motor coordinator. It integrates, for example, the many muscular motions involved in walking or in speaking. The **cerebrum,** consisting of a left and a right "hemisphere," forms the outer portions of the brain, along the top and the sides. The cerebrum contains most of the cranial c.n.s. centers. It is also the seat of the so-called higher mental capacities, i.e., those associated with consciousness, memory, intelligence, and personality.

The surface layers of the cerebrum are grooved and ridged conspicuously. In this **cerebral cortex** (Fig. 21.34) are located cell bodies of many neurons. The axons and dendrites of these neurons project into the deeper portions of the cerebrum, and since these fibers contain fatty myelin sheaths, they appear white when viewed in bulk. The deeper parts of the cerebrum are therefore designated as

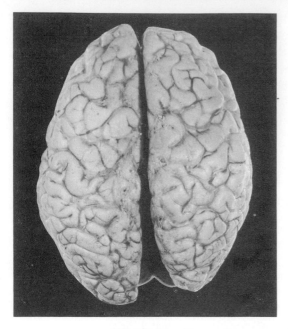

FIG. 21.34. The cerebral cortex of the human brain, seen from the top. Note that the left cerebral hemisphere is slightly larger than the right. This is usual in right-handed persons. (Institute of Pathology, Rhode Island Hospital.)

white matter, in contrast to the **gray matter** of the cerebral cortex, formed by the nonmyelinated cell bodies of neurons.

In the cerebral cortex, the location of some of the control centers is not unalterably fixed. When one area is destroyed by injury, another area may, after a long relearning process, take over the lost functions. This holds particularly for centers within the large **frontal lobe,** which controls the higher mental capacities. In this lobe one cannot pinpoint a distinct memory locus, for example, or an intelligence center. Rather, the control of higher capacities appears to be delegated diffusely to all the neurons in the frontal lobe.

FUNCTIONAL FEATURES

The Pattern

The broad functions of brain and spinal cord have already been briefly referred to in various earlier contexts. These functions may be grouped into four principal categories.

First, brain and spinal cord serve in **pathway selection.** Neural centers receive sensory impulses from receptors, and then they *select* among thousands of possible motor pathways going out to effectors; signals are sent only to *some* effectors, and only to *appropriate* effectors. As a result, the effector response of an organism to a given stimulus can be adaptively useful and can actually aid in steady-state maintenance. In all probability, the spinal cord carries out only such "switchboard" activities and none of the functions below.

Second, in addition to its role as pathway selector, the brain also serves as **reflex modifier.** It may *suppress* or *exaggerate* responses to incoming information, as when we decide not to cry out under pain, or to cry out more than necessary. It may *store* incoming information as memory and may thereby *delay* the completion of a reflex for shorter or longer periods. On occasion its modifying action may be unduly intensified, as in different mental diseases. Variously inappropriate effector responses are then produced.

Third, the brain is the principal **coordinating center.** It integrates into composite, unified sense perceptions the impulses arriving from many different receptors. And it gears together into smoothly coordinated actions the motor responses of many different effectors.

Finally, as noted above, the brain is the controller of such **higher mental capacities** as an animal possesses. The significance of these capacities to mammals in general, and to man in particular, is well appreciated.

Of these control functions, pathway selection probably is the most fundamental, and all others may be based on it. How is the selection of appropriate neural pathways accomplished? At the present state of knowledge, the answer is largely unavailable. Among several tentative suggestions and speculations, one is the idea of **pathway facilitation.** This notion emerges from the observation that nerve impulses often may travel more easily over some neural pathways than over others. For example, it is easier to perform a familiar activity than an unfamiliar one. From this, the hypothesis of pathway facilitation suggests that the more frequently impulses travel over a given neural circuit, the less resistance this circuit may offer to subsequent impulses.

As an analogy, we may imagine the brain to be like a mass of clay, and impulses, like grooves cut into the clay. Then the more often the same groove is traveled by the cutting tool, the deeper it becomes, and the more surely will the tool be guided subsequently. Preferential selection of one neural path over others therefore might be partly a matter of having used a given path repeatedly; wherever a choice of circuits exists, the well-used, *facilitated* circuits may be selected in preference over the previously little used, unfacilitated ones. To be sure, it is far from clear just how a circuit in brain or spinal cord might become different, structurally and/or functionally, when it becomes facilitated.

Learning and Association

Habit formation, and learning by repetition and by trial and error, become explainable in general terms on the basis of the hypothesis of pathway facilitation. For example, in a very young animal, few brain pathways are as yet firmly established by facilitation. In our analogy, the neural clay still has a fairly smooth surface. Incoming impulses are transmitted more or less in all directions, and behavior is relatively uncoordinated and random. But among the random impulse paths, some will initiate advantageous effector results. The same pathway pattern may then be tried time and again, and a facilitated neural route may eventually be established; the groove in the clay becomes well worn, and the animal becomes proficient in performing a particular activity.

Learning, maturing, gathering experience thus may be a matter of blazing ever new neural trails. And when the new trails become old, a **habit** has been acquired. The initial establishment of a new pathway requires mental effort, but later, impulses may travel the route with ease. It should be noted here that not all pathways need be established by learning. Many neural routes are already fully facilitated at or before birth, and these are responsible for inherited, instinctive behavior. Indeed, most animals depend almost entirely on such inborn neural circuits, and later learning plays only a minor role at best.

Neural facilitation may also be at the root of learning by **conditioned reflex.** Such reflexes have originally been demonstrated on dogs, by the Russian biologist Pavlov. When a hungry dog sights food, his saliva and gastric juice begin to flow reflexly. If, on many successive occasions, a bell is sounded every time food is presented, then the flow of digestive juices can eventually be initiated by sounding the bell alone, without giving food (Fig. 21.35). Evidently, the dog learns to associate the

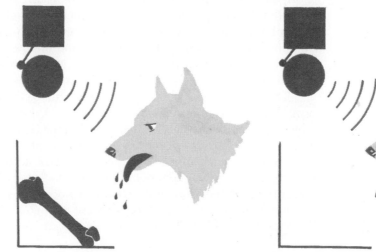

FIG. 21.35. Illustrating the principle of conditioned reflexes. Left: two simultaneous stimuli (sight of food, sound of bell) produce a response (salivation). Right: if the procedure depicted on the left is repeated often, then a single stimulus alone may eventually produce the characteristic response.

bell with food, and instead of one facilitated pathway to the digestive glands, there are now two. Either one alone, or both together, may initiate secretion.

Neural conditioning of this sort plays a considerable role in behavior development not only in dogs but in vertebrates generally, man included. Most experiences are composite, made up of many individual elements. For example, the object "bread" produces sensations of vision, of touch, of taste, of a verbal picture, of a verbal sound, etc. After all these simultaneous sensations have occurred often enough, one of them may elicit all others as well. The mere word "bread," seen or heard, enables us to produce in our mind the feel, the taste, the appearance of bread. We associate the one with the others; that is, we have become conditioned.

Association of originally separate neural circuits may account for much of intelligence, for insight,

for "getting the idea." Suppose that two well-facilitated pathways are established, each representing one item of information. "Seeing the connection" between such seemingly unrelated bits of information might mean the emission of impulses over a third neural pathway, interlinking the two. This might be accomplished by "speculation," i.e., by letting impulses travel more or less at random over existing paths, or by trying new paths. Among these might be found a route which all at once gives connected meaning to separate pieces of information. The more widely a person is able to correlate in this way, the more intelligent he is likely to be. And this might well mean that such a person can make numerous and varied path connections in his brain—possibly because he uses his brain often enough even when he does not have to—and thereby facilitates a large number of neural routes among the trillions potentially available.

RESUME   The net result of nervous operations is control of muscular movement and of glandular secretion.

But is it not really more than this? Conscious, contemplative thinking, reading, aesthetic appreciations, and all other higher mental functions, are they not more than mere reflex modulation of muscles and glands? Actually not. For *all* mental activity aims toward some *action,* potential or actual, present or future. On the one hand, we see, hear, learn, store information, correlate information, in short, we *think.* And on the other hand, we speak, walk, build, vote, in short, we *do.* All this doing requires, and is directly brought about by, muscular and glandular activity. In the final analysis, therefore, thinking sets the stage for moving muscles, and better thinking implies more judicious use of muscles. Because muscular control contributes powerfully to the maintenance of steady states, nervous systems have become vital components of animals.

Throughout these chapters on steady state, the central running theme has been that, by virtue of its built-in hierarchy of control systems, the protoplasmic unit may attain an actual life span which approaches that potentially inherent in it. When the controls fail for any external or internal reason, disease occurs. Intact controls may then be able to restore steady state. However, in time even the best-controlled system goes out of control. As the component parts age and wear out, functional and structural breakdowns occur in so rapid a succession, and in so many different places at once, that not enough controls remain intact to make the necessary repairs. Disintegration and death must be the eventual outcome.

But, as pointed out in Chap. 3, living systems here reveal their superiority of design and construction over any nonliving system. For before final disintegration supervenes, the living controls may call into action another self-perpetuating device, one which anticipates even the powerful stimulus of death: *reproduction.*

1. Describe the structure of a neuron. How do neurons in c.n.s. and a.n.s. differ structurally and functionally? Describe the components, and the structural arrangement, of a reflex arc. Distinguish between nerve fibers and nerves. What different kinds of each are known?

2. Describe the organization of the c.n.s., its nerves, and its centers. Review the detailed course of a c.n.s. reflex arc. What is a ganglion? Distinguish between a cranial and a spinal reflex.

3. Describe the organization of the a.n.s., its nerves, and its centers. What are the (*a*) structural and (*b*) functional differences between the sympathetic and the parasympathetic systems? What are sympathetic chain ganglia?

4. What are preganglionic and postganglionic fibers? Describe the detailed course of an a.n.s. reflex arc. Review the innervation of the heart. How are c.n.s. and a.n.s. interconnected (*a*) structurally and (*b*) functionally?

5. What is a nerve impulse? How is an impulse transmitted through a nerve fiber? What electrical phenomena take place during impulse transmission? What is an action potential of a nerve fiber? How is an impulse transmitted across a synapse? Distinguish between a cholinergic and an adrenergic nerve fiber. Where does each kind occur? What is choline esterase, and what is its function?

6. What is the basic function of all sensory receptors? Describe the location and general structure of receptors for pain, touch, pressure, heat, and cold stimuli. How can it be proved that the kind and localization of a sensory experience depend on neural centers? Describe the location and structure of the taste and smell receptors. What are the primary taste sensations? Are tastes and smells inherent in given substances? Discuss.

7. Describe the structure of the eye. What components form the focusing mechanism, and how is the function of focusing carried out? What is the distribution pattern of rods and cones in the retina? What eye structures does light traverse before it reaches the rods and cones? Review the chemical changes leading to impulse production in rods. Describe the pattern of the neural pathways between the eyes and the brain.

8. Describe the structure of the ear. What components form the receptors for (*a*) static body balance and (*b*) dynamic body balance? How do these receptors function? Describe the internal structure of the cochlea and the organ of Corti. Show how different sounds produce corresponding sensations of hearing.

9. What are the general functions of neural centers? Review the structural organization of the brain. What is the specific function of each major part or region? What is meant by pathway facilitation?

10. What are conditioned reflexes? Show how such reflexes might be established by pathway facilitation. How do conditioned reflexes contribute to learning, habit formation, and behavior development?

SUGGESTED COLLATERAL READINGS

The text cited first is recommended as a supplement to most topics of this chapter, particularly those dealing with nerve impulses and their transmission. The remaining sources below are first-rate accounts of various specific aspects of neural coordination.

Carlson, A. J., and V. Johnson: "The Machinery of the Body," 4th ed., University of Chicago Press, 1953.

Katz, B.: The Nerve Impulse, *Sci. American,* vol. 187, 1952.

Haagen-Smit, A. J.: Smell and Taste, *Sci. American,* vol. 186, 1952.

Beidler, L. M.: Our Taste Receptors, *Sci. Monthly,* vol. 75, 1952.

Kalmus, H.: Inherited Sense Defects, *Sci. American,* vol. 186, 1952.

Allen, F.: The Visual Apparatus as an Optical Instrument, *Sci. Monthly,* vol. 72, 1951.

Evans, R. M.: Seeing Light and Color, *Sci. American,* vol. 181, 1949.

Wald, G.: Eye and Camera, *Sci. American,* vol. 183, 1950.

Wald, G.: The Molecular Basis of Visual Excitation, *Am. Scientist,* vol. 42, 1954.

Sperry, R. W.: The Eye and the Brain, *Sci. American,* vol. 194, 1956.

Halstead, W. C.: "Brain and Intelligence," University of Chicago Press, 1947.

Walter, W. G.: The Electrical Activity of the Brain, *Sci. American,* vol. 190, 1954.

Liddell, H. S.: Conditioning and the Emotions, *Sci. American,* vol. 190, 1954.

Pavlov, I. P.: Conditioned Reflexes, in T. S. Hall, "A Source Book in Animal Biology," McGraw-Hill, 1951.

Babkin, B. P.: "Pavlov," University of Chicago Press, 1949.

Munn, N. L.: The Evolution of Mind, *Sci. American,* vol. 196, 1957.

THE MOST SPECTACULAR of self-perpetuative events among
organisms, reproduction and the attendant phenomena
of growth and development, have long held a central
position in human culture. Mystified and awed by the progenitive
forces of nature, early man has surrounded with tribal ritual
and religious ceremony the fertility of soil and of man,
the planting of seed, and the landmarks of birth, puberty,
and marriage. Many of the customs, and much of the mysticism,
have carried down to this day.

It is barely a century since the main events in plant
and animal reproduction have come to light, and barely a few
decades since the fundamental role of cells in reproduction
has been appreciated. We know today that the reproduction
and development of molecules pave the way for the
reproduction and development of cells; and that this in
turn is the necessary preliminary for the reproduction
and development of tissues, of organs, and of
whole organisms.

In this series of chapters, therefore, we begin with a
survey of the general **patterns of reproduction.** We then
continue with a detailed discussion of **cell reproduction, plant
reproduction,** and **animal reproduction.** And we conclude
with an analysis of **development,** the process which
must accompany all reproduction if preexisting
living organizations are to be recreated.

PART

5

SELF-PERPETUATION: REPRODUCTION

22

THE PATTERN OF REPRODUCTION

OF ALL PROTOPLASMIC FUNCTIONS, reproduction happens to be among the most noticeable to the casual human observer. Metabolism occurs largely on an invisible, molecular scale. Control functions result in steady state, that is, in unchanged, even conditions. Adaptation and evolution occur on a scale so vast that man does not perceive them directly or obviously. But reproduction does take place on a directly perceivable, obvious scale. Moreover, reproductive processes are universal and very dramatic: now there is one, then there are two. Hence the selection of reproduction particularly as a certain criterion of life.

To be sure, the deep significance of reproduction does not lie in its dramatic nature, but in its results. We recall that we have assigned "living" properties to the first of the ancient nucleoproteins largely because they possessed *reproductive* properties. These properties have been handed down in an unbroken succession from the first genes to all present genes, and they still form the basis of all reproductive events today.

In this chapter, we examine the patterns of **molecular, cellular,** and **organismic reproduction.** In the course of this, we also relate reproduction to **development,** to **sex,** and to the **life cycle** patterns of plants and animals.

Molecules and Cells

If we define reproduction broadly as extension of protoplasm in space and in time, then its fundamental importance as a self-perpetuative device is readily apparent. For the formation of new protoplasmic units makes possible *replacement* and *addition* at every level of organization. Among molecules or cells, among organisms or species, replacement offsets death from normal wear and tear and death from accident or disease. *Healing* and *regeneration* are two aspects of replacement. Above and beyond this purely restorative function of reproduc-

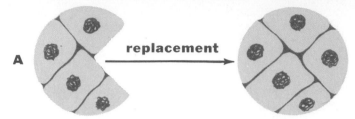

A

replacement

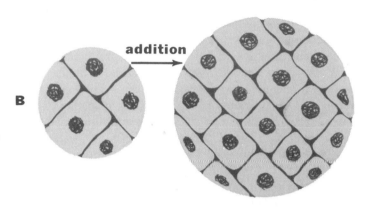

B

addition

FIG. 22.1. The principal roles of reproduction, on any level: replacement and addition. On the cellular level, replacement of lost parts leads to healing and regeneration (**A**), and addition leads to growth (**B**).

tion, addition of extra units at any level results in four-dimensional *growth,* that is, geographic, spatial expansion, and extension in time (Fig. 22.1).

Any new protoplasmic unit resembles the old, and reproduction therefore implies exact duplication. To create new units, raw materials are re-

FIG. 22.2. The four forms of molecular reproduction. **F,** fatty acids; **G,** glycerin; **A₁, A₂, A₃,** amino acids.

quired. Indeed, reproduction at any level depends on ample nutrition specifically, and on properly controlled metabolism generally. It is also clear that duplication of a large unit implies prior or simultaneous duplication of all constituent smaller ones. Hence reproduction on the molecular level is the foundation for reproduction on every other level.

MOLECULAR REPRODUCTION

The reproduction of molecules may take four different forms, according to the nature of the molecule to be reproduced. We are already familiar with all four (Fig. 22.2).

If water or another inorganic substance is to be reproduced within a cell, additional molecules of such substances must be supplied ready-made by nutrition. We note that **accumulation** is the simplest form of molecular "reproduction."

If a carbohydrate, a fat, or any of their numerous derivatives is to be duplicated, they may have to be synthesized from accumulated simpler raw materials, with the aid of appropriate enzymes. So

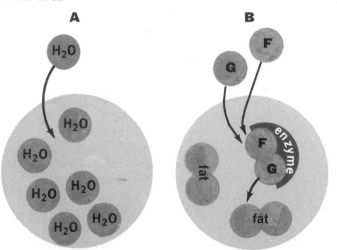

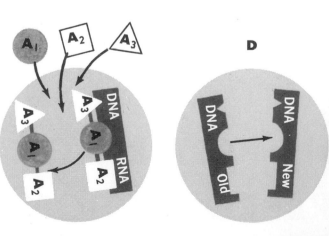

A

B

C

D

accumulation

enzymatic synthesis

template-dependent synthesis

self-duplication

long as the enzymes of a cell remain the same, most newly synthesized organic molecules will automatically be exact duplicates of molecules synthesized earlier. Thus, the second form of molecular reproduction is **enzymatic synthesis.** It includes the first form, accumulation, as a component phase.

If a protein molecule is to be duplicated, we know that enzymes, cathepsins in particular, are required to link together amino acids into a new protein. We also know that proteins are specific. Hence if the new protein is to be an exact copy of a preexisting protein, genes and RNA must provide the specific blueprint, the template, for the joining of particular amino acids in particular sequences. Clearly, the third form of molecular reproduction includes the first two forms of reproduction but is additionally characterized as **template-dependent synthesis.**

Lastly, if a gene is to be duplicated, it must serve as its own template and control its own replication (see Chap. 18). All three other forms of molecular reproduction play a part here. Phosphate must be accumulated; sugars, purines, pyrimidines must be synthesized enzymatically; and protein must be synthesized with the aid of both enzymes and genetic templates. But in addition, duplication of genetic nucleoproteins hinges on specific **self-duplication,** and this is the fourth form of molecular reproduction.

In viruses, where the structural organization does not exceed the level of the molecular aggregate, molecular reproduction is equivalent to reproduction of the whole unit. In all truly living systems, accumulation, enzymatic and template-dependent synthesis, and self-duplication contribute either to normal molecular replacement within cells or to molecular additions to cells. The result is **cell growth** (see Fig. 22.1). The rate of these processes depends on the supply of nutrients. If the parts of the protoplasmic framework wear down faster than they can be replaced, then a cell may actually decrease in size and undergo negative growth, or degrowth. Positive growth demands a rate of molecular reproduction which exceeds the rate of molecular destruction.

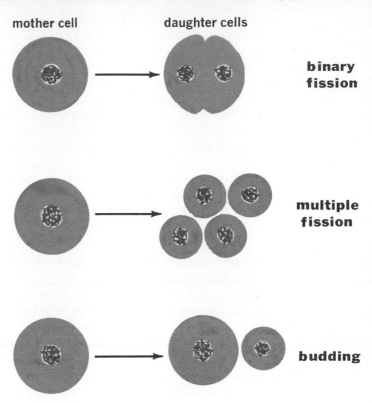

mother cell   daughter cells

binary fission

multiple fission

budding

FIG. 22.3. The principal forms of fission.

CELLULAR REPRODUCTION

Molecular duplication, resulting in increase of cell size, may be followed by reproduction of a cell as a whole. This reproductive process is **cell division,** or *fission.*

In certain cases among unicellular organisms, a mother cell may divide into *several* daughter cells, a phenomenon known as **multiple fission.** In the vast majority of cases, however, **binary fission,** or division of one cell into two, is the rule. Binary fission in most organisms produces two daughter cells of roughly equal size. In some instances, as in yeasts, distinctly unequal cells may result, a form of cell division called **budding.** In all cases, daughter cells enlarge by molecular reproduction, and they may subsequently divide in their turn. The period between two succeeding cell divisions represents a cell generation (Fig. 22.3).

In cells which possess a distinctly formed nucleus, division consists of at least two separate processes: *cleavage of the cytoplasm* into two parts and *duplication of the nucleus*. These two events normally take place more or less concurrently, but they may become ungeared from each other. In many cell types, for example, nuclear duplication often occurs without cytoplasmic cleavage, and a binucleate cell then results. The reverse is encountered as well, i.e., a binucleate cell may cleave without nuclear duplication. Such events may also be induced by experimental means. It is unknown how the normal gearing of nuclear and cytoplasmic duplications is accomplished, but since the nucleus usually begins to duplicate somewhat earlier than the cytoplasm, nuclear reproduction probably triggers cytoplasmic reproduction (Fig. 22.4).

In most cell divisions, nuclear duplication includes a mathematically precise doubling of the chromosomes. The genes in the chromosomes reproduce just before cell division begins, and at the start of cell division, two complete, identical sets of chromosomes are already present. In the course of division, one of these chromosome sets becomes incorporated into one of the daughter cells, and the second set, into the other daughter cell. Specific, very characteristic chromosome movements occur at that time. These chromosomal changes, and all events associated with them, together are known as mitosis. The type of cell division in which it occurs is referred to as **mitotic division.** We shall discuss its details in the next chapter. Here we note carefully that "mitosis" is not simply another word for cell division but is a particular series of nuclear and chromosomal events in a particular type of cell division.

Some cells, notably bacteria and blue-green algae, do not possess formed nuclei, or even chromosomes. Here cell division includes gene duplication, but not mitosis. Moreover, certain cells which do possess chromosomes on occasion divide without demonstrable mitotic changes. Any division in which mitotic events are not evident is referred to as **amitotic division.** Many different forms of it exist, and the term therefore does not designate a single distinct process, as does the term "mitotic division" (Fig. 22.5).

Mitotic or amitotic, the net result of division is the formation of two offspring cells which are genetically identical to each other and to the parent cell which produced them. In unicellular plants and animals, cell division is equivalent to reproduction of the whole organism. Daughter cells generally separate, but in some forms they remain sticking together, forming *colonies.*

In multicellular organisms, cell division either contributes to **cell replacement,** as in regeneration or wound healing, or adds to **cell number.** This leads to growth of tissues and organs. The growth of an organism, we note, may be a result either of molecular reproduction and increase in cell *size* or of cellular reproduction and increase in cell *number,* or of both (see Fig. 22.6). If the rate of cell division more than balances the rate of cell death, continued net growth occurs. In the opposite case, degrowth will take place.

FIG. 22.4. Cytoplasmic and nuclear divisions of a cell usually occur at the same time (left). But on occasion the nucleus may divide without cytoplasmic division, resulting in a binucleate cell (middle), or the cytoplasm of a binucleate cell may divide without nuclear division, resulting in two uninucleate cells (right).

nuclear duplication plus cytoplasmic cleavage
(normal cell division)

nuclear duplication without cytoplasmic cleavage
(binucleate cell forms)

cytoplasmic cleavage without nuclear duplication
(binucleate cell forms two normal cells)

mitotic:

amitotic:

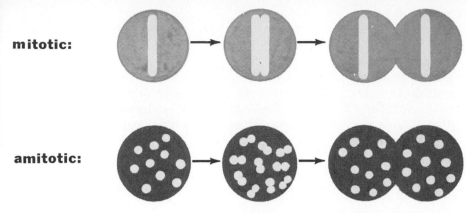

FIG. 22.5.   Illustrating the difference between mitotic and amitotic division. In mitotic division, the chromosomes of a cell are duplicated exactly, and the daughter cells possess chromosomes which are identical in number and type with those of the mother cell. Formed chromosomes are often not present in cell types which divide amitotically, and the genetic elements here are duplicated individually, without the division apparatus characteristic of mitotic division.

The rates of cellular reproduction vary greatly. For example, bacterial cells may split every 20 min or so, under optimal conditions. Hence 20 cell generations, occurring within a mere 6 to 7 hr, multiply a single bacterium into about 1 million organisms. Among multicellular organisms, the most intense rates of cell division occur in embryonic stages, the least intense in old age. Cells which form membranous sheetlike tissues retain a fairly rapid, but steadily decreasing, rate of division throughout the life of an organism. By contrast, human liver or muscle cells, for example, divide only rarely in the adult. And after being formed in the embryo, nerve cells no longer divide at all. Nerve cells may grow, but only by increase in cell size. Destroyed neurons cannot be replaced. In general, the more highly specialized a cell, the less frequently it divides, and vice versa (see Chap. 3).

Why does tissue and organ growth slow down with increasing age? With few exceptions, cellular reproductive capacity in the adult remains *potentially* as great as in the embryo. This is shown, for example, by the high rates of cell division in wound healing, in regeneration, in cancer, and in **tissue cultures.** Such cultures are prepared by separating groups of cells from an organism and growing these same cell groups in artificial nutrient solutions. Under isolated conditions of this sort, cells are found to reproduce faster than if they had remained within an organism. Moreover, if newly formed cells in a tissue culture are cut away from time to time, the original bit of tissue may live almost indefinitely long, certainly far longer than it would have lived within an organism. Through tissue culture, for example, a piece of the heart muscle of a chicken embryo has been maintained alive for over 30 years, which exceeds the life span of the whole chicken several times.

It is conceivable, therefore, that cell reproduction in intact organisms may slow down mainly because the cells are *not* isolated, as in a tissue culture. Instead, cells are integrated very finely into a larger organization. Just as, in the human population, economic, social, and other checks hold the reproduction of the individual to less than maximum rates, so evidently is the rate of cell division held down by metabolic checks in the healthy cell population. Similarly, the slower expansion of an older, established society, compared with that of a new pioneer group, provides a close parallel to comparative growth rates in adult and embryo.

The actual answer to the problem of slowing

growth, when found in the future, may well have a bearing on the observation that, in plants and many animals, growth never ceases entirely. Trees, for example, are well known to be able to grow for hundreds of years. Some of them, particularly giant redwoods and *Eucalyptus* trees, have attained heights of about 400 ft—the largest organisms ever to exist. Here, as in whales, elephants, and other large animals, bulk arises primarily through increase in cell number, not cell size. Among animals, fish are known to grow throughout life. But in other forms, as in man, net growth stops altogether at a certain stage.

Organismic Reproduction

THE PATTERNS

After periods of tissue and organ growth by molecular and cellular reproduction, the whole multicellular organism may reproduce. The general pattern consists of two phases. First, a portion of protoplasm, a **reproductive unit,** separates from the parent. Second, a duplicate organism then forms out of the reproductive unit, through **development** (Fig. 22.6).

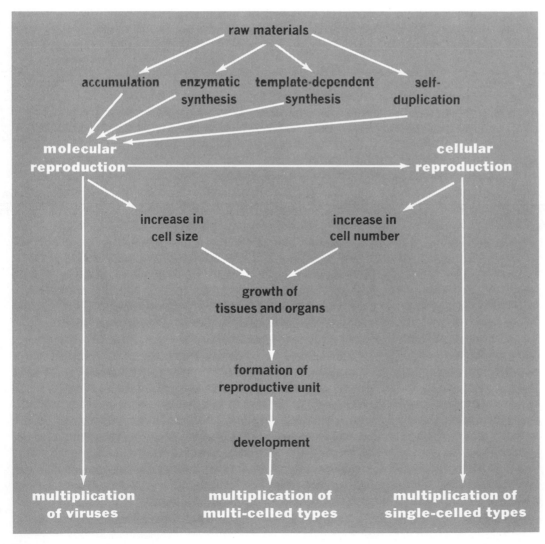

FIG. 22.6. The overall pattern of reproduction.

Vegetative Reproduction

In many cases, the reproductive unit consists of a substantial portion of the parent organism. For example, certain flatworms, sea anemones, and other animal types may on occasion pull themselves apart into two or more portions. Each portion then regenerates the missing body parts (Fig. 22.7). In unicellular organisms, the whole body is the reproductive unit. Cell division in these forms is actually the only means of making more individuals. This general type of multiplication, of particular importance in unicellular forms, is called **vegetative reproduction**. Its characteristics are that the reproductive unit is always a substantial part of the whole body and that such units are not specialized for reproduction primarily.

Closely allied to vegetative reproduction, and representing, in fact, a special form of it, is *regenerative reproduction*. Here the reproductive units arise fortuitously, as a result of injury to the parent by external agents. For example, many organisms may be cut into several pieces, and each piece may then grow into a new, whole individual. Almost any piece of a plant, a few segments of an earthworm, an arm of a starfish, a chunk of tissue from a hydra or a sponge, each is an effective reproductive unit. The parent organisms which lose such sections of their bodies regenerate the missing parts (Fig. 22.8).

In all these cases, the size and composition of the reproductive unit obviously vary with the nature and extent of damage to the parent. It is clear, also, that regeneration may become reproduction only where the capacity of regeneration is extensive, as in the examples just cited. Regenerative capacity varies with the species, and in many organisms it is highly limited. Salamanders may regenerate a whole limb, but a limb cannot regenerate a whole salamander. In vertebrates generally, the regeneration potential is not even as great as in salamanders but, as in man, is limited to the healing of relatively small wounds.

Reproductive Cells

On theoretical grounds, a reproductive unit of a multicellular organism should not have to be as large a portion of the parent organism as it is in vegetative

FIG. 22.7. Vegetative reproduction in sea anemones. This animal is splitting lengthwise into two offspring organisms. (Courtesy of D. P. Wilson, Marine Biological Laboratory, Plymouth, England.)

reproduction. The smallest protoplasmic unit which possesses the genetic information, and the operating equipment, representative of an entire multicellular organism is a *single cell*. Hence the minimum unit for the construction of such an organism should be one cell. This is actually the universal case. Regardless of whether or not it may also reproduce vegetatively, every multicellular organism is capable of reproducing through single **reproductive cells**. All such cells are more or less specialized for reproduction, and they are formed in more or less specialized reproductive tissues or organs of the parent.

FIG. 22.8.   Regenerative reproduction. Left: an arm of a starfish regenerates all missing parts and becomes a whole animal. Right: a starfish which has lost parts of each arm at least once regenerates into a whole animal. Note the lighter shading of the regenerated portions in each arm. The arm at top center has regenerated twice. (Courtesy of D. P. Wilson, Marine Biological Laboratory, Plymouth, England.)

According to the manner of their formation and their later fate, two general classes of reproductive cells may be distinguished. One includes cells which may develop into adults *directly*. Such cells are very common in plants, where they are usually called **spores.** Among animals, cells of this type are rarer, and they are given a variety of names. The designation **bud** cell is probably the most frequent.

Reproductive cells in the second general class can *not* develop directly. Instead, they must first undergo a *sexual process*, in which two reproductive cells fuse. Such cells are called *sex cells*, or **gametes.** The gametes produced by a male parent are *sperms;* those produced by a female parent, *eggs*. A **mating** process makes possible the pairwise fusion of sperms and eggs. This fusion is **fertilization,** and the fusion product is called a **zygote.** Development of gametes into adults cannot occur until fertilization has taken place. In other words, if sex occurs, it is interpolated between the two basic phases of the reproductive sequence, namely, between the formation of reproductive cells and the development of these cells into adults.

The Reproductive Repertoire

We conclude that an organism may reproduce in one or more of three general ways (Fig. 22.9):

1. Vegetatively, by means of relatively large reproductive units, variously produced and not specialized primarily for reproduction

2. By means of spores or buds, specialized reproductive cells which develop directly

3. By means of gametes, specialized reproductive cells which develop only after a sexual process

As noted, vegetative reproduction is the basic process of multiplication in unicellular forms, but variants of it also occur widely elsewhere. Multicellular types reproduce mainly by the second and third methods. We may use the term **sporulation** to identify the second method, and the term **gametic reproduction** to identify the third.

Note here that, in a strict sense, the often used terms "asexual reproduction" and "sexual reproduction" are meaningless. In all forms of multiplication, the essential "reproductive" event is the formation of *reproductive units*. The rest is *development*.

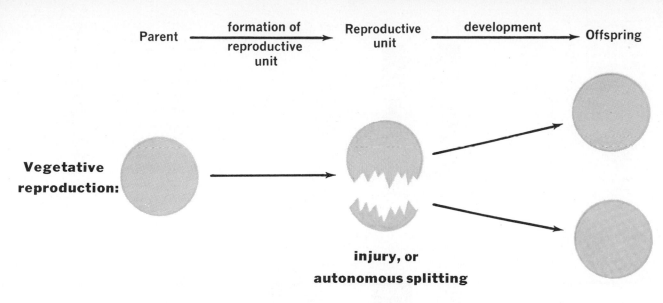

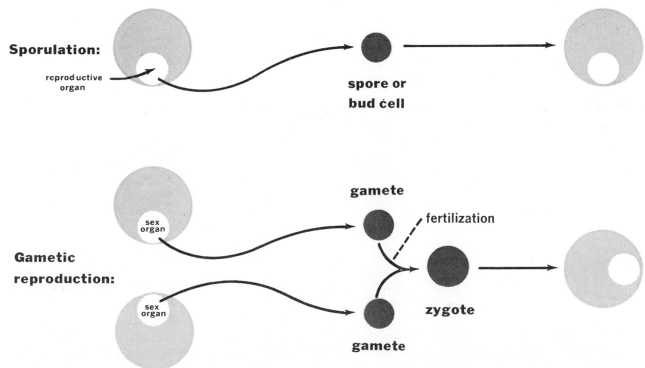

FIG. 22.9. The three principal patterns of organismic reproduction.

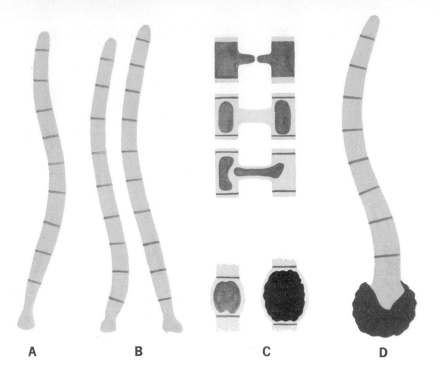

FIG. 22.10. Sexuality in *Spirogyra*. **A,** colony of cells. **B,** two filaments side by side prior to conjugation. **C,** protoplasmic bridge between opposite cells (top); migration of contents of one cell into the other cell (middle); formation of cyst, or zygospore (bottom). **D,** growth of new colony from opened zygospore. See also Fig. 22.14.

A   B   C   D

And it is this developmental phase which may or may not require sexual triggering. Reproduction as such, namely, the formation of reproductive units, is always "asexual."

What is the significance of these alternative methods of reproduction, and how does an organism choose among them? Above all, if an adult can be created adequately by the direct development of single cells, as in sporulation, what is the function and significance of sex?

SEXUALITY

Sex vs. Reproduction

The significance of sex is revealed most clearly in unicellular organisms, protozoa or certain algae, for example, where the sexual process is not even associated with reproduction.

Spirogyra is a common green alga forming dense growths in fresh-water ponds. The plant consists of a long chain of cells, each of which is capable of living independently. The whole filament thus represents a colony of distinct unicellular individ-

uals. Throughout spring, summer, and early fall, the cells reproduce vegetatively by cell division, adding to the length of the colony. Pieces of the filament may break off and settle elsewhere, starting new colonies. Later in the fall, two cells from two filaments lying side by side may **conjugate:** a protoplasmic bridge forms which interconnects the two cells. The contents of one cell then pass through the bridge into the other cell, and the two protoplasms fuse (Fig. 22.10).

That is a sexual process. What initiates its occurrence, characteristically at that season of the year? Subsequent events provide the clue. All non-conjugated cells soon die as a result of falling autumn temperatures. But the fused double cell, the zygote, is able to secrete a heavy wall around itself. The *cyst*, or **zygospore,** so formed is then able to live through the winter. In the following spring, as surface ice disappears from the pond and temperatures begin to rise, the cyst wall breaks open, and a new colony of cells develops from the surviving protoplasm.

The protozoon *Paramecium* provides another

instructive example. Here also reproduction occurs vegetatively, through cell division, and mating is achieved through conjugation. However, the sexual process does not involve *fusion* of whole cells, but merely *exchange of gene sets* (Fig. 22.11).

Note, first, that the sexual process is fundamentally quite distinct from reproduction. *Spirogyra* and *Paramecium* do not "multiply" by sex—if anything, quite the contrary. In *Spirogyra*, two cells form one, and in *Paramecium*, two cells enter the process, two cells again emerge. In all other organisms, sex and reproduction are equally distinct, even though the two processes occur together. In such cases it is sometimes possible to "ungear" sex and reproduction by experimental means. For example, a frog egg can be made to develop *before* it has been fertilized, by pricking its surface with a needle. The puncture simulates the entrance of a sperm, and development begins. But the sexual process has not taken place. Development of this sort without fertilization is called **artificial parthenogenesis**. *Natural* forms of parthenogenesis occur in a number of animals, e.g., social insects, as was pointed out in Chap. 4.

Note further that in *Spirogyra*, in *Paramecium*, and in virtually all other organisms, man not excepted, sexual activity is particularly evident during periods of persistent *stress*. Sexuality may be brought out or intensified by unfavorable climates, by widespread food shortages, by overpopulation, or by other conditions which cannot be quickly re-sponded to through steady-state control or reproduction. Indeed, most plants and animals living in temperate climates manifest sexual activity typically in the fall or in the spring. Initial unfavorable changes in the fall environment bring forth sexual responses anticipating the worse conditions of winter, and sexual activity during spring anticipates the stress conditions of summer heat and dryness.

The Function of Sex

Just how is sexuality effective against conditions of stress? Events in *Spirogyra* and *Paramecium* supply the general answer: every cell resulting from the sexual process possesses the genes of *both* cells which entered the process. Stripped to its barest essentials, sex may be defined as the accumulation, within a single cell, of genes derived from two relatively unrelated cells. One method of achieving this is cell fusion, as in *Spirogyra;* another is direct exchange of duplicate nuclei, hence of duplicate gene sets, as in *Paramecium.*

Sex therefore counteracts stress conditions on the principle of "two are better than one." If the self-perpetuating powers of two relatively unrelated parent organisms are joined, through union of their genes, then the resulting offspring organism may acquire a survival potential which is greater than that of either parent alone. If parent *A* survives in environment *a*, and parent *B* in environment *b*, then the organism *AB* formed after sexual union may survive in environment *a* or *b*, or in both (Fig. 22.12).

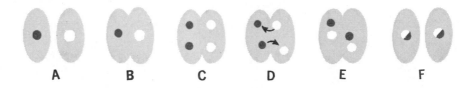

FIG. 22.11.   Sexuality in *Paramecium* and other protozoa. **A**, original partners. **B**, mating. **C**, nuclear division. **D**, gene exchange. **E**, result. **F**, nuclear fusion and separation of partners. Note that sexuality in *Spirogyra* involves fusion of two entire cells, whereas in *Paramecium* only exchanged nuclei fuse.

Moreover, a still poorly understood protoplasmic *rejuvenation,* on the biochemical, metabolic level, accompanies the sexual process. In certain protozoa, for example, if sex is experimentally prevented during an indefinite number of successive vegetative generations, then the vigor of the line eventually declines. The animals ultimately die, even under optimal environmental conditions. Internal stresses apparently appear in aged generations, and only a "rejuvenation" through sex may then save the reproductive succession and prevent the line from dying out.

We may say that reproduction is a "conservative" process. Parental characteristics are passed on faithfully by reproduction from generation to generation, and so long as the external and internal environment remains favorable, succeeding generations survive as well as preceding ones. Sex, on the other hand, is a "liberalizing" process. It may offer survival under new or changed conditions. By combining the best (and the worst) features of two parents, sex introduces *genetic change* into the resulting organisms. And to the extent that such change may be advantageous for survival in new environments, or under new conditions, *sex has adaptive value.*

That is the key point. *Sex is a process of* **adaptation, not** *of reproduction.*

Since every organism must adapt, sex has become universal. And since sex is a process involving single cells, it must be carried out at a stage when an organism consists of but a single cell. In unicellular organisms, therefore, sex may occur at any stage of the life cycle, regardless of when reproduction occurs; and it may be dissociated completely from reproduction. Indeed, the predominant life-cycle pattern among unicellular organisms is simply a succession of vegetative generations. Sex may occur at any point in such a succession, once or several times, under the influence of environmental stress.

By contrast, the life cycle of a multicellular organism passes through a unicellular stage only once, and if sex is to take place at all, it must take place then. Hence, "gametic reproduction": sex occurs *after* the formation of reproductive cells, and *before* the development of such cells into multicellu-

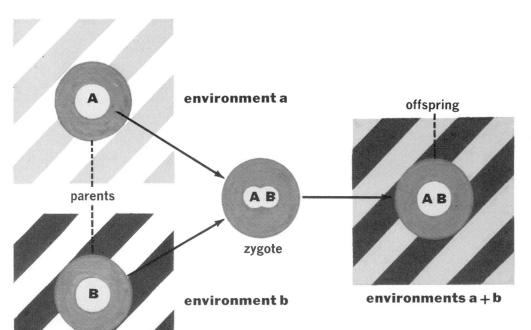

FIG. 22.12. The role of sex in combating stress. **a** and **b** represent two different environments in which live two genetically different prospective parents; **A** and **B** symbolize their genes. Through sex, the offspring acquires the genes of both parents, hence also the ability to live in either or both environments **a** or **b**. Sex combines the adaptation potential of the parents and so endows the offspring with increased adaptation potential.

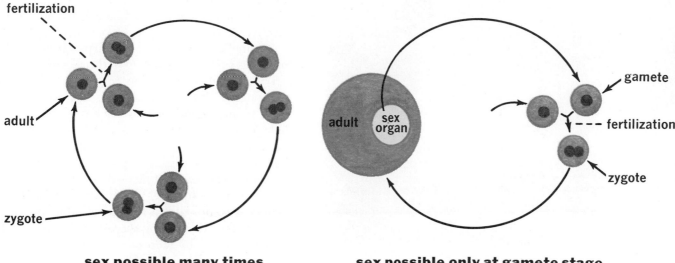

UNICELLULAR

MULTICELLULAR

fertilization

adult

zygote

**sex possible many times
during life cycle**

adult

sex
organ

gamete

fertilization

zygote

**sex possible only at gamete stage
of life cycle**

FIG. 22.13.   The relation of sex to life cycle. Since sex is a process involving single cells, it may occur at any stage in unicellular organisms, but only at the gamete stage in multicellular organisms.

lar organisms. Fertilization in such organisms has a dual function. It makes sex possible, i.e., it permits the pooling of the genes of sperm and egg. And second, it supplies the signal which triggers the start of development, thus ensuring that development does not begin before sex has occurred (Fig. 22.13).

We conclude generally that the timing of sexuality is conditioned by the unicellular or multicellular nature of the organism and that the function of sexuality is to improve the adaptedness of the species.

Males and Females

In *Spirogyra, Paramecium,* and indeed in most unicellular organisms, both sexes look exactly alike. There is no structural distinction between males and females, and the gametes are not visibly distinguishable as sperms and eggs. Nevertheless, invisible chemical and functional differences do exist. Not any two gametes can conjugate. The cells of a *Spi-*

rogyra filament, for example, have all originated from the same zygospore and may be regarded as being of the same "sex," or, better, the same **mating type.** Cells within such a filament cannot unite sexually. Two cells from two different filaments are required (Fig. 22.14). Mating types exist in *Paramecium* as well, and cells from different ones are necessary for sexual union.

In some algae and protozoa, and in all other plants and animals, chemical sex differences are accompanied by visible, structural ones. True male and female sexes may be distinguished here. Specialized sex organs, *ovaries* and *testes* in animals, *archegonia* and *antheridia* in plants, produce eggs and sperms, respectively. Accessory structures may be present which, functioning in gamete transport and the later development of embryos, make up a *reproductive system.*

In such multicellular organisms, we find, gametic reproduction functions as a combined repro-

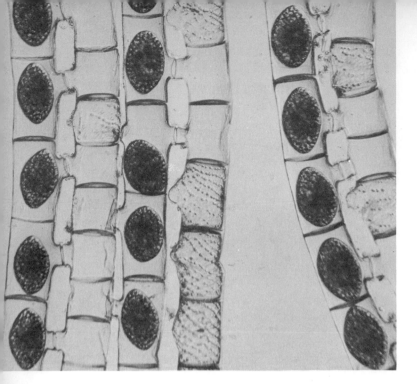

FIG. 22.14. Zygospore cysts of *Spirogyra* after conjugation. Note that all cells within a given filament have the same sexual properties: they may be either migrating sexual partners or stationary partners which receive the cells from a neighboring filament. All cells of a given filament are of the same mating type, and this accounts for the uniform sexual behavior. (General Biological Supply House, Inc.)

ductive and adaptive process. Why then is gametic reproduction in many organisms not the only form of multiplication? What is the significance of sporulation? And where both sporulation and gametic reproduction occur, how are these two reproductive processes integrated into one life cycle?

LIFE CYCLES

Gametes vs. Spores

Gametic reproduction serves well in perpetuating an organism in time, but it serves rather less well in extending living matter in space. This form of multiplication depends on locomotion, for if physical contact between sperm and egg is to occur, at least one of the gametes must move. Sperms actually

do move, usually by means of flagella. But eggs in most cases are nonmotile. This means that new offspring can form only where the adults are, for they contain the eggs. If, therefore, the adults are sessile or stationary, gametic reproduction cannot be too effective in dispersing the species geographically.

Gametic reproduction also depends on chance, for unless sperms do meet eggs, the reproductive effort of the adults will be wasted. Above all, gametic reproduction invariably requires an aquatic medium. In air, gametes would dry out quickly, unless they possessed external evaporation-resistant shells. But if two cells were so encapsulated, they could then not fuse or exchange genes.

These various limitations disappear in sporulation. A reproductive cell which need not meet with another is complete and functional on its own, and the chances of developing successfully consequently are not reduced by failures of meeting. Also, independently developing cells *can* be encapsulated, and they can therefore be effective in an aerial as well as in an aquatic medium. Moreover, a spore or bud cell can be transported to completely new territory, even far away from the parent; hence such cells are ideal for geographic dispersal. Aquatic spores are usually flagellated, and they distribute the species by active locomotion. Encapsulated terrestrial spores are dispersed passively, by wind, water, or animals.

Sporulation thus compensates for the limitations of gametic reproduction. But it has a limitation of its own; namely, it does not offer the adaptive opportunities which gametic reproduction offers through sex. Both sporulation and gametic reproduction have therefore persisted as major forms of multiplication.

The Cycle Patterns

On the basis of their reproductive repertoire, multicellular organisms may be divided into two main groups. In one are organisms which reproduce via gametes *only*, and which disperse geographically primarily through adult locomotion. Moving animals are in this group. Organisms in the other group reproduce via gametes too, but in addition they reproduce by sporulation. Species dispersal

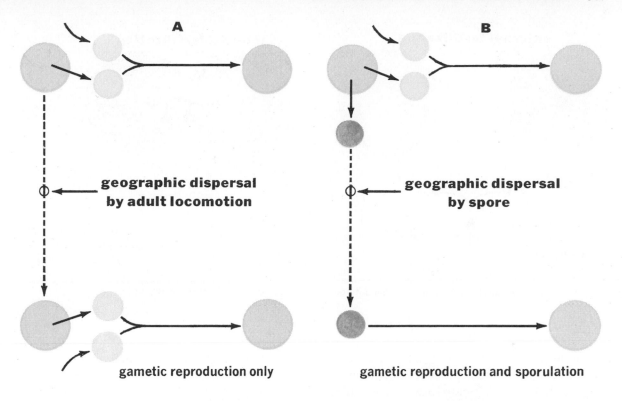

A

**geographic dispersal
by adult locomotion**

gametic reproduction only

B

**geographic dispersal
by spore**

gametic reproduction and sporulation

FIG. 22.15. Gametic reproduction and sporulation. Organisms capable of loco-motion may achieve geographic dispersal by that means, and the reproductive reper-toire then usually includes only gametic reproduction (**A**). Sessile organisms on the other hand usually reproduce both through gametes and through sporulation, the latter also serving in geographic dispersal (**B**).

here is achieved mainly through sporulation. In this group are sessile animals and all multicellular plants (Fig. 22.15).

In the first group, gametic reproduction is exe-cuted by either of two major patterns. One involves **external fertilization.** This pattern is characteristic of most motile animals which live in water and also of terrestrial animals, such as frogs and toads, which migrate to permanent bodies of water for reproduc-tion. In all these cases, males and females mate by coming into more or less close proximity and by shedding clouds of swimming sperms and of eggs directly into the water. Frequent chance collisions among the gametes then bring about fertilization.

The other pattern is characteristic of most mo-tile animals which live on land, e.g., worms, insects,

spiders, reptiles, birds, and mammals. These forms efficiently circumvent the need for natural bodies of water through **internal fertilization,** made possible by locomotion. Prospective parents move together, and the male ejects swimming sperms directly into the body of the female, over an uninterruptedly moist path (Fig. 22.16). The fertilized eggs, or zy-gotes, then are protected against evaporation in var-ious ways. They may mature within the body of the female, as in mammals. Or they may be deposited into natural bodies of water, as in mosquitoes and many other insects. Or, third, they may be deposited on land but may be protected against evaporation by shells secreted around them. For example, earth-worms, spiders, and insects such as grasshoppers and cockroaches form a cocoon or a hard casing

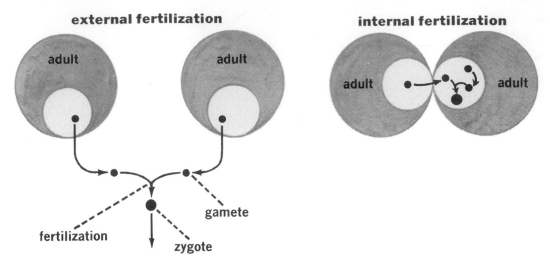

external fertilization

adult

adult

gamete

fertilization

zygote

internal fertilization

adult

adult

FIG. 22.16. Illustration of the difference between external and internal fertilization.

around batches of fertilized eggs. Other insects, and also reptiles and birds, produce individual, hard-shelled, often very elaborate **land eggs,** in which the young are surrounded by their own "private pond." The chicken egg is the most familiar example of this.

As noted, sporulation becomes necessary in most organisms incapable of locomotion, but for adaptive reasons, gametic reproduction must occur as well. In plants and sessile animals, these two methods of reproduction are integrated into one life cycle in either of two ways. The primitive way is characteristic of many multicellular algae and fungi among plants, and of sponges among sessile animals. In these forms, *both* sporulation and gametic reproduction may be carried out during the same generation of adults. A fungus, for example, may now produce spores, and at other periods, particularly under conditions of stress, it may produce gametes.

A more advanced pattern has evolved in all other multicellular plants and also in coelenterates among the sessile animals. A complete life cycle here consists of *two* successive generations. Adults of one generation reproduce *only* through gametes. These give rise to the next generation, in which the adults reproduce *only* by spores or by buds. The fol-

lowing generation is sexual again, and an **alternation of generations** so continues. By this means, the requirements of both adaptation and geographic dispersal may be satisfied in regular, two-generation cycles (Fig. 22.17).

Among these organisms, the terrestrial plants must cope with an additional problem. They must provide water for the gametes formed during the sexual generation of their life cycle. Such a water problem does not arise in the asexual generation, for spores may be encapsulated and evaporation-resistant. Nor does the water problem arise in sessile animals, for all these live in water to begin with. We shall see in Chap. 24 how stationary land plants have solved this major difficulty. Here we note only that the attempt at solution has oriented virtually all plant evolution on land, and that a successful solution has ultimately emerged in the form of seeds and flowers.

Hermaphroditism

We may here take note of a reproductive feature encountered very widely among sessile organisms, and also among sluggish, slowly moving forms. In particular species, a given individual is not distinctly male or distinctly female but possesses *both* male and female reproductive systems within the same body. This condition is known as **hermaphroditism.** Most terrestrial plants are hermaphroditic, and among animals the phenomenon occurs in clams, for example, and also in earthworms, flatworms, and many other types of worms. Hermaphroditism sometimes develops as an abnormality in vertebrates, man included.

Hermaphroditism is a direct adaptation to the slow or sessile way of life. Since a normal hermaphrodite functions both as a male and as a female, it may not have to search for a mate at all: **self-fertilization** may take place. This is actually relatively rare, but it does occur in some animals and a number of plants. Most hermaphrodites, like all other organisms, must carry out **cross-fertilization;** that is, the sperms of one individual must fertilize the eggs of

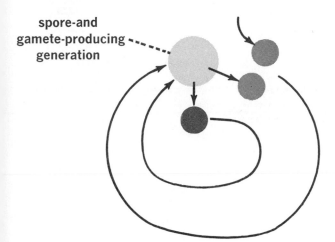

spore-and gamete-producing generation

one — generation cycle: either or both reproducing methods

FIG. 22.17. The integration of gametic reproduction and sporulation into the life cycle. In the more primitive pattern on the left, either or both reproductive methods may occur within a single generation of organisms. In the pattern on the right, sporulation alone occurs in one generation, and gametic reproduction alone in the succeeding generation. A two-generation cycle, characterized by an alternation of generations, is so established.

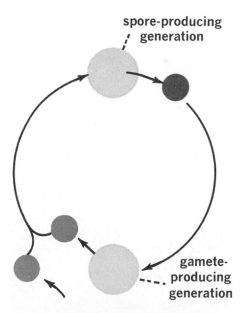

spore-producing generation

gamete-producing generation

two— generation cycle: one reproduction method per generation

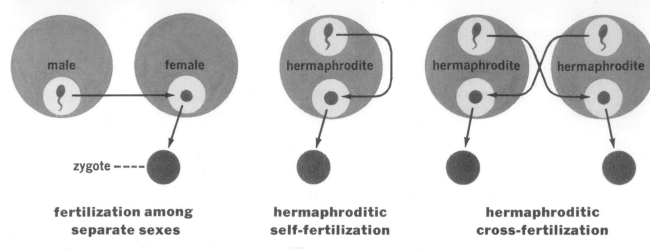

fertilization among
separate sexes

hermaphroditic
self-fertilization

hermaphroditic
cross-fertilization

FIG. 22.18.   Self- and cross-fertilization. Left: the pattern of fertilization among nonhermaphrodites, as in the majority of organisms. Middle and right: the patterns of self- and cross-fertilization among hermaphrodites.

another individual (Fig. 22.18). The advantage of hermaphroditism here is that fewer reproductive cells are wasted. For example, if a given plant species is hermaphroditic, sperms from one individual may meet eggs in *any* other individual, for every hermaphrodite contains eggs. In sessile nonher-

FIG. 22.19.   Copulating earthworms. These animals are cross-fertilizing hermaphrodites; hence whenever *any* two of them meet, each may be fertilized by the other. (General Biological Supply House, Inc.)

maphrodites, by contrast, many sperms would be wasted through chance misdistribution to the wrong sex. Similarly, if cross-fertilizing hermaphrodites are capable of some locomotion, like earthworms, for example, then fertilization becomes possible whenever *any* two individuals meet. Since sluggish individuals are not likely to meet very frequently to begin with, and since every such meeting may result in fertilization, the adaptive value of hermaphroditism is clear (Fig. 22.19).

The above outlines the broad scope of the reproductive patterns among plants and animals. We have found that the predominant pattern among unicellular organisms is a succession of vegetative generations, with sex interpolated at any point. And we have found that multicellular forms carry out either gametic reproduction only or, in most sessile types, gametic reproduction as well as sporulation. Whatever the life cycle, these processes make possible protoplasmic succession in time, distribution in space, and adaptive improvements in structure and function.

We next consider the reproduction of cells in greater detail.

1. How does reproduction contribute to steady-state maintenance? To self-perpetuation in general? Review the forms of molecular reproduction, and the nature of each. How does molecular reproduction contribute to organismic reproduction?

2. Define binary fission, multiple fission, budding. What basic events occur in all forms of cell division? What is mitosis? Distinguish between mitotic and amitotic division. How does cell division contribute to organismic reproduction?

3. What is a tissue culture? What have experiments with tissue cultures shown about rates of cell division? When and where in an organism are fission rates highest? Lowest?

4. Distinguish between reproduction and development. What is vegetative reproduction? In which organisms, under what circumstances, and in which forms, does vegetative reproduction occur?

5. What is sporulation? What is gametic reproduction? In which organisms does each of these occur? What is a spore? How is vegetative reproduction different from sporulation? How is sporulation different from gametic reproduction?

6. What are the most basic events of every sexual process? Under what conditions does sex tend to occur? In what way is sex of adaptive value? Illustrate by the example of *Spirogyra*.

7. Define mating, fertilization, zygote, gamete, mating type. What are the limitations of, and the environmental conditions required for, (*a*) gametic reproduction and (*b*) sporulation? Contrast in detail.

8. Describe the reproductive repertoire and the typical life cycle of a moving animal. Distinguish between external and internal fertilization. How do terrestrial animals with internal fertilization protect their zygotes from drying out?

9. Describe the reproductive repertoire of a sessile organism. What major life-cycle patterns are encountered among such organisms? What is alternation of generations?

10. What is hermaphroditism? In which organisms does it occur, generally and specifically? What is its adaptive function? Distinguish between self-fertilization and cross-fertilization.

**SUGGESTED
COLLATERAL
READINGS**
Most of the subject matter introduced in this chapter is rediscussed in greater detail in the following chapters. Many appropriate additional readings are cited in these later contexts. The selection below covers various aspects of cellular and organismic reproduction.

Radl, E.: Reproduction, in I. W. Knobloch, "Readings in Biological Science," Appleton-Century-Crofts, 1948.

Loeb, J.: On the Nature of the Process of Fertilization, etc., in M. L. Gabriel and S. Fogel, "Great Experiments in Biology," Prentice-Hall, 1955.

Stone, A.: The Control of Fertility, *Sci. American,* vol. 190, 1954.

Tinbergen, N.: The Courtship of Animals, *Sci. American,* vol. 191, 1954.

Milne, L. J., and M. J. Milne: Animal Courtship, *Sci. American,* vol. 183, 1950.

———— and ————: "The Mating Instinct," Little, Brown, 1954.

Zahl, P. A.: The Evolution of Sex, *Sci. American,* vol. 180, 1949.

Berrill, N. F.: "Sex and the Nature of Things," Dodd, Mead, 1953.

Wollman, E. L., and F. Jacob: Sexuality in Bacteria, *Sci. American,* vol. 195, 1956.

Delbruck, M., and M. Delbruck: Bacterial Viruses and Sex, *Sci. American,* vol. 179, 1948.

Gray, G. W.: Human Growth, *Sci. American,* vol. 189, 1953.

White, P. R.: Plant Tissue Cultures, *Sci. American,* vol. 182, 1950.

Biesele, J. J.: Tissue Culture and Cancer, *Sci. American,* vol. 195, 1956.

Braun, A. C.: Plant Cancer, *Sci. American,* vol. 186, 1952.

Conklin, G.: Cancer and Environment, *Sci. American,* vol. 180, 1949.

Greene, H. S. N.: On the Development of Cancer, *Sci. American,* vol. 179, 1948.

SINCE IT REPRESENTS the basic process of cellular reproduction, **cell division** will be the first topic of this chapter. Few biological events are as central to life, and as universally characteristic of it, as cell division. It is the sole means by which unicellular organisms multiply. It creates reproductive cells and transforms these into multicellular adults. It replaces dead cells in the adult and thereby offsets normal wear and tear. It heals wounds and regenerates body parts lost or destroyed. And cell division sometimes goes wild and produces tumors, cancers, and other abnormal overgrowths. Indeed, the life histories of organisms may be described well as changing dynamic equilibria between cell division and cell death.

The second topic will deal specifically with one of the cellular reproductions mentioned above, namely, the specialized cell divisions which lead to the formation of **reproductive cells.** This chapter thus sets the stage for a detailed discussion of the reproduction and development of whole organisms.

Cell Division: Mitosis

THE PATTERN

All cells probably possess the machinery for division, but whether or not, and with what frequency, that machinery can become effective depends on a number of factors. As noted earlier, one factor is the state of cellular nutrition. Being a process of duplication, cell division consumes energy and raw materials, and, like other reproductive events, it is therefore contingent on adequate metabolism. Another factor is the state of cellular specialization. Relatively unspecialized cells may divide at more or less regular intervals, but highly specialized cells may not divide at all.

The immediate stimulus necessary to initiate

23

CELLULAR
REPRODUCTION

division is still unknown. Many cells divide when they have grown to double their original volume. But attainment of such a volume is probably not a specific stimulus, for cells can be made to divide at any time before their volume has doubled. Moreover, they may be prevented from dividing altogether and may be allowed to grow into giant cells many times larger than twice the original. Several chemicals are known to inhibit division, and several to promote it. How do such chemicals act? Similarly, physical agents such as X rays may inhibit or promote division, depending on conditions. But although experimental procedures like these have gone far toward controlling cell division, it is still not known how such control actually operates. And it is equally unknown what normal conditions within a cell, or outside it, so stimulate it that it begins to divide.

Mitotic division is by far the most widespread form of cell reproduction. The first demonstrable event of mitotic division, and probably of amitotic division as well, is a chemical event which occurs well before microscopically visible changes can be detected: the DNA content of the cell nucleus doubles. Rapid synthesis undoubtedly occurs at this stage, and the genes of a cell reproduce, as outlined in Chap. 18. In mitotic division, gene duplication probably marks the time when the entire collection of chromosomes is doubled. At this stage, however, such doubling is not yet visible microscopically.

A certain amount of time elapses before the visible phases of cell division begin. During this period, presumably, numerous biochemical preparations are made throughout a cell for the actual execution of the reproductive process. The visible phases of mitotic division consist of four successive, arbitrarily defined stages: **prophase, metaphase, anaphase,** and **telophase.** One stage merges gradually into the next, and it is impossible to fix sharp lines of transition. The first three stages are characterized predominantly by chromosomal changes, and these stages are particularly typical of mitotic division. The last stage is primarily the stage of cytoplasmic cleavage, and the essential events here occur in all types of cell divisions.

THE PROCESS

Prophase

One of the first happenings of prophase is the division of the *centriole*. It will be recalled that such a granule is found in the cells of primitive plants and all animals, that it contains RNA-protein, and that it is situated just outside the nucleus. As soon as the centriole has divided, the two resulting granules behave as if they repelled each other. Migrating away from each other, they eventually attain stations at opposite sides of the cell nucleus.

As the centrioles migrate, they become the anchor points of conspicuous fibrillar structures which form at this time. Portions of the fluid cytoplasm surrounding a centriole transform into a less fluid gel, and fine gelated strands appear which radiate away from the centriole like the spokes of a wheel. This set of gel fibrils is appropriately called an **aster.** Gel fibrils also arise *between* the two migrating centrioles, looping from one granule to the other in flat curves. These fibrils constitute a **spindle.** As the centrioles move farther and farther apart, spindle and aster fibrils lengthen, and they increase in number (Fig. 23.1).

In most plant cells, centrioles are not present, and asters do not form. But a spindle develops nevertheless, and, as in all other cells, it ranges from one end of the cell to the other. Spindles and, where present, asters and centrioles function as a sort of scaffolding for the principal events of mitosis (Fig. 23.2).

Preparations for these main events get under way even while the scaffolding is being erected. Still during prophase, the nuclear membrane dissolves away, the nucleoli present in the nucleus disintegrate, and nuclear and cytoplasmic substances mix freely.

Distinct chromosomes now become visible. Close examination reveals that each chromosome is a *double* filament (Fig. 23.3). As noted, each chromosome has manufactured a mathematically exact double some time before prophase. Such twin chromosomes lie closely parallel, and they are joined to each other only at a single point. This attachment point is called the **centromere.** Its location varies for different chromosome pairs. Two spindle fibrils become anchored to each centromere, one from each pole of the spindle. In this way, the chromosomes become linked to the fibril scaffolding, and the stage is set for subsequent mitotic occurrences. At this general period, prophase comes to a close and *metaphase* begins.

Metaphase and Anaphase

Early during metaphase, the spindle poles, marked by centrioles in animal cells, reach their final position at opposite sides of the cell. Spindle and asters attain their maximal growth at this stage. The chromosome pairs, still scattered randomly through the central portion of the cell, now begin to migrate.

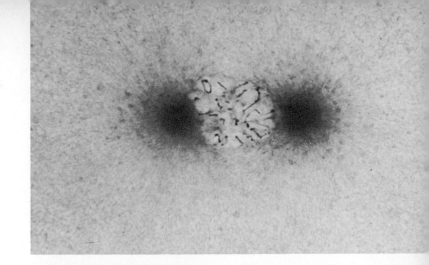

FIG. 23.1. Early prophase in animal mitosis. The nuclear membrane is just dissolving, and chromosomes are already visible. To either side of the nuclear region is a darkly stained centriole area. These areas develop after a single centriole has divided and the two daughter centrioles have migrated to opposite sides of the nucleus. From each centriole area fine fibrils are beginning to radiate out, i.e., asters are beginning to form. (General Biological Supply House, Inc.)

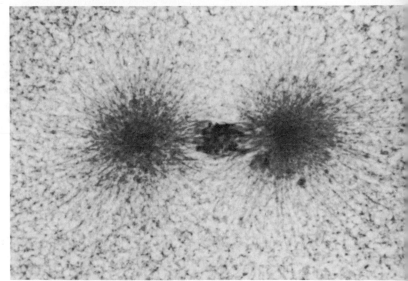

FIG. 23.2. Late prophase in animal mitosis. Asters are already conspicuous, and spindle fibrils have formed between asters and chromosomes. The chromosomes are migrating into a metaphase plate. (General Biological Supply House, Inc.)

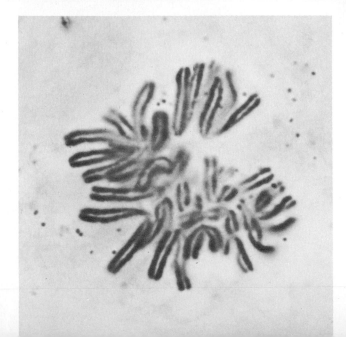

FIG. 23.3. At the time of prophase, chromosomes have already duplicated, and doubled chromosomes are therefore present. Each double is still held together at one point, the centromere. (General Biological Supply House, Inc.)

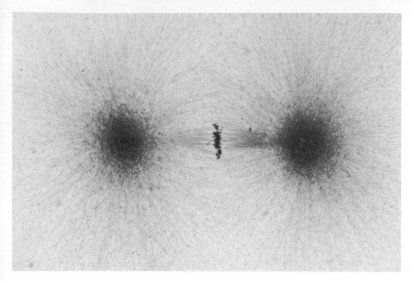

If we draw an imaginary line from one spindle pole to the other, we mark out a spindle axis. Chromosomes migrate into a plane set at right angles to the spindle axis, midway along it. Specifically, it is the centromere of each chromosome pair which comes to occupy a station precisely within this plane. During the migration, the chromosomes trail behind their centromeres like streamers. Lined up in one plane, the centromeres are said to form a **metaphase plate** (Fig. 23.4).

The lengthwise separation of the chromosome pairs now becomes complete. Each centromere divides, and so entirely independent chromosomes are produced. A small gel fibril arises at once between the centromeres of formerly joined chromosomes, and such chromosomes begin to move apart; once they are completely separated, the members of a pair of chromosomes behave as if they repelled each other. Thus, one set of chromosomes migrates away from the metaphase plate toward one spindle pole, and an identical twin set migrates in the opposite direction, toward the other spindle pole. The centromeres again lead, and the arms of the chromosomes trail. Also, the gel fibrils between twin centromeres lengthen, and fibrils between the centromeres and the spindle poles shorten. This period of poleward migration of chromosomes represents the *anaphase* of mitotic division (Fig. 23.5).

FIG. 23.4. Metaphase in animal mitosis. Note asters, spindle, and the metaphase plate, halfway along and at right angles to the spindle axis. Note also the fibrils which join the chromosomes lined up in the metaphase plate with the spindle poles. (General Biological Supply House, Inc.)

FIG. 23.5. Anaphase. Left: mid-anaphase in animal mitosis. Chromosome sets are migrating toward spindle poles. Right: anaphase in plant cell. Note absence of asters and centrioles, but presence of spindle. (General Biological Supply House, Inc.)

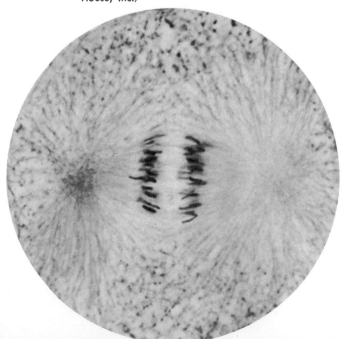

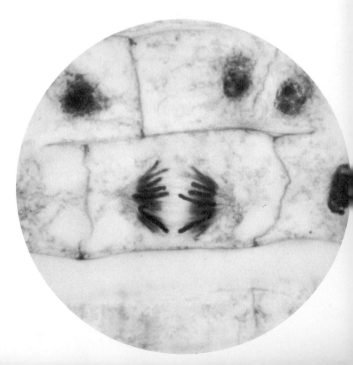

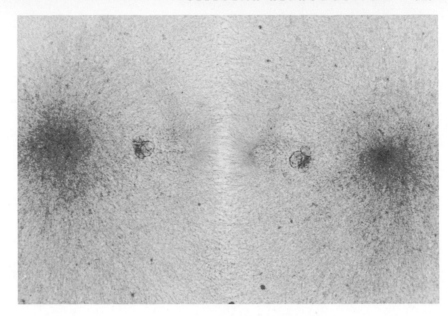

FIG. 23.6. Early telophase in animal mitosis. Asters are subsiding, nuclei are reforming, chromosome threads have become indistinct, and cytoplasmic cleavage is under way, in the same plane as the earlier metaphase plate. (General Biological Supply House, Inc.)

Telophase

The beginning of telophase is marked by the appearance of a **cleavage furrow** in animal cells and of a **division plate** in plant cells. Both furrow and plate form in the plane of the earlier metaphase plate. The cleavage furrow at first is a shallow groove circling the surface of a cell. This groove gradually deepens, cuts through the spindle fibrils, and eventually constricts the cell into two daughter cells. The process is accompanied by violent physical and chemical adjustments within the dividing cell. These internal upheavals erupt through to the surface like slow-motion, small-scale earthquakes, and the whole cell surface is thrown into deep undulations. Plant cells are enveloped by fairly rigid cellulose walls, and surface movements during division are therefore less pronounced. The plant cell is divided into two not by a deepening groove, but by a partition of cellulose, the division plate, which is laid down more or less simultaneously at all points of the plane of cleavage (Fig. 23.6).

While these events take place, the chromosomes within each prospective daughter cell aggregate near the spindle pole. Spindle fibrils and aster fibrils subside; that is, the protoplasm composing them reverts to a sol state. A new nuclear membrane now forms which envelops the chromosomes, but the centriole, if present, remains outside in the cytoplasm. Concurrently, the chromosomes in each newly forming nucleus manufacture new nucleoli, in numbers characteristic of the particular cell type. These nuclear processes terminate roughly when cytoplasmic cleavage nears completion, and mitotic division then has reached its endpoint.

The net result of these occurrences is the cleavage of one cell into two cells containing *precisely* identical gene sets, incorporated in identical chromosome sets, and *approximately* equal quantities of all other protoplasmic constituents. Consequently, the structural and functional potential of both daughter cells is the same as that of the original mother cell. The duration of mitotic division varies with species and cell type. Thirty minutes to three hours represents an average range, prophase usually being the longest of the four stages. The events of mitotic division are summarized diagrammatically in Fig. 23.7.

The Intracellular Forces

What are the mechanical forces involved in division? How do chromosomes move, and what constricts cells into two? The behavior of the spindle fibrils is highly suggestive. Do these fibrils, like guy

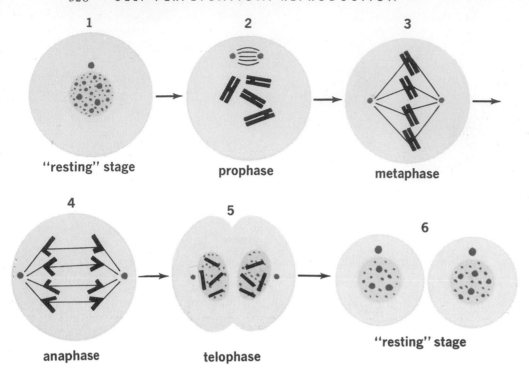

1
"resting" stage

2
prophase

3
metaphase

FIG. 23.7. Mitosis summary, diagrammatic. Note that a "resting" cell is resting only from the standpoint of reproductive activity. In all other respects it is exceedingly active.

4
anaphase

5
telophase

6
"resting" stage

ropes, pull and push chromosomes first into the metaphase plate, and later toward the spindle poles? This possibility has been tested in experiments in which spindle fibers have been cut through with needles. Under such conditions, the chromosomes still migrate in normal fashion. Moreover, in certain insects, cells have been found where demonstrable spindle fibrils from pole to chromosome never form. Yet here the chromosomes migrate nevertheless.

In view of this, the gelated fibrils would not seem to be responsible for chromosome movements. However, other lines of evidence indicate the opposite. It happens sometimes that pieces break off from chromosomes. Indeed, this can be induced by exposing cells to X rays, or to ultrasonic vibrations. In such cases, the main portion of a chromosome, which is attached to a spindle fibril, unfailingly moves toward a pole. But a piece which has broken off and is unattached invariably stays behind and clearly is unable to migrate anywhere. Futhermore, in certain animal cells, it can be shown that aster

fibrils attach to the inner surface of the cell membrane. As these fibrils shorten, the cell membrane is pulled inward, and this produces the constricting groove which eventually divides the cell.

In these instances, spindle fibrils do seem to exert a positive pull. Some investigators have suggested that the fibrils contain myosin, the same protein which makes muscles contract. We note that, on the whole, existing evidence is still conflicting, and for the present we must conclude that the forces responsible for mitotic movements have not yet been identified.

Cell division provides the bricks with which a living edifice is built and maintained. Among the many new cells continually produced by cell division in multicellular organisms, some are of particular significance. These cells contribute not so much to the growth and maintenance of various tissues and organs as to the growth and maintenance of whole new organisms; they are the *reproductive cells*. How, specifically, are they formed?

Reproductive Cells: Meiosis

THE PATTERN

Reproductive cells of all kinds are manufactured in specialized reproductive tissues or organs. In a first step, new cells are produced by mitotic division, just as in the formation of new cells in any other tissue. In a second step, the new cells then undergo a special process of *maturation*, which transforms them into cells with unique developmental properties.

The detailed pattern of this cellular maturation differs for different kinds of reproductive cells. Only cytoplasmic changes occur in some, and cytoplasmic as well as nuclear changes in others. Wherever they occur, the nuclear phases of maturation are known collectively as **meiosis.** This process follows the same universal pattern in plants and animals, and it affects primarily the chromosome number of a reproductive cell.

The Function of Meiosis

As noted in Chap. 18, the number of chromosomes per cell is a fixed, genetically determined trait of every plant and animal species. However, whenever a sexual process takes place, *two* cells or gene sets fuse together. In a fertilized egg, therefore, the chromosome number is doubled. An organism developing from such a zygote would consist of cells which would all have a doubled chromosome number. If the next generation is again produced sexually, the chromosome number would quadruple, and this process of progressive doubling would continue indefinitely, through successive sexual generations.

This does not happen in actuality. Chromosome numbers do stay constant from one generation to the next, and the constancy is brought about by meiosis. *It is the function of meiosis to reduce the chromosome number of reproductive cells by half* and so to counteract the chromosome-doubling effect of fertilization. The unreduced chromosome number,

before meiosis, is called the **diploid** number, and it is symbolized as **2n;** the reduced number, after meiosis, is the **haploid** number, and it is symbolized as **n** (Fig. 23.8).

Meiosis occurs in every plant and animal life cycle which includes a sexual process—in other words, more or less universally. If a sexual event takes place once during one life cycle, meiosis also occurs just once. The actual timing of meiosis differs in different plant and animal cycles. Adult animals typically consist of diploid cells, and meiosis takes place *during the maturation of gametes*, before fertilization. In these cases, *immature* sperms and eggs contain the diploid, 2n number of chromosomes characteristic of the species. In man, this diploid number is 48. Meiosis then occurs during gamete maturation; hence *mature* sperms and eggs are haploid and contain *half* the species-characteristic chromosome number. In man, $n = 24$. Fertilization sub-

FIG. 23.8. The relation of meiosis to life cycle.

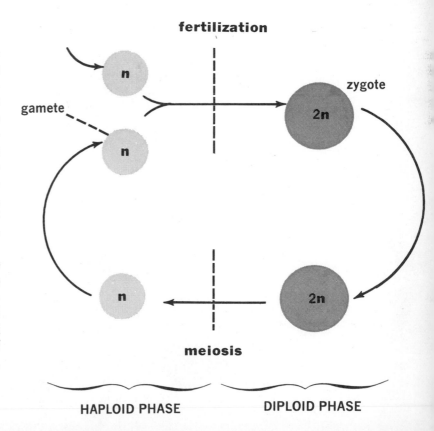

fertilization

gamete

n

n

zygote

2n

2n

n

meiosis

HAPLOID PHASE   DIPLOID PHASE

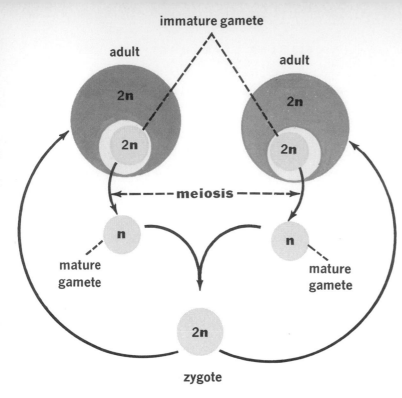

immature gamete

adult — 2n — 2n

adult — 2n — 2n

← meiosis →

n — mature gamete

n — mature gamete

2n

zygote

FIG. 23.9. Meiosis in relation to the animal life cycle. Animal meiosis occurs during the maturation of gametes. In man, the diploid (2n) number is 48, and the haploid (n) number is 24.

times during their life cycles meiosis takes place in plants. For the present, the essential point is only that meiosis occurs at *some* stage during every life cycle which includes sex, as a counterbalance to the chromosome-doubling effect of fertilization. For purposes of illustration, we shall here continue to discuss the animal pattern specifically.

The Course of Meiosis

A diploid cell actually does not contain a 2n collection of mutually different chromosomes, but a collection of n mutually different *pairs* of chromosomes. A fertilized egg receives one haploid, *n,* set of chromosomes via the sperm, and a like haploid set via the egg. Therefore, like shoes, the chromosomes of any diploid cell come in pairs. One of each pair originates initially in the sperm, the other in the egg. In an adult man, for example, 24 of the 48 chromosomes of every diploid cell are paternal, that is, they have been inherited originally from the father of that individual. The other 24 chromosomes are maternal, having been inherited from the mother (Fig. 23.11).

During gamete production in such an adult, chromosome reduction occurs in such a way that the

sequently reestablishes the diploid number (see Fig. 23.9).

If an animal also reproduces by means of bud cells, a sexual process is not involved here. Meiosis therefore does *not* occur during the maturation of such bud cells. For example, the *gametes* of a sponge mature via meiosis. But the directly developing *bud* cells of the same sponge do not, and their chromosome number stays diploid, the same as in any adult sponge cell (see Fig. 23.10).

The next chapter will show at what different

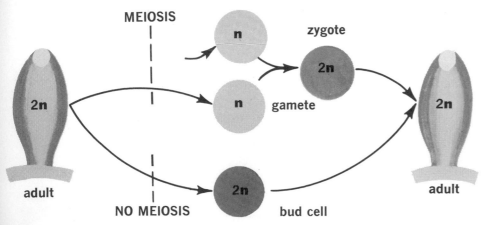

MEIOSIS

n — zygote

2n

adult — 2n

n — gamete

2n

adult — 2n

NO MEIOSIS — 2n — bud cell

FIG. 23.10. The chromosome difference between buds and gametes. In a sponge, for example, meiosis occurs during gamete production; hence gametes are haploid, and fertilization then restores the diploid condition. But bud cells of the same sponge are formed without meiosis; hence they are diploid like the cells of the parent. Fertilization then does not occur.

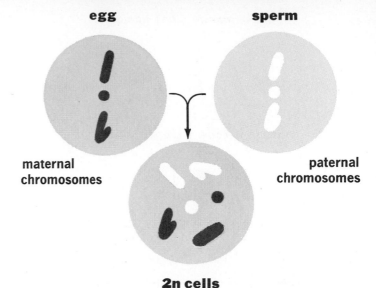

egg   **sperm**

maternal chromosomes   **paternal chromosomes**

2n cells

FIG. 23.11.   Each diploid cell contains two like sets of chromosomes, representing maternal-paternal pairs. The maternal set originated in the egg, and the paternal set in the sperm.

mature haploid gamete contains *one of each maternal-paternal pair* of chromosomes. In this haploid gamete, it is entirely a matter of chance which, and how many, chromosomes will be maternal, and which and how many will be paternal. In a human sperm or egg, for example, 24 chromosomes make up a complete haploid set; and of these, a chance-determined number will be paternal, the remainder maternal (Fig. 23.12).

The phrase "chromosome reduction" might imply that one of each pair of chromosomes is destroyed or otherwise lost. This is not the case. Instead, chromosome number is reduced to half by two **meiotic cell divisions.** The general pattern of these divisions is as follows. An immature, diploid sex cell undergoes two successive cytoplasmic cleavages, which transform the one original cell into four cells. At the same time, the chromosomes of the original cell duplicate *once*. As a result, $2n$ becomes $4n$. And of these $4n$ chromosomes, one n is incorporated into each of the four cells formed. In sum, *one* original *diploid* cell becomes *four* mature *haploid* cells. In man, the 48 chromosomes of an immature

sex cell double to 96, and the cytoplasm of that cell concurrently divides twice, producing four cells. These four share the 96 chromosomes equally. Each mature human gamete therefore contains 24 chromosomes (Fig. 23.13).

FIG. 23.12.   When the chromosome number of a diploid cell is halved by meiosis, a resulting haploid cell contains a single set of chromosomes consisting of a chance-determined number of paternal and maternal chromosomes. The diagram shows the various possible paternal-maternal combinations if $n = 3$.

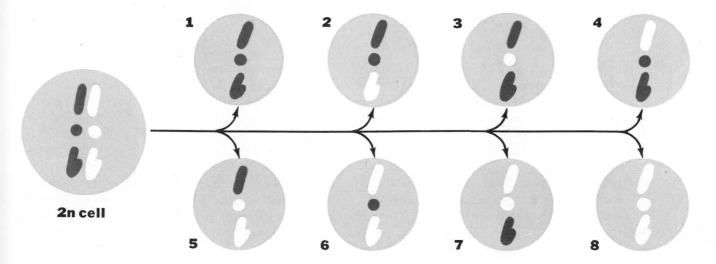

2n cell

1   2   3   4

5   6   7   8

one immature (2n) gamete

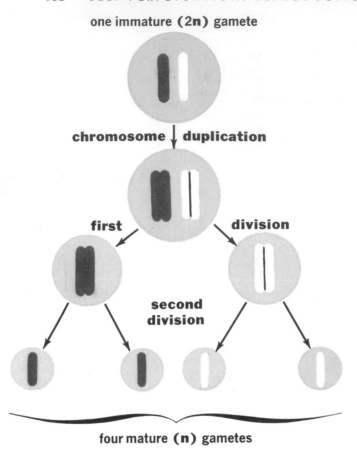

chromosome ↓ duplication

first   **division**

**second
division**

four mature (n) gametes

FIG. 23.13. The general pattern of events during meiosis, on the assumption that $2n = 2$.

THE PROCESS

The Meiotic Divisions

The two meiotic divisions occur one after the other, and they have many features in common with mitotic divisions. For example, each meiotic division passes through prophase, metaphase, anaphase, and telophase, as in mitosis. As in mitotic divisions also, the centriole divides, spindle fibrils and asters form, and the nuclear membrane dissolves during each prophase and re-forms during each telophase in meiotic divisions.

The critical difference between mitosis and the *first* meiotic division lies in their metaphases.

In mitosis, we recall, the $2n$ chromosomes, each of them already duplicated, migrate into the metaphase plate, where all the centromeres line up in the same plane. Hence the mitotic metaphase plate is made up of $2n$ pairs of chromosomes.

In the first meiotic division, the $2n$ chromosomes similarly duplicate during or before prophase. These $2n$ pairs, the members of each pair again joined at the centromere, also migrate into the metaphase plate. But now only n pairs assemble in one plane. The other n pairs migrate into a plane of their own, a plane which is closely parallel to the first. Moreover, every pair in one plane comes to lie next to the corresponding type of chromosome pair in the other plane. Hence the metaphase plate is made up of *paired chromosome pairs,* or *foursomes* of like chromosomes lying side by side. And there are n of these foursomes in the whole plate (Fig. 23.14).

During the ensuing anaphase, two chromosomes of each foursome migrate to one spindle pole, two to the other. At the end of the first meiotic division, therefore, there are two cells, each with n pairs of chromosomes. In the metaphase of the subsequent second meiotic division, the n pairs of chromosomes line up in the same plane, and n single chromosomes eventually migrate to each of the poles during anaphase. Hence, at the termination of meiosis as a whole, four cells are present, each with n single chromosomes, a complete haploid set (see Fig. 23.14, also Fig. 23.15).

Sperms and Eggs

In males, all four haploid cells produced by meiosis become functional sperms. In females, by contrast, only one cell becomes a functional egg. Of the two cells produced by the first meiotic division, one is small and it soon degenerates. Its remnants, now called the **first polar body,** remain attached to the other cell. This cell subsequently passes through the second meiotic division. Of the two cells produced here, one becomes the egg, and the other again is small and degenerates. Its remnants form

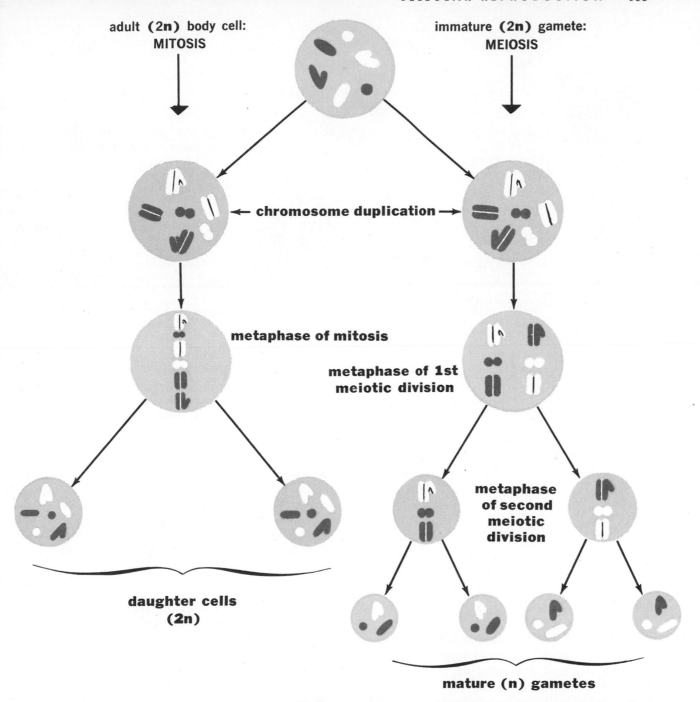

adult (2n) body cell:
MITOSIS

immature (2n) gamete:
MEIOSIS

← chromosome duplication →

metaphase of mitosis

metaphase of 1st
meiotic division

metaphase
of second
meiotic
division

daughter cells
(2n)

mature (n) gametes

FIG. 23.14.   A comparison of mitosis and meiosis, on the assumption that 2n = 6.
Note that the key difference between the two processes is the way the chromosomes
line up in metaphase.

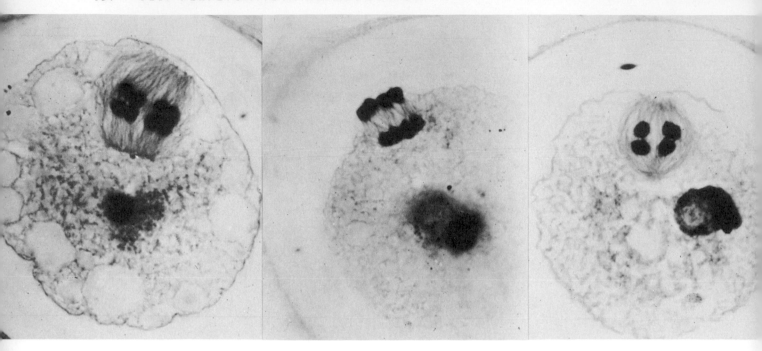

FIG. 23.15. In the nematode *Ascaris,* 2n = 4. Shown here are meiotic stages during egg maturation. The first meiotic metaphase is illustrated at left. Each of the two pairs of chromosomes has duplicated, and two foursomes are lined up in the metaphase plate. The middle photo illustrates the first telophase, when one large and one very small cell are formed, each with four chromosomes. The small cell will degenerate and form the first polar body (see also Fig. 23.17 and below). The remaining cell then undergoes the second meiotic division, the metaphase of which is shown at right. Of the two pairs of chromosomes here present, two, or *n,* will go into each of the two cells yet to be formed. One of these will be the egg, the other will degenerate and form the second polar body. The first polar body may be seen as a dark spot at the top of the photo at right. Note also the dark central spot in all three photos. This is the sperm nucleus. When meiosis of the egg is completed, sperm and egg nuclei will fuse, and fertilization will be accomplished. (Carolina Biological Supply Co.)

the **second polar body** which, like the first, remains attached to the egg (Figs. 23.16 and 23.17).

The above outlines the *nuclear* maturation of prospective gametes. In parallel with it, cytoplasmic maturation occurs. The particular form of cytoplasmic maturation varies for different animal species. In the sperms of vertebrates, for example, much of the cytoplasm degenerates altogether. The nucleus enlarges into an oval **sperm head,** and the mature sperm retains only three structures which have a cytoplasmic origin: a long **sperm tail,** which serves as locomotor flagellum; a **middle piece,** which contains mitochondria, and which joins the sperm tail with the sperm head; and an **acrosome,** a structure at the forward end of the sperm head, by means of which the sperm will make contact with an egg. As a result of losing all other cytoplasm, a mature sperm is among the smallest cells within the body.

Mature eggs, on the other hand, are among the largest cells; their cytoplasms have become special-

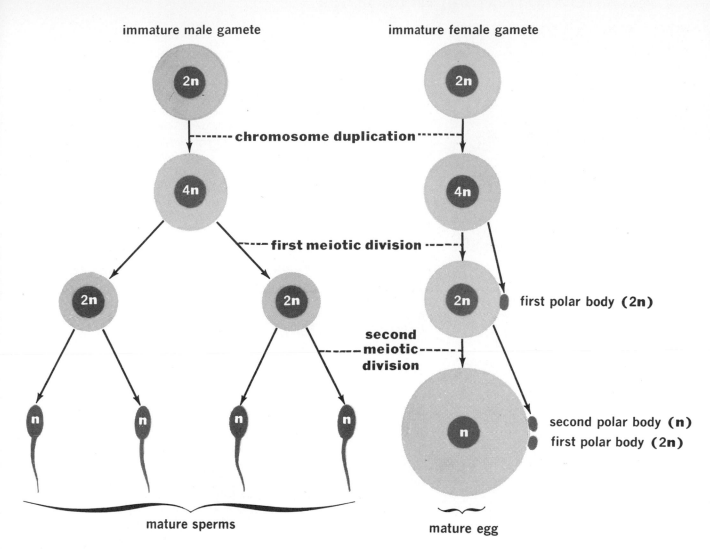

FIG. 23.16. Meiosis in males and females. In males, all four haploid cells formed become functional sperms. In females, one cell formed by the first meiotic division is small and degenerates, and becomes the first polar body. Similarly, one cell formed by the second meiotic division becomes the second polar body. Thus only one cell matures as a functional egg.

ized for the accumulation and storage of **yolk**, food reserves for the future embryos. The amount of yolk may be insignificant, as in mammals, where the blood of the female parent feeds the embryo developing in the womb. Or it may be comparatively enormous, as in birds, where yolk and albumen represent the very substance out of which an offspring bird will be constructed.

In this chapter, we have seen how cell division produces, on the one hand, the cellular raw material for tissue, organ, and individual growth, and on the other, the cellular raw material which, with or without meiosis, matures into reproductive cells. In the following chapters, we shall observe how the reproductive cells transform into whole new individuals.

FIG. 23.17. Polar-body formation. Left: the photo shows a section through the edge of an immature egg of the whitefish, and the extremely excentric position of the spindle and the chromosomes during a meiotic division. The chromosomes are in anaphase, and cleavage, which will occur at right angles to the spindle axis, will therefore produce an extremely large and an extremely small cell. Below: cytoplasmic cleavage is under way. The small cell formed will degenerate, and the remnants will persist as a polar body. (General Biological Supply House, Inc.)

REVIEW QUESTIONS

1. Review once more the distinction between cell division and mitosis. What functions does cell division serve within a multicellular organism? What molecular events within cells precede the microscopically visible phases of division?

2. Describe the processes characteristic of prophase. Define spindle, aster, centriole, centromere. How does prophase differ in plant and animal cells?

3. Describe the processes characteristic of metaphase. What, and where, is the metaphase plate? What are the events of anaphase?

4. Describe the processes characteristic of telophase. How does telophase differ in plant and animal cells? Review the history of the nucleoli during mitotic division.

5. What is the net result of mitotic division? What is known about the mechanical forces which bring about chromosome movements during mitosis? Review some of the experiments and observations which may have a bearing on this.

6. What is the basic function of meiosis, and what makes such a process neces-

sary? When, and where, does meiosis occur, generally for all organisms, and specifically for man? Define haploid, diploid.

7. How many *pairs* of chromosomes are found in a diploid cell? Of these, which and how many are maternal, and which and how many are paternal?

8. How many chromosome duplications, and how many cell duplications, occur during meiosis? In what respects are mitosis and meiosis alike?

9. What is the essential difference between the metaphase of mitosis and the metaphase of the first meiotic division? Describe the complete sequence of events during both divisions of meiosis.

10. What are the first and second polar bodies? Are they found in males as well as females? Explain. What is the general structure of a mature sperm and of a mature egg?

SUGGESTED COLLATERAL READINGS

The text listed first contains good general accounts of mitosis and meiosis. Very detailed information may be obtained from the second book. The remaining sources deal with various specific aspects of cellular reproduction.

DeRobertis, E. D. P., W. W. Nowinski, and F. A. Saez: "General Cytology," 2d ed., Saunders, 1954.

Wilson, E. B.: "The Cell in Development and Heredity," 3d ed., Macmillan, reprinted 1947.

Mazia, D.: Cell Division, *Sci. American,* vol. 189, 1953.

————: The Life History of the Cell, *Am. Scientist,* vol. 44, 1956.

Schrader, F.: "Mitosis," Columbia University Press, 1952.

Bishop, D. W.: Sperm Maturescence, *Sci. Monthly,* vol. 80, 1955.

Farris, E. J.: Male Fertility, *Sci. American,* vol. 182, 1950.

Van Beneden, E.: Researches on the Maturation of the Egg and Fertilization, in M. L. Gabriel and S. Fogel, "Great Experiments in Biology," Prentice-Hall, 1955.

24

PLANT REPRODUCTION

TERRESTRIAL PLANTS are rooted and stationary, but some phases of reproduction always require movement. If nothing more, sperms must move toward eggs. Terrestrial plants have solved the problem of dispersing their reproductive products by using the wind or, more ingeniously, by letting moving animals do the dispersing. The means of enticing animals to do the plant's reproductive work is the *flower*. Attracted by exuberant color, arresting fragrance, and nutritious nectar, animals such as bees, birds, and men make deliberate contact with one flower and then another, and in so doing they often transfer the reproductive products of plants from bloom to bloom.

It took plants a billion years to create the flower. To understand its reproductive significance, we actually must trace the evolution of reproduction within the entire plant kingdom. We shall do so here in three stages. First, we shall examine the **early patterns** of plant reproduction, still exhibited by *algae* and *fungi,* and also by *bacteria,* which generally are not considered to be true plants. In these groups, we encounter all the fundamental variants of organismic reproduction, including many different types of life cycles and forms of sexuality.

From some of these early patterns, **transitional patterns** of reproduction evolved. Still revealing an aquatic origin, but already adapted to terrestrial conditions, these patterns are exhibited today by the *bryophytes* and the primitive tracheophytes, notably the *ferns*. The third stage is reached with advanced tracheophytes, namely, the *seed plants*. Among these, truly **terrestrial patterns** of reproduction are in evidence. Through seeds, and in most cases also through flowers and fruits, these plants have become able to exploit the terrestrial way of life to the fullest.

538

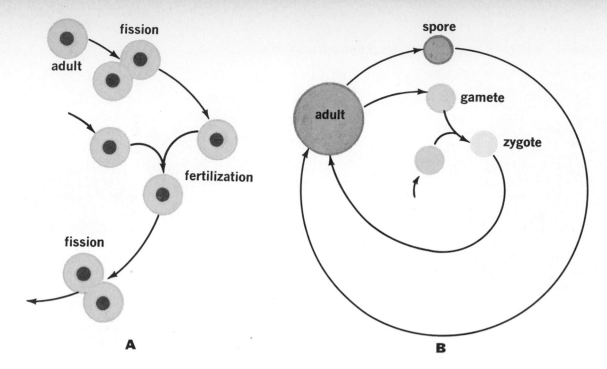

FIG. 24.1. The pattern of reproduction in unicellular and multicellular plants. The basic unicellular pattern **A** is a succession of vegetative generations, sex occurring at any time. The basic multicellular pattern **B** involves sporulation and gametic reproduction, in either a one-generation or a two-generation cycle.

Early Patterns

Bacteria are predominantly unicellular; fungi are predominantly multicellular; and algae are partly unicellular, partly multicellular. According to their cellular structure, these plants feature two principal types of life cycles.

The unicellular forms pass through successive vegetative generations, and sexual processes may occur at any time under the influence of stress conditions (Fig. 24.1). Under stress also, many of these plants may secrete heavy cyst walls around themselves, which protect the cells and keep them in a relatively inactive, **dormant** state. Such cysts are often called "spores," or "resting spores." But note that these do not function primarily in reproduction; hence they are not equivalent to the true spores formed as specialized reproductive cells by multicellular plants.

The second main pattern is exhibited by the multicellular algae and the fungi. These carry out gametic reproduction and sporulation, in most cases within the same generation of adults (see Fig. 24.1). In addition, regenerative reproduction, a variant of vegetative reproduction (see Chap. 22), occurs extensively in these as in all other multicellular plants. The adaptive importance of this is readily appreciated, for inasmuch as plants are stationary, they cannot easily escape injurious physical or biological agents. Hence the organisms are likely to be fragmented rather frequently, and it is advantageous that the fragments may regenerate into whole individuals.

UNICELLULAR PATTERNS

Life Histories

Bacteria reproduce vegetatively by cell division, here a form of amitotic division (see Chap. 22). The organisms live in all environments, and geographic distribution of these smallest of all cells is accomplished easily by wind, water, and other living organisms. Many bacterial types encyst under stress,

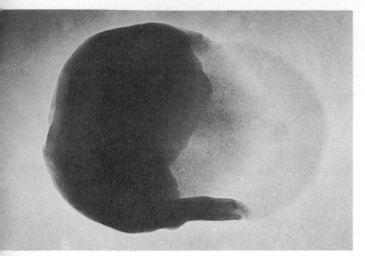 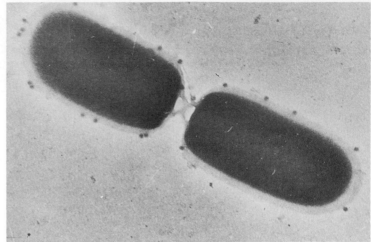

FIG. 24.2.   Left: electron micrograph of a germinating spore of the bacterium *Bacillus mycoides*. Note the bacterial cell emerging from the coat of the resting spore. Right: electron micrograph of the bacterium *Escherichia coli,* at the end of vegetative reproduction by cell division. The daughter cells are almost completely separated. Note incidentally the small dark particles adhering to the bacterial cell walls. These are bacteriophage viruses, about to infect the bacterial cells. (Society of American Bacteriologists; left: courtesy of G. Knaysi, R. F. Baker, and J. Hillier, *J. Bacteriol.,* vol. 53, 1947; right: courtesy of S. E. Luria, M. Delbruck, and T. F. Anderson, *J. Bacteriol.,* vol. 46, 1953.)

forming bacterial "spores." In this protected state, bacteria may stay dormant for years. Under favorable conditions, the enveloping capsules break open, and the emerging cells resume their vegetative multiplication (Fig. 24.2).

Sexual processes akin to conjugation are now known to take place among bacteria. Joined mating pairs may be isolated from cultures of certain bacteria, and genetic experiments show that sexual gene exchanges take place. But chromosomes have so far not been demonstrated in bacteria, and a spindle apparatus seems to be absent also. Hence the method and timing of meiosis, or its bacterial equivalent, are still unknown. Inasmuch as bacteria-like cells may have been the very first cells on earth, the occurrence of sex in modern bacteria suggests that sexuality may not be a late evolutionary invention but, on the contrary, may be as old as cellular life itself.

A few unicellular types occur among fungi, e.g., the yeasts. In these, reproductive patterns match those of bacteria. Algae include numerous unicellular forms, some growing singly, like diatoms; some in colonies, like *Spirogyra.* Here too the basic life cycle is a succession of vegetative generations. The life cycle of diatoms is particularly interesting.

As noted in Chap. 5, diatoms are unicellular plants making up much of the phytoplankton in the surface waters of the ocean. Each cell is surrounded by a delicate silica shell which consists of two halves, or *valves.* The rim of one valve fits snugly over the rim of the other valve, as a lid fits over a box (Fig. 24.3). After a cell division, each daughter cell inherits one of the valves, and the plant secretes a new second valve on its own. This newly formed valve always fits *into* the old valve and is therefore smaller. Consequently, in the course of numerous vegetative generations, diatoms become progres-

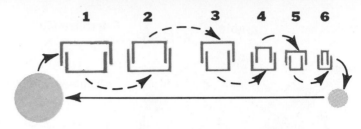

FIG. 24.3. Diagram of the life cycle of a diatom. Daughter cells form new valves on the inside of the old valves, and so the size of individuals in successive generations decreases. Eventually both valves are shed, and the cell grows back to species-characteristic size and secretes new valves.

sively smaller. However, a lower limit is reached eventually. When a certain minimum size is attained, the cell discards both its valves and grows rapidly until it is again as large as the maximum characteristic of the species. Then it secretes new valves around itself, and another succession of diminishing generations begins. Diatoms may form "resting spores," like bacteria.

Sexual processes among unicellular algae are conjugative, as in *Spirogyra*. The blue-green algae are an interesting exception: sex is so far entirely unknown for this group of unicellular types. Apparently, the ability of blue-green algae to form heavy-walled resting spores under unfavorable conditions suffices to counteract stress. Sexlessness is encountered occasionally also among animals. Amoebae, for example, appear to do without sex.

Meiosis

We may now make note of an important point: many algae, fungi, and probably also all bacteria typically are *haploid* organisms. For example, a cell of a *Spirogyra* filament is haploid. In these plants, the diploid condition is produced by fertilization, and the first developmental event *after* fertilization is meiosis. Hence the life cycle is diploid only at the zygote stage (Fig. 24.4).

This is probably very significant from an evolutionary standpoint. It suggests that the first plants, and perhaps even the first organisms of any kind, may have been haploid individuals. This primitive state may have been preserved in plants like *Spirogyra*. In other words, in ancient, ancestral organisms, meiosis may have occurred just *after* fertilization, at the *start* of a new sexual generation, as in *Spirogyra* today. Indeed it is reasonable that, in a primitive organism, a chromosome-doubling process like fertilization should occur *before* a chromosome-reducing process like meiosis. For fertilization is the stimulus to which meiosis is the response, and a stimulus ordinarily precedes a response.

But we know that, in many plants and in all animals, the adult formed after fertilization is diploid, not haploid. Such a condition could have arisen from the primitive pattern by a *postponement of meiosis*,

from its original time at the start of a sexual generation, to some later time in the life cycle. A *diploid* adult would then develop from a zygote. In animals, for example, meiosis is postponed as long as it *can* be postponed. It occurs at the time the diploid adult produces its own gametes, at the very *end* of a sexual generation (Fig. 24.5). In other words, meiosis in animals takes place just *before* fertilization, as if the response anticipated the stimulus. We shall see shortly that in many plants meiosis is postponed too,

FIG. 24.4. Chromosome numbers in the life cycle of *Spirogyra*. Meiosis occurs after fertilization, and the cells of adult colonies are haploid.

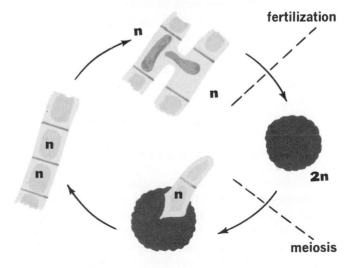

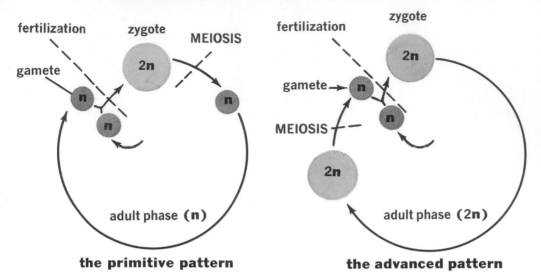

the primitive pattern   **the advanced pattern**

FIG. 24.5. The timing of meiosis in the life cycles of primitive plants and of animals. In the primitive pattern (see also *Spirogyra*, Fig. 24.4), meiosis occurs just after chromosome doubling by fertilization. In the animal pattern, meiosis is postponed to a point just before fertilization, which makes the adult diploid.

in a few cases to as late a time as in animals, in most cases to a point not quite as late.

It is probable, therefore, that at various stages during the evolution of different organisms, shifts in the timing of meiosis may have taken place, which tended to make the adults diploid rather than haploid. One general advantage of such shifts undoubtedly is an increase in the genetic stability of the species. For if every chromosome in a cell is represented twice rather than just once, then every gene is represented twice too. This increases the redundancy of the genetic information (see Chap. 17). Hence even if one gene of a pair changes in some way, e.g., by mutation, the other gene would still preserve the original message. Another advantage of the diploid state will become apparent below.

We note, however, that many modern algae, many fungi, and probably all bacteria still feature the presumably primitive condition of haploid adults.

MULTICELLULAR PATTERNS

In multicellular forms generally, cell division increases primarily the size of one individual, not the number of separate individuals. In these organisms, therefore, vegetative reproduction has a decreased importance as a method of multiplication, except in so far as it may become fortuitous regenerative reproduction. Sporulation and gametic reproduction, on the other hand, become the chief multiplicative devices.

Fungi

To illustrate the pattern of sporulation among multicellular fungi, we may examine events in the *bread molds* (Fig. 24.6). As their name indicates, these fungi subsist saprophytically on stale, decaying bread, or on other starchy plant products. The body of the fungus is a dense meshwork of whitish protoplasmic filaments, called the **mycelium,** which ramifies into the substance of bread. From these mycelial threads grow many white stalks, which project outward from the bread and appear to the unaided eye as hairy fuzz. On the upper end of each of these stalks develops a tiny round chamber, the **spore case.** The tissues of this case produce many hundreds of cells, and these accumulate within the case and mature into encapsulated **spores.** The case becomes black as the spores mature, and it eventually breaks open, allowing the ripe spores to escape. Wind or water then distributes the spores to other locations, and if the cells happen to fall on suitable raw material, they grow into new molds.

In other fungi, the functional details of sporulation are as above, even if structural details differ. For example, the familiar stalked umbrella of *mushrooms* is a spore-producing structure. It is composed

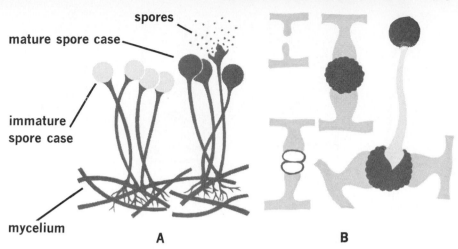

FIG. 24.6. Reproduction in bread molds. In the diagram, **A** illustrates sporulation. Note the horizontal threads of mycelium, stalks with ripening spore cases, and escape of spores from the cases. Sexuality is illustrated in **B**. Note the mycelial outgrowth on two neighboring hyphae, contact and fusion of sex cells, formation of encysted zygote, and development of zygote into stalk with spore case.

spores
mature spore case
immature spore case
mycelium

A

B

of many thousands of packed mycelial threads. On the underside of the umbrella are found vertical plates, arranged like the spokes of a wheel, which manufacture the spore cells. Mature spores break away and are dispersed passively (see also Chap. 30).

The most elaborate pattern of sporulative reproduction is encountered among the *rusts,* parasitic fungi which undergo complex life cycles involving several intermediate hosts. Within each such host, a different set of spores is produced. For example, the so-called *wheat rust fungus* manufactures, in succession, *summer spores* on wheat; *winter spores* on wheat; *early spring spores* on wheat stubble or in soil; *spring spores* on the leaves of barberry bushes, after a sexual process has occurred; and then again summer spores on wheat. Each type of spore here develops into a fungal growth which produces the next spore type in the series.

To illustrate the general pattern of gametic reproduction in multicellular fungi, we may again refer to bread molds (see Fig. 24.6). Under conditions of stress, two neighboring mycelial filaments may each develop a short side branch, one growing toward the other. The tip of each branch then matures as a sex cell. Sperm and egg cannot be distinguished, and we are evidently not dealing here with true sexes but with different *mating types.* The two gametes eventually make contact and fuse, and the resulting zygote secretes a heavy cyst wall around it-

self. Surviving adverse conditions, the cyst may subsequently break open, and the cell within may give rise to a new mycelium. We note that events here are rather similar to those in the conjugation of *Spirogyra.* And we note too that sporulation and gametic reproduction may both occur in the same fungal generation.

Algae

Among multicellular algae, sporulation and gametic reproduction may occur in the same generation too. In these predominantly aquatic plants, spores typically are flagellate, and they disperse the species through active locomotion. The filamentous green alga *Ulothrix,* which superficially resembles *Spirogyra,* illustrates the general sporulative pattern. In cells of *Ulothrix,* the cytoplasm may contract away from its cellulose housing and may divide a number of times within the housing. Each small cell so produced then matures into a flagellate spore. An opening subsequently forms in the cellulose wall, and the spores escape through it (Fig. 24.7a).

Sexual patterns in multicellular algae are highly varied, particularly with respect to the degree of distinction between males and females. No such distinction is evident in *Ulothrix,* for example. Given cells here divide within their cellulose walls, as in spore production. However, many more successive divisions occur, and many more, smaller cells are

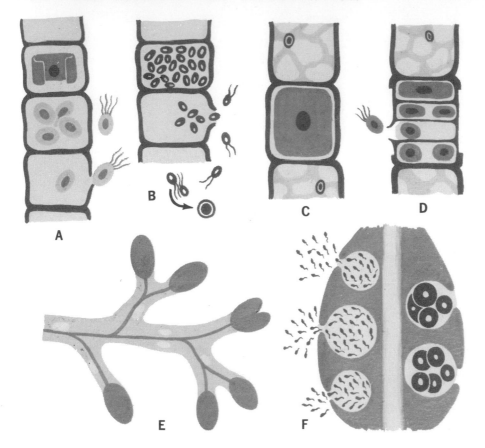

FIG. 24.7. Reproduction in a variety of algae. Diagrams: **A,** formation of flagellate spores in *Ulothrix* (top cell of diagram represents a nondividing cell). **B,** formation of flagellate gametes, and fertilization, in *Ulothrix* (note absence of sex differences among gametes). **C,** a cell of *Oedogonium* developed into an egg. **D,** a cell of *Oedogonium* divided up into a number of flagellate sperms. **E,** a piece of *Fucus,* a brown alga, with sexual reproductive structures at the tip. **F,** details of reproductive structures in *Fucus;* left half, sperm-producing organs; right half, egg-producing organs.

produced. These develop flagella, escape through an opening in the cellulose wall, and function as *gametes;* they must fuse pairwise (Fig. 24.7*b*).

Sexual definition is greater in algae such as *Oedogonium,* a green, filamentous plant structurally also rather like *Spirogyra.* In *Oedogonium,* a cell of one filament may enlarge and mature into a true, nonmotile egg. A cell of another filament may subdivide into a number of true, flagellate sperms. If such swimming sperms happen to encounter egg-bearing filaments, fertilization may occur (Fig. 24.7*c* and *d*). In *Oedogonium,* as also in *Ulothrix, Spirogyra,* and indeed in most filamentous algae, meiosis occurs just *after* fertilization, and adults are haploid.

But as already noted earlier, in many algal groups the time of meiosis has shifted to a later point in the life cycle, and so the adults are diploid. Such

is the case, for example, in *Fucus,* a common brown alga found attached to rocks on the seashore. These plants exhibit a very high degree of sexual definition. Sperms and eggs are clearly different structurally, and these gametes are produced in distinct, rather elaborate male and female reproductive organs (Fig. 24.7*e* and *f*). Meiosis in algae like *Fucus* occurs *before* fertilization, not after, the timing pattern corresponding exactly to that of animals. In some very advanced multicellular algae, a life cycle consisting of two alternating generations has developed, as in terrestrial plants. One generation is sexual and produces gametes. The adult generation then formed from the zygote is asexual and produces spores which develop into a new sexual generation (see below).

We may note in general that, among bacteria, fungi, and algae, we encounter practically all the basic variants of the reproductive repertoire of plants as a whole: the vegetative reproduction of unicellular forms, and the sporulation and gametic reproduction of multicellular forms; the motile spore of the aquatic form, and the encapsulated spore of the terrestrial form; the lack of sexual definition of the primitive form, and the true maleness or femaleness of the more advanced form; and the early meiosis and haploid condition of the primitive adult, and the late meiosis and diploid condition of the more advanced adult.

Primitive green algae, featuring early meiosis and haploid adults, appear to have been the ancestors of all green terrestrial plants, the bryophytes and the tracheophytes (see Chap. 30). During the evolution of these land plants, the ancestral reproductive patterns of the algae gave rise to new transitional patterns, which bridged the changeover from fully aquatic to fully terrestrial forms of reproduction. Modern bryophytes, and the ferns among tracheophytes, still bear witness to these reproductive transitions.

Transitional Patterns

ALTERNATION OF GENERATIONS

To a sessile land organism, a water-requiring sperm tends to be a liability. Spores can be encapsulated, but sperms cannot, for they must swim and their protoplasm must fuse with that of eggs. Yet the adaptive advantages of sex are required even more than in water, for the terrestrial environment undergoes far more drastic fluctuations. This outlines the basic dilemma the early land plant had to resolve. Land animals never faced a similar problem, for they all could move, and so either they could migrate to water and there accomplish external fertilization, or they could search out mates and achieve internal fertilization.

The general solution evolved by the first land plants consisted of three components. First, the plants stayed as close to water as they could; that is, they hugged the ground and lived in more or less perpetually moist regions. Second, they adapted the time of sperm release, and of fertilization, to the time of the rainy seasons, when films of water would cover the ground. And third, they shifted the time of meiosis to a later point in the life cycle, an adjustment which was moderately advantageous immediately but was to prove very highly advantageous in the subsequent history of land plants.

Like sex, meiosis is a cellular process. In a multicellular organism, therefore, meiosis must occur at a stage when the life cycle passes through a unicellular phase. As we have seen, meiosis actually does take place either just *after* fertilization, at the stage of the unicellular zygote, as in *Spirogyra*, or just *before* fertilization, at the stage of the unicellular gamete, as in *Fucus* and in animals. But a plant is unicellular on a third occasion, namely, at the stage of the spore. It is possible, therefore, to postpone meiosis from its primitive timing to either of *two* different later times: to the latest possible time, as in *Fucus* and animals, or to an intermediate time, when spores are produced (Fig. 24.8).

In the latter case, the individual developing from a diploid zygote will be diploid. At some time during its adult phase, that individual manufactures spores. Inasmuch as meiosis now occurs during spore manufacture, the spores will be haploid. Such spores develop into haploid individuals, and these, during *their* adult phase, produce haploid gametes. Fertilization occurs subsequently, and a diploid zygote is formed. This completes the life cycle. It is this kind of cycle which has evolved in some algae, in many terrestrial fungi, and, above all, in early terrestrial green plants and all their descendants.

In effect, the shifting of meiosis to the time of spore manufacture produces a life cycle consisting of *two* generations of individuals: a diploid, spore-producing, asexual individual, representing what is called the **sporophyte** generation; and a haploid, gamete-producing, sexual individual, representing the **gametophyte** generation (Fig. 24.9).

The immediate net advantage of such an **alternation of generations** is that the short diploid phase of the original, ancestral life cycle is prolonged considerably, into a genetically stable adult, which produces encapsulated land-adapted spores. At the same time, the originally long, water-dependent,

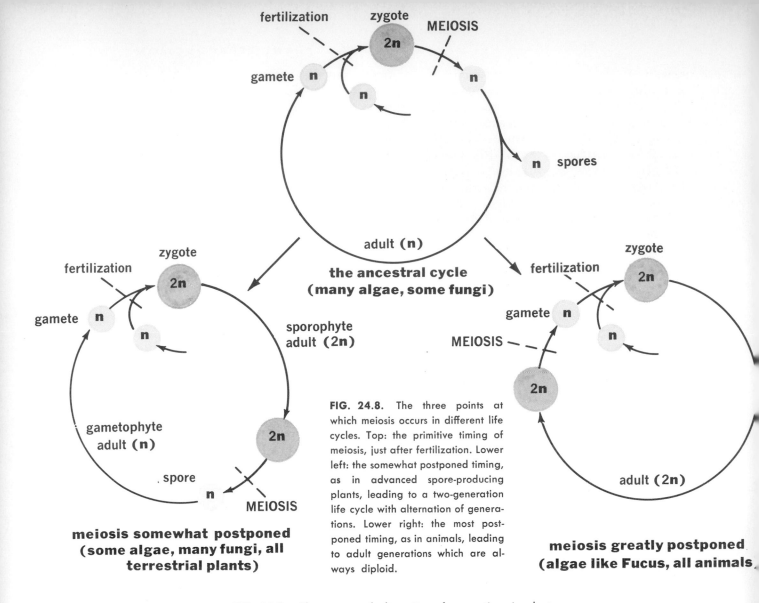

fertilization — zygote — MEIOSIS

2n

gamete — n

n

n

n — spores

adult (n)

**the ancestral cycle
(many algae, some fungi)**

zygote

fertilization

2n

gamete — n

n

sporophyte
adult (2n)

gametophyte
adult (n)

2n

spore

n

MEIOSIS

**meiosis somewhat postponed
(some algae, many fungi, all
terrestrial plants)**

zygote

fertilization

2n

gamete — n

n

MEIOSIS —

2n

adult (2n)

**meiosis greatly postponed
(algae like Fucus, all animals**

FIG. 24.8. The three points at which meiosis occurs in different life cycles. Top: the primitive timing of meiosis, just after fertilization. Lower left: the somewhat postponed timing, as in advanced spore-producing plants, leading to a two-generation life cycle with alternation of generations. Lower right: the most postponed timing, as in animals, leading to adult generations which are always diploid.

FIG. 24.9. The pattern of alternation of generations in plants.

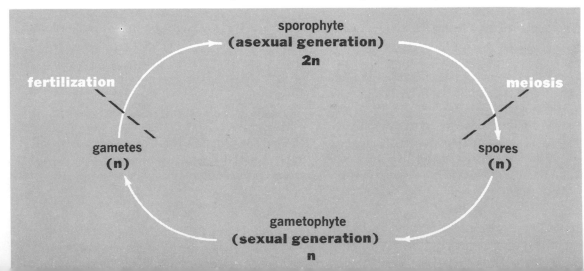

sporophyte
(asexual generation)
2n

fertilization

meiosis

gametes
(n)

spores
(n)

gametophyte
(sexual generation)
n

haploid phase is reduced correspondingly. Clearly, such a cycle is eminently suited for a sessile organism on land. We shall find, moreover, that it makes possible many additional adjustments which adapt the later land plants to terrestrial life even more fully.

However, the earliest terrestrial plants in many ways still lived like their aquatic, haploid ancestors, and their haploid gametophyte generation remained the dominant phase of their life cycle. This condition is preserved in their modern descendants, the *bryophytes*. We may illustrate the pattern by examining the life cycle of the most familiar bryophytes, the mosses.

MOSS REPRODUCTION

Mosses are low, ground-hugging plants which require shady, moist environments. The main body of a moss consists of fine threadlike strands of green cells, spread flat over the ground. Each strand rather resembles a filament of *Spirogyra*, and a tangled accumulation of such strands compares with the (nongreen) mycelium of a fungus. At certain seasons of the year, upright outgrowths develop on many points of the filamentous meshwork. These outgrowths, not higher than perhaps ¼ to ½ in., are studded with tiny leaflike blades of tissue set on a central stalk (Fig. 24.10a). Dense clusters of such outgrowths form the familiar green "carpets" of mosses. These structures bear tiny sex organs at the stalk tips (Fig. 24.10b). Some moss species are hermaphroditic, both male and female organs developing on the same stalk. In other species, given stalks produce either male or female sex organs, but not both. Swimming sperms and sessile eggs are produced in these organs.

Fertilization can occur only if rain provides a water path for the sperms. In the hermaphroditic mosses, a single drop of water usually suffices to bridge the space between the male and female structures, set closely together on the same stalk. In other species, the stalked outgrowths are generally placed so densely that continuous water films may form easily from one stalk tip to another, or that raindrops may splash sperms to nearby stalks. If the second stalk happens to be of different sex, sperms bridging the gap may effect successful fertilization (Fig. 24.10c).

We note that fertilization in mosses, as in other bryophytes, depends on the weather and on chance. Even a moderately dry climate prevents reproduction. And even if water is in ample supply, many sperms will never reach eggs; many eggs will never be fertilized. This pattern is probably uneconomical, but that it is workable is proved by the continued existence of mosses.

The parts of a moss discussed so far represent

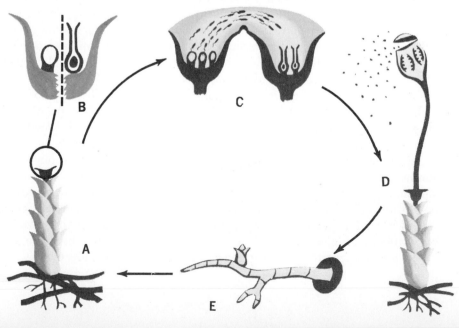

FIG. 24.10. The life cycle of a moss. **A,** moss shoot bearing sexual reproductive structures. **B,** detail of reproductive structures: left half, male sex organ; right half, female sex organ. **C,** fertilization; a drop of water forms a continuous pathway across two adjacent moss shoots. **D,** a stalk with spore case develops from the fertilized egg. **E,** a spore develops into a new moss filament.

FIG. 24.11. Reproduction in bryophytes. Left: gametophytes of liverwort with stalked female sex organs and (above) male sex organs. Eggs are produced in fingerlike processes, sperms in notched disks. Right: moss gametophytes bearing sporophytes on top. In sporophytes, note stalks and terminal spore cases. (Carolina Biological Supply Co.)

the gametophyte generation. The filamentous meshworks on the ground, the upright outgrowths, the sex organs, the gametes, all are haploid and constitute the sexual phase of the life cycle. The fertilized egg is diploid, however, and it represents the beginning of the asexual, diploid, sporophyte generation.

The zygote remains in the female sex organ and gives rise to many diploid cells. These become arranged into a thin straight stalk projecting upward for a distance of about ½ to 1 in. (Fig. 24.11). Although many cells in this stalk possess chlorophyll, the whole structure is nevertheless parasitic on the green part of the moss below. It not only withdraws needed water and inorganic materials but depends also on extra carbohydrates, since its own photosynthetic capacity is apparently inadequate. At the end of each stalk develops a chamber, a spore case, in which spore cells are manufactured (Fig. 24.10d). As the spores mature, meiosis occurs. Ripened spores consequently are haploid, and this terminates the diploid phase of the moss life cycle. The spore case eventually breaks open, mature spores escape, and from them develop new, haploid, green moss filaments, the beginnings of a new sexual generation (Fig. 24.10e). The general pattern of the whole cycle is outlined in Fig. 24.12.

We note that, in mosses, the green gametophyte represents the dominant, "main" part of the life cycle; the sporophyte is parasitic, is dependent on the gametophyte, and is produced only at certain times of the year. Yet it is clear that the gametophyte, with its water-requiring gamete, is not so well adapted to terrestrial life as the sporophyte, with its encapsulated, "dry" spore. A plant in which the sporophyte generation would be the main phase of the life cycle should be able to exist on land far more efficiently.

Such a shift of emphasis has actually occurred during the evolution of some terrestrial plants. As a first step in this direction, sporophytes have become independent of gametophytes. In certain species of bryophytes, for example, the sporophytes are still attached to the tops of the gametophytes, but they develop sufficient chlorophyll to supply most or all of their own food. Hence they are no longer parasitic. And in primitive tracheophytes, believed to have evolved directly from aquatic algae, the sporophyte is completely independent. In ferns, for example, the sporophyte is not perched atop the gametophyte, but the two are separate plants, each in direct contact with soil. Moreover, the fern sporophyte is large and conspicuous, and it persists much longer than the gametophyte. In short, the sporophyte here has actually become the main phase of the life cycle.

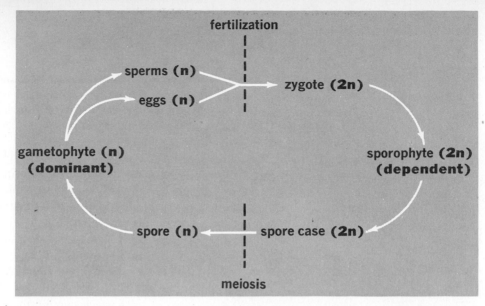

FIG. 24.12. The overall pattern of reproduction in mosses.

fertilization

sperms **(n)**

eggs **(n)**

zygote **(2n)**

gametophyte **(n)** **(dominant)**

sporophyte **(2n)** **(dependent)**

spore **(n)**

spore case **(2n)**

meiosis

FERN REPRODUCTION

The familiar plant customarily regarded as a "fern" represents the diploid, asexual, sporophyte generation. It is large, leafy, green; it persists through the winter; and, in earlier times, ferns formed huge trees and forests (see Chap. 30).

Spore-forming structures develop at certain seasons of the year on the undersides of fern leaves; regular rows of brown spots appear on the leaves. Microscopic examination demonstrates that each spot is a shield of tissue raised from the undersurface of a leaf by a stalk (Fig. 24.13a). Projecting sideways from this stalk, and covered over by the brown shield, are many smaller stalks, each bearing a hollow capsule at its tip. These capsules are spore cases. Many spores are manufactured in them, and as the spores mature, meiosis takes place; ripened fern spores, like ripened moss spores, are haploid. They represent the termination of the asexual generation and the beginning of the sexual generation.

Spore cases eventually rupture, and the spores escape. The wall of a spore case has elastic properties. As it ruptures, the parts of the torn wall may oscillate back and forth like a released watch spring. Spores held loosely along the inner surface of the walls are thereby shaken off and are catapulted out into the air (Fig. 24.13b). Even on a windless day, therefore, spores may be propelled some distance

FIG. 24.13. **A,** a section through a fern leaf bearing a brown shield on the underside. Stalks bearing spore cases project sideways, covered over by the brown shield. **B,** the recoil mechanism of spore release from spore cases in ferns.

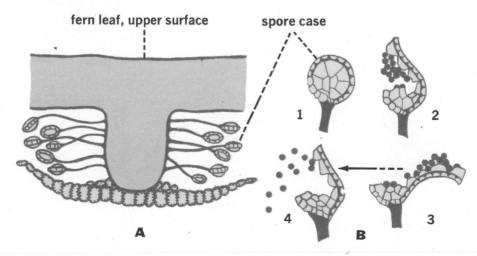

fern leaf, upper surface

spore case

1

2

4

3

A

B

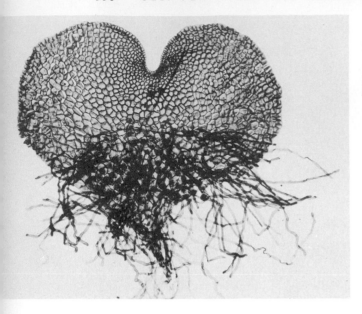

FIG. 24.14. The gametophyte of a fern. Note the rootlike processes which project into soil from the flat, heart-shaped body of the gametophyte. (Ward's Natural Science Establishment, Inc.)

away from the parent plant. A given sporophyte fern may produce new spores every year.

Spores develop into haploid gametophytes. Though everyone has seen ferns, i.e., sporophytes, few nonbiologists would be able to identify fern gametophytes. They are green plantlets consisting principally of tiny heart-shaped plates of tissue, flat on the ground, and measuring not more than about ¼ in. across (Fig. 24.14). A number of cellular fila-

ments, projecting from the underside of such a little tissue plate into the soil, serve an absorptive function. This inconspicuous gametophyte, so unlike its large sporophytic partner, requires a moist, shady environment. In size, way of life, and function, the fern gametophyte is, in fact, wholly comparable to the moss gametophyte.

Sex organs develop on the gametophyte (Fig. 24.15). As in mosses, the gametophytes of some fern species are hermaphroditic. Male sex organs are usually located near the tip of the heart-shaped plant, female sex organs near the notch. In other species, male and female organs are formed in separate individuals. The haploid sex organs manufacture haploid eggs and haploid, ciliated sperms. The pattern of fertilization is the same as in mosses; that is, rain is required to provide a water path for the sperms.

The diploid fertilized egg initiates a new sporophyte generation. Retained within the female sex organ, as in mosses, the zygote divides, and the resulting cells form a small sporophyte embryo. A tiny stem grows out from the female sex organ and curves into the soil, and a tiny embryonic leaf similarly shoots up (see Fig. 24.15). At this stage, the embryo does not possess chlorophyll but depends on food supplied by the gametophyte, to which it is still attached. All this is clearly reminiscent of mosses. Soon the embryonic fern leaf matures and greens,

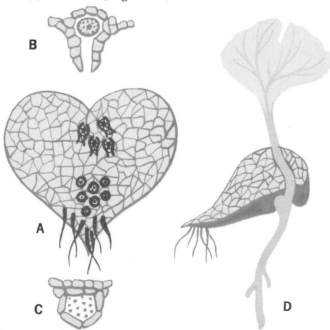

FIG. 24.15. **A,** diagram of fern gametophyte showing location of sex organs. **B,** female sex organ with egg. **C,** male sex organ with sperms. **D,** section through a gametophyte with young attached sporophyte.

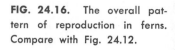

FIG. 24.16. The overall pattern of reproduction in ferns. Compare with Fig. 24.12.

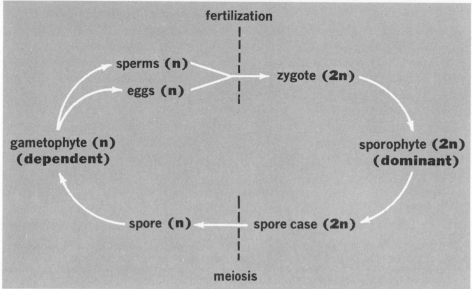

and thereafter the embryo is on its own. Indeed, the gametophyte presently degenerates and dies off, leaving the young sporophyte as a separate, independent plant. The life-cycle pattern as a whole is outlined in Fig. 24.16.

We note that mosses and ferns do not differ too greatly in their gametophytes. But whereas the moss sporophyte is a small, dependent, temporary structure, the fern sporophyte is a large, independent, permanent plant. Because of this, the reproduction of ancestral ferns, and of ancestral tracheophytes in general, was more nearly in line with the realities of the land environment. As we shall see in Chap. 30, fernlike ancestral tracheophytes gave rise to the modern ferns and to the seed plants. In all these too, emphasis is on the sporophyte.

Yet ancestral tracheophytes continued to be hampered by a fundamental difficulty. No matter how small and how temporary a structure their gametophyte may have been, a water-requiring, free-swimming sperm still represented a weak link in their reproductive cycle. This difficulty persists in modern ferns, as we have found. But some descendants of ancient tracheophytes evolved an innovation, which paved the way for a later solution of the water problem in reproduction. We have noted that,

in ferns today, spores develop into gametophytes which carry either male, or female, or both types of sex organs. The plants here are said to be **isosporous**; that is, the spores are indistinguishable, and one cannot tell ahead of time whether a given spore will become a "male" gametophyte, a "female" gametophyte, or a hermaphrodite. A different pattern has developed in certain other plant groups descended from ancestral tracheophytes. In these, the sporophytes manufacture *two kinds of spores*, one larger than the other. Larger **megaspores** consistently give rise to *female* gametophytes; smaller ones, called **microspores**, consistently to *male* gametophytes (Fig. 24.17).

This phenomenon of two kinds of spores is known as **heterospory.** It is encountered today in a few advanced fern groups and in all seed plants. How has heterospory aided in solving the problem of the water-requiring sperm?

Terrestrial Patterns

The spore, well suited to dry land, produces the gametophyte, ill suited to dry land. Would it not resolve a good part of the difficulty if the gametophyte

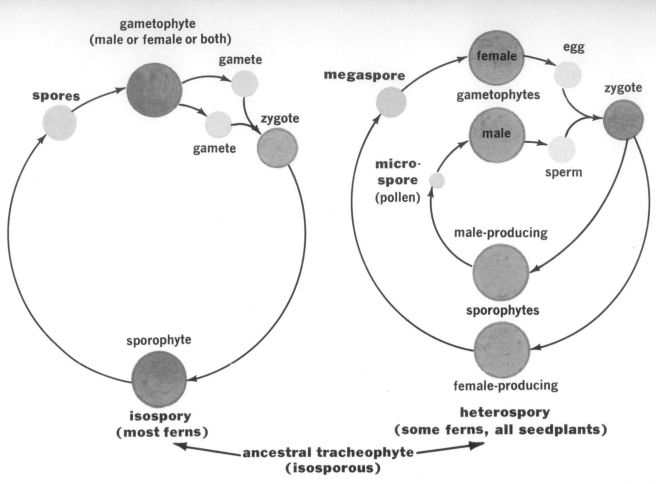

FIG. 24.17. The isosporous and heterosporous life-cycle patterns of tracheophytes. In heterospory, distinct male and female cycles exist which are merged only at fertilization.

were made so small that it would never have to leave the protective capsule of the spore from which it develops? Could not the dominant sporophytes bear parasitic gametophytes, just as the reverse takes place in mosses?

This has actually become the pattern in seed plants. *First,* sporophytes manufacture two kinds of spores, as just noted above. The smaller male-producing microspores are familiar to everyone under the name of **pollen.**

Second, a given spore cell, within its spore capsule, develops into a very small gametophyte consisting of just a few cells. And this gametophyte is *retained within the spore capsule.* Sex organs are dispensed with. Certain cells of the male gametophyte, still within the pollen capsule, develop directly into sperms. Analogously, some cells of the fe-

male gametophyte, still within its spore capsule, develop directly into eggs.

Third, instead of swimming sperms traveling through water to eggs, pollen capsules, containing male gametophytes and sperms, travel through air, wind- or animal-borne, to spore capsules containing female gametophytes and eggs. This process is called **pollination,** and it finally circumvents the need for external water.

Fourth, after a pollen grain makes contact with a megaspore, the sperm digests a path through the capsule of the megaspore, and sperm and egg meet in a moist, protoplasmic environment.

Fifth, after fertilization is thus accomplished, the capsule of the megaspore hardens and, still retaining the zygote and the remnants of the female gametophyte within it, it is then known as a **seed.**

Such a seed later develops into a new sporophyte, which in turn manufactures a new generation of spores.

The basic pattern as a whole is outlined in Fig. 24.18. It is illustrated specifically among conifers, the primitive members of the seed plants.

CONIFEROUS PLANTS

A pine tree, for example, represents the dominant, diploid sporophyte. Its spore-producing structures are the pine **cones.** Two types of cones exist. A small variety, not longer than perhaps 1 in., has fairly tightly shingled cone leaves. These are the microspore-producing cones. The second type of cone is larger, roughly 3 in. long, and its cone leaves are rather widely spaced. Such cones produce megaspores. In many species of conifers, a given tree bears either one type of cone only or the other type only. In other species, both types may be formed on the same tree.

In microspore-producing cones, the underside of each cone leaf carries a spore sac. Numerous small encapsulated spore cells, or pollen grains, are manufactured in it (Figs. 24.19 and 24.20). As they mature, meiosis occurs. A mature haploid microspore then divides a number of times within its capsule, and the resulting cells, numbering less than 100, constitute the whole male haploid gametophyte. One of the cells matures into a sperm—nonciliated for the first time in the history of land plants. As the cones ripen they dry out and become brittle, cone leaves separate a bit, spore sacs rupture, and pollen grains, containing male gametophytes and sperms, escape. The pollen grains are equipped with a pair of tiny wing blades, and as wind disperses them, some of them settle by chance in megaspore-producing cones.

In the latter, it is the upper side of each cone leaf which bears the spore sac. Just two fairly large spores are produced in each sac. Each such megaspore acquires a thick spore capsule, soft and green

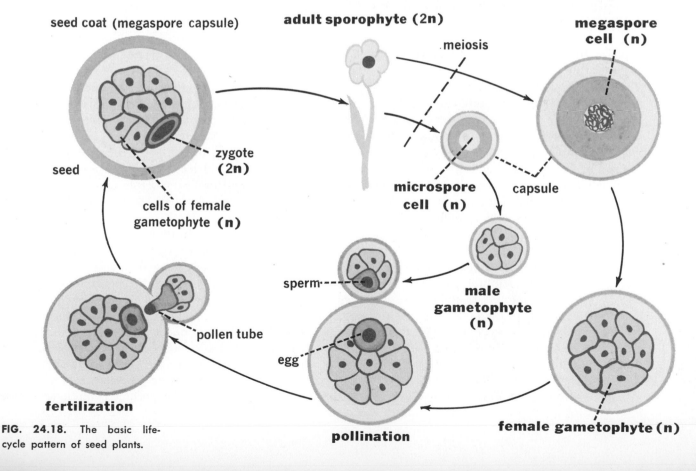

FIG. 24.18. The basic life-cycle pattern of seed plants.

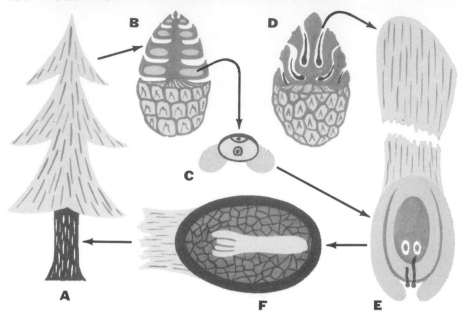

FIG. 24.19. Diagrammatic representation of the life cycle of a pine. The adult sporophyte pine tree **A** produces either male cones **B** or female cones **D**. In the spore sacs of these cones are formed microspores or pollen grains **C**, and megaspores **E**. A megaspore within its capsule develops into a small female gametophyte, which in turn produces eggs **E**. Pollination occurs, and fertilization is brought about by means of a pollen tube **E**. The remains of the megaspore then form a seed, in which the zygote develops into a sporophyte embryo **F**.

for the time being. Attached to it on one side is a long membranous wing blade. Within the capsule, the spore cell undergoes meiosis, and the resulting haploid spore then divides several times. The cells so formed represent the whole female haploid gametophyte. In some species one cell, and in others more cells of this gametophyte, mature into eggs (see Figs. 24.19 and 24.20). Ripened spore sacs rupture, exposing the capsule of the female spore.

Pollen grains approaching such a cone may fall on the outer edge of a cone leaf. Since these leaves slant, pollen is likely to slide down into the angle formed by the cone leaf and the central cone stalk, to which the leaves are attached. At this angle lie the exposed capsules of the megaspores. When pollen grains reach this region, **pollination** is accomplished.

Now the pollen capsule ruptures. The male gametophyte within elongates into a **pollen tube,** growing out through the rupture (see Figs. 24.19 and 24.20). The sperm nucleus of the gametophyte lies in the advancing tip of the pollen tube. Before long, the tip of the tube makes contact with the soft capsule of the megaspore and digests a path through it. Once inside, the pollen tube grows toward the egg, and the sperm nucleus in the tip of the tube eventually fuses with the egg. This is *fertilization*. The dip-

loid zygote so formed represents the beginning of a new sporophyte generation.

The remnants of the pollen grain and the pollen tube now degenerate, and the megaspore capsule hardens into a tough envelope. Within this envelope is found the tissue of the female gametophyte, plus a fertilized egg, which at once begins to develop into a little sporophyte embryo. The hardened megaspore capsule, together with its wing blade and its interior content, represents the **seed.** Ripe seeds loosen from the cone leaves to which they had been attached, wind pressure bears on the wing blades, and seeds are dispersed. In favorable localities, and under favorable climatic conditions, seeds germinate, and new sporophyte pine trees develop from them.

We note that, from moss to pine, reproductive emphasis has shifted completely. Not only is the gametophyte wholly dependent and parasitic, but it has become a highly reduced structure. The entire sexual, haploid phase of the life cycle has contracted in space, into the spore capsule, and in time, into a few short weeks at one season of the year, usually spring or fall. Early seed plants, and their coniferous descendants today, are the first to have completely shaken off the hampering inheritance of water-requiring sperms. This important evolutionary gain

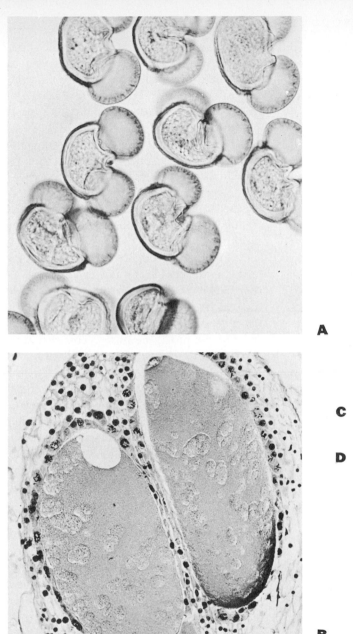

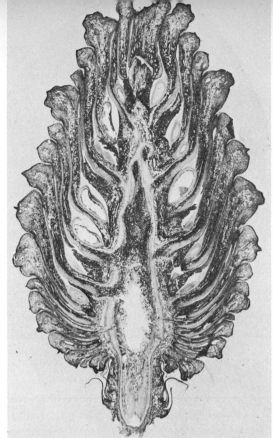

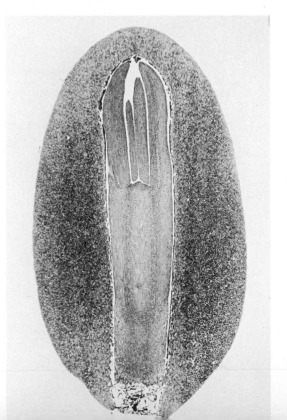

A

C

D

B

FIG. 24.20. Reproduction in the pine. **A,** high-power view of pollen grains. Note the wing blades, and the microspore cell in each grain. **B,** section through a megaspore-producing cone. Note the spore sacs between the cone leaves (actually on the upper surface of the leaves). **C,** high-power view of a portion of a female gametophyte, showing two eggs. Pollen tubes will reach the eggs through the thin gametophyte tissue just above the eggs in photo. **D,** longitudinal section through a seed, showing the central embryo and the surrounding tissue of the seed coat. (Photo of pollen, Ward's Natural Science Establishment, Inc.; others, General Biological Supply House, Inc.)

has been passed on unchanged to the later seed plants, the *flowering plants*. These have evolved various additional innovations, and through them they have become the most efficient land-reproducing plants of all.

FLOWERING PLANTS

The diagram outlining the life cycle of seed plants (Fig. 24.18) applies with full validity both to coniferous plants and to flowering plants. But the structures representing each phase are different in the two groups. In one group, the spore-producing organs are cones; in the other, they are **flowers.**

Some flowers are **composite;** that is, many individual flower units are carried collectively on a single plant as a large bloom (e.g., sunflower, dandelions, chrysanthemums, clover). Others are **simple** flowers; that is, each bloom here represents a single flower unit (e.g., tulips, lilies, buttercups). Not all flowering plants develop brightly colored blooms—consider, for example, the silks and tassels of corn. However, where colors and scents have evolved, they play an important role in pollination, by attracting pollen-dispersing animals.

FIG. 24.21.   Diagram of a simple flower.

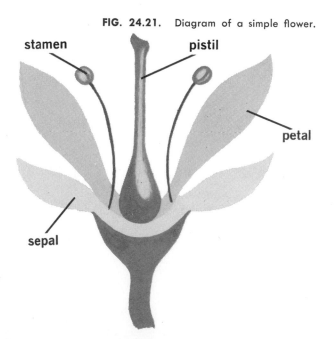

stamen

pistil

petal

sepal

A simple flower unit typically consists, from the outside in, of a whorl of green **sepal** leaves, a whorl of usually pigmented *petal* leaves, a whorl of **stamens,** and a central **pistil** (Fig. 24.21). A stamen is made up of a stalk carrying a double spore sac, the **anther,** at its tip. In such a sac (Fig. 24.22), pollen grains are manufactured. Meiosis occurs during the maturation of a microspore, and the ripe spore, within its capsule, gives rise to just *three* cells. These three represent the entire male gametophyte. Two of the three cells develop into sperms. A cleft eventually forms in each spore sac, through which pollen grains may escape.

Female reproductive parts are located in the pistil, in the center of a flower (Fig. 24.23). The upper part of the pistil, the **stigma,** is a sticky surface on which pollen grains will eventually settle. A stalk, or **style,** connects the stigma with the bulbous lower part of the pistil, the **ovary.** This structure is a new evolutionary development, without equivalent in conifers. In essence, the ovary is a thick-walled chamber which may be partitioned off into a number of sections. Each section holds a megaspore-producing sac. One or a few large encapsulated megaspores form in each sac. Meiosis occurs as a spore matures, and a megaspore eventually gives rise to just *eight* haploid cells. These eight constitute the entire female gametophyte. Typically, one of the eight cells matures as an egg (Figs. 24.23 and 24.24).

Most flowers are hermaphroditic and contain both stamens and pistil. In many groups of flowering plants, **self-pollination** is the rule. Pollen grains here simply fall on the stigma of the same flower. In other types, however, only **cross-pollination** leads to successful reproduction. In such flowers, many pollen grains undoubtedly do chance on the stigma of the same bloom. But such pollen grains may not begin to develop at all or may develop abnormally. Events proceed normally only when pollen grains from one flower are transferred to the stigmas of other flowers of the same species.

As might be expected, plants depending on wind for pollen dispersal manufacture huge numbers of pollen grains. Also, their flowers are relatively inconspicuous. By contrast, large, brightly colored, showy blooms form in plants which depend on animals for pollination. Such plants also manufacture abundant nectar, i.e., sugar water, as inducement. Many ingenious structural devices have evolved whereby only particular animal types have access to the nectar of a particular flower type. Potential "robbers" either cannot enter the flower or cannot reach the nectar stores. On the other hand, qualified animals such as bees may find landing platforms, colored guide marks on petals, and other conveniences. And as these animals reach for nectar, deep down in the flower, they brush against stamens and pistil. In the process they pick up new pollen on their body surfaces, or they deposit pollen from other flowers visited earlier. Aside from bees, animals which may carry out pollinating activity include certain wasps, butterflies, moths, in some cases small birds, and also men.

What happens after pollen grains have settled on a stigma, either through self- or through cross-pollination? One event is the rupturing of the pollen capsule and the emergence of a pollen tube, as in pines. The two sperm nuclei are again near the advancing tip of the tube. If several pollen grains have settled on a single stigma, several pollen tubes then grow. These digest a path through the stigma, through the style of the pistil, and into the ovary (see Fig. 24.23). If more than one pollen tube is

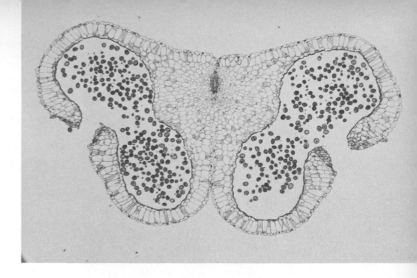

FIG. 24.22. Cross section through an anther of the lily. Note the two spore sacs, the openings in these sacs, and the microspores (pollen grains). (Ward's Natural Science Establishment, Inc.)

FIG. 24.23. Diagram: A, longitudinal section through a pistil. B, the female gametophyte, with egg, and the advancing pollen tube carrying two sperm nuclei at the tip; C, section through a seed. Photo: cross section through the ovary of a lily. Note the ovary wall (which will eventually give rise to the "meat" of a fruit) and the three pairs of spore capsules containing female gametophytes. (Photo, Ward's Natural Science Establishment, Inc.)

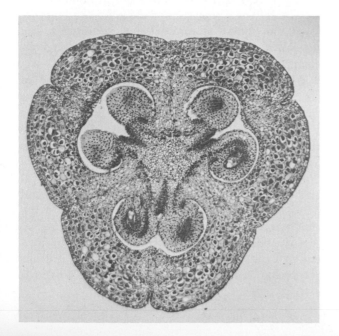

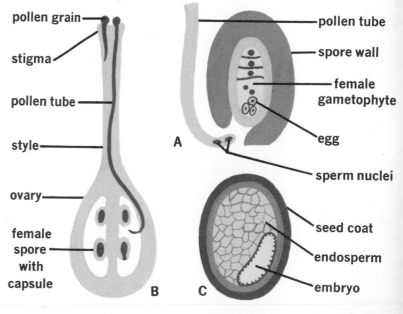

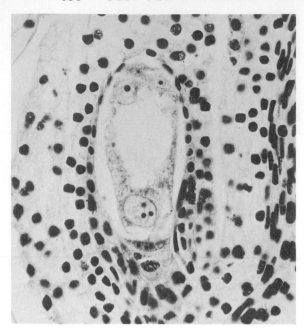

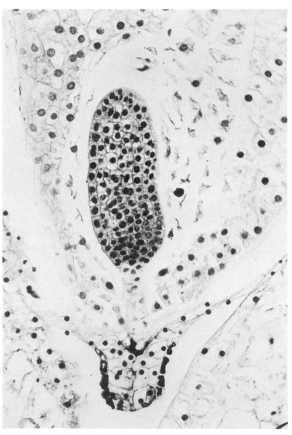

FIG. 24.24.   Top: section through a mature female gametophyte of the lily, surrounded by the tissue of the spore capsule. Eight cells are present in the gametophyte, the egg is mature, and fertilization may now occur. Bottom: fertilization has taken place, and the zygote has developed into the young embryo shown here. (General Biological Supply House, Inc.)

present, only one eventually penetrates through to each female gametophyte in the ovary.

The tip of a pollen tube, carrying two sperm nuclei, thus reaches the eight cells representing the female gametophyte. One of the sperm nuclei fuses with the egg, and the resulting zygote becomes the beginning of a new sporophyte embryo. The second sperm nucleus contributes to another evolutionary innovation. It fuses with *two* of the seven remaining female gametophyte cells. Since the sperm nucleus is haploid, and since each of the female gametophyte cells is also haploid, the fusion product of one sperm and two female gametophyte cells is a **triploid** cell; that is, it possesses *three* sets of chromosomes. This triploid cell divides repeatedly and produces the **endosperm** tissue. This tissue soon fills all available space within the megaspore capsule and surrounds the sporophyte embryo more or less completely (see Fig. 24.23). Endosperm tissue serves very largely as a reserve food store for the embryo. Until the young sporophyte has acquired a first green leaf, the endosperm provides it with nourishment.

While embryo and endosperm develop within the megaspore capsule, the capsule itself hardens and becomes the coat of a seed. At the same time also, indeed as soon as fertilization has occurred, the ovary wall begins to enlarge and develops into a **fruit.** Many fruits are **fleshy,** like apples. Here the expanded tissue of the ovary wall forms much or all of the "meat" of a fruit (Fig. 24.25). In other fruit types, e.g., nuts, the ovary wall develops into a **dry,** nonfleshy envelope surrounding the seeds.

We note that the reproductive pattern of flowering plants is characterized by three new features not encountered in coniferous plants: the flower itself; the inclusion of endosperm tissue within seeds; and the fruit, which contains a number of seeds. Each of these features is of pronounced adaptive value. The flower promotes pollination, the endosperm nourishes the embryo, and the fruit promotes seed dispersal. Fleshy fruits may be eaten by animals, and seeds may be spit out or may be expelled undigested with the feces, in new locations. Dry fruits like nuts may be carried about by squirrels, for example, and may be left by them in some forgotten hiding place. Fruits with burrs, hooks, or wing blades are distributed widely by animals and wind. And fruits which simply fall to the ground eventually decay, and this aids seed development by enriching a patch of soil.

Seed plants evidently have found a solution to the problem of terrestrial reproduction, which rather parallels the solution found by terrestrial animals. Most such animals circumvent the need for external water by internal fertilization: a diploid male animal deposits haploid sperms directly into a diploid female animal, which contains haploid eggs. In seed plants, the depositing is done by wind or animals, to be sure, but internal fertilization in a sense takes place here too. As we have seen, a diploid sporophyte produces haploid microspores and, through them, haploid sperms. Another diploid sporophyte produces haploid megaspores and, through them, haploid eggs. The sperms then reach the eggs by means of pollen tubes, which are the plant equivalent of internal fertilization in animals.

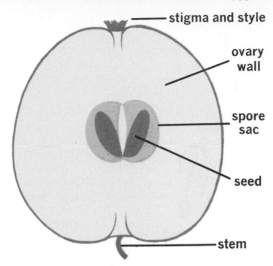

FIG. 24.25.   Diagram of a section through a fleshy fruit.

The terrestrial plant has evolved from the aquatic plant, and the terrestrial plant cannot move. That is the key to the evolution of plant reproduction. Analogously, terrestrial animals are descended from aquatic animals, but terrestrial animals are able to move. How do *they* reproduce? We know already that in moving animals the equivalents of spores and of asexual generations disappear. And we also know that the animal life cycle consists of the sequence diploid adult → haploid gametes → diploid zygote → diploid adult. How is this sequence executed?

REVIEW QUESTIONS   1. Review the basic life-cycle patterns of bacteria, algae, and fungi, with attention to differences between unicellular and multicellular forms. Describe the life cycle of diatoms.

2. Describe the processes of sporulation and gametic reproduction in (*a*) bread molds and (*b*) *Ulothrix*. Describe the process of gametic reproduction in (*a*) *Spirogyra*, (*b*) *Oedogonium*, and (*c*) *Fucus*. How does the degree of sexual definition differ in these three algal types?

3. At what points in the life cycles of different plants does meiosis occur? Which of these timing patterns is probably primitive, and in which plants is it encountered? Describe the life-cycle patterns of such plants, with attention to *n* and 2*n* phases.

4. How may other timing patterns of meiosis have evolved from the primitive

pattern, and in which plants are they encountered? Describe these patterns. What is the timing pattern of meiosis in animals?

5. Describe the basic life cycle involving alternation of generations. How may such a cycle have evolved? What are its adaptive advantages? How has availability or nonavailability of water affected the reproductive evolution of plants?

6. Describe the detailed life cycle of a bryophyte. In what respects is it poorly suited to terrestrial life?

7. Describe the detailed life cycle of a fern. Compare with the life cycle of bryophytes; what is similar and what is different? What are the adaptive advantages of a prolonged $2n$ phase?

8. Distinguish between isospory and heterospory. In which plant groups is the latter encountered? Describe the basic life cycle of seed plants. In what ways is this pattern particularly advantageous for terrestrial life? Distinguish carefully between pollination and fertilization.

9. Describe the detailed life cycle of coniferous plants. Define seed, pollen tube, self- and cross-pollination.

10. Describe the structure and adaptive significance of a flower. Define ovary, endosperm, fruit. Describe the detailed life cycle of flowering plants.

SUGGESTED COLLATERAL READINGS

Any of the texts below include accounts of plant reproduction and may be consulted for additional information. The source cited last is a popular article.

Sinnott, E. W., and K. S. Wilson: "Botany," McGraw-Hill, 1955.

Gibbs, R. D.: "Botany, an Evolutionary Approach," McGraw-Hill–Blakiston, 1950.

Weatherwax, P.: "Plant Biology," 2d ed., Saunders, 1947.

Smith, G. M., E. M. Gilbert, G. S. Bryan, R. I. Evans, and J. F. Stauffer: "A Textbook of General Botany," 5th ed., Macmillan, 1953.

Pool, R. J.: "Flowers and Flowering Plants," McGraw-Hill, 1941.

Grant, V.: The Fertilization of Flowers, *Sci. American,* vol. 184, 1951.

25

ANIMAL REPRODUCTION

As indicated in chap. 22, vegetative reproduction is standard among protozoa and is common also in many other animal groups, usually in the variant form of regenerative reproduction. Among multicellular animals, many sessile types may reproduce via sporelike, directly developing bud cells. However, gametic reproduction is the basic method, and in moving animals it is generally the only method.

The vertebrate pattern is of particular interest, for here reproduction is under the control of hormones. To illustrate these and other major features of animal reproduction, we concentrate in this chapter mainly on mammalian reproduction, and in particular on human reproduction. We first examine the structure of the **reproductive system** of males and females, and the processes by which this system manufactures gametes. We then discuss the events of **pregnancy,** in so far as these affect the female adult. Correlated events of embryonic development are left for the next chapter.

The Reproductive System

Most animals are **oviparous;** that is, they shed their eggs to the outside. Fertilization occurs either before or after the eggs are released from the female, and the young develop and hatch on their own, without nutritional support from the parents. Among vertebrates, many fish are oviparous and externally fertilizing, and all birds are oviparous but internally fertilizing.

Some animals are **ovoviviparous.** Eggs here are retained within the female reproductive system, and fertilization is internal. Development occurs within the female body, but the female does not nourish the young. Instead, as in oviparous types, they grow on food (yolk) included within the egg. However, the young are *born* rather than *hatched;* that is, the female releases fully formed animals, not eggs. Among

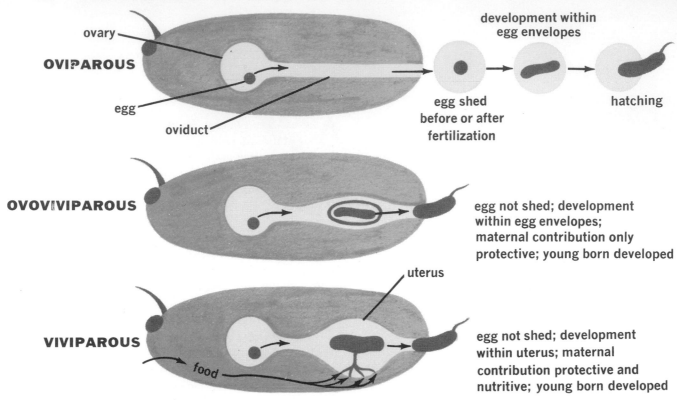

ovary

OVIPAROUS

egg

oviduct

development within
egg envelopes

egg shed
before or after
fertilization

hatching

OVOVIVIPAROUS

egg not shed; development
within egg envelopes;
maternal contribution only
protective; young born developed

uterus

VIVIPAROUS

food

egg not shed; development
within uterus; maternal
contribution protective and
nutritive; young born developed

FIG. 25.1.   The patterns of oviparity, ovoviviparity, and viviparity.

vertebrates, fish, amphibia, and reptiles include many ovoviviparous types.

Finally, some animals are **viviparous.** In these, eggs are again retained within the female, fertilization is internal, and the young are born as developed animals. But the development of the young within the female here *does* depend on maternal nutrition. Among vertebrates, the principal viviparous types are mammals (Fig. 25.1).

In all animals, vertebrate or nonvertebrate, the basic structural plan of the reproductive system is comparatively simple. The main components are a pair of gamete-producing organs, the **testes** in males, the **ovaries** in females, collectively known as **gonads.** These organs are each joined to a duct system. The ducts carry the gametes to the outside, and, in the females of ovoviviparous and viviparous forms, they house the developing young. In view of the essential similarity of the structural pattern, the reproductive system of man serves adequately as an illustrative example.

THE MALE SYSTEM

In human males, the testes are located in a **scrotum,** a skin sac between the legs. Each testis is honeycombed extensively with **testicular tubules,** groups of which are separated from one another by partitions of connective tissue (Fig. 25.2). In the partitions are found specialized endocrine cells. These manufacture and secrete **androgens,** the male sex hormones.

We recall that these hormones, *testosterone* in particular, maintain primary and secondary sex characteristics and that their manufacture in the testes is in turn under the control of pituitary gonadotropic hormones (see Chap. 19). Two such hormones are secreted by the pituitary: **FSH** and **LH.**

The function of FSH in males is still obscure, but pituitary LH is the hormone which stimulates the testes to produce androgens. If the androgen concentration in blood becomes too high, the sex hormones *inhibit* the pituitary from producing more LH. Androgen secretion then declines. Conversely, if androgen concentrations are too low, the pituitary will not be inhibited, LH will therefore be produced in greater amount, and this increases the rate of androgen production. Through this control, the androgen concentration in males is maintained automatically at a fairly steady level (Fig. 25.3).

The sperm-producing tissue of the testes is located in the testicular tubules (Fig. 25.4). The cells lining these tubules divide mitotically at a great rate. New cells so formed accumulate in the interior of the tubules, and there they mature into sperms.

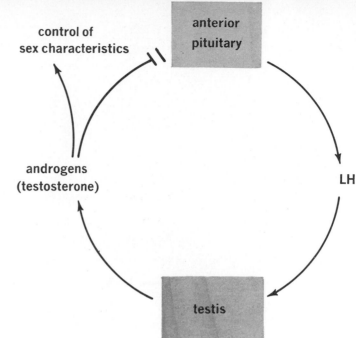

FIG. 25.3. The control of androgen secretion. LH is one of the gonadotropic hormones of the pituitary (compare Figs. 19.7 and 19.8). Arrow tipped with transverse double bar denotes inhibition.

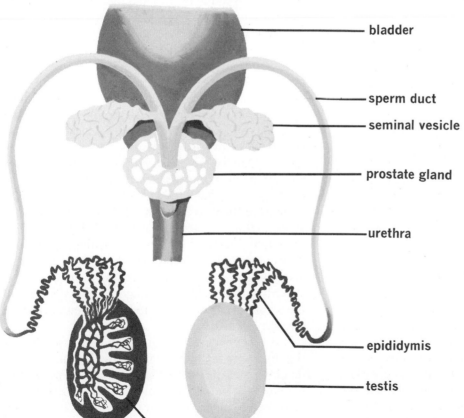

FIG. 25.2. The male reproductive system, diagrammatic. Testis on left shown in section.

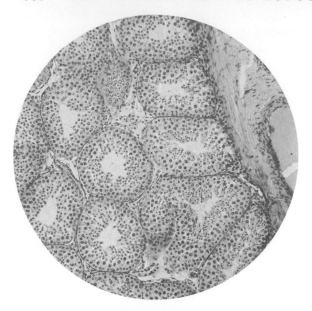

FIG. 25.4. Section through a mammalian testis, showing the tubular chambers in which sperms are produced. Mature sperms accumulate in the central spaces of the tubules. The tissue between the tubules manufactures androgens, the male sex hormones, under the stimulus of LH from the pituitary. (General Biological Supply House, Inc.)

That is, meiosis occurs, much of the cell cytoplasm degenerates, a sperm tail forms, and at the forward tip of the sperm an acrosome is elaborated (see Chap. 23). Newly formed sperms do not lash their tails. Much respiratory CO_2 tends to accumulate in the confined spaces of the testicular tubules, and CO_2 probably depresses sperm motility.

The tubules of each testis join into a common **sperm duct,** which emerges from the testis (see Fig. 25.2). Just outside the testis the duct is greatly looped and coiled, and this portion is called the **epididymis.** It *stores* sperms which are crowded out from the testicular tubules. During copulation, nerve impulses may bring about contraction of the muscular walls of the epididymis, and then the collected sperms are propelled forward, into the straight part of the sperm duct.

This part of the duct leaves the scrotum and passes through the groin. It eventually opens into the **urethra,** close to the point where the urinary bladder also opens into the urethra. Near its termination, the sperm duct receives watery secretions from the **seminal vesicle** and the **prostate gland.** These secretions, together with sperms, constitute **semen.** It is here that sperms begin to lash their tails. Semen may contain specific sperm-activating substances, and CO_2 probably becomes diluted sufficiently in this terminal part of the sperm duct to permit sperm movement.

Note that urine and semen are expelled along the same exit path, the urethra, a channel which leads to the outside through the **penis.** However, simultaneous discharges are prevented by reflexes. The bladder-urethra juncture constricts when semen is expelled, and the sperm-duct–urethra juncture constricts when urine is expelled.

Sperm-producing capacity develops at puberty and continues to old age, often until death. In man and some other mammals, sperms are manufactured the year round. But in most mammals, as in most animals generally, they are produced only during a breeding season. Possibly in correlation with this, the testes are found in different positions in different mammals. In one group, which includes the opossum, for example, the testes are located permanently where ovaries are located in females: within the body cavity, not far from the kidneys. In a second group of mammals, which includes elephants, the testes are again found within the body cavity, for most of the year. But during the breeding season, when sperms are actually produced, the testes migrate into a scrotum. After the breeding season, the testes migrate back into the body cavity. Finally, in man and a few other mammals, the testes are internal only during embryonic stages. They migrate into the scrotum before birth, and they then remain in this sac permanently.

It is known that the temperature in a scrotum is slightly lower than within the body. It is also known that lower temperatures tend to promote sperm production and that higher temperatures tend to inhibit it. Hence, temperature, location of the testes, and continuity or discontinuity of sperm manufacture may well be correlated.

THE FEMALE SYSTEM

Most female animals, like their male partners, produce gametes only during a breeding season. This holds also for most female mammals. In these, eggs are formed during the breeding season in fairly rapid succession, until the animal is fertilized and is pregnant. Some mammals, however, like apes and man, produce eggs the year round. In human females, egg production begins at puberty and continues at a rate of one per month for a period of about 30 years.

The ovaries of human females are a pair of walnut-sized organs situated at the back of the abdominal cavity, at hip level. They are partially enveloped by the funnel-shaped terminals of the **oviducts,** also called *egg ducts* or *fallopian tubes*. These ciliated channels lead into the **uterus.** The young develop in this muscular organ, which may stretch and enlarge considerably. The mouth of the uterus opens into the **vagina,** and this channel leads to the outside (Fig. 25.5). Note that, in contrast to the arrangement in males, the reproductive tract in females is entirely separate from the urinary tract. Each of these duct systems leads to the outside through its own opening.

The outer layers of the ovaries are the egg-pro-

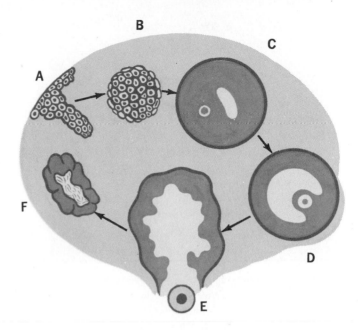

FIG. 25.6. The growth of an egg (diagrammatic). **A** and **B,** newly formed potential egg cells within the ovary. **C** and **D,** maturation of one of the cells into an egg and development of surrounding cells into a follicle. Note the enlarging follicular cavity. **E,** ovulation. **F,** the remnants of the follicle have transformed into a corpus luteum.

FIG. 25.5. Diagram of the female reproductive system.

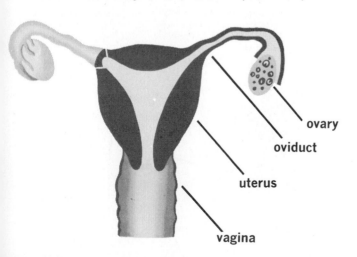

ovary

oviduct

uterus

vagina

ducing tissues. As in testes, new cells are manufactured mitotically, and these cells are crowded into the interior of the organ. But in contrast to events in the testis, not all the new cells in the ovary become eggs. In a given batch of newly produced cells, all of which are probably *potential* eggs, usually only one actually matures into a reproductive cell: the cytoplasm enlarges, and meiosis occurs. The surrounding cells are inhibited in some unknown way from also maturing as eggs (Figs. 25.6a, b, and c and 25.7).

However, these surrounding cells acquire other functions. They specialize as *endocrine* tissue and secrete **estrogens,** the female sex hormones. Like androgens in males, estrogens maintain the primary and secondary sex characteristics of females and sex

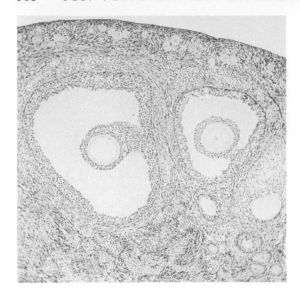

FIG. 25.7. Section through a mammalian ovary. Note the two large follicles, the follicular cavities, and the large egg cell in each follicle, embedded within a mass of cells along the follicular wall. Near the top of the photo, along the edge of the ovary, note the relatively large cells. These are immature eggs which will become mature later, within follicles yet to be formed. (Ward's Natural Science Establishment, Inc.)

drive. The endocrine cells surrounding the egg become arranged into a **follicle,** a ball of tissue which soon develops a slowly enlarging central cavity. This follicular cavity is filled with fluid, and in it, the estrogenic hormones accumulate before they are carried away by blood. In such a follicle, the egg is located eccentrically, in a thickened region of the follicular wall (Figs. 25.6*d* and 25.7).

The formation and growth of a follicle, and all subsequent reproductive events, are under the control of gonadotropic hormones released by the pituitary gland. This gland also imposes a cyclical character on the process of egg production in man. What is the course of events in such a cycle?

THE MENSTRUAL CYCLE

In one form or another, cyclical reproductive processes under hormonal control occur in all vertebrates. For example, the endocrine system plays a major role in determining whether gametes are produced the year round, or only in annual breeding cycles. Moreover, whenever females do produce gametes, short intervals separate the appearance of successive batches of eggs, as in chickens, in which the egg-laying cycle lasts approximately one day. Such cycles of egg production are usually under pituitary control. In man, apes, and old-world monkeys, rather elaborate and specialized egg-producing cycles have evolved. These are of longer duration than in most other mammals, but they too are under pituitary control. Because they terminate in **menstruation,** they are called menstrual cycles.

Ovulation

In man, a menstrual cycle lasts about one month. The cycle begins with FSH production by the pituitary. The name of this hormone, short for "*f*ollicle-*s*timulating *h*ormone," describes its function. Under its influence, a follicle grows, an egg matures within it, and the endocrine follicle cells secrete increasing amounts of estrogen.

This last has two specific consequences. First, the increasing concentration of estrogen in the blood eventually reaches a level which *inhibits* the pituitary from secreting more FSH. Second, high concentrations of estrogen *stimulate* the pituitary to begin secreting LH, the other gonadotropic hormone. In other words, continued growth of the follicle, and

FIG. 25.8. The hormonal changes during the follicular phase of a menstrual cycle, leading to ovulation. Arrow tipped with double bar denotes inhibition.

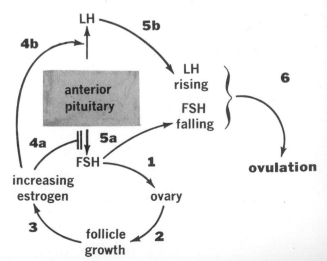

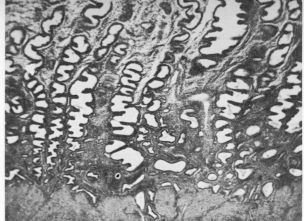

FIG. 25.9. The effect of sex hormones on the structure of the uterus. The left photo shows the inner glandular tissues of a human uterus during the follicular phase of a menstrual cycle, when progesterone is absent. Note the layer of uterine muscle underneath the glandular layer. The right photo, taken at the same magnification, shows the glandular tissues during the luteal phase, when the progesterone concentration is high. Note the tremendous increase in thickness of the glandular layer, and the increased elaboration of the glandular pockets. (Courtesy of Dr. B. J. Serber, College of Medicine, New York University.)

the correlated rising estrogen output, ultimately bring about a sharp fall in FSH concentration and a sharp rise in LH concentration (Fig. 25.8).

This stage is usually attained some 10 to 14 days after a follicle has begun to grow. During this roughly two-week-long period, the follicle has migrated within the ovary and has come to be stationed just under the ovary surface, where it may form a pronounced outward bulge. Follicle and egg are fully matured at this time, and now, as noted, FSH concentration falls rapidly, and LH concentration rises. This is the specific stimulus for **ovulation:** the ovary surface ruptures, the follicle wall ruptures too, and the mature egg falls out of the ovary (Fig. 25.6e).

The immediate consequence of ovulation is that the follicle, now eggless, loses its fluid and collapses. This remnant of the follicle is called the **corpus luteum** (Figs. 25.6f and 25.7). Its cells retain an endocrine function, but the hormone now produced is not estrogen. For inasmuch as FSH is no longer sent by the pituitary, estrogen manufacture ceases too. Instead, the cells of the corpus luteum secrete another hormone, **progesterone.** Manufacture of this substance requires the stimulus of LH from the pituitary. The name "LH" stands for "*l*uteinizing *hor*mone." We have noted above that LH begins to be secreted just before ovulation, as a result of a strong estrogen stimulation of the pituitary. As a further re-

sponse to this stimulus, the LH output thereafter continues to rise for a period of about one week. And under the influence of this pituitary hormone, the corpus luteum then secretes gradually increasing quantities of progesterone.

Menstruation

Progesterone is properly described as the "pregnancy hormone"; it prepares the uterus to receive the egg. When the egg leaves the ovary, it normally falls into the funnel of the oviduct. From there it is slowly propelled toward the uterus by the cilia which line the oviduct. The uterus in the meantime is readied by progesterone for the arrival of an egg. Under the influence of progesterone, the inner lining of the uterus thickens, becomes greatly pitted with glandular pockets, and acquires a rich supply of blood capillaries. As a result, the inner surface of the uterus is transformed into a spongy carpet of particularly well-nourished tissue (Fig. 25.9).

What happens next depends on whether the egg is fertilized or not. If fertilization does occur, the event normally takes place as the egg travels through the upper part of the oviduct. The fertilized egg then continues to migrate toward the ready uterus and arrives there some 2 days after ovulation. But if fertilization does not occur, the egg disintegrates when about halfway down the oviduct, and the uterus will have been made ready for nothing.

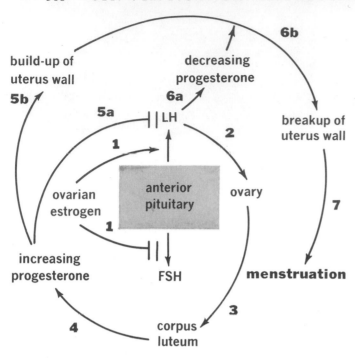

FIG. 25.10. The hormonal changes during the luteal phase of a menstrual cycle, leading to menstruation.

FIG. 25.11. The hormonal inter-relations during a menstrual cycle.

In the latter case, the following changes take place. The corpus luteum, having secreted ever increasing amounts of progesterone for about a week, ultimately produces so much hormone that it *inhibits* the pituitary from manufacturing more LH. Therefore, beginning about a week after ovulation, the pituitary produces less and less LH. Hence progesterone from the corpus luteum decreases in amount gradually too (Fig. 25.10). Indeed, the corpus luteum begins to degenerate, and it eventually produces so little progesterone that this hormone can no longer maintain the structural build-up in the uterus. The glandular uterine pockets are then resorbed, the blood capillaries break up, and the whole spongy lining disintegrates. The tissue fragments separate from the uterus wall, and some blood escapes from the torn vessels. Over a period of a few days, all this debris is expelled through the vagina to the outside. This is *menstruation.* It begins some two weeks after ovulation, and we note that it is brought about by the cessation of LH and progesterone production. At this time, the pituitary resumes FSH production, and a new month-long cycle is initiated.

Hormonal Balances

As we have seen, the first two weeks, roughly, of a menstrual cycle are dominated by FSH, estrogen, and the follicle; this is the **follicular phase.** The second two weeks are dominated by LH, progesterone, and the corpus luteum, and this is the **luteal**

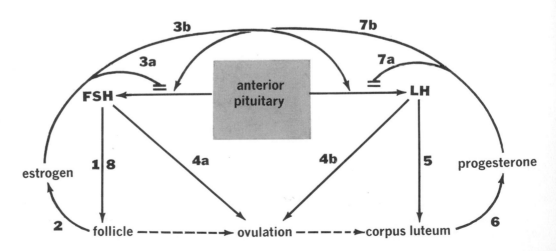

phase. FSH and estrogen are components of one control system, LH and progesterone of another, and these two are coordinated in time. This is one of the best illustrations of the way in which hormones control body functions, and how such control is self-adjusting through the intricate interplay of hormones. The sequence of events in an entire menstrual cycle is summarized in Figs. 25.11 and 25.12.

We may note now that estrogen is not absent altogether during a luteal phase. Some can be shown to be present in the blood even then, despite the absence of follicles at that time. Similarly, some progesterone is present during the follicular phase of the menstrual cycle (see Fig. 25.12). Exactly where these hormones come from is still undetermined. Im-

mature follicles, reaching maturity only during future cycles, might secrete some estrogen during the luteal phase. Analogously, corpora lutea in process of degeneration might secrete some progesterone during the follicular phase. Or other ovarian tissues might secrete the hormones. Yet, although both female sex hormones are present at every stage of the menstrual cycle, their quantities do fluctuate sharply. Estrogen reaches a definite peak late during the follicular phase and at the time of ovulation; progesterone, during the luteal phase (see Fig. 25.12).

This fluctuation has far-reaching consequences. In addition to its effect on the uterus, progesterone promotes the development of the duct system in the

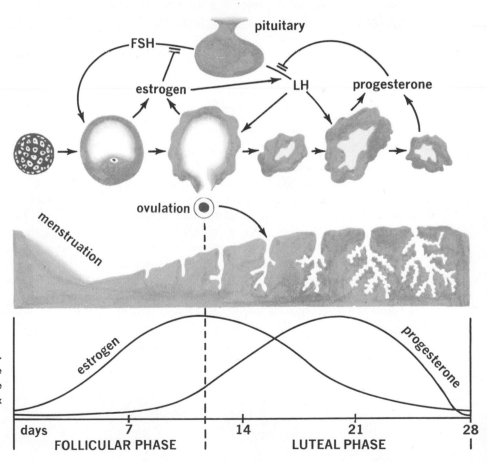

FIG. 25.12. Summary of the menstrual cycle. Top: events in the ovary and the role of the pituitary. Middle: events in the wall of the uterus. Bottom: variations in the amounts of sex hormones during a menstrual cycle.

mammary glands. Hence a slight swelling of these glands generally occurs during the luteal phase of the menstrual cycle. Body temperature increases somewhat during the follicular phase, then falls during the luteal phase. Sex drive is likely to be more pronounced during the follicular phase, since estrogen maintains it. And since estrogens, like androgens in males, affect mental processes, it is possible that the monthly fluctuation of these hormones contributes to the emotional fluctuations rather characteristic of females.

Menstrual cycles as above occur under "sterile" conditions, that is, when fertilization does not take place. Such cycles are essentially egg-producing mechanisms, more elaborate than in other animal groups, but basically representing little more than a controlled way of manufacturing female gametes. Together with the production of sperms, menstrual cycles set the stage for subsequent reproductive events.

Pregnancy

After the production of gametes, two processes occur which are common to the reproductive patterns of all animals. The first is **fertilization,** and the second is **development** of the fertilized egg into a formed animal. In oviparous forms, the pattern includes nothing further. The reproductive role of the parents here ends with fertilization, and the zygote develops independently. In ovoviviparous forms too the pattern is essentially the same, except that here the female body protects the developing zygote passively. But in viviparous types, a third process is added to the two above: active maternal participation in offspring development, or **gestation.**

Thus, pregnancy, which includes fertilization, development, and gestation, is a phenomenon confined to viviparous animals, that is, largely to mammals. We shall defer a discussion of development to the next chapter, and concentrate here primarily on fertilization, and on the subsequent gestative role of the mammalian female.

FERTILIZATION

Once it is discharged from the male reproductive system, a sperm can live only a few hours. Analogously, eggs erupted from the ovary do not persist for more than a few hours. The time of greatest fertility in man therefore coincides roughly with the time of ovulation. Sperms deposited into the female swim from the vagina through the uterine cavity into the oviducts. Defective sperms largely succumb along the arduous path. If a ripe living egg is encountered in the upper part of the oviduct, fertilization may occur.

Sperms which collide with the egg at an angle are likely to bounce off. Sperms hitting head on are likely to remain attached, for the acrosome at the sperm tip is specialized to adhere to the egg. One, and only one, sperm is able to fertilize any one egg. As soon as the *first* sperm makes contact, a **fertilization membrane** rises from the egg surface. This membrane is formed earlier, during egg maturation. On contact with a sperm, the egg rapidly secretes some water between its surface and the membrane. As a result, the membrane lifts off, the sperm which has made contact is trapped inside, and any other sperms are prevented from entering (Fig. 25.13).

Now the successful sperm rests against the egg surface proper. Contrary to wide belief, the sperm

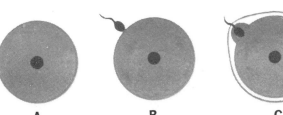
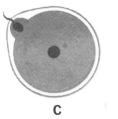
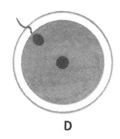

A   B   C   D

FIG. 25.13. Diagrammatic representation of fertilization. Note the egg cone engulfing a sperm, and the lifting off of a fertilization membrane (**C** and **D**).

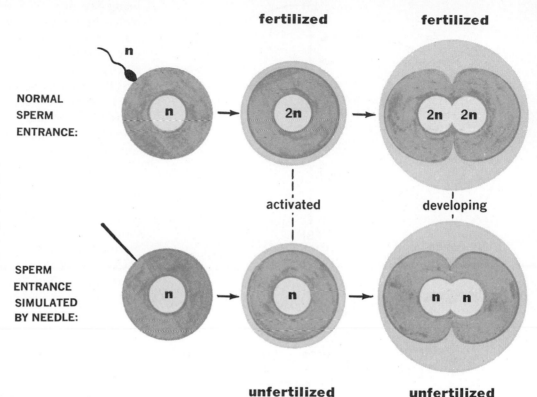

fertilized   fertilized

NORMAL
SPERM
ENTRANCE:

n → 2n → 2n 2n

activated   developing

FIG. 25.14. Initiation of development by a sperm (top), and by artificial parthenogenesis, with the help of a needle (bottom). In both cases the egg is activated and begins to develop, but in parthenogenesis the egg remains unfertilized and haploid.

SPERM
ENTRANCE
SIMULATED
BY NEEDLE:

n → n → n n

unfertilized   unfertilized

does not penetrate into the egg by boring in, but the egg *engulfs* the sperm. During this process, the sperm tail drops off. At this point the egg is **activated,** but not yet fertilized. This means that the development of the egg has been triggered off. A mature egg is ready and able to develop, but this ability remains latent until a specific stimulus makes development start. Sperm penetration into the egg normally serves as this stimulus, and such an arrangement ensures that sex occurs before development begins.

In some cases it is possible, by experimental means, to provide a substitute stimulus. In an unfertilized frog egg, for example, one may simulate the entry of a sperm by pricking the egg with a needle. The egg thereby becomes properly activated, and development then begins without sperms and without fertilization. Such an egg remains haploid, and all the cells of the resulting embryo are

haploid too. The term **artificial parthenogenesis** designates such spermless, experimentally initiated development of eggs (Fig. 25.14).

Under normal conditions, a sperm nucleus which has activated an egg moves toward the egg nucleus, and the meeting of the two haploid nuclei then does complete fertilization. The membranes of the two nuclei dissolve, and a mitotic spindle forms. The chromosomes, now diploid in number, line up in a metaphase plate, and the zygote undergoes its first **cleavage division.** Very shortly after fertilization, therefore, two cells are formed from the zygote. The two cells then divide again, and many successive cleavage divisions follow thereafter. The development of an offspring is launched in this manner.

As noted above, fertilization in man occurs in the upper part of the oviduct. Hence, after a few days, when the egg reaches the uterus, it is actually

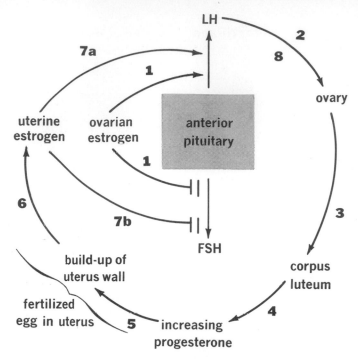

FIG. 25.15. Summary of hormonal changes when the luteal phase of menstrual cycle becomes the luteal phase of pregnancy.

being, we may infer that LH continues to be secreted by the pituitary. And since LH secretion in turn requires stimulation of the pituitary by estrogen, we may infer further that estrogen does indeed stimulate the pituitary to manufacture LH.

But what is the source of this estrogen? It cannot be the ovary, for, as we have seen, ovulation stops the secretion of ovarian estrogen; and the amount of estrogen produced before ovulation is sufficient only to start LH secretion and to maintain it for about a week or so. In all probability, the new estrogen source is the uterus. We shall find presently that the arrival of an early embryo in the uterus leads to the transformation of some embryonic and some uterine cells into endocrine tissues. These secrete many hormones throughout pregnancy, estrogen among them. Apparently, it is this estrogen source, beginning to be available some two days after ovulation and fertilization, which maintains and increases the secretion of pituitary LH beyond the first week after ovulation. Hence the secretion of progesterone continues too. At the same time, the new estrogen source continues to inhibit FSH production, and further menstrual cycles are suppressed as a result (Fig. 25.15).

The luteal phase of the menstrual cycle so merges into a luteal phase of pregnancy. In man, the corpus luteum persists for the ensuing 12 weeks. Throughout this time, the progesterone output increases, and the uterine lining becomes even more glandular and vascularized. Moreover, two other events take place. First, the developing embryo becomes anchored securely to the wall of the uterus; and second, a nutritive and general metabolic connection is established between embryo and mother. Up to the time it enters the uterus, the embryo draws energy and raw materials from the small amount of yolk included in the original egg. After arrival in the uterus, the maternal tissues supply food and oxygen and carry off wastes. The structure which so links the embryo to the uterus mechanically and metabolically is the **placenta.** This structure develops during the first 12 weeks of pregnancy, in part from **extraembryonic membranes** which form around the embryo.

already an embryo composed of several hundred cells. Further development requires the direct aid of the maternal body.

GESTATION

The Luteal Phase

We recall that, under the influence of progesterone, the inner lining of the uterus becomes a glandular, vascularized mat during the latter half of a menstrual cycle. If an egg has been fertilized in the upper oviduct, an early embryo enters the ready uterus some two days after ovulation.

This leads to the suppression of menstruation. The corpus luteum does not degenerate but continues to secrete progesterone. As a result, the uterine preparations for pregnancy persist. Inasmuch as the corpus luteum remains functional for the time

The Extraembryonic Membranes

When the ball of embryonic cells first arrives in the uterus, it bores its way deep into the spongy uterine lining (Fig. 25.16). Completely embedded within the lining tissue, the early embryo is held fast temporarily. At this stage, the embryonic cell mass contains two groups of cells. One group, in the center of the mass, represents the embryo proper. These cells will give rise to the future offspring. Surrounding this central group are cells which will not become part of the offspring body as such. Instead, these cells form into four extraembryonic membranes (Figs. 25.17 and 25.18).

One of these membranes, the **amnion,** comes to surround the embryo proper everywhere, except for an area at the future abdominal side. The *amni-*

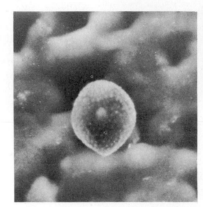
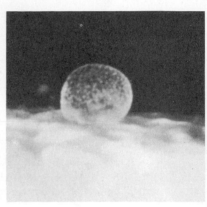

FIG. 25.16. Implantation of the egg in the uterus. Top: diagram showing position of egg relative to wall of uterus, at the time of implantation. Bottom: top and side views of early monkey embryo just arrived in the uterus and beginning to implant. (Photos courtesy of Dr. G. W. Corner and Department of Embryology, Carnegie Institution of Washington.)

FIG. 25.17. A rabbit embryo about four days after fertilization. The single, spherical layer of cells on the outside of this embryo will not become part of the adult but will develop into one of the extraembryonic membranes, namely, the chorion. Most of the dense cell mass aggregated in one area along the inner surface of the chorionic layer constitutes the embryo proper, and will develop into the adult. (General Biological Supply House, Inc.)

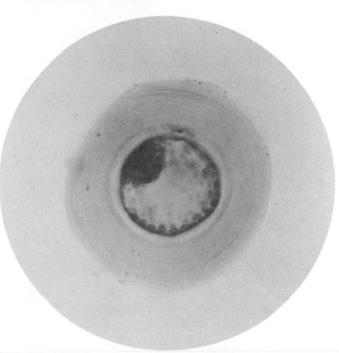

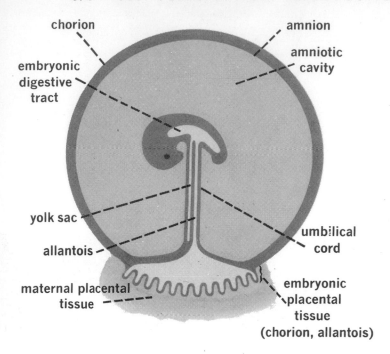

chorion

amnion

amniotic
cavity

embryonic
digestive
tract

yolk sac

allantois

umbilical
cord

maternal placental
tissue

embryonic
placental
tissue
(chorion, allantois)

FIG. 25.18. The extraembryonic membranes in mammals, and the placenta (diagrammatic). Note that yolk sac and allantois are rudimentary and collapsed.

otic cavity is the space between the embryo surface and the amnion, and this space is filled with a lymphlike *amniotic fluid*. During the later months of pregnancy, the amniotic cavity enlarges considerably, and the amount of fluid increases. This fluid serves both as a "private pond" and as a shock absorber for the embryo.

Two other membranes are attached to the future abdominal side of the embryo. One is the **yolk sac.** In reptiles and birds, this sac is relatively huge. It contains the yolk which sustains the embryo till it hatches. In mammals, the sac is empty and collapsed, the prospective mother nourishing the embryo instead. Yet the functionless yolk sac develops nevertheless, as a silent reminder of the reptilian ancestry of mammals.

The second membrane attached to the abdominal region of the embryo is also a sac, the **allantois.** In the eggs of developing reptiles and birds, this sac functions as an embryonic urinary bladder and as a breathing device. Up to the time of hatching in such eggs, urinary wastes accumulate in the sac; urine cannot escape through the hard egg shell. Also, embryonic blood vessels ramify through the allantoic membrane, which lies just under the egg shell. Gaseous oxygen and CO_2 pass through the shell readily and may diffuse into and out of the allantoic blood vessels. In other words, up to the time of hatching, the allantois serves as an embryonic *lung* (Fig. 25.19). In mammals, the allantoic membrane carries blood vessels too. As we shall see presently, these connect the embryonic circulation with that of the mother. They bring food and oxygen from the mother to the embryo and carry CO_2 and urinary wastes from the embryo to the mother. Hence the allantoic blood vessels have assumed added importance, but the allantoic sac has lost its function as a urinary bladder. It still forms in mammals, but, like the yolk sac, it remains collapsed.

The fourth extraembryonic membrane is the **chorion,** a complete outer enclosure which envelops the embryo proper, the amnion, the yolk sac, the allantois, and all their contents. It is this membrane, in direct contact with the uterine lining, which largely contributes to the growth of a placenta. Soon after the whole embryonic mass has become embedded in the uterine wall, numerous fingerlike outgrowths develop on the outer surface of the chorion. These outgrowths branch extensively and erode paths through the tissues of the spongy uterine lining. Uterus tissue and chorionic tissue become firmly attached to each other, and these two interlacing and interfingering tissues represent the placenta.

The Placenta

In the placenta, the microscopic terminals of the chorionic outgrowths dip into pools of maternal blood which has accumulated within the placental spaces. The maternal blood circulates extensively through the maternal side of the placenta. On the embryonic side, an artery leaves the embryo proper, travels through the allantoic membrane, and capillarizes abundantly in the placenta, just underneath the chorion (Fig. 25.20). The capillaries eventually

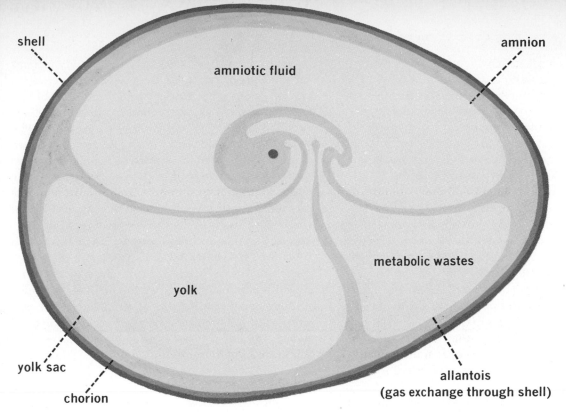

shell

amnion

amniotic fluid

metabolic wastes

yolk

yolk sac

chorion

allantois
(gas exchange through shell)

FIG. 25.19. The extraembryonic membranes in reptile and bird eggs. Note that yolk sac and allantois are large and functional.

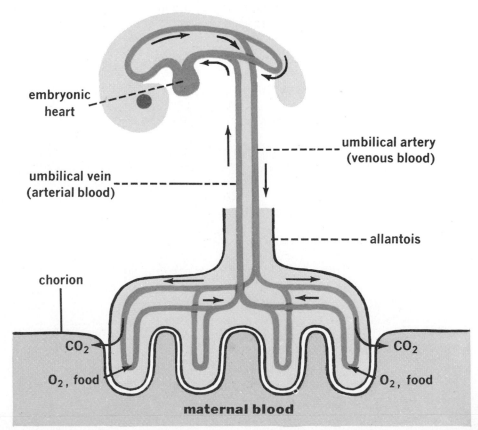

embryonic
heart

umbilical vein
(arterial blood)

umbilical artery
(venous blood)

allantois

chorion

CO_2

CO_2

O_2, food

O_2, food

maternal blood

FIG. 25.20. The embryonic blood circulation and the placenta. Note that embryonic and maternal bloods do not mix, being separated by the chorionic and allantoic membranes.

join and form a large vein, which leads back through the allantoic membrane to the embryo proper. The artery, the vein, the yolk sac, and the allantois become enveloped by connective tissue and skin, and the whole represents the **umbilical cord.** This is the life line between placenta and embryo, and its point of origin in the embryo leaves a permanent mark in the later offspring in the form of the navel.

Note that maternal and embryonic bloods do not mix in the placenta. The two circulations approach each other closely, but the chorion always separates them. This membrane forms a selective boundary. Nutrients of all kinds, and oxygen, are passed across into the embryonic circulation, and metabolic wastes are passed in the opposite direction. If a raw material is in low supply in the maternal circulation, it is usually in still lower supply in the embryonic circulation. Hence diffusion tends to occur *into* the embryo, even if this produces a pronounced deficiency in the prospective mother. In this sense, the embryo is parasitic on maternal metabolism. The placenta also ferries defensive antibodies from the maternal to the embryonic circulation. The newborn thereby acquires much of his mother's immunity for the first few months of life, usually sufficiently long to allow the newborn to manufacture his own antibodies in response to exposure to infectious agents.

The placenta also specializes as an endocrine organ. As it grows and develops during the first 12 weeks of pregnancy, it manufactures slowly increasing amounts of estrogens, progesterone, and a number of other hormones as well (Fig. 25.21). As noted earlier, it is this endocrine function which probably maintains the activity of the corpus luteum during the first 12 weeks of pregnancy. Moreover, it is the placenta which provides the main hormonal control of pregnancy *after* the twelfth week. Up to that time, the corpus luteum in the ovary exercises control through its output of progesterone. But as the twelfth week nears, the corpus luteum declines and its hormone secretion subsides. Why this is so is unknown. However, this decline is more than compensated for by progesterone increasingly produced by the placenta. After the twelfth week, and for the remaining months of pregnancy, the now fully matured placenta controls its own maintenance: the luteal phase of pregnancy changes over to the *placental phase.*

The Placental Phase

The twelfth week is a rather critical period in pregnancy. For if the corpus luteum should degenerate a little too soon, and if the placenta should reach full development a little late, then the amount of available progesterone during this gap is likely to be inadequate. And in the absence of the hormone, placental tissues cannot be maintained. Just as at the end of a menstrual cycle, the uterine lining disintegrates, and the embryo, no longer securely

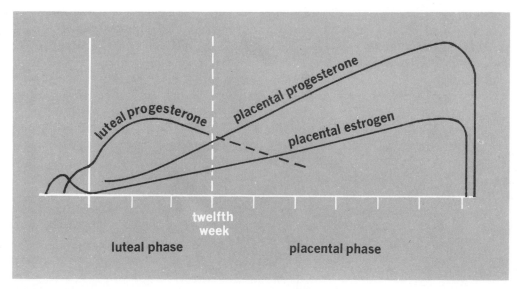

FIG. 25.21. Curves indicating the amounts and the sources of sex hormones present during pregnancy.

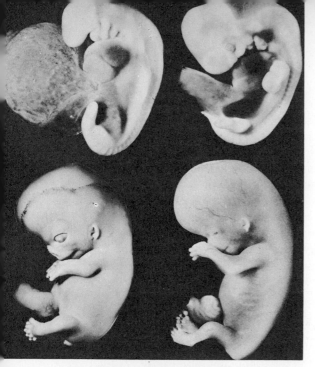

FIG. 25.22. Stages in embryonic development of man. Upper left: approximately 25 days after fertilization. Upper right: approximately 33 days old. Lower left: approximately 6 weeks old. Lower right: approximately 8 weeks old. (Courtesy of Dr. G. W. Corner and Department of Embryology, Carnegie Institution of Washington.)

prisingly rapid sequence. For example, 3 weeks after fertilization, the human embryo is about the size of a small nailhead, and three-quarters of it is head structures. It is characteristic of the development of all animals that the head end forms earlier, and faster, than other regions. Four weeks after fertilization, the eyes are partly developed, and the heart is already beating (Fig. 25.22, upper left). Limb buds appear in the fifth week, ears are elaborated at that time, and the embryo now responds to mechanical stimuli by muscular contractions (Fig. 25.22, upper right). Human form is vaguely recognizable 8 weeks after fertilization, when the embryo is about 1 in. long (Figs. 25.22, lower right, and 25.23). From this stage on, one speaks of a **fetus** rather than an embryo.

By the twelfth week fingers have formed, the semicircular canals in the ears are functional, and the embryo moves jerkily, but in balance, within

FIG. 25.23. Photograph of human embryo, about 8 weeks after fertilization, obtained after surgical removal of portions of the reproductive system of female patient. Chorion pushed to one side, revealing the amniotic sac. Note umbilical cord. (By permission, from Fig. 10, "The Embryology of Behavior," by Dr. A. Gesell and Harper & Brothers.)

anchored, may be aborted. Miscarriages occur frequently near the end of the third month of pregnancy. Such mishaps due to hormone deficiency can be forestalled by injecting some progesterone into the pregnant female.

We may note here in passing that sex hormones normally produced by the placenta pass not only into the maternal but also into the embryonic circulation. This has a curious effect; in newborn infants, the genitals and the breast region are often precociously enlarged and swollen, superficially resembling a mature condition. After a short time, however, the sex hormones in the infant are destroyed metabolically without being replaced till puberty, and the external effects then disappear.

During the twelfth week of pregnancy in man, it is already amply clear that the developing offspring will be a human being. Basic forms and functions have become elaborated earlier, in sur-

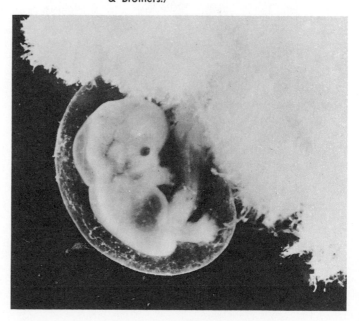

its amniotic water pool. Eyelids are still fused, yet the eyeball may rotate underneath. Five months after fertilization, the fetus is about 8 in. long, weighs about 1 lb, and his facial features show signs of individual personality. In the ensuing weeks, the breathing machinery develops rapidly, possibly an adaptive feature against the hazards of premature birth. The fetus is now in a perpetual drowsy state, neither sleeping nor waking. Overt body movements are sporadic and uneven, but important facial reflexes are being developed. For example, eyelids open and close, and lips purse rhythmically, as if the fetus were learning to suck. But there is some doubt whether these prenatal movements are being "learned," in preparation for the future. In primitive vertebrates, at least, overt movement may be suppressed experimentally, yet upon hatching the animals are fully capable of performing necessary motions.

FIG. 25.24. The fetus, within its membranes in the uterus: amnion on the inside, chorion on the outside.

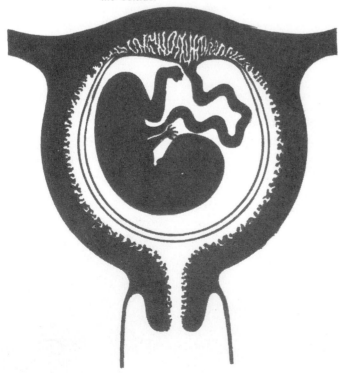

In the eighth and ninth months, periods of true wakefulness occur increasingly. Arms and legs are moved frequently, and the hand opens and closes. Body fat is being laid down, and the fetus acquires a sturdier stature generally. Growth in size has proceeded apace, and by the end of the ninth month, the microscopic fertilized egg has become a whole human being.

With several exceptions, the gestation period of mammals is roughly proportional to adult size. For example, the period of pregnancy is 3 weeks in mice, and 22 months in elephants. On the other hand, pregnancy lasts only a year, approximately, in whales.

BIRTH

In parallel with the growth and development of the fetus, the amniotic cavity gradually enlarges, and the uterus grows and stretches too (Fig. 25.24). Also, during the last months of pregnancy, the mammary glands undergo a marked enlargement, under the stimulus of the increasing quantities of sex hormones from the placenta. Numerous ducts form in the interior of the glands, and in later stages, the milk-secreting cells mature. Flow of secretion starts soon thereafter. However, the first product is not milk, but **colostrum,** a watery, lymphlike fluid.

Birth generally begins with the rupturing of the chorion and the amnion and the escape of the amniotic fluid to the outside. Labor contractions of the uterine muscles then occur with increasing frequency and strength, pressing against the fetus and pushing it out through the vagina. In these labor contractions, the possible role of hormones produced in the posterior lobe of the pituitary has already been mentioned (Chap. 19). At the time of birth, the interlocked maternal and embryonic tissues which form the placenta loosen away from the wall of the uterus, and the mechanical and metabolic connection between mother and infant is thereby severed.

An important result of this is that CO_2 produced by the infant must accumulate in his own circulation. Before long the concentration of the gas becomes high enough to stimulate the infant's breathing center.

In correlation with this switchover from placental breathing to lung breathing, several structural changes occur in the heart and in the large blood vessels around the heart. In the fetus, the dividing wall between the right and left auricles is incomplete (Fig. 25.25). A movable flap of tissue provides an opening between these two chambers, and blood may pass freely from one chamber into the other. Once lung breathing is initiated, the blood-pressure pattern within the heart changes, and the tissue flap is pressed over the opening interconnecting the auricles. The flap eventually grows into place, and so the left and right sides of the heart become separated permanently.

Another structural change involves a fetal blood vessel, the **ductus arteriosus,** which originally shunts blood from the pulmonary artery to the aorta, thereby short-circuiting blood around the nonfunctional lung (see Fig. 25.25). At birth, a specially developed muscle in this blood vessel constricts. The muscle never relaxes thereafter but degenerates into scar tissue. Blood is thus forced to pass through the lungs. The ductus arteriosus as a whole degenerates soon after birth.

The loosened placenta, still connected to the umbilical cord, is expelled to the outside as the **afterbirth,** within an hour or so after the infant is expelled. Not having the aid of hospitals and attending physicians, four-footed mammalian mothers bite the umbilical cord off their young and eat cord and placenta. We may note, incidentally, that the escaped amniotic fluid is eagerly lapped up also, perhaps quenching thirst at a time when need for water may be great but locomotion is difficult. Indeed, among carnivorous mammals, it is not uncommon that, in the course of drinking the fluid and eating the placenta, the tiny offspring is swallowed as well.

In the majority of mammals, litter size corresponds roughly to the number of nipples present on the mother's body. For the first few feedings, mammary secretions remain lymphlike, as before birth. This fluid has some laxative action, clearing the infant's alimentary tract of debris and mucus ac-

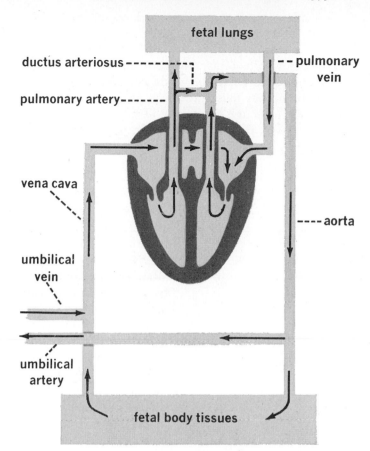

FIG. 25.25. The fetal circulation (diagrammatic). Note that the fetal lung is nonfunctional in breathing and that most of the blood flowing through the pulmonary artery is shunted through the ductus arteriosus directly into the aorta. Oxygenation of blood occurs in the placenta; hence the umbilical artery carries venous blood to the placenta, and the umbilical vein carries arterial blood to the vena cava. Note the opening between the right and left auricle, permitting blood to pass directly from the right to the left side of the heart. Compare with the adult circulation, Fig. 20.11.

cumulated during uterine development. Milk begins to be produced soon, however. Production continues as long as *lactogenic hormones* are manufactured by the pituitary, and as long as milk is not allowed to accumulate in the glands. The females of certain primitive human tribes in northern Australia have been reported to produce milk for some-times up to 6 years after a pregnancy. Cows milked after a pregnancy may "dry up" after a year or so. Incidentally, contrary to surprisingly wide belief among urban people, cows do not give milk at just any time; they must have been pregnant first.

Even though the source of progesterone is removed with the expulsion of the placenta, normal menstrual cycles in man are generally not resumed as long as nursing continues. The manufacture of lactogenic hormones by the pituitary apparently interferes with FSH production. But once the offspring is weaned, FSH is formed again in quantity, and a new ovarian follicle then begins to mature. And after a few months of establishing new hormone balances, the reproductive machinery of the female reverts to rhythmic nonpregnancy operation.

RESUME   The reproductive period of human females comes to a close in middle age, at the time of **menopause.** For ill-understood reasons, the sex-hormone control system ceases to operate, estrogen manufacture declines rapidly, and the reproductive system atrophies progressively during later life. Menopausal events are attended by profound readjustments of all hormone balances in the body, hence by more or less incisive upsets of mental and physical functions. Menopause may occur rather abruptly. In such cases, the effects may be eased by injection of estrogen in slowly decreasing doses. In males, processes equivalent to menopause may occur in old age or may not occur at all.

With appropriate modifications of detail, particularly in matters of hormone control, this account of human reproduction also outlines the reproduction of mammals in general. Considering the animal kingdom as a whole, mammalian reproduction illustrates the basic features of all animal reproduction: gamete manufacture, fertilization, development of offspring. In other respects, this common pattern varies, mainly according to how much prenatal care the developing offspring receives from the female. Here mammals are more specialized than most other animal groups, and in this sense mammalian reproduction is relatively atypical. But regardless of the degree of parental care, the offspring does develop.

Indeed, development is of universal significance. For wherever there is life, there is development. Animals develop; plants develop; buds and spores develop; organs, tissues, and cells develop; and even molecules develop. Moreover, development is characteristic not only of the "young." The young and the old are themselves only momentary expressions of a continuing, uninterrupted developmental sequence. The next chapter will examine the nature of this crucial phenomenon.

REVIEW QUESTIONS   1. Define oviparity, ovoviviparity, viviparity. In which vertebrates does each occur? Review the structure of the reproductive system of human males.

2. Where, specifically, are sperms produced? Describe the hormonal controls of sperm production. What is semen? Describe the relation of testis location and breeding season in different mammals.

3. Review the structure of the reproductive system of human females. Specifically where, and from what tissues, are eggs produced? What is a follicle, and what is its structure?

4. Describe the hormonal controls and the process of follicle growth up to the time of ovulation. What events take place during ovulation? After ovulation, what happens to (*a*) the egg and (*b*) the follicle?

5. Describe the hormonal controls and the events in the uterus up to the time of menstruation. What happens during menstruation? Review the entire menstrual cycle from the standpoint of (*a*) hormonal control, (*b*) events in the ovary, and (*c*) events in the uterus.

6. If fertilization occurs, what hormonal events (*a*) prevent menstruation and new menstrual cycles and (*b*) promote the further development of the uterus? Describe the hormonal controls during (*a*) the luteal phase and (*b*) the placental phase of pregnancy.

7. Distinguish between fertilization and activation of an egg. Where, and when, does fertilization occur? What is parthenogenesis? What happens to an egg (*a*) after fertilization and (*b*) after it arrives in the uterus?

8. Describe the location and function of the extraembryonic membranes in (*a*) reptiles and birds and (*b*) mammals. In which vertebrates, and how, is a placenta formed? What are the functions of a placenta?

9. Review the structure of the human placenta, with attention to embryonic and maternal blood circulation through it. Describe the whole pathway of the embryonic circulation. What is a fetus?

10. Review the changes in the fetal circulation at birth. What events in the uterus result in birth of offspring? How is milk production initiated and maintained? What is colostrum?

SUGGESTED COLLATERAL READINGS

Additional background information on most of the topics dealt with in this chapter may be found in the following excellent, largely popularly written accounts.

Bullough, W. S.: "Hormones and Reproduction," Methuen, 1952.

Corner, G. W.: "The Hormones in Human Reproduction," Princeton University Press, 1942.

————: "Ourselves Unborn," Yale University Press, 1944.

Pincus, G.: Fertilization in Mammals, *Sci. American,* vol. 184, 1951.

Monroy, A.: Fertilization of the Egg, *Sci. American,* vol. 183, 1950.

Loeb, J.: On the Nature of the Process of Fertilization, and the Artificial Production of Normal Larvae from the Unfertilized Eggs of the Sea Urchin, in M. L. Gabriel and S. Fogel, "Great Experiments in Biology," Prentice-Hall, 1955.

Tyler, A.: Fertilization and Antibodies, *Sci. American,* vol. 190, 1954.

Csapo, A.: Progesterone, *Sci. American,* vol. 198, 1958.

Stone, A.: The Control of Fertility, *Sci. American,* vol. 190, 1954.

Patten, B. M.: The First Heart Beats and the Beginning of the Embryonic Circulation, *Am. Scientist,* vol. 39, 1951.

Reynolds, S. R. M.: The Umbilical Cord, *Sci. American,* vol. 187, 1952.

————: Circulatory Adaptations to Birth, *Sci. Monthly,* vol. 77, 1953.

"LIVING" IMPLIES TURNOVER: continuous breakdown and destruction, counterbalanced by continuous synthesis and construction. Through turnover, protoplasm acquires a *history*. And history, or change with time, is the essence of development.

Development is one of the three universal dimensions of living matter. The other two are structure and function. Living matter can be described completely by describing its structure, its function, and its development. In this chapter we shall first outline the basic problems of development, and the answers obtained so far. That is, we shall analyze what has been learned about the **nature of development** and about the **control of development.** We shall then discuss the actual **pattern of development** of specific organisms. Emphasis will be on vertebrates, which of all plants and animals have been studied most extensively from a developmental standpoint.

The Nature of Development

The universal scope of development implies that *any* type of change, occurring on *any* level of protoplasmic organization, and at *any* time in protoplasmic history, should have developmental significance. This is so. Developmental changes can be structural or functional, quantitative or qualitative, progressive or regressive, normal or abnormal. Actually, as we shall see, development always involves all these simultaneously. But in given instances, one or the other form of change may predominate or may be more readily apparent to the observer.

Development is universal too with respect to the protoplasmic unit in which change takes place, and with respect to time. A molecule develops no less than a cell or a tissue, an organism no less than a species or a population. And whether we measure it in microseconds, as on the molecular level, or in millions of years, as on the species level, development occurs at every moment in protoplasmic his-

26

DEVELOPMENT

tory. The developmental domain, clearly, is as extended as that of biology as a whole. However, developmental studies traditionally have concentrated most on the particular events which relate to the formation of *organisms* and of their parts.

We are already familiar with the three ways in which new plant and animal organisms can arise: by vegetative regeneration, from spores or bud cells, or from zygotes. Therefore, the maximum problem of developmental studies is to explain how single cells are transformed into whole multicellular organisms (Fig. 26.1).

A simple answer here would be "by cell division." This is not incorrect, to be sure, but the answer is not very informative either. The real issues are far more subtle and far more complicated. In the following we shall dissect these issues into their basic components.

MORPHOGENESIS

If the problem is to transform single cells into whole organisms, then a first obvious developmental requirement is increase in size, or **growth.** Overall growth may occur by either or all of three types of changes. Protoplasmic parts may increase in *number*, or they may increase in *size*, or the *spaces* between the parts may enlarge.

Singly and in combination, these alternatives apply at every level of the protoplasmic organization. We already know, for example, that molecules increase in number either by being accumulated ready-made from the environment or by being newly synthesized within cells; in size, by combining with other molecules; and in spatial distribution, by dilution with water. Together, these ways of molecular growth constitute the means by which the size of cells increases. The number of cells increases by division, and the spacing, by the accumulation between cells of water, or of cementing substance, or of other secreted deposits. These ways of cellular growth in turn bring about increase in the size, the number, and the spacing of tissues and organs. The net result is overall growth of the organism. Note, however, that molecular growth is the fundamental prerequisite: the living system grows from its molecules up (Fig. 26.2).

Growth introduces qualitative as well as quantitative changes. For example, certain types of

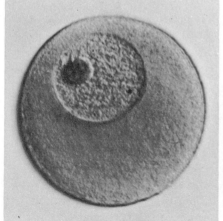

FIG. 26.1. Single egg cells, such as shown on the left, transform through development into plant and animal adults, such as shown next to the egg. Explaining and understanding transformations of this kind are the key objectives of developmental studies. (Guinea pig, Carolina Biological Supply Co.; others, General Biological Supply House, Inc.)

molecules may be synthesized or accumulated at a greater rate, or in greater amount, than others. Indeed, some molecular types may disappear altogether, while others, not previously present, may appear for the first time. Similarly, the growth of cells, of tissues, or of organs may take place dis-

proportionately in different parts of the developing system. As a result of such **differential growth,** the composition of the system may be altered not only quantitatively but also qualitatively (Fig. 26.3).

Growth does not proceed randomly in all directions. How does it happen, for example, that developmental growth stops just when the nose, the brain, the rootlet, the leaflet, and all other body parts are of the "right" proportional size, and the "right" proportional shape? How does it happen that the different parts of the fully grown adult *retain* correct proportions and shapes? And how does it happen that, when the limb of a salamander is cut off, regenerative growth stops just when the newly developing limb has the size and the shape of the original one? In short, what determines the **form** of an organism, with respect to both size of parts and geometrical configuration of parts? Evidently, development of form, in addition to growth as such, is a second requirement if a reproductive unit is to be converted into a whole organism.

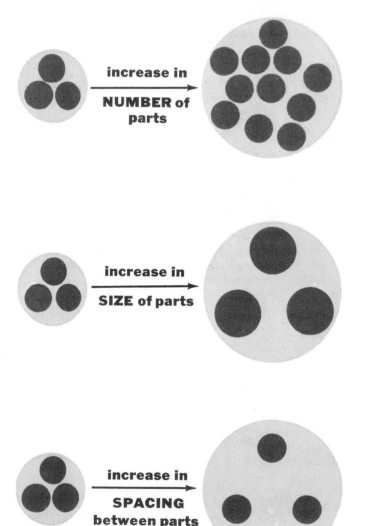

FIG. 26.2. Growth. On any level of organization, growth may occur by increase in the number of parts, the size of parts, the spacing of parts, or by a combination of any of these.

increase in
NUMBER of parts

increase in
SIZE of parts

increase in
SPACING between parts

Form

At any level of organization, the basic aspects of form are **polarity** and **symmetry.** If *they* are given, a great deal about the general appearance of an object is already specified. The polarity of a structure indicates its orientation with reference to the three axes of space. A structure is said to be polarized if one axis is in some way dominant. For example, the head-tail axis in most animals is longer than the other two. This axis is the principal guide line around which the whole animal is organized, and such organisms are said to be polarized longitudinally. Symmetry indicates the degree of mirror-image regularity. A structure may be symmetrical in three, two, one, or in no dimensions; i.e., it may be **spherical, radial, bilateral,** or **asymmetrical.**

Each plant or animal exhibits a certain polarity and a certain symmetry. Polarity and symmetry are the first and most permanent expressions of living form. Invariably, the earliest definitive features to appear during the development of any plant or animal are its polarity and its symmetry. Many features of an organism can be changed by experimental means, but its original polarity and sym-

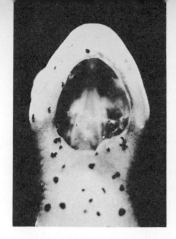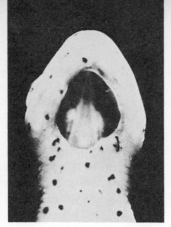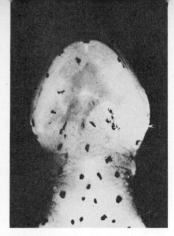

FIG. 26.3. Differential growth. The floor of the mouth of this salamander has been cut out (left). The photos show successive stages in the regeneration of a new floor. Evidently, the regenerating tissues grow faster than the rest of the animal. Unequal growth of this sort is termed "differential growth." (Courtesy of Dr. R. J. Goss and M. W. Stagg, *J. Exptl. Zool.*, vol. 137, 1958, p. 9.)

metry can hardly ever be changed. Millions of years later, long after the organism has become a fossil, polarity and symmetry may still be recognizable even if all other signs of form have disappeared. It is a fairly general principle of development that the earlier a particular feature appears, the later it disappears.

Form is first blocked out in the rough, through establishment of polarity and symmetry, and then it becomes progressively more refined in regional detail. Whereas an organism *grows* from the molecule up, it *forms* from gross shape down. For example, the organ system is delineated ahead of its component organs. The tissue acquires definitive shape in advance of its component cells. And the molecules of the organism are last to assume final form. In the living system, evidently, form develops as in a sculpture, from the coarse to the fine, from the general to the specific. In both instances, this may be the only feasible way to ensure that the small remains appropriately subordinated to the large, structurally as well as functionally.

Specifically, establishment of form requires that cellular aggregates be molded into various configurations. Cells must become arranged and re-arranged to produce regional enlargements and diminutions, to transform compact masses into sheets and vice versa, to produce channels, openings, cavities, and the like. Two general types of processes bring about such changes: **directed differential growth** and **form-regulating movements.** As a result of these two processes, an organism and its parts acquire not only particular polarities and symmetries but also particular detailed shapes.

For example, if differential growth proceeds differently in different parts of a developing system, so that the amount and rate of growth vary for different directions of space, then regional enlargements and diminutions will be produced. Local elongations, thickenings, overgrowths, altered contours, layers, and other new shapes can arise in this manner. Also, a solid mass can become hollow, if the outer layers of the mass grow faster than the core. And a hollow structure can become solid, if the inner layers of the rind grow faster than the outside. Directed differential growth of this sort can be effective at every level of developmental organization.

Form-regulating movements involve shifts and migrations of growing parts relative to one another. Directed migrations of parts can result in the piling up of protoplasm in one region, and in attenuation in others. Sheets or compact masses can slide over one another, can fuse together, or can separate. Compact masses can spread out and become sheets or loose aggregations, or aggregations can condense and form larger masses. Sheets may fold and form ducts or cavities, and compact masses may undergo internal redistribution of parts and assume any number of shapes. Clearly, with material as plastic and malleable as protoplasm, and with a built-in mechanism of moving parts, an infinite array of forms can be produced. Add directed growth to directed movements, and a sufficient machinery is available to translate the form of the reproductive unit into the specific form of the adult.

Growth and form, and all their qualitative and quantitative expressions, together determine the architectural design of protoplasm. This architectural aspect of development is called **morphogenesis.** It is the first major component of the developmental process.

DIFFERENTIATION

The Nature of Differentiation

A living system develops not only architecturally, but also operationally. For example, growth of a zygote does not simply produce an aggregate of many identical cells, but an aggregate of *mutually different* cells; some become nerve cells, some liver cells, some skin cells, etc. In every multicellular organism, a reproductive unit gives rise to a multitude of differently specialized cells. How does this come about? Cell division as such certainly does not alter the character of a cell. As we have already noted, daughter cells inherit the same set of genes, indeed the same kind of protoplasm, as is present in a mother cell. Cell division does copy faithfully, and a dividing reproductive cell therefore *should* give rise to many identical cells. Yet it does not, and cell character does change radically during development.

This holds for every other organizational level as well. Molecules, tissues, organs, whole organisms, all change in character steadily. Such changes are often in the direction of progressively greater operational novelty, but they may also be in the direction of regressively lesser operational novelty. As a result, every protoplasmic unit possesses structures, and carries out functions, which are not yet in existence at earlier developmental stages, and which may no longer be in existence at later stages. For example, the egg is merely irritable, but the mature organism can see, hear, think, feel, and act. The egg merely holds together, but the mature organism is taut with bone, muscle, and tendon. On the other hand, the mature organism reproduces, but the senile organism no longer can. The mature organism is agile and strong, but the senile organism has lost physical vigor.

These dramatic changes of operational potential are brought about by the second, and perhaps the most important, major component of the developmental process, namely, by **differentiation.** A developing system need not necessarily grow, and it need not necessarily change form, but by the very meaning of development, it must differentiate.

The term is ordinarily used to describe only the progressive aspects of operational change. Regressive changes are described as **dedifferentiation.** Thus, if not otherwise qualified, differentiation means enhancement or refinement of existing potentialities, or introduction of altogether new potentialities. Through differentiation, protoplasmic units become *specialized* in various ways. It is sometimes useful to distinguish between "chemodifferentiation," "cytodifferentiation," "histodifferentiation," "organ differentiation," etc., according to the level of organization at which operational change takes place.

The basis of differentiation, as of any protoplasmic occurrence, is **interaction.** In most interactions of protoplasmic parts with one another, or with their physical environment, the operational potentialities of the system are not altered lastingly. But in some cases they are, and then the result is differentiation. For example, if some of the many interactions among molecules lead to the continuing production of novel categories of molecules, then these interactions contribute to chemodifferentiation. Or if a cell produces a hormone which, on reaching a second cell, causes that second cell to mature, to become abnormal, to become endocrine itself, or to change operationally in some other lasting way, then this is an instance of cytodifferentiation. Or again, if in response to a persisting climatic change, organisms transform into new types able to withstand the altered conditions, then this is a case of organismic differentiation, otherwise known as evolution.

In short, to be differentiation, operational changes must have a certain degree of permanence. We may make an animal vitamin-deficient, for

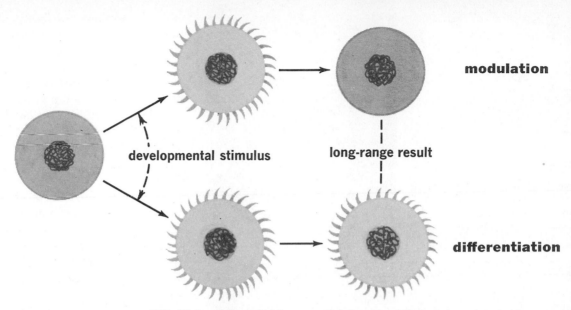

FIG. 26.4. Differentiation vs. modulation. In differentiation, the developmental change is permanent; in modulation, it is not.

example, and many of its cells will then behave differently. But if we now add the missing vitamin to the diet, normal cellular operations will probably be resumed very promptly. Here cellular capacities have not been changed in any fundamental way. Only their expression has changed temporarily, in response to particular conditions. Such easily alterable, transient, reversible changes are spoken of as **modulations.** The concept of differentiation, on the contrary, implies a more or less fundamental, relatively lasting alteration of operational potentials. A vitamin-deficient cell which, after addition of the missing vitamin, does *not* resume normal operations would have differentiated (Fig. 26.4).

The Mechanism of Differentiation

How does differentiation come about? On the organismic level, the process is understood comparatively well, and we shall discuss it in detail in the chapters on evolution. However, differentiation on the molecular and cellular levels is not really understood at all as yet, and this remains one of the most crucial unsolved problems in all biology. Three general possibilities exist.

First, cell differentiation might be a result of progressive changes in gene action. Genes themselves probably do not change during development, for, as already noted, their stability is an essential requirement for the preservation of species character. But the *activity* of different genes could vary with time. For example, in a given cell some genes might become active at certain developmental stages, whereas others might become inactive. Such differential activity patterns might occur differently in different cells, and this might contribute to differentiation.

Or, second, gene actions might remain the same, but the operations of the cytoplasm could become altered progressively. For example, one round of cytoplasmic reactions might use up a certain set of starting materials, and in the subsequent absence of these, similar reactions could then no longer take place. A next round of reactions would proceed with different starting materials and would therefore produce different endproducts. The net result could be progressive differentiation.

Or, third, nuclear and cytoplasmic changes might both occur, in reciprocal fashion. This is prob-

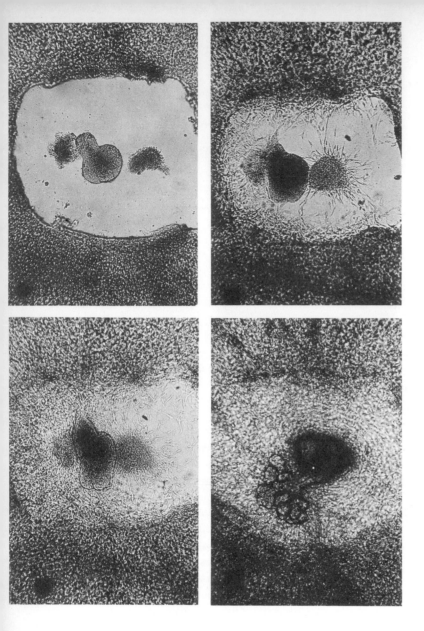

FIG. 26.5. Differentiation by interaction. Development of salivary gland of mouse in tissue culture. One piece of undifferentiated salivary ectoderm and two pieces of undifferentiated salivary mesoderm from a mouse embryo were put together into a culture (first photo). These pieces grew and interacted (second and third photos) and eventually differentiated into secretion pockets and ducts characteristic of normal salivary glands (fourth photo). (Courtesy of Dr. C. Grobstein, Stanford University.)

ably the likeliest possibility, and much current research is devoted to a study of this very complex key problem.

Even though the specific causes of differentiation cannot be identified as yet, it is possible nevertheless to describe the general nature of differentiation in terms of interactions between protoplasmic parts. We may note that, at any level of organization, a differentiating system contains at least three components: a component *A* which influences a component *C*, and a component *B* which provides the necessary physical or chemical communication between *A* and *C*. Communication may be brought about in two ways: by **contact interaction,** as in the case of colliding and reacting molecules; or by **distance interaction,** as when one cell produces a hormone which causes differentiation in another, distant cell. Ultimately, every distance interaction reduces to a contact interaction. For whether it is physical or chemical, the communicating agent eventually must impinge directly on a target, or interaction will not occur at all (Fig. 26.5).

A group of special terms has come into use in this context. The general phenomenon through which interacting elements lead to differentiation is known as **induction.** Component *A*, above, is the **inducing** component, and *C* is the **induced** component. If distance interaction occurs, the communicating agent *B* is described as an **inductor.** These terms have originated during investigations of tissue differentiation in embryos, and we shall encounter them again later in this chapter.

Every interaction changes a potentiality into an actuality. Therefore, once certain components of a system interact in a given way, they can no longer interact in another way, or with other components. Hence, if several interaction possibilities exist at the start, the actual occurrence of some of these will reduce the operational *versatility* of the system. This happens during differentiation. As a result, the nondifferentiated, relatively unspecialized, immature protoplasmic unit is more versatile than the fully differentiated, highly specialized, mature unit. For example, the cells of many early embryos are fully interchangeable. Any one of these cells can, under appropriate conditions, carry out the functions of any other and can give rise to virtually any adult cell type (see below). Later, these embryonic cells differentiate in various ways and become specialized. By that time the versatility of the cells has been reduced sharply, and they are no longer interchangeable. No mature nerve cell, for example, could take the place of a mature blood cell, or vice versa. We have already spoken of various degrees of cellular versatility in Chap. 3, in our discussion of degrees of cellular specialization. Note here that the inverse relation between differentiation and functional versatility holds generally, at any level of protoplasmic organization.

Like growth, differentiation occurs from the molecule up. Just as a house cannot be any more serviceable than its component rooms will permit, so also the operational capacities of any protoplasmic level are based on the capacities of subordinated levels. Chemodifferentiation therefore is the key to all differentiation. It is this which makes the problem of understanding so enormous. For if the process of differentiation is as complex as the totality of molecular interactions in protoplasm, then it cannot be any less complex than the very process of life itself.

METABOLISM

Morphogenesis and differentiation are two of the forces which drive developmental processes. A third is *metabolism*. To be sure, metabolism is not a uniquely developmental requirement, but there could be no growth, no establishment of form, no differentiation, if energy were not available, and if protoplasmic syntheses did not occur. On the other hand, there could be no metabolism if morphogenesis and differentiation did not develop it.

Rates of metabolism are correlated with rates of development. At no point in the life cycle of any protoplasmic unit is metabolism more intensive, and development more rapid, than during the earliest stages. Both then decline in rate, until the zero point is reached at death; the metabolic clock is wound only once, at the beginning.

This circumstance introduces a number of major problems. Early in development, just when meta-

bolic fires burn most fiercely, well-developed means of nutrition are not yet in existence. Neither the zygote nor the spore or bud, nor in many cases the regenerating fragment, possesses its own photosynthetic or alimentary system. Three general solutions of this dilemma are possible, and all three occur. First, enough food may be packed into the reproductive unit to last till it differentiates a nutritional apparatus of its own. The starchy seed among plants and the yolky egg among animals are the best examples. Or, second, the developing system may be fed more or less continuously by the parent, via a persisting functional connection between the two. This is well illustrated by the parasitic sporophytes among mosses; by animal buds, which often remain attached to the parent; and by the placental mechanism of most mammals.

A third solution is frequently necessary in vegetative regeneration, when injury has put the nutritional apparatus out of commission, and reserve food sources are not available. Under such conditions, the regenerating unit may be able to draw foods from the structural framework of its own protoplasm. One result of such partial self-destruction is decrease in size, or *degrowth*. Another is the mobilization of enough raw materials for effective redevelpment on a smaller scale. Mouthless fragments of many animals may degrow and regenerate with the foods so obtained (Fig. 26.6).

With fuel supplies assured, respiration and synthesis become possible. But initial dilemmas must be resolved here as well. Intensive respiration requires oxygen, yet reproductive cells possess neither a specialized breathing system nor a specialized circulation system. Gas exchange must therefore occur through the cell surfaces. But this requirement limits the size of the reproductive cell, for diffusion alone could not be effective in a large protoplasmic mass. The requirement of smallness, however, limits the amount of food that can be stored in the reproductive cell, and this in turn places a time limit on the amount of development possible. Clearly, the developmental consequences of so "simple" a requirement as oxygen supply are exceedingly far-reaching. Much of the difference between various patterns of development, particularly among

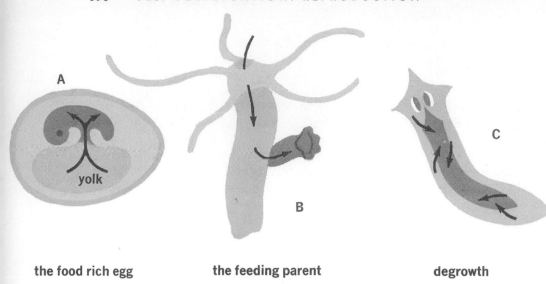

the food rich egg   the feeding parent   degrowth

FIG. 26.6. The three principal forms of nutrition in developing systems. From left to right: inclusion of food in the embryo (as in yolky egg); attachment of embryo to parent, and embryo nourished by parent (as in hydra buds); degrowth, i.e., food obtained by partial breakdown of body (as in planarians).

animals, actually results from varied evolutionary attempts to reconcile the demands of morphogenesis and differentiation with the demands of developmental metabolism.

Once gas-supply problems are solved, respiration may proceed. The molecular equipment for energy production is inherited complete by all reproductive units and is more or less fully functional from the start. This is an absolute necessity for survival. But such is not the case for protoplasmic syntheses. Only relatively few kinds of synthetic reactions are possible initially. Most of the molecular equipment required for intricate developmental syntheses must itself first develop. End-products of a first round of synthesis must become the starting materials for a second, more complex round. In this manner, synthetic capacities must be increased and broadened progressively. Evidently synthesis metabolism is as much a *result* of development as it is a prerequisite; it is one aspect of chemodifferentiation.

Morphogenesis, differentiation, and metabolism are three of the universal components of every developmental process. It should be stressed that the boundaries between these three are not at all sharp. Any one of them grades into, and overlaps with, each of the other two. Architectural development cannot be achieved without operational de-

velopment. And the nature of the operations in turn determines the design of the architecture. But operations and architecture together depend on, and at the same time make possible, metabolic development. Any one part of the developmental process thus can be regarded as "merely" a phase of any other. The point is that development is a unified, four-dimensional space-time continuum of events. And while the human observer may, for purposes of analysis, dissect from this continuum any number of parts, such parts are selected quite arbitrarily for human convenience. Development as it actually occurs in nature knows nothing of them.

The Control of Development

THE PROBLEM

How does a reproductive unit happen to give rise to just the right kinds and the right numbers of parts? If the head of an earthworm is cut off, the worm develops a new head: not two, or three, or half a head, but one, and only one; and not another tail, but another head. Even more strikingly, a single reproductive cell does not yet possess any of the features of the adult. How then does it happen to produce just one head and one tail, not two or more of each, but in a man, for example, two arms and two legs, not one of each? And why arms and legs at all—why not wings or fins?

This brings us to the most puzzling of all aspects of development. What integrates development? How do morphogenesis, differentiation, and metabolism mesh together to produce an elegant, sensibly functioning whole? By any standard, this smooth, seemingly unerring directedness, and this persistent, concerted advancing toward **wholeness,** is probably the most dramatic and most remarkable property of development. The headless earthworm, for example, never ceases its quiet internal revolution till it has a new head. The armless salamander never halts the violent shuffling of its molecules until the last finger is again in place. The transfigurations of the egg or the bud do not stop before the adult whole has come into being. Evidently, the healthy developing system behaves as if it "knew" its objectives precisely, and it proceeds without apparent trial and error. For normally, there is no underdevelopment, no overdevelopment, and there are no probing excursions along the way. Development is *directed* straight toward wholeness (Fig. 26.7).

Only one conclusion can be drawn: the course of development must somehow be rigorously *controlled.* Such control represents a fourth major component of every developmental process. The attempt to understand it, and the ways in which it produces directed wholeness, have already taken centuries of man's best thought and are likely to take several more. Today it is fashionable to say that genes control development, as they control every other living process. This is unquestionably correct. But again such an answer is not very informative and is actually little more than a restatement of the problem. *How* do genes control development? More specifically, how does a particular gene, through control over a particular enzyme or other protein, regulate a particular developmental occurrence? Answers to such small problems are just beginning to be obtained. And the collective larger issue, the controlled, directed emergence of wholeness in an entire organism, that remains a matter of future research.

Whenever in the past a pressing problem has defied easy analysis, man has turned to speculation

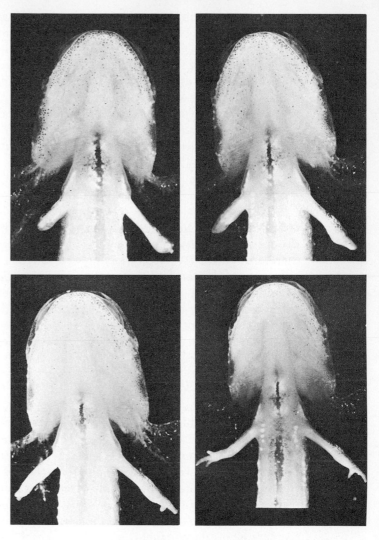

FIG. 26.7.   Both arms of this salamander larva were amputated, one above and one below the elbow. From top left to bottom right, this sequence of photos shows the degree of regeneration attained after 1, 14, 22, and 31 days, respectively. The problem of development, in this or any other living unit: how is wholeness established, how does protoplasm "know" when it is or is not whole, and in the latter case, how does it "know" what its particular pattern of wholeness must be? (Courtesy of Dr. Charles Thornton, Kenyon College.)

and generalization. The problem of developmental control provides a beautiful and famous example of this. Two opposing viewpoints have long been in vogue here. One of these is metaphysical. It is based on philosophical assumptions, and it can be described by three words: **vitalism, teleology,** and **preformation.** The other is scientific, and it is based on rational observation and experiment. It is similarly tripartite: **mechanism, causalism, epigenesis.**

VITALISM-MECHANISM

Vitalism is the doctrine of the supernatural. It holds, essentially, that supernatural powers control the operations of living matter and that such powers therefore control development and give it the direction toward wholeness. Since the supernatural is, by definition, beyond reach of the natural, it cannot be investigated by natural means. Hence the vitalistic explanation of development is untestable by experiment, and it rests entirely on faith. Rather than providing explanations, vitalism avoids explanations.

The opposing view is mechanism, which holds that the operations of living matter are governed entirely by natural law and are amenable to experimental analysis. If all physical and chemical phenomena in living matter can be accounted for, no other phenomena will remain. Therefore, the controlling agent of development must reside within the developing system itself and must consist of physical and chemical events *only.* Hence the directedness of development must be a result of internal, automatic *self-direction.*

In various guises and under various names, mechanists and vitalists have probably existed ever since man began to contemplate nature. Vitalistic ideas continue today partly because man is not notably rational, partly because nature is still very incompletely understood in mechanistic terms. Note, incidentally, that mechanism does not imply a denial of God. However, it does imply that such influence as God may have had must have ceased with His creation of natural law.

The mechanist-vitalist controversy is relatively quiescent today, largely because, during the last century, mechanists have been so signally successful in interpreting natural events, while vitalists have been signally unsuccessful. In the field of development, the last vitalist of note was the German embryologist Hans Driesch. During the closing decades of the nineteenth century, he and another German, Wilhelm Roux, carried out virtually the same types of experiments on developing animal eggs. But whereas Driesch could see in development only proof of his metaphysical preconceptions, Roux saw the phenomenon in a mechanistic light, and his work provided the momentum for all developmental studies since.

TELEOLOGY-CAUSALISM

Teleology and causalism both attempt to answer the same problem: how can a terminal state be implicit in the initial state? For example, how does an egg "know" in just what way it is supposed to develop?

The teleological view is that the beginning has actual foreknowledge of the end and that the course of a natural process is guided by this foreknowledge. All nature is therefore goal-directed and goal-seeking. Nothing happens by chance, but everything happens on purpose. The purpose is the fulfillment of preordained goals. In development, the preordained goal is the adult state, and all earlier developmental processes purposely strive to reach this state of wholeness. The striving is directed and oriented, because the egg has foreknowledge of what the adult state is to be. Evidently, teleology "explains" the end state by simply assuming it given at the beginning. And in thereby putting the future into the past, the effect before the cause, it negates time. Teleology (often also called "finalism") clearly leans toward the supernatural, and it is, in fact, a refined form of vitalism. The key difference is that in vitalism the supernatural is assumed to be external to a process, whereas in teleology it resides within the process itself.

Causalism denies foreknowledge of terminal states, preordination, purposes, and goals. It holds that natural events take place *sequentially.* Cause produces effect, and effect becomes new cause.

Events occur only as other events *permit* them to occur, not as preordained goals or purposes make them occur. End states are consequences, not foregone conclusions, of beginning states.

All biologists today agree that living phenomena are causal, not teleological. Yet teleological reasoning is still heard surprisingly often, particularly from students. For example, "eggs have yolk *in order to* provide food for development"; "the *purpose* of the heart is to pump blood"; "the ancestors of birds evolved wings *so that* they could fly." The first statement here implies that eggs can "foresee" the nutritional problem in development and that food will be required; therefore they proceed to store up some. In effect, eggs are given human mentality. The teleologist is always anthropocentric; that is, he implies that the natural events he discusses have minds like his. Substitute "and" for every "so that" or "in order to," and "function" for every "purpose" in biological statements, and they become properly nonteleological.

PREFORMATION-EPIGENESIS

The ideas of preformation and epigenesis are refined forms of teleology and causalism, respectively. They too deal with the problem of how end states are attained. Preformationist notions originated in antiquity, but they came into new vogue during the seventeenth and eighteenth centuries, following the invention of the microscope. Many who used this new tool became convinced that inside an egg one could see, fully formed though in miniature, all the structures and organs of the future adult. And that inside the miniature eggs of this miniature adult are present the even more miniature parts of the next generation, and so on ad infinitum. On this box-within-a-box-within-a-box principle, development would consist simply of the growth of the outermost "container." In preformation, as in teleology, we note, the end is given at the beginning.

The concept of preformation became extremely popular, and extremely ridiculous; like teleology and vitalism, it was an attempt to find in nature proof for philosophical preconceptions. Some of the most illustrious names of the time subscribed to preformationist notions in varying degree—Leibniz, Spallanzani, Reaumur, Swammerdam, to some extent Malpighi, and many others. Some thought to see in sperms, not in eggs, the boxed-in future generations, and violent academic debates ensued between "spermists" and "ovists." Others logically argued that the eggs of Eve must have contained the whole human race to its last member, including all the parasites which man carries. Many of the most ardent preformationists never actually bothered to look at an egg.

An epigenetic view becomes unavoidable once the egg is seen without metaphysical bias. Adult structures are simply not there, but they develop gradually, anew in each generation. Development is an unfolding, an emerging, or, in technical terminology, an epigenesis. The wholeness of the end condition is not explicit, but is merely implicit, in the beginning. And this necessitates caution in interpreting the meaning of epigenesis. For it would be incorrect to think that absolutely nothing is preformed in the egg. Genetic instructions and initial metabolic equipment certainly are given from the start. That much is preformed. Early notions were ridiculous only in their assumption of *actual* preformation of parts. *Potential* preformation cannot be denied.

Today, the great problem is to attempt to understand development as an epigenetic process, self-directing, self-controlling, and unfolding in stages from a rudimentary inheritance to a full-bodied wholeness. This is to understand how, at every developmental stage, only certain interactions occur among many possible interactions; how the kinds, the amounts, the timing, and the sequences of given interactions regulate the kinds, the amounts, the timing, and the sequences of others; how, in short, any one developmental event is both a necessary and sufficient effect of preceding events and a necessary and sufficient cause of succeeding events. The problem adds up to an identification of living control devices. For just as a heart self-adjusts the speed of its beat, as a liver self-regulates its glycogen content, so also does a reproductive unit self-control its own development.

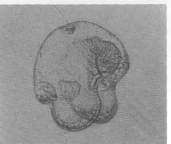

FIG. 26.8. A variety of larvae. Top left: a caterpillar. Top middle: a *pluteus* larva, characteristic of sea urchins. Far right: a *brachiolaria* larva, characteristic of starfish. Middle: a *pilidium* larva, characteristic of proboscis worms. Bottom right, a *Mueller's* larva, characteristic of flatworms. (Pilidium, courtesy of Dr. Philip Grant; caterpillar, Carolina Biological Supply Co.; others, General Biological Supply House, Inc.)

We conclude, therefore, that *development is an* **epigenetic causal mechanism.** Through morphogenesis, differentiation, and metabolism, it brings about the gametic, sporulative, or vegetative formation of organisms.

We now consider some of the ways in which these forces actually transform single cells into whole organisms.

The Pattern of Development

THE MAIN PHASES

The course of development varies considerably according to whether the starting unit is a zygote, a spore or a bud, or a regenerating fragment.

The Sexual Pattern

Zygotic development starts with **fertilization** and leads then to the formation of an **embryo.** The embryonic period is very distinct in animal development, but it occurs also, less distinctly, among plants. During the embryonic period, all basic structures and functions of the body are elaborated in at least rough detail. In most animals, the embryonic phase typically terminates with a process of **hatching,** in which the embryo emerges from its original egg envelopes and becomes a free-living **larva.**

A larval phase is characteristic of virtually all animal groups, but it does not occur in plants and is also more or less absent in given animal subgroups (e.g., birds, mammals). Larvae are transient organisms playing a variety of roles (Fig. 26.8). For example, they may function in geographic dispersal, especially if the adult is sessile or sluggish (e.g., clams, many worms, tunicates). Or they may serve as temporary feeding machines, which accumulate enough raw materials, in the form of larval protoplasm, to make lengthy further development possible (e.g., insect caterpillars). Or they may represent a developmental stage of ancestral organisms (e.g., frog tadpoles, which constitute an ancestral "fish" stage of development).

Whatever the significance of the larva, this temporary organism eventually undergoes **metamorphosis,** a more or less sudden transformation into the **adult** condition (Fig. 26.9). It should be stressed that this last phase in the developmental history of an individual is not any more static than preceding phases. On the contrary, the components of the adult are steadily being demolished and redesigned or replaced, and in this continuing turnover, internal as well as external features become altered. Adolescence so passes into maturity, maturity into senescence, and only death brings development to a halt.

Thus, the typical developmental pattern of animal gametes is a four-step sequence: *fertilization →* *embryo → larva → adult* (Fig. 26.10). Plant gametes characteristically develop in three steps, the larval phase being omitted.

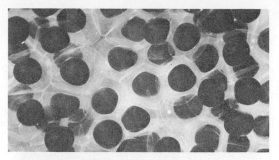

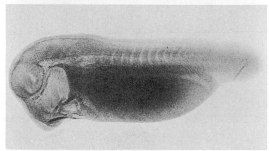

FIG. 26.9. Metamorphosis. This immature starfish, just metamorphosed, has formed from a brachiolaria larva shown in Fig. 26.8. Note the immature tube feet and the incompletely developed water-vascular system. Another illustration of metamorphosis may be found in Fig. 9.18. (General Biological Supply House, Inc.)

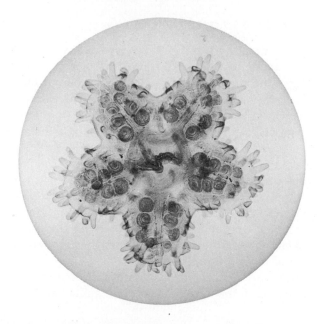

FIG. 26.10. These stages of the life cycle of frogs symbolize the main stages in the sexual development of animals generally. From top to bottom: egg, embryo, larva, adult. (Eggs, Carolina Biological Supply Co.; tadpole, American Museum of Natural History; others, General Biological Supply House, Inc.)

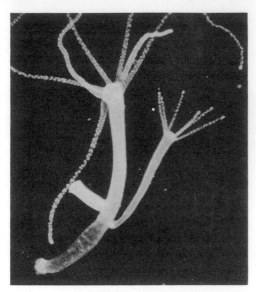

FIG. 26.11. Asexual development. Two buds are developing on this parental hydra, and when the buds are fully grown they separate from the parent and take up independent existence. Formation and maturation of such a bud do not involve any sexual processes, and development occurs in a smooth, single sequence of events. (Courtesy of Dr. Roman Vishniac, Albert Einstein College of Medicine, Yeshiva University, New York.)

The Asexual Pattern

In sharp contrast to the lengthy multistage course of sexual development, all forms of asexual development are exceedingly direct. In the development of spores, buds, or regenerating fragments, there is no sex, hence no fertilization; there is no embryo, hence also no hatching; and there is no larva, hence also no metamorphosis. Instead, the reproductive unit becomes an adult in a smoothly continuous, single developmental step (Fig. 26.11).

We recall that the only essential initial difference between sexual and asexual development is the presence or absence of the sexual process itself. It is this which makes the sexual and asexual patterns of development so radically different. For unlike spores or buds or regenerating fragments, an egg is *more* than simply a reproductive unit. As we have seen, it is also the agent for sex; that is, it is an *adaptive* device. Through fertilization, the egg acquires new genes, and this may endow the future offspring with new, better adapted features. Therefore, if the mature adult actually is to display the new features, they must be *developed* during the transition from egg to adult. Embryonic and larval periods are the result. These phases provide the opportunity for translating the genetic instructions acquired sexually by the zygote into the adaptively improved structures and functions of the adult. Spores, buds, and regenerating fragments do not acquire new genetic instructions through sex; hence equivalent time for executing such instructions is not needed. Hence also there are no embryos and no larvae here (Fig. 26.12).

Of all forms and phases of development in various plants and animals, the *embryonic* phase of animals is undoubtedly the most dramatic and spectacular. Partly for this reason, it has been studied most. Indeed, developmental investigations originally were carried out only within the field of animal *embryology*, which today is but one of many subsciences within the broad science of development. The development of animal embryos is outlined in what follows, and Chaps. 8 and 24 may be consulted again for a corresponding outline of plant development.

THE EMBRYONIC PHASE

Animals featuring external fertilization and aquatic embryos have received the most attention. Eggs and sperms of such animals may be put into a dish of water, and fertilization and development may then be observed under the microscope. Moreover, such eggs and embryos may be experimented on readily. Much of our knowledge of embryology has actually come from experiments on frog and other aquatic vertebrate embryos, and from sea urchin and other aquatic invertebrate embryos. Much has also been learned by cutting windows into developing chicken eggs, and by observing, and experimenting on, the exposed embryos. Comparative studies have shown that, although the details may often vary considerably, certain basic features are common to the development of all animal embryos.

Cleavage

The first clearly visible event after fertilization is **cleavage,** the repeated division of the zygote into many cells. Growth does not occur during this phase; hence, as cleavage proceeds, the cells become progressively smaller. The original egg, we recall, is a comparatively huge cell. Cleavage continues until the cells have a species-characteristic mature size (Fig. 26.13).

Even before cleavage begins, invisible and poorly understood molecular changes occur in the egg which establish the basic polarity and symmetry of the future embryo. Two categories of eggs may be distinguished here: **mosaic,** or *determined,* eggs and **regulative,** or *undetermined,* eggs.

The first type is encountered among mollusks, annelids, insects, and many other invertebrates. In the eggs of these animals, the future developmental fate of every portion of the protoplasm becomes fixed unalterably before or at the time of fertilization. The zygote therefore is already fully polarized, and the head-tail, dorsal-ventral, and left-right axes are firmly established. Moreover, each portion of the egg protoplasm already "knows" what it is going to develop into. When cleavage in such an egg gives rise to an increasing number of cells, it is possible by experimental means to separate these cells from

FIG. 26.12. Sexual vs. asexual development. In sexual development (top), new genetic instructions are introduced into the zygote via the gametes, and during subsequent embryonic and larval stages these instructions are elaborated explicitly. Hence the mature offspring may differ to a greater or lesser extent from the parent. In asexual development (bottom), on the other hand, new genetic instructions are not introduced, and the offspring therefore resembles the parent exactly.

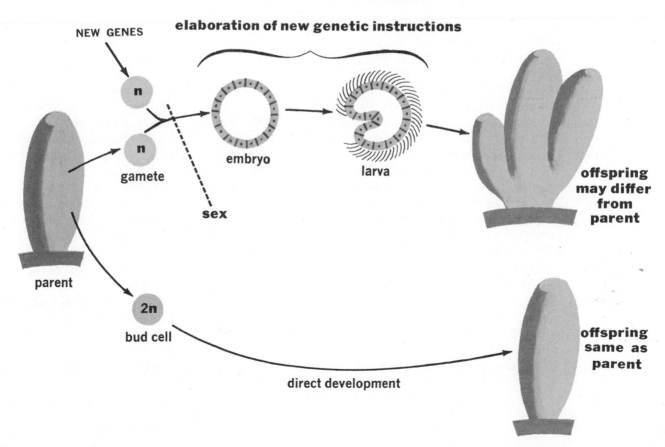

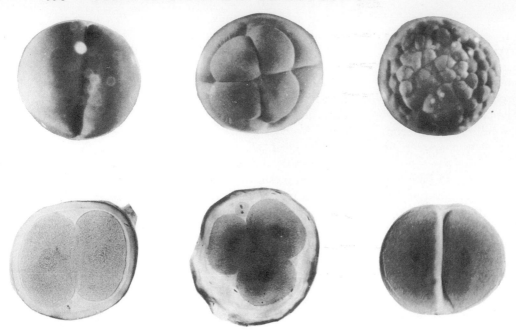

FIG. 26.13. Cleavage. Top: left to right, 2-cell stage, 8-cell stage, and later stage in cleavage of frog eggs. Bottom: left and middle, 2- and 4-cell stage in cleavage of rabbit egg. Bottom right: 2-cell stage in cleavage of starfish egg. Note, especially in top series, how cell size decreases with successive cleavage divisions. (Top, Carolina Biological Supply Co.; bottom, General Biological Supply House, Inc.)

one another. Each isolated cell then continues to develop and forms a *partial* embryo. It produces the same portion of the embryo it would have produced if the cleaving egg had been left intact (Fig. 26.14). In short, the determined egg is like a quiltwork, a mosaic, in which each protoplasmic portion contributes a fixed, unalterable part to the whole; and the nature of the mosaic is established before or, at the latest, at the time of fertilization.

By contrast, vertebrate and echinoderm eggs are examples of the regulative variety. In these, the future fate of various egg portions becomes unalterably fixed too, but such fixing occurs comparatively much later. Moreover, different features of the future animal become fixed at different times. For example, at fertilization, only the main egg axis is determined. That is, the direction of "top" and "bottom" is already given, but no other aspect of polarity and symmetry, or of any other feature, is as yet fixed (see Fig. 26.13).

That this is so can be demonstrated very strikingly by experiment. If the two cells formed by the first cleavage division are left as they are, then these two cells will eventually form the left and right halves of the future animal. Further, protoplasm in the center of the egg will develop into cen-

tral internal structures of the adult. But if the two cells are separated from one another, then the cells do *not* develop into two half animals, as would be the case in a mosaic egg. Instead, the two cells develop into two *whole* animals. Moreover, the central protoplasm of the original egg now gives rise to the right side of one whole animal, and to the left side of another. Evidently, central protoplasm at the two-cell stage does not yet "know" whether to form left, right, or internal mid-body structures. In short, it is not yet determined (Fig. 26.15).

Analogously, if the cells of later cleavage stages are isolated and grown separately, then each cell may again give rise to a whole instead of a partial animal. But a limit is reached fairly soon. After the first four cleavages, for example, 16 cells are present. If these are separated from one another, 16 whole animals cannot be obtained. Instead, each cell forms only one-sixteenth of an embryo, as it would have done if the 16-cell stage had been left intact. In other words, the developmental fate of the cells has become determined by now, and the embryo henceforth is like a mosaic.

We may conclude that mosaic and regulative eggs differ mainly in the timing of developmental determination. The early timing in mosaic eggs contrasts with the comparatively late timing in regulative eggs. During the undetermined phase in regulative eggs, any cell may substitute for any other cell and may develop into any structure, including a whole animal. Note here that developmental determination is a form of differentiation and that the underlying mechanism is still completely unknown.

Note also that the formation of two or more whole animals, from separated cells of early undetermined embryos, is equivalent to the experimental production of identical **twins**, triplets, quadruplets, etc. Natural twinning undoubtedly occurs through similar separations. But the forces or accidents which actually isolate such cells in nature are not understood. If the cells are separated incompletely, Siamese twins result. This too can be demonstrated by laboratory experiments (Fig. 26.16). Twins are **identical** when they develop from a single fertilized egg, as above. They are **fraternal** when two or more whole eggs are fertilized individually at the same time. Fraternal twins are formed normally by cats, pigs, and other litter-producing animals. The offspring here may be of different sexes, and they need not resemble one another. By contrast, identical twins are of the same sex, and they do resemble one another. Indeed they often are structural mirror images.

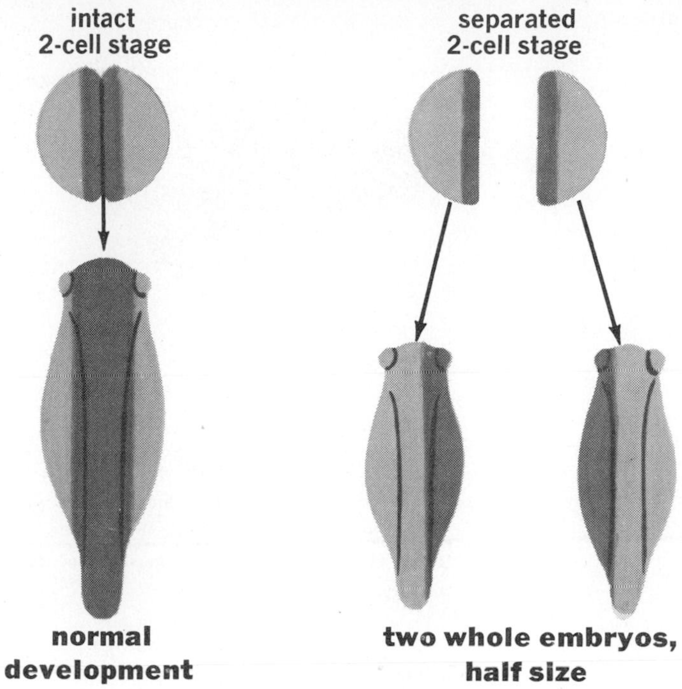

intact 2-cell stage

separated 2-cell stage

normal development

two whole embryos, half size

FIG. 26.15. Development in regulative eggs. If the cells of early cleavage stages of such eggs are isolated experimentally, each cell develops into a smaller, but whole, organism. The inference is that the fate of the protoplasm of early cleavage stages is still undetermined. For example, the central protoplasm of the 2-cell stage normally forms central body parts (left figures, shaded portions). But if the cells are separated, the central protoplasm forms left structures in one case, right structures in the other (right figures, shaded portions).

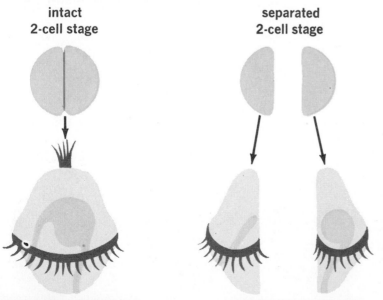

intact 2-cell stage

separated 2-cell stage

normal development

two half-embryos

FIG. 26.14. Development in mosaic eggs. If the cells of early cleavage stages of such eggs are isolated experimentally, each cell develops as it would have in any case, even if it had not been isolated. The inference is that the fate of the protoplasm of mosaic eggs is determined very early.

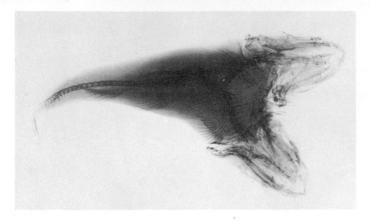

FIG. 26.16. X-ray photo of Siamese twinning in fish. Abnormalities like these result from incomplete cytoplasmic divisions of cells during early cleavage. (American Museum of Natural History.)

Gastrulation

The ultimate result of normal cleavage is a ball of a few hundred cells, called a **blastula.** This ball may be hollow or solid, and it represents a developmental stage characteristic of all multicellular animals (Fig. 26.17). Cell divisions continue in a blastula, but growth now occurs as well, and successive cell generations no longer become smaller. The main subsequent developmental event is the transformation of the blastula into an embryo consisting of three distinct layers of tissue. This process of transformation is called *gastrulation,* and the three-layered result is the **gastrula.** It too is a developmental stage common to all multicellular animals.

Patterns of gastrulation vary widely. For purposes of illustration, we may examine events in the embryos of sea urchins and other echinoderms. In these, the blastula is a hollow, one-layered sphere. When gastrulation occurs, one side of this sphere **invaginates;** that is, it becomes dented inward. A two-layered cup-shaped structure is formed in this manner. The resulting outer layer is called the **ectoderm,** and the inner layer, the **endoderm** (see Fig. 26.17).

Later, in most animals a third tissue layer, called the *mesoderm,* arises between the ectoderm and the endoderm. In echinoderms, vertebrates, and certain other animals, the mesoderm arises as an outgrowth from the endoderm. In another group of animals, the mesoderm is an outgrowth from the ectoderm. And in a third group, mesoderm forms from both ectoderm and endoderm. See Chap. 31 for a fuller discussion of these different methods and the animals in which they occur. Here we may note that, according to its manner of origin, the mesoderm may be either an **endomesoderm** or an **ectomesoderm,** or a combination of both (Fig. 26.18). Regardless of how mesoderm originates, the fully formed gastrula is a hollow, triple-walled ball with an opening at one point.

FIG. 26.17. The early development of starfish embryos. From left to right: late cleavage; blastula; invagination, early gastrula; late gastrula, beginning of mesoderm formation; mesoderm formation under way. (General Biological Supply House, Inc.)

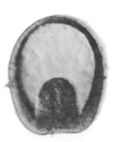

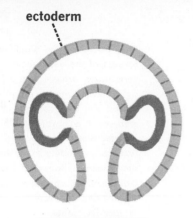
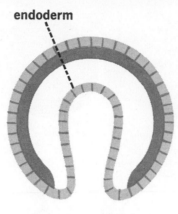
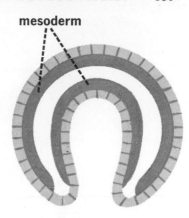

ectoderm   endoderm   mesoderm

ENDOMESODERM   ECTOMESODERM   ENDO- AND
(e.g., vertebrates)   (e.g., rotifers)   ECTOMESODERM
(e.g., mollusks)

FIG. 26.18.   Methods of mesoderm formation in different animal groups (diagrammatic). Left: pouches grow out from endoderm. Middle: cells migrate inward from ectoderm. Right: cells migrate inward from both ectoderm and endoderm. A more detailed illustration will be found in Fig. 29.7.

After gastrulation, the patterns of development of different animal groups differ very widely, according to the type of organism to be produced. But, in the gastrula, the body parts of the future offspring are already well blocked out. In vertebrates, for example, the opening in the wall of the gastrula, called the **blastopore,** marks the region of the future anus. At the opposite end of the gastrula a mouth will later break through. The interior cavity, the **archenteron,** is the future gut cavity. The endoderm which lines this cavity will develop into the alimentary system, the breathing system, and all glands and ducts associated with these: liver, pancreas, salivary glands, trachea, etc. The ectoderm will give rise to the whole nervous system and to the skin, including hair, nails, and skin glands. The mesoderm will form the remaining parts of the body, namely, bones, muscles, and the circulatory, excretory, and reproductive systems. The endocrine system arises partly from ectoderm, partly from mesoderm, and partly from endoderm (Fig. 26.19).

Clearly, with the formation of the gastrula, the basic architectural design of the body is already established. In man, the gastrula forms a few days after fertilization, roughly when the embryo reaches the uterus.

FIG. 26.19.   The general structure of a vertebrate gastrula, and the adult organ systems formed by each of the primary germ layers (diagrammatic).

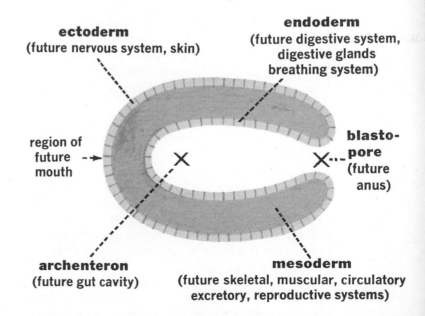

ectoderm
(future nervous system, skin)

endoderm
(future digestive system, digestive glands breathing system)

region of future mouth

blasto-pore
(future anus)

archenteron
(future gut cavity)

mesoderm
(future skeletal, muscular, circulatory excretory, reproductive systems)

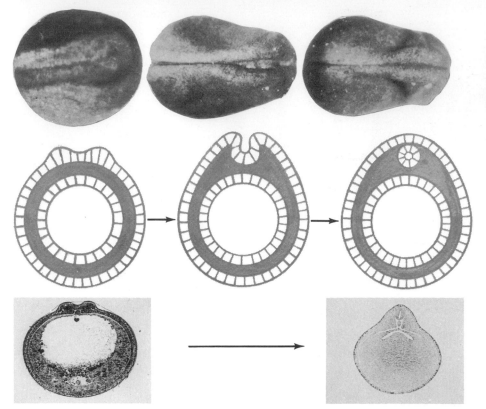

FIG. 26.20. The initial development of the nervous system in vertebrates (frogs). Top: left to right, dorsal views, progressive stages. The anterior ends of the embryos are toward the right. Middle: diagrammatic cross sections corresponding to the stages shown above. Bottom: photos of cross sections corresponding to the first and last stages illustrated in middle series. Note large amounts of yolk in bottom photos. (Top photos, courtesy of Dr. Roberts Rugh, from "Experimental Embryology," Burgess Publishing Company; bottom photos, General Biological Supply House, Inc.)

Later Events: Induction

Ectoderm, mesoderm, and endoderm are referred to collectively as the **primary germ layers.** How are these layers transformed into well-defined body parts? The principle involved is fundamentally the same in all cases. We may illustrate by considering the development of, for example, the nervous system (Fig. 26.20).

On the upper surface of the gastrula develop two ridges, one along each side of the mid-line. These ridges are folds of ectoderm, which grow upward and toward each other. Soon they meet along the mid-line. As their edges fuse, they form a tube of ectoderm which runs from front to back and is covered over by an outer ectoderm layer. This tube is the basis of the nervous system; it develops into brain in the front part of the embryo and into spinal cord in the hind part.

The essential event here, we note, is the outfolding of a tissue layer, followed by fusion of the fold edges. Virtually all other phases of embryonic development are similarly a matter of outfolding or infolding, outpouching or inpouching, of portions of the three germ layers of the gastrula. For example, limb buds form by combined outpouchings from ectoderm and mesoderm. Lungs and digestive glands develop as outpouchings from various levels of the endoderm. The eye develops in part as an outpouching from the brain. Evidently, much of development after gastrulation is *morphogenesis,* that is, directed differential growth and form-regulating movements.

But equally conspicuous at this time are progressive cell, tissue, and organ *differentiations.* These accompany, and in large measure probably are prerequisite for, the morphogenetic changes. Many of the differentiative changes occur as a result of *induction,* that is, as noted earlier, interaction among developing parts. We may illustrate by examining again the early development of the nervous system.

In amphibian embryos it is possible to cut out the dorsal ectoderm which, under normal circumstances, would fold up and form a neural tube. If this excised tissue is then put into a nutrient solution, or if it is transplanted to another region of the embryo, it will not form a neural tube, and its cells will not differentiate into neurons. This suggests that the dorsal mesoderm, which in an intact embryo lies just under the dorsal ectoderm, normally affects this ectoderm in such a way that it will fold out and differentiate into neural tissue. That this is actually so can be shown by another experiment. The dorsal *mesoderm* can be cut out and transplanted, for example, into the belly region of an embryo, just under the belly ectoderm. Normally, belly ectoderm forms only skin. But if dorsal mesoderm lies under it, it will form a neural tube, and its cells will differentiate into neural tissue (Fig. 26.21).

The implications are clear. Somehow, the dorsal mesoderm of a normal embryo *induces* the outfolding of the overlying ectoderm, hence the formation of ridges and the later differentiation of neural tissue. Analogously, induction of this sort can be shown to be at work *wherever* outfoldings or infoldings, outgrowths or ingrowths, develop in the embryo. The development of the eye provides a particularly striking example.

Eye development (Fig. 26.22) begins with the

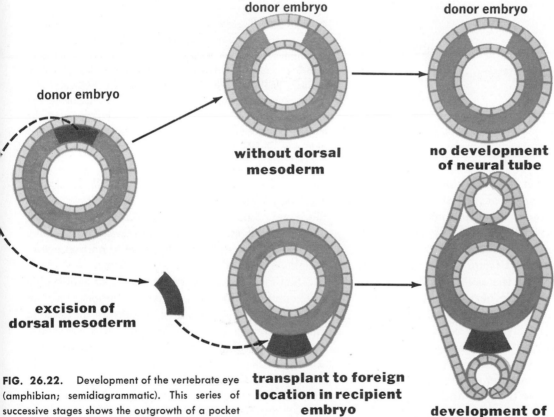

donor embryo

donor embryo

donor embryo

without dorsal mesoderm

no development of neural tube

excision of dorsal mesoderm

transplant to foreign location in recipient embryo

development of supernumerary neural tube

FIG. 26.21. Neural induction. If the dorsal mesoderm of a donor embryo is transplanted under the belly ectoderm of a host embryo, then the transplant will induce the formation of an abnormally located neural tube in the host.

FIG. 26.22. Development of the vertebrate eye (amphibian; semidiagrammatic). This series of successive stages shows the outgrowth of a pocket from the brain, contact of this pocket with the outer body ectoderm, formation of an eyecup, gradual differentiation of a lens from the outer ectoderm, and differentiation of the pigmented and other tissue layers of the eyeball. (Courtesy of Dr. Dietrich Bodenstein; from originals of figures 2 and 3, *J. Exptl. Zool.*, vol. 108, pp. 96 and 97, by permission.)

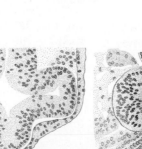
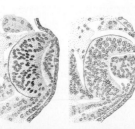

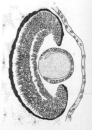

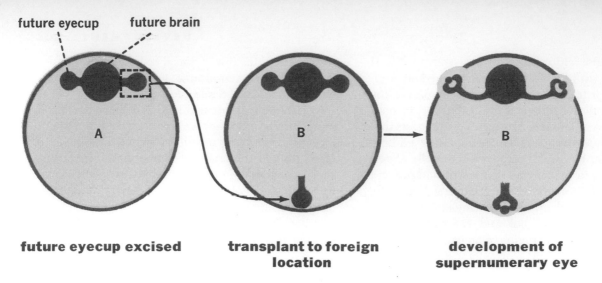

future eyecup   future brain

A

future eyecup excised

B

transplant to foreign
location

B

development of
supernumerary eye

FIG. 26.23. Experiments in eye transplantation. Diagram: if an embryonic eyecup is excised from a donor embryo **A** and is transplanted into an abnormal location in a host embryo **B**, then a structurally perfect eye will develop at that abnormal location. Photo: a larva of the amphibian *Amblystoma*, with two supernumerary eyes grafted into abnormal locations. The procedure followed that outlined in the diagram, and the photo was taken 43 days after the transplant operation. (Photo from original figure 16, S. R. Detwiler and R. H. Van Dyke, *J. Exptl. Zool.,* vol. 69, p. 157.)

growing out of a pocket from the side of the future brain. This pocket is narrow at the base and bulbous at the tip. Soon the bulbous portion invaginates, or indents, from the forward end, and a double-layered cup is formed. The cup represents the future eyeball. As it grows outward from the brain, its rim comes into contact with the outer ectoderm layer which, overlying the whole nervous system, represents the future skin. Just where the eyecup rests against it, the ectoderm layer now begins to thicken. This thickening eventually grows into a ball of cells, which is nipped off toward the inside. It fits neatly into the mouth of the eyecup, and it represents the future lens. The cells of this ball and the ectoderm overlying them later become transparent. Thus the basic structure of the eye is established.

The following type of experiment has shown dramatically how these developmental processes are brought about. It is possible to cut off the eyecup and its stalk before they have grown very far. Eyecup and stalk may then be transplanted. For example, they may be inserted into a region just under the belly ectoderm of an embryo. Under such conditions, the patch of belly ectoderm overlying

the eyecup soon thickens, a ball of cells is nipped off toward the inside, and a lens differentiates! Moreover, lens and overlying skin become transparent. In effect, the transplanted structures have caused the formation of a structurally normal eye in a highly abnormal location (Fig. 26.23).

Similarly in all other processes of embryonic development. One tissue layer interacts with an adjacent one, and the latter is thereby induced to differentiate, to grow, to develop in a particular way. This developed tissue then interacts with another one in turn and induces it to develop. In short, sequential induction must occur if progressive development is to take place. As in the sequence dorsal mesoderm → neural tube → eyecup → lens, so also generally; one tissue is the stimulus for the differentiation of the next. This accounts well for the orderly, properly timed, and properly spaced elaboration of body parts.

Although inductive processes among embryonic tissues may be identified and described, the nature of such interactions in terms of reactions within and among cells is still quite obscure.

RESUME The ultimate result of these various occurrences is a fully formed embryo, clearly recognizable as a young stage of a particular species. Whether it later hatches and forms a larva or develops into an adult directly, it leads on to the emergence of a new individual, hence to the completion of the entire reproductive process.

This concludes the series of chapters on reproduction. We have found that the extension of protoplasm in space-time undoubtedly includes some of the most fascinating of all living processes, but also some of the least understood. We firmly recognize the self-perpetuative role of reproductive events, and we may describe these events in considerable detail. But, whether we deal with cell division or with plant and animal life cycles, with morphogenesis or with differentiation, we have so far been able only to peel off the outermost of the veils which hide the actual epigenetic causal mechanisms. Throughout, the ultimate controlling activity of genes either has been demonstrated already or is strongly suspected. In this regard, reproductive processes do not differ from those of steady-state control.

This brings us directly to the last ingredient of self-perpetuation, namely, adaptation. For here, even more obviously than in reproduction or in steady-state control, genes are at the root of all happenings too. As they reproduce, these time capsules of protoplasmic tradition become the basis of heredity; and out of heredity is woven the fabric of evolution.

REVIEW QUESTIONS 1. Define morphogenesis, differential growth, form-regulating movements, polarity. Through what types of growth processes does an organism enlarge in size? Explain the meaning of the phrase "Organisms grow from their molecules up."

2. What different types of symmetries are exhibited by living units? In what ways do polarity and symmetry circumscribe the form of an organism? Specify the polarity and symmetry of (*a*) man and (*b*) a tree. What is the role of differential growth in the development of form?

3. Define, and distinguish between, differentiation and modulation. What is the relation between differentiation and specialization? Cite examples of differentiative changes on the level of (*a*) molecules, (*b*) cells, (*c*) organisms, and (*d*) societies.

4. What general kinds of changes within cells might bring about cytodifferentiation? What is meant by contact interaction and distance interaction in connection with differentiation? Define "induction." What is the effect of differentiation on the functional versatility of living units. Give specific examples.

5. What role does metabolism play in development? How does metabolic rate vary during the developmental history of an organism? In what different ways may an incompletely developed reproductive unit acquire (*a*) nutrients and (*b*) respiratory gases? What cellular metabolic capacities (*a*) are and (*b*) are not in existence in a zygote?

6. Describe the general problem which must be answered if the control of development is to be understood. Review the concepts described by the terms (*a*) vitalism and mechanism, (*b*) teleology and causalism, and (*c*) preformation and epigenesis. What

bearing do these concepts have on the problem of development? Explain the meaning of the phrase "Development is an epigenetic causal mechanism."

7. Describe, and define, the principal developmental phases in the life history of an organism, if this history (*a*) includes and (*b*) does not include a sexual process. What is the significance of the greater number of phases under condition *a*? What events usually terminate (*a*) the embryonic period and (*b*) the larval period?

8. What events occur during the cleavage of an egg? What is meant by developmental determination? Distinguish between mosaic and regulative eggs. How can it be established by experiment whether a given egg is mosaic or regulative? In which animals do each of these egg types occur? How are twins formed? Distinguish between identical and fraternal twinning. Can identical twinning take place in mosaic eggs?

9. Describe the processes leading to the formation of (*a*) a blastula and (*b*) a gastrula. Define ectoderm, endoderm, mesoderm, blastopore, archenteron. How does mesoderm form in vertebrates? Which structural components of an adult vertebrate develop from each of the primary germ layers?

10. By what general processes of morphogenesis do the primary germ layers develop into adult structures? Illustrate this in the development of the nervous system and the eye. What differentiative role does induction play in such transformations? Again illustrate in the development of the nervous system and the eye, and describe supporting experiments.

SUGGESTED COLLATERAL READINGS

The first listing below focuses attention on reprints of several original articles, which describe fundamental and classical experiments in the field of embryonic development. The three texts cited next may be consulted for additional information on all topics discussed in this chapter. And the remaining sources are very good popular treatments of various specific topics dealt with here.

Gabriel, M. L., and S. Fogel: "Great Experiments in Biology," section on Embryonic Differentiation, Prentice-Hall, 1955.

Barth, L.: "Embryology," rev. ed., Dryden, 1953.

Waddington, C. H.: "Principles of Embryology," G. Allen, London, 1956.

Willier, B. H., P. A. Weiss, and V. Hamburger: "Analysis of Development," Saunders, 1955.

Bonner, J. T.: "Morphogenesis," Princeton University Press, 1952.

Newman, H. H.: "Multiple Human Births," Doubleday, 1940.

Dahlberg, G.: An Explanation of Twins, *Sci. American,* vol. 184, 1951.

Smith, C. S.: The Shape of Things, *Sci. American,* vol. 190, 1954.

Waddington, C. H.: How Do Cells Differentiate? *Sci. American,* vol. 189, 1953.

Rose, S. M.: Transformed Cells, *Sci. American,* vol. 181, 1949.

Danielli, J. F.: On Transplanting Nuclei, *Sci. American,* vol. 186, 1952.

Weisz, P. B.: The Embryologist and the Protozoon, *Sci. American,* vol. 188, 1953.

Moog, F.: Up from the Embryo, *Sci. American,* vol. 182, 1950.

————: The Biology of Old Age, *Sci. American,* vol. 179, 1948.

Lansing, A. I.: Experiments in Aging, *Sci. American,* vol. 188, 1953.

Balm, A. J.: Teleological Arguments, *Sci. Monthly,* vol. 58, 1944.

O N THE MOLECULAR as on the organismic level, in structure as in function, the living system is *adapted* to its environment. For example, among thousands of shapes that a fish *might* possess, it possesses precisely the one which is best suited for rapid locomotion in water. A bird is cast in a form eminently suited for aerial life, yet its ancestry traces to fish. Over long periods of time, clearly, protoplasm may change its particular adaptations in response to new environments.

Being adapted is a universal attribute of all organisms, and adaptation is the long-range process of development which creates and maintains this attribute. Through adaptation, organisms change *with* their environments, and this makes them potentially immortal as a group.

Based on steady-state control and reproduction, adaptation consists of three components: *sex, heredity,* and *evolution.* In this last series of chapters, therefore, we begin with an analysis of the adaptive roles of **sex and heredity** and continue with a similar analysis of evolution. Specifically, we discuss the **mechanism of evolution,** that is, the processes through which evolution is believed to occur. We next examine the historical **course of evolution** and survey here past plants and animals which the evolutionary mechanism has created. And we conclude with an account of the plants and animals living today, which together represent the current **result of evolution.**

PART

SELF-PERPETUATION: ADAPTATION

THE KEY PROBLEM in studies of heredity is to explain the inheritance of **likeness** and of **variation:** how an offspring usually comes to resemble its parents in certain major respects but differs from the parents in many minor respects. Are such hereditary patterns in any way regular and predictable, and if so, what are the underlying principles?

It should be clear that organisms do not inherit blue eyes, clever minds, red blood, or any other trait. Organisms inherit *genes,* not traits. Visible traits *develop* in an offspring, under the control of inherited genes and within the limitations imposed by given internal and external environments.

Genes cannot be seen, but traits can be. Studies of heredity therefore consist in examining the traits of successive generations of organisms and inferring from the visible likenesses and variations what the heredity of the genes has been. The first important studies of this sort were made in the last half of the nineteenth century, by the Austrian monk Gregor Mendel. He discovered two basic rules of inheritance, which laid the foundation for all later advances in understanding of processes of heredity.

Thus, a discussion of heredity today must include an examination of the general relationship between **genes and traits;** an account of the rules of **Mendelian inheritance;** and a survey of the main aspects of **non-Mendelian inheritance,** brought to light since the time of Mendel.

Genes and Traits

HEREDITY AND ENVIRONMENT

The pattern of inheritance varies according to whether reproduction is **uniparental** or **biparental.** Where an offspring is produced by a single parent, as in vegetative reproduction and in sporulation, the genes of the parent are passed on unchanged to the offspring. In uniparental reproduction, therefore, offspring and parent are genetically identical, and they usually display the same visible traits. The only source of genetic variation in such cases is **mutation.**

27

SEX
AND HEREDITY

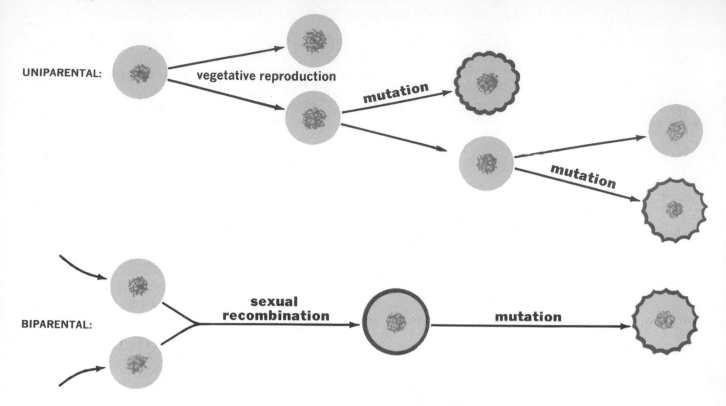

UNIPARENTAL: vegetative reproduction   mutation   mutation

BIPARENTAL: sexual recombination   mutation

FIG. 27.1.   The sources of genetic variations. In uniparental inheritance, the only source is mutation. In biparental inheritance, genetic variations may arise both by mutation and by sexual recombination of genes.

For example, if some gene of a plant spore undergoes a mutational change, then, and only then, may the offspring become genetically different from the parent. Trait variations may then be displayed too.

By contrast, *two* sources of genetic variation exist in cases of biparental, i.e., gametic, reproduction. One is again mutation, in this instance mutation in one or both gametes. The other is a direct result of sex. *Two* sets of genes are pooled in the zygote, and the genetic endowment of the offspring may therefore differ from that of either parent. Through such **sexual recombination** of genes, the offspring may become unlike the parents.

We conclude, for both uniparental and biparental reproduction, that *likeness* to parents will be inherited to the extent that the genes of the offspring are the same as those of the parents; and that *varia-*

tion will be inherited to the extent that mutation, recombination, or both, have changed the genes of the offspring (Fig. 27.1).

But inheriting a certain gene is not automatically equivalent to developing a certain trait. For the development of traits is affected by the environment. Genes supply a "reasonable promise," as it were, and the total environment of the genes subsequently permits, or does not permit, the translation of promise into reality.

The environment of genes includes, first of all, other genes. Indeed, gene-gene interactions are exceedingly common, as we shall see. The functional integration of genes in a cell is actually so intimate and so complex that it becomes relatively meaningless to speak of "a" gene, as if it were an independent, clearly distinct particle (see also Chap. 18).

Only the interacting totality of genes in a cell, called the **genome,** has functional reality.

The environment of genes also includes the cell cytoplasm, and it too influences the development of traits in major ways. For example, *all* cells of a plant possess flower-color genes, but only cells in the petals express that color. *All* cells of man possess eye-color genes, but only in iris cells does the color become explicit. Evidently, the cytoplasms of different cells are differentially sensitive to the genes they contain, and traits will be expressed differentially as a result (Fig. 27.2).

So-called "inherited" diseases must be interpreted in this light. Certain mental diseases, diabetes, alcoholism, cancer, and many other abnormalities are known to "run in families." What is inherited here is not the disease itself. A child of diabetic ancestry is not automatically diabetic. However, *susceptibility* to disease may be inherited. The genes are present, but before the disease can become explicit, specific cellular and external environments must make gene expression possible. In a similar vein, a person who performs physical exercise regularly will develop strong muscles, and so will acquire traits differing from those of a person who does not exercise. In both cases, however, the genes controlling muscular development may be the same.

We may therefore distinguish between **inherited variations** of traits, produced by basic genetic differences, and noninherited, **acquired variations** of traits, produced by environmental or developmental effects. And we are led to the fundamental principle that visible traits are always a product of inherited genes *and* of environment. To the extent that variations of traits may be advantageous to the organism in its way of life, heredity, like sex, has adaptive value.

CELLULAR AND SUPRACELLULAR TRAITS

It is almost as difficult to define "a" trait as it is to define "a" gene. For example, consider the trait of intelligence, characteristic of certain organisms and clearly hereditary in nature. Intelligence is not really "a trait." Inasmuch as it is a functional property of the brain, it is a composite property of millions of co-operating cells. Each of these contributes some particular function to the total trait, and specific genes in each of these cells control each of these functions. It is clear, therefore, that intelligence must be a combination of perhaps millions of different cellular traits, controlled by a large, equally unknown number of genes.

In very many instances, actually, what is normally regarded as a trait is of such composite nature. Body size, the fine structure and the functional capacities of organs, physical vigor, personality make-up, fertility, and many others, all are interaction

FIG. 27.2. Even though all cells of an organism possess the same kinds of genes, gene action is influenced differently by different cells, resulting in differential expression of traits. Thus all cells of a plant may have pigment-producing genes, but actual pigmentation may develop only in the cells of petals.

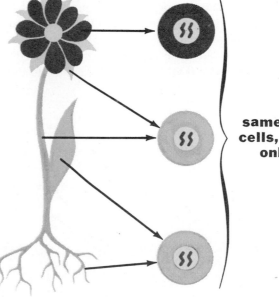

same genes in all cells, but pigment only in some

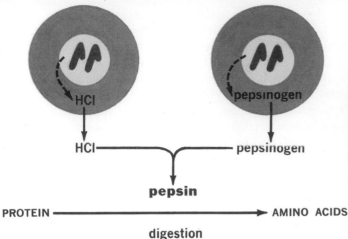

FIG. 27.3. Is the "trait" of being able to digest proteins one trait, or two or more? As shown here, capacity to digest proteins depends on at least two subordinate capacities, namely, manufacturing HCl and manufacturing pepsin or other proteinases. Hence the trait of protein digestion must be regarded as a composite rather than a single trait. Many different genes in different cells must cooperate to produce such a composite trait.

products of several dozens, or hundreds, or thousands of different genes (Fig. 27.3). Indeed, there is reason to believe that most of such highly composite traits are controlled by the collective action of possibly all genes of an organism, each contributing a tiny effect to the total trait. Such traits may then be expressed in a correspondingly great variety of ways. As is well known, for example, the expression of traits like body size or intelligence in different individuals may range from one extreme to another, through enormously varied series of intergradations.

But if *all* genes contribute to the control of a trait like body size, for example, and if *all* genes also control intelligence and other highly composite traits, then any *one* gene clearly must contribute to the control of *more* than one trait. We are led to the

generalization that *one trait may be controlled by many genes, and one gene may control many traits.* Note, however, that the meaning of such a generalization depends on the meaning of the terms "one" gene and "one" trait (Fig. 27.4).

In some instances, the functional relation between genes and traits is comparatively less complex. We know from Chap. 18 that the general pattern of gene action within a cell may be symbolized by the sequence: gene → enzyme → reaction → reaction product. Sometimes such a reaction product does not participate in the elaboration of a more complex trait, but constitutes a final trait itself. For example, a *pigment* produced within a cell is a gene-controlled reaction product, and it is often a visible *end*product, representing a final trait. In

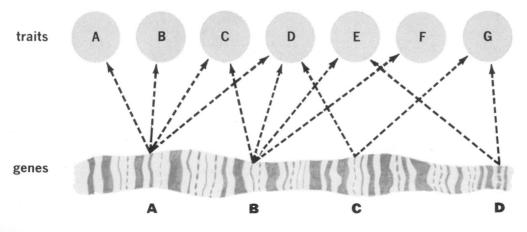

FIG. 27.4. Illustrating the principle that one trait (e.g., **D**) is controlled by many genes, and that one gene (e.g., **B**) controls many traits.

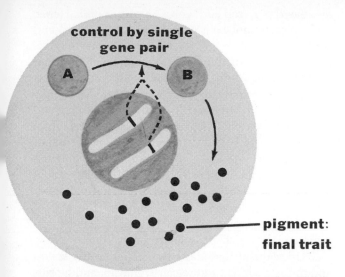

FIG. 27.5. In certain special cases, one gene is known to control just one trait. A cytoplasmic pigment may be a final trait, and a single gene may govern the metabolic reaction which produces such a pigment.

cases of this sort, a readily specifiable trait is linked directly with one particular gene (Fig. 27.5). From the pattern in which such a trait is expressed visibly in successive generations, one may readily infer the pattern of gene inheritance. It was from studies of just such color traits in plants that Mendel deduced his two rules of heredity. If he had happened to investigate, instead, any of the numerous composite traits of plants, then regularities in hereditary patterns would not have been clearly apparent and his name might not be immortal today.

Mendelian Inheritance

THE LAW OF SEGREGATION

Blending and the Chromosome Theory

In his spare time, Mendel bred and raised several kinds of garden plants, and he kept records of the kinds and numbers of offspring obtained from each mating. He knew, as did others, that a mating of two red-flowered snapdragons, for example, produced exclusively red-flowered offspring. Moreover,

all later generations too developed only red flowers. Similarly, a mating of two white-flowered snapdragons yielded exclusively white-flowered progeny in all subsequent generations. Evidently, red and white flower color were **true-breeding** traits (Fig. 27.6).

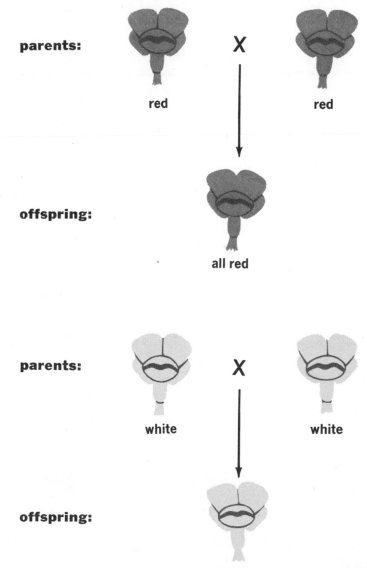

FIG. 27.6. True-breeding in snapdragons. If two red-flowered plants are mated, all offspring will be red-flowered (top); and if two white-flowered plants are mated, all offspring will be white-flowered (bottom).

parents: X

red   red

offspring:

all red

parents: X

white   white

offspring:

all white

It was also well known that when a red-flowered snapdragon was mated with a white-flowered plant, all offspring developed *pink* flowers. In Mendel's time, it was generally supposed that such pinkness resulted from a *blending* of red and white plant pigments, as if paints had been mixed together. Mendel now reasoned that if blending really occurred, pinkness should be true-breeding too, and a mating of two pink-flowered plants should yield pink offspring exclusively.

However, the actual results of such a mating are strikingly different. Two pink-flowered parents consistently produce pink *and* red *and* white offspring. Numerically, an average of 50 per cent of the offspring are pink, roughly 25 per cent are red, and the remainder are white (Fig. 27.7). Evidently, pinkness does *not* breed true, for from pink can be

re-created pure red and white, as well as pink. Hence pink color cannot be a permanent blend of red and white.

From data of this kind, Mendel concluded that blending inheritance does not occur and that, instead, traits remain distinct and intact. They may become joined temporarily in one generation and may again become separated, or **segregated,** from one another in a following generation. This denial of blending was Mendel's most significant contribution. It ultimately reoriented the thinking about heredity completely and paved the way for all modern insights. Mendel himself supplied the first of such insights, for he not only negated the old interpretation, but also postulated a new one.

He realized that traits trace back to the sperm and the egg which produce an organism, and he sus-

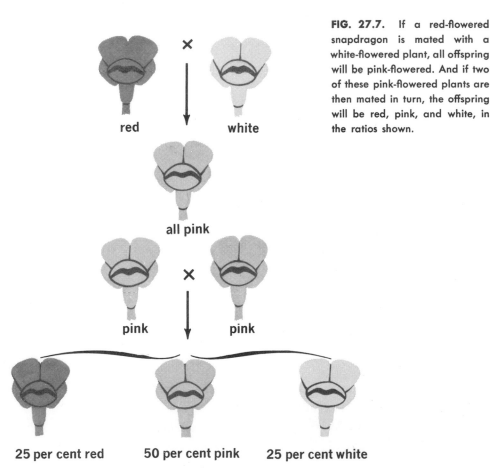

red   ×   white

all pink

pink   ×   pink

25 per cent red   50 per cent pink   25 per cent white

FIG. 27.7. If a red-flowered snapdragon is mated with a white-flowered plant, all offspring will be pink-flowered. And if two of these pink-flowered plants are then mated in turn, the offspring will be red, pink, and white, in the ratios shown.

pected that some specific components within the sperm and the egg controlled the later development of traits. Mendel called these hypothetical components "factors." For any given trait, he argued, an organism must inherit at least one factor from the father and one from the mother. Therefore, the offspring must possess at least two factors for each trait. When that offspring in turn becomes a parent, it must similarly contribute *one* factor to its progeny. Hence, at some point before gamete production, two factors must be reduced to one. Mendel consequently postulated the existence of a factor-reducing process.

With this he in effect predicted the occurrence of meiosis. When near the end of the nineteenth century meiosis was actually discovered, it was recognized that the reduction of chromosomes at some point before fertilization matched precisely the postulated reduction of Mendel's factors. Hence chromosomes came to be regarded as the carriers of the factors, and the **chromosome theory of heredity** so emerged. This theory has since received complete confirmation, and Mendel's factors became the genes of today.

The Transmission of Genes

On the basis of the chromosome theory, we may interpret the snapdragon data above as follows. A true-breeding red-flowered plant possesses a pair of red-pigment-producing genes in each cell. These genes, which we may symbolize by the letters *AA*, are located on a given pair of chromosomes, of which one is maternal and one is paternal in origin. We say that the **genotype,** or gene content, of the plant is *AA* and that the **phenotype,** or visible appearance, is *red*. When such a plant produces gametes, meiosis occurs. Mature gametes therefore contain only one of the two chromosomes, hence only one of the two genes (Fig. 27.8).

Note that it is entirely a matter of chance which of the two adult chromosomes will become incorporated into a given gamete. Since both adult chromosomes here carry the same color gene, all gametes will be genetically alike in this respect. We may un-

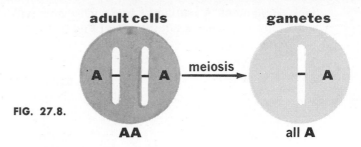

FIG. 27.8.

derstand now why *AA* plants are true-breeding, i.e., why a mating of *AA* × *AA* will produce only red-flowered, *AA* offspring (Fig. 27.9).

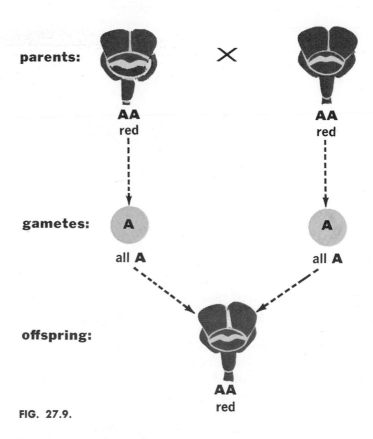

FIG. 27.9.

In precisely analogous manner, we may symbolize the genotype of a true-breeding white-flowered snapdragon as *aa*. The letters here represent genes which do not produce any pigment at all. The white coloration in such flowers is a result of this lack of pigment. A mating of two such plants will yield only white-flowered offspring (Fig. 27.10).

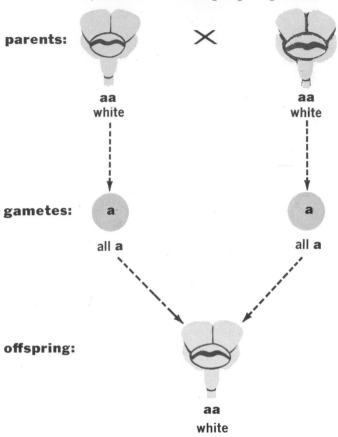

parents:

aa
white

X

aa
white

gametes:

a

all **a**

a

all **a**

offspring:

aa
white

FIG. 27.10.

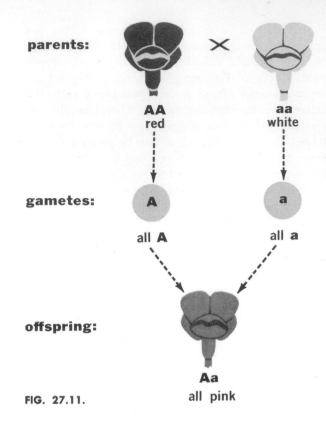

parents:

X

AA
red

aa
white

gametes:

A

all **A**

a

all **a**

offspring:

Aa
all pink

FIG. 27.11.

If we now mate a red-flowered and a white-flowered plant, *all* offspring will be *pink* (Fig. 27.11).

We may note here that an *Aa* offspring plant possesses only *one* pigment-producing gene per cell, namely, *A*. Such a cell consequently develops only *half* as much pigment as an *AA* cell, which possesses two pigment-producing genes. This lesser amount of pigment in the *Aa* offspring appears as a dilute red or a pink.

If now two pink-flowered *Aa* plants are mated, meiosis in each plant will give rise to *two* types of gametes. For, given the genes *Aa*, either the *A* gene or the *a* gene could become incorporated into any given gamete. What actually happens in each spe-

cific case is determined by chance. Hence if, as is usually the case in most organisms, large numbers of gametes are produced, each possibility will be realized with roughly equal frequency. Consequently, approximately 50 per cent of the gametes will carry the *A* gene, the other 50 per cent the *a* gene. We may write: *Aa* parent → 50% *A* gametes, 50% *a* gametes, or, diagrammatically, as in Fig. 27.12.

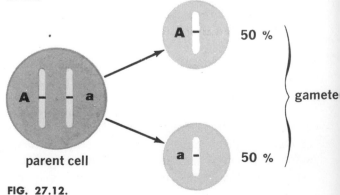

A ─── **a**

parent cell

A ─ 50 %

a ─ 50 %

} gamete

FIG. 27.12.

parents:

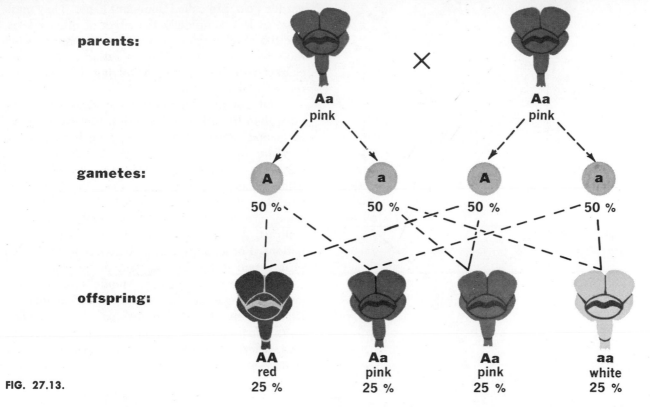

gametes:

Aa
pink

×

Aa
pink

A   **a**   **A**   **a**

50 %   50 %   50 %   50 %

offspring:

AA
red
25 %

Aa
pink
25 %

Aa
pink
25 %

aa
white
25 %

FIG. 27.13.

Now fertilization occurs. Each parent produces two genetically different gamete types, and it is wholly a matter of chance which of the two sperm types fertilizes which of the two egg types. If many fertilizations occur simultaneously, as is usually the case, then all possibilities will be realized with appropriate frequency (Fig. 27.13).

We note that half the offspring are pink-flowered and resemble their parents in this respect. One quarter are red-flowered, one quarter white-flowered, and these offspring resemble their grandparents. We may conclude that Mendel's results can be explained adequately on the basis of nonblending, freely segregating genes and the operations of chance.

Genetic Dominance

Genes like *A* and *a*, which control the same trait but produce different expressions of that trait, are called allelic genes, or **alleles.** In the snapdragon example above, trait expression evidently depends on the number of *A* alleles. Presence of *A* in single dose, as in *Aa* plants, gives only half as much pigment as presence of *A* in double dose, as in *AA* plants. Most traits are affected in this way by gene dosage.

In some cases, however, a maximum trait may be produced even if an allele is present only in single dose. Mendel discovered an instance of this in garden peas. In these, as in snapdragons, true-breeding red-flowered plants may be symbolized as *AA*, true-breeding white-flowered plants as *aa*. But when two such plants are mated, *all* offspring are *red*, not pink (Fig. 27.14).

Evidently, the single *A* gene in *Aa* plants suffices to bring out the full red color; and two *A* genes, as in *AA*, do not produce substantially more redness.

Therefore, if two red-flowered *Aa* plants are mated, three out of every four offspring will be red-flowered (Fig. 27.15).

Genes which produce a maximum trait even when present only in single dose, like the *A*'s of

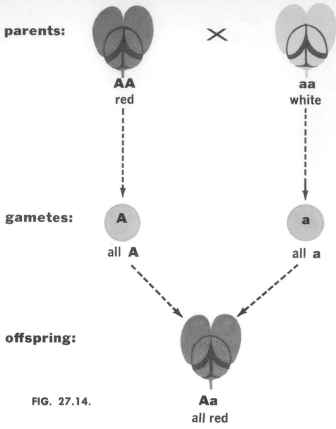

parents:

AA
red

×

aa
white

gametes:

A

all **A**

a

all **a**

offspring:

FIG. 27.14.

Aa
all red

garden peas, are called **dominant** genes. They mask more or less completely the effect of other alleles, like the *a*'s of garden peas. These latter are called **recessive** alleles. Offspring in ratios of ¾:¼ are characteristic for matings involving dominant and recessive alleles, as above.

But complete dominance of this sort is far rarer than the allelic relationship illustrated above for snapdragons. There the *A* gene is said to be *partially* dominant, the *a* gene, *partially* recessive. Offspring ratios of ¼:½:¼ are then characteristic. We may note in this connection that allelic pairs like *AA* or *aa*, in which both genes are the same, are called **homozygous** combinations. By contrast, *Aa* pairs are called **heterozygous** combinations. For example, an *AA* genotype in garden peas is said to be "homozygous dominant."

In modern terminology, Mendel's first law, the **law of segregation,** may now be stated as follows: *Genes do not blend, but behave as independent units. They pass intact from one generation to the next, where they may or may not produce visible traits, depending on their dominance characteristics.*

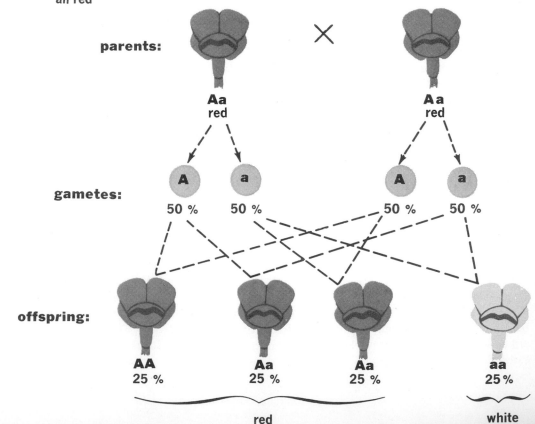

parents:

Aa
red

×

Aa
red

gametes:

A
50 %

a
50 %

A
50 %

a
50 %

offspring:

FIG. 27.15.

AA
25 %

Aa
25 %

Aa
25 %

aa
25 %

red

white

And genes segregate at random, thereby producing predictable ratios of traits in the offspring. Implied in this law are chromosome reduction by meiosis and the operation of chance in the transmission of genes.

THE LAW OF INDEPENDENT ASSORTMENT

Mendel knew that mature organisms do not express traits one at a time, but exhibit all their traits simultaneously. Analogously, we know today that genes are not inherited one at a time, but that all of them are inherited together. Therefore, given certain parents, what will the offspring be like with respect to two or more simultaneous traits?

Mendel discovered a fundamental rule here. Phrased in modern terms, this **law of independent assortment** states: *The inheritance of a gene pair located on a given chromosome pair is unaffected by the simultaneous inheritance of other gene pairs located on other chromosome pairs.* In other words, two or more traits, produced by genes located on two or more chromosome pairs, "assort independently"; that is, each trait will be expressed independently, as if no other traits were present.

The Evidence

Suppose we analyze, as Mendel did, the simultaneous inheritance of two traits of garden peas, *seed shape* and *seed color*. Seed shape can be either **round** or **wrinkled.** Mendel had found round to be dominant over wrinkled, and the possible alleles can be symbolized as *R* for round and *r* for wrinkled. Therefore, on a given chromosome pair of peas is located either an *RR,* an *rr,* or an *Rr* pair of alleles. Similarly, Mendel had found **yellow** seed color (*Y*) to be dominant over **green** seed color (*y*). Hence on another chromosome pair is located a *YY,* or a *yy,* or a *Yy* pair of alleles (Fig. 27.16).

Mendel mated two *RrYy* plants, that is, individuals which were heterozygous for both traits and which therefore had matured from round, yellow seeds. He obtained four categories of offspring, in the proportions given in Fig. 27.17.

Mendel here noted that a total of 76.1 (56.7 plus 19.4) per cent of the offspring were round-seeded and that a total of 74.9 (56.7 plus 18.2) per cent were yellow-seeded. In other words, each of the two dominant traits, considered *separately,* amounted to very nearly 75 per cent, or three-fourths of the total. And the two recessive traits, considered separately, each amounted to about 25 per cent, or one-fourth of the total. Evidently, as expected on the basis of the law of segregation, each dominant and its correlated recessive appeared in ratio of $\frac{3}{4} : \frac{1}{4}$; that is, dominants were three times as abundant as recessives.

Moreover, the two dominants were also three times as abundant *even if they were considered together.* For among the 76.1 per cent total of round-seeded offspring, 56.7 per cent, or very nearly

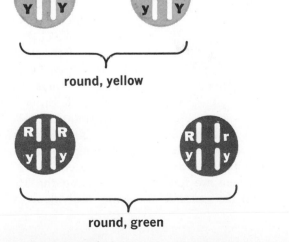
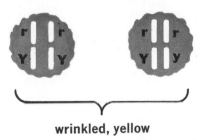

FIG. 27.16. Seed color and seed shape in garden peas. Four kinds of seed types may occur, namely, round-yellow, round-green, wrinkled-yellow, and wrinkled-green. Some of the possible gene combinations which could produce such seed types are shown in the diagram.

round, yellow

wrinkled, yellow

round, green

wrinkled, green

parents matured from seeds of this type:

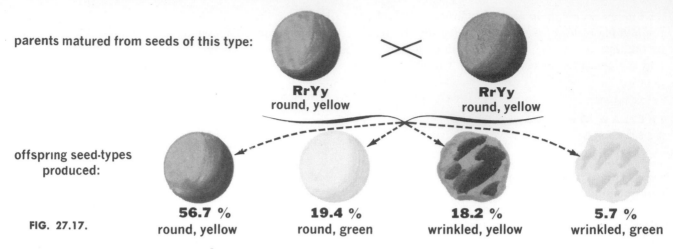

RrYy
round, yellow

RrYy
round, yellow

offspring seed-types
produced:

FIG. 27.17.

56.7 %
round, yellow

19.4 %
round, green

18.2 %
wrinkled, yellow

5.7 %
wrinkled, green

three-fourths, were at the same time also yellow-seeded. And among the 74.9 per cent total of yellow-seeded offspring, 56.7 per cent, or again nearly three-fourths, were at the same time also round-seeded. In other words, the 56.7 per cent round-*and* yellow-seeded offspring amounted to *three-fourths of three-fourths*, or *nine-sixteenths*, of the total. The overall ratio thus was very nearly $9/16 : 3/16 : 3/16 : 1/16$. Mendel concluded that such a ratio could be obtained only if *each* trait obeyed the law of segregation and if it were therefore expressed independently of other traits. Hence his law of independent assortment.

The validity of this second law may be appreciated readily if we consider chromosomes, meiosis, and gametes. In the mating above, the cells of the parents are shown in Fig. 27.18.

parental cells:

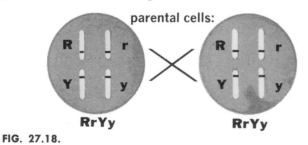

RrYy

RrYy

FIG. 27.18.

After meiosis, each gamete will contain only *one* seed-shape gene and only *one* color gene. But which of each pair? The dominant or the recessive gene? This is a matter of chance. There are four possibilities. A gamete might contain the genes R

and Y, or R and y, or r and Y, or r and y. Many gametes are produced; hence all four combinations will occur with roughly equal frequency (Fig. 27.19).

parents

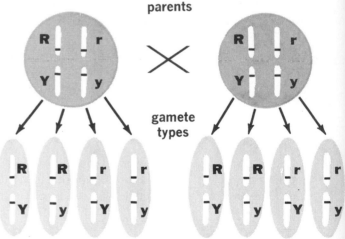

gamete
types

FIG. 27.19.

Fertilization is governed by chance too. Therefore, *any* one of the four sperm types might fertilize *any* one of the four egg types. Hence there are 16 different ways in which fertilization can occur, and if large numbers of fertilizations take place simultaneously, all 16 ways will be realized with roughly equal frequency. We may determine these 16 ways by using a grid where the gametes of one parent are put along a horizontal edge and the gametes of the other parent along a vertical edge (Fig. 27.20).

Among the 16 offspring types here, we find some individuals which contain *both* dominant

parents:

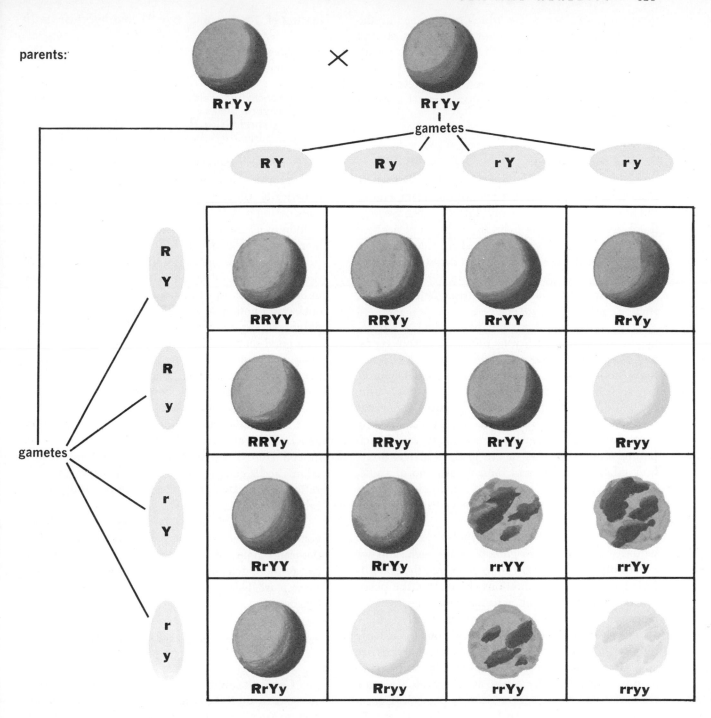

FIG. 27.20.

genes at least once, some which contain one *or* the other of the dominant genes at least once, and some which contain none of the dominant genes. A count reveals round-yellow, round-green, wrinkled-yellow, and wrinkled-green to be present in a ratio of 9:3:3:1. This is the ratio Mendel actually obtained, as we have seen.

The Consequences

Mendel's second law applies specifically to gene pairs located on *different* chromosome pairs. Hence the law will hold for as many different gene pairs as there are chromosome pairs in each cell of a given organism. Suppose we considered the inheritance of *three* different gene pairs, each located on a different chromosome pair. For example, what would be the offspring of a mating of two triple heterozygotes, such as $AaBbCc \times AaBbCc$?

We have found above that a double heterozygote $AaBb$ produces *four* different gamete types; and it should not be too difficult to verify that a triple heterozygote produces *eight* different gamete types, namely, ABC, ABc, AbC, Abc, aBC, aBc, abC, and abc. To determine all possible genotypes of the offspring, we may make a grid 8 squares by 8 squares, and place the 8 gamete types of each parent along the sides of the grid, as above. Sixty-four offspring types will then result, and of these, 27 will express all three traits in dominant form. The complete phenotype ratio may easily be verified as 27:9:9:9:3:3:3:1.

Two quadruple heterozygotes, $AaBbCcDd$, would manufacture 16 gamete types each, and we would need a grid 16 by 16 to represent the 256 different genotype combinations. Evidently, the possibilities rapidly become astronomical once we consider more than a few traits simultaneously.

Organisms which are heterozygous for a large number of traits are known as **hybrids.** Aa types are sometimes referred to as **monohybrids,** $AaBb$ types as **dihybrids,** $AaBbCc$ types as **trihybrids.** In man, there are 24 pairs of chromosomes per cell. Consequently, Mendel's second law will apply to any 24 different traits controlled by genes located on different chromosome pairs. We might then study a

mating of, for example, two 24-fold hybrids: $AaBb$ $\ldots WwXx \times AaBb \ldots WwXx$. How many gamete types would each such hybrid produce? We know that:

a monohybrid yields 2^1 = 2 gamete types
a dihybrid yields 2^2 = 4 gamete types
a trihybrid yields 2^3 = 8 gamete types
a quadruple hybrid yields 2^4 = 16 gamete types

Carrying this progression further, we find that a 24-fold hybrid will produce 2^{24}, or nearly 17 million, genetically different gamete types. Therefore, in considering just 24 traits, we would require a grid 17 million by 17 million to represent the nearly 300 trillion possible genotypes.

A particular individual then inherits just *one* of these genotypes. Of all the possible genotypes, a few millions or billions will produce resemblance to parents, and another few millions or billions to grandparents or earlier ancestors. But there are bound to be a good many million or billion genotypes which have never yet become expressed during the entire history of man. Hence there is a very excellent chance that every newly born human being differs from every other human being, past or present, in at least some genes controlling just 24 traits. And the genetic differences for *all* traits must be enormous indeed. Here is one major reason for individual variations, and a genetic basis for the universal generalization that no two protoplasms are precisely identical.

Any given chromosome contains not just one gene, but anywhere from a few hundred to a few thousand genes. What is the inheritance pattern of two or more gene pairs located on the *same* chromosome pair? This question leads us beyond Mendel's two laws.

THE LAW OF LINEAR ORDER

Linkage

Genes located within the same chromosome are said to be **linked:** as the chromosome is inherited, so are all its genes inherited. Such genes clearly do *not* assort independently, but they are transmitted together in a block. Hence the traits controlled by linked genes are expressed in a block too. For example, assume that in the heterozygote *AaBb* the two gene pairs are linked (Fig. 27.21).

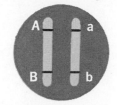

FIG. 27.21.

When such an organism produces gametes, only *two* different gamete types are expected, 50 per cent of each (Fig. 27.22).

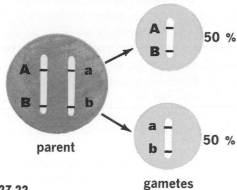

parent   gametes

FIG. 27.22.

We recall that if the gene pairs *Aa* and *Bb* were *not* linked, we should expect *four* gamete types through independent assortment, namely, *AB*, *ab*, *Ab*, and *aB*, 25 per cent of each.

Crossing Over

Linkage studies were first undertaken by T. H. Morgan, a renowned American biologist of the early twentieth century. Experimenting with fruit flies, *Drosophila*, Morgan discovered a curious phenomenon. When genes were linked, the expected result of two gamete types in a 50:50 ratio was obtained relatively rarely. Instead, there were usually somewhat fewer than 50 per cent of each gamete type, and there were correspondingly small percentages of two additional, completely unexpected gamete types.

For example, fruit flies possess a gene for *gray* body color (*B*), dominant over a gene for *black*

body color (*b*). These alleles are located on the same chromosomes which also carry genes controlling wing shape: an allele for *normal* wings (*V*), dominant over an allele for highly reduced, *vestigial* wings (*v*) (Fig. 27.23). If now a gray-bodied, nor-

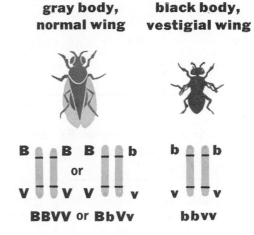

FIG. 27.23.   Linked genes in the fruit fly *Drosophila*.

mal-winged heterozygous female fly, *BbVv*, produces gametes, only two types should be expected, namely, *BV* and *bv* (Fig. 27.24).

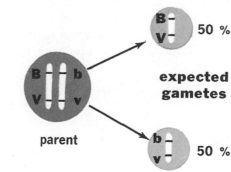

FIG. 27.24.

However, Morgan consistently obtained *four* gamete types, in the proportions given in Fig. 27.25.

If these four types had formed to an extent of about 25 per cent each, the experiment could have been regarded simply as a case without linkage, governed by Mendel's second law. But the actual results included significantly *more* than 25 per cent

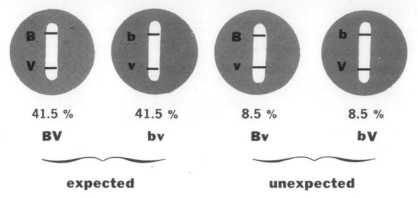

41.5 %   41.5 %   8.5 %   8.5 %

BV   **bv**   **Bv**   **bV**

expected   unexpected

FIG. 27.25.

each of the expected gamete types *BV* and *bv*, and significantly *fewer* than 25 per cent each of the unexpected types *Bv* and *bV*.

To explain these odd results, Morgan proposed a new hypothesis. He postulated that during meiosis, paired chromosomes in some cases might *twist around each other,* might break where twisted, and the broken pieces might fuse again in the "wrong" order. This is shown diagrammatically in Fig. 27.26.

This would account for the large percentage of expected and the small percentage of unexpected gamete types. To test the validity of this hypothesis, cells undergoing meiosis were examined carefully under the microscope: could chromosome twists and breaks actually be seen? They could indeed, and the phenomenon of **crossing over** was so proved.

The implications of this discovery were far-

reaching. It was reasoned that the frequency of crossovers should be an index of the *distance* between two genes. For if two genes on a chromosome are located near each other, the chances will be relatively small that a twist will occur between these close points. But if two genes are relatively far apart, then twists between these points should be rather frequent. In general, the frequency of crossovers should be proportional to the distance between two genes (Fig. 27.27).

Inasmuch as the crossover percentage of two genes could be determined by breeding experiments, it became possible to construct **gene maps,** showing the actual location of given genes on a chromosome. Since Morgan's time, the exact position of a few hundred genes has been mapped in the fruit fly, and smaller numbers of genes have similarly

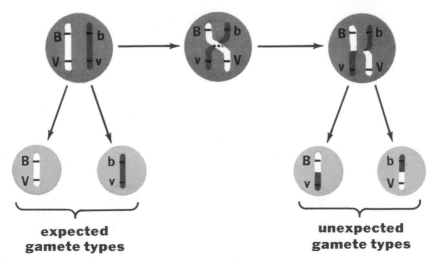

FIG. 27.26.   expected
                    gamete types   unexpected
                                                   gamete types

been located in corn among plants, and in mice among mammals. Many of these determinations have been corroborated by X-ray work. When irradiated, a chromosome may break into pieces, and a small piece of this sort may be lost from a gamete. Offspring resulting from such deficient gametes will be abnormal in certain traits. Since microscopic examination shows where a chromosome piece is missing, a trait can be correlated with a particular spot on a chromosome.

Another implication of crossing over is that genes on a chromosome must be lined up single-file. Only if this is the case can linkage and crossing over occur as it actually does occur. This generalization has become known as the **law of the linear order of genes,** and it constitutes the third major rule which governs Mendelian inheritance.

Finally, crossing over has provided a functional definition of "gene": *A gene is the smallest section of a chromosome within which crossovers do not take place at all.* The assumption here is that the minimum chromosome unit able to cross over is one *whole* gene, not a fractional part of one gene. Recall the two other acceptable definitions of "gene" discussed in Chap. 18.

The three rules of heredity here outlined describe and predict adequately the patterns of Mendelian inheritance, that is, the parent-to-offspring transmission of one or more independent gene pairs, controlling *an equal number* of independent traits. But, as noted earlier, a great deal of heredity involves *complexes* of genes and *complexes* of traits, where one gene pair may contribute to the control of many traits and where many gene pairs may cooperate toward the production of just one major trait. This leads beyond the subject of Mendelian inheritance.

Non-Mendelian Inheritance

GENE-GENE INTERACTIONS

We have noted earlier that gene action is influenced greatly by the environment and that genes themselves are part of this environment. It is impor-

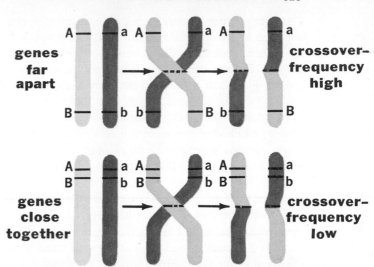

FIG. 27.27. Crossover frequency in relation to gene distance. If two genes are far apart, crossing over between them is likely to occur rather frequently (top). But if genes are close together, crossing over between them is less likely. In general, crossing over will be the more frequent, the farther apart given genes are on a chromosome.

tant now to reemphasize the occurrence of gene-gene interactions. For preoccupation with segregating genes, independently assorting genes, and linearly arranged genes might leave the impression that the units of heredity are simply so many discrete, functionally self-sufficient particles.

If genes were merely independent "beads on a string," haphazardly lined up on given numbers of chromosomes, then it should not matter functionally if the position of genes relative to one another were rearranged. But experiment shows that such rearrangement actually does matter. For example, in *Drosophila* it is possible to change the position of given sections of a chromosome. A piece lost by one chromosome may become attached to another, or may become reattached to the same chromosome, but in inverted position, or at the other end. Genes here are neither removed from nor added to a cell, and only their position relative to one another is rearranged. Under such conditions, the cell may nevertheless develop altered traits. Evidently, genes normally interact very subtly with their neighbors, and they are functionally interdependent, not independent.

Many other illustrations of gene interdependence are in evidence. Partial or complete dominance relationships among alleles are good pertinent examples. Even a completely dominant pigment-producing gene acts as it does not only because of its inherent characteristics, but also because other genes *permit* it to act in dominant fashion. If the functional characteristics of the recessive allele of a given dominant gene were to change, then the status of dominance of that gene would change too. And if the functional characteristics of any other genes in the cell were to change, then the status of dominance of that gene would again change. It is now well established that given gene pairs boost, suppress, partially inhibit, or otherwise modify the effects of other gene pairs. Indeed it is probable that every gene in a cell is a more or less decisive **modifier** of one or more other genes present.

Thus, whereas the pre-Mendelians thought that *traits* were inherited, whereas the Mendelian era advanced to the concept that individual factors, or *genes*, were inherited, the present post-Mendelian era recognizes that actually neither traits nor genes are inherited. Instead, what are inherited are whole chromosome *sets*, coordinated *complexes* of genes, subtly integrated **genetic systems.** And the individual chromosome has emerged as the more significant functional unit of inheritance than the undefinable gene. For what really segregates, assorts independently, and crosses over are *chromosomes,* and parts of chromosomes, not genes.

One case is known which shows particularly well that a complex trait is controlled not so much by separate genes as by whole chromosomes acting as functionally integrated units. The trait in question is sexuality, and its expression provides a good example of non-Mendelian inheritance in general.

INHERITANCE OF SEX

Sex Determination

In mammals, birds, certain groups of insects, and some other animal types, the primary determiners of sex are chromosomes. These in turn control secondary determiners like sex hormones. In these organisms, the cells of males and females differ with respect to one particular pair of chromosomes. The members of this pair are identifiable by unique shape and size, and they have come to be known as **sex chromosomes.** For contrast, all other chromosomes are referred to as **autosomes.** In human cells, for example, there are 23 pairs of autosomes and one pair of sex chromosomes.

In the females of fruit flies and mammals, the two sex chromosomes in each cell are alike; they are called **X chromosomes.** In males, each cell possesses one X chromosome, but the other member of the pair is visibly different. This member is called the **Y chromosome** (Fig. 27.28). Therefore,

in all cells of human *females:*
23 pairs of autosomes plus XX, or (46A + XX)

in all cells of human *males:*
23 pairs of autosomes plus XY, or (46A + XY)

All X chromosomes, like all autosomes, carry genes. The function of Y chromosomes is still rather obscure. They contain but few genes, and the bulk of their substance appears to be genetically inert. Y chromosomes may be lost from cells without appreciable interference with the expression of traits. In effect, therefore, cells of human males contain only 47 functional chromosomes, but female cells contain 48. This difference of one whole X chromosome, with its hundreds of genes, lies at the root of the sexual differences between males and females. In a sense, an X chromosome in its entirety may be regarded as a "gene" for sex.

It can be shown that it is the *ratio of autosomes to X chromosomes* which is significant in the expression of sex. *Autosomes* promote the development of *maleness,* and *X chromosomes* the development of *femaleness.* In a human (46A + XX) cell, the total feminizing influence of the two X chromosomes outweighs the total masculinizing influence of the 46 chromosomes. Individuals composed of such cells are females. But if the cells contain (46A + XY), then the masculinizing effect of the 46 autosomes is sufficiently strong to override the feminizing effect of the single X chromosome. Such individuals are male.

Hence the sexual nature of certain groups of or-

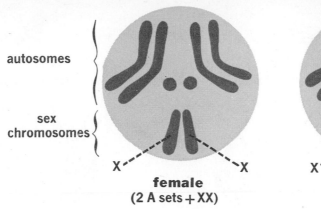

FIG. 27.28. The chromosomes of the fruit fly *Drosophila*. In each cell, 2n = 8. Note the differences in the sex chromosomes of males and females. In man 2n = 48, sex chromosome differences being as in fruit flies.

autosomes

sex chromosomes

X —————— X
female
(2 A sets + XX)

X —————— Y
male
(2 A sets + XY)

ganisms appears to depend on a particular *balance* between two genetic influences. If this is correct, should it not be possible to alter the expression of sex by experimentally altering the numerical balance between autosomes and X chromosomes? This is indeed possible. Experiments of this kind actually have given the first clues that chromosome balances play a role in sex determination.

In *Drosophila*, for example, the numbers of autosomes and X chromosomes in sperms and eggs can be varied by certain laboratory procedures. One may then obtain offspring characterized by normal paired sets of autosomes, but by *three* X chromosomes instead of two. These individuals grow into so-called **superfemales:** all sexual traits are greatly accentuated in the direction of femaleness. **Supermales** and **intersexes** may be produced analogously. In intersexes, sexual traits are intermediate between those of males and females. The chromosome balances are shown in Fig. 27.29. Paradoxically, supersexes, and also intersexes, are generally sterile. For as a result of the abnormal chromosome numbers, meiosis occurs abnormally, and the sperms and eggs then produced are defective.

In the light of such balances, we may appreciate readily how the sex of an offspring is inherited normally. Females (46A + XX) give rise to eggs of which each contains (23A + X) after meiosis. Males (46A + XY) produce *two* kinds of sperms, namely, (23A + X) and (23A + Y), in roughly equal numbers. Fertilization now occurs at random; that is, a sperm of either type may unite with an egg (Fig. 27.30).

Note that it is the prospective father who, at the moment of fertilization, determines the probable sex of the offspring. When only a single offspring is produced, there exists a 50:50 chance of its being a son or a daughter. When many offspring are produced, the number of males will generally equal the number of females.

Sex Linkage

The absence of a functional mate to the X chromosome in males has far-reaching consequences. In females, the effect of a recessive gene located on one X chromosome may be masked by the effect of a dominant located on the other X chromosome. But in males, recessive genes on the X chromosome may exert their effect, since another X chromosome with

FIG. 27.29. Sex and chromosome balance in the fruit fly. The sexual character of an individual is determined by the specific balance of autosomes and X chromosomes.

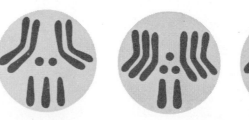

Superfemale
(2 A sets + 3 X)

Intersex
(3 A sets + 2 X)

Supermale
(3 A sets + 1 X)

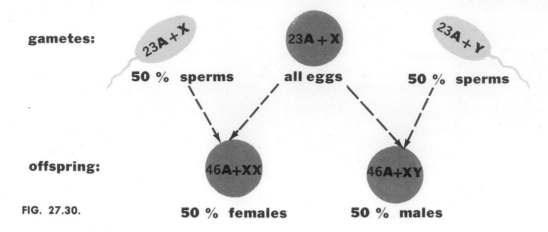

gametes:

50 % sperms   all eggs   50 % sperms

offspring:

FIG. 27.30.

50 % females   50 % males

masking dominants is never present. Genes located on *X* chromosomes are called **sex-linked** genes.

Because males possess only a single *X* chromosome, such genes are inherited according to a characteristic pattern. For example, red-green color blindness in man is traceable to a sex-linked recessive gene *c*. Suppose a color-blind male, X_cY, marries a normal female, *XX*. In this symbolization, an *X* chromosome without the subscript *c* is tacitly assumed to contain the dominant gene *C*, which prevents the expression of color blindness. The offspring of such a mating will be as shown in Fig. 27.31.

We note that daughters and sons are produced in equal numbers. The daughters carry the recessive gene *c*, but *all* offspring have normal vision.

Suppose now one of these daughters marries a normal male, as shown in Fig. 27.32.

All daughters here are normal, but half the sons are color-blind. Note that the trait has been transmitted from color-blind grandfather, via normal mother, to color-blind son. Such a zigzag pattern of inheritance is characteristic of all recessive sex-linked traits. Males typically exhibit the trait; females merely transmit it. Evidently, the presence of a second *X* chromosome may protect females from expressing recessive sex-linked traits. Color blindness is one of several characteristically male, sex-linked abnormalities. Another is *hemophilia*, a bleeder's disease resulting from absence of blood platelets.

NON-MENDELIAN VARIATIONS

To the extent that genetic variations are brought about by the sexual pooling of different genetic systems in the zygote, the pattern is Mendelian, and as we have seen, it obeys the laws of Mendel and Morgan. But inheritable variations in genetic systems may arise also in non-Mendelian fashion.

Transduction and Transformation

One rather limited source of non-Mendelian genetic variations is **transduction**. This phenome-

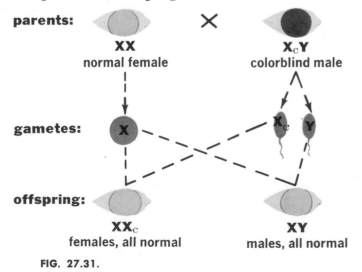

parents:

XX
normal female

X_cY
colorblind male

gametes:

X

X_c Y

offspring:

XX_c
females, all normal

XY
males, all normal

FIG. 27.31.

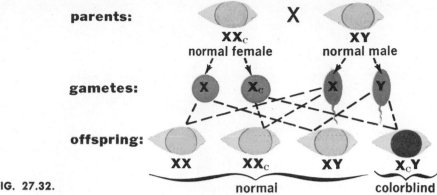

parents:

XX$_c$
normal female

X

XY
normal male

gametes:

X   X$_c$ X   Y

offspring:

XX   XX$_c$ XY   X$_c$Y

normal   colorblind

FIG. 27.32.

non was discovered in bacteria, and at the present time it is not known to occur in any other group of organisms. Transduction involves the transfer of genetic material from one bacterium to another, through the agency of particular viruses. These viruses are *bacteriophages;* that is, they parasitize bacteria (see Chap. 4). A virus infects a bacterium and reproduces within the host at the expense of host protoplasm. The host then dies, and the offspring viruses are released, free to infect more bacteria. It happens on occasion that bits of the genetic material of a host bacterium become incorporated into newly forming offspring viruses. When the latter subsequently infect new bacterial hosts, they carry the DNA of the old hosts into the new. In this way the new hosts acquire additional hereditary agents and may develop changed or new traits as a result (Fig. 27.33).

Transduction is related in principle to bacterial **transformation,** another limited source of non-Men-

FIG. 27.33. The principle of transduction. Newly forming bacteriophage viruses may incorporate into their own structure pieces of the genetic material of the host bacterium. When such viruses infect new bacterial hosts, these hosts acquire additional bacterial genes.

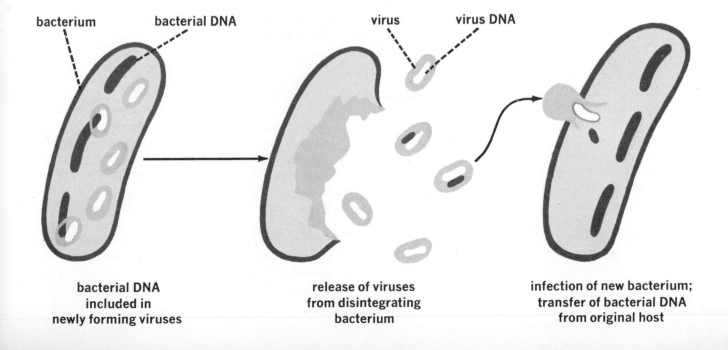

bacterium   bacterial DNA   virus   virus DNA

bacterial DNA
included in
newly forming viruses

release of viruses
from disintegrating
bacterium

infection of new bacterium;
transfer of bacterial DNA
from original host

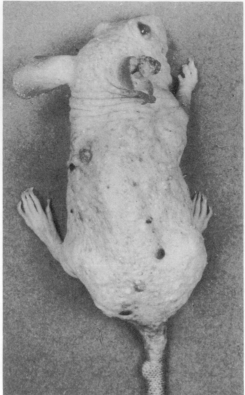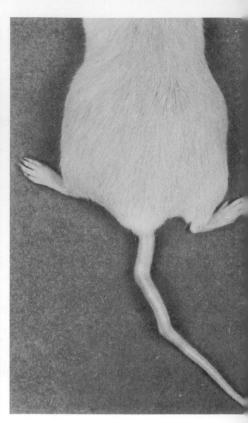

FIG. 27.34.   Mutant types in mice. Left: the effects of the mutation "eyelessness." Middle: the effects of the mutation "hairlessness." Right: the effects of the kinky-tail mutation. Each of these alterations of structure is correlated with a single mutant gene, and the alterations are stable and inheritable. (Courtesy of Dr. Herman B. Chase and R. Hughes, Brown University.)

delian variations. This phenomenon has already been referred to briefly in Chap. 18. It is possible by laboratory methods to extract genetic DNA from one strain of bacteria and to expose another strain to the DNA extract. This second strain may then absorb some of the DNA molecules, incorporate them into its own genetic system, and develop new or altered traits as a result (see Fig. 18.2). We note that transformation differs from transduction, first, in that a human rather than a viral agency brings about the genetic transfers, and second, in that it is an experimental method of producing variations which, unlike transduction, does not otherwise occur in nature.

Mutation

Transduction and transformation have strictly limited significance. By far the most important source of non-Mendelian variations, of universal significance in all organisms, is *mutation*. Any stable, inheritable change in the basic genetic system with which every cell is equipped constitutes a mutation. For example, the accidental doubling, tripling, etc., of the normal chromosome number represents a stable, transmissible change. This is a **chromosome mutation**. Accidental loss or addition of a whole chromosome; loss of a chromosome piece; fusion of such a piece with another chromosome, or fusion with the original chromosome in inverted position—these are chromosome mutations too. They occur on rare occasions in nature, and they may also be produced experimentally.

By far the most common type of mutation is a **point mutation,** a stable physical and/or chemical change of one gene (Fig. 27.34). We do not know how such mutational gene changes are produced in nature. One possible explanation has emerged from the discovery that high-energy radiation could increase mutation rates. The more radiation a cell is exposed to, the more mutations will occur in it. This has suggested that natural mutations might be caused by cosmic rays and other space radiation, and by radioactive elements in the earth. However, it can be shown that such unavoidable "background radiation," which affects all organisms, is not sufficiently intense to account for the mutation frequency known to be characteristic of genes generally. This frequency has been estimated as about 1 mutation per million cells, on the average. To be sure, natural radiation does produce some mutations. Others perhaps represent "errors" in gene reproduction (see Chap. 18). And still others are undoubtedly caused by man-made radiation, which adds to, and so increases, the natural background radiation.

As far as can be ascertained, mutations are completely random events. Any gene may mutate at any time, in unpredictable ways. A given gene may mutate several times in rapid succession, then not at all for considerable periods. It may mutate in one direction, then mutate back to its original state or in new directions. There is little question that *every* gene existing today is a **mutant** which has undergone many mutations during its past history.

The effect of a mutation on a trait is equally unpredictable. Some are "large" mutations; that is, they affect a major trait in a radical, drastic manner. Others are "small," with but little effect on a trait. Some mutations are dominant, producing immediate positive alterations of traits. Other mutations are recessive and remain masked by normal dominant alleles.

Most mutations are disadvantageous. For inasmuch as a living cell is an exceedingly complex, very finely adjusted whole, it is to be expected that *any* change of operational character would be more or less disruptive and harmful. In many cases, therefore, dominant mutations tend to be eliminated as soon as they arise, through death of the affected cell. In other cases, the effect of a dominant mutation, particularly a "small" dominant mutation, may become integrated successfully into cellular functions, and such a cell, though exhibiting an altered trait, may survive. By and large, however, recessive mutations are likely to persist more readily, since their effects may be masked by normal dominant alleles. Accumulated evidence actually shows that the large majority of surviving mutations are recessive ones.

A minority of mutants produces advantageous traits and new traits which are neither advantageous nor disadvantageous. Consider mutations in man, for example. Many trillions of cells compose the human body, and mutations occur at an average rate of 1 in every million cells. Therefore, several million mutations are likely to occur in each person. Many of these may be lethal to the cells in which they occur, and many others will remain masked by normal dominants. But some mutations may produce traits which do not kill a cell. Such new traits, arising in individual cells, are then transmitted to all cells arising from the original ones by division. For example, "beauty spots" probably develop in this manner.

Gene changes of this type, occurring in body cells generally, are known as **somatic mutations.** They affect the heredity of the cell progeny, that is, a patch of tissue at most. But in multicellular organisms they have little direct bearing on the heredity of the individual. Entire multicellular offspring are affected only by so-called **germ mutations,** stable genetic changes in immature and mature gametes. Such mutations will be transmitted to the fertilized egg, and from there to all cells composing the offspring (Fig. 27.35). In so far as such germ mutations may be recessive and masked by normal dominants, the traits of the offspring will not be altered. But if the offspring is homozygous recessive for a mutation, or if a mutation is dominant, then a particular trait may be expressed in altered form. Provided such a new trait is not lethal, it will persist as an individual

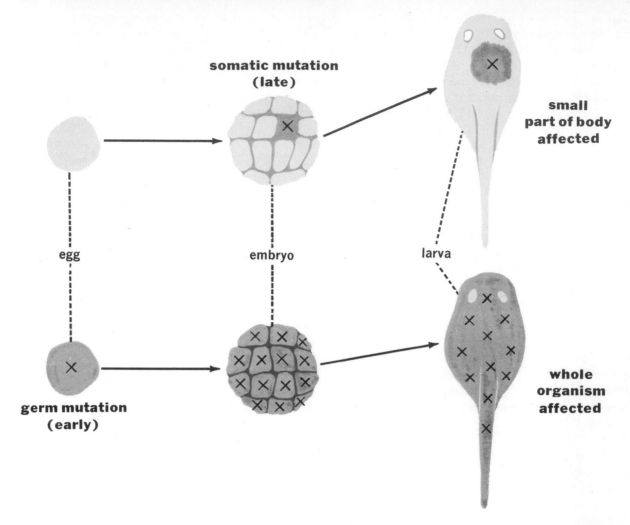

FIG. 27.35. The effects of germ mutations and somatic mutations. If a mutation occurs late during development, in a somatic cell, then only the progeny of that cell will inherit the mutation and the total effect on the adult organism will be small. But if a mutation occurs early during development, e.g., in a gamete, then all cells of the resulting adult will inherit such a germ mutation, and all cells may feature altered traits.

variation. We note that mutations may affect the adaptation of an individual as much as sexual recombination of genes.

In this chapter we have found that the inheritance of genetic systems, and of the traits they control, is governed by the biological nature of sex, by various probabilistic Mendelian rules, by non-Mendelian gene-gene interactions, by random mutational changes, and by the manifold effect of the environment on gene-trait relationships. In the individual organism, this interplay between sex, heredity, and environment produces relative adaptedness. In the long reproductive succession as a whole, this interplay becomes *evolution*.

1. What are the sources of genetic variations in (*a*) uniparental, (*b*) biparental inheritance? Distinguish between inherited and acquired variations. What contributions are made to the expression of traits by (*a*) genes, (*b*) the environment? What is an "inherited disease"? Distinguish between simple and composite traits.

2. What was meant by "blending inheritance"? Describe the experiments through which Mendel came to deny blending. What hypothesis did Mendel substitute for the blending concept? State the chromosome theory of heredity. What is the evidence that genes are actually contained within chromosomes?

3. Define: genome, true-breeding, phenotype, genotype, allele, dominant gene, recessive gene, homozygous, heterozygous, hybrid.

4. Review the interpretation of Mendel's snapdragon experiments in terms of genes and chromosomes. What are the quantitative results of the mating $Aa \times Aa$ if (*a*) *A* is dominant over *a*, (*b*) neither gene is dominant over the other?

5. In your own words, state the law of segregation. If *A* is dominant over *a*, what phenotype ratios of offspring are obtained from the following matings: (*a*) $Aa \times aa$, (*b*) $AA \times aa$, (*c*) $Aa \times Aa$, (*d*) $Aa \times AA$?

6. In your own words, state the law of independent assortment. By what kinds of breeding experiments, and by what reasoning, did Mendel come to discover this law? Interpret the law in terms of genes, meiosis, and gametes. How many genetically different gamete types will be produced by an organism heterozygous in 10 gene pairs? If two such organisms were mated, how many genetically different offspring types could result?

7. Define linkage. Why does inheritance of linked genes not obey Mendel's second law? What are the quantitative and qualitative differences here? What were Morgan's observations which led him to the hypothesis of crossing over? Describe this hypothesis. How do crossover data permit the construction of gene maps? State the law of the linear order of genes. What definition of gene is based on the phenomenon of crossing over? Review other definitions (see Chap. 18).

8. What are modifier genes? Describe specific instances of gene-gene interactions. Review the genetic basis of sex determination in man. What is the significance of a given numerical balance between autosomes and sex chromosomes? What are supersexes and intersexes? How, and in what organisms, have they been produced? How does it happen that, globally, the number of men roughly equals the number of women?

9. What are sex-linked genes? Describe the inheritance pattern of the sex-linked recessive hemophilia gene *h*, assuming that a hemophilic male mates with a normal female. What are transduction and transformation? In what organisms, and how, do these processes occur?

10. Distinguish between chromosome mutations and point mutations and between somatic mutations and germ mutations. What is the relation between mutation frequency and radiation intensity? What are the characteristics of mutations from the standpoint of (*a*) predictability, (*b*) functional relation to normal alleles, (*c*) effects on traits, and (*d*) relative advantage to the organism?

SUGGESTED COLLATERAL READINGS

The original work of the founder of modern genetics will always be of special interest:

Mendel, G.: "Experiments in Plant Hybridization." A translation of the original (1865) was published by Harvard University Press, 1941.

Two standard texts on genetics, recommended as supplements to topics covered in this chapter:

Snyder, L. H.: "The Principles of Heredity," Heath, 1951.

Srb, A., and R. D. Owen: "General Genetics," Freeman, 1955.

Of the readings below, the first is a collection of reprints of classical original articles on which much of modern genetics is based. The second is a "progress report" after the first fifty years of genetics and consists of essays written by eminent biologists.

Gabriel, M. L., and S. Fogel: "Great Experiments in Biology," section on Genetics, Prentice-Hall, 1955.

Dunn, L. C. (ed.): "Genetics in the 20th Century," Macmillan, 1951.

Scheinfeld, A.: "The New You and Heredity," Lippincott, 1950.

Goldschmidt, R. B.: "Understanding Heredity," Wiley, 1952.

Dunn, L. C., and T. Dobzhanski: "Heredity, Race, and Society," Penguin, 1946.

Muller, H. J., C. C. Little, and L. H. Snyder: "Genetics, Medicine, and Man," Cornell University Press, 1947.

Muller, H. J.: Radiation Damage to the Genetic Material, *Am. Scientist,* vol. 38, 1950.

————: Radiation and Human Mutation, *Sci. American,* vol. 193, 1955.

Hollander, W. F.: Lethal Heredity, *Sci. American,* vol. 187, 1952.

Spoerl, E.: The Lethal Effects of Radiation, *Sci. American,* vol. 185, 1951.

Knight, C. A., and D. Fraser: The Mutation of Viruses, *Sci. American,* vol. 193, 1955.

Flanders, S. E.: Control of Sex in the Honeybee, *Sci. Monthly,* vol. 71, 1950.

Strong, L. C.: Genetics and Cancer, *Sci. American,* vol. 183, 1950.

Stern, C.: Two or Three Bristles, *Am. Scientist,* vol. 42, 1954.

————: Man's Genetic Future, *Sci. American,* vol. 186, 1952.

Snyder, L. H.: Human Heredity and Its Modern Applications, *Am. Scientist,* vol. 43, 1955.

28

THE MECHANISM
OF EVOLUTION

No one today seriously questions the principle that species arise from preexisting species. Evolution on a small scale can be brought about in the laboratory, and the forces which drive and guide evolutionary processes are understood quite thoroughly.

That evolution actually occurs did not become definitely established till the nineteenth century. For long ages man was unaware of the process, but he did wonder about the origin of his kind and of other living creatures. Indeed, he developed a succession of simple, rather crude theories about evolution. Unsupported by real evidence, these were ultimately proved untenable one by one. Yet the early ideas today occasionally still color the views of those who are unacquainted with the modern knowledge.

It is advisable, therefore, that we begin this chapter with a brief survey of the historical **background** of evolutionary thought. Based on such a perspective, we may then discuss the **forces of evolution,** as these are understood today, and conclude with an analysis of the **nature of evolution,** as determined by the underlying forces.

Background

EARLY NOTIONS

The earliest theory of organic creation is contained in the Old Testament: God made the world and its living inhabitants in six days, man coming last. On this were based the theological ideas of *special creation* and of *immutability of species,* which largely held sway until the eighteenth and nineteenth centuries. Each species was considered to have been created separately, completely developed, from dust, dirt, and other nonliving sources. And once created, a species was held to be immutable, unable to change its characteristics.

In the sixth to fourth centuries B.C., Anaximander, Empedocles, and Aristotle independently considered the possibility that living forms might represent a *succession,* rather than unrelated, randomly created types. But the succession was thought of in an essentially philosophical way, as a progression from "less nearly perfect" to "more nearly perfect" forms. The *historical* nature of succession and the continuity of life were not yet recognized. Nor was the notion of continuous succession exploited further in later centuries, for clerical dogma by and large discouraged thinking along such lines.

Francesco Redi, an Italian physician of the seventeenth century, was the first to disprove the idea of special creation, by showing experimentally that organisms could not arise from nonliving sources. Contrary to notions held at the time and earlier, Redi demonstrated that maggots would never form "spontaneously" in meat if flies were prevented from laying their eggs on the meat. But old beliefs die slowly, and it was not until the nineteenth century, chiefly through the work of Louis Pasteur, that the notion of special creation finally ceased to be influential.

By this time, the alternative to special creation, namely, the idea of continuity and historical succession, or **evolution,** had occurred to a number of thinkers. Some of these recognized that any concept of evolution demanded an earth of sufficiently great age, and they set out to estimate this age. Newton's law of gravitation provided the tool with which to calculate the weight of the earth. One could then bring a small weighed ball of earth to white heat and measure its rate of cooling. From such measurements, one could calculate how long it must have taken the whole earth to cool to its present state. This provided the many millions of years required to fit evolution into, and this time span gradually lengthened as techniques of clocking improved. As a result of these efforts, the notion of evolution was clearly in the air when the nineteenth century began. And in 1809, the first major theory of evolution was actually published. This was the theory of the French biologist Lamarck.

LAMARCK

Lamarck considered the reality of evolution as established, and he believed, correctly, that to explain *how* evolution occurred was equivalent to explaining *adaptation*—how individual variations arise among plants and animals, and how such variations lead to the emergence of different species, suited to different environments and ways of life. To account for this, Lamarck proposed the two ideas of **use and disuse of parts** and of **inheritance of acquired characteristics.** He had observed that if a part of an organism was used extensively, such a part would enlarge and become more efficient. And that if a structure was not fully employed, it would degenerate and atrophy. Therefore, by differential use and disuse of various parts during its lifetime, an organism would change to some extent and would acquire individual variations. Lamarck then thought that such acquired variations were inheritable and could be transmitted to offspring.

Evolution, according to the Lamarckian scheme, would come about somewhat as follows. Suppose a given short-necked ancestral animal feeds on tree leaves. As it clears off the lower levels of a tree, it stretches its neck to reach farther up. During a lifetime of stretching, the neck becomes a little longer, and a slightly longer neck therefore is inherited by the offspring. These in turn feed on tree leaves and keep on stretching their necks; and so on, for many generations. Each generation acquires the gains of previous generations and itself adds a little to neck length. In time, a very-long-necked animal is formed, for example, something like a modern giraffe.

This theory was exceedingly successful, and it did much to spread the idea of evolution. But Lamarck's views ultimately proved to be untenable. That use and disuse *do* lead to acquired variations is quite correct. For example, it is common knowledge that much exercise builds big muscles. However, Lamarck was mistaken in assuming that such acquired variations were inheritable. We may say categorically that *acquired characteristics are not inheritable.* They are effects produced by environment and development, not by genes (see Chap. 27).

Only *genetically* controlled variations of traits are inheritable, for only genetic systems are actually inherited. And what happens to body cells through use and disuse does not affect the genetic systems of the gametes. Hence, although Lamarck observed the effects of use and disuse correctly, such effects cannot play a role in evolution.

One famous experimental refutation of Lamarckism was carried out by Weismann, an eminent biologist of the nineteenth century. The tails of mice were cut off for very many successive generations. According to Lamarck, such enforced disuse of tails should eventually lead to tailless mice. Yet mice in the last generation of the experiment still grew tails as long as their ancestors. Inheritance of acquired characteristics in essence implies that a person who spends his life lying on a beach acquiring a tan will have children who are *born* slightly tanned! Even so, Lamarckism is occasionally still met with today in speech and thought. For example, quite a number of people still believe that playing the piano during pregnancy will produce a musically gifted child.

DARWIN AND WALLACE

The year in which Lamarck published his theory was also the year in which Charles Darwin was born. During his early life, Darwin undertook a five-year-long circumglobal voyage as the biologist on the naval expeditionary ship *H.M.S. Beagle.* He made innumerable observations and collected a large number of specimens of plants and animals, in many parts of the world. Returning home, he spent nearly twenty years sifting and studying the collected data. In the course of this work, he found evidence for certain generalizations. Another biologist, Alfred Wallace, had independently been led to substantially the same generalizations, at the same time as Darwin. Darwin and Wallace together then announced a new theory of evolution, which was to supplant that of Lamarck. Darwin subsequently elaborated the new theory into book form. This famous work, entitled "The Origin of Species by Means of Natural Selection, or the Preservation of Favored Races in the Struggle for Life," was published in 1859.

In essence, the Darwin-Wallace **theory of natural selection** is based on three observations and on two conclusions drawn from these observations.

Observation: Without environmental pressures, every species tends to multiply in geometric progression.

In other words, a population doubling its number in a first year possesses a sufficient reproductive potential to quadruple its number in a second year, to increase eightfold in a third year, etc.

Observation: But under field conditions, although fluctuations occur frequently, the size of a population remains remarkably constant over long periods of time.

We have already spoken of this in the discussion of food pyramids (Chap. 4).

Conclusion: Hence not all eggs and sperms will become zygotes; not all zygotes will become adults; and not all adults will survive and reproduce; there must be a "struggle for existence."

Observation: Not all members of a species are alike; that is, there exists considerable individual variation.

Conclusion: Hence in the struggle for existence, individuals featuring favorable variations will enjoy a competitive advantage over others. They will survive in proportionately greater numbers and will produce offspring in proportionately greater numbers.

Darwin and Wallace thus identified the environment as the principal cause of natural selection. Through the processes above, the environment would gradually weed out organisms with unfavorable variations but preserve those with favorable variations. Over a long succession of generations, and under the continued selective influence of the environment, a group of organisms would eventually have accumulated so many new, favorable variations that a new species would in effect have arisen from the ancestral stock.

Nonbiologists today often are under the impression that Darwin's and Wallace's theory is *the* modern theory of evolution. This is not the case. Indeed, Darwinism was challenged even during Darwin's lifetime. What, it was asked, is the *source* of the all-important individual variations? How do individual variations arise? Here Darwin actually could do no better than fall back on the Lamarckian idea of inheritance of acquired characteristics. Ironically, the correct answer regarding variations began to be formulated just six years after Darwin published his theory, when a monk named Mendel announced certain rules of inheritance! But Mendel's work went unheeded for more than thirty years, and progress in understanding evolutionary mechanisms was correspondingly retarded.

Another objection to Darwinism concerned natural selection itself. If this process simply preserves or weeds out what already exists, it was asked, how can it ever create anything new? As we shall see, natural selection actually does create novelty, and the earlier criticism arose in part because the meaning of Darwin's theory was widely misinterpreted. Social philosophers of the time thought that the essence of natural selection was described by the phrase "struggle for existence," and they coined alternative slogans like "survival of the fittest" and "elimination of the unfit." Natural selection so came to be conceived almost exclusively as a negative, destructive force, and this had two unfortunate results. First, a major implication of Darwin's theory, namely, the creative role of natural selection, was missed; and second, the wrong emphasis carried over into the popular thinking concerning evolution.

Such thinking proceeded in high gear in Darwin's day. Many still did not accept the reality of evolution and were prompted variously to debate, to scorn, and to ridicule the merits of the evidence. It was felt also that evolution implied "man descended from the apes," and man's sense of superiority was duly outraged. Moreover, because evolutionary views denied the special creation of man, they were widely held to be antireligious. In actuality, the idea of evolution is not any more or less antireligious than the idea of special creation, for neither really strengthens, weakens, or otherwise affects belief in God. To the religious person, only the way God operates, not God as such, is in question.

But many were properly convinced by the evidence for evolution. However, under the banner of phrases like "survival of the fittest," evolution was interpreted to prove an essential cruelty of nature; and human behavior, personal and national, often came to be guided by the ethic of "jungle law," "might is right," "every man for himself." Only in that way, it was thought, could the "fittest" prevail. Indirectly, these feelings undoubtedly fanned the fires of political nationalism already intense at the time, and so contributed to setting the stage for World War I. Even today, unfortunately, the mechanism of evolution is still commonly—and erroneously—thought to be a matter of "survival of the fittest."

By now, a full century after Darwin and Wallace, the emotion-charged atmosphere has cleared, and the impact of their theory may be assessed calmly. That Darwin made the greater contribution cannot be questioned. In voluminous writings, he, far more than Wallace, marshaled the evidence for the occurrence of evolution so extensively, and so well, that the reality of the process has never been in doubt since. Moreover, the theory of natural selection was the most convincing explanation of the evolutionary mechanism offered up to that time. Indeed, carrying new meaning today, it still forms a part of the modern theory of evolution. As now understood, however, evolution is preeminently a peaceful process, and it has very little to do with "struggle," "weeding out," or "the fittest." Also, we know that Darwin and Wallace, like Lamarck, were unsuccessful in identifying the actual sources of individual variations. In short, Darwin and Wallace supplied an incomplete explanation, but as far as it went, theirs was the first to point in the right direction.

The modern theory of evolution is not the work of any one man, and it did not arise by "special creation," fully developed. Rather, it evolved slowly during the first half of the current century, many biologists of various specializations contributing to it. The theory is the spiritual offspring of Mendel and of Darwin, but the family resemblance, though present, may not be immediately evident. We shall be concerned with this modern theory in the following pages.

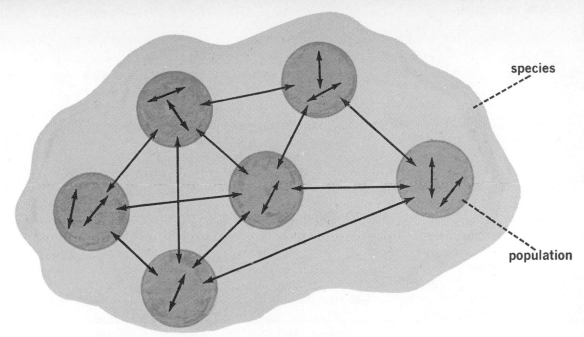

FIG. 28.1. The concept of "gene pool." In a species, gene flow occurs within and between populations. The total gene content of the species thus represents a gene pool to which all members of the species have access. Gene flow cannot occur between the gene pools of two different species.

The Forces of Evolution

THE EVOLUTIONARY PROCESS

The medium of evolution is the *population*. The raw materials of the evolutionary process are the *inheritable variations* which appear among the individuals of a population. And the mechanism of evolution may be described as **natural selection acting on the inheritable variations of a population.**

We already know from Chap. 4 that a population is a geographically localized group of organisms of the same species in which the members interbreed preferentially with one another and also interbreed occasionally with members of neighboring populations. We may note now that the result of the close sexual communication within a population is a **free flow of genes.** Hereditary material present in a part of a population may in time spread to the whole population, through the gene-pooling and gene-combining effect of sex. Therefore, in the course of successive sexual generations, the total genetic content of a population may become shuffled and reshuffled thoroughly. We may say that a population possesses a given **gene pool** and that the interbreeding members of the population have free access to all components of that pool. Moreover, inasmuch as sister populations are in occasional reproductive contact, the gene pool of one population is connected also to the gene pools of sister populations. In this way, the total genetic content of an entire species continues to be shuffled about among the member organisms (Fig. 28.1).

Evolution operates via the gene pools of populations. We already know from Chap. 27 how changes in genetic systems, hence inheritable variations, may arise: by **sexual recombination** and by **mutation.** In each generation, some individuals may appear featuring new trait variations, as a result of either recombinational or mutational processes. If these variant organisms survive and have offspring of their own, then their particular genetic innovations will persist in the gene pool of the population. And in the course of successive generations, the genetic novelty may spread to many or all members of the population.

Whether or not such spreading actually takes

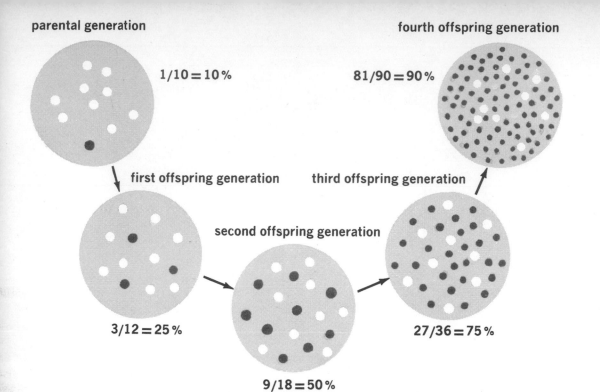

parental generation

$1/10 = 10\%$

first offspring generation

$3/12 = 25\%$

second offspring generation

$9/18 = 50\%$

third offspring generation

fourth offspring generation

$81/90 = 90\%$

$27/36 = 75\%$

FIG. 28.2. Illustrating the effect of differential reproduction or natural selection. Assume that a variation arises in one individual of a parental generation (black dot), and that the variant organism is able to leave three offspring. Each nonvariant organism (white dot) on the other hand only manages to leave one offspring. The complexion of the population will then change as shown during subsequent generations; i.e., the variant type will represent a progressively larger fraction of the numerical total. Such spreading of variations, brought about by differential reproduction, constitutes natural selection.

place depends on natural selection. This term is synonymous with **differential reproduction**, a phrase which indicates simply that some individuals of a population have more offspring than others. Clearly, those which leave more offspring will contribute a proportionately greater percentage of individuals to the numerical total of the next generation than those which leave fewer offspring. Hence if differential reproduction continues in the same manner over many generations, the abundant reproducers will contribute a progressively larger fraction to the whole population. As a result, *their* genetic systems will become preponderant in the gene pool of the population (Fig. 28.2).

Which individuals leave more offspring than

others? Usually, but by no means necessarily, those that are best adapted to the environment. Being well adapted, such individuals on the whole are healthier and better fed, may find mates more readily, and may care for their offspring appropriately. However, circumstances may on occasion be such that comparatively poorly adapted individuals have the most offspring. Instances of this are sometimes encountered in human populations, for example. In any event, what counts in evolution is not how well or how poorly an organism copes with its environment, but only how many offspring it manages to leave. The more there are, the greater a role will the parental genes play in the total genetic content of the population. By and large, the well-adapted organism contributes most to the gene pool.

Hence if an inheritable variation appears in an organism, and if, through differential reproduction in successive generations, the progeny of that organism becomes numerically more and more abundant, then a given genetic novelty will spread rapidly throughout the population. As a result of such natural selection, the genetic innovation will become a common component of the hereditary repertoire of most or all member organisms. In effect, a trait variation originating in one organism will have become a standard feature of the population as a whole.

This is the unit of evolutionary change. Many such unit changes must accumulate in a population before the organisms are sufficiently altered in structure or function to be unable to interbreed with sister populations. But once such a reproductive barrier does come into existence, the population represents a new species. We shall return to these and larger evolutionary alterations below. Here we may note that all evolution operates through the basic mechanism just described, namely, appearance of inheritable variations by sexual recombination and mutation, and spreading of these variations through a population by differential reproduction.

Inasmuch as inheritable variations originate randomly, evolutionary innovations, too, appear at random. And inasmuch as the best reproducers are generally the best adapted, evolution as a whole is directed by adaptation and is oriented toward continued or improved adaptation.

Note that, in this modern view of evolution, natural selection is fundamentally a creative force. For its important effect is to *spread genetic novelty,* hence new traits, through a population. It is also a peaceful force, involving *reproduction,* not "struggle for existence" or "survival of the fittest." Organisms actually struggle rather rarely. Indeed they try to avoid struggle and attempt to pursue life as inconspicuously as possible, eating when they can, reproducing when they can. Moreover, natural selection does not "eliminate the unfit." The "fit" may be the mightiest and grandest organism in the population, but it might happen to be sterile. And the "unfit" could be a sickly weakling, yet have numerous offspring. The point is that neither "survival" nor "elimination" is actually at issue. The only issue of consequence here is comparative reproductive success. Indirectly, to be sure, health, fitness, and even actual physical struggles may affect the reproductive success of organisms. To that extent such factors can have evolutionary consequences. But what in Darwin's day was regarded as the whole of natural selection is now clearly recognized to have only a limited, indirect effect on evolution. The whole of natural selection, directly and indirectly, undoubtedly is differential reproduction.

THE GENETIC BASIS

The Hardy-Weinberg Law

From the preceding, we may describe evolution as a progressive change of **gene frequencies.** This means that, in the course of successive generations, the proportion of some genes in the population increases and the proportion of others decreases. For example, a mutation may at first be represented by a single gene, but if by natural selection this mutation spreads to more and more individuals, then its frequency increases, whereas the frequency of the original, unmutated gene decreases. Clearly, the *rates* with which gene frequencies change will be a measure of the *speed* of evolution. What determines such rates?

Suppose we consider a large population in which two alleles, *A* and *a,* occur in certain frequencies. In such a population, three kinds of individuals will be found, namely, *AA, Aa,* and *aa.* Let us assume that the numerical proportions happen to be:

AA	Aa	aa
36%	48%	16%

Assuming further that the choice of sexual mates is entirely random, that all individuals produce roughly equal numbers of gametes, and that the genes *A* and *a* do not mutate, we may then ask how the frequency of the genes *A* and *a* will change from one generation to the next.

Since *AA* individuals make up 36 per cent of the total population, they will contribute approximately 36 per cent of all the gametes formed in the population. These gametes will all contain one *A* gene. Similarly, *aa* individuals will produce 16 per cent of all gametes in the population, and each will contain one *a* gene. The gametes of *Aa* individuals will be of two types, *A* and *a,* in equal numbers. Since their total amounts to 48 per cent, 24 per cent of them will be *A* and 24 per cent will be *a.* Hence the overall gamete output of the population will be:

parents	gametes	parents	gametes
36% AA	⟶ 36% A	16% aa	⟶ 16% a
48% Aa	⟶ 24% A	48% Aa	⟶ 24% a
	60% A		40% a

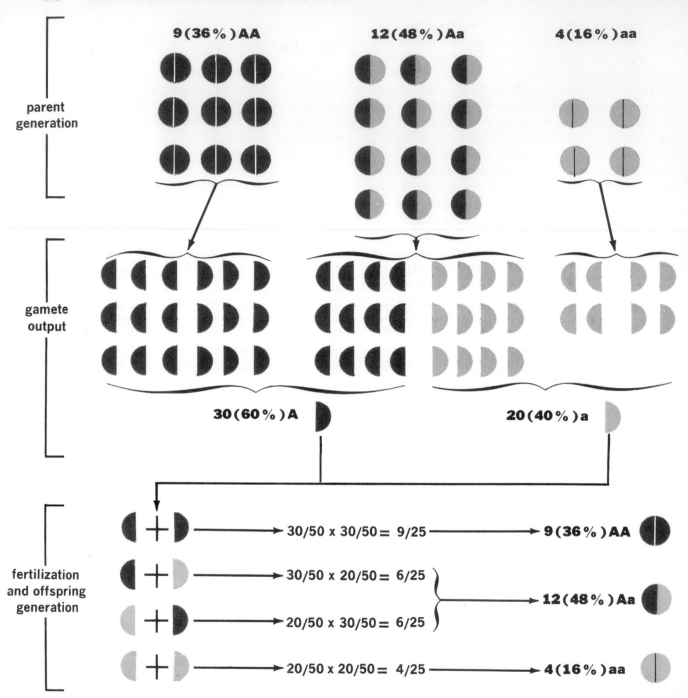

FIG. 28.3. Illustrating the Hardy-Weinberg law. If mating is random, if mutations do not occur, and if the population is large, then gene frequencies do not change from one generation to the next.

Fertilization now occurs in four possible ways: two *A* gametes join; two *a* gametes join; an *A* sperm joins an *a* egg; and an *a* sperm joins an *A* egg. Each of these possibilities will occur with a frequency dictated by the relative abundance of the *A* and *a* gametes. There are 60 per cent *A* gametes. Hence *A* will join *A* in 60 per cent *of 60 per cent* of the cases, i.e., in 60 × 60, or 36 per cent of the time. Similarly, *A* sperms will join *a* eggs in 60 × 40, or 24 per cent of the cases. The total result:

sperms		eggs			offspring
A	+	*A*	⟶ 60 × 60 ⟶	36% *AA*
A	+	*a*	⟶ 60 × 40 ⟶	24% *Aa*
a	+	*A*	⟶ 40 × 60 ⟶	24% *Aa*
a	+	*a*	⟶ 40 × 40 ⟶	16% *aa*

We note that the new generation in our example population will consist of 36 per cent *AA*, 48 per cent *Aa*, and 16 per cent *aa* individuals. These are precisely the same proportions we started with originally. Evidently, *gene frequencies have not changed*.

It can be shown that such a result is obtained regardless of the number and the types of gene pairs considered simultaneously. The important conclusion is that, *if mating is random, if mutations do not occur, and if the population is large, then gene frequencies in a population remain constant from generation to generation*. This generalization is known as the **Hardy-Weinberg law.** It is to the theory of evolution what Mendel's laws are to the theory of heredity (Fig. 28.3).

The Hardy-Weinberg law indicates that, when a population is in genetic equilibrium, the rate of evolution is zero; that is, genes continue to be reshuffled by sexual recombination, and as a result, individual variations continue to originate from this source. But the overall gene frequencies do not change, and of themselves, therefore, the variations are *not* being propagated differentially. Evolution consequently does not occur.

What does make evolution occur are deviations from the "ifs" specified in the Hardy-Weinberg law. Thus, mating is decidedly not random whenever natural selection takes place; genes actually do mutate; and populations are not always large. Singly and in combination, these three factors may disturb the genetic equilibrium of a population and may produce evolutionary change.

The Effect of Nonrandom Mating

This effect may be appreciated readily if we assume that, in our example above, *AA*, *Aa*, and *aa* individuals are not adapted equally well. Suppose that the *A* gene in double dose, as in the *AA* combination, has a particular metabolic effect, such that death in infancy will occur in one-third of the individuals possessing these genes. Under these conditions, 36 per cent *AA* individuals will be born, but only two-thirds of their number will reach reproductive age. Consequently, the *Aa* and *aa* individuals will constitute a proportionately larger fraction of the reproducing population, and they will contribute proportionately more to the total gamete output. The ultimate result over successive generations will be a progressive decrease in the frequency of the *A* gene and a progressive increase of the *a* gene. A certain *intensity* of natural selection, or **selection pressure,** here operates *against* the *A* gene and *for* the *a* gene (Fig. 28.4). Whenever such selection pressures exert an effect, Hardy-Weinberg equilibria are not maintained. Instead, as gene frequencies become altered more or less rapidly, given traits spread or disappear, and this represents evolutionary change. In nature, most traits are being steadily selected for or selected against, and in the course of many generations, even a very slight selection pressure substantially affects the genetic complexion of a population.

The Effect of Mutations

Mutations disturb genetic equilibria too. It has been found that given genes mutate at characteristic rates. For example, man possesses a recessive gene *h* which produces the bleeder's disease *hemophilia* (see Chap. 27). A dominant gene *H* masks the effect of *h* and allows blood to clot normally. It is known that among roughly every 50,000 *H* genes in human gametes, one is likely to mutate and become *h*. Clearly, each such mutation reduces the frequency of *H* and increases the frequency of *h*.

This implies that *h* genes should slowly accu-

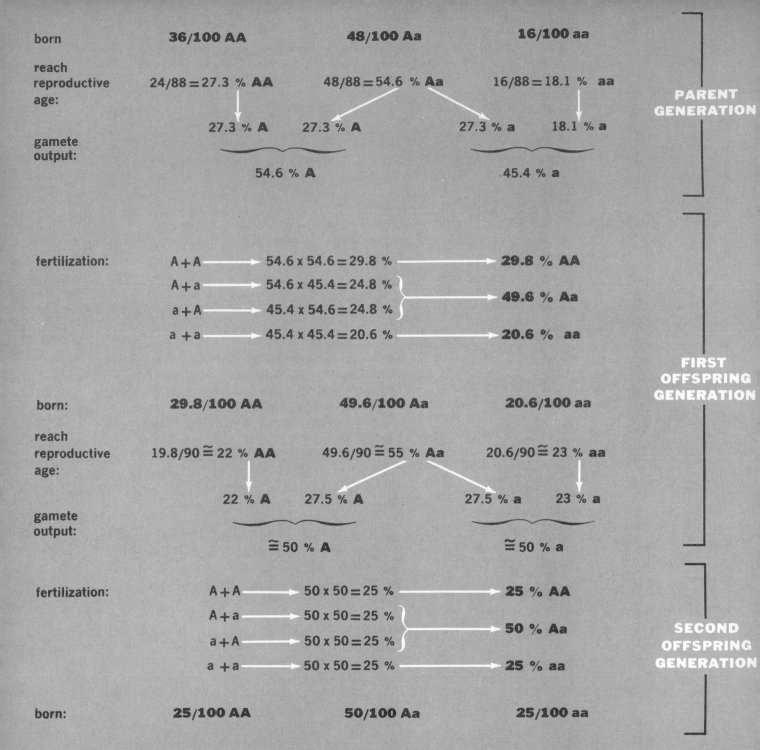

FIG. 28.4. The effect of nonrandom mating. If only two-thirds of all *AA* individuals reach reproductive age, then in the course of two generations the frequency of the *A* gene will decrease and the frequency of the *a* gene will increase, as shown in the calculation.

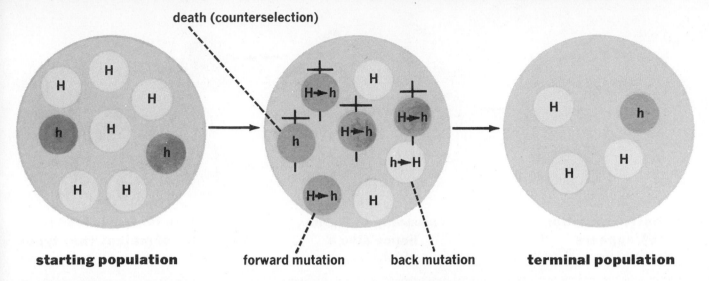

death (counterselection)

starting population   **forward mutation**   **back mutation**   **terminal population**

FIG. 28.5.   The effect of mutations. In a population containing mutant types, new mutants may arise by forward mutation; also, the number of mutants may be reduced both by backward mutation and by death through counterselection. Gene frequencies may or may not change through these forces.

mulate in human populations and that hemophilia should therefore be an increasingly common disease. Actually, the disease is exceedingly rare. Two conditions account for this. One is *back mutation*, that is, mutation of h to H. Back mutations are not at all unusual among genes generally, and they have their own characteristic rates. In the case of $h \to H$, the rate is lower than that of $H \to h$. Even so, back mutations do reduce the equilibrium-disturbing effect of the "forward" mutations.

The second condition which reduces the actual frequency of the h gene is that a powerful selection pressure operates against this gene. For persons afflicted with hemophilia rarely reach reproductive age, but die when young from even minor wounds. So also most mutations are affected by selection pressures which operate either for or against them. Therefore, whenever mutations occur, they produce a disturbance of genetic equilibria; and natural selection acting on these mutations then modifies the disturbances further, in some cases increasing them, in others decreasing them (Fig. 28.5).

We may note here that the evolutionary effect of mutations varies according to whether the gene changes are dominant or recessive. A newly originated dominant mutation will affect traits immediately, and selection for or against it will take place at once. But if a mutation is recessive, it does not affect

traits immediately. Hence natural selection does not influence it immediately either. This is the case with most mutations since, as noted in Chap. 27, most actual mutations are recessive.

Nevertheless, recessive mutations may spread through a population. For example, an organism may carry a recessive mutant gene a', and it may also carry a dominant gene B, which produces an adaptively very desirable trait. Natural selection will then operate *for* the gene B; that is, the organism possessing B will reproduce abundantly, and its genes will spread through the population. But in the process, the mutant gene a' will be spread at the same time. Many recessive mutations actually do propagate in this way, by being inherited along with other, adaptively useful dominant genes.

Recessive mutants simply accumulate in the gene pool, without visible effect. However, if two individuals carrying the same recessive mutation happen to mate, then one-fourth of their offspring will be homozygous recessive: $Aa' \times Aa' \to 25\%$ $a'a'$. These offspring will feature altered visible

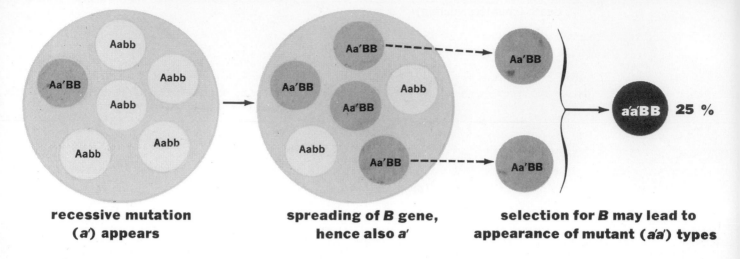

recessive mutation   **spreading of B gene,**   **selection for B may lead to**
(a') appears   **hence also a'**   **appearance of mutant (a'a') types**

FIG. 28.6. If a recessive mutation a' appears in an organism, and if that organism also carries a gene B which is strongly selected, then both B and a' may spread through a population. The appearance of mutant phenotypes a'a' then becomes rather likely.

traits, and natural selection will then affect the mutation directly (Fig. 28.6).

Mutational effects in evolution also vary according to how greatly a given mutation influences a given trait. A "large" mutation, affecting a vital trait in major ways, is likely to be exceedingly harmful and will usually be lethal. For example, *any* change in the principal structure and function of the human heart is likely to cause immediate death. Indeed, large variations are usually eliminated as soon as they arise. By contrast, an organism may survive far more readily if a mutation is "small." We may note here that evolutionary alterations of organisms occur almost exclusively through the accumulation of *many, small* changes in traits, not through single, large changes.

The Effect of Population Size

The third condition affecting Hardy-Weinberg equilibria is population size. If a population is large, any regional imbalances of gene frequencies, arising by chance, are quickly smoothed out by the many random matings among the many individuals. The principle underlying this holds in statistical systems generally. In a coin-flipping experiment, for example, "heads" and "tails" will each come up 50 per cent of the time, but only if the number of throws is large. If only three or four throws are made, it is quite possible that *all* will come up heads, by chance alone. Analogously, gene combinations attain Hardy-Weinberg equilibria only if a population is large. In small groups, chance alone may produce major deviations.

Assume, for example, that AA, Aa, and aa individuals are expected in a certain ratio, in accordance with existing gene frequencies. If the population contains many hundreds of individuals, this ratio will actually materialize. But if the population consists of a few individuals only, *all* these might by chance turn out to be of the *same* genotype, rather than of the three expected genotypes (Fig. 28.7). We say that, in small populations, chance leads to **genetic drift**, that is, to the random establishment of genetic types which numerically are not in accordance with Hardy-Weinberg equilibria.

This effect resembles that of natural selection. For if several genotypes are possible, a particular one would likewise come to predominate if there

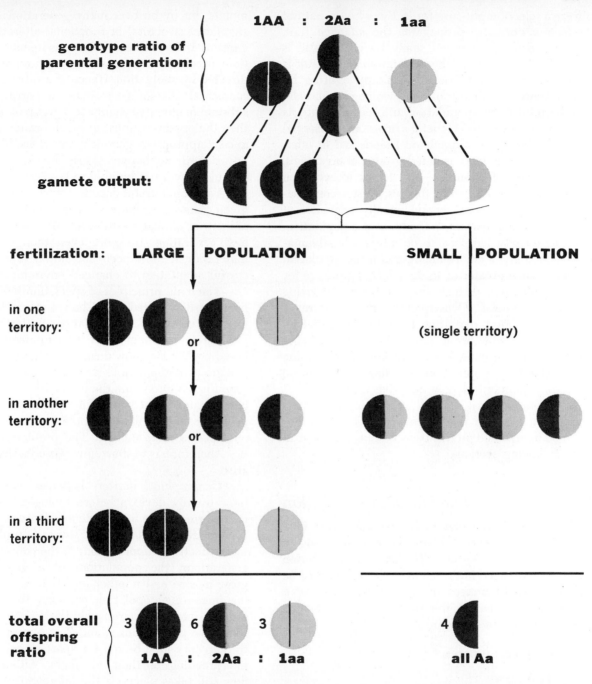

FIG. 28.7.   Genetic drift. Given a population as at top of figure, then the genetic constitution of offspring populations is influenced by population size. In large populations (left), gene combinations produced in different territories will average out to form a total offspring population in which gene frequencies are as in the parent population. But in small populations (right), chance alone may produce significant deviations from Hardy-Weinberg expectations.

were a selection pressure for it. But whereas natural selection normally propagates the *adaptive* trait, genetic drift is governed solely by chance and is therefore not oriented by adaptation. The result is that, in small populations, nonadaptive, often bizarre traits become established, which may actually be harmful to the population and may promote its getting even smaller. Genetic drift is often observed among plants and animals on islands and in other small, reproductively isolated groups of organisms.

By way of summary, the forces of evolution may now be described as follows. First, recombinational or mutational genetic novelty originates at random among certain individuals of a population. If this novelty happens to be adaptively advantageous in a given environment, and if the population is large, then greater or lesser selection pressure for the novelty will disturb the equilibria of existing gene frequencies. Consequently, this pressure of natural selection, operating through differential reproduction, will bring about a correspondingly rapid or slow propagation of the genetic innovation throughout the population. The final result will be the establishment of new adaptive traits.

Evolution as it actually occurs must be interpreted in terms of this mechanism. That it in fact can be interpreted on this basis will become clear in the following section.

The Nature of Evolution

The key processes to be explained are, first, *speciation*, i.e., evolutionary events culminating in the origin of new species. The term **microevolution** is sometimes used in this context. Second, it must be shown how differences among organisms arise on a scale beyond that of the species. The contrasting term here is **macroevolution.**

MICROEVOLUTION

The Process

Even on the species level, evolution is an exceedingly slow process. As noted, a very large number of very small variations of traits must accumulate, bit by bit over many generations, before a significant structural or functional alteration of organisms is in evidence. Moreover, genetic innovations occur at random, whereas natural selection is directed by adaptation. Hence, if a substantial environmental change necessitates a correspondingly substantial adaptive change in a group of organisms, then the organisms must *await* the random appearance of appropriate genetic innovations. If useful innovations do not happen to arise by chance, then the organisms will not be able to readapt and will die out. Yet even if useful genetic novelty does arise in a given generation, there is no guarantee that more novelty of similar usefulness will originate in the next generation. In short, even though evolution may occur, it could occur too slowly to permit successful adaptation to changed environments.

The main principles of speciation have already been briefly referred to in Chap. 4. A species, we recall, is a collection of populations within which reproductive communication is maintained by interbreeding. We may now define a species alternatively as a group of populations sharing the same gene pool (see Fig. 28.1). Within the pool a free flow of genes is maintained, but genetic flow between two such pools does not occur; a reproductive barrier isolates one species from another. The problem of speciation, therefore, is to show how reproductive barriers arise.

Geographical barriers between sister populations usually develop before biological, reproductive barriers come into existence. Among geographical isolating mechanisms, *distance* is probably the most effective. Suppose that, in the course of many generations, the populations of a given species grow in size and number and that, as a result of the increasing population pressure, the organisms radiate into a progressively larger territory. In time, two populations A and Z at opposite ends of the territory may be too far apart to permit direct interbreeding of their members. Although gene flow still takes place via the interconnecting populations between A and Z, individuals of A and Z no longer come into reproductive contact directly (Fig. 28.8).

initial species territory

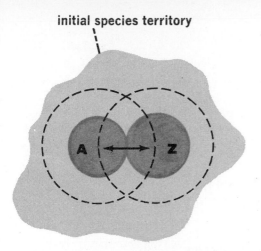

reproductive ranges of **A** and **Z** overlap:
gene flow direct

expanded species territory, after population growth

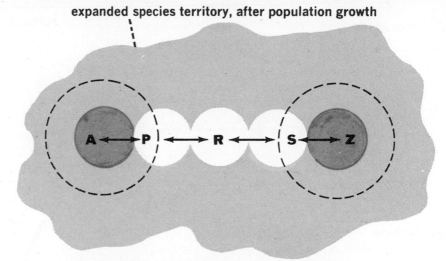

reproductive ranges of **A** and **Z** no longer overlap:
gene flow indirect, via populations **P, R,S**

FIG. 28.8. Diagram illustrating how species populations may in time become separated by distance, leading to a comparative reproductive isolation, hence a reduction of gene flow.

It is then almost certain that, by chance, different genetic innovations arise in *A* and *Z* and that different ones will be propagated within *A* and *Z* by natural selection. Such an effect will be particularly pronounced if the environments of *A* and *Z* are, or become, more or less different. If now the evolutionary changes *within* *A* and *within* *Z* occur faster than the speed of genetic flow *between* *A* and *Z*, then *A* and *Z* will actually become progressively different in structure or function. These two populations thus may come to represent two distinct **subspecies** (Fig. 28.9).

Geographical isolation here has set the stage for the development of initial differences between members of *A* and *Z*. And if the differences accumulate, they may eventually become so great that gene flow between *A* and *Z* will stop altogether. For example, population *A* (or *Z*) may undergo a change in the reproductive organs, such that mating with neighboring populations becomes mechanically impossible. Or the protein specificities of *A* may change, such that the gametes become incompatible with those of neighboring populations. Or the time of the annual breeding season in *A* may become advanced or delayed relative to that

of neighboring populations. Or the individuals of *A* may become changed psychologically, such that they no longer accept mates from neighboring populations. *Biological* barriers of this sort will interrupt all gene flow between *A* and *Z*, and these subspecies, isolated reproductively, then in effect will have become two different **species** (Fig. 28.10).

Although an initial distance isolation is probably the most common kind, other forms of geographical isolation are encountered also. The development of terrestrial islands surrounded by water, or of aquatic islands surrounded by land, the interposition of a forest belt across a prairie, or of a prairie belt across a forest, the appearance of mountain barriers, river barriers, temperature barriers, or of many another physical barrier, each may result in geographical isolation. This may be followed in time by biological reproductive isolation and speciation. The evolution of a new species takes, on the average, roughly one million years.

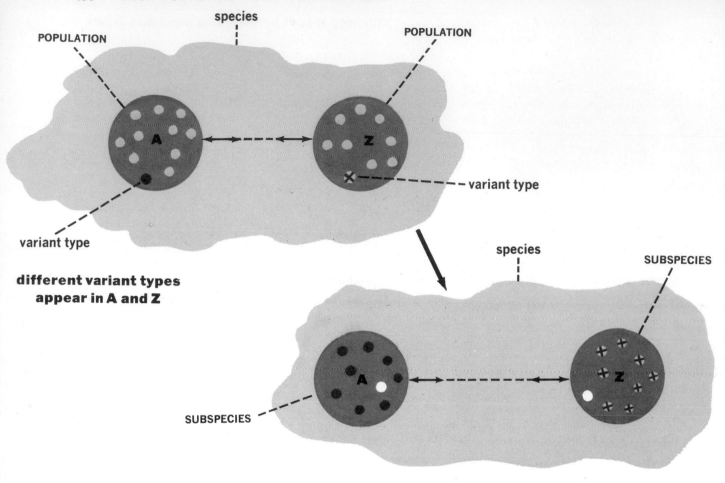

species

POPULATION

POPULATION

variant type

A

Z

variant type

**different variant types
appear in A and Z**

species

SUBSPECIES

A

Z

SUBSPECIES

variant types dominant, but gene flow still possible

FIG. 28.9. Diagram illustrating how different populations of a species may, by selective spreading of variant types, develop into different subspecies.

The Evidence

In many cases, man has been, and is now, contributing deliberately to the microevolution of other organisms. Here may be found direct proof that evolution actually operates according to the mechanism described above.

The most ancient evolution-directing effort of man is his successful *domestication* of various plants and animals. Darwin was the first to recognize the theoretical significance of domestication, and indeed it was this which led him to his concept of natural selection. He reasoned that if man, by **artificial selection,** can transform wild varieties of given plants and animals into domesticated varieties, then perhaps natural selection, acting for far longer periods, can bring about even greater evolutionary transformations in nature. We know now that the

THE MECHANISM OF EVOLUTION

domesticating process actually does involve all the elements of natural evolution: first, deliberate physical, hence genetic, isolation of a wild population by man; and second, long-continued, carefully controlled, differential reproduction of individuals "adapted" to human desires, i.e., of individuals featuring traits considered desirable by man. The result is the creation of new strains, races, subspecies, and even species (Fig. 28.11).

Furthermore, during the last few decades, rather rapid, man-directed evolution has taken place among certain viruses, bacteria, insects, various parasites, and other pest organisms. These live now in an environment in which antibiotics and numerous pest-killing drugs have become distinct hazards. And the organisms have evolved, and are still evolving, increasing resistance to such drugs as these. Indeed, the very rapid evolution of viruses and bacteria becomes a problem in research. For laboratory populations of microorganisms may evolve resistance to a drug even while the drug is being tested. Because microorganisms have exceedingly short generation times, because their populations are physically small, compact, and eas-

ily reared, and because high mutation rates may be induced readily by X rays, they have become favorite test objects in evolution experiments.

Clearly, then, small-scale evolution unquestionably occurs and is observable directly. Moreover, it may be made to occur under conditions based on the postulated modern mechanism of evolution. That this mechanism actually operates as implied by theory is therefore no longer in doubt. Does the same mechanism operate in macroevolution, in the transformation of species into more divergent types?

MACROEVOLUTION

According to their similarities and differences in structure, function, and development, plants and animals are classified into a hierarchy of *taxonomic categories* (see Chap. 8). The **species** is the unit from which higher categories are built up. A group of related species forms a **genus.** Several related

FIG. 28.10. Diagram illustrating the origin of two new species from two subspecies of a single ancestral species.

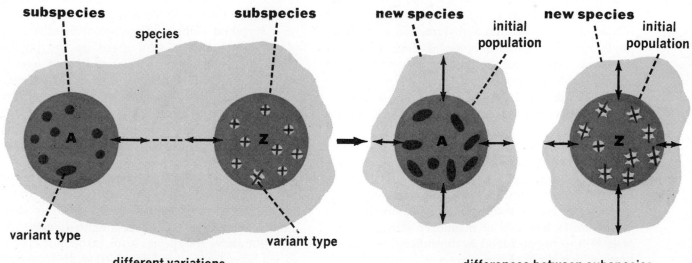

different variations accumulate in each subspecies

differences between subspecies eventually so extensive that gene flow no longer possible; new species formed

FIG. 28.11. Red jungle fowl, an example of a wild animal from which man has bred domesticated varieties by artificial selection. (New York Zoological Society.)

genera form a **family.** Several families make up an **order.** Related orders comprise a **class.** A group of related classes constitutes a **phylum.** And a group of phyla forms a **kingdom.** Finer-rank distinctions are sometimes made, and the prefixes *sub-* and *super-* are then added to the designations of the main categories. For example, several families may make up a **superfamily,** and several of these a **suborder** (Fig. 28.12).

The higher the category, the more subordinate categories are included in it and the more general are the features which unify the group. All mammals, for example, form a class. This class consists of some twenty orders, and the unifying feature of all is possession of hair and of mammary glands. Mammals in turn are included in the subphylum Vertebrata, which also includes, among others, the class of birds, characterized by possession of feathers, and the class of reptiles, comprising terrestrial verte-

brates with scaly skin. As the name indicates, the unifying feature of all Vertebrata is the possession of a vertebral column. Together with other subphyla, vertebrates in turn make up the phylum Chordata, all members of which possess an internal stiffening rod, the *notochord*, at least during early stages of their life cycle. Thus, the category of phylum represents a large basic grouping in which all members share one or more unique architectural features, distinct from those of other phyla (see also Chaps. 30, 31).

Up to the level of the species, as we have seen, the criteria of gene flow and reproductive contact determine whether or not two organisms differ enough to be regarded as belonging to different species. But above the species level, taxonomic classification becomes more or less arbitrary. It depends in large measure on a consensus of opinion among qualified biologists as to how greatly two organisms must differ before they may be put into separate genera, orders, phyla, etc. In most cases, such consensus is arrived at readily. For example, there is no doubt that a tapir and a tiger represent two different orders within the class of mammals, or that a bear and a dog represent two different families within the mammalian order Carnivora. In some cases, the rank distinction between two types of organism is not easily determined, but it is usually quite clear when the differences exceed the species level. The problem at issue is to show *how* the differences among organisms evolve beyond the species level.

The biologist R. Goldschmidt believes that the mechanism of macroevolution is not the same as that of microevolution. Differences between orders, classes, and phyla are far too great, Goldschmidt argues, to be accounted for by a gradual accumulation of many small, minor variations among organisms. Goldschmidt agrees that the origin of species, and even of genera, can be explained on this basis, but he maintains that, for higher taxonomic categories, a different machinery may be required.

Here he postulates a mechanism involving "large" mutations. According to this hypothesis, a major mutation, affecting many vital traits simultaneously, transforms an organism suddenly, in one jump, into a completely new type which represents a new, high-ranking taxonomic category. In most cases, such an organism could not survive, for it would undoubtedly be entirely unsuited to the local environment. But Goldschmidt considers that, in ex-

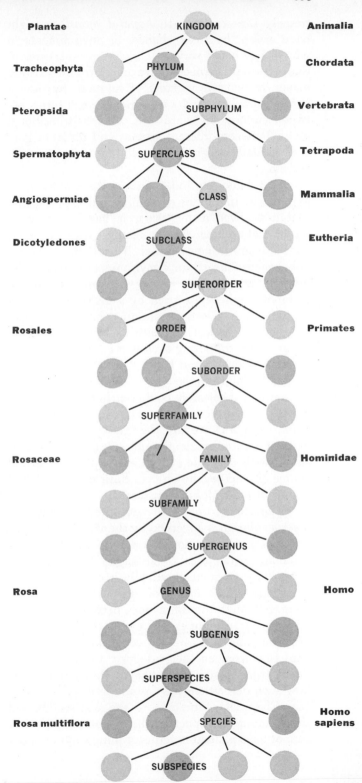

FIG. 28.12. The hierarchy of taxonomic categories. To serve as specific examples, the taxonomic classifications of a rose and of man are given to the left and right of the center diagram.

tremely rare cases, such *hopeful monsters* might have arisen, by freak chance, in environments in which they could survive. Only a few successes of this sort would be needed to account for the existing major taxonomic variants. Evolution by jumps would explain also why transitional fossil forms between various phyla are rare, whereas transitional fossils between different species and different genera, created by gradual evolution, are extremely common.

Few biologists today accept the Goldschmidt hypothesis. In studies of natural and experimental mutations over many years, it has always been found that sudden genetic changes with major effects are immediately lethal. This is the case not only because the external environment is unsuitable, but also, and perhaps mainly, because the internal metabolic upheaval caused by a major mutation is far too drastic to permit continued survival. Indeed, large mutations lead to death well before hatching or birth. But supposing even that a hopeful monster could develop beyond birth, it would by definition be so different from the other individuals of the population that it certainly could not find a mate. Also, although transitional fossils between major taxonomic categories are rare, they are by no means nonexistent. On the whole, therefore, it is far more consistent with available evidence to explain the actual course of macroevolution on a basis other than that of fortuitous hopeful monsters.

The almost universally accepted view is that macroevolution is governed by the very same mechanism as microevolution. The origin of high-ranking taxonomic categories is envisaged to involve the same kinds of small, gradually accumulating trait variations as the origin of species, only more of them. Although the differences between phyla and other major categories are great, they are not so great that one such category could not have evolved gradually from another category. Indeed, the evidence from fossils and embryos shows quite well how such derivations have probably been achieved (see Chap. 29). Moreover, as the next section will show, important aspects of the evolutionary process cannot be explained in terms of jump evolution, but

can be explained rather well in terms of gradual evolution. And we may note that the designations microevolution and macroevolution actually become almost superfluous, for they do not identify different mechanisms.

THE CHARACTERISTICS OF EVOLUTION

Rates of Change

On the basis of the common mechanism for all evolution, a number of general features of past evolution may be explained readily. A first such feature is that the *speeds* of evolution, though slow in all instances, have varied considerably for different types of organisms, differently at different times. As a rule, the more stable a given environment has been, the slower has been the evolution of the organism living in it. Thus, terrestrial organisms by and large have evolved faster than marine organisms. Also, during periods of major geologic upheavals, e.g., in times of glaciation or of mountain building (see Chap. 29), evolution has been fairly rapid generally. On the other hand, in a few existing animal types, the rate of evolution has been practically zero for hundreds of millions of years. Horseshoe crabs, certain lampshells (see Chap. 31), and radiolarian protozoa are among the oldest of such "living fossils" (Fig. 28.13). In these and similar cases, the specific environment of the organisms has been stable enough to make the ancient way of life still possible. Given the general evolutionary mechanism of small random variations acted on by adaptively oriented natural selection, it is not surprising that speeds of evolution should have varied in keeping pace with environmental changes.

Adaptive Radiation

Another general feature in past evolution has been the phenomenon of **adaptive radiation.** We have seen how, in speciation, one ancestral species gives rise simultaneously to two or more descendant species. A similar pattern of *branching* descent has characterized evolution on all levels. A new type evolves, and it then becomes a potential ancestor for many different, simultaneous descendant lines. For example, the ancestral mammalian type has given rise *simultaneously* to several lines of grazing plains animals (e.g., horses, cattle, goats), to burrowing animals (e.g., moles), to flying animals (bats), to several lines of aquatic animals (e.g., whales, seals, sea cows), to animals living in trees (e.g., monkeys), to carnivorous predators (e.g., dogs, cats), and to many others. Evidently, the original mammalian type branched out and exploited many different available environments and ways of life. Each descendant line thereby became adaptively specialized in a particular way, and the sum of the various lines, all leading away from the common ancestral type, formed an "adaptive radiation."

Within each such line, furthermore, adaptive radiations of smaller scope took place. For example, the line of tree-living mammals in time evolved several simultaneous sublines, and each of these in turn gave rise to subsublines, etc. The specific results today are animals as varied as monkeys, lemurs, tarsiers, apes, and men. Evidently, man did not "descend from the apes." Rather, apes and men have had a common ancestor, and they are *contemporary* members of the same adaptive radiation.

The important implication here is that evolution is *not* a "ladder" or a "scale." The pattern is more nearly that of a greatly branching bush, where the tips of all uppermost branches represent currently living species (Fig. 28.14). Note that none of these actually is "higher" or "lower" than any other. Instead, they are simply contemporary groups of different structure, function, and history. The ameba too may be found on one of the top branches, and it too is a contemporary of man. The all-too-frequent picture of evolution as a "progression from ameba to man" is, and always has been, utterly without foundation. Leading down from the branch tips to progressively thicker branches, the evolutionary bush goes backward in time. Junctions of branches represent common ancestors, and these are the higher in taxonomic rank the more closely the main stem is approached.

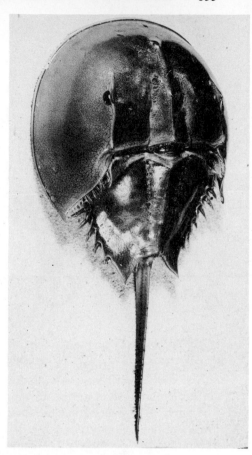

FIG. 28.13. The horseshoe crab *Limulus*. This arthropod may be regarded as a "living fossil," having persisted more or less unchanged for 200 million years or more. (Carolina Biological Supply Co.)

Extinction

Not all the branches on a bush ramify right to the top, but some terminate abruptly at various intermediate points. In past evolution, too, **extinction** has been a general feature. In many actual cases of extinction, the specific causes may never be known. But the general cause of all extinctions emerges from the nature of the evolutionary mechanism. That cause is change in environment, without rapid enough readaptation of organisms to the change. Evidently, unlike death, which is inherent in the life history of every individual, extinction is *not* a

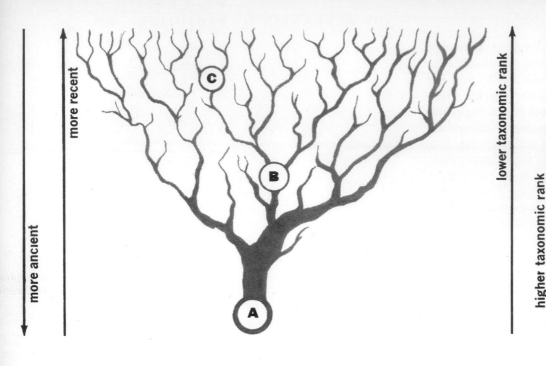

FIG. 28.14. The bush pattern of evolution. The uppermost tips of the branches represent currently living forms, and branches terminating below the top represent extinct forms. Fork points such as **B** and **C** are ancestral types. **B** is more ancient and of higher taxonomic rank than **C**. **A** represents the archancestor of all living types.

foregone conclusion inherent in the evolutionary history of every group. Rather, extinction occurs only if and when the group cannot make adaptive adjustments to environmental change (Fig. 28.15).

Such change need not necessarily be physical. For example, biological *competition* between two different types occupying the same territory often has led to the extinction of one. However, note that competition most often does not involve direct combat or "struggle." Characteristically, the competition is usually quite indirect, as when two different types of herbivores draw on the same limited supply of grass. The more narrowly specialized type here usually prevails over the more generalized type. A herbivore like a rabbit, *specialized* to feed on vegetables, is likely to have the competitive advantage over an omnivore like a man or a bear, if that omnivore, though capable of feeding on varied foods, happens by circumstance to be forced to eat only vegetables. The rabbit will be able to find vegetables more easily and to make more efficient use of them. On the other hand, if vegetables should disappear locally, the specialized herbivore would quickly become extinct, whereas the generalized omnivore might find other food and survive. Clearly, specialization and adaptive flexibility each has certain evolutionary advantages and certain disadvantages. The issue of survival or extinction depends on a fine balance between the two.

This probably accounts for the observation that extinction is the more common the lower the taxonomic category. Extinction of species, and even of genera, has been a nearly universal occurrence, but relatively few orders and still fewer classes have become extinct. And practically all phyla that ever originated continue to be in existence today. The phylum evidently includes so broad and so far-flung an assemblage of different adaptive types that at least some of them have always persisted, regardless of how environments have changed. Species, on the other hand, are usually adapted rather narrowly to limited, circumscribed environments, and the chances for extinction are therefore greater.

Replacement

In conjunction with extinction, **replacement** has been another common occurrence in evolution. As noted, competition may be a direct cause for the replacement of one group in a given environment by another. For example, pouched marsupial mammals were very abundant in the Americas a few million years ago, but with the exception of forms like the opossum, they were replaced in the Western Hemisphere by the competing placental mammals. Competition is not a necessary prerequisite for replacement, however. A group may become extinct for some other reason, and another group may then evolve into the vacated environment and way of life. A good example of this is provided by the *ammonites,* fossil mollusks related to the living chambered nautilus (see Chap. 29). Some 200 million years ago, ammonites were represented by about a dozen families. All but one of these later became extinct, and the surviving group rapidly evolved into some two dozen new families of ammonites. These latter then exploited the adaptive niche vacated by the earlier ammonites.

Replacement in this case was more or less immediate. But on occasion, many millions of years may elapse before a new group evolves into a previously occupied environmental niche. *Delayed replacement* of this sort took place, for example, in the case of the ichthyosaurs. These large, marine, fishlike reptiles became extinct some 100 million years ago, and their particular niche subsequently remained unoccupied for about 40 million years. Dolphins and porpoises evolved then, and these mammals replaced the ichthyosaurs. Similarly delayed replacement occurred between the flying reptilian pterosaurs and the later mammalian bats (Fig. 28.16; also Chap. 29).

Convergence and Divergence

The phenomenon of replacement is often accompanied by that of **convergence**, a frequent feature in evolution generally. We have seen how, in an adaptive radiation, a common ancestral type gives rise to two or more descendant lines, all adapted in different ways to different environments. Such development of dissimilar characteristics in closely related groups is often called evolutionary **divergence**. By contrast, when two or more *unrelated* groups adapt to the *same* type of environment,

then their evolution is oriented in the same direction. Such organisms may come to resemble one another in one or more ways. Evolution of a common set of characteristics in groups of different ancestry is called convergence (Fig. 28.17).

For example, the development of wings in both pterosaurs and bats, or of finlike appendages in both ichthyosaurs and dolphins, illustrates evolutionary convergence in replacing forms. Inasmuch as the replacing type occupies the same adaptive niche as the type which is being replaced, the appearance of convergent features is not surprising. But convergence is also encountered in nonreplacing forms. For example, the eyes of squids and of fish are remarkably alike. Squids and fish are not related directly, and neither replaces the other. However, both groups comprise large, fast swimmers, and good eyes of a particular construction are a distinct advantage in the ways of life of both. Selection ac-

FIG. 28.15. An animal which has become extinct relatively recently. The dodo survived till just a few hundred years ago. (American Museum of Natural History.)

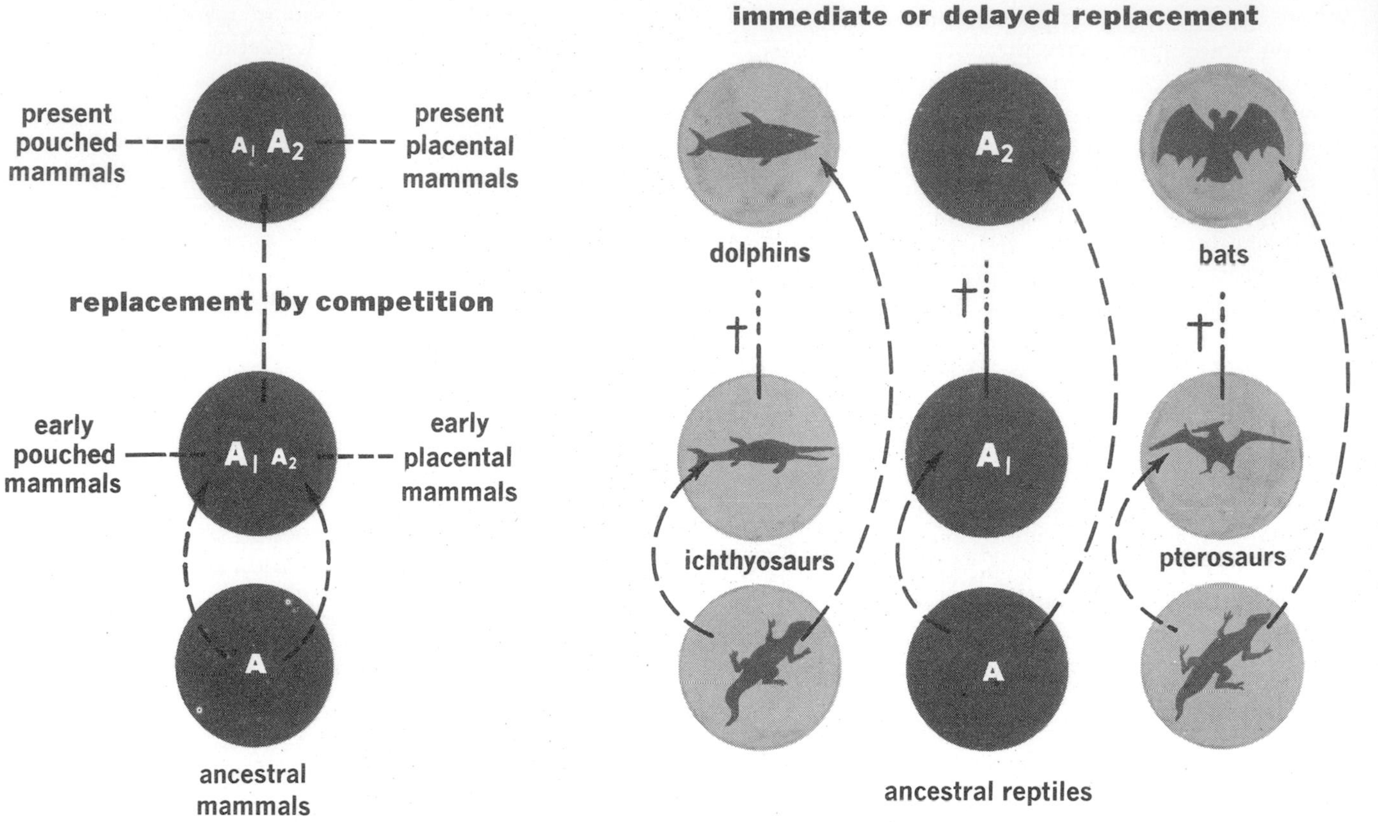

immediate or delayed replacement

present
pouched
mammals

present
placental
mammals

A_1 A_2

replacement by competition

early
pouched
mammals

early
placental
mammals

A_1 A_2

A

ancestral
mammals

dolphins

A_2

bats

ichthyosaurs

A_1

pterosaurs

A

ancestral reptiles

FIG. 28.16. Diagrams of evolutionary replacement.

tually has promoted variations which have led to eyes of similar structure, and the observed convergence is the result.

Opportunism

We may note that although the eyes of squids and fish are strikingly alike, they are by no means identical. Similarly, although the wings of pterosaurs and bats, and also of insects and birds, are convergent, in the sense that all carry out the same functions of flying, the various wing types are quite different structurally, and they operate in different ways (see Chap. 9). Convergence leads to *similarity*, never to identity. Moreover, neither squids nor fish possess a theoretically "best" eye structure for fast swimmers, and none of the flying groups possesses a theoretically "best" wing design. Engi-

neering specialists in optics and aviation can probably point out numerous operational imperfections in all these organs and can design devices for vision or flight which are theoretically far more efficient.

The point is that eyes, wings, or any other structures need not be theoretically best. They only need to be practically workable. In a way of life based on flying, wings of *some* sort are clearly essential. But virtually all requirements for living can have *multiple* solutions, and so long as a given solution works at all, it does not matter how the solution is arrived at. The various animal wings do represent multiple solutions of the same problem, each evolved from a different starting point and each functioning in a different way. Similarly for all other instances of evolutionary convergence.

We are led to one of the most important and

most universal characteristics of evolution, that of **random opportunism.** Evolution has produced not what is theoretically desirable or best, but what is practically *possible*. There has been no predetermined plan, no striving for set "goals," but only the exploitation of actually available opportunities offered by selection among random hereditary changes. For example, it might have been adaptively

exceedingly useful for terrestrial plants to grow legs, or for terrestrial animals to grow wheels. But neither occurred, because it could not occur. The ancestors in each case simply did not possess the necessary structural and functional potential. However, they did possess the potential to evolve adequate, workable, alternative solutions. In the case of plants, already existing spores could be encapsulated and

FIG. 28.17.   In evolutionary divergence (**A**), a common ancestor gives rise to different descendant lines. In evolutionary convergence (**B** and **C**), relatively unrelated ancestors give rise to rather similar lines.

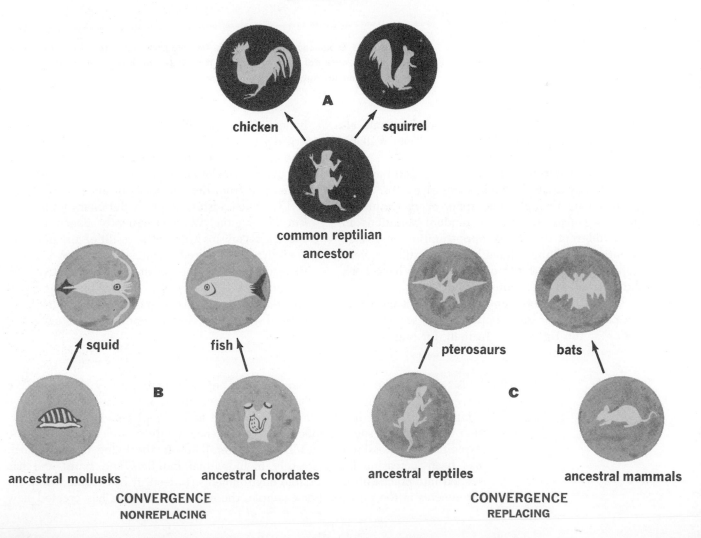

DIVERGENCE

A

chicken   squirrel

common reptilian
ancestor

squid   fish ↑   pterosaurs   bats ↑

B   C

ancestral mollusks   ancestral chordates   ancestral reptiles   ancestral mammals

CONVERGENCE   CONVERGENCE
NONREPLACING   REPLACING

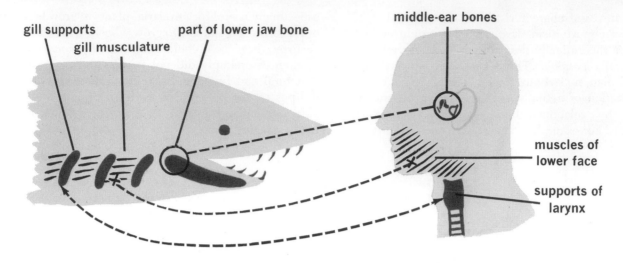

FIG. 28.18. Evolutionary opportunism. The diagram illustrates the evolutionary origin among ancestral fishes of one of the middle-ear bones, the muscles of the lower face, and laryngeal cartilages of men.

distributed by wind, and in the case of animals, already existing fins could be reshaped into walking legs.

Thus, evolution can only remodel and build on what already exists, in small, successive steps. Since, given a long enough time span, *every* feature of *every* organism undergoes random variations in many different directions, opportunities for diverse evolutionary changes have been, and still are, very numerous. Some of these opportunities have been and are actually exploited.

Therefore, every organism, man not excepted, is a patchwork of good opportunities seized by selection at the right time. In man, for example, the

bones of the middle ear have arisen opportunistically from pieces of earlier vertebrate jawbones. The musculature of the lower face has evolved from the gill muscles of ancestral fish. The voice box has developed from the gill bones of ancient fish (Fig. 28.18). Such instances of evolutionary opportunism are legion. We consequently conclude that specific organisms are *not* the result of any planned, goal-directed, or predetermined course of creation. Instead, they are the result of a cumulative, opportunistic process of piece-by-piece building, based on preexisting organisms and governed entirely by natural selection acting on random variations.

RESUME   This outlines the general characteristics of the evolutionary process. We have found that the course has proceeded at various rates through successive adaptive radiations, has led to extinction here and to replacement there, to further divergence in some instances, to convergence in others, and to opportunistic exploitation of possibilities in all. As an overall result, the living mass on earth has been increasing fairly steadily in individual numbers and types and has seeped into practically all possible environments. Indeed, it has created new environments in the process. For example, the evolution of trees has created new possibilities of life in the treetops, exploited later by some new plants and by very many new animals, including our own ancestors. The evolution of warm-blooded birds and mammals has created a new environment in the blood of these animals, exploited later by many new parasites. The evolution of man has created numerous new environments in human installations, and these have been exploited by a large variety of new plants and animals. We recognize here yet another general characteristic of evolution: a progressive, creative **expansiveness,** as regards both living mass and ways of life. The expansion is still under way, faster in some cases than in others, and the end cannot be predicted as yet.

REVIEW QUESTIONS

1. Describe the essential points of the evolutionary theories of (*a*) Lamarck, (*b*) Darwin and Wallace. How could the evolution of giraffes from short-necked ancestors be explained in terms of each of these two theories? What were the weaknesses of each theory?

2. What different kinds of inheritable variations may arise in organisms? Do such variations appear randomly, or are they oriented toward usefulness? How do noninheritable variations arise, and what role do they play in evolution?

3. Define the modern meaning of natural selection. Show how natural selection has little to do with "survival of the fittest," or "struggle," or "weeding out" and how it is both a peaceful and a creative force. How does it happen that natural selection is oriented toward improved adaptation?

4. State the Hardy-Weinberg law. If a population consists of 49% *AA*, 42% *Aa*, and 9% *aa* individuals, show by calculation how the law applies. If a Hardy-Weinberg equilibrium exists in a population, what are the rate and amount of evolution?

5. What three conditions disturb Hardy-Weinberg equilibria? For each condition, show in what way such equilibria are disturbed and how evolution is therefore affected. What are back mutations? How do recessive genes spread through a population? What is genetic drift, and where is it encountered?

6. Define "species" in genetic terms. Describe the process of speciation. What are some common geographical isolating conditions, and what is their effect on gene pools? What is a subspecies? How do reproductive barriers arise between populations?

7. Review some actual evidence for past and present microevolution. Classify man taxonomically. Describe Goldschmidt's hypothesis of macroevolution. What are its weaknesses, and what is the commonly accepted alternative hypothesis?

8. How have rates of evolution varied in the past? What is an adaptive radiation? Illustrate in the case of mammals. How many, and which, implications are wholly erroneous in the following statement: "If we examine the evolutionary scale, we find that the lowly ameba has given rise to higher forms such as man." Rephrase this statement into an appropriate number of correct ones.

9. What are the general causes of extinction? What has been the pattern of extinction on different taxonomic levels? How do narrow specialization and broad adaptability contribute to either extinction or survival? What is evolutionary replacement? Distinguish between immediate and delayed replacement, and give examples. Distinguish between evolutionary divergence and convergence, and again give examples.

10. In what important way is evolution randomly opportunistic? List 10 structural and functional features of man, and show for each (*a*) how it has evolved opportunistically, and (*b*) that it cannot be labeled as being "theoretically best." What has been the general evolutionary trend regarding the total quantity of life on earth? Show how evolution has created new environments, hence new opportunities for evolution.

SUGGESTED COLLATERAL READINGS

This first group of references is of outstanding historical importance:

Redi, F.: "Experiments on the Generation of Insects." Translation of 1688 original in M. L. Gabriel and S. Fogel, "Great Experiments in Biology," Prentice-Hall, 1955.

Pasteur, L.: "Examination of the Doctrine of Spontaneous Generation." Translation of 1862 original in Gabriel and Fogel.

de Lamarck, J. P. P. A.: "Evolution through Environmentally Produced Modifications." Translation of 1809 original in T. S. Hall, "A Sourcebook in Animal Biology," McGraw-Hill, 1951.

Darwin, C., and A. R. Wallace: "On the Tendency of Species to Form Varieties; and on the Perpetuation of Varieties and Species by Natural Means of Selection." Original 1858 statement of theory of natural selection, reprinted in Gabriel and Fogel.

Darwin, C.: "The Origin of Species, etc.; and the Descent of Man," Modern Library, 1948.

Any of the following books, especially the first, is recommended for background reading on evolutionary theory as a whole:

Simpson, G. G.: "The Meaning of Evolution," Yale University Press, 1949, or Mentor Books, M66, 1951.

————: "The Major Features of Evolution," Columbia University Press, 1953.

Dobzhanski, T.: "Genetics and the Origin of Species," 3d ed., Columbia University Press, 1951.

————: "Evolution, Genetics and Man," Wiley, 1955.

Blum, H.: "Time's Arrow and Evolution," Princeton University Press, 1951.

Huxley, J. S.: "Evolution: The Modern Synthesis," Harper, 1943.

Dodson, E. O.: "A Textbook of Evolution," Saunders, 1951.

Mayr, E.: "Systematics and the Origin of Species," Columbia University Press, 1942.

The articles and books below discuss various specific topics in the field of evolution.

Hardy, G. H.: "Mendelian Proportions in a Mixed Population." In Gabriel and Fogel.

Ryan, F. J.: Evolution Observed, *Sci. American,* vol. 189, 1953.

Dobzhanski, T.: The Genetic Basis of Evolution, *Sci. American,* vol. 182, 1953.

————: Evolution in the Tropics, *Am. Scientist,* vol. 38, 1950.

————: "Adaptive Changes Induced by Natural Selection in Wild Populations of Drosophila." In Gabriel and Fogel.

Lack, D.: Darwin's Finches, *Sci. American,* vol. 188, 1953.

Blum, H.: Perspectives in Evolution, *Am. Scientist,* vol. 43, 1955.

Metcalf, R. L.: Insects vs. Insecticides, *Sci. American,* vol. 187, 1952.

Stebbins, G. L.: Cataclysmic Evolution, *Sci. American,* vol. 184, 1951.

Dunn, L. C.: Genetic Monsters, *Sci. American,* vol. 182, 1950.

Deevey, E. S.: The End of the Moas, *Sci. American,* vol. 190, 1954.

Horowitz, N. H.: "On the Evolution of Biochemical Syntheses." In Gabriel and Fogel.

Florkin, M.: "Biochemical Evolution," Academic Press, 1949.

29

THE COURSE OF EVOLUTION

ONE OF THE MAIN LINES of investigation which reveals the time course of past evolution is **paleontology,** the study of fossils. Representing the remains of formerly living plants and animals, fossils provide the most direct evidence of the kinds of organisms in existence at various earlier times. A second main line of investigation is **comparative morphology,** the study of the structure of *presently* living organisms. Being the products of past plants and animals, modern organisms reflect in their architecture the evolutionary history of their antecedents. In particular, three aspects of structure embody the record of past evolution: molecular structure, revealed by studies in *comparative biochemistry;* embryonic structure, revealed through *comparative embryology;* and adult structure, revealed through *comparative anatomy.*

Unfortunately, the fossil record does not go back more than 500 million years, a span of time representing only the last quarter or so of living history. Events during the crucial first three-quarters must therefore be inferred indirectly through morphological investigations. The critical happenings during this long initial phase were the origin of life; the origin of cells; the primary diversification of cells and of cell groups into the first representatives of the plant and animal kingdoms; and lastly, further diversification of these early plant and animal types into basic forms which represented, or foreshadowed, the various phyla of today. The first section below will deal with this gradual **evolution of early groups.**

Paleontological as well as morphological evidence documents the events of the last quarter of living history. This period was characterized primarily by enormous diversification of types, within the various plant and animal phyla already in existence. Frequent replacement accompanied this phase of evolution, and it also led to the expansion of life from the ocean into fresh water, to land, and into the air. Modern plants and animals are the result. This **evolution of modern groups** will be the subject of the second section of this chapter. A third and concluding section will concentrate on one of the modern groups in particular and will deal with the **evolution of man.**

The Evolution of Early Groups

THE FIRST RADIATION

The Common Ancestor

As already noted in Chaps. 2 and 3, the first steps of evolution were the creation of cells and the subsequent development of a large variety of unicellular organisms. Most of the latter are still abundantly represented today through their modern descendants, the bacteria, the single-celled algae, and the protozoa.

A basic problem confronts us here. Did the different unicellular organisms originate **monophyletically,** from *one* common ancestral cell type, or **polyphyletically,** from *several* different cell types, each created independently in the early ocean? The answer is not known and may never be known. Even so, many biologists tend to favor a monophyletic view. Later evolution is known to have involved

FIG. 29.1. The basic structure of a flagellate, suggesting what the first flagellate ancestor may have looked like.

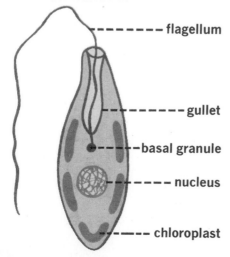

- - - - - - flagellum

- - - - - gullet

- - - - - basal granule

- - - - - nucleus

- - - - chloroplast

adaptive radiations branching away from common ancestors, and it may therefore be supposed that the same kind of branching evolution occurred also at the beginning. Moreover, unicellular plants and animals are not so different that a common ancestral cell type cannot be envisaged readily. How such a type would be related to modern bacteria is not clear, but that it could have been ancestral to both algae and protozoa is entirely likely.

Indeed, living *flagellates* could be the most direct descendants of this postulated single ancestral cell type. Some modern flagellates feature both plant and animal characteristics. They possess chlorophyll and photosynthesize, but they also possess locomotor flagella, as well as animallike capacity to engulf minute bulk food (see Chap. 30). A common ancestor of plants and animals would be expected to be similarly equipped. Therefore, an ancestral flagellate type, free-living in the open ocean some one to two billion years ago, is widely thought to be the likeliest candidate for a common starting point of both plant and animal evolution. Undoubtedly, such an ancestor would itself be a derivative of still earlier, possibly bacterialike cells, and these in turn, of molecular, viruslike units (Fig. 29.1).

If we assume that an ancestral flagellate population actually existed, then from it must have evolved a first major adaptive radiation consisting of at least three more or less simultaneous descendant lines. One such line continued the ancestral way of life and led directly to the modern flagellates. These are still classified either as plants, as animals, or as both. In another line, the animal characters must have been deemphasized and lost, whereas the plant characters became emphasized more and more. This line would represent the basic stock of the plant kingdom. Conversely, the photosynthetic machinery must have been lost in a third line, and such organisms would represent the basic stock of the animal kingdom (Fig. 29.2).

The First Plants

Within each of these stocks, an extensive exploitation of the cellular way of life must then have taken place. In the young plant kingdom, a subradiation must have produced a variety of **algae:** blue-green algae, green algae, brown algae, red algae, and others (see Chap. 30). These different algal lines are distinguished basically by their different pigments, formed in conjunction with chlorophyll. New adaptive opportunities undoubtedly arose through these pigments. For example, possession of brown or red pigment in addition to chlorophyll would allow an alga to absorb light of lesser intensity, hence would permit it to live at somewhat greater water depths.

In parallel with such evolutionary "experiments in pigmentation," a multicellular condition evolved in many of the algal lines. Among green algae today, multicellular types are as numerous as unicellular ones. Brown and red algae became very largely multicellular. Note here that the innovation of multicellularity probably was developed independently in each algal group in which it occurs today.

Each of the main algal lines is commonly accorded the rank of a phylum (see Chap. 30). Algae as a whole could therefore be regarded as a superphylum. These plants were, and still are, exceedingly successful. Within each phylum they diversified abundantly and came to populate the sunlit parts of all oceans. The green algae among them appear to have been the most progressive evolutionally. They are probably related most directly to the ancestral flagellates, and some of the early green algae in turn may have been the ancestors of several of the other major algal groups. Moreover, green algae appear to have given rise to some of the **fungi**; they probably were the first to invade the fresh waters, and they were also the first, and indeed the only ones, to colonize the land. One group evolved a symbiotic partnership with certain fungi and developed into the terrestrial, rock-encrusting **lichens**. Other green algae reached the land on their own, and as we shall see below, some of these probably became the ancestors of all advanced terrestrial plants.

But these events did not occur till well into the last quarter of living history. For a billion years before that, algal evolution remained confined to the ocean. Major categories established then persisted as such, and minor categories within them replaced one another successively and increased in numbers. In parallel with this, the ancestral stock of unicellular animals underwent its own diversification.

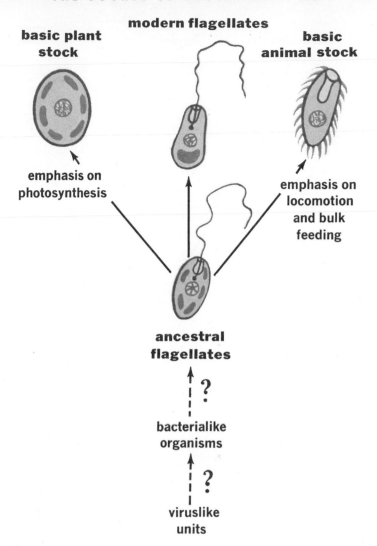

FIG. 29.2. The general pattern of the first radiation. Here, as in all subsequent illustrations of this kind, read from the bottom up.

The First Animals

The original animal flagellate stock represented the first group of the **protozoa**. From it arose other protozoan types by adaptive radiation: the ameboid group, the ciliate group, and the parasitic sporozoan group (see Chap. 31). Like algae, these exploited the cellular way of life, and they specialized particularly in varied forms of cellular locomotion. But unlike algae, protozoa largely did not evolve multicel-

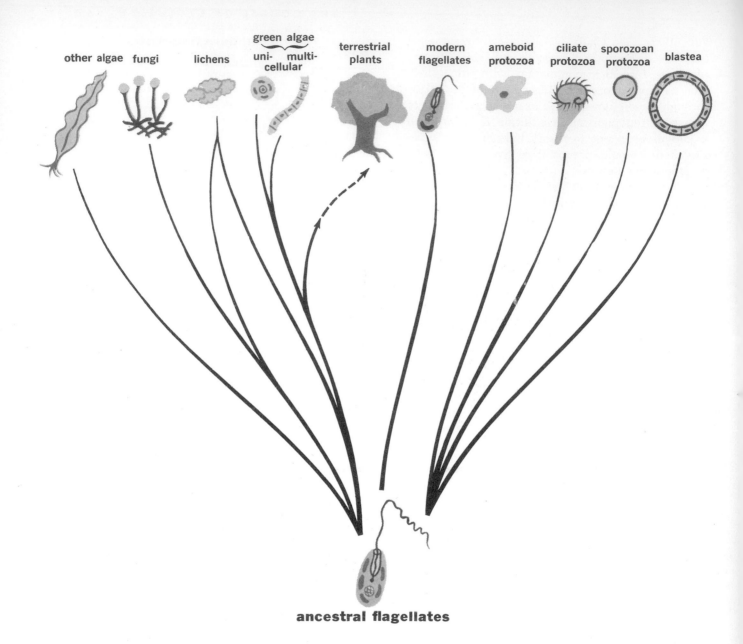

other algae fungi lichens green algae uni- multi- cellular terrestrial plants modern flagellates ameboid protozoa ciliate protozoa sporozoan protozoa blastea

ancestral flagellates

FIG. 29.3. A comprehensive outline of the first radiation.

lular sublines. Instead, as already outlined in Chap. 3, their evolution tended to exploit the possibilities of increased cell size and of internal cell specialization. Living ciliates in particular include some of the largest and most specialized unicellular forms. Like algae, protozoa came to be extremely

successful organisms, and they too eventually invaded the fresh waters and the land. Again like algae, protozoa may be regarded as a superphylum, each main group constituting a distinct phylum.

The ancestral animal flagellate stock not only originated the various protozoan lines, but must also have produced a separate line which culminated in ancestral *multicellular* animals. It is very unlikely that any adult animal living today is a direct descendant of this multicellular ancestor. Nevertheless, we may reconstruct the probable appearance of this ancestor. There is little question that, in the absence of a circulatory system, all cells of a first multicellular type must have remained in direct contact with the nutrient-supplying ocean. With this specification, two general architectural designs are possible: a *sheet* of cells or a hollow *sphere* of cells. To a passively floating, light-dependent organism like an alga, a sheet design is likely to be more advantageous. Indeed, multicellular algae are organized predominantly on a sheet pattern. But to a light-independent, actively moving organism, the more compact architecture of a hollow sphere is likely to be of greater advantage. We suspect, therefore, that the first multicellular animal was a hollow, single-layered sphere. Recall that practically all multicellular animals living today pass through an embryonic *blastula* stage, which is essentially a sphere of cells (see Chap. 26). This observation has suggested the name **blastea** for the hypothetical ancestral multicellular animal.

Thus, on the assumption of a monophyletic origin of plants and animals, the first major adaptive radiation may be envisaged as in Fig. 29.3. The algal and protozoan groups currently in existence are modern members of this first radiation. And the blastea, no longer represented today except as an embryonic stage, must have become the starting point of a second radiation among animals.

THE SECOND RADIATION

The Pattern

Did the many multicellular animal phyla now in existence originate separately, as independent lines radiating away from a blastea? Or did the blastea give rise to only some of the phyla, these in turn then producing others? Since fossil data are lacking, we must again attempt to find the answers from currently living forms.

The guiding principle here is that the greater the structural similarity of two organisms, the more closely are they likely to be related historically. On the human level, this principle is commonplace. If two persons *look* rather alike, they are properly judged to be closely related members of the same family. Note that structural similarity, or **homology**, is a more reliable index of relatedness than functional similarity, or **analogy**. Clearly, two persons performing the same job may not be related at all. So also in evolution. The wings of birds and insects are analogous; that is, they function in similar manner. But they are not homologous, and indeed birds and insects are known not to be closely related. On the other hand, bird wings and mammalian forearms *are* homologous, and even though they are not analogous, they reveal a close relationship of birds and mammals (see Fig. 9.32).

Homologies exist not only in adult organisms, but also among their embryos. The greater the structural similarity of two embryos, and therefore the longer these embryos develop in similar ways, the closer is their evolutionary relationship. For example, the embryos of monkeys and of men are more alike, and remain alike for longer periods, than the embryos of mice and of men. This suggests that men are more closely related to monkeys than to mice, a conclusion confirmed independently by fossil data and adult homologies. We may note generally that evolutionary interrelations among multicellular animals may be deduced by comparing their embryonic histories and their adult architectures and by determining how much or how little homology is in evidence.

If such comparisons are made, we find that modern multicellular animals may be classified into two broad groups. In one, each animal possesses a body which consists essentially of *two* basic tissue layers. The embryo of such an animal first passes through a single-layered *blastula* stage, and later it develops into a double-layered *gastrula*, composed of an outer *ectoderm* and an inner *endoderm* (see Chap. 26). The gastrula then transforms directly into the adult. This group of double-layered **diploblastic** animals includes the sponges, the ctenophores (comb jellies), and the coelenterates (see Chap. 31). Inasmuch as these animals are fundamentally homologous in their embryonic patterns and their adult anatomy, we may infer that they are histori-

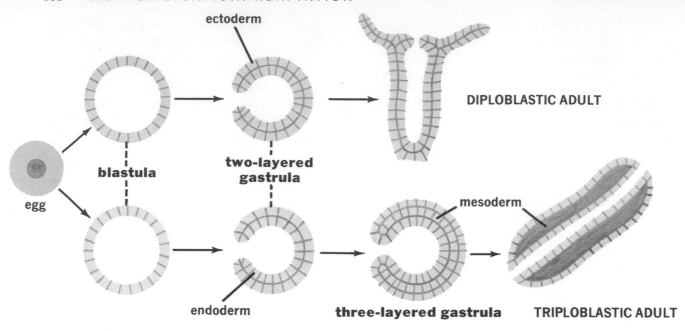

FIG. 29.4.   Diagram of the development and basic architecture of diploblasts and triploblasts.

cally more closely related to one another than to other animal groups (Fig. 29.4).

All other multicellular animals comprise a large second group. Blastula and gastrula stages occur here too, but the gastrula does not transform into an adult directly. Instead, it gives rise to further embryonic stages. One such stage possesses a third tissue layer, the *mesoderm,* developed between the ectoderm and the endoderm (see Chap. 26). The adult body later formed from such embryos is therefore **triploblastic,** constructed from three primary germ layers rather than two (see Fig. 29.4). In view of these homologies in embryonic development and adult structure, we again conclude that triploblastic animals are more closely related to one another than to other animal groups. Moreover, we infer that in evolution, as in embryonic development, the triploblastic type originates from, and after, the diploblastic type.

Therefore, the general course of animal evolution must have been somewhat as follows. The blastea, produced during the first radiation of animals and corresponding to the single-layered blastula, must have evolved into a basic diploblastic type, corresponding to the double-layered gastrula. This diploblastic ancestor then must have given rise to various diploblastic descendants, as well as to a basic triploblastic type. The latter subsequently became the ancestor of all triploblastic animals (Fig. 29.5). On these assumptions, how did the blastea evolve into a basic double-layered type?

Blastea to Gastrea

Direct descendants of an ancestral diploblast are no longer in existence, but we may reconstruct its probable origin and architecture. Being motile and independent of light, the blastea could have left the surface waters of the ocean and could have descended to an advantageous new environment, at the sea bottom along the continental shelves. Gliding or creeping in this region of the ocean floor, it could have fed on the very abundant dead organisms which rained down in a steady stream from the surface waters. In time, an adaptively useful invagination could have evolved on the lower surface of the blastea, enabling the animal to station itself firmly over a bit of food, like an inverted cup. In this manner, it might have developed an advantageous double-layered architecture, with an alimentary opening at the underside connecting the interior cavity and the external environment. The inner endoderm could in time have become specialized for digestion, and the outer ectoderm for locomotion, protection, and reconnoitering the surroundings. Inasmuch as this hypothetical ancestral diploblast resembles a gastrula, the name **gastrea** has been proposed for it.

According to our assumptions above, the gastrea then produced an adaptive radiation in which the new double-layered architecture was exploited extensively. Modern diploblastic animals are the latest results of this second major radiation among animals. Specifically, one descendant line must have led to the phylum Coelenterata, comprising specialized animals with tentacles around the alimentary opening, and sting cells on the tentacles for paralyzing prey. Another descendant line probably gave rise to the free-swimming comb jellies, which form the phylum Ctenophora. A third line must have produced another phylum, the sessile sponges. In these, the diploblastic architecture is today somewhat obscured, but distinct blastula and gastrula stages do occur during their embryonic development.

Finally, the gastrea must also have evolved a fourth line, characterized by possession of a third body layer, the mesoderm. Direct descendants of this line again are no longer in existence, but its early representatives must have included the ancestor of all triploblastic animals living today.

The second adaptive radiation among animals may therefore be symbolized as in Fig. 29.6.

THE THIRD RADIATION

The development of mesoderm in the ancestral triploblast undoubtedly was of great adaptive advantage. It permitted a broader distribution of body functions among a larger number of tissues; hence it made possible a more nearly complete specialization of each function. For example, reproductive functions, formerly executed by the endoderm, could now be carried out by the new mesoderm. This allowed the endoderm to specialize more fully in alimentation. Similarly, excretory and muscular functions, formerly performed by ectoderm, became

localized in mesodermal tissues. This freed the ectoderm to specialize more fully in sensory and protective roles. Moreover, mesoderm made possible the eventual evolution of a circulatory system. This in turn permitted a general increase in body size, for the transport system could bring respiratory gases and nutrients even to deep interior tissues of the animal.

Triploblastic Types

A study of homologies among the triploblasts now living suggests the existence of at least four major subgroups. All possess mesoderm, but they differ partly in the way the mesoderm originates in the embryo, partly in the way this mesoderm develops during later embryonic stages.

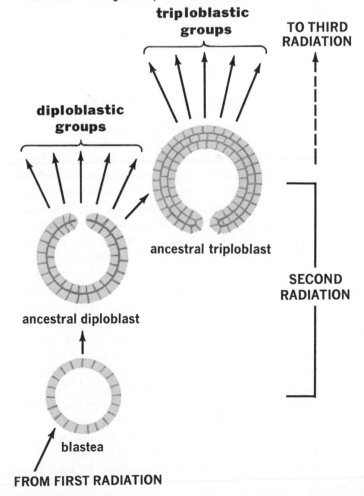

FIG. 29.5. The general pattern of the second animal radiation.

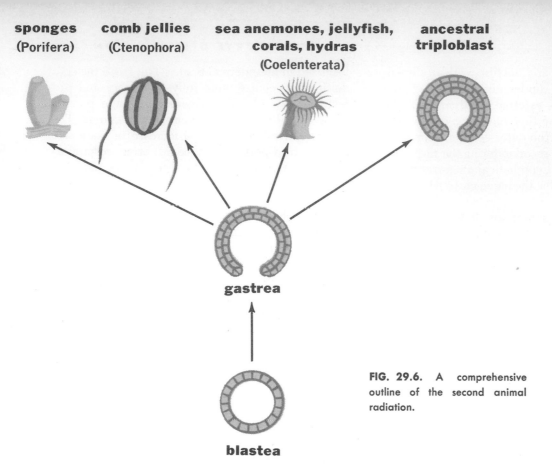

sponges
(Porifera)

comb jellies
(Ctenophora)

sea anemones, jellyfish,
corals, hydras
(Coelenterata)

ancestral
triploblast

gastrea

blastea

FIG. 29.6. A comprehensive outline of the second animal radiation.

In one group, mesoderm arises from the *endoderm* (Fig. 29.7). On both sides of the endoderm, pouches grow out and enlarge, eventually filling most of the space between ectoderm and endoderm. These mesodermal pouches later constrict off the endoderm and persist as separate, fundamentally hollow entities. A space so enclosed by mesoderm tissue is called a **coelom.** It forms an internal body cavity, and its existence is of considerable advantage to the animal; by separating the external body wall from the intestine, it makes these two parts of the body mechanically independent. Hence the animal may be physically active regardless of whether food is present in the gut. Since such a coelom originates from the future digestive cavity, it is called an **enterocoel.** And the animals possessing enterocoels are called **enterocoelomates.** The most prominent members of this group are the echinoderms, which include starfish and sea urchins, and the chordates, which include the vertebrates.

In a second living triploblastic group, mesoderm arises predominantly from *ectoderm,* by an inwandering of ectodermal cells. These cells accumulate between the ectoderm and the endoderm, and eventually they become so abundant that they form a solid mesodermal layer. The animal subsequently retains a solid mesoderm, and a coelom does not develop. Because of this absence of an internal body cavity, animals comprising this group are called **acoelomates.** The most prominent types here are the flatworms and the proboscis worms (see Fig. 29.7).

In a third group of triploblasts, mesoderm arises from *both* the ectoderm and the endoderm. At early embryonic stages, ectodermal cells wander in from the surface and contribute some of the mesoderm. Later, a single pair of large cells buds off from the endoderm, and these eventually give rise to the bulk of the mesoderm. After the mesoderm layer becomes established in the embryo, a split develops in this layer, dividing it into an outer and an inner lining. Thus a space appears within the mesoderm, and this again is a coelom. But since this type of coelom arises by splitting, it is called a **schizocoel.** Accordingly, animals possessing schizocoels are called **schizocoelomates.** The main types in this category are the segmented worms, or annelids, among which the earthworm is the most familiar; the mollusks, which include clams, snails, and squids; and the arthropods, an enormous group including the crustacea, the insects, and the spiders (see Fig. 29.7).

Finally, the fourth group of living triploblasts consists of a varied collection of types in which mesoderm arises in varied ways. In some cases, mesoderm is formed exclusively from ectoderm. In others, both ectoderm and endoderm contribute to mesoderm formation. The unifying feature here is that mesoderm does not become so extensive as in the other three groups. Instead of filling the whole available space between ectoderm and endoderm, mesoderm collects in localized regions only. This

gives the animal an internal body cavity, but the cavity is not a true coelom, since it is lined by ectoderm and endoderm, not by mesoderm. The name **pseudocoel** is applied here, and the animals forming this group are designated as **pseudocoelomates.** Among the many types included, rotifers, roundworms, and hairworms are the most common (see Fig. 29.7).

Interrelations of Triploblasts

The homologies here outlined for each of these four groups are not the only ones to suggest close intragroup relationships. For example, the developmental patterns of certain marine annelids and mollusks are so similar that their embryos, and even their free-swimming larvae, the so-called **trochophores,** are practically indistinguishable. Accord-

FIG. 29.7.   Mesoderm formation in the four main groups of triploblasts (diagrammatic).

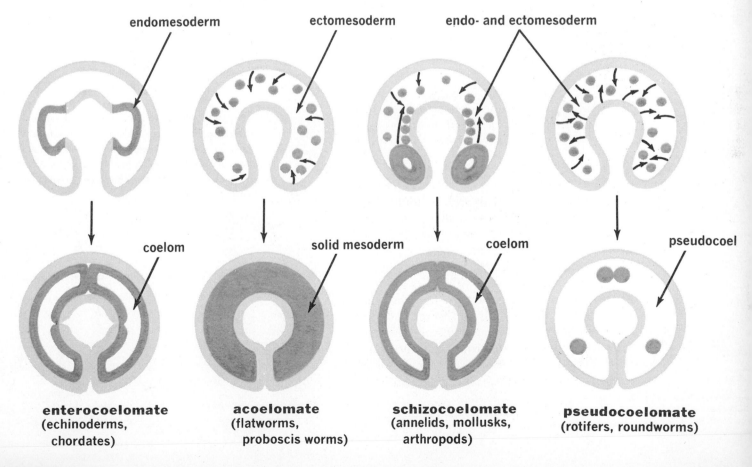

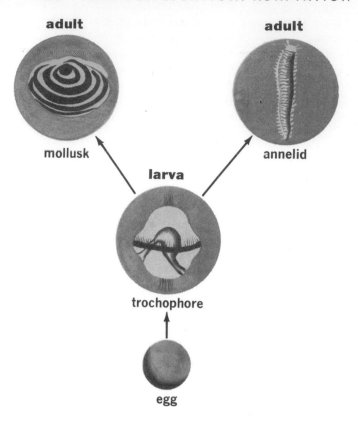

adult

mollusk

adult

annelid

larva

trochophore

egg

FIG. 29.8. Although the adults of mollusks and annelid worms resemble one another very little, the embryos and larvae of both groups are hardly distinguishable. Trochophore larvae are characteristic of both.

ingly, although an adult clam and an adult earthworm do not *appear* to be particularly close relatives, their embryos and larvae indicate that they are (Fig. 29.8). Similarly, earthworms and insects are not noticeably alike as adults, but their embryos are very much alike. Indeed, earthworms are more closely related to insects, and also to clams, than to tapeworms or other kinds of "worms." In like manner, despite the profound differences between adult chordates and echinoderms, the embryos and larvae of these forms in some cases are so similar that only expert biologists can tell them apart (Fig. 29.9).

We may conclude, in general, that demonstrable homologies give relatively clear evidence of the close evolutionary relationship of the animals *within* each of the four groups above. In many instances, moreover, the evidence is extensive enough to reveal the finer interrelations of the subgroups within each group.

The problem now is to determine evolutionary relationships *among* the four basic groups. Did all four radiate independently from a common triploblastic ancestor, or did they arise successively from one another? Fossil data are lacking—and homological studies so far have proved to be inconclusive. The weight of available data tends to suggest that the enterocoelomates arose from ancestral triploblasts as an independent main line, and that a second main line led to acoelomates, pseudocoelomates, and schizocoelomates. In other words, these three groups appear to be more closely related to one another than to enterocoelomates.

One basis for this conclusion is the manner of mesoderm formation. The development of distinct pouches from the endoderm, as in enterocoelomates, appears to be unique, whereas inwandering cells from the ectoderm are a more or less common feature in the other three groups (see Fig. 29.7). Another distinction is the manner in which mouth and anus form. In all triploblasts, as in diploblasts,

FIG. 29.9. Although the adults of echinoderms and chordates are very dissimilar, their larvae in many cases are quite alike. On the left is a diagram of an echinoderm larva; on the right, a diagram of a larva of hemichordates, a primitive chordate subphylum.

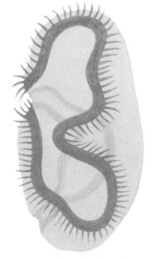

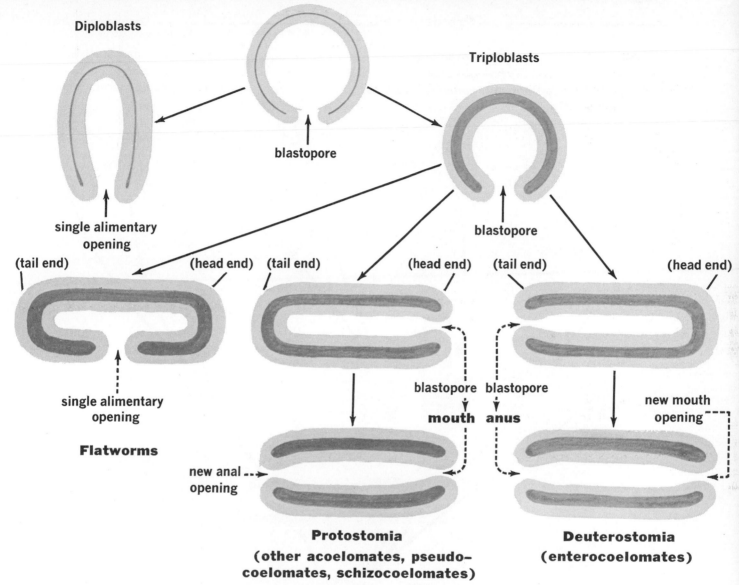

FIG. 29.10. Development of the alimentary openings in multicellular animals. Diploblasts and flatworms acquire a single opening serving both as mouth and as anus. In enterocoelomates, the blastopore becomes the anus; and in all other triploblasts, the blastopore becomes the mouth.

an opening connects the interior of the gastrula with the outside. This *blastopore* (see Chap. 26) becomes the single alimentary opening of adult diploblasts, as noted earlier. Flatworms, which are members of the triploblastic acoelomates, have retained this ancestral condition of a single alimentary opening. This suggests that they, and acoelomates in general, may be the most ancient of the triploblasts.

But in all other acoelomates, as well as in all pseudocoelomates and schizocoelomates, the blastopore develops into a true *mouth*, an anus later breaking through at the opposite end of the embryo. By contrast, in enterocoelomates the blastopore becomes the *anus*, and a mouth is developed later as a new opening at the opposite end of the embryo (Fig. 29.10).

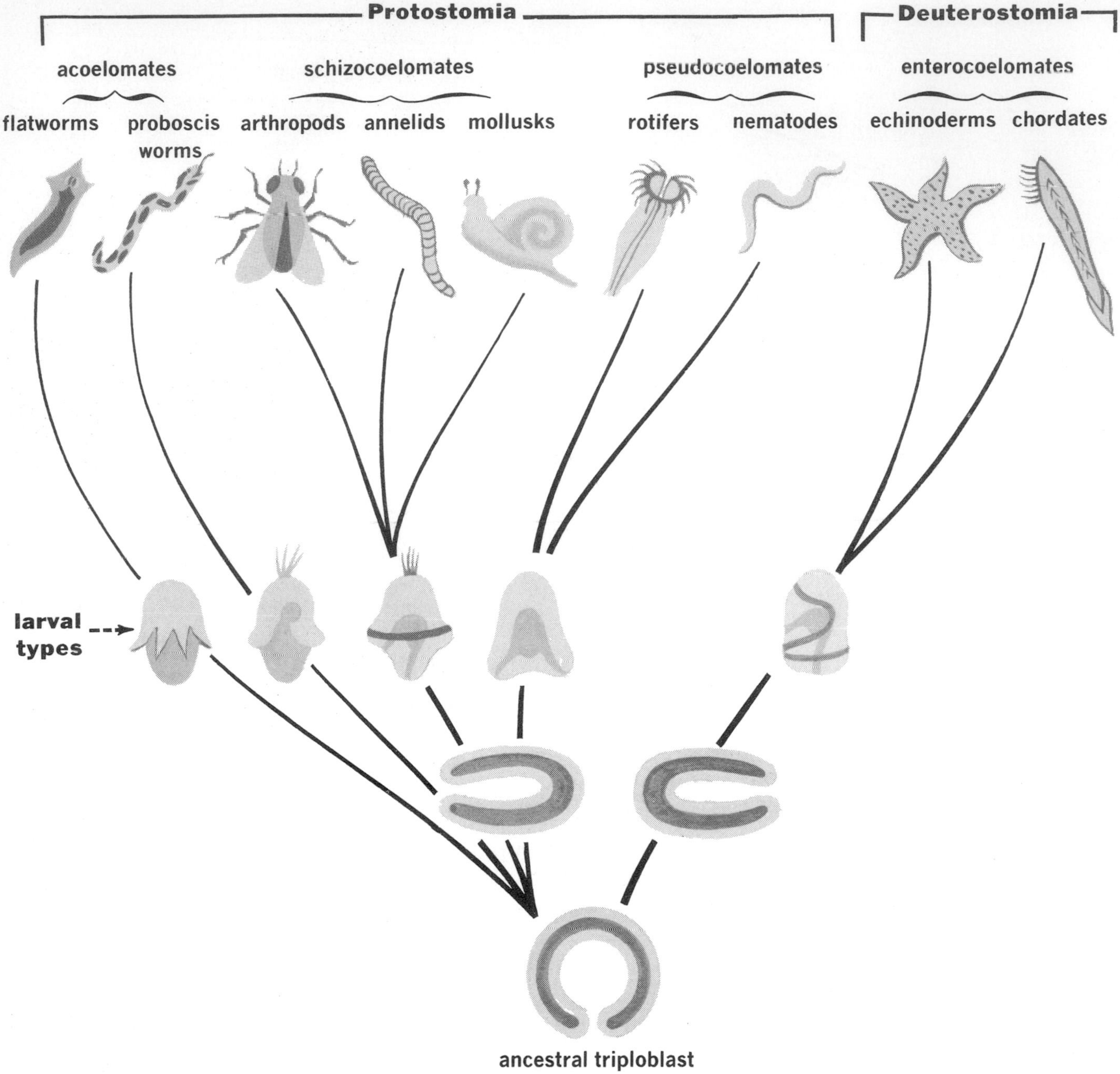

FIG. 29.11. A comprehensive outline of the third animal radiation.

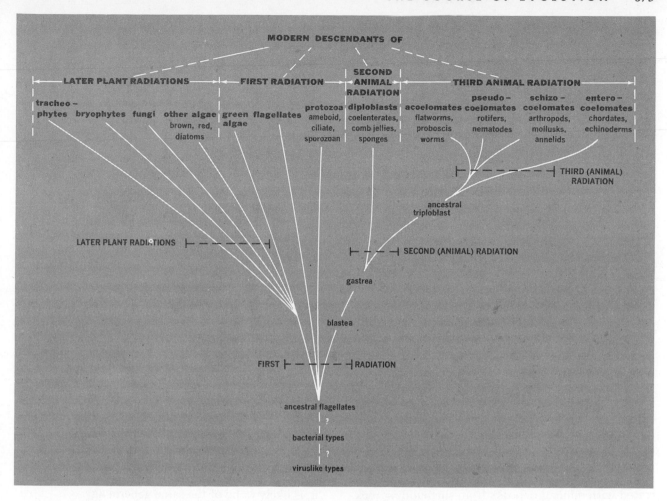

FIG. 29.12. Summary of the first three main radiations among animals.

These various considerations suggest that the third adaptive radiation among animals may have occurred as in Fig. 29.11.

We may note here that triploblastic animals fundamentally are *bilaterally symmetrical*. The triploblastic ancestor undoubtedly was bilateral also. Diploblastic animals, on the other hand, are largely *radially symmetrical*. Various views have been proposed regarding the evolution of animal symmetry. According to one, the diploblastic ancestor could have been radial, and bilaterality could have evolved during the transition to the triploblastic type. Alternatively, the diploblastic ancestor could have been bilateral from the start, and the radiality of living diploblasts could have evolved secondarily, as an adaptation to a basically sessile way of life. Recent studies tend to favor this second view.

The complete pattern of all three radiations is summarized in Fig. 29.12. Whether or not all these adaptive radiations occurred in precisely this way, they certainly occurred well before the last 500 million years. For at that time mark, fossils began to form abundantly in the earth's crust, and among them, most of the animal types referred to above were already represented. To be sure, these representatives were ancient species, no longer in existence today. Nevertheless they were members of main categories which had evolved earlier and which are still flourishing now.

A few major groups among both plants and animals evolved *after* the 500-million-year mark. These comparative newcomers included mainly the terrestrial organisms: among plants, the mosses, the ferns, the seed plants, and their various relatives; and among animals, the insects, spiders, and other land arthropods, and all vertebrates, including even their aquatic members.

What does the fossil evidence reveal about this later course of evolution, as regards both the new groups and the modern members of the early groups?

The Evolution of Modern Groups

FOSSILS AND GEOLOGY

Fossils are any long-preserved remains of organisms. They may be skeletons or shells, perhaps recrystallized under heat and pressure and infiltrated with mineral deposits from surrounding rock. They may be footprints later petrified, or the remnants of organisms trapped in arctic ice, amber, quicksand, gravel pits, tar pits, and swamps. Or they may be imprints of carbon black on rock, left when the soft parts of plants or animals vaporized under heat and pressure. Whenever a buried organism, or any part of it, becomes preserved in some way before it decays, it will be a fossil.

Fossils formed in the past are embedded in earth layers of different ages. In a geologically undisturbed section of the earth's crust, the deeper layers are the older layers. Material eroded from high-lying land gradually piles up on low land and on the sea bottom; hence a deep layer today was on the surface in past ages, and the earth's surface today will be a deep layer in the future. Fossils embedded in successive layers so provide a time picture of evolution. To be sure, deep-lying fossils are normally not accessible. But on occasion, a canyon-cutting river, an earthquake fracture, or an upbuckling and consequent breaking of the earth's crust may expose a cross section through the rock strata. Moreover, erosion gradually wears away top layers, exposing deeper rock. Geological changes of this sort have been sufficiently abundant to expose layers of all different ages in various parts of the world (Fig. 29.13).

How is the actual age of a rock layer determined? Very excellent clocks are built right into the earth's crust: radioactive substances. The disintegration rate of these substances is known accurately, as are the endproducts of disintegration. For example, a given quantity of radium is known to "decay" into lead in a certain span of time. When radium and lead are found together in one mass within a rock, the whole mass presumably had been radium originally, when the rock was formed. From the relative quantities of radium and lead present today, one can then calculate the time required for that much lead to form. This dates the rock, exactly to about 10 per cent of its total age. Fossils themselves often help in fixing the age of a rock layer. If such a layer contains a fossil which, on the basis of other evidence, is known to be of a definite age, then the whole layer, including all other fossils in it, is likely to be of the same general age.

Based on data obtained from radioactive and fossil clocks, geologists have constructed a *geologic time table,* which indicates the age of successive earth layers and so provides a calendar of the earth's past history. This calendar consists of five successive main divisions, so-called **eras.** The last three of these are subdivided in turn into a number of successive **periods.** The names of the eras and periods and their approximate durations are indicated in Table 13.

The beginning and terminal dates of the eras and periods have not been chosen arbitrarily, but have been made to coincide with major geological events known to have occurred at those times. The transitions between eras in particular were times of great upheaval, characterized by mountain building

FIG. 29.13. Rock layers of different ages are often exposed to view, as in this photo. The deeper a layer in the earth's crust, the older it is. (American Museum of Natural History.)

and by severely fluctuating climates. For example, the transition from the Paleozoic to the Mesozoic dates the **Appalachian revolution,** during which the mountain range of that name was built up. By now, these mountains are already greatly reduced by erosion. Similarly, the transition between the Mesozoic and the Cenozoic was marked by the **Laramide revolution,** which produced the high mountain ranges of today: the Himalayas, the Rockies, the Andes, and the Alps. As we shall see, these major geological events led to major biological ones, marked by evolutionary crises and large-scale replacement of types.

The first geologic era, the immensely long Azoic, spans the period from the origin of the earth to the origin of life. The subsequent pre-Cambrian era covers the time of the basic radiations among plants and animals, as outlined in the preceding section. Fossils are not lacking altogether from these distant pre-Cambrian ages. But the record is exceedingly fragmentary, and it shows mainly that life, simple cellular life at least, was actually in existence as early as about 1 billion years ago. A continuous and on the whole a rather abundant fossil record becomes available with the beginning of the first period of the Paleozoic, the Cambrian.

It is a very curious circumstance that rocks older than about 500 million years are so barren of fossils, whereas rocks younger than that not only are

comparatively rich in them, but also include representatives of most major categories of organisms. Many hypotheses have been proposed to account for this sudden and simultaneous appearance of different fossil groups. But to date, a satisfactory explanation has not been found. Has the pre-Cambrian environment somehow precluded the forma-

TABLE 13. The geologic time table*

Era	Period	Duration		Beginning date
Cenozoic ("new life")	Quaternary	75	1	1
	Tertiary		74	75
Mesozoic ("middle life")	Cretaceous	130	60	135
	Jurassic		30	165
	Triassic		40	205
Paleozoic ("ancient life")	Permian	300	25	230
	Carboniferous		50	280
	Devonian		45	325
	Silurian		35	360
	Ordovician		65	425
	Cambrian		80	505
Pre-Cambrian		1,500		2,000
Azoic ("without life")		3,000		5,000

* All numbers refer to millions of years; older ages are toward bottom of table, younger ages toward top.

FIG. 29.14. Seascapes of the early Paleozoic. Restorations. Top: Cambrian seas. Various algae, trilobites, eurypterids, sponges, jellyfish, brachiopods, and different types of worms are the most prominent organisms shown. Bottom: Ordovician seas. The large animal in foreground is a straight-shelled nautiloid. (Top, American Museum of Natural History; bottom, Chicago Natural History Museum.)

tion of fossils? Have fossils become destroyed in some way before the Paleozoic? Or is the pre-Cambrian fossil record so scanty because the organisms then were still too unsubstantial to leave fossilizable remains, whereas their descendants all had evolved hard parts during the Cambrian?

Note here that the simultaneous appearance of different types in the fossil record actually is not, on second glance, really so "simultaneous." The Cambrian lasted about 80 million years, and such an enormous time span, longer than the whole Cenozoic era, is highly significant even by geological standards. A great deal of evolution could and did occur during this period. Some groups entered the fossil record early during the Cambrian, others rather later. Hence it is certainly *possible* that many different groups all evolved fossilizable hard parts during the Cambrian but not before. Yet whether this or some other interpretation is correct is simply not known.

Once it was under way, what was the course of fossil history?

THE PALEOZOIC

Whereas, on the phylum level, every group in existence in the Cambrian has persisted to the present, on the species level no group has persisted. So far as is known, only a single genus has survived from the Ordovician, the period after the Cambrian. This genus is *Lingula,* of the phylum Brachiopoda (see Chap. 31). Apart from this 400-million-year-old relic, all ancient genera have become extinct, like all ancient species. This points up the dominant theme of the fossil record as a whole: very extensive, and repeated, replacement within major groups and relatively few additions of new major groups.

Cambrian and Ordovician

During these two periods, the land surface was as yet free of living organisms, with the possible exception of bacteria. But the sea abounded with diverse types of algae, and among animal groups, sponges, coelenterates, brachiopods, bryozoa, echinoderms, mollusks, arthropods, and a large variety of worms were particularly common (Fig. 29.14). The most prominent arthropods were the now extinct **eurypterids,** large animals resembling crustacea to some extent but more nearly related to horseshoe crabs and scorpions; and the similarly extinct **trilobites,** whose bodies were marked into three lobes by two longitudinal furrows (Fig. 29.15). Among mollusks, archaic clams and snails were present, as were the **nautiloids.** Related to modern squids, octopuses, and particularly to the living chambered nautilus, the nautiloids probably included the largest animals of the time: some had uncoiled shells 5 to 6 yards long. During the later Devonian period, the nautiloids gave rise to, and were in turn replaced by, the **ammonites,** which came to be the dominant mollusks for long ages.

From the human standpoint, the most important event of the early Paleozoic was the rise of the subphylum Vertebrata. The chordate ancestors of vertebrates probably were marine tunicates, already present at the start of the Paleozoic. Some of the descendants of these ancestral tunicates later evolved into vertebrates, presumably in fresh-water rivers (see Chap. 5). The first fossil vertebrates date to the late Ordovician. These were members of the class Agnatha, the **jawless fishes.** Lampreys and

FIG. 29.15.   Fossils of trilobites (left), a eurypterid (middle), and a crinoid or sea lily, a sessile echinoderm (right). (American Museum of Natural History.)

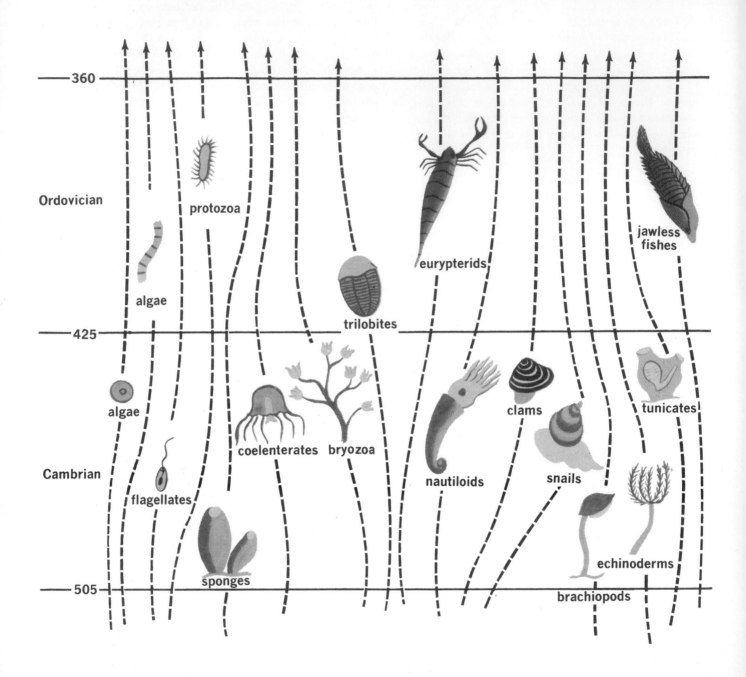

FIG. 29.16. Summary of Cambrian-Ordovician events. The level at which jawless fishes are drawn corresponds roughly with the time of their first appearance in the fossil record. All other forms were present throughout the time period shown, and all groups represented in the chart continued on into later periods.

FIG. 29.17. Devonian land plants. Note tree ferns, as on right. Psilopsids are shown in middle foreground, along shore, as are sphenopsids, toward left and behind small ferns. The large trees on extreme left are lycopsids. (American Museum of Natural History.)

hagfishes are the only surviving descendants of these forms (see Chap. 31). The Cambrian-Ordovician record is summarized in Fig. 29.16.

Silurian and Devonian

During the Silurian, the aquatic flora and fauna underwent very few essential changes. However, the first invasions of the land occurred in this period. Plants led the move. In the middle Silurian, the first members of the phylum Tracheophyta appear in the fossil record. These archaic representatives of modern land plants were the **psilopsids,** now virtually extinct (see Chap. 30). The actual origin of psilopsids, hence of tracheophytes generally, is rather obscure. The best guess is that they trace back directly to green algae.

Once they had reached the land, the early tracheophytes rapidly made the most of the new opportunities. The psilopsids gave rise to three other major tracheophyte lines, the **lycopsids,** the **sphenopsids,** and the **pteropsids.** The first two of these groups have since become almost extinct, being

represented today only by the *club mosses* and the *horsetails,* respectively. But the third line, the pteropsid stock, flourished ever since it arose. The earliest representatives of the pteropsids were the **ferns,** which became well established by Devonian times. Some of these ancestral ferns grew to tree size, and they formed the first forests (Fig. 29.17).

Animals followed the plants to land. Fossil scorpions from the late Silurian are the earliest known terrestrial animals, and other land arthropods appeared in the Devonian: spiderlike creatures, archaic mites, and probably the ancestors of insects. Moreover, at the very end of the Devonian, the first terrestrial vertebrates made their appearance.

The Devonian as a whole is often called the age of fishes. During the early Silurian, ancestral jawless fishes had given rise to a new line, the *jawed fishes,* or **placoderms.** The name of this separate class of vertebrates refers to the armor plates with which the skins of these fishes were equipped (Fig. 3.5). Most likely evolved in fresh water, placoderms became abundant when the De-

FIG. 29.18. A modern lungfish from West Africa. (American Museum of Natural History.)

vonian began, spread into the ocean, and thus replaced the jawless fishes more or less completely in all aquatic environments. Some of the placoderms were small, but others reached lengths of 12 or more yards, and most exploited the possession of jaws by adopting a fiercely carnivorous way of life. But the dominance of the placoderms was relatively short-lived. Early during the Devonian, ancestral placoderms had given rise to two new lines of fishes, and these came to replace the later placoderms. By the end of the Devonian, placoderms had disappeared completely, and we may note that this is the only vertebrate class which has become extinct.

The two new types of fishes evolved from early placoderms during the Devonian were the **cartilage fishes** and the **bony fishes,** each representing a separate class. The former includes sharks, skates, and rays, which today, as in Devonian times, are adapted largely to the marine environment. The bony fishes at first remained in fresh water, where they had probably evolved, and during the Devonian they radiated into three main subgroups: the so-called **paleoniscoid fishes,** the **lungfishes,** and the **lobe-finned fishes.** The paleoniscoids later became the ancestors of virtually all modern fresh-water and marine bony fishes. The lungfishes were common in Devonian and later Paleozoic times, but they are represented today by only three surviving genera (Fig. 29.18). The lobe-fins too are practically extinct today (Fig. 29.19).

But the Devonian representatives of the lobe-fins included the ancestors of the first land vertebrates, the **amphibia.** As indicated by their name, the lobe-fins had fleshy appendages, usable to some extent as walking legs. These fishes probably lived in fresh waters which dried out periodically, and their fins may have enabled them to crawl overland to other bodies of water. We note that terrestrial vertebrates arose not because certain fish preferred the land, but because they had to use the land if they were to survive as fish.

Thus, when the Devonian came to a close, sharks dominated in the ocean, and bony fishes in fresh waters. On land, forest-forming ferns and other tracheophytic plants were well established, terrestrial arthropods had become abundant, and the first amphibia had made their appearance (Fig. 29.20).

FIG. 29.19. Restoration of fossil lobe-finned fishes. (American Museum of Natural History.)

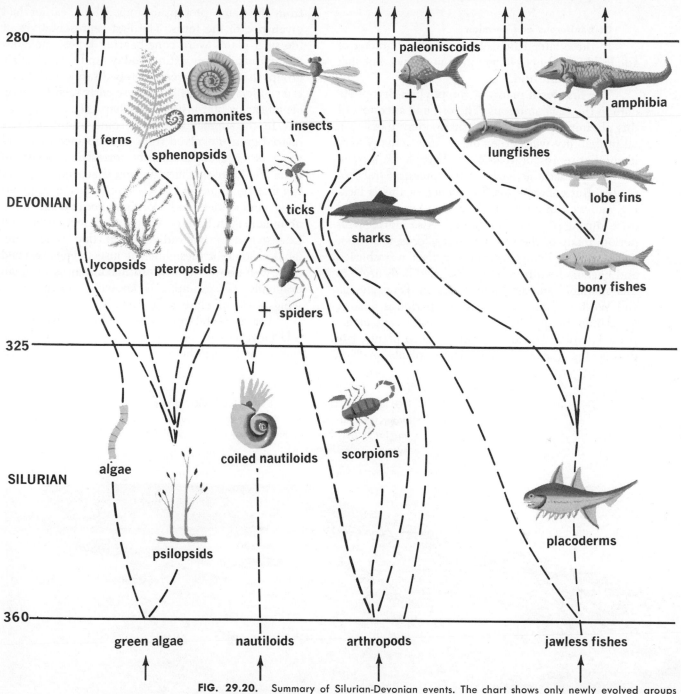

FIG. 29.20. Summary of Silurian-Devonian events. The chart shows only newly evolved groups and those which became extinct during the time period under consideration. Groups already established during earlier periods are not otherwise indicated. The level at which a given group is placed here corresponds roughly to the time of its first appearance in the fossil record. Daggers signify extinction, at the appropriate time level.

Carboniferous and Permian

In these later Paleozoic times, the character of aquatic life did not change in major ways, but that of terrestrial life did.

The first fossil plants of the phylum Bryophyta date to the Carboniferous. The original ancestors of this phylum, which includes the modern mosses, in all probability were green algae. It is actually very likely that representatives of the bryophytes were in existence at least as early as the ancestral tracheophytes. But concrete fossil evidence of this is lacking, and we can be certain only that bryophytes did exist during the Carboniferous. Also during this period, many of the forest-forming ferns, and other tracheophytes living in swamp regions, were buried and became fossilized. Extensive coal beds arose in this manner, among them those in Pennsylvania and West Virginia, for which the period is named.

Undoubtedly the most important event in the plant kingdom was the rise of the **seed plants,** late during the Carboniferous. These plants evolved from the same pteropsid stock which earlier had given rise to the ferns. The first representatives of the seed plants were cone-bearing types: ginkgoos and cycads, largely extinct today, and several other groups that have now completely disappeared. Modern *conifers* too arose from these early seed-forming, cone-bearing pteropsids (see Chap. 30).

In the animal kingdom, some additional terrestrial groups evolved from aquatic ancestors, and some other groups, already terrestrial, began to diversify. More specifically, land snails appeared for the first time during the Carboniferous, centipedes arose, and spiders and scorpions became still more abundant than before. Above all, insects produced extensive adaptive radiations at that time (Fig. 29.21). Some of these ancient insect types reached sizes well above the modern maximum. A Permian dragonfly, for example, is known to have had a wingspread of close to a yard.

Among vertebrates, the amphibia gave rise to a large variety of more or less clumsy, often bizarre forms, the **labyrinthodonts** (Fig. 29.22). During the

FIG. 29.21.   The wing of a Permian insect, shown in actual natural size. Insects larger than this existed in the Permian era, but even the owner of the wing shown was far larger than any insect today. (Courtesy of Dr. C. O. Dunbar and Peabody Museum, Yale University.)

FIG. 29.22. Labyrinthodonts. Reconstruction of *Diplovertebron*, a Permian amphibian. (American Museum of Natural History.)

Permian, these began to be overshadowed by members of a new vertebrate class, the **reptiles.** The latter had evolved from ancestral labyrinthodonts late during the Carboniferous and were represented at first by one main group, the **cotylosaurs,** or *stem reptiles.* Inasmuch as they laid hard-shelled land eggs, they were the first completely terrestrial vertebrates. The cotylosaurs produced a major reptilian radiation during the Permian, and so they set the stage for an age of reptiles, which followed during the Mesozoic era.

The long Paleozoic era terminated with the **Permo-Triassic crisis,** precipitated by the Appalachian revolution (see page 677). This geologically unstable time of transition was marked by rapid evolution in many groups, by widespread extinction of archaic forms and replacement with new types, and by a general but temporary decrease in the total amount of life. In the sea, the trilobites disappeared altogether; the previously very abundant brachiopods declined; and archaic echinoderms, mollusks, and crustacea were replaced by newly evolved representatives. Similar intragroup replacement occurred among the cartilage and bony fishes. On land, the fern forests gave way to coniferous forests, and the labyrinthodonts became extinct. This left the amphibian tradition up to a small group of inconspicuous types, the direct ancestors of the modern salamanders, frogs, and toads. When the new Mesozoic era opened, reptiles were already dominant. The Carboniferous-Permian record is summarized in Fig. 29.23.

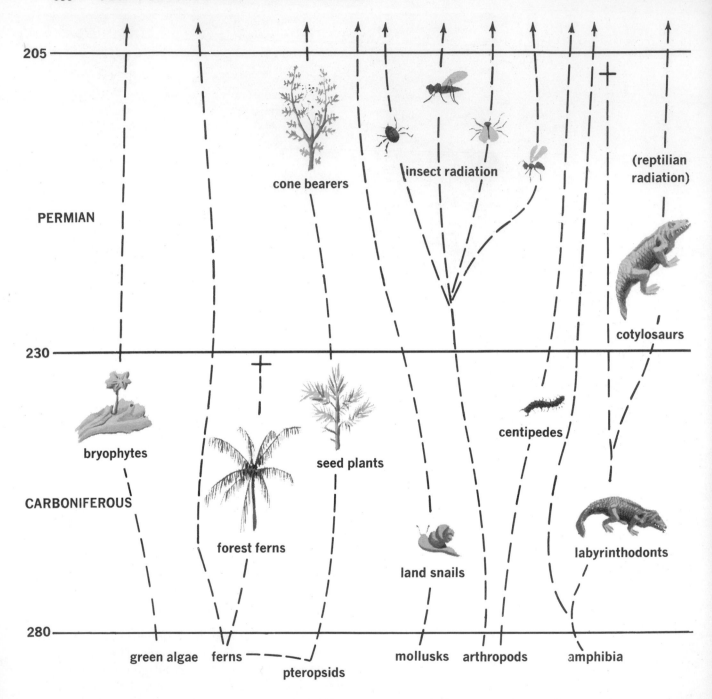

205

PERMIAN

cone bearers

insect radiation

(reptilian radiation)

230

cotylosaurs

bryophytes

seed plants

centipedes

CARBONIFEROUS

forest ferns

land snails

labyrinthodonts

280

green algae   ferns

pteropsids

mollusks   arthropods   amphibia

FIG. 29.23. Summary of Carboniferous-Permian events. Placement of groups corresponds roughly with time of first appearance in the fossil record. Only newly evolved groups are indicated.

THE MESOZOIC AND CENOZOIC

The whole Mesozoic era is often referred to as the age of reptiles. Apart from reptilian evolution, it was characterized by several other major events.

During the late Triassic or early Jurassic, the **flowering plants** arose, probably from cone-bearing pteropsid ancestors. In the Cretaceous, the flowering plants underwent an expansion which established them as the dominant terrestrial plant types from then on. In parallel with this, **insects** reradiated enormously, and their present importance traces to this Mesozoic expansion. An equally extensive radiation occurred among the bony fishes. During the Cretaceous, the paleoniscoid fishes gave rise to a multitude of new fresh-water and marine types, the **modern bony fishes.** These became the dominant animals of the aquatic environment, a status they still retain today. Thus both the sea and the land began to acquire a relatively modern character (Fig. 29.24).

However, the most spectacular Mesozoic event was the expansion of the reptiles. These animals not only evolved many different terrestrial ways of life, but also invaded the water and the air. As a group they reigned supreme on earth for 130 million years, longer than any other animals to date. When their dominance was eventually broken, they were replaced by two new groups they themselves had given rise to, the birds and the mammals.

Reptiles

At the beginning of the Mesozoic, five major reptilian stocks were in existence, all evolved during the Permian from the cotylosaurian stem reptiles (Fig. 29.25). One group, the so-called **thecodonts,** reradiated extensively during the Triassic, and in turn gave rise to the following types: the ancestral **birds;** the ancestors of the modern **crocodiles, lizards,** and **snakes;** the flying **pterosaurs;** and two other groups, referred to collectively as **dinosaurs.** A second reptilian stock was ancestral to the modern **turtles.** A third and fourth produced two kinds of

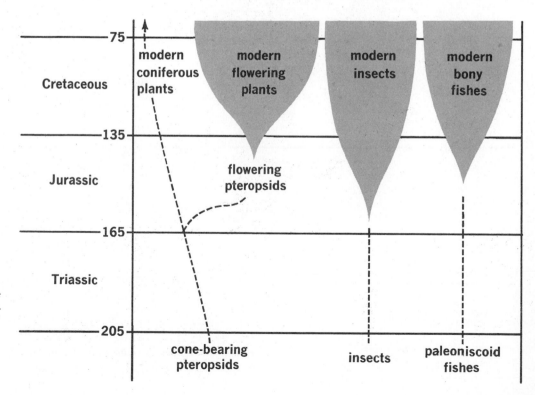

FIG. 29.24. The major non-reptilian radiations of the Mesozoic.

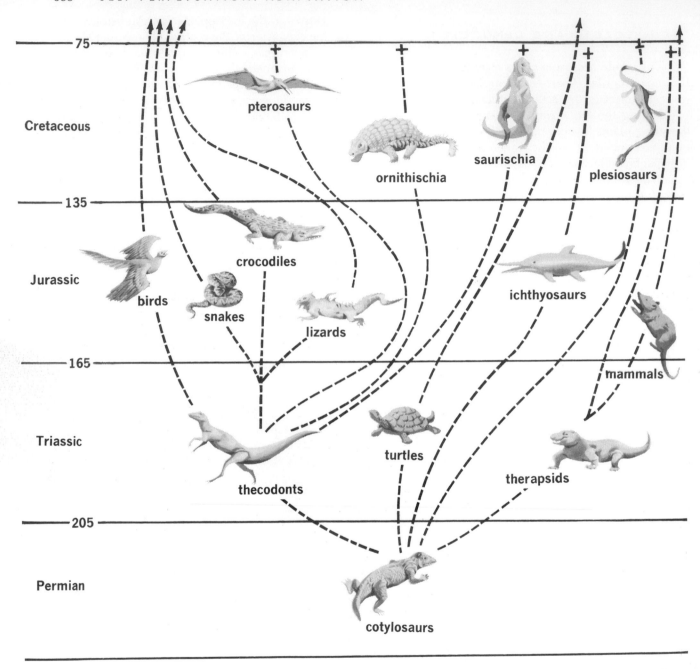

75

Cretaceous

pterosaurs

ornithischia

saurischia

plesiosaurs

135

crocodiles

Jurassic

birds

snakes

lizards

ichthyosaurs

165

mammals

Triassic

turtles

thecodonts

therapsids

205

Permian

cotylosaurs

FIG. 29.25. The great reptilian radiation of the Mesozoic. Placement of groups corresponds roughly with the time of their greatest abundance.

marine reptiles, the porpoiselike **ichthyosaurs** and the unique, long-necked **plesiosaurs.** The fifth stock comprised the so-called **therapsids,** mammallike reptiles which included the ancestors of the true **mammals** (Fig. 29.26).

These various reptilian types did not all flourish at the same time. The Triassic was dominated largely by the ancestral thecodonts and the therapsids. The former were rather birdlike in appearance. They featured large hind limbs for walking, an enormous supporting tail, and diminutive forelimbs, often not even long enough to shovel food into the mouth. Therapsids, on the other hand, walked on all fours, and some of them gradually became less reptilelike and more mammallike. True mammals arose from this stock during the late Triassic or early Jurassic. However, these new fur-bearing vertebrates were greatly overshadowed by the reptiles, and they remained small and inconspicuous during the rest of the Mesozoic, that is, for a period of about 80 or 90 million years.

During the Jurassic, ichthyosaurs became abundant in the ocean, and one of the thecodont groups evolved into birds. This transition is documented beautifully by a famous fossil animal called *Archeopteryx* (Fig. 29.27). The organism possessed teeth

FIG. 29.26. Therapsids, mammal-like reptiles of the Triassic. (American Museum of Natural History.)

FIG. 29.27. Cast of *Archeopteryx*. Note feathered tail, wings. Head is bent back, and teeth-bearing mouth is not easily visible here. (American Museum of Natural History.)

FIG. 29.28. Reconstruction of plesiosaurs (left) and ichthyosaurs (right). (Chicago Natural History Museum.)

and a lizardlike tail, two features which are distinctly reptilian. But it also possessed feathers and wings, and presumably it flew like a bird. Like the early mammals, ancestral birds too were inconspicuous during the whole remaining Mesozoic. They were overshadowed particularly by their thecodont kin, the pterosaurs. These flying reptiles had their heyday during the Cretaceous, the period when reptiles as a whole attained their greatest abundance and variety (Fig. 29.28). Plesiosaurs then were common in the ocean, and the dinosaurs came into undisputed dominance on land.

The two dinosaurian groups are called the **Ornithischia** and the **Saurischia.** Both evolved from the thecodonts. Not all dinosaurs were large, but some of the group were enormous. The saurischian *Brontosaurus* was the largest land animal of all time, exceeded in size only by the modern blue whale. This dinosaur was herbivorous, and it probably lived in swamps or lagoons, where it could support its 20- to 30-ton bulk in water. Another saurischian, the giant *Tyrannosaurus*, probably was the fiercest land carnivore of all time. Among its victims undoubtedly were animals like *Ankylosaurus* and *Triceratops*, herbivorous and heavily armored ornithischian giants.

As the Cretaceous came to a close, virtually all the reptilian multitude became extinct. Today the class is represented only by turtles, crocodiles, lizards, snakes, and *Sphenodon,* a lizardlike "living fossil" in New Zealand (Fig. 29.29). The specific reasons for this large-scale dying out have been sought for a long time, but fully satisfactory explanations have not yet been found. Climatic changes at the end of the Mesozoic, coincident with the Laramide revolution, are believed to have played a decisive role. Mesozoic reptiles were adapted to rather warm environments, as their modern descendants still are. However, climates appear to

FIG. 29.29. *Sphenodon,* the tuatara from New Zealand. (American Museum of Natural History.)

have become colder toward the close of the Cretaceous, as a result of the Laramide revolution. Much tropical and subtropical vegetation then must have died out, which must have meant that herbivorous reptiles lost their food supplies. And as the herbivorous stocks so declined, the carnivorous reptiles would have had to die out too.

Whatever the precise causes, the extinction of the Mesozoic reptiles cleared the way for a great expansion of mammals and birds.

Mammals

The radiation of mammals and birds came to be the key feature of the new Cenozoic era. Terrestrial mammals replaced the dinosaurs; aquatic mammals eventually took the place of the former ichthyosaurs and plesiosaurs; and bats, but more especially birds, gained the air left free by the pterosaurs. The Cenozoic is often designated as the age of mammals, but it might equally well be called the age of birds.

At the beginning of the 75-million-year-long Cenozoic, ancestral mammals gave rise to a large-scale radiation of some two dozen independent lines. Some of these became extinct, but most persist today. They represent three subclasses and some twenty orders within the class of mammals. The subclasses are the **Prototheria,** or *egg-laying* mammals, of which the duck-billed platypus is the most familiar representative that is living today; the **Metatheria,** or *pouched* mammals, which include the opossum, the kangaroo, and a large variety of other *marsupials* now confined largely to the Australian continent; and the **Eutheria,** or *placental* mammals, the most abundant group. To

FIG. 29.30. Reconstruction of horse evolution, based on abundant fossil evidence. The evolutionary sequence begins at bottom of photo, with the fossil horse *Eohippus*, and ends at top, with the modern horse *Equus*. The drawings are to scale, and show how the average size and the outline shape of horses have changed during their evolution in the Cenozoic. Progressive reduction in the number of toes occurred as well as changes in dentition and size changes. Note that the animals shown represent a *selected* series, and it should not be inferred that horse evolution followed a straight-line pattern. Here, as elsewhere, a bush pattern is actually in evidence. (American Museum of Natural History.)

the latter belong the most familiar mammals: cats, dogs, seals, and walruses; rodents; whales and dolphins; bats; moles and shrews; cattle, sheep, pigs, and camels; horses and zebras; elephants and tapirs; monkeys and men; and many others (see Chap. 31).

The fossil record of this mammalian radiation is fairly extensive for most groups and extremely good for a few, such as horses and elephants (Fig. 29.30). In the following we shall concentrate primarily on the history of one of the mammalian groups, namely, the line which produced man.

The Evolution of Man

THE PRIMATE BACKGROUND

The Origin of Primates

Just as each geological era may be subdivided into periods, so each period in turn may be sub-

divided into **epochs.** The periods and epochs of the Cenozoic era are shown in Table 14. As noted earlier, the era as a whole began with the great upheavals of the Laramide revolution, which produced the present high mountain ranges. Their emergence substantially changed the pre-Cenozoic patterns of air circulation between ocean and land, and the new patterns led to new climatic conditions. For example, the east-west barrier of the Himalayas in Asia, and of the Alps in Europe, prevented warm south winds from reaching the northern portions of Eurasia. These regions became cooler as a result. In turn, this undoubtedly facilitated the development of ice ages during the recent Pleistocene epoch.

Ice ages had occurred before during the earth's history, and during the last million years there were four. In each, ice sheets spread from the North Pole southward, covered much of the land of the Northern Hemisphere, then receded. Warm interglacial periods intervened between successive glaciations.

FIG. 29.31.   Some of the main features of the mammalian radiation during the Cenozoic.

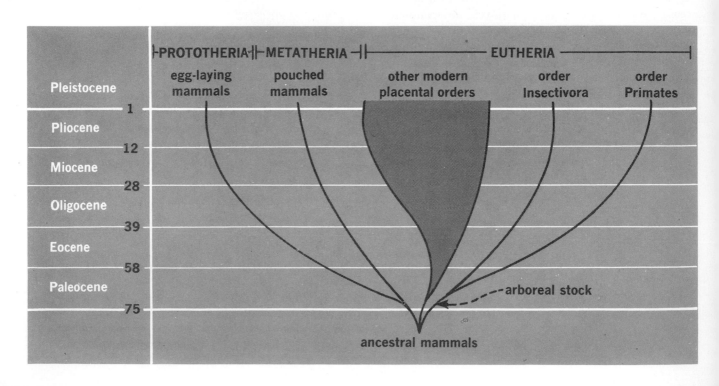

The last recession began some 20,000 years ago, at the beginning of the Recent epoch, and it is still in progress: polar regions are still covered with ice. The biological importance of Cenozoic climates in general, and of Pleistocene ice in particular, is great, for these environmental conditions materially influenced the evolution of all mammals, man not excepted. Man in a sense is one of the products of the ice ages.

When the Cenozoic began, the great mammalian radiation was just getting under way (Fig. 29.31). Each descendant mammalian line exploited a particular way of life available at the time and came to occupy either a new environmental niche or one left free after the extinction of the Mesozoic reptiles. One mammalian line is of particular interest, for it eventually led to man. This line exploited a relatively new environmental possibility. Its members took to the trees, then already abundantly available, and adapted to an *arboreal* life.

Soon after such a stock of arboreal mammals had evolved during the early Paleocene, it must have reradiated and produced two major sublines, the order **Insectivora** and the order **Primates** (see Fig. 29.31). Most modern insect-eating mammals, particularly the moles and the hedgehogs, are clearly distinct from modern primates, of which man is a late member. But some of the shrews now living are exceedingly like insectivores, on the one hand, and like primitive living primates, on the other. Indeed, one group of shrews is actually classified with the Insectivora, and another with the Primates. Fossil data too support the view that insectivorous mammals and primates are very closely related,

FIG. 29.32. Arboreal squirrel shrew. This animal belongs to the order Insectivora. (American Museum of Natural History.)

through a common, shrewlike, arboreal, insect-eating ancestor (Fig. 29.32).

The Primate Radiation

The first distinct primates evolved from this insect-eating ancestor during the Paleocene are known as the **early prosimians**. They were small, still shrewlike in appearance, with a fairly long snout and a long bushy tail. They were also agile and nimble, an important adaptation in a life among the treetops. Undoubtedly they possessed good eyes and good neuromuscular coordination, but in these respects they were probably not equipped very much better than early mammals in general. Of the many lines which radiated from the early prosimians during the Paleocene, four major ones survive today (Fig. 29.33).

One of these four largely retained the prosimian characteristics and gave rise to a number of sublines during subsequent epochs. The **modern prosimians**

TABLE 14. The epochs and periods of the Cenozoic era

Period	Epoch	Duration	Beginning date
Quaternary	Recent	20,000 years	20,000 B.C.
	Pleistocene	1	1
Tertiary	Pliocene	11	12
	Miocene	16	28
	Oligocene	11	39
	Eocene	19	58
	Paleocene	17	75

* Unless otherwise stated, all figures refer to millions of years.

are the collective result. This group includes the *lemurs* and the *aye-ayes,* found today largely on the island of Madagascar (Fig. 29.34). These animals still possess long snouts and long tails, but instead of claws they possess flat nails, a general primate characteristic. Nails probably interfere less with locomotion along tree branches than long claws; hence nails may be a specific adaptation to arboreal life. The modern prosimians also include the *tarsiers* of Southern Asia and Indonesia (Fig. 29.35). In these, the snout has receded considerably, and a fairly well-defined face has appeared. Moreover, the eyes, which in lemurs are still more or less on the side, have moved well into the face. As a result, tarsiers are able to focus on one point with both eyes, and this endows them with stereoscopic vision and efficient depth perception.

These features are additional adaptations to a tree-dwelling existence. In a plains animal such as a horse, for example, the eyes are located advantageously on the side, where they enable the animal to scout the open environment, even while grazing.

But among the branches of a tree, lateral vision is less important. Quite the contrary, it becomes important to look ahead along a branch, almost a necessary requirement if balance is to be retained during precarious limb-over-limb locomotion. Note too that tarsiers possess fairly well-defined fingers, with a gripping pad at the end of each.

The second of the main groups descended from the early prosimians comprises the **ceboids,** or *New World monkeys.* These attained their present diversity during the Oligocene and Miocene. Ceboid monkeys today are confined to South and Central America, and they are characterized by long, strong tails, which are used as fifth limbs. The third main group evolved independently from Paleocene prosimians consists of **cercopithecoids,** or *Old World monkeys.* They too radiated during the Oligocene and Miocene, and they are found today in Africa and Asia. These monkeys possess tails, but they are not used as limbs.

In both groups of monkeys, adaptations to arboreal life have evolved a good deal farther than in

FIG. 29.33. Diagram of the radiation of primates.

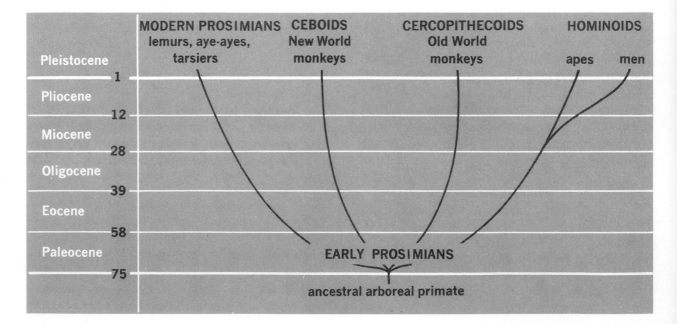

modern prosimians. A monkey possesses a very well developed face, stereoscopic vision, and in addition, independently movable fingers on all four limbs. Moreover, it possesses opposable thumbs, which allow it to grip tree branches very firmly. Also, limbs may be rotated freely within their sockets. In a plains animal like a horse, limbs move predominantly back and forth. The limb sockets here permit very little lateral play, and this is an energy-saving feature in running. In jumping among tree branches, on the other hand, freely movable limbs are clearly advantageous.

Correlated with such skeletal specializations to arboreal life, monkeys have also evolved important muscular, sensory, and neural adaptations. Through a general enlargement of the cerebral cortex and a particular enlargement of the optic lobes, monkeys have become capable of precision timing, of judging distances to the inch, and of coordinating limb and finger muscles in new, complex ways. In turn, increase in brain size has led to a quickness of mind and a level of intelligence well above the prosimian average. We may note here that the evolution of intelligence has been correlated particularly with the improvement of coordination between the eyes and the limbs. Evidently, primate intelligence too is basically an adaptation to the arboreal way of life.

The Hominoid Radiation

Trends of the same kind, but developed very much farther than in monkeys, are apparent also in the fourth group of living primates. Descended independently from Paleocene prosimians, this group comprises the so-called **hominoids.** During the early Miocene, some 30 million years ago, the hominoid line radiated into two main sublines. One of these led to the *apes,* the other to *men* (see Fig. 29.33). Both groups are characterized by the absence of an external tail and by an increase in body size over the average of other primates. Moreover, they feature a still further, very remarkable enlargement and elaboration of the brain.

Apes are represented today by four genera: gibbons, orangutans, chimpanzees, and gorillas. The group is fundamentally arboreal, and the ancestral hominoid stock undoubtedly was too. But modern

FIG. 29.34. A modern lemur from Madagascar. (American Museum of Natural History.)

FIG. 29.35. A modern tarsier from Indonesia. (American Museum of Natural History.)

apes include types which abandoned the arboreal way of life more or less completely. Orangutans, for example, and especially chimpanzees, can be quite at home out of trees. And gorillas are ground animals altogether, using trees as little as men. Correlated with this abandonment of life in trees is a tendency toward more or less two-legged walking and toward a more or less upright posture. In this, arboreal adaptations can be used to advantage. For example, the long arms of a gorilla enable it to assume a half-erect, crouching stance, and the animal may also support itself on its hind legs and walk bipedally for short distances. This frees the agile forelegs and fingers for other tasks.

These trends became very much more elaborated in the line leading to man. After branching away from the common hominoid stock during the Miocene, the human line left the trees completely. Forelimbs remained adapted for gripping, but the feet evolved into flat walking platforms. A half-erect, bent-kneed, four-limbed shuffle must have been characteristic for a long time, but as the feet became perfected, forelimbs were completely relieved of a locomotor function. Undoubtedly, it was this total freeing of arms and fingers for many new functions which made possible the evolution of the most basic human characteristics. For, correlated with new opportunities for exceedingly complex hand-eye coordination, brain size enlarged still further, and intelligence increased spectacularly.

These and other features which now distinguish men and apes came to be superimposed on the characteristics of pre-Miocene arboreal primates. We recognize, therefore, that the modern human type could not have evolved if the ancestral type had not first been specialized for life in trees.

THE PREHUMAN LINE

Early History

Leaving the trees was clearly essential to the emergence of man. What prompted our Miocene ancestors, and also some of the early apes, to abandon arboreal life? A certain answer is not available, but a reasonable guess may be made: in the ancestral territories, trees may have become scarce.

A thinning out of deciduous forests may have been generally characteristic of the late Tertiary, as a result of steadily cooling climates (see p. 692). Small annual plants and evergreens would be favored under such conditions, but dense accumulations of perennial deciduous trees would become confined largely to tropical regions. Elsewhere, such trees would become sparser, and continuous overhead canopies of branches and foliage would therefore disappear. Hence our prehuman ancestors would have had to travel on the ground if they wished to move from one stand of trees to another. However, such forced excursions may well have been fraught with considerable danger. For saber-toothed carnivores and other large mammals dominated the ground at those times. Consequently, ability to dash quickly across open spaces may have had

great selective value, and this may have oriented the evolution of running feet in the human direction. Moreover, strong muscles would be required to move the hind limbs in new ways. Indeed, a unique trait of the human line is the possession of such muscles, in the form of enlarged buttocks.

It is conceivable, therefore, that the prehumans came out of the trees because they had to, and that this in turn promoted the gradual evolution of running feet, bipedal locomotion, newly functioning forelimbs, complex hand-eye coordination, and powerful brains.

We may note here that the early evolutionary history of the human line must necessarily be speculative, for fossil data of Miocene and Pliocene prehumans are almost completely lacking. Indeed, the whole human fossil record is tantalizingly scanty, and we can trace the recent evolution of almost any other mammal far better than our own. Virtually the entire fossil evidence of human evolution is of Pleistocene origin, that is, no older than 1 million years. However, this epoch includes the development of modern man, and some fossil documentation of this event is available.

Dominated by intermittent ice ages, the Pleistocene as a whole was a period of severe and fluctuating climates. It was marked by extinction of many forms and by rapid evolution of others. Adaptation to cold was of prime importance. Many mammals and other forms migrated south beyond the reaches of ice, and their descendants are found today among the animal populations of equatorial and subequatorial regions. Others, like the woolly mammoth, possessed rich fur and could hang on for a time in the cold lands. Still others withdrew into caves, forests, and ground holes and managed to eke out a precarious existence. But they survived, and today bears, moose, and many small mammals still live in northern regions. Among the cave dwellers may have been a number of subhuman types, descended from Tertiary prehuman ancestors. As noted, it is not known what the specific ancestors of these subhumans may have been. Nor is it known which of the subhumans finally gave rise to modern man. Nevertheless, fossils of Pleistocene subhumans provide a good indication of how far the human line had evolved since Miocene times.

Pleistocene Subhumans

It is not necessary to find whole fossilized skeletons to reconstruct the probable appearance of their once-living owners. The proportions of body parts to one another may be deduced with reasonable accuracy from living man, from apes, and from such whole skeletons of subhuman types as have been found. For example, a tooth, a jawbone, a skullcap, or a leg bone may not only be identified from its shape as belonging to a particular subhuman, but may also give important clues about the missing remainder. By and large, the features of the skull tell most. Thick or thin bones, prominent or reduced eyebrow ridges, receding or vertical forehead, small or large brain case, poorly or well-defined chin, all indicate fairly well whether or not a fossil is from a primitive or an advanced subhuman type. Much may also be learned from various signs of cultural activity often associated with a fossil find. For example, the type of tool, the type of camp site, the type of weapon found with a fossil, each may reveal a great deal about the evolutionary status of the subhuman in question.

Some of the known aspects of subhuman history during the last million years or so are outlined in Fig. 29.36. The oldest subhuman fossil found to date has been assigned the generic designation *Australopithecus*. Rather more apelike than manlike, this humanoid dates to the late Pliocene. It is believed to be fairly closely related to the unknown ancestral stock from which Pleistocene subhumans must have evolved (Fig. 29.37).

Among several known subhumans of the early Pleistocene, one is documented fairly well. This is *Pithecanthropus erectus*, the **Java ape man,** dating back perhaps 500,000 years and probably more (Fig. 29.38). *Pithecanthropus* was already more manlike than apelike. He possessed a brain measuring about 1,000 cm³ by volume, which compares with 600 cm³ for the gorilla and about 1,500 cm³ for the brain of modern man. *Pithecanthropus*, in addition, featured a flat sloping forehead, thick eyebrow ridges, and a rounded, practically chinless jaw. He had relatively long arms, and he probably crouched like a gorilla. Also, he may have practiced cannibalism: separate skullcaps have been found, detached cleanly from the rest of the skeletons. Sheer accident

is not likely to have caused such neat separations.

The best known of the subhumans is undoubtedly *Homo neanderthalensis,* the **Neanderthal man** (Figs. 29.38, 29.39). He was sufficiently like modern man to be put into the same genus, *Homo,* but he represented a distinctly different species. The Neanderthalers flourished during the latter half of the Pleistocene, roughly from about 500,000 to 50,000 years ago. Therefore, the first Neanderthalers could have been contemporaries of the last members of the *Pithecanthropus* stock. The Neanderthalers still had practically no chin, still had heavy brow ridges, fairly long arms, short legs, and a crouching gait. But their brain case was deeper and higher, enclosing a volume of about 1,500 cm³. This approximates the brain size of modern man, but the Neanderthal brain was proportioned differently. The skull jutted out in back, where we are relatively rounded, and the forehead was low and receding.

Culturally, the Neanderthalers were Stone Age cave men. All Pleistocene human and subhuman types are generally regarded as belonging to the **Old Stone Age.** But whereas earlier subhumans made only crude stone implements, Neanderthal man fashioned a variety of weapons, tools, hunting axes and clubs, and household equipment. Yet he was still a nomad living from hand to mouth, and he had neither agriculture nor domesticated animals. He did not make pottery, and he did not leave any art. His territory covered most of Europe, with fringe populations along the African and Asian coasts of the Mediterranean.

Neanderthal man, and his contemporary subhumans in other parts of the world, held their own till relatively recently, paleontologically speaking. Then they became extinct and were replaced by already existing representatives of our own species, *Homo sapiens.*

MODERN MAN

History

The time of origin of modern man cannot be pinpointed very precisely. The oldest known fossil of *Homo sapiens* is probably the **Swanscombe skull plate,** and this skeletal fragment may date back about 300,000 years. At that time, modern man

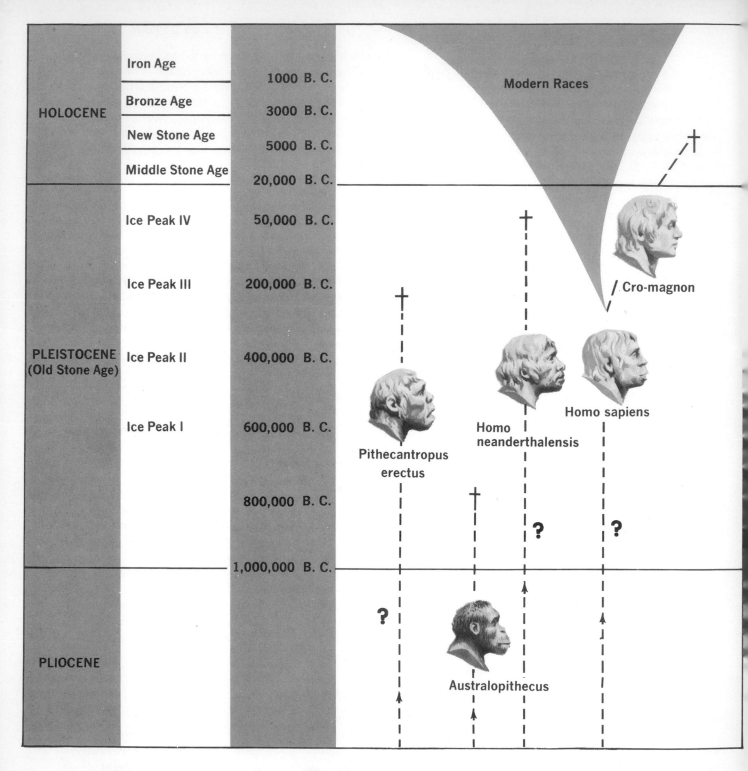

FIG. 29.36. The Pleistocene and man. Each humanoid type is shown at a time level at which that type is actually known to have existed. It is not clearly established when a given type first originated, nor when exactly it became extinct.

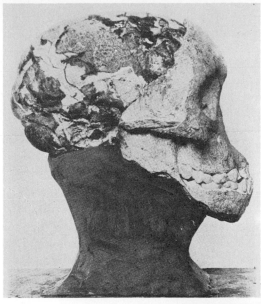

FIG. 29.39. Restoration of a Neanderthal group. (Chicago Natural History Museum.)

clearly was already in existence. It is possible, therefore, that *Homo sapiens* may have arisen as long as half a million years ago. His early representatives, like the Neanderthalers, may have been contemporaries of *Pithecanthropus*.

The specific derivation of modern man is still in question too. Neither *Pithecanthropus* nor Neanderthal man is likely to have been ancestral to us. Instead, *Homo sapiens* and the subhuman types of the Pleistocene appear to be separate branches of a humanoid radiation. The original ancestor of this radiation is not known, and with one exception, namely,

ourselves, all other branch lines of the radiation are now extinct (see Fig. 29.36).

The modern men who replaced the Neanderthalers in Europe are known as the **Cro-Magnon** race (Figs. 29.38, 29.40). This group flourished from about 50,000 to 20,000 years ago, roughly the peak period of the last ice age. Cro-Magnon was fully erect, 6 ft tall on the average, with a brain volume of about 1,700 cm^3. His culture still belongs to the Old Stone Age, but in addition to stone implements, Cro-Magnon used bone tools. Bone needles have been found with which he may have sewn animal skins into crude garments. The dog became his companion, but he still did not domesticate food animals, and he did not practice agriculture; Cro-Magnon was a cave-dwelling hunter. He developed a remarkable art, however, as his murals on cave walls indicate.

In other parts of the world there lived other races of *Homo sapiens*. The racial division of modern man into **caucasoids, negroids,** and **mongoloids** may have taken place then. But the original racial traits became diluted or obliterated fairly rapidly, through interbreeding among the extensively migrating human populations. None of the present human types represents a "pure" race.

As the Pleistocene came to a close, Cro-Magnon disappeared in Europe, and other groups of modern men replaced him. At that time, some 20,000 years ago, the ice sheets started to retreat, milder climates gradually supervened, and eventually man no longer needed to shelter in caves. For the next 15,000 years he produced what is known as the **Middle Stone Age** culture. It was characterized chiefly by great improvements in stone tools. Man was still a nomadic hunter.

The **New Stone Age** began around 5,000 B.C., about the time Abraham settled in Canaan. A great cultural revolution took place then. Man learned to fashion pottery; he developed agriculture; and he was able to domesticate animals. From that period

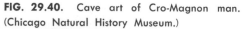

FIG. 29.40. Cave art of Cro-Magnon man. (Chicago Natural History Museum.)

on, modern civilization moved on with rapid strides. By 3,000 B.C. man had entered the **Bronze Age,** and during the ensuing 2,000 years, the **Iron Age,** he was to find out how to produce and to work iron. Not very long after he discovered steam, electricity, and now the atom and outer space. Measured by geological standards, the hairy beast which lumbered down from the trees 30 million years ago turned into college professor in a flash.

The Status of Man

That modern man has evolved through the operation of the same forces which produced all other organisms is clear. And it should also be clear that this organism is by far the most remarkable product of evolution. Man is sometimes described rather offhandedly as being "just" another animal. Often, on the contrary, he is considered to be so radically distinct that the appellation "animal" assumes the character of an insult. Neither view is justified.

Man certainly *is* an animal, but an animal with very unique attributes. Structurally, man is fully erect and possesses a double-curved spine, a prominent chin, and walking feet with arches. He is a fairly generalized type in most respects, being not particularly specialized for either speed, strength, agility, or rigidly fixed environments.

At some stage during his evolution, his rate of embryonic development slowed down, and his whole life cycle became stretched out in duration. Thus man became perhaps the longest-lived of all animals. This stretching of the life cycle also lengthened substantially the period of postnatal growth and adolescence. In this manner, another uniquely human characteristic emerged, namely, a proportionately very long *youth*. A chimpanzee, mature at the age of two, is senile at the age of twenty, when man is only beginning to attain adulthood. Man therefore has *time* to learn and to gather experiences, and in his learning capacity man is also unique. To be sure, other animals may learn too, but the quantitative difference is so great that it is in effect a qualitative difference.

Learning presupposes a powerful brain, and in this department man clearly has no equal. Note here again that the human nervous system develops as it does because it has *time* to do so, because the em-

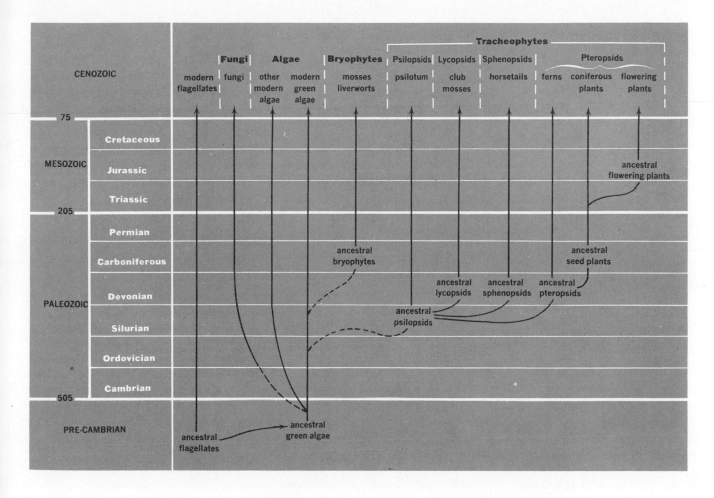

FIG. 29.41. Overall summary of the course of plant evolution.

bryonic period is greatly stretched out. The most characteristically human traits depend directly or indirectly on man's brain. Man is far more aware of himself and far more individualized in personality and behavior than any other creature. He displays a greater range of emotions than any other animal, and he is the only animal able to laugh and to weep. Moreover, only man knows beauty, and the human capacities of planning ahead, of having reasoned purposes, and of making considered choices far outclass anything similar in the animal kingdom.

Above all, only man has traditions, and only he *accumulates* knowledge over successive generations.

The transmission of knowledge occurs by nonbiological means, and we actually deal here with a new kind of evolution. The old is biological evolution, and its vehicle is the gene. The new is social evolution, and its vehicle is spoken and written *speech*. Man is quite unique in having evolved, and in continuing to evolve, through inherited traditions passed on not only by genes, but also by *words*.

Conceivably, this changeover from the merely biological to the human may have as much future significance as the earlier changeover, 2 billion years ago, from the inorganic to the biological. The first transition placed matter on a totally new plane, and

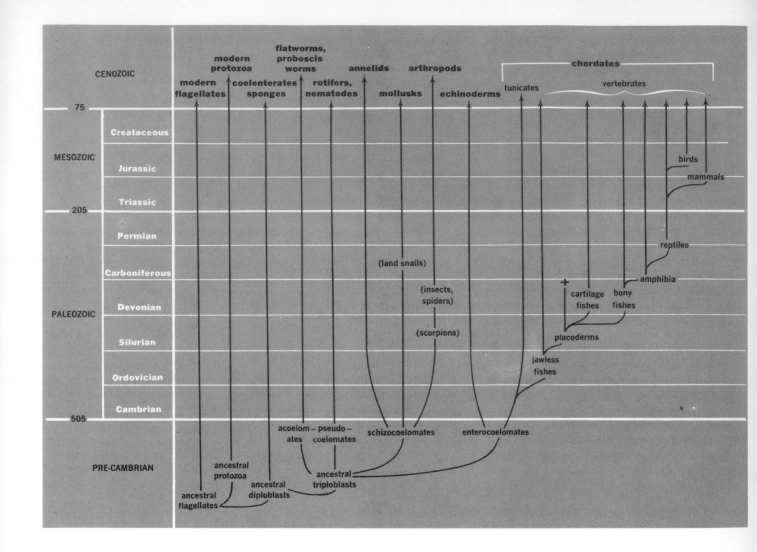

FIG. 29.42. Overall summary of the course of animal evolution.

on this plane it became organized into a wealth of previously nonexistent arrangements. The recent transition may create new possibilities of like scope. But the realization of this potential is now in the hands of man. For with the coming of man, the chance operations of nature have begun to be modified and manipulated by human purpose. The activities of man block chance increasingly, and man's fate will therefore be decided by man's purpose.

We have outlined the past course of human evolution, and of evolution in general. A comprehensive summary of plant evolution is given in Fig. 29.41, and a comprehensive summary of animal evolution in Fig. 29.42. Clearly, man is not the only living product of the evolutionary process, even though he is the most interesting. Evolution has the pattern of a bush, and man represents but one of a few million topmost branches which have radiated up through past ages.

In the two concluding chapters, we turn to these contemporary upper branches and examine the currently living product of evolution as a whole.

REVIEW
QUESTIONS

1. Review the probable events of the first radiation among (a) plants, (b) animals. What lines of reasoning support a hypothesis of a monophyletic origin of plants and animals, and why are flagellates the likeliest candidates for a common ancestor? What was the blastea, and what lines of reasoning suggest that it may actually have existed?

2. Distinguish between biological homology and analogy. Give examples. What use is made of homologies in evolutionary studies? Distinguish between diploblastic and triploblastic animals. Which groups of living animals are diploblastic? Show how a blastea might have given rise to a gastrea. Summarize the probable events of the second radiation among animals.

3. What is the adaptive advantage of mesoderm? Describe the four basic ways in which mesoderm develops, and name the main animal groups in which each of these ways is encountered. Show how the mouth and the anus develop in each of these groups. Summarize the probable events of the third radiation among animals.

4. What is a fossil? How can the age of a fossil be determined? Review the names and dates of the geological eras and periods. What were the Appalachian and Laramide revolutions? List the major groups of plants and animals not yet in existence 500 million years ago.

5. Describe the key events of both plant and animal evolution during the (a) Cambrian-Ordovician, (b) Silurian-Devonian, (c) Carboniferous-Permian. Review the course of vertebrate evolution during the entire Paleozoic.

6. Describe the main events of both plant and animal evolution during the Mesozoic and Cenozoic. Review the principal features, and the time pattern, of the Mesozoic reptilian radiation. Name reptilian stocks now extinct and stocks now in existence. How many, and which, vertebrate classes have evolved since the Cambrian, and which ones survive today? Trace the ancestry of flowering plants since the Cambrian.

7. Name the subclasses of mammals. Describe the principal features of the Cenozoic mammalian radiation, with special attention to the origin of primates. Describe the major features and the time pattern of the primate radiation, and name living animals representing each of the main lines. When, and from where, did the line leading to man branch off?

8. Describe the various adaptations of each of the primate stocks to arboreal life. Which structural, functional, and behavioristic features of man trace back specifically to the arboreal way of life of his ancestors? How does the hominoid line differ from other descendants of early prosimians? How does the human line differ from that of the apes?

9. Why did the prehuman line probably cease to be arboreal? What structural and functional developments were made possible by this descent to the ground? Describe the climatic pattern of the Pleistocene. Show how the Pleistocene glaciations may in part have been consequences of the Laramide revolution. Describe and contrast the main fossil subhumans. When was each of them probably in existence? What culture was associated with each?

10. Roughly when did modern man evolve? Review in detail the biological characteristics which man shares with (a) all other hominoids, (b) all other primates, (c) all other mammals. Review in detail the biological characteristics which distinguish man uniquely from all other animals. Study carefully the data in Figs. 29.41 and 29.42.

SUGGESTED COLLATERAL READINGS

The following, partly textbooks, partly popular works, supplement the topics dealt with in this chapter:

Croneis, C., and W. C. Krumbein: "Down to Earth," Chicago University Press, 1936.

Raymond, P. E.: "Prehistoric Life," Harvard University Press, 1939.

Simpson, G. G.: "Life of the Past," Yale University Press, 1953.

Matthew, W. D.: "Climate and Evolution," 2d ed., New York Academy of Science, 1939.

Dunbar, C. O.: "Historical Geology," Wiley, 1949.

Mayr, E., E. B. Lindsley, and R. L. Usinger: "Methods and Principles of Systematic Zoology," McGraw-Hill, 1953.

Richards, A.: "Outlines of Comparative Embryology," Wiley, 1931.

Nelson, O. E.: "Comparative Embryology of the Vertebrates," McGraw-Hill–Blakiston, 1953.

Arnold, C. A.: "An Introduction to Paleobotany," McGraw-Hill, 1947.

Andrews, H. N.: "Ancient Plants and the World They Lived in," Comstock, 1947.

Stebbins, G. L.: "Variation and Evolution in Plants," Columbia University Press, 1950.

Moore, R. C., C. G. Lalicker, and A. G. Fisher: "Invertebrate Fossils," McGraw-Hill, 1952.

Shrock, R. R., and W. H. Twenhofel: "Principles of Invertebrate Paleontology," McGraw-Hill, 1953.

Colbert, E. H.: "The Dinosaur Book," American Museum of Natural History, 1954.

————: "Evolution of the Vertebrates," Wiley, 1955.

Berrill, N. J.: "The Origin of Vertebrates," Oxford University Press, 1955.

Romer, A. S.: "Vertebrate Paleontology," University of Chicago Press, 1945.

Clark, W. E. LeG.: "History of the Primates," 4th ed., British Museum, 1954.

————: "The Fossil Evidence for Human Evolution," University of Chicago Press, 1935.

Hooton, E. A.: "Up from the Ape," Macmillan, 1945.

Moore, R.: "Man, Time, and Fossils," Knopf, 1953.

Berrill, N. J.: "Man's Emerging Mind," Dodd, Mead, 1955.

The following are popular articles on specific aspects of past evolution:

Abelson, P. H.: Paleobiochemistry, *Sci. American,* vol. 195, 1956.

Deevey, E. S.: Radiocarbon Dating, *Sci. American,* vol. 185, 1951.

Brues, C. T.: Insects in Amber, *Sci. American,* vol. 185, 1951.

Janssen, R. E.: The Beginnings of Coal, *Sci. American,* vol. 179, 1948.

Jarvik, E.: The Oldest Tetrapods and Their Forerunners, *Sci. Monthly,* vol. 80, 1955.

Millot, J.: Coelacanth, *Sci. American,* vol. 193, 1955.

Bogert, C. M.: The Tuatara: Why Is It a Lone Survivor? *Sci. Monthly,* vol. 76, 1953.

Colbert, E. H.: The Ancestry of Mammals, *Sci. American,* vol. 180, 1949.

Eiseley, L. C.: Antiquity of Modern Man, *Sci. American,* vol. 179, 1948.

————: Fossil Man, *Sci. American,* vol. 189, 1953.

————: Man, the Firemaker, *Sci. American,* vol. 191, 1954.

Broom, R.: The Ape-men, *Sci. American,* vol. 181, 1949.

Krogman, W. M.: The Man-apes of South Africa, *Sci. American,* vol. 178, 1948.

————: What We Do Not Know about Race, *Sci. Monthly,* vol. 57, 1943.

30

THE RESULT OF EVOLUTION: PLANTS TODAY

THE GROUND PLAN ADOPTED in this and the following chapter is taxonomic; that is, we shall be concerned with the structures and functions which all organisms within a given major taxonomic group have in common, and which uniquely distinguish this group from all others. In this manner, we shall become acquainted not only with the different kinds of organisms in existence today, but also with their identifying characteristics.

Our unit of discussion will be the *phylum*. As noted earlier, a phylum is a broad grouping of historically closely related classes, orders, families, genera, and species of organisms, all characterized by the same basic structural and functional body organization. Such organisms often differ radically in their ways of life, yet they use the same kind of internal equipment in solving the different problems of their different environments. In some cases, it is not universally agreed whether a given group represents a distinct phylum, or a superphylum containing several smaller phyla, or a class within a larger phylum. We may note also that the term "phylum" is primarily a zoological one, botanists preferring the designation "division" for the major categories of plants. For convenience, we shall use the first term throughout this and the next chapter, and we may keep in mind that the important issue is not what a group is called, but what it contributes to, and reveals about, the richness of life.

Where warranted in the following, a classification of each phylum down to classes and subclasses is included, as is the approximate number of species known and described to date. We turn our attention first to the modern descendants of **ancient organisms**, then to the phyla within the **plant kingdom**.

Ancient Organisms

The preceding chapters should have made clear that given groups of organisms *cannot* be regarded as being "higher" or "lower," or "more com-

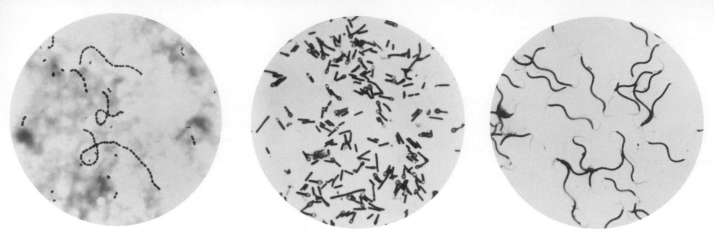

FIG. 30.1. Bacteria. Left: cocci, growing in chains. Middle: bacilli. Other bacilli are illustrated in Figs. 2.13, 9.24, and 24.2. Right: spirilla. (General Biological Supply House, Inc.)

plex" or "less complex," or "simpler" than others. Such characterizations do not emerge from features inherent in organisms, but are arbitrarily man-made and are largely lingering byproducts of erroneous concepts which envisage evolution as a "scale." We may note too that it is quite impossible to define comparative terms like "higher" and "lower" in any biologically meaningful way.

This is not to imply, however, that valid comparisons between groups of organisms cannot be made. Structurally and functionally, for example, various groups are certainly *different;* and historically, given ones are *more ancient* or *less ancient,* in the sense that the first of their kind appeared earlier or later during evolution. If used in this temporal sense, designations like "primitive," "modern," or "advanced" are reasonably acceptable, and indeed often useful.

Considered in this manner, the four living groups of organisms to be examined here are unquestionably very primitive, probably the most primitive now in existence. They are the **bacteria,** the **blue-green algae,** the **slime molds,** and the **flagellates.** Apart from their great age, these organisms have in common also the fact that their historical connection to one another, and to other groups, is far from clear. In the past, some have been classified with the plant kingdom, others with the animal kingdom. But it has become increasingly evident that the four properly fit into neither of these categories, and they are best treated as a separate collection of ancient, still more or less unrelatable types.

Phylum Schizophyta: Bacteria (2,500 Species)

The evolutionary affinities of the bacteria have not been determined satisfactorily. These organisms, or at least some of them, *could* be the direct descendants of original bacterialike cells evolved when life first arose (see Chap. 2). Alternatively, all or some of them *could* be degenerate descendants of a later ancestral group, for example, the early flagellates. Evidence obtained from living bacteria to date has been insufficient to decide this issue.

As a group, bacteria represent the smallest cells now in existence. The tiniest of them are smaller even than certain gigantic viruses, and the largest are not substantially larger than very small cells of other organisms. Bacteria usually possess a cell wall, made of a chitinlike material or of complex polysaccharides. The polysaccharide *cellulose* occurs rather rarely. Internally, bacteria feature clumps of genetic material not organized into a well-defined nucleus. This may be either a primitive or a degenerate trait. Many bacteria occur as single cells, but many others grow in clumps, forming chains, plates, or compact aggregates. Many also possess exceedingly fine surface flagella, which endow them with a certain amount of self-powered mobility. On the basis of shape, three kinds of bacteria may be distinguished. A **coccus** is a spherical type, a **bacillus** a rod-shaped type, and a **spirillum** a coiled or spiraled type (Fig. 30.1).

As noted in various earlier contexts, some bacteria are chemosynthetic or photosynthetic autotrophs. Most are heterotrophic, however, and of these, some live as independent saprophytes and others as parasitic, commensalistic, or mutualistic symbionts. Also, some are strictly aerobic, some strictly anaerobic, and others may survive both with and without oxygen. Bioluminescence is fairly common. The most important bacteria are those which, in soil and ocean, cause decay and play major roles in the global nitrogen cycle and those which cause disease, called **pathogenic** bacteria. The phylum evidently is highly diversified, and in spite of the exceedingly small size of the individual bacterium, there is certainly nothing "simple" about it: its molecular and chemical complexity is quite as great as that of any other cell type.

Phylum Cyanophyta: Blue-green Algae (2,500 Species)

The group name of these organisms is somewhat misleading, since many of them are not blue-green, but are of red, yellow, green, blue, and various intermediate shades. These colors are produced by chlorophyll *a*, various carotenes and xanthophylls, and by a blue **phycocyanin** and a red **phycoerythrin** pigment, both unique to the group (see Table 15). Blue-green algae, moreover, are probably not even true "algae," since they appear to be rather more closely related to the bacteria.

Like bacteria, the cyanophytes are fundamentally single cells, very small, and equipped with cell walls composed in part of cellulose (Fig. 30.2). Like bacteria also, they lack a distinct nucleus internally. Moreover, like photosynthetic bacteria, but unlike all other photosynthesizing organisms, the cyanophytes do not possess plastids. Instead, chlorophyll and all other pigments occur dispersed

TABLE 15. Comparative biochemical characteristics of various plant groups*

Group	Pigments Chlorophyll	Others	Food stored as	Cell wall contains
Cyanophyta	a	phycocyanin, phycoerythrin (both unique)	cyanophycean starch (unique)	cellulose
Chlorophyta Bryophyta Tracheophyta	a, b		starch	cellulose
Dinoflagellata	a, c	fucoxanthin		cellulose in some, others no wall
Chrysophyta	a, c	fucoxanthin	oils	silica
Phaeophyta	a, c	fucoxanthin, unique xanthophylls	mannitol, laminarin	cellulose
Rhodophyta	a, d	phycocyanin, phycoerythrin (both unique)	flurodean starch (unique)	cellulose

*Note: Most groups contain a variety of common carotene and xanthophyll pigments, which are not specially indicated in the table.

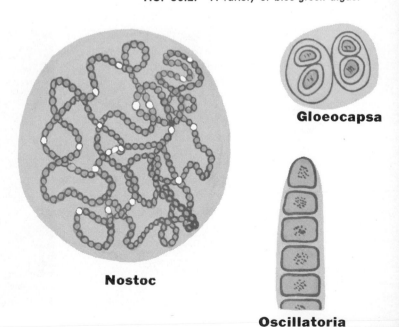

FIG. 30.2. A variety of blue-green algae.

Gloeocapsa

Nostoc

Oscillatoria

1 solitary flagellate cells   **2** solitary ameboid cells   **3** clumping

6
release
of spores

5 spore production
in fruiting body

4 formation of stalked
fruiting body

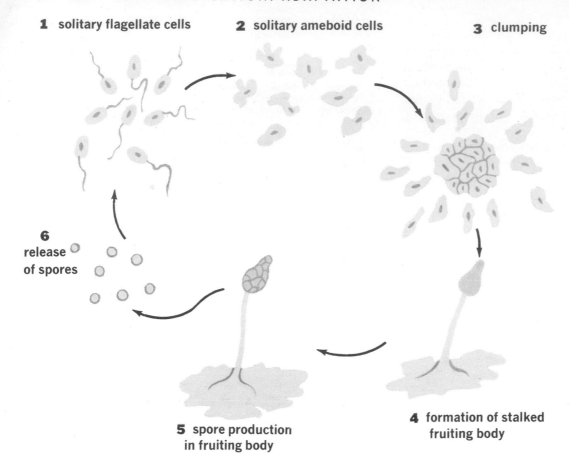

FIG. 30.3. Slime molds. The diagram illustrates the life cycle of a slime mold. Note the animal-like and plantlike phases. In the photo, fruiting bodies of the genus *Acryria* are shown. Slime molds are illustrated also in Fig. 3.18. (General Biological Supply House, Inc.)

through the cytoplasm. Again like certain bacteria, many cyanophytes may fix molecular nitrogen from the atmosphere, and many are bioluminescent. Food is stored in the form of a unique type of starch. The composition of this compound is still undetermined, and it has been called **cyanophycean starch.**

Most blue-greens are fresh-water forms, but some are marine. The organisms characteristically grow in colonial filaments, often greatly branched, or in clumps of various shapes. In many cases, such colonies are embedded in a gelatinous material secreted by the cells. The blue-greens reproduce by fission, like bacteria, and sexual processes are entirely unknown.

Because of the great similarity of bacteria and cyanophytes, both groups are sometimes classified as subphyla or classes of a single phylum *Schizophyta,* or fission plants.

Phylum Myxophyta: Slime Molds

These organisms are sometimes grouped with fungi in the plant kingdom, or, equally unjustifiably, with protozoa in the animal kingdom. At present it is certain only that slime molds combine certain plant and animal characteristics and that their evolutionary affinities are more or less completely unknown.

Slime molds undergo a remarkable life cycle (Fig. 30.3; see also Fig. 3.18). In an initial stage, the organisms exist as solitary flagellate cells, greatly resembling animallike flagellates. These solitary cells are haploid, and they reproduce by fission. At a later stage, the cells lose the flagella and become strikingly amebalike in locomotion, feeding behavior, and reproduction. Still later, ameboid cells which come into contact with one another clump together, and in many species the cell membranes dissolve in addition. The result is a huge colonial or continuous mass of protoplasm, in some cases as much as 1 ft or more in diameter. Up to this point the life cycle is rather animallike. A plantlike phase then supervenes. From the protoplasmic mass grow out one or more upright stalks, and the tips of these expand into **fruiting bodies.** Within them, nuclei fuse pairwise, meiosis occurs, and haploid nuclei are formed. The substance of a fruiting body later divides up into numerous *spores,* each containing one haploid nucleus and a hard shell on the outside. The spores eventually scatter, and in suitable environments they may develop into solitary flagellate cells. These begin a new cycle.

Evidently, any designation of these organisms as either plants or animals would be completely arbitrary. A proper classification will depend in large part on evidence showing whether the characteristics of slime molds are primitively original or secondarily degenerate.

Phylum Mastigophora: Flagellates

Class Phytomastigina
  Cryptomonas, Chilomonas, Chlamydomonas, Volvox, Euglena, Astasia
Class Dinoflagellata
  Noctiluca, Ceratium, Gymnodinium, Blastodinium, Peridinium
Class Zoomastigina
  Trypanosoma, Proterospongia, Trichonympha, Trichomonas

As noted in the preceding chapter, these whip bearers may well be the descendants of ancestral organisms from which true plants and animals also arose. Conceivably, ancestral flagellates may in addition have been the stock from which bacteria, blue-green algae, and slime molds have evolved. If so, the connection is not particularly direct or obvious. On the other hand, flagellates, as well as the three phyla discussed above, may be derivatives of still more ancient cellular types. In either event, ancestral flagellates qualify best as the evolutionary source of all the plants and animals to be dealt with below.

Modern flagellates possess one or more locomotor flagella, which in most cases are permanent structures. In some types, however, the flagella disappear at certain stages of the life cycle, and the organisms then may move like amoebae. Flagellates are most often unicellular, but colony-forming types do occur. In colonial forms like *Volvox,* for example, the cells are interdependent to a substantial degree (see Fig. 3.21). Flagellates characteristically do not possess rigid cell walls, but pliable surfaces cov-

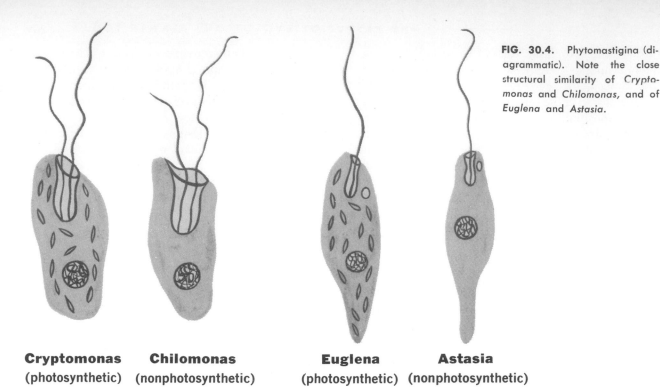

FIG. 30.4. Phytomastigina (diagrammatic). Note the close structural similarity of *Cryptomonas* and *Chilomonas*, and of *Euglena* and *Astasia*.

Cryptomonas
(photosynthetic)

Chilomonas
(nonphotosynthetic)

Euglena
(photosynthetic)

Astasia
(nonphotosynthetic)

ered with thin cuticles. Some dinoflagellates are exceptional in this respect, possessing walls made of a material resembling cellulose (see below).

The class Phytomastigina includes types which are plantlike, types which are animallike, and types which are both (Fig. 30.4). For example, *Volvox* is photosynthetic, *Chilomonas* is a colorless heterotroph, and *Euglena* not only photosynthesizes but also may, and probably must, feed heterotrophically as well. Three methods of heterotrophic feeding are encountered in the group. In some cases the organism is a saprophyte, living on molecular foods resulting from decay processes. In other cases the flagellate is symbiotic, living mutualistically or commensalistically or parasitically with other organisms. And in still other cases the flagellate engulfs bulk food like a free-living animal.

Some of the exclusively heterotrophic forms bear a striking resemblance to given autotrophic types. For example, *Chilomonas* is a colorless saprophyte exceedingly similar to the photosynthetic *Cryptomonas*. In like manner, the nongreen, always saprophytic *Astasia* remarkably resembles the green, partly photosynthetic and partly saprophytic *Euglena*. Paired types of this sort undoubtedly represent branch lines from a relatively recent common ancestor, one line having retained, the other lost, the photosynthetic method of nutrition. Experimental procedures may duplicate such evolutionary processes. For example, it has been possible to convert certain photosynthetic flagellates into variant strains which lack chlorophyll and photosynthetic capacity. Such animallike variants thrive perfectly well if a ready-made source of carbohydrates is supplied them from the outside. Very probably, experiments of this sort also simulate the ancient natural process by which original flagellate stocks may have given rise to the plant and animal kingdoms.

The dinoflagellates too include types which are either plantlike, or animallike, or both (Fig. 30.5). For example, *Ceratium* is photosynthetic, *Blastodinium* is parasitic in animals, and *Noctiluca* both photosynthesizes and may feed like a free-living animal. Closely related pairs of types with different nutrition are known in this class also.

Most free-living dinoflagellates are marine and form a major component of plankton. One group, which includes *Peridinium* and *Ceratium*, is charac-

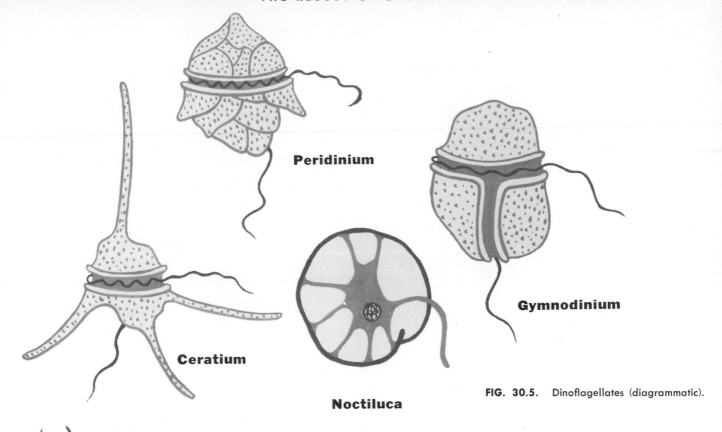

Peridinium

Ceratium

Gymnodinium

Noctiluca

FIG. 30.5.   Dinoflagellates (diagrammatic).

FIG. 30.6.   Zooflagellates.

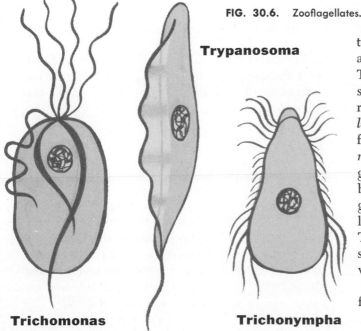

Trypanosoma

Trichomonas

Trichonympha

terized by the presence of an external celluloselike armor, consisting of two or more interlocking plates. These organisms are encircled by a groove which shelters one of the two locomotor flagella. Many marine dinoflagellates are bioluminescent (e.g., *Noctiluca*), and some on occasion proliferate locally in fantastic numbers. For example, the reddish *Gymnodinium* often produces so-called "red tides." As a group, the autotrophic dinoflagellates show certain biochemical resemblances to diatoms and brown algae: they possess chlorophylls *a* and *c* and the yellow-brown pigment **fucoxanthin** (see below; also Table 15). For these reasons, dinoflagellates are sometimes classified as an independent phylum within the plant kingdom.

Flagellates of the class Zoomastigina are either free-living or symbiotic heterotrophs (Fig. 30.6).

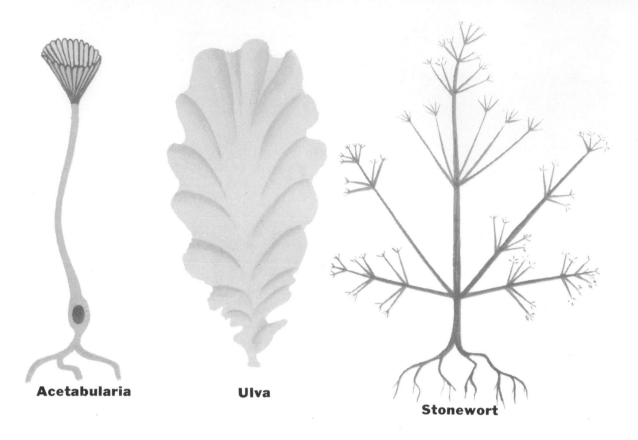

Acetabularia   **Ulva**

Stonewort

FIG. 30.7.   Three types of green algae (diagrammatic).

Among the free-living types are *Proterospongia*, the so-called **collar flagellates,** which feed on debris and minute organisms. Food is trapped within the collar of these cells, and the flagellum then creates a current which sweeps the food toward the cell body, where it is engulfed. Among symbiotic types, some are parasites. For example, different species of *Trypanosoma* live in the bloods of various vertebrates, and one species causes sleeping sickness in man. *Trichonympha* is a mutualistic wood-digesting symbiont in the gut of termites, and *Trichomonas* is a commensal in the gut of man and other vertebrates.

The Plant Kingdom

The true plants include the algae, the fungi, the bryophytes, and the tracheophytes. The various algal groups are undoubtedly related to one another and probably trace back to ancestral plantlike flagellates. Presumably, early green algae in turn gave rise independently to fungi, to bryophytes, and to tracheophytes (see Fig. 29.41).

ALGAE

Algal groups are best distinguished by biochemical features, and only secondarily by criteria of gross structure. As noted in the preceding chapter, algal evolution has been fundamentally an exploitation of the cellular, photosynthetic way of life, and adaptive differences therefore should be expected to be evident largely on a molecular level. Recent attempts to classify algae have taken this into account, and subgroups are now defined on the basis of pigmentation, the chemical composition of the cell wall, and the chemical nature of the principal food-storage compounds (Table 15).

Phylum Chlorophyta: Green Algae (5,000 Species)

Class Chlorophyceae: green algae proper
Chlorella, Pleurococcus, Ulothrix, Ulva, Spirogyra, desmids, *Oedogonium, Acetabularia*

Class Charophyceae: stoneworts
Chara, Nitella

This group of plants is characterized by the possession of chlorophylls *a* and *b* and of various carotenes and xanthophylls. The principal food-storage compound is **starch.** The cell wall is composed of two layers, cellulose being the building material of one. These features are characteristic also of bryophytes and tracheophytes and are a major reason for regarding green algae as ancestral to the terrestrial plants.

Green algae today are exceedingly widespread and are found wherever there is water (Figs. 30.7, 30.8). As noted in several preceding contexts, many green algae grow as single cells (e.g., *Chlorella*), and many are colonial and multicellular (e.g., *Spirogyra, Ulva*). Reproduction is variously vegetative, sporulative, and gametic, and the sexes may be indistinguishable, or more or less fully differentiated (see Chap. 24). An alternation of generations as in terrestrial plants is developed in *Ulva* and various other chlorophytes. Flagellate spores and gametes are common among many green algae.

Special mention may here be made of the **tubular algae,** which may reach lengths of several inches yet consist of single cells. A famous example is *Acetabularia*, found in warm seas. The plant is 2 to 4 in. long and consists of a stalk tipped by an umbrellalike cap. The whole is a single cell, and a single nucleus is present in the stalk. This nucleus eventually divides, and several resulting small nuclei then migrate into the cap, which becomes divided up into several cells. Spores subsequently arise from these cells, and the spores in turn give rise to gametes. After fertilization, the zygote develops into a new plant, in a maturation process lasting several years. Because of its large size and unicellular nature, *Acetabularia* is a favorite organism in research on developmental processes.

Similarly single-celled, but microscopic in size, are the **desmids,** or pond scums. These have beautifully sculptured shapes, and they are characterized

by a median constriction which unites perfectly symmetrical cell halves. The nucleus is located within the constriction, and during fission, the cell divides through the constriction. The sexual process is conjugative, fundamentally as in *Spirogyra*.

Structurally probably the most complicated green algae are the stoneworts, usually found in fresh-water ponds. These multicellular algae resemble miniature trees, with whorls of leaflike branches attached at more or less regular intervals to a stemlike stalk. This stalk is anchored to the ground by

FIG. 30.8. Green algae. Below, close-up of some desmids, or pond scums. Right, upper portions of the stonewort *Chara*. (General Biological Supply House, Inc., Chicago.)

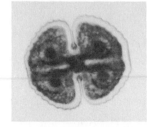

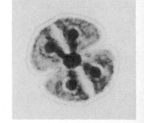

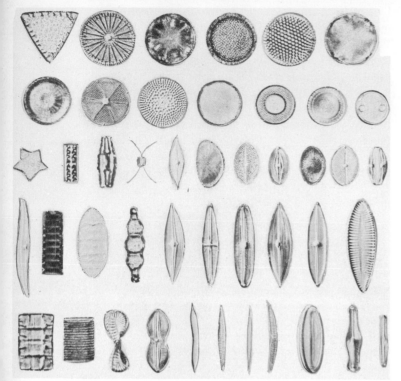

FIG. 30.9. An array of diatoms. A close-up of a single diatom is illustrated in Fig. 5.2. (General Biological Supply House, Inc.)

the chrysophytes, and particularly in the diatoms, foods are stored as *oils*, and in some cases also in the form of a carbohydrate of undetermined composition. Starch is not present. The cell walls are characterized by the presence of silicon compounds (see Table 15).

Chrysophytes other than diatoms have relatively little importance in the economy of nature, but the diatoms more than make up for this. As already pointed out in Chap. 5, diatoms are the most abundant single group of plankton organisms, and as such they support much of the flora and fauna of the oceans and the fresh water (Fig. 30.9, also Fig. 5.2). The life cycle of the diatoms has been outlined in Chap. 24. We may note that the silica shells of dead diatoms make up large tracts of the ocean floor, and that geologically uplifted parts of this floor are the source of *diatomaceous earth*, mined for its abrasive properties. We may note too that much of the petroleum used in industry today is probably derived from the oils synthesized by diatoms of past ages.

Phylum Phaeophyta: Brown Algae (1,000 Species)

These plants possess chlorophylls *a* and *c* and a series of xanthophylls of which some are unique to the group, while others, like the prominent yellow-brown **fucoxanthin,** are not. Food is stored either as **mannitol,** a polysaccharide formed from the 6-carbon sugar *mannose,* or as **laminarin,** a unique polysaccharide formed from glucose and found only in these algae. The cell walls contain an inner layer of cellulose (see Table 15).

Brown algae are exclusively multicellular, and they include the largest and most differentiated of all algae. They are almost entirely marine and include most of the **seaweeds.** The majority of species are found in shallow water and in the intertidal zone. A notable exception is the genus *Sargassum,* the predominant seaweed in the open waters of the Sargasso Sea (see Fig. 5.4). Coastal types are normally attached to rocky bottoms by holdfasts. Ebb tides may expose them to the air for periods of several hours. The most familiar of the brown algae is probably the rockweed *Fucus,* which we have already encountered in the discussion of plant reproduction (Chap. 24; see also Fig. 5.6). Undoubtedly the most spectacular in the seaweed group are the **kelps.**

rootlike processes. The sex organs are distinct and far more complex in structure than in other green algae. As a group, the stoneworts may represent an evolutionary experiment in advancing the basic algal organization in a direction actually taken later by terrestrial plants.

Phylum Chrysophyta: Golden-Brown Algae
Class Xanthophyceae: yellow-green algae
Class Chrysophyceae: yellow-brown algae
Class Diatomeae: diatoms

As indicated by the names of the subgroups, the phylum is characterized by the presence of a variety of pigments. The chief ones are chlorophylls *a* and *c,* carotenes, and xanthophylls, the latter including the yellow-brown pigment **fucoxanthin.** In these respects the chrysophytes to some extent resemble the brown algae, but the food-storage compounds and cell-wall compositions differ in the two groups. In

The giant kelp *Macrocystis* will sometimes attain lengths of more than 100 yd, which makes it longer than a full-grown blue whale. Not quite so long is *Laminaria,* the commonest of the kelps. This genus features alternation of generations, a reproductive pattern probably quite widespread also among other brown algae.

Phylum Rhodophyta: Red Algae (3,000 Species)

The plants of this phylum are characterized by the possession of chlorophylls *a* and *d* and the pigments **phycocyanin** and **phycoerythrin**. The last two are of unique composition and are chemically not the same as similarly named pigments in the blue-green algae. Red algae store food in the form of **flurodean starch,** chemically distinct from the common starch found in other plants. The cell walls are of cellulose (see Table 15).

Red algae are exclusively multicellular and almost exclusively marine (Fig. 30.10). They live in somewhat deeper water than the brown algae, and their red pigment phycoerythrin appears to be an adaptation to their dimmer environment. For phycoerythrin absorbs "blue" light particularly well, and "blue" wavelengths of sunlight actually penetrate deeper into water than "red" wavelengths. Indeed, phycoerythrin has been found to play an important auxiliary role in the photosynthesis of these algae. Red algae are lacier and more delicate than the sturdy brown algae. The latter are adapted to withstand pounding surf, but in deeper water the red algae are not so subject to wave action.

Rhodophytes as a whole are a relatively advanced group. Reproductive patterns are complex, and alternation of generations occurs in a number of types. Some of the red algae are used commercially. The genus *Gelidium* is the source of agar jelly, and *Porphyra, Rhodymenia,* and *Chondrus crispus,* the Irish moss, are among several types prized as vegetables in various parts of the world.

FUNGI

The fungi are saprophytic and variously symbiotic heterotrophs, showing affinities to green algae, and in some cases also to other algal groups. In many classifications, bacteria and slime molds are still in-cluded under fungi, but as noted, justification for this is largely lacking. Fungi are exceedingly common in all environments which contain organic materials. The decay- and disease-causing activities of these plants make them a group of major importance.

FIG. 30.10.   Red algae. *Polysiphonia.* Note the delicate structure. (General Biological Supply House, Inc.)

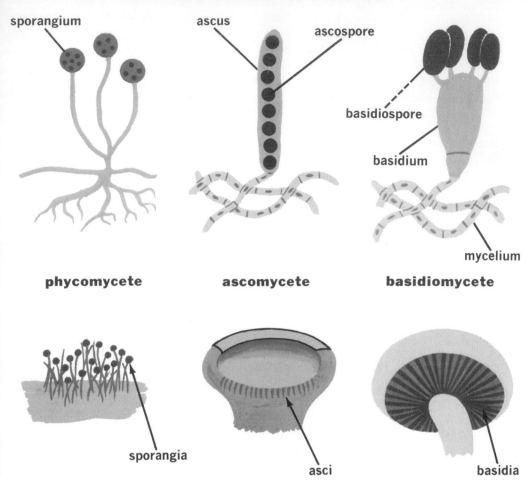

sporangium

ascus

ascospore

basidiospore

basidium

mycelium

FIG. 30.11. Diagram of the spore-producing structures in three classes of fungi. Views of the whole spore-producing organs are shown in bottom row, close-ups in top row.

phycomycete   **ascomycete**   **basidiomycete**

sporangia

asci

basidia

FIG. 30.12. Diagram of the sexual structures of the water mold *Saprolegnia*.

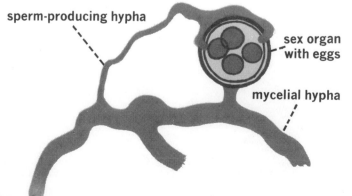

sperm-producing hypha

sex organ with eggs

mycelial hypha

Phylum Mycophyta: Fungi (90,000 Species)
Class Phycomycetes: tubular fungi
  Bread molds: *Rhizopus*
  Water molds: *Saprolegnia*
  Downy mildews, blights, white rusts
Class Ascomycetes: sac fungi
  Molds: *Neurospora, Penicillium*
  Yeasts: *Saccharomyces*
  Powdery mildews, truffles, lichens
Class Basidiomycetes: club fungi
  Mushrooms, toadstools, rusts, smuts, bracket fungi, puffballs, lichens
Class Fungi Imperfecti
  A heterogeneous collection of types which, because of unknown reproductive patterns, cannot yet be assigned to any of the above groups

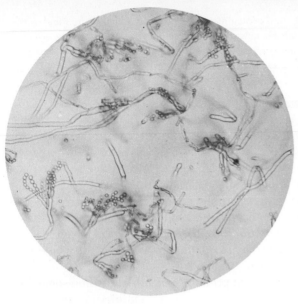

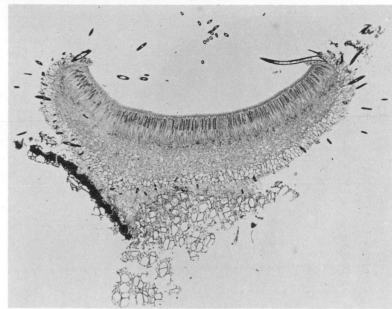

FIG. 30.13. Ascomycetes. Top left: *Penicillium*. Note the ascospores budding off from hyphal filaments. Top right: section through a cup fungus, showing layer of asci just under inner surface of cup. Bottom: detail of layer of asci. Note the spores in each ascus. (Penicillium, General Biological Supply House, Inc.; cup fungus and detail, courtesy of G. H. Conant, Triarch Products.)

As already noted in Chap. 8, the basic unit of fungal structure is a **hypha,** a tubular, multinucleate filament which may be branched. A mass of meshed hyphae forms a **mycelium,** and this constitutes the main body of a fungus. Mycelia may be underground, but growing from them are spore-forming **fruiting bodies** of varied construction, and these are the exposed parts of the fungi (Fig. 30.11).

The class Phycomycetes is probably related to green algae. Some members of the tubular fungi are unicellular, but most are multinucleate syncitia, like the bread mold *Rhizopus,* which has been described in Chap. 24.

Water molds like *Saprolegnia* form dense whitish growths on the bodies of aquatic animals, and the fruiting bodies of the water molds then produce aquatic, flagellate spores. Unlike *Rhizopus,* in which the sexes are indistinguishable, *Saprolegnia* forms hyphal branches producing distinct eggs and others carrying sperm nuclei at the tip (Fig. 30.12).

The sac fungi (Fig. 30.13) are so called because

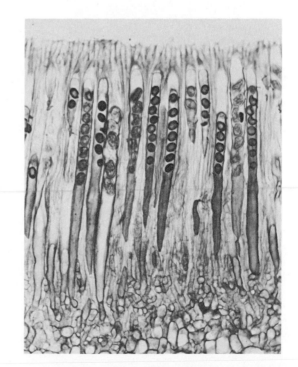

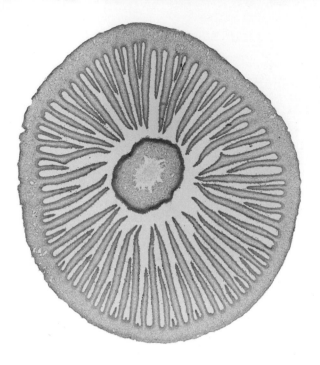

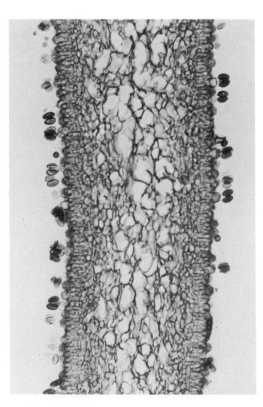

FIG. 30.14. Top: section through the cap of a mushroom, showing the arrangement of the gills. Bottom: close-up of a gill. Note the mycelial meshwork in the interior, and the spores, attached to basidia and projecting from the surface. (General Biological Supply House, Inc.)

their spores are manufactured in sacs, or **asci.** Each ascus usually arises from a zygote which forms within the mycelium, and such a sac then typically produces eight spores. Ascomycetes are almost exclusively terrestrial. The hyphae of most are divided up into distinct cells and may become thick and fleshy, as in truffles. Some of the ascomycetes are degenerate and unicellular, like the yeasts. Under certain conditions, the cell content of given species of yeasts may divide into four spores, the whole representing a modified ascus.

Sac fungi produce many diseases, and some, like *Penicillium*, are sources of antibiotics which cure disease. Ascomycete molds also produce the characteristic flavor of Roquefort, Camembert, and other kinds of cheeses. As noted in Chap. 4, symbiotic combinations of fungi and algae form **lichens.** The fungal members of these combinations in most cases are ascomycetes, and the photosynthetic members, blue-green and green algae. As a group, the sac fungi show no obvious relation to the Phycomycetes, and some authorities trace their ancestry to the red algae.

The Basidiomycetes are believed to have evolved from the Ascomycetes, and they are structurally the most complex of all of the fungi. They are characterized by a specialized spore-producing unit, the **basidium.** This is an enlarged, club-shaped, terminal cell of a hypha, from which grow four spores. The whole is believed to represent a modified ascus (see Fig. 30.11). Many basidium-bearing hyphae may be combined into a large, stalked fruiting body, familiarly known as a mushroom. In many cases, the cap of a mushroom has radially arranged plates on its underside, called gills. On these, the spore-bearing basidia are exposed to the external environment (Fig. 30.14).

Not all basidiomycetes form mushrooms, however. Among those which do not are the parasitic **rusts,** distinguished by possibly the most complicated life cycles of all organisms (see Chap. 24).

Smuts too are largely parasitic. Special mention may be made of the **puffballs** and **stinkhorns,** in which the basidia are not exposed to the air, as in mushrooms, but are initially embedded within the fruiting body. This body eventually breaks open, and the mass of spores is then extruded. Giant puffballs are known to reach diameters of about 5 yd, and they probably have the distinction of being reproductively the most prolific organisms of all. A single giant puffball may manufacture as many as 100 *trillion* spores. It has been estimated that if each of these were to grow into a mature plant, a mass of tissue close to 1,000 times the size of the earth would be produced.

BRYOPHYTES

As noted earlier, these "amphibia" of the plant kingdom are undoubtedly derived from the green algae. Of all plant types today, bryophytes are probably the least important from an economic standpoint. But they have considerable biological interest, for they show how a primitive water-requiring plant can adapt successfully to a terrestrial existence.

Phylum Bryophyta: Moss Plants (25,000 Species)
Class Musci: mosses
  Sphagnum, Mnium
Class Hepaticae: liverworts
  Marchantia, Sphaerocarpus
Class Anthocerotae: hornworts
  Anthoceros

The life cycle of mosses, outlined in Chap. 24, serves to characterize the phylum as a whole. None of the bryophytes is marine; some live in fresh water; and most are terrestrial. They are all rather small plants, requiring moist, shady environments. Alternation of generations is well established, and the gametophyte phase is dominant. Mosses are characterized by more or less radially symmetrical, upright gametophytes, bearing leaflike blades. In liverworts, on the other hand, the gametophyte is flat and ground-hugging and resembles a notched leaf with midribs. Hornworts are flat and prostrate too, but the gametophyte is not notched, and it does not have midribs (Fig. 30.15).

Bryophytes as a whole have remarkable powers of regeneration, and many have developed a very specialized method of vegetative reproduction.

FIG. 30.15. Bryophytes (diagrammatic). Representative individuals of the three classes are drawn. See also Chap. 24 for other illustrations of bryophytes.

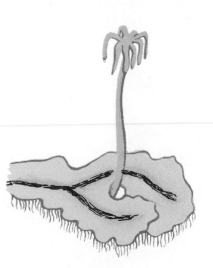

mosses   **liverworts**   **hornworts**

This involves **gemmae,** which are localized, often cup-shaped outgrowths on the surface of the gametophyte (Fig. 30.16). If such a gemma is dislodged from the parent and is deposited on suitable ground, it may develop into a whole new gametophyte. Special mention may be made of *Sphaerocarpus,* in which distinct sex chromosomes of the *XY* type are known to exist. Sex determination here is as in mammals and insects.

In the past, the hornworts have been regarded as the most primitive members of the phylum, and the mosses as the most advanced. Morphological considerations, however, suggest that the first mosses may have been ancestral to the whole phylum, the three modern classes being the result of radiation from mosslike ancestors.

TRACHEOPHYTES

In terms of numbers of species, these true land plants form the bulk of the plant kingdom. The unifying features of the group are the presence of specialized vascular tissues, namely, xylem and phloem; a dominant, upstanding sporophyte generation; and, in most groups, a more or less clear-cut subdivision of the sporophytes into roots, stems, and leaves.

FIG. 30.16. The liverwort *Marchantia,* showing gemma cups. (Carolina Biological Supply Co.)

Four major subgroups are recognized, each of subphylum rank. As noted in Chap. 29, fossil data suggest that one of the subphyla, the psilopsids, may be ancestral and that the other three have radiated independently from early psilopsid stock.

Phylum Tracheophyta: Vascular Plants
Subphylum Psilopsida: *Psilotum* (2 species)
　　　　　　　　　　　Tmesipteris (1 species)
Subphylum Lycopsida
　Club mosses: *Lycopodium* (100 species)
　　　　　　　　Selaginella (500 species)
Subphylum Sphenopsida
　Horsetails: *Equisetum* (25 species)
Subphylum Pteropsida
　　Class Filicineae: ferns (10,000 species)
　　Class Gymnospermiae: conifers, cycads, ginkgoes (600 species)
　　Class Angiospermiae: flowering plants (200,000 species)
　　　Subclass Dicotyledones
　　　Subclass Monocotyledones

The first three subphyla above, spectacularly successful in the past, today are little more than evolutionary relics. Of the **psilopsids,** only three species now remain, and they still feature characteristics remarkably similar to those of their fossil ancestors. *Psilotum* grows with forked branches, very small scalelike, paired leaves, and bulbous spore cases between the members of each pair of leaves. The spores are all alike, as in modern ferns. The life cycle resembles that of a fern, and this is true also for lycopsids and sphenopsids.

Lycopsids, or club mosses, are more widely represented, and the ground pine *Lycopodium* in particular is still relatively common (Fig. 30.17). This lycopsid possesses forked stems covered with small, somewhat needle-shaped, spirally arranged leaves and terminal cones containing the spore cases. In this genus all spores are alike, but *Selaginella* produces distinct microspores and megaspores, an evolutionary development paralleling that of the seed plants.

The living **sphenopsids,** or horsetails, all belong

FIG. 30.17.   Living lycopsids. The ground pine *Lycopodium* is shown at left, the club moss *Selaginella* at right. (Brooklyn Botanic Garden photos.)

to the single genus called *Equisetum*. This particular group is characterized by small scalelike leaves, arranged in whorls at the nodes of hollow stems. Spore-bearing cones grow at the tips of the stems. The spores are all alike in modern horsetails, but some fossil forms are known to have manufactured micro- and megaspores.

The **pteropsids** today include the most abundant and most important of the terrestrial plants. An ancestral pteropsid group probably arose from early psilopsids, and subsequently branched into two main lines, one leading to the modern ferns, the other to the first seed plants. The latter eventually gave rise to the modern gymnosperms and angiosperms (see Fig. 29.41). All three pteropsid classes evolved large leaves, very distinct from the foliation patterns in the other tracheophyte subphyla. Undoubtedly, this contributed greatly to the past and present success of the pteropsids. Gymnosperms and angiosperms in addition developed seeds, and we have already seen in Chap. 24 how this enhanced their adaptation to terrestrial conditions (Fig. 30.18).

A very abundant group in Paleozoic times, **ferns** today inhabit few areas other than tropical rain forests, where many still reach the dimensions of trees. The far smaller ferns of temperate regions feature simple roots, which extend from horizontal stems growing on, or just under, the soil surface. As noted in Chap. 24, the life cycle of ferns passes through an independent, green gametophyte stage, and the dominant sporophyte forms spores which in most cases are all alike. In a few groups, however, distinct microspores and megaspores are produced. The xylem of ferns is relatively unspecialized, consisting of tracheids rather than continuous vessels without cross-walls (see Chap. 8). This is true also of gymnosperm xylem.

Gymnosperms were undoubtedly the most ancient of the seed plants. The first representatives of the class were rather fernlike in appearance, and some of these fossil gymnosperms are actually called, rather misleadingly, "seed ferns." The living cycads still resemble ferns superficially. Ginkgoes are another example of a once abundant group, now reduced to a single species. The most common gymnosperms today are the *conifers*, of which the pines, firs, and spruces are familiar examples. As outlined in Chap. 24, the gametophyte phase of gymnosperms is dependent and nongreen and is parasitic on the sporophyte phase. Spores are borne on cones or conelike structures in the sporophytes of all gymnosperm groups, although, as just noted, not all gymnosperms are classified as conifers. Cycads and ginkgoes still possess *flagellate* sperms, a primitive feature reminiscent of ferns. As we have found in Chap. 24, after pollination in conifers, a pollen tube carries the sperm nucleus to the egg. In cycads and ginkgoes, on the other hand, pollen tubes do not form and the sperms *swim* to the eggs, as in ferns.

Elaborate pollen tubes are characteristic also of the **angiosperms,** the most varied and most abundant group of all plants. They differ from other pteropsids principally in the possession of flowers and fruits, in the extreme reduction of the gametophyte phase, and in the presence of uninterrupted xylem vessels (see Fig. 30.18). The exact ancestry of angiosperms is unknown, but it is generally believed that they arose from early gymnospermlike seed plants. Thus they are the most recent of all plants. However, by virtue of their adaptive innovations and the massive aid of insects, they have become so successful that they have replaced all other terrestrial plants to a very large extent.

FIG. 30.18.   The subphyla of tracheophytes and the classes of pteropsids. The main diagnostic features of each group are shown.

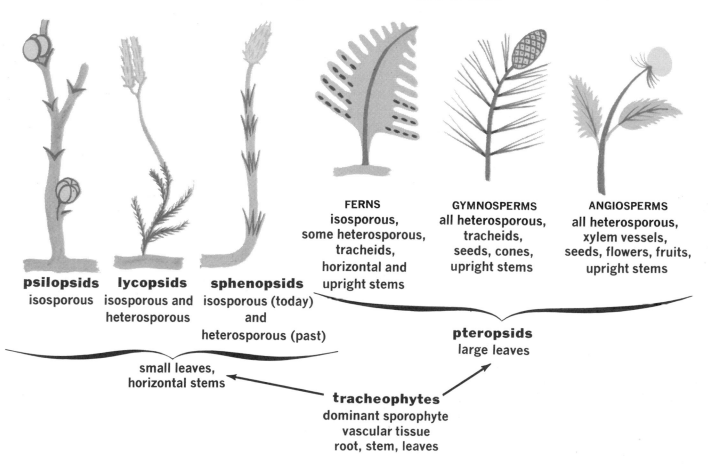

FERNS
isosporous,
some heterosporous,
tracheids,
horizontal and
upright stems

GYMNOSPERMS
all heterosporous,
tracheids,
seeds, cones,
upright stems

ANGIOSPERMS
all heterosporous,
xylem vessels,
seeds, flowers, fruits,
upright stems

psilopsids
isosporous

lycopsids
isosporous and
heterosporous

sphenopsids
isosporous (today)
and
heterosporous (past)

pteropsids
large leaves

small leaves,
horizontal stems

tracheophytes
dominant sporophyte
vascular tissue
root, stem, leaves

Flowering plants today inhabit virtually all environments except the open ocean. They include aquatic types, parasitic types, saprophytic types, and partly carnivorous types. They enrich the world with color and scent, but they also exude poison and stench. Some survive only a single growing season; others live for centuries. Some complete an entire generation, from seed to seed, within a few days; others require decades. Only the algae and the heterotrophic plants collectively approach the success and diversity of the angiosperms. And we may note here that heterotrophs in general, plant or animal, owe their continued existence largely to angiosperms. For these plants are the essential food producers for all terrestrial life.

The class of angiosperms is subdivided into the Monocotyledones and the Dicotyledones. As noted in Chap. 8, a cotyledon is a food-containing leaflike structure within the seed. Monocots possess one such seed leaf; dicots, two. A corn kernel and a peanut seed illustrate this difference. Monocots also feature flowers in which the petals and other structures occur in threes or in multiples of three; leaves which have smooth edges and parallel veins; and xylem and phloem formed into vascular bundles, which are scattered through the stem. Dicots, on the other hand, possess flower parts in fours or fives or multiples of these; leaves which are net-veined and have variously notched contours; and vascular tissues arranged into a compact core or ring within the stem (Fig. 30.19).

The dicots are the more abundant group, and they may be more primitive. They include virtually all familiar trees and shrubs, as well as roses, strawberries, peaches, cabbages, cotton, tobacco, cucumbers, dandelions, beans, and innumerable other familiar plants. But plants classified as monocots have at least equal economic importance, for in this group are wheat, corn, rice, barley, sugar cane, and all other grasses, as well as date and coconut palms, pineapples, bananas, and orchids.

FIG. 30.19. Diagram illustrating the structural differences between monocots and dicots.

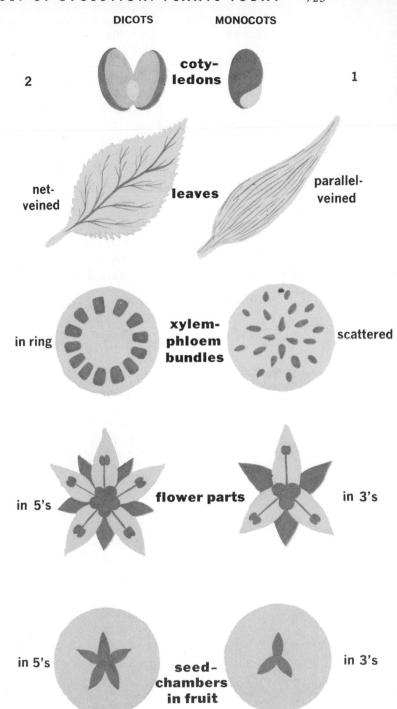

1. Describe the structural characteristics of bacteria. Review here the various autotrophic and heterotrophic patterns of life encountered among bacteria and their role in global nitrogen turnover.

2. Describe the structural characteristics of blue-green algae. In which respects do these organisms resemble the bacteria? Review the life cycle of a slime mold.

3. What are the different classes of Mastigophora? Describe the common diagnostic features of the phylum as a whole and the special characteristics which distinguish the classes. What nutritional patterns are encountered among each of the flagellate classes? Why are dinoflagellates sometimes regarded as a separate phylum?

4. Review the (a) pigments, (b) food-storage compounds, (c) cell-wall compounds, encountered in each plant phylum. On the basis of this, what evolutionary affinities among the phyla appear to be suggested?

5. Describe the chief structural characteristics of (a) green, (b) golden-brown, (c) brown, (d) red algae. To which environments is each of these groups adapted? Which phyla contain (a) unicellular, (b) multicellular types? Review the reproductive patterns of each group. For each phylum, give as many names of representative genera as you can.

6. Describe the basic structure of all fungi. What diagnostic features distinguish the different classes? What representative kinds of fungi are included in the different classes? What makes a yeast cell a fungus rather than a bacterium? Review the reproductive patterns of fungi.

7. Describe the basic structure of all bryophytes. What diagnostic features distinguish the different classes? What are gemmae? Review the life cycle of a bryophyte. How many species of bryophytes, and of each other plant phylum, are known to exist?

8. Describe the group characteristics of (a) the phylum Tracheophyta, (b) the tracheophyte subphyla, (c) the pteropsid classes, and (d) the angiosperm subclasses.

9. Review the general structure, and the reproductive patterns, of psilopsids, lycopsids, and sphenopsids. How are these groups related historically, and how abundant are they today? Review the structure and life cycle of (a) ferns, (b) gymnosperms. In what respects are cycads and ginkgoes primitive?

10. Review the structure and life cycle of angiosperms. Describe the distinction between monocots and dicots. Name representative plants of each subclass.

The references cited last at the end of Chap. 8, and also the additional ones at the end of Chap. 24, may be consulted for more detailed discussions of various plant groups. The books and articles below supplement this subject matter further.

Sporne, K. R.: The Phylogenetic Classification of Angiosperms, *Biol. Revs.,* vol. 31, 1956.

Jones, G. N.: On the Number of Species of Plants, *Sci. Monthly,* vol. 72, 1951.

Smith, G. M.: "Cryptogamic Botany," 2d ed., McGraw-Hill, 1955.

Milner, H. W.: Algae as Food, *Sci. American,* vol. 189, 1953.

Weiss, F. J.: The Useful Algae, *Sci. American,* vol. 187, 1952.

Chapman, V. F.: "Seaweeds and Their Uses," Methuen, 1950.

Tiffany, L. H.: "Algae, the Grass of Many Waters," Charles C Thomas, 1939.

Quisenberry, K. S.: The World's Principal Food Plants, *Sci. Monthly,* vol. 79, 1954.

Mangelsdorf, P. C.: The Mystery of Corn, *Sci. American,* vol. 183, 1950.

————: Wheat, *Sci. American,* vol. 189, 1953.

Salaman, R. N.: The Social Influence of the Potato, *Sci. American,* vol. 187, 1952.

Schery, R. W.: "Plants for Man," Prentice-Hall, 1952.

Platt, R.: "Our Flowering World," Dodd, Mead, 1947.

31

THE RESULT OF EVOLUTION: ANIMALS TODAY

O F THE TWO DOZEN OR SO ANIMAL PHYLA now recognized, about half include mostly rare animals of more or less limited distribution. These have relatively little importance to man, and in the account below we shall treat them rather briefly. The remaining phyla include the majority of animals, and the discussion of these will follow the pattern adopted in the preceding chapter.

It should already have become apparent that the border line between animals and plants is neither sharp nor unequivocal. In general, animals are heterotrophs, most are motile, and their cells typically do not possess cellulose walls. Moreover, animals on the whole react far more quickly and variedly to environmental stimuli than plants, their metabolic rates tend to be higher, and multicellular types contain a greater variety of highly differentiated cells and tissues. Unicellular types will occupy our attention first.

Protozoa

Although these "first animals" are typically single-celled, most possess a very highly differentiated body. A cuticle or secreted shell protects the exterior, and in given species there may be up to several hundred nuclei internally. Protozoa are classified on the basis of their different locomotor devices. In the past, each major group has been ranked as a class within a single protozoan phylum, but today the groups are properly considered sufficiently distinct to be accorded independent phylum rank. In some classifications, the phylum Mastigophora is included under protozoa. As already noted, whether or not flagellates should be so included, they are undoubtedly ancestral to protozoa as a whole.

The number of existing protozoan species has been underestimated fairly consistently. Figures often quoted are in the order of 15,000, but there are known to be more than that many foraminiferan species alone. Moreover, most other animal species harbor at least one more or less specific protozoan

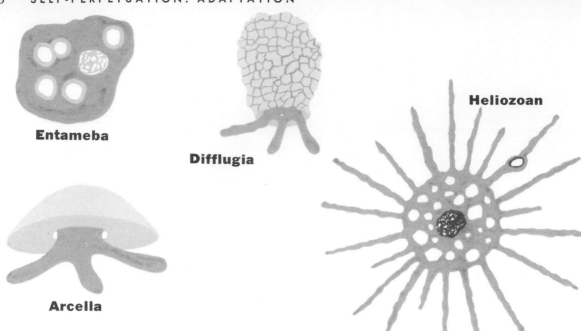

Entameba

Difflugia

Heliozoan

Arcella

FIG. 31.1. A variety of sacrodine protozoa. See also Figs. 31.2, 31.3, and 9.6.

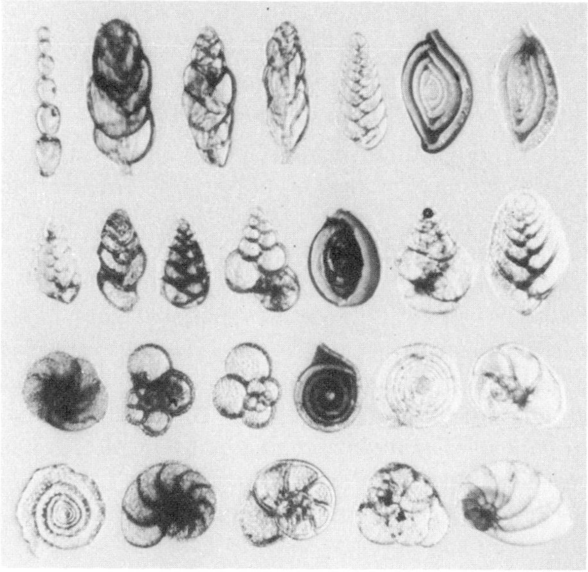

FIG. 31.2. Foraminifera. The shells of these sarcodine protozoa are made of calcium salts.

parasite, which means that protozoan species could well number in the hundreds of thousands. As a conservative figure, at least 100,000 species of protozoa may be presumed to exist.

Phylum Sarcodina: Amoebae, Foraminifera, Radiolaria

These animals (Fig. 31.1) move and feed by means of **pseudopods.** Some, like the various species of *Ameba* (see Figs. 3.9, 9.6), are naked cells, and these include a good many parasitic forms. For example, *Entameba histolytica* causes amebic dysentery in man.

Other sarcodines enclose their bodies in secreted shells. A chitinous housing is present in *Arcella,* the animal extruding pseudopods through an opening in the shell. *Difflugia* cements tiny sand particles to a chitinous envelope. The **foraminifera** manufacture calcareous shells of many different forms, all resembling tiny snail shells (Fig. 31.2). Pseudopods are extruded through holes in these shells, hence the name hole bearers. As noted in

Chap. 5, foraminiferan shells may accumulate in given tracts of ocean floor in such numbers that they form the predominant bottom deposit in such regions. This is true also of **radiolarian** shells, which consist of silica (Fig. 31.3). Foraminiferan deposits may become transformed into chalk, radiolarian deposits into flint. When either of these is uplifted geologically, they may contribute massively to the formation of land (e.g., the chalk cliffs of Dover).

Phylum Ciliophora

Class Ciliata: *Paramecium, Stentor, Euplotes, Vorticella*

Class Suctoria: *Podophrya, Tokophrya*

These protozoa (Fig. 31.4; also Fig. 3.14) move and feed by means of **cilia,** arranged in most species into orderly rows. The phylum is characterized also by the presence of *two* kinds of nuclei in each animal. The so-called **micronucleus** functions principally in sexual processes, and the **macronucleus** controls metabolism, development, and most other cellular processes. Several of both kinds of nuclei may be present in a single animal. This unique nuclear differentiation is paralleled by a very high degree of cytoplasmic differentiation. For example, ciliates typically possess permanent mouths, excretory vacuoles, contractile fibrils, neural fibrils, holdfasts, and locomotor apparatus.

Some ciliates are colonial and sessile, and many are parasitic. The class Suctoria comprises animals which are ciliated and free-swimming only during

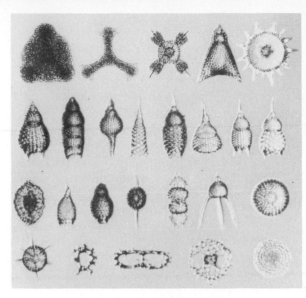

FIG. 31.3. Radiolaria. The shells of these sarcodine protozoa are made of silicon compounds. (General Biological Supply House, Inc.)

FIG. 31.4. Various ciliophorans. The photo shows *Paramecium* stained to reveal the macronucleus (large dark central body) and the micronucleus (small dark body partly overlapping the macronucleus on the right). Ciliates are also shown in Figs. 3.14 and 7.15. (Carolina Biological Supply Co.)

Didinium   Euplotes   Spirostomum   Vorticella

young stages. Adults are sessile and unciliated, and they feed by means of tentaclelike protrusions, which capture and suck up the protoplasm of other protozoa.

Phylum Sporozoa: Plasmodium

All sporozoa are parasitic. They are characterized by wholly **passive locomotion** and by very complex life cycles which often involve multiple hosts. The most familiar genus is undoubtedly *Plasmodium,* various species of which cause malaria in man and other mammals and in birds. In human malaria, the *Anopheles* mosquito is the specific intermediate host of the protozoan parasite (Fig. 31.5).

Diploblasts

As outlined in Chap. 29, the multicellular diploblastic animals pass through a two-layered developmental stage, and their adult bodies are fundamentally two-layered also. Three phyla are included in this group, the sponges, the coelenterates, and the comb jellies.

Phylum Porifera: Sponges (15,000 Species)

Class Calcarea: chalk sponges
Class Hexactinellida: glass sponges
Class Demispongiae: horn sponges

All sponges are sessile as adults, but their larvae are ciliated and free-swimming. The larvae are gastrulalike in structure, but when they settle and become adult sponges, the neatly layered arrangement of the cells becomes greatly obscured. Nevertheless, the adults possess different cell types on the outside and the inside (Fig. 31.6).

The outer cells are of several kinds, the most distinctive being those which secrete the intracellular **spicules,** or skeletal elements. These have different characteristic shapes in different species, and they are the basis of sponge classification. In chalk sponges, the spicules consist of calcium salts; in glass sponges, of silica; and in horny sponges, of complex organic materials.

The most characteristic cells on the inside of a sponge are the so-called **collar cells,** which are flagellate and remarkably resemble the collar flagellates of the phylum Mastigophora. These cells line a sys-

FIG. 31.5. The life cycle of the sporozoan malarial parasite *Plasmodium.* The successive stages of the cycle are indicated by numbers.

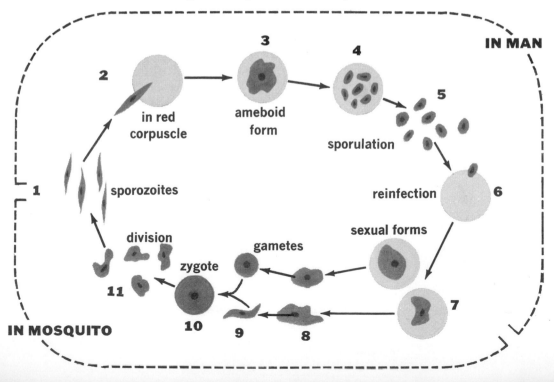

IN MAN

2   in red corpuscle

3   ameboid form

4

5   sporulation

6   reinfection

sexual forms   7

1   sporozoites

division

11

zygote   10   gametes

9   8

IN MOSQUITO

tem of interconnecting channels, which communicates with the environment through entry and exit pores located on the surface of the sponge body. The collar cells create a water current which flows through the entry pores into the channel system and out through the exit pores. Food present in the current is trapped by the collar cells.

All sponges are aquatic, and most are marine in habitat. As a group they have changed very little since Cambrian times, an indication that they are very well adapted to a continuously available way of life. See Chaps. 9, 17, and 22 for other data.

Phylum Coelenterata (10,000 Species)

Class Anthozoa: sea anemones, corals
Class Scyphozoa: jellyfishes
Class Hydrozoa: *Obelia, Hydra, Physalia*

Coelenterates are characterized by a digestive cavity with a single opening; by tentacles which surround this opening; and by **sting cells,** unique to the phylum coelenterata, located on the tentacles. The body wall consists of an outer ectodermal cell layer containing sensory cells of various sorts, and an inner endodermal layer containing digestive ameboid cells. Between these two cell layers is a gelatinous secretion of varying thickness, the **mesogloea.** In it is embedded a simply constructed nerve net (Fig. 31.7).

The gastrulalike larva of coelenterates is ciliated and free-swimming, and the adult is either a sessile **polyp** or a free-swimming, bell-shaped **medusa.** Hydrozoa characteristically pass through alternate polyp and medusa stages. In *Obelia,* for example, the larva settles and grows into a colony of polyps. Most of these are feeding polyps. But some develop as specialized reproductive polyps, which bud off medusae by vegetative means. The free-swimming medusae eventually differentiate sex organs, and after fertilization, the zygote becomes a larva which gives rise to a new polyp (Fig. 31.9).

In Scyphozoa, the polyp phase is greatly reduced. For example, in the common jellyfish *Aurelia,* the larva settles and grows directly into a single reproductive polyp which buds off medusae. These develop sex organs and produce new larvae. In Anthozoa, on the contrary, it is the medusa phase

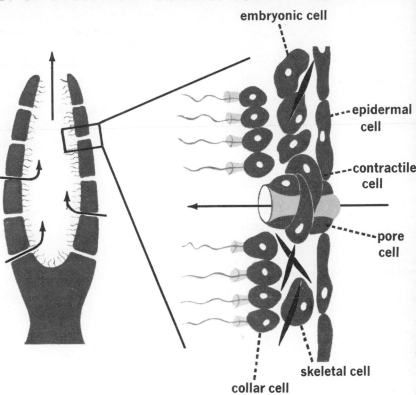

FIG. 31.6. The organization of a simple sponge (diagrammatic). Left: cross-sectional view showing the flow direction of water. Right: detail of a portion of the body wall.

which is reduced, and indeed that phase is absent altogether: the sessile adult is a feeding polyp which develops sex organs. After fertilization a larva forms, which settles and grows into a new adult polyp (see Figs. 31.8, 9.4). Such polyps may also reproduce vegetatively, bisecting lengthwise (see Chap. 22).

Whether sessile or free-swimming, coelenterates are efficient carnivores, which catch crustacea, small fish, and other prey by means of tentacles and sting cells. Most genera are marine, but some, like the familiar *Hydra,* live in fresh water (see Fig. 26.11). Note that *Hydra* is a highly specialized form in which the characteristic hydrozoan life cycle does not occur. In particular, a medusa phase is suppressed. Hydrozoa also include specialized colonial types like *Physalia,* the Portuguese man-of-war, characterized by several different kinds of polyps of

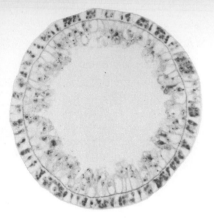

FIG. 31.7. Cross section through the body of a hydra. Note the two layers of cells, ectoderm on the outside, endoderm on the inside. The cavity enclosed by endoderm is the alimentary sac. (Ward's Natural Science Establishment, Inc.)

FIG. 31.8. The life cycles of coelenterates. Polyp and medusa generations alternate in Hydrozoa like *Obelia;* polyp phases are suppressed in Scyphozoa like *Aurelia* and other jellyfish; and medusa phases are suppressed in Anthozoa like sea anemones.

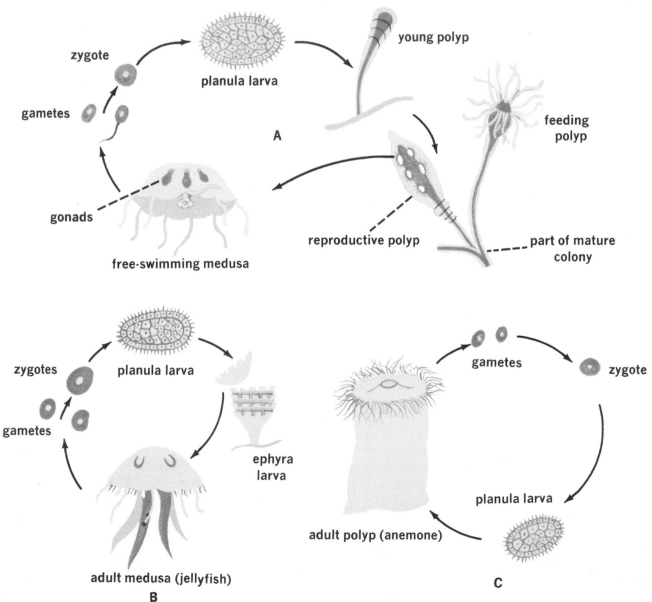

zygote

planula larva

young polyp

feeding polyp

gametes

gonads

reproductive polyp

part of mature colony

free-swimming medusa

A

zygotes

planula larva

gametes

ephyra larva

adult medusa (jellyfish)

B

gametes

zygote

planula larva

adult polyp (anemone)

C

FIG. 31.9. *Obelia.* Left: a colony of polyps. Note feeding polyps with tentacles, and club-shaped reproductive polyps. The latter produce medusae. Right: a medusa. Dark region in center is the mouth. Note the four sex organs. Other coelenterates are illustrated in Fig. 22.8. (Carolina Biological Supply Co.)

 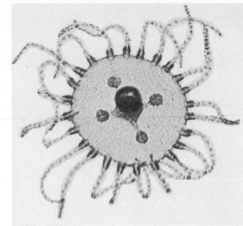

distinct form and function (see Fig. 4.8). Anthozoa manufacture often very elaborate exoskeletons of calcium salts, and the group includes the builders of coral reefs and atolls.

Phylum Ctenophora: Comb Jellies (100 Species)

In some respects these animals resemble coelenterate medusae, but in others they are quite unique (Fig. 31.10). The body is transparent, two-layered, and contains a bulky gelatinous mesogloea. The digestive cavity leads from a single opening into eight pouches, and we may note that the number eight is of considerable significance in the phylum. For example, there are also eight nerve cords, which underlie eight external rows of **comb plates**, the locomotor organs of the animals. Ctenophores possess a pair of tentacles, which are not equipped with sting cells and which may be withdrawn into ectodermal pouches. All ctenophores are marine and hermaphroditic, and many species are bioluminescent.

Acoelomates

As noted in Chap. 29, animals in this group are triploblastic and bilateral, and the mesoderm does not develop coelomic cavities. Three groups of worms belong in this category: the flatworms, the proboscis worms, and the spiny-headed worms.

Phylum Platyhelminthes: Flatworms (10,000 Species)
Class Turbellaria: free-living flatworms
Class Trematoda: flukes
Class Cestoda: tapeworms

As a group, flatworms are distinguished by a dorsoventrally compressed body and by a digestive system which resembles that of coelenterates; that is, a single opening serves as both mouth and anus, and the digestive cavity is lined with ameboid cells, which engulf small food particles and digest them intracellularly.

The most familiar free-living flatworms are the **planarians**, of which *Dugesia* is a good example

FIG. 31.10. Ctenophores, photo and diagram of structure. (Photo, General Biological Supply House, Inc.)

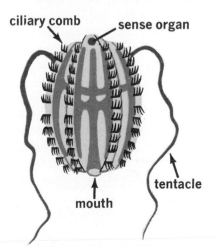 

ciliary comb   sense organ

mouth   tentacle

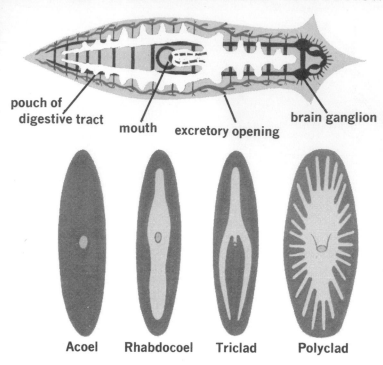

pouch of
digestive tract
mouth   excretory opening   brain ganglion

Acoel   Rhabdocoel   Triclad   Polyclad

FIG. 31.11. Top: the internal structure of a planarian. Bottom: the types of free-living flatworms, based on the structure of the alimentary cavity.

to consider. The body here has definite front and rear ends, but the digestive opening is located in the middle, on the underside. An eversible **pharynx** breaks larger food into particles suitable for ingestion. A pair of **eyes** is present at the head end, and the head also contains a concentration of nervous tissue, the **brain ganglion.** From it lead a pair of **ventral nerve cords,** which are interconnected at more or less regular intervals by transverse strands of nerves. The whole has the appearance of a ladder (Fig. 31.11). Circulatory and breathing systems are not present in flatworms, but planarians possess excretory and elaborate reproductive systems. The animals are hermaphroditic. Locomotion is accomplished by undulating muscular movements which result in swimming, or by the beat of cilia on the underside of the body, which propel the animal on a solid surface.

Turbellaria are largely free-living scavengers,

found in both ocean and fresh water. The **acoels** are a group in which a digestive cavity is lacking and in which food is introduced from the alimentary opening directly into endodermal digestive cells. These animals are probably the most primitive of the flatworms. In **rhabdocoels,** the digestive cavity is straight and unbranched, and in **triclads,** to which the planarians belong, the digestive cavity forms three pouches, one pointing anteriorly, two posteriorly. The largest of the turbellarians are the exclusively marine **polyclads,** distinguished by multiple-branched digestive cavities and by unique, free-swimming larvae (see Fig. 31.11).

The two remaining classes of flatworms are exclusively parasitic, and of considerable general importance to man. We have already discussed their characteristic life cycles in Chap. 4.

Phylum Nemertinea: Proboscis Worms (600 Species)

These worms resemble flatworms in embryonic development and general structure, but they are unique in several important respects. First, they possess separate anterior mouth and posterior anal openings, connected by a straight alimentary tube. Second, they possess a simple closed circulatory system, blood moving forward in a dorsal vessel, backward in a ventral vessel. And third, they possess a unique and identifying proboscis apparatus. This is a long tubular organ lying inside a cavity above the mouth opening. It can be extruded rapidly and wrapped around suitable animal prey. In some cases, the tip of the proboscis contains a pointed stylet which pierces the body of a victim, and a gland which secretes poison into the wound made by the stylet (Fig. 31.12). Proboscis worms occur in the ocean as well as in fresh water.

Phylum Acanthocephala: Spiny-headed Worms (300 Species)

All animals of this phylum are parasitic in vertebrates. They are so named because the head bears a retractile proboscis armed with hooks (Fig. 31.12). By means of this structure, the parasite clings to the intestinal lining of the host. Spiny-headed worms are without digestive systems, and they absorb food directly through their cuticles, like tapeworms.

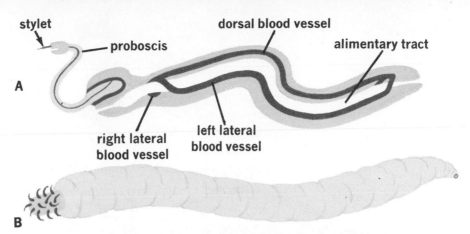

stylet

proboscis

dorsal blood vessel

alimentary tract

A

right lateral
blood vessel

left lateral
blood vessel

B

FIG. 31.12. Top: a proboscis worm, showing proboscis apparatus, one-way alimentary tract, and the primitive circulatory system. Bottom: an acanthocephalan. Both illustrations are diagrammatic.

Pseudocoelomates

The unifying features of this group of seven phyla are the reduction of mesoderm to localized regions and the presence of a pseudocoel, a body cavity lined with ectoderm and endoderm, not mesoderm. Also, cell boundaries in many cases disappear in the adult, and the animals become syncitial. The first six of the seven phyla below comprise worm-shaped animals, and most of these exhibit a tendency toward superficial, external segmentation. In some classifications, these six phyla are considered to be classes within the single phylum *Aschelminthes.* But the group is actually relatively heterogeneous, and the ancestry of many is obscure. Independent phylum rank for each major type is therefore justified. The pseudocoelomates as a whole include some of the rarest and least known, as well as some of the most abundant, of all animals.

Phylum Rotifera (1,500 Species)

These microscopic animals are very largely free-living, and they are found predominantly in fresh water, where they are exceedingly common.

They possess an identifying anterior crown of cilia surrounding the mouth, hence the name wheel bearers for the phylum. The cilia are the organs of locomotion, and they also create food currents. The mouth leads into a muscular grinding organ, the **mastax,** and then into a straight intestine which terminates at the anus. At the hind end are located ce-

ment organs, which anchor the animal during feeding and which also make possible a second form of locomotion resembling caterpillarlike creeping. The nervous system consists mainly of a brain ganglion dorsal to the mouth and of a series of nerve cords leading away from it. Rotifers possess excretory systems, but circulatory and breathing systems are absent (Fig. 31.13).

One of the long-known peculiarities of these animals is that the number of cells in late embryos, and the number of nuclei in adults, is constant for each species and that the nuclei occupy fixed positions in each individual. The body plan of each species may thus be mapped out nucleus by nucleus.

During spring and summer, female rotifers produce eggs which develop into new females parthenogenetically, that is, without being fertilized. The new females in turn reproduce parthenogenetically, and many generations of females succeed one another in this manner. In the fall, the females lay some eggs which are smaller than the rest. These hatch into small males, degenerate individuals lacking digestive systems but capable of producing sperms. Fertilization may then occur. The resulting zygotes differ from the parthenogenetic eggs in that they possess thick, hard shells. Such eggs may resist unfavorable environments for very long periods. Under suitably favorable conditions, for example, in the following spring, the shelled eggs develop into females. In some types of rotifers males are unknown altogether, the species being propagated exclusively by parthenogenesis (Fig. 31.14).

A

FIG. 31.13. The structure of a rotifer, diagrammatic. **A,** dorsal external view. **B,** sagittal section.

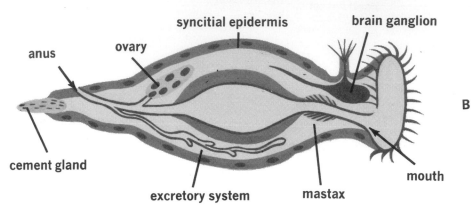

syncitial epidermis

brain ganglion

anus

ovary

B

cement gland

excretory system

mastax

mouth

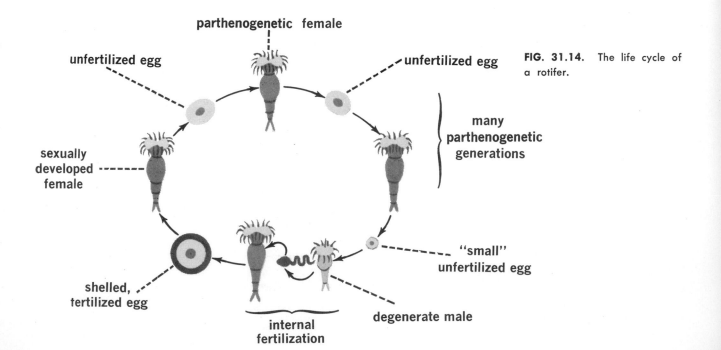

parthenogenetic female

unfertilized egg

unfertilized egg

FIG. 31.14. The life cycle of a rotifer.

many parthenogenetic generations

sexually developed female

"small" unfertilized egg

shelled, fertilized egg

internal fertilization

degenerate male

FIG. 31.15. Diagrams, various invertebrates. Photos: Middle right, larvae of trichina worms, encapsulated in pig muscle. If infected pork is improperly cooked, the larvae are digested out in the intestine of the host, and the worms then invade the host tissues; bottom right, a group of nematodes called "vinegar eels." (Trichina worms, Ward's Natural Science Establishment, Inc.; vinegar eels, General Biological Supply House, Inc.)

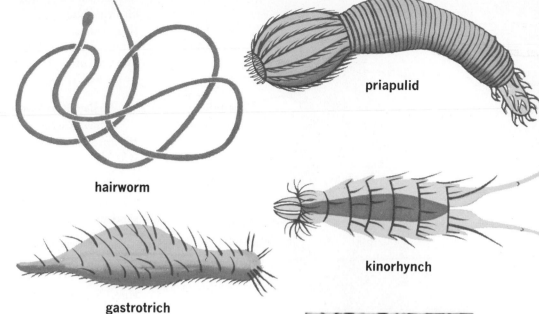

priapulid

hairworm

gastrotrich

kinorhynch

Phylum Nematoda: Roundworms (10,000 Species)

It has been estimated that probably more individual roundworms exist than any other multicellular animals except possibly insects. Many nematodes are free-living in soil and water, and they occur in such numbers that a spadeful of garden earth is likely to contain up to a million worms. Many nematodes are parasitic in plants and animals, and they are usually implicated when an animal is said to suffer from "worms." Man alone harbors some 50 species. Most of these are relatively harmless, but some cause serious diseases (Fig. 31.15).

All nematodes are remarkably alike. The body is slender, cylindrical, with tapered ends, and is covered with a tough chitinous cuticle. As in rotifers, the number of nuclei is constant for each species, and cell boundaries are absent in the adult. The worms possess mouth, straight intestine, and anus. Circulatory and breathing systems are not present, and excretory systems are constructed relatively simply. Males are usually smaller than females, and fertilization is internal.

Among the serious nematode pests of man are

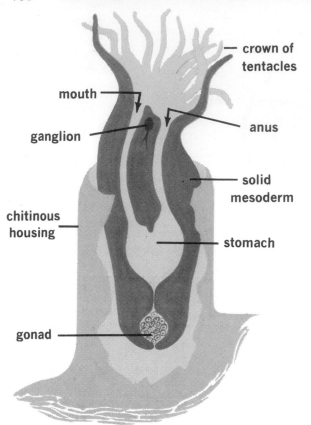

crown of
tentacles

mouth

ganglion

anus

solid
mesoderm

chitinous
housing

stomach

gonad

FIG. 31.16. The structure of an entoproct individual (diagrammatic cutaway). Note absence of true coelom, and position of anus within tentacle ring.

the **trichina worms,** introduced via insufficiently cooked pork; the **hookworms,** which live in soil and infect man by boring through his skin; and the **filaria worms,** which are transmitted by mosquitoes and cause blocks in lymph vessels. The disease resulting from filarial infections is characterized by immense swellings and is known as *elephantiasis.*

Phylum Nematomorpha: Hairworms (80 Species)

These are very long, very thin animals which resemble nematodes in general structure (Fig. 31.15). Larval hairworms are parasitic in insects; adults are free-living but nonfeeding.

Phylum Gastrotricha (200 Species)

The phylum comprises microscopic marine and fresh-water animals, which move by means of cilia

located on the underside of the body. In some species the body surface is covered with bristles, and this makes the animals resemble ciliate protozoa. However, the internal structure is in some respects like that of rotifers, in others like that of nematodes (Fig. 31.15).

Phylum Kinorhyncha (30 Species)

Marine worms with surface spines and retractile proboscis, resembling nematodes in general structure (Fig. 31.15).

Phylum Priapulida (3 Species)

Thick-bodied marine worms living in mud and sand in coastal regions (Fig. 31.15).

Phylum Entoprocta (60 Species)

One species of this group of minute, sessile animals is known to live in fresh water; the rest are marine (Fig. 31.16). The animals form shallow-water colonies which encrust rocks, shells, and seaweeds. Each entoproct is attached by a stalk, and at the other end it possesses a crown of ciliated tentacles. The cilia create feeding currents. Mouth and anus lie side by side within the ring of tentacles, and the digestive tract is U-shaped. We note that entoprocts are the only pseudocoelomate animals which are not shaped like worms. The larvae of entoprocts are unique, types like them being not found in any other phylum.

Schizocoelomates

Of the seven phyla in this important group, two rank first and second among multicellular types in number of species. In two phyla the body is segmented, and all seven are characterized by the presence of true coelomic body cavities, formed by a splitting of the embryonic mesoderm. Where development includes larval stages, a **trochophore** or trochophorelike stage is typical (Fig. 31.17; also Fig. 29.8).

Phylum Ectoprocta (2,500 Species)

These are minute marine and fresh-water animals which resemble entoprocts superficially; that

FIG. 31.17. Diagram of a trochophore larva. Note alimentary tract, also band and tufts of cilia.

is, they are sessile, colonial, and form mats on rocks and seaweeds. Moreover, they possess a U-shaped digestive tract, as well as a crown of ciliated tentacles (Fig. 31.18). Because of these similarities, ectoprocts and entoprocts used to be regarded as subgroups of a single phylum (*Bryozoa* or *Polyzoa*). But the differences between the entoprocts and ectoprocts are quite pronounced, and each is now properly accorded the rank of a separate phylum.

Ectoprocts are coelomate, and the anus opens outside the ring of tentacles. Each animal is encased in a calcareous or chitinous cup, from which the tentacles may be protruded. Polymorphism is characteristic of the group. Some individuals of a colony may mature as highly modified animals resembling the heads of birds. These are called **avicularia**, and they consist largely of a pair of muscle-operated jaws, which prevent other organisms from settling on the colony. Ectoprocts may reproduce by budding, and through this a colony may grow vegetatively. The animals may also reproduce gametically, and this results in free-swimming trochophorelike larvae which disperse the species geographically. The larvae transform into adults through a very drastic metamorphosis.

Phylum Phoronidea (15 Species)

These are wormlike, sedentary, tube-dwelling animals, living in the bottom of shallow seas. The straight tubular housing of a phoronid lies vertically in mud or sand, and from the top protrudes a horseshoe-shaped crown of ciliated, food-catching tentacles. The digestive tract is U-shaped. Larvae are of the trochophore type, and in this and other respects phoronids resemble ectoprocts to some extent (Fig. 31.19).

Phylum Sipunculoidea (250 Species)

This group comprises small, flask-shaped animals, found in sand or mud of shallow seas (Fig. 31.19). The narrow anterior part of the body bears a fringe of ciliated tentacles, and the whole foreregion of the animal may be retracted into a thicker hind part. The mouth, within the ring of tentacles, leads into a U-shaped, coiled intestine, which terminates at an anus located dorsally behind the tentacle ring. The larva is of the trochophore type.

FIG. 31.18. The structure of an ectoproct individual, diagrammatic cutaway. Note presence of a true coelom and position of anus outside of tentacle ring.

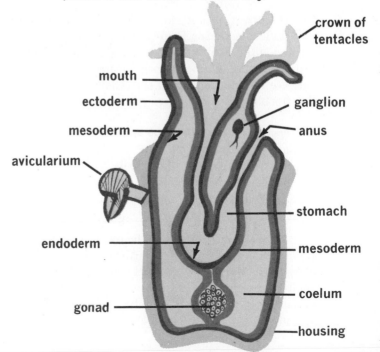

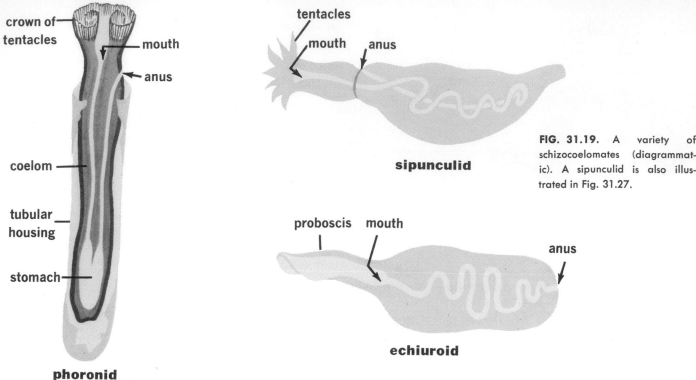

crown of tentacles

mouth

anus

coelom

tubular housing

stomach

phoronid

tentacles

mouth   anus

sipunculid

FIG. 31.19. A variety of schizocoelomates (diagrammatic). A sipunculid is also illustrated in Fig. 31.27.

proboscis   mouth

anus

echiuroid

Phylum Echiuridea (60 Species)

The wormlike animals in this group (Fig. 31.19) possess an anterior proboscislike, nontentacled, mucus-secreting food-catching organ, a mouth located at the base of the proboscis, and a coiled intestine leading to a posteriorly located anus. Echiurids are marine mud dwellers. Their larvae are of the trochophore type.

Phylum Mollusca (100,000 Species)

Class Amphineura: chitons
Class Scaphopoda: tooth shells
Class Gastropoda: snails, slugs, whelks
Class Pelecypoda: clams, mussels
Class Cephalopoda: squids, octopuses, nautiluses

Among multicellular animals, this enormous phylum is second only to the arthropods in numbers of species. Mollusks are mostly marine, but many snails and clams live in fresh water, and one group of snails is terrestrial. Mollusks are exceedingly abundant in all aquatic habitats. As a group, they il-

lustrate the general principle that successful phyla are highly diversified in structural adaptations and ways of life. We may note too that the phylum includes the largest of all nonvertebrate animals, namely, the giant squids, which may reach lengths of 50 ft.

Despite the external dissimilarities of the members of different classes, all mollusks share a common fundamental body organization. The molluscan body consists of a ventral, muscular **foot,** which is the principal organ of locomotion; a **visceral mass,** located dorsal to the foot, which contains most of the internal organs; and a **mantle,** a tissue layer which covers the visceral mass and which in most cases secretes a calcareous **shell** (Fig. 31.20). The larvae characteristically are trochophores. In most mollusks, the trochophore develops into a so-called **veliger** larva, which eventually metamorphoses into the adults.

Class Amphineura. The animals of this class are probably the least specialized mollusks, and they reveal the basic molluscan architecture most nearly in

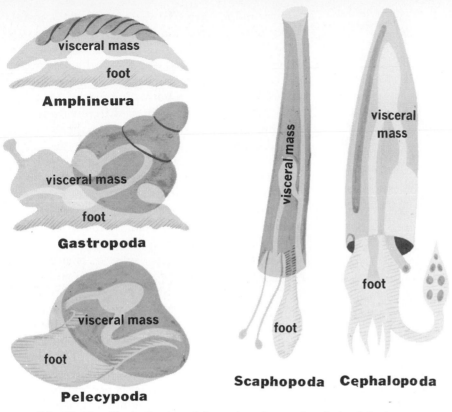

Amphineura

Gastropoda

Pelecypoda

Scaphopoda   **Cephalopoda**

visceral mass

foot

visceral mass

foot

visceral mass

foot

visceral mass

foot

visceral mass

foot

FIG. 31.20. The body plan of the various classes of mollusks. A basic structure is seen to be common to all. Shells are in dark gray; the foot is cross-hatched.

FIG. 31.21. A chiton, member of the molluscan class Amphineura. The animal is seen from the dorsal side. Note the eight shell plates and the edge of the foot. (American Museum of Natural History.)

its primitive form (Fig. 31.21). Chitons occur abundantly on rocks along the seashore, where they creep sluggishly with their broad foot. The dorsal surface of a chiton is protected by a shell of eight overlapping plates, and under the rim of this shell, in the so-called **mantle cavity,** are lateral gills for breathing. The head is greatly reduced, probably a specialized feature of chitons. Between shell and foot is the visceral mass. It contains the alimentary system, which consists of an anterior mouth, a tubular digestive tract, and a posterior anus. Behind the mouth is a pharynx, in which is found a **radula,** a horny rasping organ characteristic of mollusks generally. When it is protruded through the mouth, the radula may move back and forth over algal vegetation and rasp off small fragments. Chitons possess a circulatory system with a simply constructed heart.

The cavity in which this pumping organ is located represents the main part of the molluscan coelom. Also present in the visceral mass are excretory and reproductive organs and a nervous system. The latter consists of a ring of neural tissue which encircles the alimentary tract behind the mouth and of a ventral ladder-type array of nerve cords.

Class Scaphopoda. In these mollusks (see Fig. 31.20), the body is greatly elongated in a dorsoventral direction, and the animal is tubular. The shell is a tube open at both ends, and the foot of a scaphopod protrudes from the wider ventral end. The mouth is surrounded by delicate sensory and prehensile tentacles. Scaphopods are the least common of the mollusks. They are all marine, and they live partly buried in sand or mud bottoms of shallow waters.

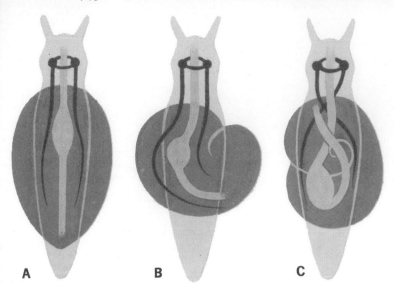

FIG. 31.22. Coiling of shell and torsion of internal organs in snails, as a result of faster development on one side of the body.

Class Gastropoda. Snails have the general architecture of chitons, with two major differences (Fig. 31.22). First, a distinct head is present, which bears retractile tentacles and eyes. Second, during development, the visceral mass becomes rotated through an angle of 180° relative to the foot. This makes the intestine U-shaped and brings the anus anteriorly above the mouth. Also, rotation twists the two main trunks of the ladder-type nervous system into a figure 8. Correlated with the visceral rotation, one side of the body, usually the left, grows much more slowly than the other, and this unequal growth produces a coiling of the shell.

Rotational development of this sort undoubtedly is an adaptation to the gastropod way of life. For the shell is open only at one end, and when a snail withdraws into its shell, it is advantageous to have both mouth and anus near the opening. Shells are cumbersome even then, and we may note that in many gastropods the shells are reduced or absent altogether. In such animals, the visceral mass is more or less completely rotated back into the original position. Aquatic snails breathe by means of gills, like chitons, and in terrestrial snails parts of the mantle cavity have become adapted to function as lungs. Some land snails have returned secondarily to water, and these must surface periodically for air.

Class Pelecypoda. Clams are highly specialized mollusks, adapted to a burrowing way of life (Figs. 31.23, 31.24). They are flattened from side to side, the hinge of the two shells, or **valves,** being dorsal.

Lining the valves on the inside are the mantle tissues, which form two openings at the posterior end, one for the entry and one for the exit of water. In many species, these posterior tissues are drawn out into a long retractile tube, which may be pushed out into free water if the clam is embedded in several inches of sand or mud. Hanging freely into the mantle cavity are the gills, folds of ciliated tissue which function both as breathing organs and as food filters. Pelecypods subsist on microscopic food particles brought into the animals by the incoming water current. The gills strain and collect these particles, and the cilia carry them to the mouth. This opening is located anteriorly between the left and right gills, in the visceral mass. The digestive tract within the visceral mass consists of stomach, digestive gland, and intestine. A radula is not present in this class of mollusks. The anus opens posteriorly and discharges into the outgoing water current.

The other organs of the visceral mass are largely as in other mollusks, except that the nervous system is highly reduced, a feature undoubtedly correlated with the sluggish way of life of these animals. A head is not present either. The muscular foot, continuous with the visceral mass, may be protruded between the valves. Clams use the foot as a burrowing organ, and by expanding the tip of the foot in sand and pulling the body after it, they may propel themselves forward. Many pelecypods are permanently attached, however. This is true, for example, of oysters, and also of the giant clam *Tridacna,* which may be 2 yd long and weigh ¼ ton.

Class Cephalopoda. All these most highly organized mollusks are marine, predatory animals (Fig. 31.25). Nautiluses have coiled, chambered shells, the animals living in the newest, largest chambers. Squids have a highly reduced horny shell em-

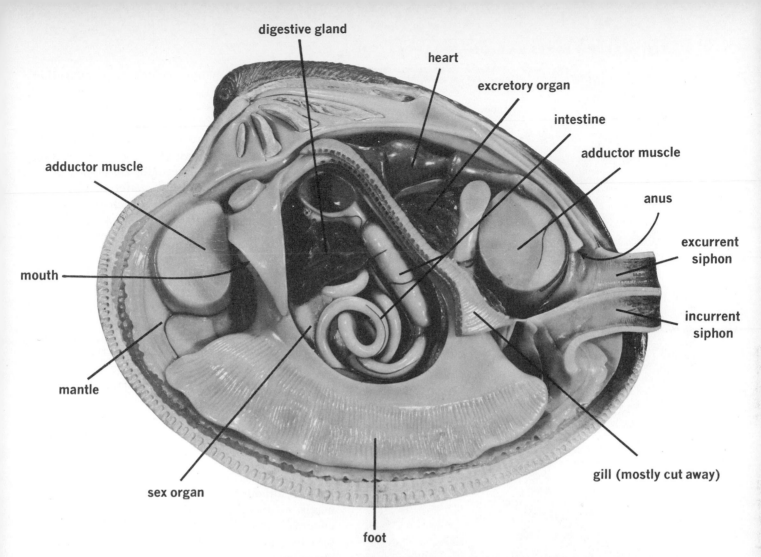

digestive gland

heart

excretory organ

intestine

adductor muscle

anus

excurrent siphon

incurrent siphon

adductor muscle

mouth

mantle

sex organ

gill (mostly cut away)

foot

FIG. 31.23. The internal structure of a clam. In this model, most of the gill flap is cut away, to expose the organs of the visceral mass. Water enters via the incurrent siphon and passes over the gills, where food particles are strained out and conducted to the mouth, hidden under a flap of tissue. Water and elimination products of all kinds leave the clam via the excurrent siphon. The two adductor muscles control the closing of the valve shells. (American Museum of Natural History.)

FIG. 31.24. A horse clam, showing the extensible tube containing the incurrent and excurrent siphons. When the animal is deeply embedded in mud or sand, the siphon tube may be extended upward into clear water. (Courtesy of V. B. Scheffer, U.S. Fish and Wildlife Service.)

FIG. 31.25. Cephalopod mollusks. Top: an octopus. Note funnel, here visible under right eye. Bottom: the chambered nautilus. A section through the shell is shown in lower photo.

bedded within the mantle. Octopuses are altogether without shells.

Like scaphopods, cephalopods are elongated dorsoventrally. In squids, for example, the sucker-equipped tentacles represent the foot, and the body represents the visceral mass (see Fig. 31.20). Within the wreath of tentacles is a highly developed head, with a large brain and large, vertebratelike eyes. The head also bears a mouth, which is equipped with strong horny jaws as well as a radula behind them. The digestive tract is U-shaped, the anus opening into the mantle cavity. The role of this cavity in the jet locomotion of cephalopods has already been discussed in Chap. 9. Larval stages in cephalopods are suppressed, the young hatching as miniature adults.

Phylum Annelida: Segmented Worms (10,000 Species)

Class Polychaeta: sandworms, clamworms, tube-worms
Class Oligochaeta: earthworms
Class Hirudinea: leeches
Class Archiannelida

This is another major group of schizocoelomate animals, although in numbers of species they are not nearly so abundant as the mollusks. The phylum comprises animals in which the body is divided internally and externally into numerous segments, separated from each other by membranous partitions. Except for the segments of the head and the hind end, all others are more or less alike. The digestive, nervous, and circulatory systems run uninterruptedly from front to rear, but all other organs are arranged on a segmental basis (Fig. 31.26). Where the life cycle includes larval stages, the larvae are trochophores, often indistinguishable from molluscan trochophores. Veliger stages are not present, however, the annelid trochophore elongating directly into a segmented worm.

The first three segments of an annelid form the head, and the last segment represents the hind end. The mouth, located anteriorly in the head, leads into an alimentary tract which terminates in the last segment. The head also contains the brain ganglia,

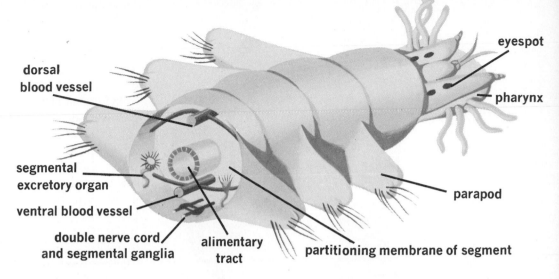

dorsal
blood vessel

eyespot

pharynx

segmental
excretory organ

ventral blood vessel

double nerve cord
and segmental ganglia

alimentary
tract

partitioning membrane of segment

parapod

FIG. 31.26. Anterior part of the polychaete *Nereis* and cross section through the body (diagrammatic).

FIG. 31.27. Polychaetes. Section through the tube of the parchment worm *Chaetopterus*. The head of the worm is on the left. Note the greatly elaborated parapodia, used to draw water currents through the tube. Between the arms of the U tube is a sipunculid worm, a member of another phylum. (American Museum of Natural History.)

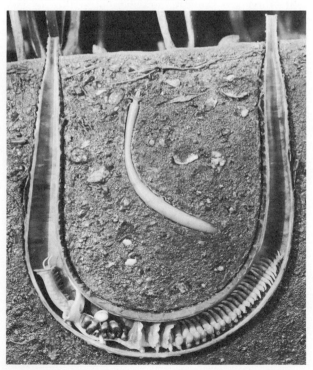

which form a ring around the pharynx. The rest of the nervous system is essentially of the ladder type, consisting of ventral nerve trunks thickened into ganglia in each segment. The circulatory system is closed and is composed principally of a longitudinal dorsal vessel, a longitudinal ventral vessel, and segmental connecting channels between these two. Blood flows forward dorsally and backward ventrally, propelled by peristaltic contractions of the dorsal blood vessel. Among oligochaetes, blood is kept in motion additionally by the connecting vessels of some of the anterior segments. These vessels are enlarged and function as pumping hearts. A pair of excretory organs with separate openings is found in each body segment. The cuticle-covered body surface of an annelid serves for breathing.

The Polychaeta (Fig. 31.27) form the largest and probably the most primitive class. These worms are mostly marine. Some are free-swimming. Others manufacture tubes in mud or sand in which they live permanently. And still others are burrowers. All are distinguished by the presence of a pair of fleshy lobes, the **parapodia,** on each body segment (see Fig. 31.26). Numerous chitinous bristles grow out from these lobes, hence the name polychaetes, or many-bristled worms, for this class. Parapodia provide a large surface for breathing, and the beating of the lobes also aids in locomotion, or in drawing wa-

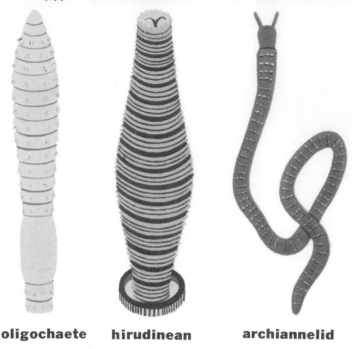

oligochaete   hirudinean   archiannelid

FIG. 31.28.   Various annelids (diagrammatic).

ter in and out of tubes and burrows. Polychaetes are characterized further by the presence of eyes, and of other specialized sense organs, in the head segments. The sexes are separate in this class. During the breeding season, the coelomic mesoderm in some or all body segments buds off gametes, which accumulate in the coelom. Gametes then reach the exterior through the excretory organs, or by bursting through the body wall. Trochophore larvae are typical of the group.

The Oligochaeta include the familiar earthworms, which belong to the genus *Lumbricus*. The annelids of this class differ from polychaetes mainly in four ways. First, eyes and other head appendages are absent. Second, parapodia are absent, and each body segment bears only a few bristles (Fig. 31.28). Third, the animals are hermaphrodites, each individual containing permanent male and female sex organs in specific segments (see Fig. 22.19). And fourth, fertilization is internal, and free-swimming larval stages are suppressed. Oligochaetes live in the ocean, in fresh water, and on land. Some attain remarkable size. For example, the giant earthworms of

Australia may reach lengths of over 10 ft and diameters of several inches.

Early oligochaete stocks have probably given rise to the Hirudinea, the class comprising the leeches (see Fig. 31.28). These animals are without bristles, and unlike other annelids, they possess a fixed number of segments throughout life. Moreover, the external segmentation does not match the internal, external segments being the more numerous (see Fig. 31.28). Each end of the body is equipped with a sucker. The most familiar leeches are bloodsucking ectoparasites, but we may note that not all members of the class pursue this way of life. The bloodsuckers possess digestive tracts equipped with spacious pouches, which may store enough blood to make a single meal suffice for many months. These worms produce **hirudin,** an anticoagulant which prevents blood from clotting during ingestion.

Archiannelids are a minor group which may be either very primitive or very specialized and simplified. These worms are unsegmented externally, and in most species parapodia and bristles are absent. Cilia are present, however, a feature of the trochophore larva which is carried over into the adult (see Fig. 31.28).

Annelids as a whole have been derived from the same common ancestor which also has produced the mollusks (see Fig. 29.42). The main innovation in the annelid line has been adult segmentation, a trait of considerable adaptive advantage. It permits the development of different specializations in different segments, just as, on a lower level of organization, division of protoplasm into cells makes possible divergent specializations. In modern annelids, to be sure, divergent segmental differentiation has not proceeded very far, and most segments are still rather alike. However, the inherent possibilities were exploited to the utmost in another phylum, which in turn arose from primitive annelid stock: the arthropods.

**Phylum Arthropoda: Jointed-legged Animals
(1 Million Species)**
Class Onychophora: *Peripatus*
Class Crustacea: shrimps, lobsters, crabs, barnacles

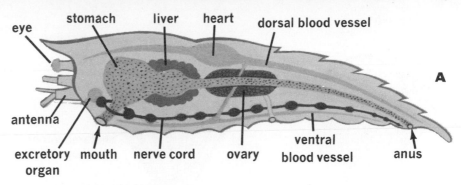

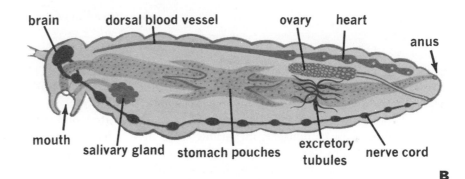

FIG. 31.29. The internal structure of a lobster (top) and a grasshopper (bottom); diagrammatic.

Class Insecta: insects
Class Chilopoda: centipedes
Class Diplopoda: millipedes
Class Arachnida: spiders, scorpions, mites, ticks
Class Merostomata: horseshoe crabs

By any standard, this is the most successful group of organisms, plant or animal. Arthropods are encountered in all environments in which life occurs at all, and in many tropical environments they maintain supremacy over even man. The insects are by far the most abundant and most diversified of all arthropods, being represented by at least three-quarters of a million species.

General characteristics. The body plan of arthropods as a whole is a highly elaborated variant of that of annelid worms (Fig. 31.29). A segmented design is fundamental, and the different segments are specialized in often greatly divergent ways. The body of an arthropod is composed of a **head,** a **thorax,** and an **abdomen.** The whole is covered by a chitinous exoskeleton (see Chap. 9), which is molted at intervals. Jointed appendages are present

on most or all segments. The head consists of six segments. Fused together in the adult, each head segment characteristically bears a pair of appendages having either a sensory or an ingestive function. The head also contains either or both of two kinds of eyes (Fig. 31.30). In so-called **simple eyes,** a single lens covers many light-sensitive cells. In **compound eyes,** on the other hand, many complete visual units are grouped together into a composite structure. Each visual unit here contains a separate lens and a light-sensitive cell. Compound eyes are unique to arthropods.

The alimentary tract consists of foregut, midgut, and hind gut. The first and last of these sections are lined with chitin, which is continuous with the exoskeleton. Hence only the midgut functions digestively. Nervous structures include dorsal brain ganglia in the head, ventral nerve cords, and paired ganglia either in each segment or grouped together in head and thorax. The circulatory system is open, a dorsal tubular heart being the only vessel present. Blood flows out from it anteriorly, circulates freely through the body tissues, and reenters the heart pos-

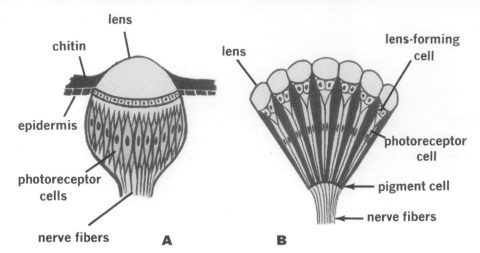

chitin

lens

lens

lens-forming
cell

epidermis

photoreceptor
cells

photoreceptor
cell

pigment cell

nerve fibers

nerve fibers

A   **B**

FIG. 31.30. Diagram of a simple arthropod eye (left) and a portion of a compound eye (right).

teriorly (Fig. 31.31). Either the excretory organs are located in the head appendages, as in crustaceans, or, as in insects, they are attached to the midgut and lead to the outside via the anus.

Breathing is accomplished in various ways in the different groups. Aquatic arthropods typically possess **gills** of some kind. In lobsters, for example, feathery gills are attached to the upper parts of the walking legs. Terrestrial arthropods like insects breathe by means of **tracheal tubes** (see Chap. 14), a unique, chitin-lined system of channels which originates on the body surface and ramifies to all interior tissues.

The sexes of arthropods are usually separate. Eggs are large and extremely yolky, and in many aquatic types they develop into free-swimming larvae. These resemble annelid worms to a consider-

able extent. This is true also for some terrestrial larvae, for example, the insect caterpillars. In other arthropods, the annelidlike stage is greatly abbreviated, and when the larvae hatch they already look like miniature adults. All larval types develop through a series of molting steps, the last of which produces the adult. Insects do not molt after adulthood is attained, but crustaceans do molt throughout life.

Class Onychophora. The members of this small class are of very great importance, for they indicate strikingly the close relation between annelids and arthropods.

The onychophoran *Peripatus* (Fig. 31.32), rather caterpillarlike in general appearance, possesses a head composed of three segments, as in annelids. These segments are fused, however, and

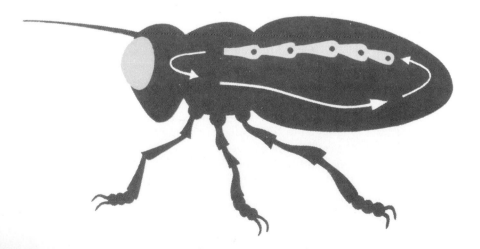

FIG. 31.31. The open circulatory system of arthropods. Blood is pumped forward in an open-ended dorsal main vessel. After circulating freely through the body tissues, blood again enters the posterior end of the dorsal vessel.

FIG. 31.32. *Peripatus.* This animal combines annelid and arthropod features. (Carolina Biological Supply Co.)

their appendages include antennae, as in arthropods. Each body segment bears fleshy, parapodia-like, unjointed legs, rather like annelids. But these legs terminate in claws, typical of arthropods. Like annelids, *Peripatus* possesses a pair of excretory organs in each body segment, leading to the outside by separate openings. But like terrestrial arthropods, *Peripatus* breathes by means of tracheal tubes. Also as in arthropods, the circulatory system of *Peripatus* is open, yet as in annelids, the reproductive ducts are ciliated, a feature not found elsewhere among arthropods.

Onychophora evidently represent a unique mixture of annelid and arthropod traits. Indeed, these animals are sometimes ranked as a separate phylum, sometimes as a subphylum within arthropods. Whatever the ranking, there is little doubt that they are remnants of an evolutionary line which branched off the ancestral arthropod stock, very soon after that stock itself had evolved from annelid ancestors.

Class Crustacea. This large group of arthropods is represented by some 50,000 species. Most crustaceans are aquatic, and most of these are marine in habitat. Many, like the *copepods* (see Fig. 5.5), are microscopic and planktonic, but others, like the giant crabs, may be some 12 ft across from one leg tip to the other. Most crustaceans are free-living and free-swimming. But some are parasitic either as larvae or as adults, and the barnacles are sessile as adults. In their internal structure, crustacea display a typically arthropod organization. Externally, they show particularly clearly how different segments

may become specialized for different functions. The segmental appendages of the lobster *Homarus* may serve to illustrate this point.

The body of a lobster consists of 21 segments (Fig. 31.33). The six segments of the head and the eight of the thorax are fused into a **cephalothorax** and are covered dorsally and laterally by a chitinous, lime-impregnated shield, the **carapace.** By contrast, the seven abdominal segments are marked off from one another distinctly. During embryonic stages, all segments bear paired appendages which are rather alike and which later differentiate in different ways. The first head segment is without appendages in the adult, but it bears a pair of stalked **compound eyes.** On the second and third segments are two pairs of sensory **antennae.** The excretory organs open at the bases of the second pair. Toothed chitinous **jaws** are present on the fourth segment. The fifth and sixth are equipped with **maxillae,** which pass food to the mouth.

To each of the first three segments of the thorax are attached a pair of **maxillipeds,** which aid in macerating food and also in passing it to the mouth. Moreover, the second and third maxillipeds are each equipped with a feathery gill. A pair of large pinching **claws** is present on the fourth thoracic segment, and on the remaining four segments of the thorax are **walking legs.** At the base of each of these is a gill, protected by the overhanging carapace.

In the abdomen, the first segment contains a pair of sperm-transferring structures in the male and greatly reduced appendages in the female. On each of the next four segments is a pair of **swimmerets,**

FIG. 31.33. Dorsal view of a crayfish, a freshwater crustacean structurally very much like the marine lobster. Note the antennae, eyes, large claws, walking legs, uropods, and telson. The fused cephalothorax, covered by the carapace, is clearly set off from the abdominal segments. (Carolina Biological Supply Co.)

small paddlelike structures used in forward locomotion. In female lobsters, the swimmerets also serve as attachment sites for eggs. The next-to-last segment bears platelike **uropods.** These, together with the similarly platelike last segment, the **telson,** form a fan-shaped tail structure used in backward locomotion.

Inasmuch as all these segmental appendages originate in the embryo in like manner, they are mutually *homologous*. Later, their functions come to differ, and this varied functional exploitation of segmental homologies lies at the root of the wide adaptability of arthropods generally, and of crustaceans specifically.

Class Insecta. This largest of all animal groups differs from other arthropods in a number of distinct ways (Fig. 31.34).

First, the head is marked off clearly from the thorax, and the thorax from the abdomen. The head again consists of six fused segments. On the first are a pair of compound eyes, as well as one or more simple eyes. Only a single pair of antennae is encountered in insects, located on the second head segment. The mouth parts on the remaining four head segments vary greatly in structure, according to whether or not the animal feeds by **biting** like a grasshopper, by **sucking** like a housefly, or by **piercing and sucking** like a mosquito.

FIG. 31.34. The external structure of an insect.

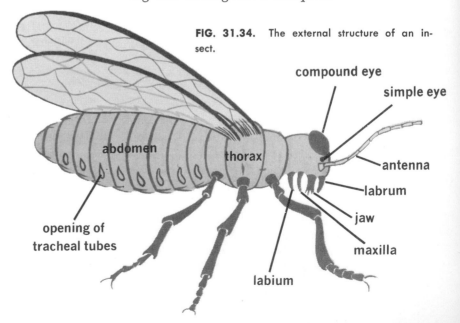

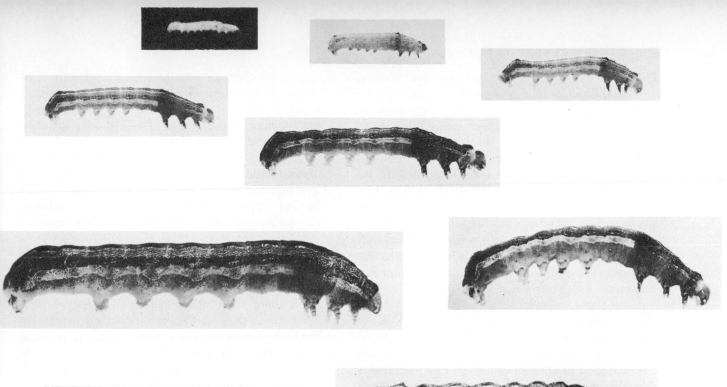

FIG. 31.35. Complete metamorphosis in insects. Note, top left to bottom right, the successive annelidlike larval stages (caterpillars), the pupa (next to last stage), and the winged adult stage. Each stage is connected to the preceding and succeeding one through a molt. In insects with incomplete metamorphosis, the larvae look like miniature adults. (Courtesy of Dr. Dietrich Bodenstein, Gerontology Branch, Baltimore City Hospitals.)

The thorax consists of three segments, each bearing a pair of walking legs. Also, in all except the most primitive insects, which are flightless, and secondarily flightless insects like fleas, each of the last two thoracic segments typically bears a pair of wings. Both pairs may be membranous, as in dragonflies and butterflies. Or the first pair may be heavily chitinized, as in beetles. Or the second pair may be reduced to tiny stalks, as in houseflies and mosquitoes. The abdomen of insects characteristically is without appendages. The segments here differ in number in different groups, and they may be variously fused.

Insects become adults either by **incomplete** or by **complete metamorphosis** (Fig. 31.35). In the former, larva resembles the adult in general features and reaches adult condition gradually, in the course of usually five molting steps. Grasshoppers, earwigs, termites, true bugs, aphids, and many other insect types belong to this group. In the second case, the larva is annelid- or caterpillarlike. It eventually transforms into a **pupa**, and the pupa in turn becomes the adult. Butterflies, moths, houseflies, beetles, bees, and ants are in this group. In either group, we may note, only the *adult* stages fly.

Insects are classified into some 20 orders, each representing a very wide range of ways of life. For example, the order of beetles includes parasites, commensals, carnivores, herbivores, omnivores, aquatic types, subterranean types, arboreal types, diurnal and nocturnal types, and dozens of others, each adapted to a particular, often highly specialized mode of living. Analogous diversity is in evidence within most other orders. We may note, incidentally, that beetles alone number some 300,000 species, and they form the largest of all orders, within the largest of all classes, within the largest of all phyla.

Classes Chilopoda, Diplopoda. Centipedes and millipedes (Fig. 31.36) are exclusively terrestrial. The two groups resemble each other in many ways, but they are nevertheless sufficiently distinct to be ranked as separate classes. In both groups, the rather wormlike animals are subdivided into numerous segments. The first six form the head, and their appendages resemble those of insects. However, compound eyes are usually absent, and clusters of simple eyes are typical. Body segments bear walking legs, *one* pair per segment in centipedes, *two* pairs per segment in millipedes. The first pair in centipedes is modified into poison claws. Centipedes are carnivorous, whereas millipedes are largely herbivorous. Despite the comparatively greater number of legs in millipedes, these arthropods cannot run as fast as centipedes. In their general internal structure, centipedes and millipedes are rather like insects.

Class Arachnida. This class comprises terrestrial arthropods too. The various types of arachnids within the group differ structurally in many ways, but they share a number of features which distinguish them from other arthropods (Fig. 31.37). Thus, in spiders, scorpions, and allied arachnids, the body is composed of a fused cephalothorax and an abdomen. The head is without compound eyes, without antennae, and without true jaws. Instead, there are simple eyes, sensory bristles, and two pairs of appendages, of which one is sensory and one is used for seizing and tearing prey. These are the **cheliceras** on the third head segment and the **pedipalps** on the fourth. In spiders, the cheliceras are sharp-pointed poison-injecting claws, and the pedipalps serve a sensory function. In scorpions, it is the pedipalps which function in tearing prey apart. The thoracic segments bear four pairs of walking legs, and this feature distinguishes arachnids from insects most readily. The abdomen is without segmental appendages, but spiders possess several

FIG. 31.36.   Left: a millipede. Right: a centipede. Note the two pairs of legs per segment in millipedes, the single pair per segment in centipedes. (Carolina Biological Supply Co.)

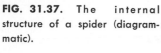

FIG. 31.37. The internal structure of a spider (diagrammatic).

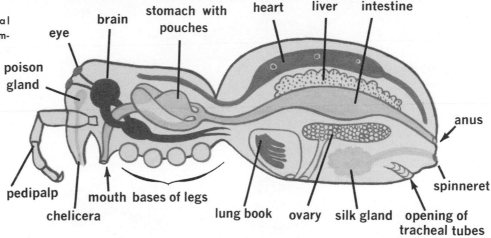

pairs of posterior **spinnerets,** organs which secrete web-forming silk. Arachnids have reduced abdominal tracheal tubes, and in addition they breathe by means of unique **lung books,** leaflike, richly vascularized plates of tissue present in an abdominal pouch. This pouch communicates with the outside through a slitlike opening.

Class Merostomata. Closely related to the arachnids, and often classified with them, are the marine **horseshoe crabs,** or king crabs. These are represented by five living species, all belonging to the genus *Limulus* (see Fig. 28.13). The animals are archaic "living fossils," and they probably are survivors of an early branch of the aquatic stock which also gave rise to the modern arachnids. Horseshoe crabs possess compound as well as simple eyes, and they breathe by means of **gill books.** These are similar to, and may well represent the forerunners of, the lung books of the arachnids.

Enterocoelomates

The four phyla in this group are characterized by the possession of mesodermal body cavities which form as pouches growing out from embryonic endoderm. Beyond this, the phyla have relatively little in common, and the evolutionary connection

of the first two to the last two, and to each other, is quite obscure. Inasmuch as the chordates are included among the enterocoelomates, this broad group of animals is of very special interest.

Phylum Brachiopoda: Lamp Shells (250 Species)

These are surviving remnants of a once very abundant group. The genus *Lingula* is considered to be the most ancient type of "living fossil" known, being already represented as early as the late Cambrian period or the early Ordovician period. Living brachiopods are all marine, and they resemble clams superficially. But whereas in clams the valves are on the left and the right of the animal, in brachiopods they are dorsal and ventral, opening anteriorly. A muscular stalk protruding posteriorly between the valves attaches the animal to rock. Internally, two large, coiled arms are studded with short, ciliated tentacles. The beat of the cilia creates feeding and breathing currents (Fig. 31.38).

The blastopore of a brachiopod embryo becomes the *mouth* of the adult. In this respect brachiopods are like schizocoelomates, but unlike other enterocoelomates, in which the blastopore becomes the anus (see Chap. 29). Therefore, although brachiopods do possess an enterocoelous body cavity, these animals are difficult to relate to others; we may note that their evolutionary affinities are unknown.

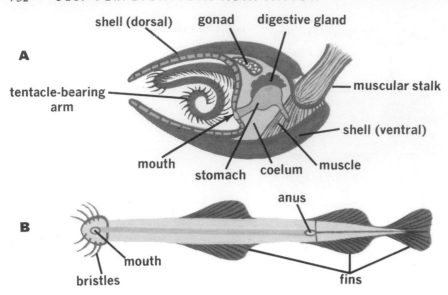

A

shell (dorsal)   gonad   digestive gland

tentacle-bearing arm

muscular stalk

mouth

stomach   coelum   muscle

shell (ventral)

FIG. 31.38. Diagram of the internal structure of a brachiopod and outline drawing of a chaetognath.

B

anus

mouth

bristles   fins

Phylum Chaetognatha: Arrowworms (30 Species)

These are small, transparent, marine animals (Fig. 31.38). Although relatively few species are known, individual arrowworms at given seasons become so enormously abundant that they form an important constituent of the food of marine fish. The chaetognath body is roughly torpedo-shaped, and it is equipped with lateral "fins," used presumably in balancing. Internal transverse partitions mark the body into head, trunk, and tail, and a longitudinal partition divides the body cavity into left and right halves. Around the mouth are curved bristles, which aid in catching minute food organisms as the arrowworms dart about in shallow water. The anus is located at the junction of trunk and tail. The evolutionary affinities of this group are unknown, but the developmental pattern clearly tends to place the chaetognaths with the enterocoelomates.

Phylum Echinodermata: Spiny-skinned Animals (6,000 Species)

Class Asteroidea: starfishes
Class Ophiuroidea: brittle stars
Class Echinoidea: sea urchins, sand dollars
Class Holothuroidea: sea cucumbers
Class Crinoidea: sea lilies, feather stars

The members of this phylum are exclusively marine, and their unique identifying feature is the water-vascular system for locomotion, already referred to in Chap. 9. The larvae are bilateral, but the adults are radially symmetrical. Starfishes may serve to illustrate the structure of echinoderms generally (Fig. 31.39).

A starfish of the familiar genus *Asterias* is composed of a central region from which five **arms** radiate out. In other genera, there may be as many as 20 or more arms. The shell-like skeleton is an endoskeleton, made up of small, flat, **calcareous plates,** which are held together by muscles and connective tissue (see Chap. 9). Short **calcareous spines,** some of them movable, project from the skeletal plates. Covering the skeleton are epidermal tissues, which are studded with many tiny fingerlike protrusions, the **skin gills.** The internal cavities of these gills are parts of the coelom, and they communicate with the interior body cavity through spaces left among the skeletal plates. Also present on the body surface are numerous, very small pincers, the **pedicellariae.** These protect the skin gills from interference by small animals.

The water-vascular system (Fig. 31.40) communicates with the outside through the **madre-**

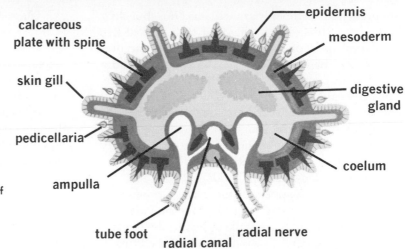

FIG. 31.39. Cross section through the arm of a starfish (diagrammatic).

porite, a sievelike device located excentrically on the upper surface of the animal. A series of ducts leads from the madreporite into five **radial canals,** one passing into each arm. Short side branches from these canals connect with the hollow, muscular **tube feet,** which project from the underside of the arms. At the base of each tube foot is a muscular sac, the **ampulla,** which may force water into the foot and make it turgid.

The **mouth** is on the undersurface in the center of the body, and in the center of the upper surface is a small **anal pore.** Connecting mouth and anus is a **stomach,** into which open five pairs of **digestive glands,** one pair from each arm. Starfishes feed largely on clams. The tube feet, working in relays, are used as suckers to pull on the valves of a clam, until the clam is exhausted and opens its housing. The stomach of the starfish then turns inside out through the mouth and digests the soft tissues of the clam. Starfishes are without brain, and the nervous system is not very elaborate. It consists of a ring of nerve tissue around the mouth, from which nerve trunks radiate into each arm. The circulatory system is also greatly reduced. Excretion is accomplished partly by diffusion, partly by migrating ameboid cells. These are dispersed freely in the body cavity, and they carry wastes to and through the epidermis.

The members of the other echinoderm classes largely resemble starfishes in their general features. Among the brittle stars the five arms are elongated and slender, and their sinuous movements aid materially in locomotion. In some ophiuroids the arms

FIG. 31.40. The components and the internal arrangement of the water-vascular system in a starfish. Water enters and leaves the system through the sievelike madreporite (sieve plate) at the upper side.

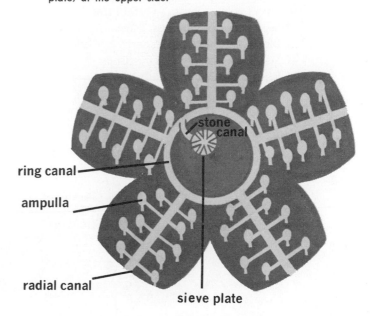

are branched. Echinoids are without arms, but their bodies nevertheless are organized on a plan of five or of multiples of five. For example, sea urchins possess five bands of long, slender tube feet and a mouth equipped with five radially placed teeth. Long movable spines are characteristic of these animals. The sea cucumbers are elongated along the mouth-anus axis, and they are further distinguished by a highly reduced skeleton, a leathery body covering, and a circlet of tentacles around the mouth. Five longitudinal bands of tube feet are typical of most members of this class. Crinoids are far less abundant today than they were in Paleozoic times. These animals are stalked, sessile, deep-water forms, characterized by numerous feathery arms.

In echinoderms generally, the sexes are usually separate, and fertilization is external. As noted in earlier chapters, the early embryonic development of these animals is quite similar to that of chordates, and there is little doubt that echinoderms and chordates are closely related.

Phylum Chordata (50,000 Species)

Subphylum Hemichordata: acorn worms
Subphylum Urochordata: tunicates
Subphylum Cephalochordata: lancelets
Subphylum Vertebrata: vertebrates
    Class Agnatha: jawless fishes
    Class Chondrichthyes: cartilage fishes
    Class Osteichthyes: bony fishes
    Class Amphibia: amphibians
    Class Reptilia: reptiles
    Class Aves: birds

Class Mammalia: mammals

Because this phylum includes man and the animals most directly important to man, it is unquestionably the most interesting from almost any standpoint. The phylum also has a special evolutionary significance, for it comprises what is by far the most progressive group of animals. Other phyla may include more species and may be more diversified. But only among chordates do we encounter, within one and the same phylum, types as primitively organized as acorn worms and types as complexly organized as men. Evidently, the ancestral chordate body plan was richer in major evolutionary potentialities than the body plans of other phyla.

Chordates as a whole are characterized by the possession of a **notochord,** a hollow, **dorsal nerve cord,** and paired **gill slits** (Fig. 31.41). These structures are present either throughout life or only at some stage of development. The notochord is a dorsal stiffening rod formed from embryonic mesoderm. The formation of the nerve cord from the embryonic ectoderm has already been described in Chap. 26. Gill slits break through laterally from the pharynx to the exterior. Thus a continuous water channel is established from the mouth to the pharynx, and from the pharynx to the outside through the gill slits. Food present in the water taken in by mouth is collected in the pharynx and is passed on into the esophagus. The water returns to the environment via the gill slits past the gills, where oxygen is absorbed into the circulatory system.

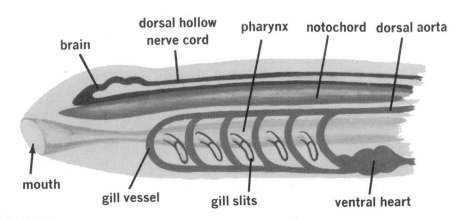

FIG. 31.41. The anterior portion of a hypothetical chordate, to show the basic diagnostic features of the phylum Chordata.

The body is segmented in two of the four chordate subphyla, the lancelets and the vertebrates. This feature is shared in common with the annelid-arthropod group of organisms, but it has here evolved independently. A distinct head is present only in vertebrate chordates, and these animals are therefore designated alternatively as *Craniata.* The representatives of the other chordate subphyla, all headless, are collectively called *Acrania* (Table 16).

Subphylum Hemichordata. These wormlike chordates number about 100 species. They are marine and live in sand or mud. The body consists of an anterior **proboscis,** which is used in burrowing, and of a **collar** and a posterior **trunk** (Fig. 31.42). The mouth is situated ventrally, where the proboscis joins the collar. Behind the collar are many pairs of pharyngeal gill slits. The poorly developed notochord is a short internal rod, which projects from the collar into the proboscis and probably supports that organ. The nervous system includes two nerve cords in the trunk, one dorsal and one ventral, the dorsal cord in some species extending into the collar as a thickened, hollow tube. These cords connect with a network of nerve cells, present under the epidermis of the worms.

FIG. 31.42.   Left: section through the anterior part of a hemichordate (diagrammatic). Right: model of the hemichordate *Dolichoglossus.* Note proboscis, collar, trunk, and the gill slits in anterior part of trunk, just behind collar. (Photo, American Museum of Natural History.)

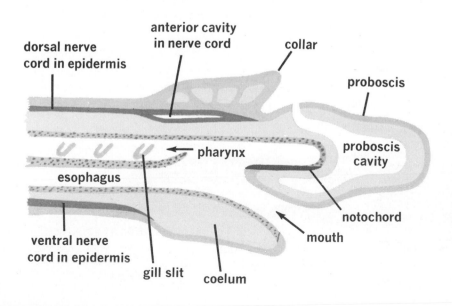

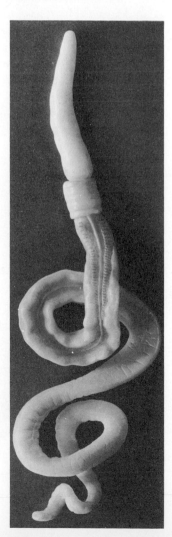

TABLE 16. Some diagnostic features of chordates

Group	Subphylum	Head	Segmentation	Skeleton	Paired gills	Nervous system	Tail
Acrania	Hemichordata	—	—	short, anterior notochord	many	dorsal and ventral nerve cord	without tail
	Urochordata	—	—	larval notochord	many	larval dorsal nerve cord	larval tail
	Cephalochordata	—	+	permanent notochord	many	permanent dorsal nerve cord	larval and adult tail
Craniata	Vertebrata	+	+	embryonic notochord; vertebral column in adult	few	permanent dorsal nerve cord and brain	larval and adult tail

The embryos and larvae of some hemichordates are remarkably like those of some echinoderms, and this is one of the main clues indicating close relationship between echinoderms and chordates (see Fig. 29.9). Indeed, hemichordates may be related to echinoderms at least as closely as to other chordates, and the group probably represents a very early independent offshoot from an ancestral echinoderm-chordate stock. Some authorities actually rank the hemichordates as a separate phylum within the enterocoelomates.

Subphylum Urochordata. Tunicates too are marine. Of the approximately 2,000 known species, most are sessile, and many form extensive colonies in the water. The adults are quite unlike typical chordates, but their larvae clearly reveal the chordate character of these animals. A tunicate larva has the general form of a tadpole (Fig. 31.43). It possesses a large, muscular tail, a very-well-developed notochord, and a dorsal hollow nerve cord, expanded anteriorly into a primitive brain. A complete alimentary system is present, as are pharyngeal gill slits.

After a free-swimming existence of some hours, such a larva attaches with its anterior end to a rock or other solid object and undergoes a remarkable metamorphosis. In the adult (see Fig. 9.13), the tail is resorbed, the notochord has disappeared completely, and the nervous system has become reduced to a single ganglion. The pharynx has enlarged, however, and has developed many additional gill slits. Also, the region of the mouth has shifted so that the alimentary tract is roughly U-shaped. A cellulose-containing covering, the **tunic,** has developed around the whole animal, leaving only two openings, the **incurrent** and the **excurrent**

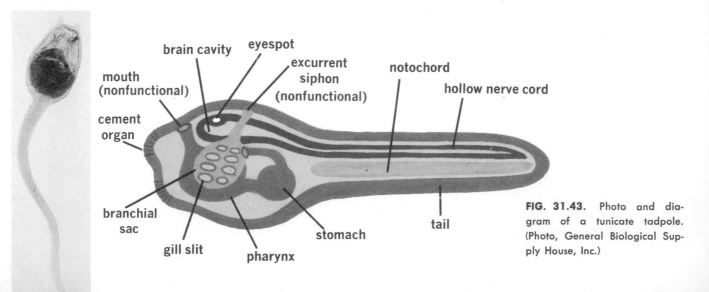

FIG. 31.43. Photo and diagram of a tunicate tadpole. (Photo, General Biological Supply House, Inc.)

siphon. Water and food enter the animal via the incurrent opening. Food is filtered out in the pharynx and is carried over a ciliated groove into the esophagus. Water passes through the gill slits and leaves via the excurrent siphon. This opening also conducts waste products and gametes to the outside.

It was probably the tadpole stage of ancestral tunicates, not the adult stage, which gave rise to the remaining chordate subphyla.

Subphylum Cephalochordata. The lancelets, often better known by the group name **amphioxus,** comprise some 30 species of small, marine sand burrowers. These animals are more or less fish-shaped, slender, and compressed laterally (Fig. 31.44). They possess a notochord which persists throughout life and which extends through the whole length of the body. The nerve cord is dorsal and tubular, but there is no brain, and a head is not present. The mouth leads into a ciliated pharynx with 60 or more pairs of gill slits. Water passing through these emerges into an **atrium,** an ectodermal chamber which surrounds the pharynx and opens ventrally, anteriorly to the anus.

Amphioxus is a segmented animal. This is shown most obviously by the musculature, which is formed into segmental bundles, or **somites.** The nerves leading to these muscles, and the excretory and reproductive organs, are arranged on a segmental pattern too. Lancelets therefore are clearly, and very closely, related to vertebrates. They differ from vertebrates principally in the permanence of the notochord and in the absence of a head. They probably are a marine offshoot of an evolutionary line which has led from ancestral marine tunicates to ancestral fresh-water vertebrates. This offshoot may have been unable to make the transition from ocean to river and has adapted instead to a life in shallow coastal waters and estuaries.

Subphylum Vertebrata. The vast majority of chordates are vertebrates, so named because, in late embryonic stages, a segmented vertebral column develops in addition to, or more generally as a replacement of, the notochord. The individual vertebrae are made of cartilage or bone. Segmentation is a general feature of vertebrate structure, but in many

FIG. 31.44. Amphioxus, the lancelet. The many pharyngeal gill slits are very prominent just behind the mouth. Note also the notochord —the very dark rod just above the gill slits, running from front to back. A head is absent. (Carolina Biological Supply Co.)

groups the segmental patterns become somewhat obscured in adult stages. Vertebrates possess a well-developed head, with brain, brain case, and paired sense organs. The nerve cord is dorsal and tubular, as in other chordates. Pharyngeal gills are present too, and in most groups an outpouching from the pharynx develops into a **lung.** Gills and lungs rarely occur at the same time, the gills usually forming first, the lungs thereafter. A distinct adult tail is a virtually unique vertebrate characteristic. The base of the tail is marked ventrally by the anus.

Vertebrates are believed to have arisen in fresh water and to have invaded the ocean and the land from there. Aquatic vertebrates, in particular the bony fishes, are still the most numerous representatives of the subphylum. These, and all other classes of fishes, including the extinct class of placoderms (see Chap. 29), are sometimes grouped into a *superclass Pisces.* On the other hand, the four classes of four-legged land vertebrates are collectively referred to as the *superclass Tetrapoda.* Most of the fundamental features of vertebrates are shared in common by all classes and have already been dealt with in some detail in many preceding chapters. Here we shall concentrate mainly on the principal identifying characteristics of the various classes (see also Table 17).

AGNATHA. These are roughly eel-shaped animals, with smooth, scaleless skin and without paired

TABLE 17. Some diagnostic features of vertebrates

Group	Super-class	Class	Skin	Skeleton	Appendages	Breath-ing	Heart chambers	Fertili-zation	Develop-ment	Other
Anamniota	Pisces	Agnatha	smooth	permanent notochord plus car-tilage skeleton	without paired fins	gills	2	external	in water	without jaws; cold-blooded; without neck; without lungs
		Chondrich-thyes	denticles	embryonic notochord; adult car-tilage skeleton	paired fins	gills	2	external	in water	with jaws; cold-blooded; without neck; without lungs
		Osteich-thyes	scales	embryonic notochord; adult bony skeleton	paired fins	gills; lungs in some	2	external	in water	swim bladder in most; cold-blooded; without neck
	Tetrap-oda	Amphibia	smooth, glan-dular	embryonic notochord; adult bony skeleton	2 pairs legs	gills and lungs	3	external	in water	cold-blooded; without neck
Amniota		Reptilia	scales	embryonic notochord; adult bony skeleton	2 pairs legs	lungs	4	internal	on land	with neck; cold-blooded
		Aves	feathers	embryonic notochord; adult bony skeleton	legs and wings	lungs	4	internal	on land	with neck; warm-blooded
		Mammalia	hair	embryonic notochord; adult bony skeleton	2 pairs legs	lungs	4	internal	mostly within female	warm-blooded; nurse young; nonnucleated red corpuscles

fins (Fig. 31.45). The anterior end of the body is modified into a funnellike sucker, in the center of which is the mouth. Jaws are absent. The notochord persists throughout life, and the adult in addition possesses a brain case and segmental vertebral elements made of cartilage. There are seven pairs of gills, and lungs do not form. The heart is ventral as in all vertebrates, and as in all fishes it consists of two chambers, one auricle and one ventricle. The sense organs include, apart from lateral eyes, a functional **pineal eye,** located dorsally along the mid-line of the head (see also Chap. 19). Lampreys comprise fresh-water as well as marine species, but even the latter migrate into rivers for spawning. Fertilization is external, and the adults die after shedding their gametes. The larvae develop in fresh water. Hagfishes are marine, and they spawn and develop in the sea.

CHONDRICHTHYES. In this and all subsequent vertebrate classes, the notochord is an embryonic structure only and is replaced completely by a vertebral column. In the chondrichthians, this column and all other skeletal parts consist of cartilage. The class includes sharks, skates, and rays, most of them marine, but some living in fresh water (Fig. 31.46). The skin of these animals is studded with tiny, pointed **denticles,** which in structure and development are homologous to the teeth of vertebrates generally. Two pairs of fins are present in addition to several unpaired fins, as are upper and lower jaws, characteristic also of subsequent classes. Breathing is by gills, of which there are five to seven pairs. The cartilage fishes are strongly muscled, and most are active, open-water predators. Some are plankton feeders, and these include the whale sharks, which sometimes reach lengths of approximately 50 ft and are the largest vertebrates after the true whales.

OSTEICHTHYES. At least half the number of all vertebrate species are bony fishes. As indicated by the name of this class, the adult skeleton is made largely of bone, a feature characteristic also of all four-legged vertebrates. Bony fishes typically have scaly skin, paired fins, and gills covered by a hinged bony plate, the **operculum,** on each side of the pharynx (Fig. 31.47). The animals also develop an internal membranous sac, pouched out ventrally from the pharynx. In most species this sac becomes a swim bladder. In the lungfishes, however, the sac functions partly like a lung. It is likely that in ancestral bony fishes the sac served as a lung primarily and that in most descendant forms it became adapted secondarily as a swim bladder, the breathing function being lost. Lungfishes appear to be one exception to this. The lobe-finned ancestors of the land vertebrates must have been another (Fig. 31.48; also Chap. 29).

AMPHIBIA. The two main groups of this class are, first, the salamanders and newts, in which a tail is present throughout life; and second, the frogs and toads, which are tailless only as adults. Both frogs and toads may be distinguished by their dentition; frogs possess teeth on their upper jaws, toads do not. All amphibia have smooth, moist, glandular skins without scales, and two pairs of legs, homologous to the paired fins of fishes. Larval amphibia typically live in fresh water, are fishlike in

FIG. 31.45. Lamprey, lateral view. Note gill slits. (Carolina Biological Supply Co.)

FIG. 31.46. Left: a skate, member of the class of cartilage fishes. Right: close-up of sharkskin, showing the toothlike denticles. (Left: Carolina Biological Supply Co. Right: General Biological Supply House, Inc.)

FIG. 31.47. Anterior portion of a carp, a member of the class of bony fishes. Note scales and also the operculum, a bony plate behind the eyes which covers the gills and lets water out at its rear edge. (Courtesy of E. P. Haddon, U.S. Fish and Wildlife Service.)

most respects, and breathe by means of gills and through the skin. The adults of all newts, some salamanders, and some toads are aquatic, and the adults of all others are terrestrial. Virtually all adults have lungs, and the newts and some of the aquatic salamanders in addition retain the gills throughout life. The heart of amphibia is three-chambered: two auricles and one ventricle. Fertilization is usually external and in most species takes place in water.

REPTILIA. Many people tend to confuse these true land vertebrates with amphibia. But reptiles are easily identified by their dry, scaly skin, by the presence of a fairly well-defined neck, and by their large shelled eggs, which are always laid on land, even where the adults are aquatic (see Table 17). The living representatives of this class are the turtles and tortoises, the snakes and lizards, the alligators and crocodiles, and the tuatara, or *Sphenodon*, a lizard-

like relic of the Mesozoic found today only in New Zealand. The legs of reptiles are typically five-toed and equipped with claws. But in sea turtles they are modified into flippers, and in snakes and some lizards limbs are not present at all. Gills are nonfunctional embryonic structures, and breathing is always by lung. This, and a four-chambered heart, is characteristic also of birds and mammals. Reptiles, birds, and mammals are alike also in that fertilization is internal and the embryos are equipped with amnion, allantois, yolk sac, and chorion (see Chap. 25). For this reason these three terrestrial classes are often referred to as *Amniotes*, and all other vertebrate classes as *Anamniotes*. Reptiles, like the anamniotes, have variable body temperatures, determined by the temperature of the environment. Partly because they can be active only in warm climates, most reptilian species are adapted to tropical and subtropical regions.

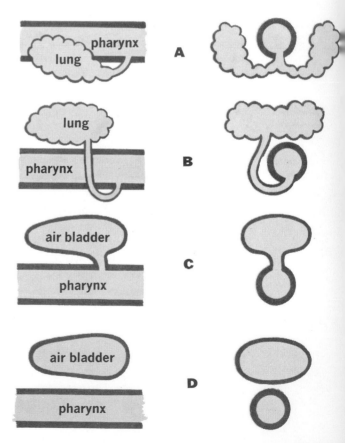

FIG. 31.48. The interrelation of lung, air bladder, and alimentary tract in fishes. Left figures: longitudinal view. Right figures: cross-sectional view. A, the pattern in tetrapods and some lungfishes. B, the pattern in other lungfishes and probably also in ancestral lobe-fins. C, the pattern in some modern bony fishes. D, the pattern in all other modern bony fishes. The connecting duct between pharynx and air bladder has disappeared.

FIG. 31.49. Top left: a spiny anteater, one of the few existing egg-laying mammals, or Protheria. Top right: a platypus. Bottom: an opossum. These three are pouched mammals, marsupials, or Metatheria. Other illustrations of Prototheria and Metatheria may be found in Fig. 29.36. (Opossum, Carolina Biological Supply Co.; other photos, American Museum of Natural History.)

AVES. In their internal structure, these feathered vertebrates greatly resemble primitive reptiles. Apart from the presence of feathers, birds are characterized by forelimbs which are modified into wings and by the absence of teeth, the mouth armature being a horn-covered beak or bill. Birds maintain a constant body temperature, like mammals. Undoubtedly because of the aerodynamic requirements of flight, birds are more like one another than the members of any other vertebrate class. We may note, however, that many birds have reduced wings and cannot fly. Ostriches, emus, moas, kiwis, and penguins are among the flightless types. Of the 10,000 or so avian species, more than half belong to a single order, the *passerine*, or *perching*, birds, which include the songbirds and most of the other familiar bird types.

MAMMALIA. The female members of this class possess milk-producing mammary glands, and they nurse their young. Three other identifying features are the possession of hairy skin, the transverse division of the body cavity by a diaphragm, and the nonnucleated condition of mature red blood corpuscles. The class comprises some 6,000 species, which, as noted also in Chap. 29, are grouped into three subclasses. The subclass **Prototheria** consists of egg-laying types. These are the least progressive mammals, and they still display many ancestral reptilian features. The group today includes only the duck-billed platypus and the spiny anteaters. Pouched or marsupial mammals form the subclass **Metatheria**. In these, the young are born in a very incompletely developed state, and development is completed in an abdominal skin pouch of the female. Opossums and the kangaroos, koala bears, wombats, and other marsupials of Australia belong to this group. The vast majority of mammals are included in the subclass **Eutheria,** the placental mammals, in which the young develop within the uterus of the female. Among these most familiar of all living organisms, shrews are the tiniest, whales the largest, rodents the most numerous, and primates certainly the brainiest and in all respects by far the most interesting and important (Fig. 31.49).

1. Describe the diagnostic group characteristics of protozoa. What features uniquely distinguish the various protozoan phyla? Which phyla are included among diploblastic animals, and what diagnostic features distinguish these phyla?

2. Name the classes of coelenterates, and describe the life cycles characteristic of each. Distinguish between polyps and medusae. Which phyla are included among acoelomates? Name the classes of flatworms, and describe the main structural features of Turbellaria. Review the life cycles of flukes and tapeworms.

3. Which are the pseudocoelomate phyla, and what features characterize the group as a whole? Describe the structure and the life cycle of rotifers. Distinguish between entoprocts and ectoprocts, and describe the basic structure of each. Which are the schizocoelomate phyla?

4. What is the fundamental body plan of mollusks? Describe the internal structure of animals within each of the molluscan classes, and show what features distinguish each class from the others. Which mollusks develop via (a) trochophores, (b) veligers, (c) neither?

5. Describe the diagnostic features of annelids. Name the annelid classes, and describe the internal structure of polychaetes. How do the other classes differ? What evidence relates annelids to mollusks on the one hand and to arthropods on the other? Describe the characteristic features of *Peripatus*.

6. Describe the group characters and the basic body organization of arthropods. Name the classes and the distinguishing features of each. Show how segmentation is exploited adaptively in (a) crustacea, (b) insects.

7. How do arachnids, centipedes, and millipedes differ structurally from insects? How is breathing accomplished in the various arthropod classes? Describe the structure of simple and compound eyes, and show in which arthropod classes each type of eye is found.

8. Which phyla are included among the enterocoelomates, and for what reasons? How do these phyla differ from one another? State the group characteristics of echinoderms, and name the various classes. Describe the structure of a starfish.

9. Review the classification of chordates. Contrast the diagnostic features of the four subphyla. Which subphylum is believed to be ancestral to the vertebrates, and for what reasons? Describe the basic structure of the various nonvertebrate chordates.

10. Describe the group characteristics of vertebrates. Name the classes, and describe the identifying features of each. Which classes are (a) amniotes, (b) anamniotes, (c) tetrapods, (d) jawless, (e) warm-blooded, (f) gill breathers, (g) lung breathers?

Any of the following books may be consulted for further information on given animals.

Buchsbaum, R.: "Animals without Backbones," University of Chicago Press, 1948.

Borradaile, L. A., F. A. Potts, L. E. S. Eastham, and J. T. Saunders: "The Invertebrata," Cambridge University Press, 1951.

Hyman, L.: "The Invertebrates," McGraw-Hill, 1940–1959.

Romer, A. S.: "Man and the Vertebrates," 3d ed., University of Chicago Press, 1941.

————.: "The Vertebrate Body," Saunders, 1950.

Young, J. Z.: "The Life of the Vertebrates," Oxford University Press, 1950.

Storer, T. I., and R. L. Usinger: "General Zoology," 3d ed., McGraw-Hill, 1957.

Particular animals are discussed in the following popular articles:

Russell, P. F.: The Eradication of Malaria, *Sci. American,* vol. 186, 1952.

Ladd, H. J., and J. I. Tracey: The Problem of Coral Reefs, *Sci. Monthly,* vol. 69, 1949.

GLOSSARY[1]

Acanthocephala (ȧ·kăn'thŏ-sĕf'ȧ·lȧ) [Gr. *akantho,* a thorn, + *kephalē,* head]: spiny-headed worms, a small phylum of acoelomate parasitic animals.

acoel, acoelomate (ă·sēl') [Gr. *a,* not, + *koilos,* cavity]: (1) without coelom; also a group of free-living flatworms without digestive cavity; (2) an animal without coelom, i.e., flatworms, proboscis worms, and spiny-headed worms.

acrania (ȧ·krā'nĭ·ȧ) [Gr. *a,* not, + *kranion,* skull]: headless chordates, including the hemichordates, the urochordates, and the cephalochordates.

acromegaly (ăk'rŏ·mĕg'ȧ·lĭ) [Gr. *akros,* outermost, + *megas,* large]: a condition characterized by skeletal overgrowths, particularly in the extremities, produced by excessive growth-hormone secretion from the pituitary.

acrosome (ăk'rŏ·sōm) [Gr. *akros,* outermost, + *soma,* body]: structure at the tip of the sperm head (nucleus) which makes contact with the egg during fertilization.

adenine (ăd'ĕ·nēn): a pyrimidine component of nucleotides and nucleic acids.

adenosine (di-, tri-) phosphate (ADP, ATP) (ȧ·dĕn'-ŏ·sēn): phosphorylated organic compounds functioning in energy transfers within cells.

adipose (ăd'ĭ·pōs) [L. *adipis,* fat]: fat, fatty, fat-storing tissue.

adrenal, adrenalin (ăd·rē'năl, ăd·rĕn'ăl·ĭn) [L. *ad,* to, + *renalis,* kidney]: (1) endocrine gland; (2) the hormone produced by the adrenal medulla.

adrenergic (ăd'rĕn·ûr'jĭk): applied to nerve fibers which release adrenalinlike substance from their axon terminals when impulses are transmitted across synapses.

adventitious (ăd'vĕn·tĭsh'ŭs): appearing not in usual place; as in adventitious root, which may sprout from anywhere on a stem.

aerobe, aerobic (ā'ĕr·ōb, —ō'bĭk) [Gr. *aeros,* air, + *bios,* life]: (1) oxygen-requiring organism; (2)

[1] The system of indicating pronunciation is used by permission of the publishers of Webster's New Collegiate Dictionary. Copyright 1949, 1951, 1953, 1956, 1958 by G. & C. Merriam Co.

pertaining to oxygen-dependent form of respiration.

Agnatha (ăg'nȧ·thȧ) [Gr. *a,* not, + *gnathos,* jaw]: jawless fishes, a class of vertebrates including lampreys and hagfishes.

alga (ăl'gȧ), *pl.* **algae** (—jē): any member of a group of ancient plant phyla; blue-green, green, golden-brown, brown, red algae.

allantois (ă·lăn'tŏ·ĭs) [Gr. *allantoeidēs,* sausage-shaped]: one of the extra-embryonic membranes in reptiles, birds, and mammals; functions as embryonic urinary bladder or as carrier of blood vessels to and from placenta.

allele (ă·lēl') [Gr. *allēlōn,* of one another]: one of a group of alternative genes which may occupy a given locus on a chromosome; a dominant and its correlated recessive are allelic genes, as are two correlated dominants or two correlated recessives.

alveolus (ăl·vē'ŏ·lŭs), *pl.* **alveoli** (—lī) [L. dim. of *alveus,* a hollow]: a small cavity or pit, e.g., a microscopic air sac of the lungs.

amino, amino acid, amination (ă·mē'nō, ă·mĭnā'shŭn): (1) —NH_2 group; (2) acid-containing amino group, general structure NH_2—R—COOH, constituent of protein; (3) addition of amino group to other compound.

amitosis (ăm'ĭ·tō'sĭs) [Gr. *a,* not, + *mitos,* thread]: form of cell division in which mitotic nuclear changes do not occur; the term applies to a large variety of different kinds of cellular reproduction.

amnion, amniote, amniotic (ăm'nĭ·ŏn) [Gr. dim. of *amnos,* lamb]: (1) one of the extra-embryonic membranes in reptiles, birds, and mammals, forming a sac around the embryo; (2) any reptile, bird, or mammal, i.e., any animal possessing an amnion during the embryonic state; (3) pertaining to the amnion, as in amniotic fluid.

Amphineura (ăm'fĭ·nū'rȧ) [Gr. *amphi,* both, + *neuron,* nerve]: a class of mollusks, including the chitons, characterized by a primitive ladder-type nervous system.

amylase (ăm'ĭ·lās) [L. *amylum,* starch]: an enzyme promoting the decomposition of polysaccharides into smaller carbohydrate units.

anaerobe, anaerobic (ăn·ā'ĕr·ōb, —ō'bĭk) [Gr. *an,* not, + *aeros* + *bios*]: (1) an oxygen-independent organism; (2) pertaining to an oxygen-independent form of respiration.

anamniote (ăn·ăm'nĭ·ōt): any vertebrate other than a reptile, bird, or mammal, i.e., one in which an amnion does not form during the embryonic phase.

anaphase (ăn′à·fāz) [Gr. *ana,* up, + *phasis,* appearance]: a stage in mitotic cell division, characterized by the migration of chromosome sets toward the spindle poles.

anatomy (à·năt′ô·mĭ) [Gr. *ana,* up, + *temnein,* to cut]: the gross structure of an organism, or the science which deals with gross structure; a branch of the science of morphology.

androgen (ăn′drô·jĕn) [Gr. *andros,* man, + *genēs,* born]: one of a group of male sex hormones.

angiosperm (ăn′jĭ·ô·spûrm′) [Gr. *angeion,* a vessel, + *sperma,* seed]: a member of a class of tracheophytic plants, characterized by the possession of flowers and fruits; a flowering plant.

anhydrase (ăn·hī′drās) [Gr. *an,* not, + *hydōr,* water]: an enzyme promoting the removal of water from a given type of compound, e.g., carbonic anhydrase, which specifically catalyzes the conversion of carbonic acid into water and carbon dioxide (or the reverse).

annelid, Annelida (ăn′ĕ·lĭd) [L. *anellus,* a ring]: (1) a segmented worm; (2) the phylum of segmented worms.

antheridium (ăn′thēr·ĭd′ĭ·ŭm) [Gr. *anthēros,* flowery]: the sperm-producing organ of plants.

anthocyanin (ăn′thô·sī′à·nĭn) [Gr. *anthos,* flower, + *kyanos,* blue]: a water-soluble pigment in plants, producing red, purple, and blue colors.

antibody (ăn′tĭ·bŏd′ĭ): a substance, produced within an organism, which opposes the action of another substance; in specific usage, an antibody is a globulin type of protein which combines and renders harmless an antigen, i.e., a foreign protein introduced into an organism by infectious processes.

antigen (ăn′tĭ·jĕn): a foreign substance, usually protein in nature, which elicits the formation of specific antibodies within an organism.

apical (ăp′ĭ·kăl) [L. *apex,* tip]: belonging to an apex, being at or near the tip; as in apical meristem, the embryonic plant tissue at the tip or root or stem.

archegonium (är′kĕ·gō′nĭ·ŭm) [Gr. *archegonos,* first of a race]: the egg-producing organ of plants.

archenteron (är·kĕn′tēr·ŏn) [Gr. *archein,* to be first, + *enteron,* gut]: the central cavity of a gastrula, lined by endoderm, representing the future digestive cavity of the adult.

arthropod, Arthropoda (är′thrô·pŏd, är·thrŏp′ô·dà) [Gr. *arthron,* joint, + *podos,* foot]: (1) a jointed-legged invertebrate, such as an insect or a crustacean; (2) the phylum of jointed-legged invertebrates.

ascus (ăs′kŭs) [Gr. *askos,* a bladder]: the tubular spore sac of a class of fungi; eight spores typically form within an ascus.

atom (ăt′ŭm) [Gr. *atomos,* indivisible]: the smallest whole unit of a chemical element; composed of given numbers of protons, neutrons, and other particles which form an atomic nucleus, and of given numbers of electrons, which orbit around the nucleus.

auricle (ô′rĭ·k′l) [L. dim. of *auris,* ear]: a chamber of the heart receiving blood from the circulation and pumping it into a ventricle.

autosome (ô′tô·sōm) [Gr. *autos,* self, + *soma,* body]: any chromosome which is not a sex chromosome.

autotroph, autotrophism (ô′tô·trŏf′, —ĭz′m) [Gr. *autos,* + *trophos,* feeder]: (1) an organism which manufactures organic nutrients from inorganic raw materials; (2) a form of nutrition in which only inorganic substances are required as raw materials.

auxin (ôk′sĭn) [Gr. *auxein,* to increase]: one of a group of humoral agents in plants, promoting cell elongation, hence growth.

avicularium (ā·vĭk′ũ·lā′rĭ·ŭm) [L. dim. of *avis,* bird]: a specially differentiated individual in a colony of ectoprocts, shaped like a bird's head, serving a protective function.

axon (ăk′sŏn): an outgrowth of a nerve cell, conducting impulses away from the cell body; a type of nerve fiber.

bacillus (bà·sĭl′ŭs) [L. dim. of *baculum,* rod]: any rod-shaped bacterium.

bacteriophage (băk·tēr′ĭ·ô·fāj) [*bacterium* + Gr. *phagein,* to eat]: one of a group of viruses which infect, parasitize, and eventually kill bacteria.

bacterium (băk·tēr′ĭ·ŭm) [Gr. dim. of *baktron,* a staff]: a small, typically unicellular organism characterized by the absence of a formed nucleus; genetic material is dispersed in clumps through the cytoplasm.

basidium (bà·sĭd′ĭ·ŭm) [Gr. dim. of *basis,* base]: a spore-bearing organ of a class of fungi; typically, four spores are formed on each basidium.

benthos, benthonic (bĕn′thŏs) [Gr., depth of the sea]: (1) collective term for organisms living along the bottoms of oceans and lakes; (2) adjective.

beriberi (bĕr′ĭ·bĕr′ĭ) [Singhalese *beri,* weakness]: disease produced by deficiency of vitamin B₁ (thiamine).

bicuspid (bī·kŭs′pĭd) [L. *bi,* two, + *cuspis,* point]: ending in two points, as in bicuspid heart valve, two flaps of tissue guarding opening between left auricle and left ventricle; see also *mitral*.

biennial (bī·ĕn′ĭ·ăl) [L. *bi*, two, + *annus*, year]: occurring once every two years, as in biennial plant, which flowers and forms seeds every second year.

bioluminescence (bī′ō·lū′mĭ·nĕs′ĕns) [Gr. *bios*, life, + L. *lumen*, light]: emission of light by living organisms.

biotin (bī′ō·tĭn): one of the B vitamins.

blastea (blăs·tē′a) [Gr. *blastos*, sprout]: hypothetical blastulalike ancestral animal, consisting of single layer of cells shaped into hollow sphere; may have given rise to double-layered gastrea.

blastopore (blăs′tō·pōr): opening connecting archenteron of gastrula with outside; represents future mouth in some animals, future anus in others.

blastula (blăs′tŭ·la): stage in early animal development, when embryo is a hollow, and in some cases a solid, sphere of cells; the sphere typically is constructed from a single layer of cells.

brachiopod, Brachiopoda (brā′kĭ·ō·pŏd, brā·kĭ·ŏp′ō·da) [L. *brachium*, arm, + Gr. *podos*, foot]: (1) a sessile, enterocoelomate, marine organism, possessing a pair of shells (valves), and internally a pair of coiled arms which bear ciliated tentacles; (2) phylum name.

bronchus, bronchiole (brŏng′kŭs, brŏng′kĭ·ōl) [Gr. *bronchos*, windpipe]: (1) a main branch of the trachea; (2) a smaller branch of a bronchus.

bryophyte, Bryophyta (brī′ō·fĭt) [Gr. *bryon*, moss, + *phyton*, a plant]: (1) a moss, liverwort, or hornwort, i.e., any terrestrial green plant which is neither algal nor tracheophytic; (2) phylum name.

bud, budding (bŭd): (1) an undeveloped organism or part of an organism; may be single-celled (e.g., bud of yeast, bud cell of sponge) or multicellular (e.g., leaf bud, Hydra bud); (2) a form of cell division in which the daughter cells are of unequal size (e.g., yeast).

buffer (bŭf′ēr): a substance which prevents appreciable changes of pH in solutions to which small amounts of acids or bases are added.

caecum (sē′kŭm) [L. *caecus*, blind]: cavity open at one end, e.g., the blind pouch at the beginning of the large intestine, connecting at one side with the small intestine.

Calorie (kăl′ō·rĭ) [L. *calor*, heat]: unit of heat, defined as that amount of heat required to raise the temperature of 1 kg of water by 1°C; a **small calorie**

is a thousandth part of the unit above, which is often designated as a "large" Calorie.

cambium (kăm′bĭ·ŭm) [L., exchange]: embryonic tissue in roots and stems of tracheophytes, giving rise to xylem and phloem (secondary growth).

carapace (kăr′a·pās) [fr. Sp. *carapacho*]: a hard case, or shield, covering the back of certain animals, e.g., the calcareous carapace of lobsters, the horny carapace of turtles.

carbohydrate, carbohydrase (kär′bō·hī′drāt): (1) an organic compound consisting of a chain of carbon atoms to which hydrogen and oxygen, present in a 2:1 ratio, are attached; (2) an enzyme promoting the synthesis or decomposition of a carbohydrate.

carboxyl (kär·bŏk′sĭl): the acid group of organic molecules: —COOH.

carnivore, Carnivora (kär′nĭ·vōr, kär·nĭv′ō·ra) [L. *carnivorus*, flesh-eating]: (1) any bulk-feeding organism subsisting on animals or parts of animals; (2) an order of mammals; includes cats, dogs, seals, walruses.

carotene, carotenoids (kăr′ō·tēn, ka·rŏt′ē·noid) [L. *carota*, carrot]: (1) a pigment producing creamyellow to carrot-orange colors; precursor of vitamin A; (2) a class of pigments of which carotene is a member.

catalysis, catalyst, catalytic (ka·tăl′ĭ·sĭs) [Gr. *katalysis*, dissolution]: (1) acceleration of a chemical reaction by a substance which does not become part of the endproduct; (2) a substance which accelerates a reaction as above; (3) adjective.

cathepsin (kă·thĕp′sĭn): one of a group of enzymes within cells promoting the synthesis or decomposition of proteins.

causalism (kôz′ăl·ĭz′m): view which holds that a terminal state of any natural process is an effect resulting from the properties of the initial state and that the initial state does not have foreknowledge of the terminal state; opposing nonscientific view is teleology.

ceboid (sē′boid): a New World monkey; uses its tail as a fifth limb.

Cenozoic (sē′nō·zō′ĭk) [Gr. *kainos*, recent, + *zōē*, life]: geological era after the Mesozoic, dating approximately from 75 million years ago to present.

centriole (sĕn′trĭ·ōl): cytoplasmic body forming spindle pole during mitosis and meiosis; present in cells of primitive plants and most animals.

centromere (sĕn′trō·mēr): region on chromosome at which spindle fibril is attached during mitosis and meiosis.

Cephalochordata, Cephalopoda, cephalothorax (sĕf′-à·lŏ—) [Gr. *kephalē,* head]: (1) a subphylum of chordates; the lancelets or amphioxus; (2) a class of mollusks; squids, octopuses, nautiluses: (3) the fused head and thorax in certain arthropods, e.g., crustacea.

cercaria (sûr·kā′rĭ·à) [Gr. *kerkos,* tail]: a larval stage in the life cycle of flukes; produced by a redia, and infects fish, where it encysts.

cercopithecoid (sûr′kŏ·pĭ·thē′koĭd): an Old World monkey; possesses tail, which is not used as limb.

cerebellum (sĕr′ĕ·bĕl′ŭm) [L. dim. of *cerebrum*]: a part of the vertebrate brain, controlling muscular coordination.

cerebrum (sĕr′ĕ·brŭm) [L., brain]: a part of the vertebrate brain, especially large in mammals; controls many voluntary functions and is seat of higher mental capacities.

chaetognath, Chaetognatha (kē′tŏg·năth, —à) [Gr. *chaitē,* hair, + *gnathos,* jaw]: (1) small marine wormlike enterocoelomate, with curved bristles on each side of mouth; (2) phylum name.

chelicera (kĕ·lĭs′ēr·à) [Gr. *chēlē,* claw]: a pair of pincerlike head appendages in spiders, scorpions, and arachnids generally.

chemosynthesis (kĕm′ŏ·sĭn′thĕ·sĭs): a form of autotrophic nutrition in certain bacteria, in which energy for the manufacture of carbohydrates is obtained from inorganic raw materials.

chitin (kī′tĭn): a horny organic substance forming the exoskeleton of arthropods and the epidermal cuticle of many other invertebrates.

chloroplast, chlorophyll, chlorophyte (klō′rŏ—) [Gr. *chloros,* green]: (1) chlorophyll-containing plastid; (2) green light-trapping pigment essential as energy donor in photosynthesis; (3) a green alga, member of the phylum Chlorophyta.

cholinergic (kō′lĭn·ûrjĭk): refers to a type of nerve fiber which releases acetyl-choline from the axon terminal when impulses are transmitted across synapses.

Chondrichthyes (kŏn·drĭk′thĭ·ēz) [Gr. *chondros,* cartilage, + *ichthyos,* fish]: fishes with cartilage skeleton, a class of vertebrates comprising sharks, skates, rays, and related types.

Chordata (kôr·dā′tà) [L. *chorda,* cord]: animal phylum in which all members possess notochord, dorsal nerve cord, and pharyngeal gill slits at least at some stage of the life cycle; four subphyla, the Hemichordata, the Urochordata, the Cephalochordata, and the Vertebrata.

chorion (kō′rĭ·ŏn) [Gr.]: one of the extra-embryonic membranes in reptiles, birds, and mammals; forms outer cover around embryo and all other membranes and in mammals contributes to structure of placenta.

choroid (kō′roid): mid-layer in wall of eyeball, between retina and sclera; carries blood supply to eye and contains light-absorbing black pigment.

chromosome (krō′mŏ·sōm) [Gr. *chroma,* color, + *soma,* body]: gene-containing filamentous body in cell nucleus, becoming conspicuous during mitosis and meiosis; the number of chromosomes per cell nucleus is constant for each species.

chrysophyte, Chrysophyta (krĭs′ŏ·fīt) [Gr. *chrysos,* gold, + *phyton,* a plant]: (1) a golden-brown alga, e.g., a diatom; (2) phylum name.

Ciliophora (sĭl′ĭ·ŏf′ôrà) [L. *cilium,* eyelid, + Gr. *phoros,* bearing]: a protozoan phylum, in which member organisms possess cilia on body surface; includes ciliates, e.g., *Paramecium.*

cilium (sĭl′ĭ·ŭm): microscopic bristlelike process, present on surfaces of many cell types and capable of vibratory motion; functions in cellular locomotion and in creation of currents in water.

coagulation (kŏ·ăg′ŭ·lā′shŭn) [L. *coagulare*]: change in physical state of proteins, when internal architecture of protein molecule is destroyed and molecule collapses; gross result is solidification of previously liquid or jellylike proteins.

coccus (kŏk′ŭs), *pl.* **cocci** (kŏk′sī) [Gr. *kokkos,* a grain]: a spherical bacterium.

cochlea (kŏk′lĕ·à) [Gr. *kochlias,* snail]: part of the inner ear, coiled like a snail shell; houses the organ of Corti.

coelenterate, Coelenterata (sĕ·lĕn′tēr·àt) [Gr. *koilos,* hollow, + *enteron,* gut]: (1) an invertebrate animal possessing a body wall of two cell layers, a single alimentary opening, and tentacles with sting cells; e.g., jellyfish, corals, sea anemones, hydroids; (2) phylum name.

coelom (sē′lŏm) [Gr. *koilōma,* a hollow]: body cavity of triploblastic animals, lined entirely by mesoderm.

coenzyme (kō·ĕn′zīm): a substance, usually organic, required if a given enzyme is to be active.

colloid (kŏl′oid) [Gr. *kolla,* glue]: a substance divided into fine particles, where each particle is larger than a particle of a true solution but smaller than one in a coarse suspension; a colloid system contains particles of appropriate size and a medium in which the particles are dispersed.

colon (kō'lŏn): the large intestine, portion of alimentary tract between caecum and rectum.

colostrum (kŏ·lŏs'trŭm): the first, lymphlike secretion of the mammary glands of pregnant mammals.

commensal, commensalism (kŏ·mĕn'săl, —ĭz'm) [L. *cum,* with, + *mensa,* table]: (1) an organism living symbiotically with a host, where the host neither benefits nor suffers from the association; (2) noun.

compound (kŏm'pound) [L. *componere,* to put together]: a substance consisting of identical molecules.

conjugation (kŏn·jŏŏ·gā'shŭn) [L. *conjugare,* to unite]: a mating process characterized by the temporary fusion of the mating partners; occurs particularly in unicellular organisms.

convergence (kŏn·vûr'jĕns) [L. *convergere,* to turn together]: the evolution of similar characteristics in organisms of widely different ancestry.

corpus luteum (kôr'pŭs lū'tĕ·ŭm), *pl.* **corpora lutea** [L.]: progesterone-secreting bodies in vertebrate ovaries, formed from remnants of follicles after ovulation.

cortex (kôr'tĕks), *pl.* **cortices** [L., bark]: the outer tissue layers of an organ or body part, e.g., adrenal cortex, cerebral cortex; also, in young plant stems, the tissue between epidermis and phloem.

cotyledon (kŏt'ĭ·lē'dŭn) [Gr. *kotylēdōn,* a cup shape]: the first leaf of a seed plant, developed by the embryo within the seed.

cotylosaur (kŏt'ĭ·lŏ·sôr') [Gr. *kotylē,* anything hollow, + *sauros,* lizard]: a member of a group of Permian fossil reptiles, evolved from labyrinthodont amphibian stock and ancestral to all other reptiles.

Craniata (krā'nĭ·ā'tà) [Gr. *kranion,* skull]: head-possessing chordates, i.e., vertebrates.

cretinism (krē'tĭn·ĭz'm) [fr. L. *christianus,* a Christian]: an abnormal condition resulting from underactivity of the thyroid in the young.

crossing over: exchange of parts between two paired chromosomes during meiosis, resulting in unexpected combinations of linked genes within the gametes.

crystalloid (krĭs'tăl·oid) [Gr. *krystallos,* ice]: a system of particles within a medium, able to form crystals under appropriate conditions; a true solution.

ctenophore, Ctenophora (tĕn'ŏ·fôr, tĕ·nŏf'ŏ·rà) [Gr. *ktenos,* comb, + *phoros,* bearing]: (1) a marine animal possessing a body wall of two cell layers, tentacles without sting cells, and a locomotor apparatus consisting of eight comb plates; a comb jelly; (2) phylum name.

cutaneous (kŭ·tā'nĕ·ŭs) [L. *cutis,* skin]: pertaining to the skin; e.g., cutaneous sense organ.

cyanophyte, Cyanophyta (sī·ăn'ŏ·fīt) [Gr. *kyanos,* dark blue, + *phyton,* plant]: (1) a blue-green alga; (2) phylum name.

cyclosis (sī·klō'sĭs) [Gr. *kyklos,* circle]: circular streaming and eddying of cellular protoplasm.

cytochrome, cytolysis, cytoplasm, cytosine (sī'tŏ—, sī-tŏl'—) [Gr. *kytos,* vessel]: (1) one of a group of hydrogen carriers in aerobic respiration; transfers hydrogen from flavoprotein to oxygen; (2) dissolution or disintegration of a cell; (3) the protoplasm of a cell between cell membrane and nucleus; (4) a purine, present in nucleotides and nucleic acids.

deamination (dē·ămĭ·nā'shŭn): removal of an amino group, especially from an amino acid.

decarboxylation (dē·kär·bŏk'sĭ·lā'shŭn): removal of a carboxyl group (—COOH).

deciduous (dĕ·sĭd'ů·ŭs) [L. *decidere,* to fall off]: to fall off at maturity, as in plants which shed foliage during the autumn.

dedifferentiation (dē·dĭf'ĕr·ĕn'shĭ·ā'shŭn): a regressive change toward a more primitive, embryonic, or earlier state; e.g., a process changing a highly specialized cell to a less specialized cell.

degrowth (dē'grōth): negative growth; becoming smaller.

dehydrogenation, dehydrogenase (dĕ·hī'drŏ·jĕn·ā'shŭn): (1) removal of hydrogen, as from a molecule; (2) an enzyme promoting dehydrogenation.

denaturation (dē·nă'tŭr·ā'shŭn): partial physical disruption of the internal architecture of a protein molecule; denaturation is usually reversible, whereas coagulation is not.

dendrite (dĕn'drīt) [Gr. *dendron,* tree]: filamentous outgrowth of a nerve cell, conducting nerve impulses from its free end toward the cell body.

denitrify, denitrification (dē·nī'trĭ·fī): (1) to convert nitrates to ammonia and molecular nitrogen, as by denitrifying bacteria; (2) noun.

denticle (dĕn'tĭ·k'l) [L. *denticulus,* small tooth]: small toothlike scale on shark skin.

dephosphorylation (dē·fŏs'fŏ·rĭ·lā'shŭn): removal of organic phosphate from a molecule.

desoxyribose (dĕs·ŏk'sĭ·rī'bōs): a 5-carbon sugar having one oxygen atom less than parent-sugar ribose; component of desoxyribose nucleic acid (DNA).

diabetes (dī′a·bē′tĕz) [Gr. *diabainein,* to pass through]: abnormal condition marked by insufficiency of insulin, sugar excretion in urine, low blood-glucose levels.

diastole (dī·ăs′tŏ·lē) [Gr. *diastolē,* moved apart]: phase of relaxation of auricles or ventricles, during which they fill with blood; preceded and succeeded by systole, i.e., contraction.

diastrophism (dī·ăs′trŏ·fĭz′m) [Gr. *diastrophē,* distortion]: geological deformation of the earth's crust, leading to slow rise or fall of land masses.

dicotyledon (dī·kŏt′ĭ·lē′dŭn) [Gr. *dis,* twice, + *kotylēdōn,* a cup shape]: a plant having two seed leaves or cotyledons; often abbreviated as dicot.

differentiation (dĭf′ĕr·ĕn′shĭ·ā′shŭn): a progressive change toward a permanently more mature or advanced state; e.g., a process changing a relatively unspecialized cell to a more specialized cell.

diffusion (dĭ·fū′zhŭn) [L. *diffundere,* to pour out]: migration of particles from a more concentrated to a less concentrated region; the process tends to equalize concentrations throughout a system.

dimorphism (dī·môr′fĭz′m) [Gr. *dis,* twice, + *morphē,* form]: difference of form between two members of a species, e.g., as between males and females; a special instance of polymorphism.

diploblast, diploblastic (dĭp′lŏ·blăst) [Gr. *diploos,* double, + *blastos,* sprout]: (1) an animal constructed from two primary germ layers, i.e., ectoderm and endoderm, e.g., sponges, coelenterates, ctenophores; (2) adjective.

diploid (dĭp′loid): a chromosome number twice that characteristic of a gamete of a given species.

disaccharide (dī·săk′a·rĭd) [Gr. *dis,* twice, + *sakcharon,* sugar]: a sugar composed of two monosaccharides; usually refers to 12-carbon sugars.

dissociation (dĭ·sō′sĭ·ā′shŭn) [L. *dissociare,* to disassociate]: the breakup of an electrolyte molecule in water, resulting in the formation of ions; synonymous with ionization.

divergence (dī·vûr′jĕns) [L. *divergere,* to incline apart]: evolutionary development of dissimilar characteristics in two or more lines descended from the same ancestral stock.

DNA: abbreviation of desoxyribose nucleic acid.

dominance: a functional attribute of genes; a dominant gene exerts its full effect regardless of the effect of its allelic partner.

DPN: abbreviation of diphosphopyridine nucleotide; a hydrogen carrier in respiration, transferring hydrogen from fuel either to flavoprotein (aerobic) or to pyruvic acid (anaerobic).

ductus arteriosus (dŭk′tŭs är·tē′rĭ·ō′sŭs): an artery, present only in the embryo and fetus, which conducts blood from the pulmonary artery to the aorta; shrivels at birth, when the lungs become functional.

duodenum (dū′ŏ·dē′nŭm) [L. *duodeni,* twelve each]: most anterior portion of the small intestine, continuation of the stomach; bile duct and pancreatic duct open into it.

echinoderm, Echinodermata (ĕ·kī′nŏ·dûrm) [Gr. *echinos,* urchin, + *derma,* skin]: (1) one of the spiny-skinned animals, i.e., starfishes, sea urchins, brittle stars, sea cucumbers, sea lilies; (2) phylum name.

Echiuroidea (ĕ·kī·ûr·oi′dĕ·a): a phylum of wormlike, schizocoelomate animals.

ectoderm, ectoparasite, Ectoprocta (ĕk′tŏ——) [Gr. *ektos,* outside]: (1) outer tissue layer of an embryo; (2) a parasite attached to the outside of a host, i.e., to skin, hair, etc.; (3) a phylum of sessile schizocoelomate animals, in which the intestine is U-shaped, the mouth is surrounded by a ring of ciliated tentacles, and the anus opens outside this ring.

egestion (ĕ·jĕs′chŭn) [L. *egerere,* to discharge]: the elimination from the alimentary system of unusable and undigested material.

electrolyte (ĕ·lĕk′trŏ·līt) [Gr. *ēlektron,* amber, + *lytos,* soluble]: a substance which ionizes in aqueous solution and so makes possible the conduction of electric current through the solution.

element (ĕl′ĕ·mĕnt): one of about 100 distinct natural or man-made types of matter, which, singly or in combination, compose all materials of the universe; an atom is the smallest representative unit of an element.

emulsion (ĕ·mŭl′shŭn) [L. *emulgere,* to milk out]: a colloidal system in which both the dispersed and the continuous phase are liquid.

endergonic (ĕn′dĕr·gŏ′nĭk): energy-requiring, as in a chemical reaction.

endocrine (ĕn′dŏ·krĭn) [Gr. *endon,* within, + *krinein,* to separate]: applied to type of gland which releases secretion not through a duct but directly into blood or lymph; functionally equivalent to hormone-producing.

endoderm, endodermis (ĕn′dŏ·dûrm): (1) inner tissue layer of an embryo; (2) single layer of tissue in a root which separates the cortex from the vascular tissues in the root core; the layer is waterproofed with suberin, but contains nonwaterproofed passage cells.

endoparasite (ĕn'dŏ·păr'a·sīt): a parasite living in the interior tissues of a host, i.e., not on surface tissues.

endoplasm, endoplasmic (ĕn'dŏ·plăz'm): the inner portion of the cytoplasm of a cell, i.e., the portion immediately surrounding the nucleus; contrasts with ectoplasm or cortex, i.e., the portion of cytoplasm immediately under the cell surface.

endoskeleton (ĕn'dŏ·skĕl'ĕ·tŭn): a skeleton in the interior of an animal, providing support from within.

endosperm (ĕn'dŏ·spûrm): triploid, often nutritive tissue within seed, formed by union of one sperm nucleus with two cells of female gametophyte.

energy (ĕn'ēr·jĭ) [Gr. *energos*, active]: capacity to do work; the time rate of doing work is called power.

enterocoel, enterocoelomate (ĕn'tēr·ŏ·sēl') [Gr. *enteron*, gut, + *koilos*, hollow]: (1) a coelom formed by the outpouching of a mesodermal sac from the endoderm; (2) an animal possessing an enterocoel, e.g., echinoderms, vertebrates.

enterokinase (ĕn'tēr·ŏ·kī'nās) [Gr. *enteron* + *kinētos*, moving]: an enzyme present in intestinal juice, which converts trypsinogen into trypsin.

Entoprocta (ĕn'tŏ·prŏk'ta) [Gr. *entos*, within, + *prōktos*, anus]: a phylum of sessile, pseudocoelomate animals, possessing a U-shaped alimentary tract, a mouth surrounded by a ring of ciliated tentacles, and an anus opening within this ring.

enzyme (ĕn'zīm) [Gr. *en*, in, + *zymē*, leaven]: a protein produced within an organism, capable of accelerating a particular chemical reaction; a type of catalyst.

epidermis (ĕp'ĭ·dûr'mĭs) [Gr. *epi*, over, + *derma*, skin]: the outermost surface epithelium of an organism.

epididymis (ĕp'ĭ·dĭd'ĭ·mĭs) [Gr. *epi* + *didymos*, testicle]: the greatly coiled portion of the sperm duct adjacent to the testis.

epigenesis (ĕp'ĭ·jĕn'ĕ·sĭs): view which holds that the terminal state of a living system is not contained explicitly within the initial state and that the terminal state develops step by step, each step being an operational consequence of the immediately preceding step.

epiglottis (ĕp'ĭ·glŏt'ĭs) [Gr. *epi* + *glōssa*, tongue]: a flap of tissue above the glottis; contains elastic cartilage, and in swallowing folds back over the glottis, so closing the air passage to the lungs.

epithelium (ĕp'ĭ·thĕ'lĭ·ŭm) [Gr. *epi* + *thēlē*, nipple]: a tissue in which the cells are packed tightly together, leaving little intercellular space.

esophagus (ĕ·sŏf'a·gŭs) [Gr. *oisō*, I shall carry, + *phagein*, to eat]: part of alimentary tract connecting pharynx and stomach.

estrogen (ĕs'trŏ·jĕn) [Gr. *oistros*, frenzy, + *genēs*, born]: one of a group of female sex hormones, produced by a follicle.

euphotic (ū·fō'tĭk) [Gr. *eu*, well, + *phōtos*, light]: applied to that surface layer of ocean or lake water through which sunlight can penetrate.

eurypterid (ū·rĭp'tēr·ĭd) [Gr. *eurys*, wide, + *pteron*, wing]: extinct Paleozoic arthropod, related to spiders and horseshoe crabs.

eustachian (ŭ·stā'kĭ·ăn): applied to canal connecting middle-ear cavity with the nasopharynx.

exergonic (ĕk'sēr·gŏ·nĭk): energy-yielding, as in a chemical reaction.

exocrine (ĕk'sŏ·krĭn) [Gr. *exō*, outside, + *krinein*, to separate]: applied to type of gland which releases secretion through a duct.

exoskeleton (ĕk'sŏ·skĕl'ĕ·tŭn): an external skeleton of an animal, providing support from the outside.

exteroceptor (ĕk'stēr·ŏ·sĕp'tēr): a sense organ receptive to stimuli from the external environment of an organism.

fat: an organic compound formed by union of glycerin with fatty acids.

feedback: information passing from an effector to a receptor, i.e., a signal indicating the action performed by an effector.

fermentation (fûr'mĕn·tā'shŭn): synonym for anaerobic respiration, i.e., fuel combustion in the absence of oxygen.

fetus (fē'tŭs) [L., offspring]: prenatal stage of development in man and other mammals, following the embryonic stage; roughly from third month of pregnancy to birth.

fiber (fī'bēr) [L. *fibra*, thread]: a strand or filament of protoplasmic material produced by cells but located outside of cells.

fibril (fī'brĭl) [L. dim. of *fibra*]: a strand or filament of protoplasmic material produced by cells and located within cells.

fibrin, fibrinogen (fī'brĭn, fī·brĭn'ŏ·jĕn): (1) coagulated blood protein forming the bulk of a blood clot; (2) a protein present in blood which upon coagulation forms a clot.

flagellate, flagellum (flăj′ĕ·lāt, —ŭm) [L., whip]: (1) equipped with one or more flagella; an organism possessing flagella; (2) a microscopic, whiplike protoplasmic filament serving as locomotor structure in flagellate cells.

flavoprotein (flā′vŏ—) [L. *flavus*, yellow]: a hydrogen carrier in aerobic respiration, derived from riboflavin; passes hydrogen from DPN to the cytochrome system.

fluorescence (floo′ŏ·rĕs′ĕns) [L. *fluere*, to flow]: emission of radiation (light) by a substance which has absorbed radiation from another source.

follicle (fŏl′ĭ·k'l) [L. *folliculus*, small ball]: hollow ball of cells in the ovary, containing a maturing egg.

foraminifera (fŏ·răm′·ĭ·nĭf′ĕr·à) [L. *foramen*, hole, + *ferre*, to bear]: a group of sarcodine protozoa, characterized by delicate calcareous shells with holes, through which pseudopods are extruded.

fovea centralis (fō′vĕ·à·sĕn·trā′lĭs) [L., central pit]: small area in the optic center of the retina; only cone cells are present here, and stimulation leads to the most acute vision.

fucoxanthin (fū′kŏ·zăn′thĭn): a brownish pigment found in diatoms, brown algae, and dinoflagellates.

fundus (fŭn′dŭs) [L., bottom]: the bottom or base of a hollow structure, i.e., the fundus of the stomach, the part to the left of the esophagus, farthest away from the intestinal opening.

gamete (găm′ēt) [Gr. *gamein*, to marry]: reproductive cell which must fuse with another before it can develop; sex cell.

gametophyte (găm·ē′tŏ·fīt): a gamete-producing plant; phase of life cycle in certain plants which alternates with a sporophyte phase.

ganglion (găng′glĭ·ŭn) [Gr., a swelling]: a collection of cell bodies of neurons located outside the brain or the spinal cord.

gastrea (găs·trē′à) [Gr. *gastros*, stomach]: hypothetical gastrulalike ancestral animal, consisting of a double layer of cells shaped into a hollow sphere with a single opening; may have given rise to modern diploblastic animals and to ancestor of triploblasts.

gastrin (găs′trĭn): a hormone produced by the stomach wall when food makes contact with the wall; stimulates other parts of the wall to secrete gastric juice.

Gastropoda (găs·trŏp′ŏ·dà) [Gr. *gastros* + *podos*, foot]: a class of mollusks; comprises snails and slugs.

Gastrotricha (găs′trŏt′rĭ′kà) [Gr. *gastros* + *trichos*, hair]: a phylum of minute, multicellular, aquatic, pseudocoelomate animals, possessing cilialike bristles on the body surface.

gastrula, gastrulation (găs′troo·là, —lā′shŭn): (1) a two-layered, and in most cases later three-layered, stage in the embryonic development of animals; the layers are the ectoderm, mesoderm, and endoderm, and they typically form a hollow sac, the opening being the blastopore; (2) the process of gastrula formation.

gel (jĕl) [L. *gelare*, to freeze]: quasi-solid state of a colloidal system, where the solid particles form the continuous phase and the liquid medium forms the discontinuous phase.

gemma (jĕm′à) [L., a bud]: cup-shaped vegetative bud in bryophytes, capable of developing into whole plant.

gene (jēn) [Gr. *genēs*, born]: a segment of a chromosome, definable only in operational terms; repository of a unit of genetic information, contributing to control and maintenance of cell character.

genome (jēn′ōm): the totality of genes in a haploid set of chromosomes, hence the sum of all different genes in a cell.

genotype (jĕn′ŏ·tīp): the particular set of genes present in an organism and its cells; the genetic constitution.

genus (jē′nŭs) [L., race]: a rank category in taxonomic classification, between species and family; a group of very closely related species.

geotropism (jĕ·ŏt′rŏ·pĭz′m) [Gr. *gē*, earth, + *tropē*, a turning]: behavior governed and oriented by gravity, i.e., growth of roots toward center of earth.

germ layer, germ mutation: (1) ectoderm, mesoderm, or endoderm of animal embryo; (2) mutation occurring in a germ cell, i.e., a gamete or other reproductive cell.

gestation (jĕs·tā′shŭn) [L. *gestare*, to bear]: process or period of carrying young in uterus.

globin (glō′bĭn) [L. *globus*, globe]: a protein; together with pigment heme forms hemoglobin.

globulin (glŏb′ŭ·lĭn): one of a class of proteins present in blood plasma; may function as antibody.

glomerulus (glŏ·mĕr′ŭ·lŭs) [L. dim. of *glomus*, ball]: a small meshwork of blood capillaries found in the cup-shaped capsule of a nephron.

glottis (glŏt′ĭs) [Gr. *glōssa*, tongue]: slitlike opening in the larynx, formed by the vocal cords.

glucogenic (gloo′kŏ·jĕn′ĭk): glucose-producing, e.g., certain amino acids after deamination.

glucose (glōō′kōs) [Gr. *gleukos,* sweet wine]: a 6-carbon sugar; principal form in which carbohydrates are transported from cell to cell in plants and animals.

glycerin (glĭs′ĕr·ĭn) [Gr. *glykeros,* sweet]: an organic compound possessing a 3-carbon skeleton; may unite with fatty acids and form a fat.

glycogen (glī′kŏ·jĕn): a polysaccharide consisting of some 12 to 18 glucose units; a principal storage form of carbohydrates in animals.

goiter (goi′tēr) [L. *guttur,* throat]: an enlargement of the thyroid gland; may be an overgrowth resulting in excessive secretion of thyroid hormone, or may be a compensatory overgrowth occasioned by undersecretion of thyroid hormone.

Golgi body (gôl′jĕ): a particulate component of cell cytoplasm; probably plays a role in the manufacture of certain cell secretions.

gonad (gōn′ăd) [Gr. *gonē,* generator]: collective term for the reproductive organs of males and females, i.e., testes and ovaries.

gradation (grȧ·dā′shŭn) [L. *gradus,* step]: leveling of land by the geological effects of erosion.

granum (grăn′ŭm) [L., grain]: a functional unit of a chloroplast; smallest particle capable of carrying out photosynthesis.

gymnosperm (jĭm′nŏ·spûrm) [Gr. *gymnos,* naked, + *sperma,* seed]: a plant belonging to a class of seed plants in which the seeds are not enclosed in an ovary; includes the conifers.

haploid (hăp′loid) [Gr. *haploos,* single, simple]: a chromosome number characteristic of a mature gamete of a given species.

hemichordate (hĕm′ĭ·kôr′dāt) [Gr. *hēmi,* half, + L. *chorda,* cord]: a member of a subphylum of chordates; wormlike, body composed of proboscis, collar, and trunk; head absent, notochord rudimentary.

hemoglobin (hē′mŏ·glō′bĭn) [Gr. *haima,* blood, + L. *globus,* globe]: oxygen-carrying constituent of red blood corpuscles; consists of red pigment heme and protein globin.

hemophilia (hē′mŏ·fĭl′ĭ·ȧ) [Gr. *haima* + *philos,* loving]: a hereditary disease characterized by excessive bleeding from even minor wounds; clotting mechanism is impared by failure of blood platelets to rupture after contact with torn edges of blood vessels.

hepatic (hĕ·păt′ĭk) [Gr. *hēpar,* liver]: pertaining to the liver; as in hepatic vein, hepatic portal vein.

herbaceous (hûr·bā′shŭs) [L. *herbaceus,* grassy]: having the character of an herb; contrasts with woody.

herbivore (hûr′bĭ·vōr) [L. *herba,* herb, + *vorare,* to devour]: a plant-eating animal.

hermaphrodite (hûr·măf′rŏ·dīt) [fr. Gr. Hermes + Aphrodite]: an organism possessing both male and female reproductive systems.

heteroauxin (hĕt′ēr·ŏ·ôk′sĭn) [Gr. *heteros,* other, + *auxein,* to increase]: the most potent of the auxins, growth hormones in plants; chemically heteroauxin is indole acetic acid.

heterosporous (hĕt′ēr·ŏs′pŏrŭs): producing two different types of spores, viz., microspores and megaspores; microspores give rise to male gametophytes, megaspores to female gametophytes.

heterotroph, heterotrophism (hĕt′ēr·ŏ·trŏf) [Gr. *heteros* + *trophos,* feeder]: (1) an organism which must obtain both inorganic and organic raw materials from the environment; (2) form of nutrition characteristic of heterotrophs.

heterozygote, heterozygous (hĕt′ēr·ŏ·zī′gōt) [Gr. *heteros* + *zygotos,* yoked]: (1) an organism in which a pair of alleles for a given trait consists of different (e.g., dominant and recessive) kinds of genes; (2) adjective.

hirudin (hĭr′ŭ·dĭn) [L. *hirudo,* leech]: a chemical produced by leeches which prevents clotting of blood.

hominoid (hŏm′ĭ·noid) [L. *homo,* man]: manlike; applied especially to various extinct fossil relatives of man.

homology (hŏ·mŏl′ŏ·jĭ) [Gr. *homologia,* agreement]: similarity in embryonic development and adult structure, indicative of common evolutionary ancestry.

homozygote, homozygous (hō′mŏ·zī′gōt) [Gr. *homos,* same, + *zygotos*]: (1) an organism in which a pair of alleles for a given trait consists of the same (e.g., either dominant or recessive, but not both) kinds of genes; (2) adjective.

humerus (hū′mĕr·ŭs) [L., shoulder]: the bone of the upper part of the forelimb, from shoulder to elbow.

humoral (hū′mĕr·ȧl) [L. *humor,* fluid]: pertaining to the body fluids; as in humoral agent, a substance carried in the body fluids and having specific effects on specific tissues.

humus (hū′mŭs) [L., soil]: the organic portion of soil.

hybrid (hī′brĭd) [L. *hibrida,* offspring of tame sow and wild boar]: an organism which is heterozygous for one or more (usually many) gene pairs.

hydrolysis (hī·drŏl′ĭ·sĭs) [Gr. *hydōr,* water, + *lysis,* a loosening]: dissolution through the agency of water; especially decomposition of a chemical by the addition of water.

hydroponics (hī′drŏ·pŏn′ĭks) [Gr. *hydōr* + *ponos,* labor]: growing plants without soil, by immersing the roots in a nutrient-rich water medium.

hydroxyl (hī·drŏk′sĭl): OH⁻, a negatively charged ion released by alkalies in water solution.

hyperparasitism (hī′pēr—) [Gr. *hyper,* above]: infection of a parasite by one or more other parasites.

hypertonic, hypertonicity (hī′pēr·tŏn′ĭk): (1) exerting greater osmotic pull than the medium on the other side of a semipermeable membrane, hence possessing a greater concentration of particles and acquiring water during osmosis; (2) noun.

hypha (hī′fȧ) [Gr. *hyphē,* a web]: a filamentous protoplasmic unit of a fungus; a meshwork of hyphae forms a mycelium.

hypothalamus: a region of the forebrain, containing various centers of the autonomic nervous system.

hypothesis (hī·pŏth′ĕ·sĭs) [Gr. *hypo,* under, + *tithenai,* to put]: a guessed solution of a scientific problem; must be tested by experimentation and, if not validated, must then be discarded.

hypotonic, hypotonicity (hī′pŏ·tŏn′ĭk): (1) exerting lesser osmotic pull than the medium on the other side of a semipermeable membrane; hence possessing a lesser concentration of particles and losing water during osmosis; (2) noun.

ichthyosaur (ĭk′thĭ·ŏ·sôr) [Gr. *ichthyos,* fish, + *sauros,* lizard]: extinct marine Mesozoic reptile, with fish-shaped body and porpoiselike snout.

induction, inductor (in·dŭk′shŭn) [L. *inducere,* to introduce]: (1) process in embryo in which one tissue or body part causes the differentiation of another tissue or body part; (2) an embryonic tissue which causes the differentiation of another.

ingestion (in·jĕs′chŭn) [L. *ingerere,* to put in]: intake of food from the environment into the alimentary system.

inorganic (ĭn·ôr·găn′ĭk): applied to noncarbon compounds and those carbon compounds which are derived from or related to carbon dioxide.

insulin (ĭn′sŭ·lĭn) [L. *insula,* island]: a hormone produced by the islets of Langerhans in the pancreas; promotes the conversion of blood glucose into tissue glycogen.

integument (in·tĕg′ŭ·mĕnt) [L. *integere,* to cover]: covering; external coat; skin.

intermedin (ĭn·tēr·mē′dĭn): hormone produced by the mid-portion of the pituitary gland; adjusts degree

of extension of pigment cells in skin of certain vertebrates, e.g., frogs.

internode (in′tēr·nōd′): section of a plant stem located between two successive nodes.

interoceptor (in′tēr·ŏ·sĕp′tēr): a sense organ receptive to stimuli generated in the interior of an organism.

invagination (in·văj′ĭ·nā′shŭn) [L. *in—,* in, + *vagina,* sheath]: local infolding of a layer of tissue, leading to the formation of a pouch or sac; as in invagination during gastrulation.

invertase (in·vûr′tās) [L. *invertere,* to invert]: enzyme promoting the splitting of sucrose into glucose and fructose, or the reverse.

iodopsin (ī′ŏ·dŏp′sĭn): pigment present in cone cells and functioning in chemistry of color vision.

ion, ionization (ī′ŏn, —ī·zā′shŭn) [Gr. *ienai,* to go]: (1) an electrically charged atom or group of atoms; (2) splitting of a molecule into ions in water solution.

isosporous (ī′sŏs′pŏ·rŭs) [Gr. *isos,* equal]: producing a single kind of spore which develops into either a male or a female gametophyte.

isotonic (ī′sŏ·tŏn′ĭk): exerting the same osmotic pull as the medium on the other side of a semipermeable membrane; hence possessing the same concentration of particles; the net gain or loss of water during osmosis is zero.

isotope (ī′sŏ·tōp) [Gr. *isos* + *topos,* place]: one of several possible forms of a chemical element, differing from other forms in atomic weight, but not in chemical properties.

keratin (kĕr′ȧ·tĭn) [Gr. *keratos,* horn]: a protein formed by certain epidermal tissues, e.g., those of mammalian skin.

ketogenic (kē′tŏ·jĕn′ĭk): fatty-acid-producing, e.g., certain amino acids after deamination.

Kinorhyncha (kĭn′ŏ·rĭng′kȧ): a small phylum of pseudocoelomate animals.

labyrinthodont (lăb′ĭ·rĭn′thŏ·dŏnt) [Gr. *labyrinthos,* labyrinth]: extinct, late Paleozoic fossil amphibian.

lacteal (lăk′tĕ·ăl) [L. *lactis,* milk]: lymph vessel in a villus of the intestinal wall.

lactogenic (lăk′tŏ·jĕn′ĭk): milk-producing; as in lactogenic hormone, secreted by the pituitary.

larva (lär′vȧ), *pl.* **larvae** (—vē) [L., mask]: period in developmental history of animals, between embryo and adult; the larval period begins at hatching and terminates at metamorphosis.

larynx (lăr′ĭngks) [Gr.]: voice box; sound-producing organ in mammals.

leucocyte (lū′kȯ·sīt) [Gr. *leukos*, white, + *kytos*, vessel]: a type of white blood cell, characterized by a beaded, elongated nucleus.

leukemia (lŭ·kē′mĭ·à): a cancerous condition of blood, characterized by overproduction of leucocytes.

lichen (lī′kĕn) [Gr. *leichēn*]: a symbiotic, mutualistic association of an algal type and a fungal type.

lignin (lĭg′nĭn) [L. *lignum*, wood]: a substance related to cellulose, present in substantial quantities in wood.

lipase (lī′pās) [Gr. *lipos*, fat]: an enzyme promoting the conversion of fat into fatty acids and glycerin, or the reverse.

lipid, lipoid (lĭp′ĭd): (1) fat, fatty, pertaining to fat; (2) fatlike.

littoral (lĭt′ȯ·răl) [L. *litus*, seashore]: the sea floor from the shore to the edge of the continental shelf.

luciferase, luciferin (lŭ·sĭf′ĕr·ās, —ĭn) [L. *lux*, light, + *ferre*, to bring]: (1) enzyme contributing to the production of light by living organisms; (2) a group of various substances essential in the production of bioluminescence.

lycopsid (lī·kŏp′sĭd) [Gr. *lykos*, wolf]: a member of a subphylum of tracheophytes; the club mosses.

lymph (lĭmf) [L. *lympha*, goddess of moisture]: the body fluid outside of the blood circulation; leaks out of, and eventually returns to, the blood circulation.

lymphocyte (lĭm′fȯ·sīt): a type of white blood cell, characterized by a rounded or kidney-shaped nucleus.

macronucleus (măk′rȯ·nū′klĕ·ŭs) [Gr. *makros*, long, + *nucleus*, kernel]: a large type of nucleus found in ciliate protozoa; controls all but reproductive functions in these animals.

madreporite (măd′rĕ·pȯ·rīt) [It. *madre*, mother, + *poro*, passage]: a sievelike opening on the upper surface of echinoderms, connecting the water-vascular system with the outside.

maltose (môl′tōs): a 12-carbon sugar formed by the union of two glucose units.

marsupial (mär·sū′pĭ·ăl) [Gr. *marsypion*, little bag]: a pouched mammal, member of the mammalian subclass Metatheria.

mastax (măs′tăks): the grinding and chewing organ of rotifers.

Mastigophora (măs′tĭ·gŏf′ȯ·rȧ) [Gr. *mastix*, scourge, whip, + *phoros*, bearing]: a phylum of primarily unicellular, flagellate organisms; syn. Flagellata.

maxilla (măk·sĭl′ȧ) [L.]: in arthropods, one of the head appendages; in vertebrates, one of the upper jaw-bones.

maxilliped (măk·sĭl′ĭ·pĕd) [L. *pedis*, foot]: one of three pairs of segmental appendages in lobsters and other crustacea, located posterior to the maxillae.

mechanism (mĕk′à·nĭz′m) [Gr. *mēchanē*, machine]: a view which holds that natural events can be accounted for entirely by the laws of physics and chemistry.

medulla (mĕ·dŭl′à) [L.]: the inner tissue layers of an organ or body part, e.g., adrenal medulla; the medulla oblongata is a region of the hindbrain which connects with the spinal cord.

medusa (mĕ·dū′sà): the free-swimming stage in the life cycle of coelenterates; a jellyfish.

megaspore (mĕg′à·spōr) [Gr. *megas*, great]: a type of spore which develops into a female gametophyte.

meiosis (mī·ō′sĭs) [Gr. *meioun*, to make smaller]: process occurring at different points in the life cycles of different organisms in which the chromosome number is reduced by half; compensates for the chromosome-doubling effect of fertilization.

menopause (mĕn′ȯ·pôz) [Gr. *menos*, month, + *pauein*, to cause to cease]: the time at the end of the reproductive period of (human) females when menstrual cycles cease to occur.

menstruation (mĕn′strŏŏ·ā′shŭn) [L. *mensis*, month]: the discharge of uterine tissue and blood from the vagina, at the end of a menstrual cycle in which fertilization has not occurred.

meristem (mĕr′ĭ·stĕm) [Gr. *meristos*, divided]: embryonic tissue in adult plants, capable of giving rise to additional adult tissues, e.g., apical shoot or root meristem, cambium.

mesoderm (mĕs′ȯ·dûrm) [Gr. *mesos*, middle, + *derma*, skin]: the middle tissue layers of an embryo, between ectoderm and endoderm.

mesogloea (mĕs′ȯ·glē′à) [Gr. *mesos* + *gloios*, glutinous substance]: the jellylike layer between the ectoderm and endoderm of coelenterates and comb jellies.

mesophyll (mĕs′ȯ·fil) [Gr. *mesos* + *phyllon*, leaf]: tissue in the interior of leaves, composed of chlorophyll-containing cells arranged either into compact layers (palisade mesophyll) or into loose aggregations (spongy mesophyll).

metabolism (mĕ·tăb'ô·lĭz'm) [Gr. *metabolē,* change]: a group of life-sustaining processes including principally nutrition, production of energy (respiration), and synthesis of more protoplasm.

metamorphosis (mĕt'a·môr'fô·sĭs) [Gr. *metamorphoun,* to transform]: the transformation of a larva into an adult.

metaphase (mĕt'ă·fāz) [Gr. *meta,* between]: a stage during mitotic cell division in which the chromosomes line up in a plane at right angles to the spindle axis.

micron (mī'krŏn), *pl.* **microns, micra** [Gr. *mikros,* small]: one-thousandth part of a millimeter, a unit of microscopic length.

micronucleus (mī'krô·nū'klĕ·ŭs): a small type of nucleus found in ciliate protozoa; controls principally the reproductive functions of these organisms.

microsome (mī'krô·sōm) [Gr. *soma,* body]: a particulate constituent of cytoplasm; contains RNA and is the site of protein synthesis.

microspore (mī'krô·spōr): a type of spore which develops into a male gametophyte; syn. pollen.

mimicry (mĭm'ĭk·rĭ) [Gr. *mimos,* mime]: the superficial resemblance of certain animals, particularly insects, to other more powerful or more protected ones, resulting in a measure of protection for the mimics.

miracidium (mī'ră·sĭd'ĭ·ŭm): a larval stage in the life cycle of flukes; develops from an egg and gives rise in turn to numerous sporocyst larvae.

mitochondrion (mī'tô·kŏn'drĭ·ŏn) [Gr. *mitos,* thread, + *chondros,* grain]: a particulate constituent of cytoplasm; the site of respiration.

mitosis (mī·tō'sĭs) [Gr. *mitos,* thread]: a form of cell division characterized by complex chromosome movements and exact chromosome duplication.

mitral (mī'trăl) [fr. *miter*]: applied to valve between left auricle and ventricle of heart; syn. bicuspid.

modulator (mŏd'ŭ·lā'tẽr): general term for one of the components of steady-state control systems; receives and interprets signals from a receptor and selects and sends out signals to an effector.

molecule (mŏl'ĕ·kūl) [L. *moles,* mass]: the smallest whole unit of a compound; consists of two or more atoms of the same or of different elements.

Mollusca, mollusk (mŏ·lŭs'kà, mŏl'ŭsk) [L. *molluscus,* soft]: (1) a phylum of schizocoelomate animals; unsegmented, body composed of visceral mass, foot, and shell; comprises chitons, snails, clams, squids, and others; (2) a member of the phylum Mollusca.

monocotyledon (mŏn'ô·kŏt'ĭ·lē'dŭn) [Gr. *monos,* single]: a plant having a single seed leaf or cotyledon; often abbreviated as monocot.

monophyletic (mŏn'ô·fī·lĕt'ĭk) [Gr. *monos* + *phylon,* tribe]: developed from a single ancestral type; contrasts with polyphyletic.

monosaccharide (mŏn'ô·săk'a·rīd) [Gr. *monos* + *saccharon,* sugar]: a simple sugar, which cannot be decomposed into smaller sugar molecules; 5- and 6-carbon sugars are monosaccharides.

morphogenesis (môr'fô·jĕn'ĕ·sĭs) [Gr. *morphē,* form, + *genēs,* born]: development of size, form, and other architectural features of organisms.

morphology (môr·fŏl'ô·jĭ) [Gr. *morphē* + *logos,* study]: the study or science of structure, at any level of organization; e.g., cytology, study of cell structure; histology, study of tissue structure; anatomy, study of gross structure of organisms.

mucosa (mŭ·kō'sà) [L. *mucosus,* mucus]: a mucus-secreting membrane, e.g., the inner lining of the intestine.

mutation (mŭ·tā'shŭn) [L. *mutare,* to change]: a stable change of a gene, such that the changed condition is inherited by offspring cells.

mycelium (mī·sē'lĭ·ŭm) [Gr. *mykēs,* mushroom]: the vegetative portion of a fungus, consisting of a meshwork of hyphae.

Mycophyta (mī'kô·fī'tà) [Gr. *mykēs* + *phyton,* plant]: the plant phylum comprising the fungi.

myelin (mī'ĕ·lĭn) [Gr. *myelos,* marrow]: a fatty material which surrounds the axons of nerve cells in the central nervous system.

myofibril (mī'ô·fī'brĭl) [Gr. *myos,* muscle]: a contractile filament within a cell, especially a muscle cell or muscle fiber.

myosin (mī'ô·sĭn): a protein which can be isolated from muscle; forms an integral component of the contraction machinery of muscle.

myxedema (mĭk'sĕ·dē'mà) [Gr. *myxa,* slime, + *oidēma,* a swelling]: a disease resulting from thyroid deficiency in the adult, characterized by local swellings in and under the skin.

myxomycete (mĭk'sô·mī·sēt') [Gr. *myxa* + *mykēs,* mushroom]: a slime mold, member of the phylum Myxophyta.

nekton (nĕk'tŏn) [Gr. *nēktos,* swimming]: collective term for the actively swimming organisms in the ocean.

nematode (něm′á·tōd) [Gr. *nēmatos,* thread]: a round-worm, member of the pseudocoelomate phylum Nematoda.

Nematomorpha (něm′á·tŏ·môr′fá) [Gr. *nēmatos + morphē,* form]: hairworms, a pseudocoelomate phylum.

Nemertinea (něm·ēr·tĭn′ē·á) [Gr. *Nemertēs,* a Nereid]: proboscis worms, an acoelomate phylum.

nephric, nephron (něf′rĭk, —rŏn) [Gr. *nephros,* kidney]: (1) pertaining to a nephron; (2) a functional unit of the vertebrate kidney, consisting of glomerulus, capsule, convoluted tubules, Henle's loop, and collecting tubule.

neritic (nĕ·rĭt′ĭk) [fr. *Nereus,* a seagod]: oceanic habitat zone, subdivision of the pelagic zone, comprising the open water above the continental shelf, i.e., above the littoral.

neuron (nū′rŏn) [Gr., nerve]: nerve cell, including cell body, dendrites, and axons.

nitrify, nitrification (nī′trĭ·fī, —fĭ·kā′shŭn): (1) to convert ammonia and nitrites to nitrates, as by nitrifying bacteria; (2) noun.

node (nōd) [L. *nodus,* knot]: in plants, a joint of a stem; place where branches and leaves are joined to stem.

nonelectrolyte: a substance which does not ionize in water solution, hence does not conduct electric currents through the solution; e.g., glucose.

notochord (nō′tŏ·kôrd) [Gr. *noton,* the back, + L. *chorda,* cord]: longitudinal elastic rod of cells serving as internal skeleton in the embryos of all chordates and in the adults of some; in most adult chordates the notochord is replaced by a vertebral column.

nucleic acid (nŭ·klē′ĭk): one of a class of molecules composed of joined nucleotide complexes; the principal types are desoxyribose nucleic acid (DNA), found only in cell nuclei (chromosomes), and ribose nucleic acid (RNA), found both in cell nuclei (chromosomes and nucleoli) and in cytoplasm (e.g., microsomes).

nucleolus (nŭ·klē′ŏ·lŭs): an RNA-containing body within the nucleus of a cell; a derivative of chromosomes.

nucleoplasm (nū′klĕ·ŏ·plăz′m): the protoplasm which forms a nucleus; also specifically the nuclear sap.

nucleoprotein (nū′klĕ·ŏ—): a supermolecule composed of nucleic acid and protein; occurs in two variant forms, according to whether the nucleic acid portion is DNA or RNA.

nucleotide (nū′klĕ·ŏ·tīd): a molecule consisting of joined phosphate, 5-carbon sugar (either ribose or desoxyribose), and a purine or a pyrimidine (adenine, or guanine, or uracil, or thymine, or cytosine).

nucleus (nū′klĕ·ŭs) [L., a kernel]: a body present in all cell types except the bacteria and the blue-green algae and consisting of external nuclear membrane, interior nuclear sap, and chromosomes and nucleoli suspended in the sap.

olfaction, olfactory (ŏl·făk′shŭn, —tŏ·rĭ) [L. *olfacere,* to smell]: (1) the process of smelling; (2) pertaining to smell.

omnivore (ŏm′nĭ·vōr) [L. *omnis,* all, + *vorare,* to devour]: an animal which may subsist on plant foods, animal foods, or both.

operculum (ŏ·pûr′kŭ·lŭm) [L., a lid]: a lidlike structure, e.g., the plate on each side of the head of bony fishes which covers and protects the gills.

organ (ôr′găn) [fr. Gr. *organon*]: a group of different tissues joined structurally and cooperating functionally to perform a composite task.

organic (ôr·găn′ĭk): applied to molecules containing carbon, except those which are derivatives of carbon dioxide; virtually all organic molecules contain linked carbon atoms.

organism (ôr′găn·ĭz′m): an individual living creature, either unicellular or multicellular.

ornithine (ôr′nĭ·thēn) [Gr. *ornithos,* bird]: an amino acid which, in the liver of vertebrates, contributes to the conversion of ammonia and carbon dioxide into urea.

osmosis (ŏs·mō′sĭs) [Gr. *ōsmos,* impulse]: the process in which water migrates through a semipermeable membrane, from a side containing a lesser concentration of particles to the side containing a greater concentration; migration continues until particle concentrations are equal on both sides (i.e., until the relative concentrations of water are the same).

Osteichthyes (ŏs·tĕ·ĭk′thĭ·ēz) [Gr. *osteon,* bone]: a class of vertebrates, comprising the bony fishes.

ovary (ō′vá·rĭ) [L. *ovum,* egg]: the reproductive organ of female organisms; in plants, contains one or more megaspores (hence female gametophytes and eggs); in animals, manufactures eggs.

oviparity, oviparous (ō′vĭ·păr′ĭ·tĭ, ŏ·vĭp′á·rŭs) [L. *ovum + parere,* to bring forth]: (1) reproductive pattern in which eggs are released by the female; offspring development therefore occurs outside the maternal body; (2) adjective.

ovoviviparity, ovoviviparous (ō′vŏ·vĭv′ĭ·păr′ĭ·tĭ, ō′vŏ·vī·vĭp′a·rŭs): (1) reproductive pattern in which eggs develop within the maternal body, but without nutritive or other metabolic aid by the female parent; offspring are born as miniature adults; (2) adjective.

ovulation (ō′vŭ·lā′shŭn): expulsion of an egg from the ovary, and deposition of egg into the oviduct.

oxidation (ŏk′sĭ·dā′shŭn): internal rearrangement of a molecule so as to create a high-energy bond; often achieved by dehydrogenation.

paleoniscoid (pā′lĕ·ŏ·nĭs′koid): extinct Devonian bony fish, ancestral to modern bony fishes, lungfishes, and lobe-fin fishes.

paleontology (pā′lĕ·ŏn·tŏl′ŏ·gĭ) [Gr. *palaios*, old, + *onta*, existing things]: study of past geological times, principally by means of fossils.

Paleozoic (pā′lĕ·ŏ·zō′ĭk) [Gr. *palaios* + *zōē*, life]: the geological era between the pre-Cambrian and the Mesozoic, dating approximately from 500 to 200 million years ago.

parapodia (păr′a·pō′dĭ·a) [Gr. *para*, beside, + *podos*, foot]: fleshy segmental appendages in polychaete worms; serve in breathing, locomotion, and creation of water currents.

parasite (păr′a·sīt) [Gr. *para* + *sitos*, food]: an organism which lives symbiotically on or within a host organism, more or less detrimental to the host.

parasympathetic (păr′a·sĭm′pa·thĕt′ĭk): applied to a subdivision of the autonomic nervous system; centers are located in brain, most anterior part of spinal cord, and most posterior part of spinal cord.

parathyroid (păr′a·thī′roid): an endocrine gland, usually paired, located near or within the thyroid; secretes parathormone, which controls calcium metabolism.

parenchyma (pa·rĕng′kĭ·ma) [Gr. *para* + *en*, in, + *chein*, to pour]: in plant stems and roots, the tissue of the pith and the cortex.

parthenogenesis (pär′thĕ·nŏ·jĕn′ĕ·sĭs) [Gr. *parthenos*, virgin, + *genēs*, born]: development of an egg without fertilization; occurs naturally in some organisms (e.g., rotifers) and may be induced artificially in others (e.g., frogs).

pathogenic (păth′ŏ·jĕn′ĭk) [Gr. *pathos*, suffering, + *genēs*]: disease-producing, e.g., many bacteria, fungi, and other parasites.

pedicellaria (pĕd′ĭ·sĕl′a′rĭ·a) [L. *pedicellus*, little stalk]: a tiny pincerlike structure on the surface of starfish and other echinoderms; protects skin gills.

pedipalp (pĕd′ĭ·pălp): one of the paired head appendages in spiders and other arachnids.

pelagic (pĕ·lăj′ĭk) [Gr. *pelagos*, ocean]: oceanic habitat zone, comprising the open water of an ocean basin; subdivided into the neritic zone and the oceanic zone.

Pelecypoda (pĕ·lĕ′sĭp′ŏ·da): a class of the phylum Mollusca, comprising clams, mussels, oysters.

pepsin (pĕp′sĭn) [Gr. *peptein*, to digest]: a protein-digesting enzyme present in gastric juice.

peptidase (pĕp′tĭ·dās) [Gr. *peptein*]: an enzyme promoting the liberation of individual amino acids from a peptide, i.e., an amino acid complex smaller than a whole protein.

perennial (pĕr·ĕn′ĭ·ăl) [L. *perennis*, throughout a year]: a plant which lives continuously throughout the year and persists in whole or in part from year to year.

peristalsis (pĕr′ĭ·stăl′sĭs) [Gr. *peristaltikos*, compressing]: successive contraction and relaxation of tubular organs such as the alimentary tract, resulting in a wavelike propagation of a transverse constriction.

permeability (pûr′mĕ·a·bĭl′ĭ·tĭ) [L. *permeare*, to pass through]: penetrability, as in membranes which let given substances pass through.

petiole (pĕt′ĭ·ōl) [L. *petiolus*, little foot]: leafstalk; the slender stem by which a leaf blade is attached to a branch or a stem.

pH: a symbol denoting the relative concentration of hydrogen ions in a solution; pH values run from 0 to 14, and the lower the value, the more acid is a solution, i.e., the more hydrogen ions it contains.

Phaeophyta (fē′ŏ·fī′t·a): the phylum of brown algae.

pharynx (făr′ĭngks) [Gr.]: the part of the alimentary tract between mouth cavity and esophagus; it is also part of the air channel from nose to larynx.

phenotype (fē′nŏ·tīp) [Gr. *phainein*, to show]: the physical appearance of an organism resulting from its genotype, i.e., its genetic constitution.

phloem (flō′ĕm) [Gr. *phloos*, bark]: one of the conducting tissues in tracheophytic plants; consists of sieve tubes and companion cells and transports organic nutrients both up and down.

Phoronidea (fōr′ŏ·nĭd′ĕ·a): a phylum of wormlike, marine, tube-dwelling, schizocoelomate animals.

phosphagen (fŏs′fă·jĕn): collective term for creatine-phosphate and arginine-phosphate, i.e., compounds which store and may be sources of high-energy phosphates.

phosphorylation (fŏs′fŏ·rĭ·lā′shŭn): the addition of a phosphate group (for example, —H₂PO₃) to a compound.

photolysis (fŏ·tŏl′ĭ·sĭs) [Gr. *phōtos*, light, + *lysis*, a loosening]: a component process of photosynthesis in which water is split into hydrogen and oxygen through the energy of light.

photosynthesis (fō′tŏ·sĭn′thĕ·sĭs) [Gr. *phōtos*, light, + *syn*, together, + *tithenai*, to place]: process in which energy of light and chlorophyll are used to manufacture carbohydrates out of carbon dioxide and water.

phototropism (fŏ·tŏt′rŏ·pĭz′m) [Gr. *phōtos* + *tropē*, a turning]: behavior oriented by light, e.g., growth of plant stems toward light source.

phrenic (frĕn′ĭk) [Gr. *phrenos*, diaphragm]: pertaining to the diaphragm, e.g., phrenic nerve, innervating the diaphragm.

phycocyanin, phycoerythrin (fī′kŏ·sī′ă·nĭn, fī′kŏ·ĕ′rĭth·rĭn) [Gr. *phykos*, seaweed]: blue and red pigments found in blue-green and other algae.

phylum (fī′lŭm), *pl.* **phyla** [Gr. *phylon*, race, tribe]: a category of taxonomic classification, between class and kingdom.

physiology (fĭz′ĭ·ŏl′ŏ·jĭ) [Gr. *physis*, nature, + *logos*, study]: study of living processes, activities, and functions generally; contrasts with morphology, the study of structure.

phytoplankton (fī′tŏ·plăngk′tŏn) [Gr. *phyton*, plant, + *planktos*, wandering]: collective term for the plants present in plankton; contrasts with zooplankton.

pineal (pĭn′ē·ăl) [L. *pinea*, pine cone]: a structure in the brain of vertebrates; functions as a median dorsal eye in a few (e.g., lampreys), but has no demonstrable function in most.

pistil (pĭs′til) [L. *pistulus*, a pestle]: the female reproductive parts of a flower; consists of stigma, style, and ovary.

pituitary (pĭ·tū′ĭ·tĕrĭ) [L. *pituita*, phlegm]: a composite endocrine gland in vertebrates, attached ventrally to the brain; composed of anterior, intermediate, and posterior lobes, each representing a functionally separate gland.

placenta (plà·sĕn′tà) [L., cake]: a tissue complex formed in part from the inner lining of the uterus and in part from the chorion of the embryo; develops in most mammals, and serves as mechanical, metabolic, and endocrine connection between the adult female and the embryo during pregnancy.

placoderm (plăk′ŏ·dûrm) [Gr. *plakos*, flat plate, + *derma*, skin]: a member of a class of Devonian vertebrates (fishes), all now extinct; ancestral to cartilage and bony fishes.

planarian (plà·nâr′ĭ·ăn) [L. *planarius*, level]: any member of the class of free-living flatworms.

plankton (plăngk′tŏn) [Gr. *planktos*, wandering]: collective term for the passively floating or drifting flora and fauna of a body of water; consists largely of microscopic organisms.

plastid (plăs′tĭd) [Gr. *plastēs*, a molder]: a cytoplasmic, often pigmented body in plant cells; plastids which contain chlorophyll are called chloroplasts.

Platyhelminthes (plăt′ĭ·hĕl·mĭn′thēz) [Gr. *platys*, flat, + *helminthos*, worm]: flatworms, a phylum of acoelomate animals; comprises planarians, flukes, and tapeworms.

plesiosaur (plē′sĭ·ŏ·sôr) [Gr. *plesios*, near, + *sauros*, lizard]: a long-necked, marine, extinct Mesozoic reptile.

plexus (plĕk′sŭs) [L., braid]: a network, especially of nerves or of blood vessels.

ploidy (ploi′dĭ) [Gr. *ploos*, fold]: the number of chromosome sets per cell; e.g., haploidy, diploidy.

pluripotent (plōōr′ĭ·pō′tĕnt) [L. *pluris*, several, + *potis*, able]: capable of developing several different specializations, as in certain types of cells.

polarization (pō′lēr·ĭ·zā′shŭn) [L. *polaris*, pole]: in nerves and muscles, the establishment of positive electric charges on one side of a surface membrane and negative electric charges on the other side.

polyclad (pŏl′ĭ·klăd): a member of a group of free-living flatworms, characterized by a digestive cavity with many branch-pouches.

polymorphism (pŏl′ĭ·môr′fĭz′m) [Gr. *polys*, many, + *morphē*, form]: differences of form among the members of a species; individual variations affecting form and structure.

polyp (pŏl′ĭp) [L. *polypus*, many-footed]: the sessile stage in the life cycle of coelenterates; a sea anemone.

polypeptide (pŏl′ĭ·pĕp′tĭd): a molecule consisting of many joined amino acids, not so complex as a protein.

polyphyletic (pŏl′ĭ·fī·lĕt′ĭk) [Gr. *polys*, many, + *phylon*, tribe]: derived from more than one ancestral type; contrasts with monophyletic.

polysaccharide (pŏl′ĭ·săk′à·rīd): a carbohydrate composed of many joined monosaccharide units, e.g., glycogen, starch, cellulose, all formed out of glucose units.

Porifera (pŏ·rĭf′ĕr·a̱) [L. *porus*, pore, + *ferre*, to bear]: the phylum of sponges.

preformation (prē′fôr·mā′shŭn): an outdated view which holds that the adult features of an organism are already established in miniature in the undeveloped egg; contrasts with epigenesis.

Priapulida (prī′a̱·pŭ′lĭ·da̱): a small phylum of pseudocoelomate animals.

proboscis (prŏ·bŏs′ĭs) [L.]: any tubular process or prolongation of the head or snout.

progesterone (prŏ·jĕs′tĕr·ōn): hormone secreted by the corpus luteum and the placenta; prepares the uterus for the reception of a fertilized egg and later maintains the capacity of the uterus to hold the embryo and fetus.

prophase (prō′fāz′): a stage during mitotic cell division, in which the nuclear membrane dissolves, chromosomes become distinct, and a spindle forms.

prosimian (prŏ·sĭm′ĭ·a̱n) [L. *pro*, before, + *simia*, ape]: an ancestral primate and certain of primitive living primates, e.g., a lemur, a tarsier.

protein (prō′tĕ·ĭn) [Gr. *prōteios*, primary]: one of a class of organic compounds composed of many joined amino acids.

proteinase (prō′tĕ·ĭn·ās): an enzyme which promotes the conversion of a protein into smaller units, e.g., amino acids, or the reverse; also called protease.

prothrombin (prŏ·thrŏm′bĭn) [L. *pro* + Gr. *thrombos*, clot]: a constituent of blood plasma; converted to thrombin by thrombokinase in the presence of calcium ions, and so contributes to blood clotting.

protoplasm (prō′tŏ·plăz′m) [Gr. *protos*, first, + *plasma*, form, mold]: synonym for living matter, living material, or living substance.

protovirus (prō′tŏ·vī′rŭs): hypothetical viruslike nucleoprotein-containing body believed to have been ancestral to the first truly living organisms on earth.

protozoon (prō′tŏ·zō′ŏn) [Gr. *protos* + *zōion*, animal]: a unicellular animal; a member of either of three phyla (Sarcodina, Ciliophora, Sporozoa); name often also given to animallike flagellates (class Zoomastigina, phylum Mastigophora).

pseudocoel, pseudocoelomate (sū′dŏ·sēl, —ŏ·māt) [Gr. *pseudēs*, false]: (1) an internal body cavity lined not by mesoderm but by ectoderm and endoderm; (2) an animal possessing a pseudocoel, e.g., rotifers, roundworms.

Psilopsida (sī·lŏp′sĭ·da̱) [Gr. *psilos*, bare]: a subphylum of tracheophytes; includes the earliest, now extinct, representatives of the vascular plants; evolved probably from green algae, and in turn ancestral to all living tracheophytes.

Pteropsida (tĕ·rŏp′sĭ·da̱) [Gr. *pteridos*, fern]: a subphylum of tracheophytes; includes ferns and all seed plants, i.e., large-leafed vascular plants; probably evolved from psilopsids.

pterosaur (tĕr′ŏ·sôr) [Gr. *pteron*, feather, + *sauros*, lizard]: a flying, extinct Mesozoic reptile.

pulmonary (pŭl′mŏ·nĕr′ĭ) [L. *pulmonis*, lung]: pertaining to the lungs, e.g., pulmonary artery, vein.

pylorus (pī·lō′rŭs) [Gr. *pylōros*, gatekeeper]: the opening from stomach to intestine.

Radiolaria (rā′dĭ·ŏ·lā′rĭ·a̱) [L. dim. of *radius*]: a group of sarcodine protozoa, characterized by silicon-containing shells.

radius (rā′dĭ·ŭs): in vertebrates, one of the two bones of the forelimb, located on the side of the thumb.

radula (răd′ŭ·la̱) [L. *radere*, to scrape]: the horny rasping organ in the alimentary tract of chitons, snails, squids, and other mollusks.

receptor (rĕ·sĕp′tĕr) [L. *recipere*, to receive]: general term for one of the components of a steady-state control system; it is sensitive to a stimulus and in turn transmits a signal to the modulator.

recessive (rĕ·sĕs′ĭv) [L. *recedere*, to recede]: a functional attribute of genes; the effect of a recessive gene is masked if the allelic gene is dominant.

redia (rē′dĭ·a̱): a larval stage in the life cycle of flukes; produced by a sporocyst larva, and in turn gives rise to many cercariae.

reflex (rē′flĕks) [L. *reflectere*, to bend back]: the unit action of the nervous system; consists of stimulation of a sense receptor, interpretation and emission of nerve impulses by a neural center, and execution of a response by an effector organ.

renal (rē′nǎl) [L. *renes*, kidneys]: pertaining to the kidney.

renin (rē′nĭn): a hormone produced by the kidneys; probably contributes to blood-pressure control.

rennin (rĕn′ĭn) [Middle Engl. *rennen*, to run]: an enzyme present in gastric juice; promotes the coagulation of milk.

respiration (rĕs′pĭ·rā′shŭn) [L. *respirare*, to breathe]: the liberation of metabolically useful energy from fuel molecules within cells; may occur anaerobically or aerobically.

retina (rĕt′ĭ·na̱) [L. *rete*, a net]: the innermost tissue layer of the eyeball; contains the receptor cells sensitive to light.

rhabdocoel (răb′dȯ·sēl) [Gr. *rhabdos*, rod, + *koilōma*, a hollow]: a member of a group of free-living flatworms possessing a straight, unbranched digestive cavity.

Rhodophyta (rȯ′dŏf′ĭ·tȧ) [Gr. *rhodon*, rose, + *phyton*, plant]: the phylum of red algae.

Rotifera (rȯ·tĭf′ēr·ȧ) [L. *rota*, wheel, + *ferre*, to bear]: a phylum of microscopic pseudocoelomate animals, characterized by whorls of motile bristles around the mouth.

saccule (săk′ūl) [L. *sacculus*, little sack]: portion of the inner ear containing the receptors for the sense of static balance.

salt (sôlt): an interaction product of an acid and a base.

saprophyte (săp′rȯ·fīt) [Gr. *sapros*, rotten]: an organism subsisting on dead or decaying matter.

Sarcodina (sär′kȯ·dī′nȧ) [Gr. *sarkos*, flesh]: a phylum of protozoa; includes amoebae, foraminifera, radiolaria, and others.

Scaphopoda (skȧ·fŏp′ȯ·dȧ) [Gr. *skaphē*, boat]: tooth shells, a class of the phylum Mollusca.

schizocoel, schizocoelomate (skĭz′ȯ·sēl) [Gr. *schizein*, to split]: (1) a coelum formed by a splitting of embryonic mesoderm; (2) an animal possessing a schizocoel, e.g., mollusks, annelids, arthropods.

Schizophyta (skĭz′ŏf′ĭ·tȧ) [Gr. *schizein* + *phyton*, plant]: the phylum of bacteria.

sclera (sklē′rȧ) [Gr. *sklēros*, hard]: the outermost coat of the eyeball, continuous with the cornea.

scrotum (skrō′tŭm) [L.]: external skin pouch containing the testes of most mammals.

semiherbaceous (sĕm′ĭ·hûr·bā′shŭs) [L. *semi*, half, + *herbaceus*, grassy]: applied to stem type intermediate in character between woody and herbaceous types; young parts of stem possess strips of cambium, as in herbaceous types; old parts possess tube of cambium, as in woody types.

semipermeable (sĕm′ĭ·pûr′mĕ·ȧ·b′l): permeable to small particles (e.g., water, certain inorganic ions), but not to larger particles (e.g., proteins, fat molecules).

sepal (sē′pȧl): one of the leaves in the outermost whorl of a flower.

serum (sēr′ŭm) [L.]: the fluid remaining after removal of fibrinogen from blood plasma.

simian (sĭm′ĭ·ăn) [L. *simia*, an ape]: pertaining to monkeys; also used as noun.

sinus (sī′nŭs) [L., a curve]: a cavity, recess, or depression, especially in bone.

siphon (sī′fŏn) [Gr. *siphōn*, a pipe]: tubular structure for drawing in or ejecting fluids, as in mollusks, tunicates.

Sipunculoidea (sī·pŭng′kŭ·loi′dĕ·ȧ): a phylum of wormlike schizocoelomate animals.

sol (sŏl): quasi-liquid state of a colloidal system, where water forms the continuous phase and solid particles the dispersed phase.

somatic (sȯ·măt′ĭk) [Gr. *sōma*, body]: pertaining to the body, e.g., somatic mutation, stable gene change occurring in a cell of the body generally, rather than in a reproductive, or germ, cell.

somite (sō′mīt): one of the longitudinal series of segments in segmented animals; especially an incompletely developed embryonic segment, or a part thereof.

speciation (spē′shĭ·ā′shŭn): the evolution of two or more species by the splitting of one ancestral species.

species (spē′shĭz), *pl.* **species** (spē′shēz) [L. kind, sort]: a category of taxonomic classification, below genus rank, defined by breeding potential or gene flow: interbreeding and gene flow occur among the members of a species but not between members of different species.

specificity (spĕs′ĭ·fĭs′ĭ·tĭ): uniqueness, especially of proteins in a given organism and of enzymes in given reactions.

Sphenopsida (sfĕ·nŏp′sĭ·dȧ) [Gr. *sphēn*, a wedge]: a subphylum of tracheophytes; includes the horsetails.

sphincter (sfĭngk′tēr) [Gr. *sphingein*, to bind tight]: a ring-shaped muscle capable of closing a tubular opening by constriction, e.g., pyloric sphincter, which closes the opening between stomach and intestine.

spicule (spĭk′ūl) [L. *spiculum*, little dart]: a slender, pointed, often needle-shaped secretion of sponge cells; may be calcareous or siliceous and serves as skeletal support.

spirillum (spī·rĭl′ŭm) [L. *spirilla*, little coil]: any bacterium possessing a wavy, coiled, or spiral body.

spore (spōr) [Gr. *spora*, a seed]: a reproductive cell of plants, capable of developing into an adult directly.

sporocyst (spō′rȯ·sĭst): a larval stage in the life cycle of flukes; produced by a miracidium larva and in turn gives rise to many rediae.

sporophyte (spōr′ȯ·fīt): a spore-producing plant; phase of life cycle in certain plants which alternates with a gametophyte phase.

Sporozoa (spō′rŏ·zō′á): a phylum of parasitic protozoa; most familiar member is the organism which produces malaria.

stamen (stā′mĕn) [L., a thread]: a male reproductive part of a flower; consists of stalk and anther.

sterol, steroid (stĕr′ōl, stĕr′oid): one of a class of organic compounds containing a molecular skeleton of four fused carbon rings; includes cholesterol, sex hormones, adrenocortical hormones, and vitamin D.

stigma (stĭg′má) [Gr., the mark of a pointed instrument]: the uppermost part of a pistil, serving as landing platform for pollen grains.

stimulus (stĭm′ŭ·lŭs) [L.]: any environmental change which activates a receptor.

stoma (stō′má), *pl.* **stomata** [Gr., a mouth]: a microscopic opening in the epidermis of a leaf, formed by a pair of guard cells; interconnects the interior air spaces of a leaf with the external atmosphere.

style (stīl) [Gr. *stylos*, a pillar]: stalklike part of a pistil which connects the stigma with the ovary.

substrate (sŭb′strāt) [L. *substratus*, strewn under]: a substance which is acted upon by an enzyme.

symbiont, symbiosis (sĭm′bĭ·ŏnt, sĭm′bĭ·ō′sĭs) [Gr. *syn*, with, + *bios*, life]: (1) an organism which lives in symbiotic association with another; (2) the intimate living together of two organisms of different species, for mutual or one-sided benefit; the principal variants are mutualism, commensalism, and parasitism.

sympathetic (sĭm′pá·thĕt′ĭk): applied to a subdivision of the autonomic nervous system; centers are located in the mid-portion of the spinal cord.

synapse (sĭ·năps′) [Gr. *synapsis*, conjunction]: the microscopic space between the axon terminal of one neuron and the dendrite terminal of another adjacent neuron.

syncitium (sĭn·sĭ′shĭ·ŭm) [Gr. *syn* + *kytos*, vessel]: a multinucleate tissue or mass of protoplasm without internal cell boundaries.

synergistic (sĭn′ĕr·jĭs′tĭk) [Gr. *syn* + *ergon*, work]: cooperative in action, e.g., hormones or other metabolic agents which reinforce each other's activities.

synthesis (sĭn′thĕ·sĭs) [Gr. *syn* + *tithenai*, to place]: the joining of two or more molecules resulting in a single larger molecule.

syrinx (sĭr′ĭngks) [Gr., a pipe]: the vocal organ of birds, located where the trachea branches into the bronchi.

systole (sĭs′tŏ·lē) [Gr. *syn* + *stellein*, to place]: the phase of contraction of auricles or ventricles, during which blood is pumped forward along the circulation path.

taiga (tī′gá) [Russ.]: terrestrial habitat zone characterized by large tracts of coniferous forests, long, cold winters, and short summers; bounded in the north by tundra; found particularly in Canada, northern Europe, and Siberia.

taxonomy (tăks·ŏn′ŏ·mĭ) [Gr. *taxis*, arrangement, + *nomos*, law]: plant and animal classification, based as far as possible on natural relationships.

tectorial membrane (tĕk·tō′rĭ·ăl): component of the organ of Corti in cochlea of ear.

teleology (tĕl′ĕ·ŏl′ŏ·jĭ) [Gr. *telos*, end, + *logos*, study]: view which holds that natural events are goal-directed and occur according to preordained purposes; contrasts which scientific view of causalism.

telophase (tĕl′ŏ·fāz) [Gr. *telos*, end]: a stage in mitotic cell division, during which cell cytoplasm cleaves into two and nuclei form in daughter cells.

template (tĕm′plĕt): a pattern or mold guiding the formation of a duplicate; term applied especially to gene duplication, which is explained in terms of a template hypothesis.

temporal lobe (tĕm′pŏ·răl) [L. *tempora*, the temples]: a part of the vertebrate cerebrum; contains neural centers for speech and hearing.

testis (tĕs′tĭs) [L.]: male reproductive organ; produces sperms.

tetrapoda (tĕ·trăp′ŏ·dá) [Gr. *tetrapodia*, four feet]: four-legged vertebrates; a superclass including amphibia, reptiles, birds, and mammals.

therapsid (thĕ·răp′sĭd): extinct Mesozoic mammallike reptile, of a group from which true mammals evolved.

thorax (thō′răks) [L.]: part of animal body between neck or head and abdomen.

thrombin (thrŏm′bĭn) [Gr. *thrombos*, clot]: substance participating in blood clotting; formed from prothrombin, and in turn converts fibrinogen into fibrin.

thrombokinase (thrŏm′bŏ·kĭn′ās): enzyme released from blood platelets during clotting; transforms prothrombin into thrombin, in presence of calcium ions; also called thromboplastin.

thrombus (thrŏm′bŭs): a blood clot within the circulatory system.

thymus (thī′mŭs) [fr. Gr.]: a lymphoid gland in most young and many adult vertebrates; disappears in man at puberty; located in lower throat and upper part of thorax.

thyroxin (thī·rŏk′sĭn): the hormone secreted by the thyroid gland.

tissue (tĭsh′ū) [L. *texere*, to weave]: an aggregate of cells of similar structure performing similar functions; the cells may be packed tightly or may be separated by greater or lesser amounts of intercellular material.

trachea, tracheal (trā′kĕ·*à*) [Gr. *trachys*, rough]: (1) air-conducting tube, as in windpipe of mammals and breathing system of insects; (2) adjective.

tracheid (trā′kĕ·ĭd): plant cell formed from and to the inside of cambium and maturing into a component of the xylem system.

tracheophyte, Tracheophyta (trā′kĕ·ò·fīt): (1) a vascular plant, i.e., one possessing xylem and phloem; term applicable to all plants other than algae, fungi, and bryophytes; (2) phylum name.

transduction (trăns·dŭk′shŭn): transfer of genetic material from one bacterium to another through the agency of a virus.

translocation (trăns·lŏ·kā′shŭn): transport of organic substances in phloem.

transpiration (trăn′spĭ·rā′shŭn) [L. *trans*, across, + *spirare*, to breathe]: evaporation of water from leaves or other exposed surfaces.

triclad (trī′klăd): a member of a group of free-living flatworms, characterized by a digestive cavity with three branch-pouches; a planarian.

tricuspid valve (trī·kŭs′pĭd) [L. *tri*, three, + *cuspis*, a point]: valve consisting of three flaps, guarding opening between right auricle and right ventricle of heart.

trilobite (trī′lŏ·bīt): an extinct, marine Paleozoic arthropod, marked by two dorsal longitudinal furrows into three parts or lobes.

triploblast, triploblastic (trĭp′lŏ·blăst) [Gr. *triploos*, triple, + *blastos*, sprout]: (1) an animal constructed from three primary germ layers, i.e., ectoderm, mesoderm, and endoderm; (2) adjective.

trochophore (trŏk′ò·fōr) [Gr. *trochos*, wheel, + *phoros*, bearing]: a free-swimming ciliated marine larva, characteristic of schizocoelomate animals.

trophic (trŏf′ĭk) [Gr. *trophos*, feeder]: pertaining to nutrition, i.e., autotrophic, heterotrophic.

tropic, tropism (trŏp′ĭk) [Gr. *tropē*, a turning]: (1) pertaining to behavior or action brought about by specific stimuli; i.e., phototropic (light-oriented-growing), gonadotropic (stimulating the gonads); (2) noun.

trypsin (trĭp′sĭn) [Gr. *tryein*, to wear down]: enzyme promoting digestion of proteins; acts in small intestine, but produced as inactive trypsinogen by pancreas.

tundra (tŏon′drà) [Russ.]: terrestrial habitat zone, between taiga in south and polar region in north, characterized by absence of trees, short growing season, and frozen ground during much of the year.

turgor (tûr′gŏr) [L. *turgere*, to swell]: the distention of a plant (or animal) cell by its fluid content.

ulna (ŭl′nà) [L., elbow]: one of the two bones of the vertebrate forelimb; located on the side of the little finger.

umbilicus (ŭm·bĭl′ĭ·kŭs) [L.]: the navel; during pregnancy, an umbilical cord connects the placenta with the offspring, and the point of connection with the offspring later becomes the navel.

urea (ŭ·rē′à) [Gr. *ouron*, urine]: an organic compound formed in the liver out of ammonia and carbon dioxide and excreted by the kidneys; represents principal means of ammonia disposal in mammals and some other animal groups.

ureter (ŭ·rē′tēr) [fr. Gr.]: duct carrying urine from a kidney to the urinary bladder.

urethra (ŭ·rē′thrà) [fr. Gr.]: duct carrying urine from the urinary bladder to the outside of the body; in the males of most mammals, the urethra also leads sperms to the outside during copulation.

Urochordata (ŭ′rò·kôr·dà′tà) [Gr. *oura*, tail, + L. *chorda*, cord]: a subphylum of chordates; comprises the tunicates.

uropod (ū′rò·pŏd) [Gr. *oura* + *podos*, foot]: an abdominal appendage in lobsters and other crustaceans; contributes to the formation of a "tail."

uterus (ū′tēr·ŭs) [L., womb]: enlarged region of the female reproductive duct in which offspring develops during pregnancy and receives maternal nourishment.

utricle (ū′trĭ·k'l) [L. *utriculus*, little bag]: portion of the inner ear containing the receptors for dynamic body balance; the semicircular canals lead from and to the utricle.

vacuole (văk′ù·ōl) [L. *vacuus*, empty]: a small, usually spherical space within a cell, bounded by a membrane and containing fluid, solid matter, or both.

vagus (vā′gŭs) [L., wandering]: the tenth cranial nerve; it is a mixed nerve, innervating many organs in the chest and the abdomen.

vascular bundle (văs′kŭ·lēr) [L. *vasculum,* small vessel]: a small group of xylem and phloem channels, with and without cambium, traversing roots, stem, and leaves; characteristic of nonwoody tracheophytes.

vasomotion (văs′ŏ·mō′shŭn) [L. *vasum,* vessel]: collective term for the constriction (vasoconstriction) and dilation (vasodilation) of blood vessels.

venous (vē′nŭs) [L. *vena,* vein]: pertaining to veins; also applied to oxygen-poor, carbon dioxide–rich blood.

ventricle (vĕn′trĭ·k'l) [L. *ventriculus,* the stomach]: a chamber of the heart which receives blood from an auricle and pumps out blood from the heart.

vestigial (vĕs·tĭj′ĭ·ăl) [L. *vestigium,* footprint]: degenerate or incompletely developed, but more fully developed at an earlier stage or during the evolutionary past.

villus (vĭl′ŭs), *pl.* **villi** [L., a tuft of hair]: a tiny fingerlike process projecting from the intestinal lining into the cavity of the gut; contains blood and lymph capillaries and is bounded by the intestinal mucosa.

virus (vī′rŭs) [L., slimy liquid, poison]: a submicroscopic noncellular particle, composed of a nucleoprotein core and a protein shell; parasitic, and within a host cell it may reproduce and mutate.

vitalism (vī′tăl·iz'm) [L. *vita,* life]: view which holds that natural processes are controlled by supernatural forces and cannot be explained through the laws of physics and chemistry alone; contrasts with scientific view of mechanism.

vitamin (vī′tá·mĭn) [L. *vita,* life]: one of a class of organic substances contributing to the formation or action of cellular enzymes; synthesized by plants, but animals cannot manufacture many vitamins, and these must be supplied prefabricated in food.

vitreous (vĭt′rĕ·ŭs) [L. *vitrum,* glass]: glassy; as in vitreous humor, the clear transparent jelly which fills the posterior part of the eyeball.

viviparity, viviparous (vĭv′ĭ·păr′ĭ·tĭ, vī·vĭp′á·rŭs) [L. *vivus,* alive, + *parere,* to bring forth]: (1) reproductive pattern in which eggs develop within female body, with nutritional and other metabolic aid of maternal parent; offspring are born as miniature adults; (2) adjective.

xanthophyll (zăn′thŏ·fĭl) [Gr. *xanthos,* yellow, + *phyllon,* leaf]: one of a group of yellow pigments found widely among plants and animals; the xanthophylls are members of the carotenoid group of pigments.

xylem (zī′lĕm) [Gr. *xylon,* wood]: tissue in plants which conducts water from roots to leaves; consists of columns of tracheids or of uninterrupted cellulose channels (xylem vessels); derived from cambium, and in bulk represents wood.

zooplankton (zō′ŏ·plăngk′tŏn) [Gr. *zōion,* animal]: collective term for the animals present in plankton; contrasts with phytoplankton.

zygospore (zī′gŏ·spōr) [Gr. *zygon,* yoke, pair]: an encysted zygote, as in *Spirogyra.*

zygote (zī′gōt) [Gr. *zygōtos,* yoked]: the cell resulting from the sexual fusion of two gametes; a fertilized egg.

INDEX

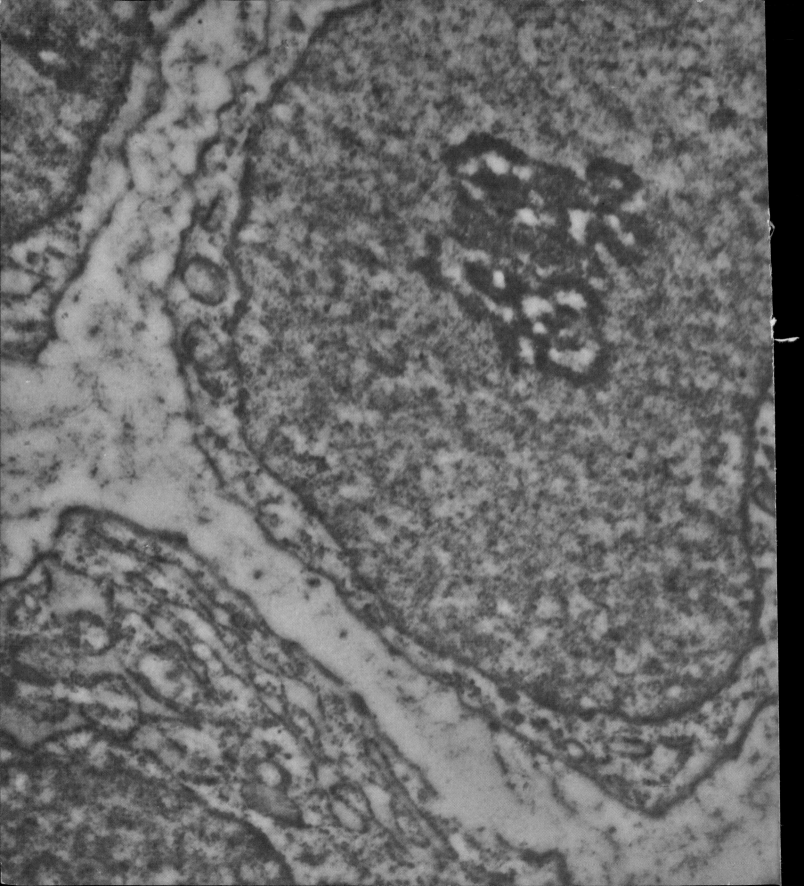